Fire Engineering's Handbook
for Firefighter I & II
2013 Update

FIRE ENGINEERING'S HANDBOOK FOR FIREFIGHTER I & II
2013 UPDATE

Copyright © 2013 by
PennWell Corporation
1421 South Sheridan Road
Tulsa, Oklahoma 74112-6600 USA

Phone: 918.835.3161
Fax: 918.831.9555
800.752.9764
+1.918.831.9421

sales@pennwell.com
www.fireengineeringbooks.com
www.pennwellbooks.com
www.pennwell.com

Chairman Frank T. Lauinger

President and CEO Robert F. Biolchini

Senior Vice President, Finance and Administration, CFO Mark Wilmoth

Vice President, Controller Brian Conway

Director Mary McGee

Managing Editor Marla Patterson

Acquisitions Editor Jerry Naylis

Technical Editor Glenn Corbett

Development Editor Brad Epperley

Production Manager Sheila Brock

Production Editor Tony Quinn

Cover Design Karla Womack

Marketing Manager Sarah De Vos

National Account Manager Cindy J. Huse

Printed in the United States of America

3 4 5 6 7   19 18 17 16 15

CONTENTS

FIREFIGHTER I

1 THE TRADITIONS AND MISSION OF THE FIRE SERVICE

2 FIRE SERVICE HISTORY

3 FIRE DEPARTMENT ORGANIZATION

4 FIRE DEPARTMENT COMMUNICATIONS

5 FIRE BEHAVIOR

6 FIRE EXTINGUISHERS

11 FIREFIGHTING BASIC TOOLS

12 FORCIBLE ENTRY

13 LADDERS

14 VENTILATION

23 ANALYZING THE HAZMAT/WMD INCIDENT

24 PLANNING THE HAZMAT/WMD RESPONSE

25 IMPLEMENTING THE PLANNED RESPONSE TO A HAZMAT/WMD INCIDENT

26 EMS IN THE FIRE SERVICE

FIREFIGHTER II

27 INCIDENT COMMAND SYSTEM

28 ADVANCED COMMUNICATIONS

GLENN CORBETT, EDITOR

GLENN P. CORBETT

is a licensed fire protection engineer, former assistant chief of the Waldwick (N.J.) Fire Department, associate professor of fire science at John Jay College of Criminal Justice in New York City, and technical editor for *Fire Engineering*. He previously held the position of administrator of engineering services with the San Antonio Fire Department. Corbett has a master of engineering degree in fire protection engineering from Worcester Polytechnic Institute in Massachusetts and is pursuing a Ph.D. in public administration from Rutgers University. He authored two chapters on fire prevention/ protection in *The Fire Chief's Handbook, 5th Edition* (Fire Engineering, 1995) and is the coauthor of the late Francis L. Brannigan's *Building Construction for the Fire Service, 5th Edition*. Corbett is the recipient of the 2013 Tom Brennan Lifetime Achievement Award from Fire Engineering/PennWell Publishing.

CONTRIBUTING AUTHORS

ANTHONY AVILLO

is a 23-year veteran, and a Deputy Chief in North Hudson Regional (N.J.) Fire & Rescue. Chief Avillo has a B.S. in Fire Science from New Jersey City University. He is an instructor at the Bergen County (N.J.) Law & Public Safety Institute and the Monmouth County (N.J.) Fire Academy. Avillo, an FDIC instructor, is also an editorial advisor, advisory board member and contributing editor to *Fire Engineering* magazine. He is the author of *Fireground Strategies* (Fire Engineering 2008) and *Fireground Strategies Scenarios Workbook* (Fire Engineering 2009). Anthony is coauthor of the *Fire Engineering's Handbook for Firefighter I and II Study Guide*.

JOHN M. BEST

is an associate with Emergency Services Consulting Inc. and a lecturer for John Jay College of Criminal Justice. During his 35-year career in the fire and rescue service, Best has served as fire chief and manager of Reedy Creek Emergency Services in Florida, and deputy fire and rescue chief of Montgomery County (Md.) Fire Rescue Service. He has a master's degree in organizational management from the University of Phoenix, a bachelor's degree in business administration from Columbia Union College, and an associate's degree in fire science from Montgomery College. He received a presidential appointment to the *America Burning Recommissioned: America at Risk* panel and is the recipient of three fire rescue governor's citations from the State of Maryland. He serves on the National Fire Protection Association (NFPA) and the Fire Service Training Committee, and he is a member of the International Association of Fire Chiefs, the Florida Fire Chiefs' Association, and the International Society of Fire Service Instructors.

STEVE BERNOCCO

is a 17-year veteran of the Seattle (Wash.) Fire Department, where he is a lieutenant on Ladder 10. He has served as a training officer, and is currently a member of the SFD's Operational Skills Enhancement Development Team. Lt. Bernocco has written numerous articles, is coauthor of *Air Management for the Fire Service* (Fire Engineering 2008), and is a national instructor on air management, firefighter safety and survival, and fireground strategy and tactics with the "Seattle Guys."

ALAN BRUNACINI

joined the Phoenix (Ariz.) Fire Department in 1958. He was promoted to fire chief in 1978 and retired in 2006 after 48 years of service. He is a graduate of the fire protection technology program at Oklahoma State University. Brunacini has a bachelor's degree and an MPA from Arizona State University. He is the past Chairman of the Board of the NFPA and the NFPA Fire Service Occupational Safety Committee (standard 1500). He is chairman of the NFPA Career Fire Service Career Organization and Deployment Committee (standard 1710). He is the author of *Fire Command* (2002), *Command Safety* (2004), *Timeless Tactical Truths* (2003), *Essentials of Fire Department Customer Service* (1996), and *The Anatomy and Physiology of Leadership* (2006). He and his son John own and operate the fire service website www.bshifter.com.

JOHN BRUNACINI

is a retired fire captain from the Phoenix (Ariz.) Fire Department. He served 26 years as a firefighter and engineer and his last 14 years as captain. As a captain, he developed and managed the Phoenix Fire Network, worked in the field as the company officer on Ladder 11 B-shift for nine years, and managed the Command Training Center his last three years, where he developed the curriculum media packages used for command and battalion training. He is currently instructing and developing curriculum packages for the Blue Card Command Certification process and www.bshifter.com.

NICK BRUNACINI

is a retired 29-year veteran of the Phoenix (Ariz.) Fire Department. He worked seven years as a firefighter on engine companies, was promoted to captain, and worked nine years on a ladder company. He served as battalion chief for five years. He was promoted to shift commander and for five years ran the PFD's Command Training Center.

DON CANNON

(1937-2010) was a noted fire historian, history professor at Saint Peter's College in New Jersey, and an adjunct fire science instructor at John Jay College of Criminal Justice. Cannon joined Yonkers (N.Y.) Fire Department Auxiliary in 1962, became chief in 1975, served with the Rockaway Point Fire Department in Queens, N.Y., was a 1960s Bronx

FDNY Auxiliary, and was with the Midway (S.C.) Fire Department. He was the author of the firefighting history book Heritage of Flames (1977).

MICHAEL N. CIAMPO

is a 22-year veteran of the fire service. He is a lieutenant in the Fire Department of the City of New York and served with the District of Columbia Fire Department. He has a bachelor's degree in fire science from John Jay College of Criminal Justice. He is the lead instructor for FDIC's H.O.T. portable ladder program and a contributing editor and editorial advisor to *Fire Engineering*.

LARRY COLLINS

is a 28-year member of the County of Los Angeles Fire Department and a captain, US&R specialist, and paramedic assigned to Rescue Task Force 103. He is a search team manager for LACoFD's FEMA/OFDA US&R task force for domestic and international response and serves as an US&R specialist on the Red FEMA US&R IST. His deployments include the Oklahoma City bombing; the 9-11 Pentagon collapse; Hurricanes Frances, Ivan, Dennis, Katrina, Rita, and Wilma; and several national security events. He is the author of many articles published in *Fire Engineering* since 1989 and of *Technical Rescue Operations, Volumes I and II* (Fire Engineering 2004, 2005).

JAY COMELLA

entered the Oakland (Calif.) Fire Department in 1989 and is a captain. He is preceded in the OFD by his father, Bob; uncle, Tom; and grandfather, Cosmo. He graduated from the University of California. Comella has conducted extensive research and testing regarding fire streams, is published in *Fire Engineering*, and is an engine company H.O.T. instructor at FDIC.

DAVID DALRYMPLE

is a career EMS provider for the RWJUH Emergency Medical Services in New Brunswick, N.J. and he is a Rescue Services Captain for Clinton EMS/Rescue in Clinton, N.J. Dave is the education chair of the Transportation Emergency Rescue Committee - US (TERC). In 2007 he received the Harvey Grant award for excellence in rescue. Certified as a fire service instructor by the State of New Jersey, Dave has been actively teaching transportation rescue topics for over 14 years. He is currently the lead instructor for vehicle rescue programs at the Hunterdon County Emergency Services Training Center and is the executive educator for RoadwayRescue LLC. He also currently writes the "Extrication Tactics" column for *Fire Engineering* magazine.

PAUL T. DANSBACH

has worked in code enforcement for the past 30 years and has served as fire marshal in the Bureau of Fire Safety in Rutherford, N.J. for the past 23 years. He has been a member of the Rutherford Fire Department for 31 years, where he was chief and a chief officer for 10 years. He is a fire instructor at the Bergen County (N.J.) Law & Public Safety Institute at the Fire Academy. He teaches CEU classes for fire inspectors, fire subcode, and building subcode officials at Kean and Rutgers Universities and is an FDIC H.O.T. and classroom instructor. He is a member of the *Fire Engineering* editorial advisory board and the FDIC executive advisory board, and is coauthor of *Fireground Size-Up Study Guide* (Fire Engineering 2003).

STEVE M. DELISI

retired after 27 years in the fire service, most recently as the deputy chief for the Virginia Air National Guard Fire Rescue at the Richmond International Airport. He is a hazardous materials specialist, an adjunct instructor for the Virginia Department of Fire Programs, and a former member of the NFPA committee on hazardous materials protective clothing. He began his career in hazardous materials response in 1982 as a member of the Newport News (Va.) Fire Department Hazmat Team. He has also served as a hazardous materials officer for the Virginia Department of Emergency Management. In that capacity, he provided on-scene assistance to hazmat first responders for an area that included 20 jurisdictions. He has a master's degree in public safety leadership.

JASON EMERY

has 20 years of experience in the fire service. He has been a career firefighter with the City of Waterbury (CT) for 15 years, with 14 of those assigned to the City's Heavy Rescue/Haz-Mat Company. Jason also serves as a volunteer EMT for his hometown ambulance service. Captain Emery has been a certified fire service instructor since 1997 and is a member of ISFSI. He is an instructor for the Burrville Regional Fire Training School and is an FDIC lecturer. He holds a bachelor's degree in Fire Science from University of New Haven as well as numerous fire service certifications.

FRANK L. FIRE

is an accomplished author with more than 30 years' experience teaching the chemistry of hazardous materials to firefighters and other emergency responders. He retired from his position as executive vice president, marketing and international, at Americhem, Inc. and is currently a member of the editorial advisory board for *Fire Engineering*. He is the author of *The Common Sense Approach to Hazardous Materials* (Fire Engineering 2009) and its study guide, *Chemical Data Notebook: A User's Manual* (Fire Engineering 1992), and *Combustibility of Plastics* (1992), as well as coauthor of *SARA Title III: Intent and Implementation of Hazardous Materials Regulations* (1990). He has also published more than 120 articles on individual hazardous materials and other fire service topics.

TIMOTHY J. FLANNERY

has a fire service career of more than 30 years. Currently an adjunct professor at John Jay College of Criminal Justice, as well as Passaic County Community College in New Jersey, he spent 15 years as an active firefighter with the Oakland (NJ) Fire Department. He has served as Lieutenant, Training Officer, Rescue Squad Captain, and Fire Inspector, later becoming Senior Fire Instructor at Bergen County (NJ) Police and Fire Academy. He then became Director of the Middlesex County Fire Training Center in central New Jersey. Flannery holds a bachelor's degree in fire service administration from Empire State College/SUNY, a master's degree in protection management from John Jay College, and certifications as Fire Official, Level 2 Fire Instructor, Level 3 Incident Management, Officer Level 1, and is trained as a NIMS/ICS instructor up to ICS-400. He has been involved with the New Jersey State Fire Commission's Training and Education Advisory Council for more than 15 years.

CHRISTOPHER FLATLEY

is a 19-year veteran of the Fire Department of the City of New York, and is currently a lieutenant assigned to Ladder Company 21 in Hell's Kitchen. He is a Master Exercise Practitioner and a member of the FDNY Exercise Design Team and the Incident Management Team, as well as a nationally certified fire instructor I. Flatley is an instructor at the Rockland County Fire Training Center in Pomona, N.Y., and has a degree in fire protection technology. He has presented at FDIC and has written numerous articles for *Fire Engineering*.

RICHARD A. FRITZ

has been an active member of the fire service since 1973. He has served with various career and volunteer fire departments, including the Muscatine and Davenport (Iowa) fire departments; Penfield, N.Y., and Hampton, Ill.; Union Fire Company No. 1 in Carlisle, Pa., and Williamsport (Md.) Company No. 2 volunteer fire departments. Until recently, he was a training captain and battalion chief of training for the High Point (N.C.) Fire Department. He has served on the NFPA 1001 committee. He is the author

of *Tools of the Trade: Firefighting Hand Tools and Their Use* (Fire Engineering 1997) and four supporting training videos on firefighting hand tools.

MIKE GAGLIANO

has 20 years of fire, crash, and rescue experience with the Seattle (Wash.) Fire Department and the U.S. Air Force. He is the captain of training and a member of the SFD Operational Skills Enhancement Development Team. He has written numerous fire service articles, is coauthor of *Air Management for the Fire Service* (Fire Engineering 2008), and is a national instructor on air management and firefighter safety.

CHARLES JENNINGS, PH.D., MIFIREE, CFO

began in the fire service in 1979 and has served in operational and administrative positions from firefighter, line officer, director, and commissioner in West Elmira (N.Y.), Ithaca (N.Y.), Hillandale (Montgomery County, Md.) and White Plains (N.Y.), where he served as Deputy Commissioner of Public Safety from 2002-2008. He is an active fire service policy researcher and consultant. He is an associate professor at John Jay College of Criminal Justice and is also the director of the Christian Regehard Center for Emergency Response Studies at John Jay College.

PHILLIP JOSE

is a 21-year veteran of the Seattle (Wash.) Fire Department where he is a Battalion Chief. He has served as a lieutenant and captain in the Training Division, and is a member of the SFD Operational Skills Enhancement Development Team. Chief Jose teaches nationally on tactics, air management, and firefighter safety. He is coauthor of *Air Management for the Fire Service* (Fire Engineering 2008) and numerous articles in fire service publications.

RON KANTERMAN

entered the fire service in 1975 with the Fire Department of the City of New York, from which he resigned in 1989 as assistant chief inspector of the Bureau of Fire Prevention. He is chief of emergency services for a Fortune 100 pharmaceutical company in New Jersey. He is currently fire chief at the Mohegan Tribe Fire Department in Connecticut. He has a bachelor's degree in fire administration and master's degrees in fire protection management and environmental science. Kanterman is also an advocate for the National Fallen Firefighters Foundation and is COO each year at the National Memorial Weekend ceremonies.

TOM KIURSKI

is a 26-year veteran of the fire service and has served Livonia (Mich.) Fire & Rescue for the past 21 years, where he is training coordinator. He also serves as a lieutenant, paramedic, and director of fire safety education. He is the author of *Creating a Fire Safe Community: A Guide for Fire Safety Educators* (Fire Engineering 1999). Kiurski has written 150 fire safety articles that have appeared in *Fire Engineering* and other fire service publications. He has an associate's degree in fire science, a bachelor's degree in fire and safety engineering technology, and a master's degree in public administration. He is a Michigan-certified fire instructor and teaches at Michigan fire academies.

JERRY KNAPP

is a training officer at the Rockland County Fire Training Center in Pomona, N.Y. He is a 34-year veteran firefighter and EMT with the West Haverstraw (N.Y.) Fire Department. He has a degree in fire science, was a nationally registered paramedic, and is an assistant chief with the Rockland County Hazmat Team. He is a frequent contributor to *Fire Engineering*, an FDIC presenter, and a H.O.T. class instructor.

RICK LASKY

is a 27-year veteran of the fire service and chief of the Lewisville (Tex.) Fire Department. He began his career as a firefighter in the suburbs on the southwest side of Chicago. He received the ISFSI 1996 Innovator of the Year award for his part in developing the Saving Our Own program. He was colead instructor for the FDIC H.O.T. firefighter survival program for 10 years and is a member of the *Fire Engineering* editorial advisory board and the FDIC executive ddvisory board. He is a participant in *Fire Engineering*'s Roundtable and the author of *Pride and Ownership—A Firefighter's Love of the Job* (Fire Engineering 2006) leadership series.

DENNIS LEGEAR

entered the fire service in 1994. He has served with state, county, and local fire agencies in California, providing him with a strong foundation in many aspects of the fire service. He has an associate's degree in fire science and a bachelor's degree in vocational education from California State University-Long Beach. He has consulted with major water municipalities assisting in the development of emergency response plans for a variety of water infrastructure problems related to seismic events and other disasters. He is a captain in the Oakland Fire Department and also serves as the water supply officer.

DOUG LEIHBACHER

is a 28-year veteran of the fire service and retired as an assistant chief in the Yonkers (N.Y.) Fire Department. He has an associate's degree in fire protection technology and a bachelor's degree in education. He is a certified fire instructor and municipal training officer and has served as senior instructor for the YFD Probationary Firefighter Training School and as an adjunct instructor at the Westchester County Training Academy. He has certifications in incident safety, code enforcement, and fire investigation, and he is a hazardous materials technician. He has also been a classroom and H.O.T. instructor at FDIC as well as a contributing author for *Fire Engineering* since 1994 and www.Fire Nuggets.com since 2000.

W. JACK MILLER

has been involved in the fire service and fire protection equipment for more than 30 years. He is secretary of the Wyckoff (N.J.) Fire Department and president of Protection Fire Company No. 1 Association. Miller is vice president of sales of New Jersey and New York for Amerex Corporation, a manufacturer of hand portable and wheeled fire extinguishers. He is a recipient of the Dana Hannon Distinguished Service Award.

JOHN MITTENDORF

is a 30-year veteran of the Los Angeles City Fire Department who retired as a battalion chief in 1993. He is a former member of the fire science advisory boards of five colleges and the author of numerous fireground articles in U.S. and European fire service-related magazines. He is the author of *Ventilation Methods and Techniques* (1988), *Truck Company Operations* (Fire Engineering 1998), and *Facing the Promotional Interview* (Fire Engineering 2003). He lectures in the United States and United Kingdom on strategy and tactics, truck company operations, fireground operations, ventilation operations, and the complete fire officer. He is a member of the *Fire Engineering* editorial advisory board.

JACK J. MURPHY

is the principal of JJM & Associates, LLC. He is a retired fire marshal and former deputy chief of the Leonia (N.J.) Fire Department. He has a master's degree in education and several undergraduate degrees. He serves as a New Jersey state deputy fire coordinator (Bergen Region), the vice chairman of the New York City High-Rise Fire Safety Directors Association, a member of the NFPA High-Rise Building Safety Advisory Committee, and an International Code Council active member within the code development process. He is the author of many fire service articles and a field workbook on Rapid Incident Command System. He is a contributing editor and an advisory board member of both *Fire Engineering* and FDIC.

MIKE NASTA

is a 23-year veteran of the Newark (N.J.) Fire Department serving as deputy chief in charge of the training division. He is also a member of the South Hackensack (N.J.) Volunteer Fire Department, having served two terms as department chief. He is a New Jersey state-certified level II fire instructor and a senior fire instructor at the Bergen County (N.J.) Law & Public Safety Institute at the Fire Academy. He coauthored the fireground officer development course with Anthony Avillo and has written numerous fire service articles. He is an FDIC H.O.T. class coordinator.

JERRY NAYLIS

has been in the fire service for 35 years as both a career and volunteer firefighter. Additionally, he worked for FM Global and its legacy company Arkwright for 15 years performing loss prevention and loss control engineering work. Naylis has written extensively in fire service publications and has lectured and taught fire-related topics throughout the United States, Canada and the United Kingdom. He is a past president of the International Association of Arson Investigators. Naylis is the fire series book acquisitions editor for Fire Engineering Books & Videos.

CASEY PHILLIPS

is a 20-year veteran of the fire service, serving the last 13 years with the Seattle (Wash.) Fire Department. He currently holds the position of captain on Engine 28, and is a member of the SFD Operational Skills Enhancement Development Team. Captain Phillips is coauthor of *Air Management for the Fire Service* (Fire Engineering 2008) and teaches across the country on air management and firefighter safety.

TIM PILLSWORTH

is a past chief of the Winona Lake Engine Company No. 2 in Orange County, N.Y., and has been an active volunteer firefighter and EMT since 1986. He is a past presenter at FDIC East and a contributor to *Fire Engineering*. He is employed as a civil engineer and project manager with the U.S. Army Corps of Engineers at West Point, N.Y.

FOREST REEDER

began his fire service career in 1979. He currently serves as battalion chief/director of training & safety with the Pleasantview Fire Protection District and is the director of training for Southwest United Fire Districts. In these capacities, he is responsible for the design, implementation, and coordination of in-service training activities as well as a full-service fire training academy program. He holds numerous Illinois fire service certifications and has an associate of applied science degree in fire science technology, a bachelor's degree in fire department administration, and a master's degree in public safety administration from Lewis University.

FRANK RICCI

serves as the Director of Fire Services for ConnectiCOSH (Connecticut Council on Occupational Safety & Health). He is an adjunct instructor for the New Haven Fire Department, Emergency Training Solutions, Middlesex County Fire School and an FDIC H.O.T. instructor and lecturer. Ricci is a contributing author of *Carbon Monoxide Poisoning* (2008) and a regular contributor to *Fire Engineering* magazine. He developed the *Fire Engineering* film "Smoke Showing" and is a member of the IAFC Safety and Survival Section. Frank created the DVD *Firefighter Survival Techniques: From Prevention to Intervention* and also appeared in *Live Fire Training in Acquired Structures* – both from Fire Engineering Books & Videos (2008).

DAN SHERIDAN

began his fire service career in 1986 with the Fire Department of the City of New York where he is a battalion chief. He is a division supervisor with the FDNY Incident Management Team in the operations section. Sheridan serves as the executive officer to the chief of training and is a national level II instructor. Previously Sheridan worked as captain of the 6th Division, on Tower Ladder 17 in the South Bronx, in Squad 41, in SOC as a lieutenant, and on Engine 58. He has been cited eight times for bravery, three individual and five unit awards.

JEFF SHUPE

has been a career firefighter for 31 years and is a member of the Cleveland (Ohio) Fire Department. He has also served as a volunteer firefighter. He is an Ohio-certified fire instructor and has served as training coordinator for volunteer and career fire departments. He has an associate's degree in fire technology and attended the University of Cincinnati fire protection program. He is an FDIC

H.O.T. team member for engine company operations and a classroom presenter.

VICTOR STAGNARO

is a lieutenant colonel with the Prince George's County (Md.) Fire/EMS Department. He has been with the department for 24 years and oversees its Emergency Operations Command. He is responsible for the 44 Fire/ EMS Stations, all technical and Special Operations, and the Advanced Emergency Medical Services office. Stagnaro is a contributing author to *Fire Engineering* magazine.

MARK A. SULCOV

is a 33-year veteran of the fire service with the Fort Lee (N.J.) Fire Department. He has been a lieutenant for several years and is serving as assistant training officer, the department safety officer, and a member of the technical rope rescue team. He is a New Jersey state-certified fire inspector, level II fire instructor, and a senior fire instructor at the Bergen County (N.J.) Law & Public Safety Institute at the Fire Academy. He is also a member of the Fair Lawn (N.J.) Fire Department.

ROBERT TILL

is a licensed professional engineer and associate professor teaching and researching fire science at John Jay College of Criminal Justice. In 2001 he received his Ph.D. in fire protection engineering from Worcester Polytechnic Institute, where his thesis addressed the evaluation of buildings for fire department intervention. He is special expert member of the NFPA Standard for Fixed Guideway Transit and Passenger Rail Systems (NFPA 130) Committee and is chairman of the Controls Reliability task group. He is also a member of the Society of Fire Protection Engineers Fire Department Operations task group.

CHRISTINE WAGNER

is an on-scene coordinator for the U.S. Environmental Protection Agency. She takes part in environmental cleanup projects for Region 3. Based in Richmond, Va., Region 3 serves Delaware, the District of Columbia, Maryland, Pennsylvania, Virginia, and West Virginia. Along with her work in the field, Wagner provides training in hazardous materials and emergency response to fire marshals, emergency responders, and emergency management personnel.

RICHARD S. WOLFSON CFEI

is the senior fire and explosion cause analysis expert with Atlantic Professional Services of Clifton, N.J. He is a member of the International Association of Arson Investigators and is a qualified expert witness in federal and state courts in New Jersey and New York. He has taught at the Bergen County (N.J.) Law and Public Safety Institute at the Fire Academy and is a volunteer firefighter and fire investigator with the City of Garfield (N.J. Fire Department.

JOHN WORON

a 26-year fire service veteran, is an assistant chief with the Middletown (Conn.) Fire Department. He's a certified Fire Officer IV, Fire Service Instructor II, Safety Officer, and Hazardous Materials Technician. Woron holds a bachelor's degree in fire administration, is an adjunct senior instructor for the Connecticut Fire Academy, and the director of training for the Middlesex (Conn.) Regional Fire School. He is a Task Force Leader of the CT-TF-1 USAR Team.

ALAN R. YOUNG

retired in 2002 from the Sacramento (Calif.) City Fire Department as an assistant chief with 30 years of fire service experience. His last assignment was as chief of communications for the Sacramento Regional Fire and EMS Communication Center. He graduated from Sacramento State University with a bachelor's degree in business administration and is a certified fire officer with the California State Fire Marshal's Office. He has an extensive background in education concentrating in the command field. He has taught emergency operational command procedures at several community colleges.

ACKNOWLEDGMENTS

This project wouldn't be complete without acknowledging and thanking those who had a hand in its creation.

Fire Engineering magazine: Bobby Halton, Editor in Chief; Diane Feldman, Executive Editor; and Nate DeMarse, Photo Editor, for their editorial assistance and support.

Special thanks to these members of the fire service community who served as reviewers and provided invaluable guidance and feedback:

Jack Alderton, Chief, Morris County Fire Academy (NJ)

John Buckheit, Battalion Chief, FDNY (NY)

Mike Cardwell, Asst. Chief, Urbandale FD (IL)

Al Gerber, Senior Fire Instructor, Bergen County Law & Public Safety Institute (NJ)

Steve Kerber, Deputy Chief, College Park Volunteer FD (IL)

Nick Morgan, Firefighter, St. Louis FD (MO)

Cary Roccaforte, Program Coordinator, ESTI Recruit Training Academy (TX)

Rob Schnepp, Captain/Paramedic, Alameda County FD (CA)

Michael Walker, Chief, Oklahoma City FD (OK)

Devon Wells, Chief, Hood River FD (OR)

Mike Witten, Captain, Tulsa FD (OK)

Many thanks to these individuals, fire departments, academies, organizations, and state entities that generously gave their time and cooperation:

Additional Technical Contributors

Penny Adams, Center Manager, Sacramento Regional Fire EMS Communication Center (CA)

Brian Arnold, Captain, Oklahoma City FD (OK)

Peter Bertocchi, CFI, FDNY (NY)

David Collado, Firefighter, FDNY (NY)

Rick Dempsey, CFI, Eastchester FD (NY)

Benjamin Dockstader, Firefighter, Brook Park FD (OH)

Bill Gustin, CFI, Miami-Dade FD (FL)

Robert Halpin, Captain, Carmel FD (Ret.) (IN)

William Hicks, Asst. Professor, Fire and Safety Engineering Technology, Eastern Kentucky University (KY)

Leigh Hollins, CFI, Cedar Hammock Fire Rescue (FL)

International Society of Fire Service Instructors (ISFSI)

Jim Jadkowski, CFI, Westchester County Dept. of Emergency Services (NY)

Adam Knight, Engineer, Kootenai County Fire & Rescue (ID)

Ralph McNemar, USAF Fire Protection (Ret.)

Charles Metcalf, Captain, DeSoto FD Dist. 8, Mansfield (LA)

Richard Nagle, NYS Office of Fire Prevention and Control (NY)

Brian Ohleth, CFI, Stamford FD (CT)

Chris Pepler, Firefighter, Torrington FD (CT)

Glen Rudner, Hazardous Materials Officer, Virginia Dept. of Emergency Management (VA)

David Russell, CFI, FDNY (NY)

John Van Voorhies, CFI, White Plains FD (NY)

Photo/Video/Drill Assistance

Marion W. Anderson, Lieutenant, Mask Service Unit, FDNY (NY)

Andrew Antoni, Firefighter, Mask Service Unit, FDNY (NY)

Don Arterburn, Chief, Rockland County Technical Rescue Team (NY)

David and Lisa Barthold, Waldwick EMS (NJ)

Thomas Bierds, Instructor, Rockland County Fire Training Center (NY)

Peter Byrne, Coordinator for Safety and Compliance, Rockland County (NY)

Dannie Caldwell, Captain, Tulsa FD (OK)

Sharon Corbett, Waldwick EMS (NJ)

Dusty Danderson, Captain, Collinsville FD (OK)

George Drescher, Deputy Fire Coordinator, Rockland County (NY)

Brian Duddy, Photographer, Central Nyack FD (NY)

Jason Emery, Lieutenant, Waterbury FD (CT)

Rick Fisher, Major, Broken Arrow FD (OK)

Phil Greer, Firefighter, Dan Leghorn Engine Company #1, Orange Lake Fire District, Newburgh (NY)

Kristopher M. Grills, Firefighter, Mask Service Unit, FDNY (NY)

Peter Grosbek, Chief, Blauvelt Volunteer FD (NY)

James Hester, Captain, Tinker Air Force Base FD (OK)

Thomas F. Hoey Jr., Firefighter, Winona Lake Engine Company #2 (NY)

Chris Hohol, Live Fire Training by Fire LLC

Tom Jenkins, Chief, Sand Springs FD (OK)

Nathaniel Johnson, Firefighter, Mask Service Unit, FDNY (NY)

Mark Joslin, Chief, Sand Springs FD (OK)

John P. Kay, Detroit FD (MI)

Kyle Knapp, Firefighter, West Haverstraw FD (NY)

Ryan Lawson, Training Officer, Broken Arrow FD (OK)

Dan Madrzykowski, Fire Protection Engineer, National Institute of Standards and Technology

Chris Mancuso, Haight Fire Equipment Supply

John Marlar, Captain, Tulsa FD (OK)

Ray McCormack, Lieutenant, FDNY (NY)

Neil Moses, Firefighter, Waldwick FD (NJ)

Bryan Myrick, Training Officer, Broken Arrow FD (OK)

Paul Newton, Chief, Glenpool FD (OK)

Terrell Ogilvie, Firefighter, Glenpool FD (OK)

Frank Ogno, MES Northeast

John Peeters, Chief, Tomahawk FD (WI)

Mike Percival, Captain, Collinsville FD (OK)

Tony Piontek, Live Fire Training by Fire LLC

Rick Pisani, Asst. Chief, Orange Lake Fire District (NY)

Larry Rauch, Chief, Bergen County Law and Public Safety Institute (NJ)

Mike Reise, Captain, Broken Arrow FD (OK)

Jennie Ross, Firefighter, Collinsville FD (OK)

James Russell, Firefighter, Mask Service Unit, FDNY (NY)

Justin Shelby, Captain, Collinsville FD (OK)

Vinni Spampinato, Chief, Orange Lake Fire District (NY)

Andy Teeter, Chief, Tulsa FD (OK)

Mike Wood, Chief, Sand Springs FD (OK)

Gordon Wren, Director of Fire and Emergency Services, Rockland County (NY)

Russell Young, Chief, Collinsville FD (OK)

Bergen County Law and Public Safety Institute (NJ)

Bergenfield FD (NY)

Bergenfield Fire Training Center (NY)

Blauvelt Volunteer FD (NY)

Broken Arrow FD (OK)

Chelsea FD (MI)

Collinsville FD (OK)

Detroit FD (MI)

Eastern Oklahoma County Fire Training Center (OK)

Fort Bliss FD (TX)

Glenpool FD (OK)

Lewisville FD (TX)

New York FD (NY)

Orangeburg Volunteer FD (NY)

Pittsfield Township FD (MI)

Rockland County Fire Training Center (NY)

Rockland County Haz-Mat Response Team (NY)

Sand Springs FD (OK)

Superior Township FD (MI)

Tulsa FD (OK)

West Nyack Volunteer FD (NY)

Ypsilanti Township FD (MI)

INTRODUCTION

It's no coincidence that the creation of one of the first American training schools for firefighters centered on the use of a then-new piece of equipment—the "Pompier" scaling ladder. Introduced as part of a new "life-saving corps" school of the New York City Fire Department (FDNY) in 1887, this new ladder with a gooseneck hook at the top and a set of rungs on a center beam allowed individual firefighters to vertically ascend the entire height of a building, traveling from window to window.

It is also no fluke that it was Chris Hoell, a St. Louis fire captain, who introduced the scaling ladder to the United States and the FDNY. Hoell had earlier created his own life-saving corps in the St. Louis Fire Department in 1877. He invented the ladder belt, still used by many fire departments today. The use of a scaling ladder requires upper body strength as well as a significant amount of inner strength and fortitude. The scaling ladder was used for decades by many fire academies to instill confidence in each new recruit.

Hoell's efforts are just one example of how the fire service has improved over the years. Training is at the heart of these improvements, founded upon the shared history, experience, and innovation of firefighters from across the United States. We learn from each other, improving techniques and developing new tools. Many of the training protocols that you will be taught came at the greatest price—*the supreme sacrifice*. It is up to you to study these "lessons learned" and to use them in your career. It is also your responsibility to stay current with new protocols and equipment as the fire service continues to evolve during your career.

Fire Engineering's Handbook for Firefighter I and II that you hold in your hands was created upon this solid foundation of history, experience, and innovation. It builds upon the works of such fire service luminaries as Fred Shepperd, Warren Isman, Frank Brannigan, Lloyd Layman, Ray Downey, Andy Fredericks, Tom Brennan, and many others (as you advance in your career, learn about these individuals and their contributions). It also builds upon the legacy of *Fire Engineering* magazine, the most respected fire service journal and one of the oldest trade publications in the nation, with its roots dating back to 1877.

Captain Chris Hoell, one of many early and important contributors to the fire service training legacy.

There are nearly a thousand years of collective experience among the authors of this *Handbook*. They are among the best educators in the fire service. As editor, I asked each of them to prepare a state-of-the-art chapter, to provide you with the most effective and safest techniques available. Reading and practicing the skills contained in these pages will lead you down the path to becoming an effective firefighter. It will also help you to perform the most important of duties, to save lives: the lives of the citizens you have sworn to protect as well as you and your fellow firefighters.

HOW TO USE THE HANDBOOK

Fire Engineering's Handbook is organized into two sections: *Firefighter I and Firefighter II*. The chapter topics are ordered so that students learn the basic components and safety issues of firefighting first--from fire behavior all the way up to fire streams--then pulls all of that training together to apply it in Fire Attack and more complex topics. Each chapter ends with study questions for you to review. The Fireground Notes provide short tips of the trade and words of wisdom from fire training greats. Many authors have provided personal Lessons from the Fireground to underscore their topic issues.

In many chapters you will also see a special Skill Drill icon. This points you to the spiral-bound Skill Drill Book for the chapter's related drills. Each skill drill includes step-by-step photos and instructions. We hope that you will take the smaller (and lighter!) skill drill book out on the training field with you when you practice your knot tying, ladder-raising, hose-stretching, and many other skills.

UPDATES FOR 2013

The *Fire Engineering Handbook 2013 Update* has been adjusted to include all changes to knowledge and skill requirements for the *NFPA 1001 Standard for Firefighter Professional Qualifications, 2013 Edition*, as well as the related Hazmat Awareness, Operations, and Mission-Specific requirements from the 2013 Edition of NFPA 472. The NFPA Knowledge Correlations following this Introduction will demonstrate the coverage for both Standards.

Finally, we encourage instructors and students alike to read the following position statement from the International Society of Fire Instructors (ISFSI) on Fire Dynamics Research in Tactical Operations, and to stay updated on these discussions going forward, so that you can be informed on these important new factors in firefighting safety.

I'm sure that you are very excited as you begin your fire service career, wanting to learn all you can about firefighting. I know I was when I began my firefighting journey, just as it was for my father when he became a firefighter. I encourage you to keep that excitement burning inside of you in the years to come—*never stop learning and training.* Learn from others and share what you have learned. Remember, it's a brotherhood and sisterhood that you have joined—we depend upon each other.

Welcome to the fire service family!

Glenn P. Corbett, editor

Waldwick, N.J.

December 2013

Editor's note: *A project of this size and scope is the result of the work of many talented hands. I would like to express my sincere gratitude to the core group who made it happen—dedicated professionals who spent days and many nights and weekends toiling away on this effort. They endured countless twice-weekly conference calls and endless email improvements, ensuring that this* Handbook *and its associated materials would set a new standard for excellence. I can't thank these people enough: Mary McGee, Marla Patterson, Brad Epperley, Sheila Brock, Mark Haugh, Jerry Naylis, Steve Hill, Tony Quinn, Susan Ormston, Jane Green, Tim Flannery, and Jason Emery.*

I also want to send a "tip of the helmet" to our authors—thanks to each and every one of them. They know how important this book is to America's new firefighters.

STATEMENT ON FIRE DYNAMICS RESEARCH

Since the 2008 edition of the 1001 Standard, ground-breaking fire dynamics research has been at the forefront of fire training safety discussions. While the findings from the National Institute of Standards and Technology (NIST) and United Laboratories (UL) have been eye-opening, the effect on firefighter training is yet to be seen. The recommendations are not yet a part of the NFPA 1001 requirements for Firefighter I and II certification. Still, there is no doubt they will impact future training, with the goal of greater firefighter safety so that *Everybody Goes Home*.

In 2012, the International Society of Fire Service Instructors (ISFSI) received grant funding to partner with NIST and South Carolina Fire Academy for research and creation of a training module to improve firefighter safety. In October 2013, the following position statement was released by ISFSI. With their permission, we include this statement for instructor and student benefit.

International Society of Fire Service Instructors
Position Statement on Fire Dynamic Research in Tactical Operations

Given the latest research in fire dynamics and the potential impact on firefighter safety, the ISFSI board of directors unanimously releases this position statement. The ISFSI encourages all fire departments to incorporate the fire dynamics research into their tactical operations through any and all means necessary.

"Given the potential to improve firefighter safety, we believe fire departments should review their tactical operations and update their tactics. The ISFSI is proud to stand behind those conducting this research and will continue to support their efforts," said ISFSI president Doug Cline.

The International Society of Fire Service Instructors (ISFSI) states its position on the importance of recent research in fire dynamics and firefighting tactics, as conducted by the National Institute of Standards & Technology (NIST) and Underwriters Laboratories (UL). The ISFSI believes that fire departments should take action to adjust their tactical plans and training programs to incorporate this research into their emergency response operations. Additionally, the ISFSI believes that professional standards should be updated to reflect the latest information in fire dynamic research as soon as possible.

Size-Up. Size-up must occur at every fire. Consideration must be given to the resources available and situational conditions, such as weather, fire location, size of the fire and building, and the construction features. A tactical plan for that fire must be developed, communicated and implemented.

Ventilation. Fire departments should manage and control the openings to the structure to limit fire growth and spread, and to control the flow path of inlet air and fire gases during tactical operations. All ventilation must be coordinated with suppression activities. Uncontrolled ventilation allows additional oxygen into the structure which may result in a rapid increase in the fire development and increased risk to firefighters due to increased heat release rates.

Suppression. Given the fuel rich environment that the fire service operates in, water should be applied to the fire as soon as possible. In many cases, water application through an exterior opening into a fire compartment may be the best first action, prior to committing firefighting resources to the interior.

Fire departments should cool the interior spaces of a fire building with water from the safest location possible, prior to committing personnel into spaces with, or adjacent to, fully developed or smoldering (ventilation limited) fire conditions.

Rapid Intervention. Fire department rapid intervention procedures should be updated to provide water on the fire as soon as possible and ventilation openings controlled during firefighter "Mayday" incidents.

Tactical Applications. Fire departments should consider revised tactical guidelines for suppression, such as the S.L.I.C.E. - R.S. acronym. This stands for the following:

Sequential actions

Size up

Locate the fire

Identify and control the flow path

Cool the heated space from a safe location

Extinguish

Actions of opportunity that may occur at any time

Rescue

Salvage

The ISFSI acknowledges the resistance to change, but believes it is important for fire departments to act on this information in a timely manner to enhance firefighter safety. Additionally, the ISFSI believes that chief officers, instructors, company officers, firefighters and all entities that support the fire service should make incorporating the latest in fire dynamic research into regular tactical operations a high priority.

We encourage instructors and students to visit ISFSI's Online Training Courses (http://learn.isfsi.org) and *Fire Engineering's* Fire Dynamics Topic Center (www.fireengineering.com/fire-dynamics.html) for new information and instruction on fire dynamics topics and firefighter safety.

NOTE: The tactical recommendations in this statement are offered as options for educational and safety consideration. *As always, readers should follow the standard operating guidelines of their department and authority having jurisdiction (AHJ).*

NFPA 1001 KNOWLEDGE CORRELATIONS

JPR	FFI Requisite Knowledge	Chapter	Page(s)
5.1.1	Organization of FD	3	30–32
	Role of FF 1 in the organization	3	34
	Mission of fire service	1, 3	4, 30
	FD's standard operating procedures and rules and regulations	3	42
	Role of other agencies as they related to the FD	3	43–45
	Aspects of the FD's member assistance program	3, 17	41, 488–489
	Importance of physical fitness and a healthy lifestyle	3, 17	41, 472
	Critical aspects of NFPA 1500 as applied to FF 1	3, 17	41–44, 183, 187, 192, 482
5.2.1	Procedures for reporting an emergency	4	58
	Departmental SOPs for taking and receiving alarms	4	58–59
	Radio codes or procedures	4	69
	Information needs of dispatch center	4	57–59
5.2.2	Fire department procedures for answering nonemergency telephone calls		57
5.2.3	Departmental radio procedures and etiquette for routine traffic, emergency traffic, and emergency evacuation signals		64–65
5.2.4	Personnel accountability systems	4, 17	61, 502
	Emergency communication procedures	17	527–529
	Emergency evacuation methods.	4, 17	62–65, 514, 524–528
5.3.1	Conditions that require respiratory protection	10	183–186
	Uses and limitations of SCBA	10	183–187
	Components of SCBA	10	187–192
	Donning procedures	10	172–173
	Breathing techniques	10	174–175
	Indications for and emergency procedures used with SCBA	10	199–203
	Physical requirements of the SCBA wearer	10	187
5.3.2	Mounting and dismounting procedures for riding fire apparatus	17	491
	Hazards and ways to avoid hazards associated with riding apparatus	17	400–499
	Prohibited practices	17	479–491
	Types of department personal protective equipment and the means of usage	9, 17	160–164, 490
5.3.3	Potential hazards involved in operating on emergency scenes including vehicle traffic, utilities, and environmental conditions	17	483–484
	Proper procedures for dismounting apparatus in traffic	17	491
	Procedures for safe operation at emergency scenes	17	491
	Protective equipment available for members' safety on emergency scenes	17	491–493
	Work zone designations	17, 24	493, 752
5.3.4	Basic construction of typical doors, windows, and walls within the department's community or service area	7	115–119
	Operation of doors, windows, and locks	12	232, 239–245
	Dangers associated with forcing entry through doors, windows, and walls	12	251

JPR	FFI Requisite Knowledge	Chapter	Page(s)
5.3.10	Principles of fire streams	15, 16	380–382, 433–434, 445–446
	Types, design, operation, nozzle pressure effects, and flow capabiliites of nozzles	16	435–439
	Precautions to be followed when advancing hose lines to a fire	16	446–447
	Observable results that a fire stream has been properly applied	16	446–457
	Dangerous building conditions created by fire	7, 20	115–116, 620–623
	Principles of exposure protection	16, 20	460, 644
	Potential long-term consequences of exposure to products of combustion	10	183–186
	Physical states of matter in which fuels are found	5	77–79
	Common types of accidents or injuries and their causes	17	471–475
	Application of each size and type of attack line	15, 16	397–398, 439–442
	Role of the backup team in fire attack situations	16, 30	455–457, 612–613
	Attack and control techniques for grade level and above and below grade levels	17, 20, 31	506, 635–636, 906, 908–911
	Exposing hidden fires	20, 21	632, 650, 662–668
5.3.11	Principles, advantages, limitations and effects of horizontal, mechanical, and hydraulic ventilation	14, 16, 20	326–328, 623–624
	Safety considerations when venting a structure	14	327
	Fire behavior in a structure	5, 14	86–90, 327–332
	Products of combustion found in a structure fire	10, 14	184, 318–319, 327, 365
	Signs, causes, effects and prevention of backdrafts	5	88, 90
	Relationship of oxygen concentration to life safety and fire growth	5, 14	76–90, 324–330
5.3.12	Methods of heat transfer	5	83–85
	Principles of thermal layering within a structure on fire	5, 14, 20	87, 323–324, 621
	Techniques and safety precautions for venting flat roofs, pitched roofs and basements	31	906–909
	Basic indicators of potential collapse or roof failure	7	135
	Effects of construction type and elapsed time under fire conditions on structure integrity	7, 14	116, 135–137, 342–343
	Advantages and disadvantages of vertical and trench/strip ventilation	14	318–321
5.3.13	Types of fire attack lines and water application devices most effective for overhaul	16	460
	Water application methods for extinguishment that limit water damage	16	460
	Types of tools and methods used to expose hidden fire	21	656–669
	Dangers associated with overhaul	21	663–669
	Obvious signs of area of origin or signs of arson	21	663–664
	Reasons for protection of fire scene	21	656, 662, 669
5.3.14	Purpose of property conservation and its value to the public	21	656
	Methods used to protect property	21	656–657
	Types of and uses for salvage covers	21	658–659
	Operations at properties protected with automatic sprinklers	21	661–662
	How to stop the flow of water from an automatic sprinkler head	21	661
	Identification of the main control valve on an automatic sprinkler system	21	661
	Forcible entry issues related to salvage	21	656–657
	Procedures for protecting possible areas of origin and potential evidence.	21	656–669

JPR	FFI Requisite Knowledge	Chapter	Page(s)
5.3.15	Loading and off-loading procedures for mobile water supply apparatus	15	392–393
	Fire hydrant operation	15	387–389
	Suitable static water supply sources, procedures, and protocol for connecting to various water sources	15	391–392
5.3.16	Classifications of fire	6	93
	Types of, rating systems for, and risks associated with each class of fire	6	93–100
	Operating methods of and limitations of portable extinguishers	6	101–105
5.3.17	Safety principles and practices	17	495–496
	Power supply capacity and limitations	17	495–496
	Light deployment methods	17	495–496
5.3.18	Properties, principles, and safety concerns for electricity, gas, and water systems	17	497
	Utility disconnect methods and associated dangers	17	497–499
	Use of required safety equipment	17	497–499
5.3.19	Types of ground cover fires	20	648–649
	Parts of ground cover fires	20	648–649
	Methods to contain or suppress	20	648–649
	Safety principles and practices	20	648–649
5.3.20	Knot types and usage	8	145–148
	Difference between life safety and utility rope	8, 14	142–143, 353
	Reasons for placing rope out of service	8	152–153
	Types of knots to use for given tools, ropes, or situations	8	145–148
	Hoisting methods for tools and equipment	8	149
	Using rope to support response activities	8, 13, 14	145–151, 272, 329, 347
5.5.1	Types of cleaning methods for various tools and equipment	8, 9, 10, 11, 13	152, 175, 203, 216, 223, 269
	Correct use of cleaning solvents	11	216
	Manufacturer's or departmental guidelines for cleaning equipment and tools	11, 20	216, 223, 628
5.5.2	Departmental procedures for noting defective hose and removing from service	15	411–412
	Cleaning methods	15	411
	Hose rolls and loads	15	415–419

JPR	FFII Requisite Knowledge	Chapter	Page(s)
6.1.1	Responsibilities of the FF 2 in assuming and transferring command within an incident management system	27	835–836
	Performing assigned duties in conformance with applicable NFPA and other safety regulations and AHJ procedures	17, 27	500, 834
	Role of FF 2 within the organization	27, 31	837, 906
	Purpose and usefulness of accurate reports	28	853–854
	Consequences of inaccurate reports	28	853–854
	How to obtain necessary information	28	853–854
	Required coding procedures	28	853–854
6.2.2	SOPs for alarm assignments	28	846
	Fire department radio communication procedures	28	847–853
6.3.1	Methods by which foam prevents or controls a hazard	31	931–940
	Principles by which foam is generated	31	931–940
	Causes for poor foam generation and corrective measures	31	936–937
	Difference between hydrocarbon and polar solvent fuels and the concentrates that work on each	31	932
	Characteristics, uses, and limitations of fire-fighting foams	31	931–940
	Advantages and disadvantages of using fog nozzles versus foam nozzles for foam application	31	937–938
	Foam stream application techniques	31	937–939
	Hazards associated with foam usage	31	939–940
	Methods to reduce or avoid hazards	31	939–940
6.3.2	Selection of the nozzle and hose for fire attack, given different fire situations	16	461–463
	Selection of adapters and appliances to be used for specific fireground situations	16	461–463
	Dangerous building conditions created by fire and fire suppression activities	31	906–931
	Indicators of building collapse	7, 31	135–136, 906–931
	Effects of fire and fire suppression activities on wood, masonry (brick, block, stone), cast iron, steel, reinforced concrete, gypsum wallboard, glass, and plaster on lath	7	116
	Search and rescue and ventilation procedures	19, 31	577–591, 907–913
	Indicators of structural instability	7	135–136
	Suppression approaches and practices for various types of structural fires	16, 31	442–445, 907–931
	Association between specific tools and special forcible entry needs	12	232–235
6.3.3	Characteristics of pressurized flammable gases	31	923–931
	Elements of a gas cylinder	31	927–928
	Effects of heat and pressure on closed cylinders	31	928–929
	Boiling liquid expanding vapor explosion (BLEVE) signs and effects	31	928–929
	Methods for identifying contents	23	689–705
	How to identify safe havens before approaching flammable gas cylinder fires	31	929
	Water stream usage and demands for pressurized cylinder fires	31	929–930
	What to do if the fire is prematurely extinguished	31	929–930
	Valve types and their operation	31	927–930
	Alternative actions related to various hazards	31	929–930
	When to retreat	31	929–930

NFPA 472 KNOWLEDGE CORRELATIONS

			Chapter	Page
4.2.1 Continued	(18)	Identify at least four indicators of possible criminal or terrorist activity involving illicit laboratories (clandestine laboratories, weapons lab, ricin lab).	24	772
	(19)	Identify at least four indicators of possible criminal or terrorist activity involving explosives.	24	772
	(20)	Identify at least four indicators of secondary devices.	24	772
4.2.2	(1)	Identify difficulties encountered in determining the specific names of hazardous materials/WMD at facilities and in transportation.	23	710
	(2)	Identify sources for obtaining the names of, UN/NA identification numbers for, or types of placard associated with hazardous materials/WMD in transportation.	23	726
	(3)	Identify sources for obtaining the names of hazardous materials/WMD at a facility.	23	691
4.2.3	(1)	Identify the three methods for determining the guidebook page for a hazardous materials/WMD.	23	725
	(2)	Identify the two general types of hazards found on each guidebook page.	23	725
4.4.1	(1)	Identify the location of both the emergency response plan and/or standard operating procedures.	22	679
	(2)	Identify the role of the awareness level personnel during hazardous materials/WMD incidents.	22	676
	(3)(a)	Identify the precautions necessary when providing emergency medical care to victims of hazardous materials/WMD incidents.	25	798
	(3)(b)	Identify typical ignition sources found at the scene of hazardous materials/WMD incidents.	25	785
	(3)(c)	Identify the ways hazardous materials/WMD are harmful to people, the environment, and property.	23	716
	(3)(d)	Identify the general routes of entry for human exposure to hazardous materials/WMD.	23	722
	(4)(a)	Emergency action (fire, spill, or leak and first aid)	23	727
	(4)(b)	Personal protective equipment necessary	23	727
	(4)(c)	Initial isolation and protective action distances	23	728
	(5)(a)	Street clothing and work uniforms	23	727
	(5)(b)	Structural fire-fighting protective clothing	23	727
	(5)(c)	Positive pressure self-contained breathing apparatus	23	727
	(5)(d)	Chemical-protective clothing and equipment	23	727
	(6)(a)	Isolation of the hazard area and denial of entry	24	750
	(6)(b)	Evacuation	24	750
	(6)(c)	Sheltering in-place	24	751
	(7)	Identify the size and shape of recommended initial isolation and protective action zones.	23	740
	(8)	Describe the difference between small and large spills as found in the Table of Initial Isolation and Protective Action Distances in the DOT Emergency Response Guidebook	23	728
	(9)	Identify the circumstances under which the following distances are used at a hazardous materials / WMD incidents:	23	728
	(9)(a)	Table of Initial Isolation and Protective Action Distances	23	728
	(9)(b)	Isolation distances in the numbered guides	23	728
	(10)	Describe the difference between the isolation distances on the orange-bordered guidebook pages and the protective action distances on the green-bordered ERG (Emergency Response Guidebook) pages.	23	728
	(11)	Identify the techniques used to isolate the hazard area and deny entry to unauthorized persons at hazardous materials/WMD incidents.	24	750
	(12)	Identify at least four specific actions necessary when an incident is suspected to involve criminal or terrorist activity.	24	769
4.4.2		Initiating the Notification Process. Given scenarios involving hazardous materials/WMD incidents, awareness level personnel shall identify the initial notifications to be made and how to make them, consistent with the emergency response plan and/or standard operating procedures.	22	676

			Chapter	Page
5.2.1.3.2		Identify each of the following pieces of information on a pesticide label, then match the piece of information to its significance in surveying hazardous materials incidents:		
	(1)	Active ingredient	23	696
	(2)	Hazard statement	23	696
	(3)	Name of pesticide	23	696
	(4)	Pest control product (PCP) number (in Canada)	23	696
	(5)	Precautionary statement	23	696
	(6)	Signal word	23	696
5.2.1.3.3		Identify the type or category of label, contents, activity, transport index, and criticality safety index as applicable for a radioactive material	23	694
5.2.1.4		Identify and list the surrounding conditions that should be noted when a hazardous materials/WMD incident is surveyed	23	688
5.2.1.5		Give examples of ways to verify information obtained from the survey of a hazardous materials/WMD incident	23	723
5.2.1.6		Identify at least three additional hazards that could be associated with an incident involving terrorist or criminal activities	24	777
5.2.2	(1)	Match the definitions associated with the UN/DOT hazard classes and divisions of hazardous materials/WMD, including refrigerated liquefied gases and cryogenic liquids, with the class or division.	23	709
	(2)	Identify two ways to obtain an MSDS in an emergency.	23	730
		Using an MSDS for a specified material, identify the following hazard and response information:		
	(3)(a)	Physical and chemical characteristics	23	730
	(3)(b)	Physical hazards of the material	23	730
	(3)(c)	Health hazards of the material	23	730
	(3)(d)	Signs and symptoms of exposure	23	730
	(3)(e)	Routes of entry	23	730
	(3)(f)	Permissible exposure limits	23	730
	(3)(g)	Responsible party contact	23	730
	(3)(h)	Precautions for safe handling including hygiene practices, protective measures, and procedures for cleanup of spills and leaks	23	730
	(3)(i)	Applicable control measures, including personal protective equipment	23	730
	(3)(j)	Emergency and first-aid procedures	23	730
	(4)(a)	Type of assistance provided by CHEMTREC/CANUTEC/ SETIQ and governmental authorities	23	732
	(4)(b)	Procedure for contacting CHEMTREC/CANUTEC/SETIQ and governmental authorities	23	732
	(4)(c)	Information to be furnished to CHEMTREC/CANUTEC/SETIQ and governmental authorities	23	732
	(5)	Identify two methods of contacting the manufacturer or shipper to obtain hazard and response information.	23	729
	(6)	Identify the type of assistance provided by governmental authorities with respect to criminal or terrorist activities involving the release or potential release of hazardous materials/WMD.	24	778
	(7)	Identify the procedure for contacting local, state, and federal authorities as specified in the emergency response plan and/or standard operating procedures.	22	679
		Describe the properties and characteristics of the following:		
	(8)(a)	Alpha radiation	23	716
	(8)(b)	Beta radiation	23	716
	(8)(c)	Gamma radiation	23	716
	(8)(d)	Neutron radiation	23	716

JPR CORRELATIONS

FIREFIGHTER I

The Traditions and Mission of the Fire Service

by Rick Lasky

This chapter provides required knowledge items for the following NFPA Standard 1001 Job Performance Requirements:

FFI 5.1.1

OBJECTIVES

Upon completion of this chapter, you should be able to do the following:

- Identify important historical figures and their relation to the fire service
- Describe what it means to be a firefighter
- List at least three fire service-related traditions
- Understand your commitment to being a firefighter

INTRODUCTION

When you look at today's fire service—our apparatus, tools, equipment, and technology—it's hard to imagine how it was way back when. Look at pictures from the olden days or read history books and you'll be amazed at what firefighters used. Considering that they had to carry almost everything to fires, including the first fire pump, we have made amazing advances. We've moved from fire buckets and **bucket brigades** to firefighters pulling their engines, hose tenders, or ladder tenders behind them, to horses pulling steam fire engines (fig. 1–1). Back then, more than just prestige came with saying one was a volunteer or paid firefighter. Firefighters knew they were making a commitment, changing their lifestyle, and joining a family. There was nothing like it.

Fig. 1–1. Horse-drawn steam fire engines were used from the 1860s to the 1920s.

EARLY VOLUNTEERS

There was a time when most volunteer firefighters were socially established or of affluence. Famous volunteer firefighters included George Washington, Thomas Jefferson, even Benedict Arnold. Firefighters were the *who's who* of the community, anyone of importance, and especially those who wanted to climb politically or socially. Let's not forget Benjamin Franklin, often called the Father of the American Fire Service (fig. 1–2). Franklin was born on January 17, 1706. He was the first American diplomat, an ambassador, storyteller, published scientist, postmaster general, inventor, and economist. He organized the first lending library, medical center, scientific society, philosophical society, volunteer fire department, and fire insurance company. He invented the lightning rod, bifocals, the static electric generator, and the Franklin stove. He was the only American founding father who signed all four major documents that established American independence: the Declaration of Independence, the treaty with France, the treaty with England, and the Constitution. (Punishment for signing these documents if caught by the British was hanging.) Showing bravery, intelligence, wit, creativity, and a will to make the world better, Franklin exhibited the personality traits of a firefighter.

Fig. 1–2. Benjamin Franklin, one of our most revered founding fathers, created America's first fire company.

GLORY DAYS

There was a glamour associated with the fire service. How one's firehouse looked, the detail given to a fire engine, and artwork associated with one's speaking trumpet or company crest were all areas of pride (fig. 1–3). **Musters** and contests determined who had the best fire company, who could get water first, and whose fire stream could go the farthest. All created exciting competition, but sometimes tussles between competing fire companies resulted. Nevertheless, whenever the bell rang, a runner or torchbearer shouted as firefighters ran down the street pulling their equipment to a fire. Residents, business owners, and children gave in to the excitement of watching their firefighters.

Fig. 1–3. The first fire trumpet, or speaking horn, was introduced in 1749 in New York City for fire department officers to amplify their voices. The first "working" trumpets (used at fire scenes) were made of toleware and later made of brass. Presentation or "parade" trumpets were nickel- or silver-plated (as seen in this photograph) or even solid silver or glass. By the 1800s they were only used for ceremonies. The use of trumpets as the insignia of rank is one of our oldest traditions.

With time, the prestige placed upon the fire service by the public began to splinter and fragment. The gallantry of horse-drawn fire engines racing down cobblestone streets, their bells ringing, and the seriousness on firefighters' faces meant a little less to those of high society. Many still held the fire department in high regard, but growing numbers considered firefighting a profession for the poor or those in need of a job. Firefighter and police officer wages were some of the lowest.

BIRTH OF THE MODERN FIRE SERVICE

So began the filling of firefighting positions by people who were not looking for financial gains but rather community service. Those who volunteered at local fire departments soon realized their commitments. When the bell rang, a firefighter was expected to stop everything to help others. Those who joined the fire service to provide a family income realized that a regular paycheck was not necessarily a big paycheck. The fire service has historically fought for every penny to run operations and, in some cases, survive. Firefighters had to be creative in budgeting and acquiring funds to protect those they swore to serve.

FIREGROUND NOTE

Our mission is very clear: to be there for people when they really need us.

As a city's population grew, so did the need to properly and safely protect those who lived there. Civilian and business populations grew steadily, but fire department budgets remained the same or decreased. North American fire departments often found themselves fighting for better equipment and more staffing—a fight we still wage. One case was in New York City. Chief Edward F. Croker served as chief of the Fire Department of the City of New York from 1899 to 1911 (fig. 1–4). When faced with budget and manpower cuts, Croker wrote and read the following statement to the city powers:

I have no ambition in the world but one, and that is to be a fireman. The position may, in the eyes of some, appear to be a lowly one; but we who know the work which a fireman has to do believe that his is a noble calling. There is an adage which states that 'Nothing can be destroyed except by fire.' We strive to preserve from destruction the wealth of the world, which is the product of the industry of men, necessary for the comfort of both the rich and the poor. We are the defenders from fire, of the art, which has

beautified the world, the product of the genius of men and the means of refinement of mankind. But, above all, our proudest endeavor is to save lives of men—the work of God himself. Under the impulse of such thoughts, the nobility of the occupation thrills us and stimulates us to deeds of daring, even at the supreme sacrifice. Such considerations may not strike the average mind, but they are sufficient to fill to the limit our ambition in life and to make us serve the general purpose of human society.

Fig. 1–4. Chief Edward F. Croker

That statement, though dated, still serves to define the passion associated with being a firefighter. "I have no ambition in the world but one, and that is to be a fireman." Man, oh man, that is the kind of desire you need in your chest to be good at what we do. This job isn't for everybody. *It takes someone special to be a firefighter.*

WHAT IS THE FIRE SERVICE?

FFI 5.1.1 But what do the words "fire service" mean to you? What does the word "firefighter" mean? The difference in definitions between a civilian and a firefighter might surprise you. Many times civilians ask us what we do, and often we explain about fighting fires, rescuing people, etc. But what is it really all about? How did we get here? First, if you're not willing to examine our heritage, nothing else about the fire service will make sense to you. That's the only way to identify what we're all about. But the fire service has evolved into more than fighting fires. We're trained in emergency medical services, hazardous materials, specialized rescue, weapons of mass destruction, and just about everything else you can come up with if it involves helping people. We have become journeymen of public service.

The fire service is based on something bigger than any of us realized when we entered our careers as firefighters. Whether you'll serve as a volunteer, paid-on-call, or paid firefighter, you'll realize that it takes a special person with special qualities to do what we do. This person must dig deeply into our history to research where we began and how we got here. This person must be willing to protect our heritage, defend our fire service family, and bring the honor that the job deserves. (See fig. 1–5.)

Fig. 1–5. Christian Michael Otto Regenhard, 28, was a probationary firefighter on September 11th, 2001 and was one of the 343 members of the FDNY killed at the World Trade Center. Pictured here are his mother, father, and sister at his memorial service held in St. Patrick's Cathedral. As a legacy to Christian, the Regenhard family created the "Skyscraper Safety Campaign" which advocates for safer high-rises through better building codes as well as improved emergency responder safety and communications. Will you study the 9/11 disaster and other emergency responses where firefighters have made the supreme sacrifice, and will you learn from them? (Courtesy of Susan Watts/New York Daily News)

WHAT DOES IT TAKE TO BE A FIREFIGHTER?

So what does it take to be a firefighter? What kind of person? It takes a person who lives within a system of values built upon family. Everything we do in the fire service has to do with family, whether it's protecting someone's home, children, belongings, or business. Every time we answer a call, it has to do with family. Now, that can be a slight problem for those who don't live by a set of values. These are the people who constantly seem to be banging into walls. They blame others and have excuses for everything. Fortunately for the fire service, it doesn't take long for these rarities to realize that family is the foundation of our success. They support it or move on. To expand on that success, you must expand your value system to include pride associated with ownership, honor bound to loyalty, and integrity, which requires you to be honest and a person of character. Once you grab these values, good things start to happen.

As a rookie firefighter, you must understand that you create your own legacy from the moment you walk into the firehouse. It's hard to make a second first impression. Ideally, you've led a good life so far and haven't muddied your resume by doing something that "seemed like the thing to do" when you were young. Ideally, you've been hanging with the right people. Constantly ask yourself, "Why did I get into the fire service, and why did I want to be a firefighter?" If your answers are to help people, to make a difference, to be part of a special family, then you're on the right track. Remember three things to be successful:

1. Do what's right.

2. Do your best.

3. Treat others the way you want to be treated.

Doing what's right means being a person of integrity. *Doing your best* means giving the job the effort it deserves and remembering why you chose this profession. *Treating people the way you would want to be treated* means treating everyone like family. People are watching. You might think otherwise, but they are. Show your fire department that you will do what it takes to be part of their team and family. Prove that they made the right choice in bringing you on as a volunteer or paid firefighter. Never lose that vision or passion.

You should have one other passion: **safety**. Make no mistake about it—firefighting is a dangerous profession. While vast improvements in equipment and procedures have been made over the last several years, injuries and death are still a part of the business. It is up to you to practice safe habits and to look out for the safety of others. Safety is the job of *every* firefighter.

FIRE SERVICE TRADITIONS

Some fire service traditions go back to its birth in North America. The traditions we must examine created passion for the fire service. Wetting down a new apparatus, pushing out an old rig and pushing in a new one, and opening a new firehouse all have importance. The swearing in and badge pinnings are just a start. It's the first step. Company logos, insignias, and tools all require understanding of their needs and importance.

How about our uniform? Do you know what it represents? It's disappointing when a fellow firefighter at a funeral says, "It's a shame. It seems we only wear our **Class A uniforms** for funerals." My usual reply is, "You're right. It is a shame . . . shame on you. That uniform is not just a funeral uniform. It represents our profession, our heritage. It stands as a symbol for what we are all about and for those who bled, sweat, and went before us. It stands for something bigger than we are. It represents something special. It's a uniform of which few are unfamiliar. When someone sees you standing straight and proud in that uniform, he or she knows you are firefighter, one of America's bravest" (fig. 1–6).

Fig. 1–6. The Class A uniform represents our profession, heritage, and all who came before us.

WHERE DO YOU GO FROM HERE?

So now what? Where do you go from here? Now that you're a new firefighter, what's your next step? You are taking that first step in climbing the mountain we call the fire service. It's full of challenges, tasks, and experiences. But each step comes with a view so awesome that, at times, it's indescribable. Sometimes that feeling will be challenged. Now and then, it will come from someone close to you in your own firehouse.

While addressing a rookie or probationary school academy graduation, I often have the candidates sit right in the front row. I ask them to close their eyes and feel that feeling of uncontrollable excitement, the one that fills them with energy. After all that time spent on classroom work, the drill field, and the physical fitness, it's graduation day. "Where will I go next?" "Where will I go to work?" "Which firehouse will I be assigned?" "Which rig?" "The engine, the ladder truck, a rescue, or the ambulance?" "Who will be my partner, and who will be my officer?" The excitement is overwhelming. You can feel it throughout your body.

Then I ask them to flash forward about two years when they're sitting at the firehouse, around the kitchen table, or on drill night complaining about the chief or their pay. *What happened to them? What changed? Or maybe the better question is whom are they hanging around? What happened to their passion? What happened to their love for the job? Who poisoned that feeling?* There's one thing I've never understood about firefighters. There is not a firefighter alive who would let a burglar break into his or her home to steal things. There isn't a firefighter who would let somebody break into his or her car and steal from them without wanting the police to arrest, prosecute, and hang the person by his toenails. But firefighters let somebody reach into their hearts and steal their passion. When I was going through such a time, a friend told me that I was being weak and letting the other side win. He said people who are weak let other people steal from them. Never allow anyone to reach into your heart and steal your passion about this wonderful profession. Defend it with everything you have. Don't ever let go of that feeling.

WHAT NEXT?

As you work through this first phase of your firefighting career, ask yourself the following questions. Allow them to guide you into and through this journey.

1. Are you ready for the challenge?

2. If you are, are you ready for the reward the challenge brings?

3. Are you ready to protect what was accomplished by those before us to make the fire service great?

4. Are you ready to defend and protect our fire service family?

5. Will you remember that you represent all of us, in and out of the firehouse, on and off duty? Whether you wear a Maltese Cross on your shirt or not, people will know that you are one of us and base their opinions of all of us by your actions. They will expect you to be a professional. Do not tarnish our image.

6. Are you willing to commit to a lifelong pursuit of continuing education, hands-on training, and mentoring those who come after you with that knowledge and those skills? Will you show them the way?

7. Will you commit to memory that "Never forgetting means never forgetting"?

8. Can you commit to a life led by values such as pride, honor, and integrity and allow those to be served by a foundation on family values?

9. Will you remember to treat retired firefighters with honor and respect, remember what they did for us, and always make them feel welcome in your firehouse? They earned it.

10. Will you train as if your life depends on it? It does.

11. Will you be a brother or sister to our fire service family? It takes a 24-hour, seven-day commitment. It's not a part-time thing.

12. Will you remember what you owe the public, and that the public doesn't owe you jack? When you raised your right hand and took an oath, pinned on that badge, or put on that fire helmet, you became a public servant.

13. Will you develop a list of mentors, people who will steer, train, and develop you, and get you fired up about the job?

14. Will you treat your firehouse like it is your home?

15. Will you take care of your apparatus, tools, and equipment? Remember, it's not just an image thing. Think about it.

16. Will you brag about the fire service both off duty and on duty?

17. Will you be that person of integrity and of character?

18. Will you show up on time for your shift or drill night? It says a lot about you and whether we can count on you. And if you're sick, stay home. If you're not, come to work!

19. Will you wear your uniform and be proud of it? It stands for a lot more than any one person. It represents our heritage.

20. Will you celebrate and participate enthusiastically in the ceremonies and traditions that promote and protect our fire service?

21. Will you always remain physically and mentally prepared to do whatever it takes?

22. Will you become a student of our fire service history and protect our heritage?

23. Will you adhere to the following rules to combat complacency?

    a. Every time we go out the door, we're going to a fire. No matter what, never let down your guard and always be prepared for the fight.

    b. When we arrive on the scene, there is no fire only if *we* say there is no fire. Listen to civilians, but don't allow yourself to be snookered or fooled.

    c. There is nobody in the building only if *we* say no one is in the building. Even when occupants are standing outside, we still search the building for fire and occupants who might be unaccounted for or overlooked.

    d. The fire is not out unless *we* say it's out.

24. Will you build relationships within your community, city, or township?

25. If you become a company officer, will you lead with distinction, remember it takes courage to lead, and make decisions because they are right, not popular? Popular decisions hurt and kill firefighters. Be their leader first, then be their buddy.

26. If you make it to chief, will you always remember where you came from?

27. Will you learn from the past and study line-of-duty deaths so history won't repeat itself?

28. Will you leave it a little better for the next guy?

29. Will you profess that the fire service is the greatest profession in the world?

30. Will you be as prepared as possible and train, train, train?

31. Will you think safety, safety, safety?

32. Will you do everything you can so everyone goes home?

Will you agree to live up to the high standards of being a firefighter?

If you can't or don't think you can make that commitment, then don't. It's probably time for you to make a different choice. Not everyone can be a firefighter. If you want the kind of life that is dedicated to protecting men, women, children, and their possessions, then welcome, brother or sister!

Good luck, be safe, and enjoy the journey.

LESSON FROM THE FIREGROUND

My love for the job came from people such as Chief Jack MacCastland who taught my Firefighter I class when I was 18 years old. Mac said, "You want to be a good firefighter? You need to know building construction and fire behavior. You have to know how the building is going to react with the fire and how the fire is going to react with the building. Anyone can go out there and chop, but you still need to know building construction and fire behavior." How very true. The first time I saw Mac was at a fire. Here was this big guy, leather helmet all bent up in the front, pulling drywall with a pike pole in one hand and using his chin to open and close the nozzle with the other hand. I said, "Man, I want to be like this guy."

Then there was Chief Eddy Enright who taught me about caring for and respecting your guys. He'd always say, "Look for their positives, Rick. Anyone can pick out the negatives. You do that and the negatives tend to go away. Catch them doing something right. It's easy to catch them doing something wrong."

One of my best friends, Chief Tom Freeman, one of the smartest firefighters I've ever met, also shared his knowledge with me. He said things such as, "A good officer or incident commander is the one who can predict his next alarm. Any mope in a white helmet can stand outside and handle what he's got right now and burn it to the ground, but it's the guy who can predict his next alarm, knows when he needs more resources before he runs out, where the fire's going, and can think out of that box who does well."

MY POINT

Perhaps the most important thing my mentors taught me was that to be a good firefighter you must have core values such as pride, honor, and integrity. And every last bit of it starts with integrity.

Rick Lasky

QUESTIONS

1. _____ is often called the Father of the American Fire Service.

2. What are some of the areas that firefighters need to be trained in to be proficient at their jobs?

3. Throughout your career as a firefighter, you should remember three things to be successful. Name them.

4. When should we wear Class A uniforms?

5. Is everyone cut out to be a firefighter? What questions can we ask ourselves to be sure we are ready to be firefighters?

Fire Service History

by Don Cannon

OBJECTIVES

Upon completion of this chapter, you should be able to do the following:

- Identify the origins of the fire service from the 5th century A.D. through the 14th century A.D.
- Identify major events that impacted the fire service during the 18th century
- Identify major events that impacted the fire service during the 19th century
- Identify major events that impacted the fire service during the 20th century
- Identify major events that are impacting the fire service during the 21st century

INTRODUCTION

The ancient Greeks recognized that the essential forces that act upon our physical world are fire, air, earth, and water. And thus mankind's ability to control and direct each of those factors has determined the success or failure of communities since they were first established.

5TH CENTURY A.D. TO 14TH CENTURY A.D.

While there were many cities in the ancient world of India and Mesopotamia and the classical world of the Greeks, Rome provided us with the first model of a major urban society in the West. Its population of more than a million made it the largest city in the West. The Emperor Augustus (63 B.C.–14 A.D.) is credited with transforming Rome from a city of brick into a city of marble by sponsoring a planned infrastructure of buildings, monuments, roads, aqueducts, and sewers. He is also credited with creating the **Vigiles**, the watchmen of the city and first public force of firefighters (fig. 2–1). Equipped with primitive though familiar apparatus and tools, the Vigiles coped with dozens of fires a day and fought several conflagrations, the most notable of which occurred in 68 A.D. during the reign of the Emperor Nero. With the collapse of the Empire, the cities of Rome declined as well and the Vigiles passed into history. Not until the age of Charles Dickens's 19th-century London would there be another city of similar size in the West. Inevitably for centuries thereafter, fire continued to ravage Europe's surviving small towns and settlements during the Middle Ages.

Fig. 2–1. The Vigiles of Rome were the first organized group of firefighters in recorded world history. Besides buckets of water, they actually used a primitive pump to apply water to a burning building. They also used hooks to tear down buildings, creating fire breaks—a technique that was subsequently used for more than 1,000 years.

15TH CENTURY A.D. TO 18TH CENTURY A.D.

The emergence of the modern world in the 16th century gave new impetus to the idea of commercial expansion. Great imperial cities began to grow again and connect to overseas settlements in every hemisphere. Colonial American towns were the offspring of those forces and each became subject to the same opportunities and dangers as its sponsoring community in the old world. Within a few years of the establishment of Jamestown, Plymouth, and Boston in the 17th century, the residents of each town considered fleeing back to England after they encountered midwinter fires. Adriaen Block, the Dutch explorer and trader, never intended to establish the first settlement in the area that was to become known as New Amsterdam when he and his crew were forced to spend the winter at the foot of Manhattan. Their ship the *Tyger* burned to the waterline late in 1613, a dozen years before Fort Amsterdam was constructed in the same area. Quickly, Peter Stuyvesant, governor of Nieuw Amsterdam, devoted himself to fire prevention by appointing a night patrol known as "the prowlers" or **Rattle Watch** (1648) and fire wardens to inspect chimneys, thatched roofs, and household cooking fires. Before the English took over the town in 1664, Stuyvesant required every householder to have buckets at hand and posted hooks and ladders for use by civilians in case of fire.

The **Great Fire of London**, which destroyed almost 80% of that city in 1666, exerted a direct influence on William Penn's original design for the city of Philadelphia. The wide streets, large tracts of land, and squares were intended to make the City of Brotherly Love a *"greene country towne . . . which will never be burnt, and always be wholesome."* Philadelphia escaped a major conflagration. Other towns were not so lucky. Charleston, South Carolina became known as a "city of fires." In Boston, one blaze after another, many suspected as arson, destroyed more than 100 buildings during a three-year period. Finally, capped in 1678 by the loss of "fourscore of thy . . . dwelling houses and seventy of thy warehouses in a ruinous heap," Boston imported fire engines from England and appointed men to operate them.

Articles in Benjamin Franklin's newspaper, the *Philadelphia Gazette*, led to the forming of America's first volunteer fire brigade, the Union Fire Company (1736). A year later in 1737, six years after two London-built **Newsham hand pumpers** arrived in New York from London, 30 "strong, able, discreet, honest, and sober men" were appointed the first firemen in New York City (fig. 2–2). In a parallel, private-sector effort to cushion the economic impact of fire losses, The Friendly Society of Charleston (1736) and the Philadelphia Contributionship (1752), America's first fire insurance companies were organized. Beginning in the 1750s, first in Philadelphia, insurance companies began to display **fire marks** on structures covered by them. Fire marks were wood or iron plaques with a unique design identifying the insurer of a building. They were initially displayed as advertisements that deterred vandals who feared being tracked down, and they encouraged fire companies to work hard in hopes of a future contribution in the annual distribution of awards by the various insurance companies (fig. 2–3).

Fig. 2–2. One of two Newsham engines New York City imported in 1731 from London, now on display in the American Museum of Firefighting in Hudson, New York. The two wooden handles on the sides of the engine—called "brakes"—were lifted up and down to pump the engine.

Fig. 2–3. Fire marks were used as forms of advertisement. This one of the mid-19th century is from an insurance company called the Fire Association of Philadelphia, and portrays a wooden hydrant and coil of hose.

One myth historians have recently laid to rest is that early American firefighters would only work on structures where fire marks were clearly displayed. As the myth goes, a purse or reward was associated with getting first water on such an insured property. It was said, falsely, that fire companies would fight each other to prevent later arriving companies from getting such a reward, even as in some cases the fire building burned to the ground. American and British historians have conclusively proved that fire brigades provided services to all who were in need, regardless of insurance. On the one hand, this was a practical matter intended to prevent extension of fire to their client properties. On the other hand, services to the uninsured were provided out of goodwill and for the positive effect it had on a company's image. In other words, fire marks were primarily posted as advertising only. Insurance companies did contribute annually to various fire companies, in some cases supplying them with needed equipment to sustain their operations, but contributions for specific fires were rare.

Arson—intentionally set fires—became a serious problem in 18th century New York. On two occasions, New York suffered a rash of arson fires attributed to discontented slaves and their sympathizers. In each case, the town's new fire companies responded. The first, in 1712, was put down quickly. In 1741, the New York Negro Plot hysteria in the city, partially triggered by a series of fires of unknown origin, culminated in the Fort George conflagration at the lower end of Manhattan. As a result, 17 blacks and 4 whites were hanged, and 13 slaves were burned at the stake. By 1790, New York City had the highest percentage of black residents other than Charleston.

Many volunteer engine companies were organized prior to the American Revolution. Shortly before the Revolution began, American inventors began to manufacture and sell their own hand pumpers. This was a clear indication that the colonial economic system was becoming less dependent upon Britain. The various trading and manufacturing restrictions imposed by London between 1763 and 1775 became increasingly viewed by merchants, mainly in the coastal cities, as an effort to strangle the emerging American economy. In the 10 years prior to the Declaration of Independence, many colonial firefighters active as Sons of Liberty seized and destroyed ships in Newport and Providence in opposition to the British Stamp Tax and trade policies. Firemen participated in the Boston Tea Party and tossed and burned cargoes of tea in Annapolis, Maryland, Greenwich, New Jersey, and Providence in protest against a British-imposed monopoly. In spring 1770, in what has become known as The Boston Massacre, a cry of "Fire!" intended to cause the town's church and fire bells to bring others to the scene caused British troops to open fire on an unarmed group of colonial protesters, killing several.

Fire Service History

FIREFIGHTER I

Chapter 2

Real shooting began in April 1775. Fire was a cruel weapon. British forces withdrawing from skirmishes at Lexington and Concord lit up houses as they retreated back to Boston. In May, 30 buildings were set afire in the dock district of Boston. In mid-June 1775, British warships set fire to 380 dwellings in Charlestown, Massachusetts, as the Battle of Bunker Hill proceeded. Beginning in fall 1775, moving down the coast from Falmouth (now Portland), Maine, continuing south to Norfolk, Virginia, and ultimately to Charleston, the British leveled towns by naval bombardment, shelling from the seaside as shore parties set waterfront structures afire. The Revolutionaries were not guilt-free, for in the winter of 1775–76 as they withdrew from their failed invasion of Quebec, burning homes, barns, and mills along the way.

The American Revolution was a brutal war, all around. In his Declaration of Independence, Thomas Jefferson condemned King George III for using fire as a terror weapon, writing: "He has plundered our seas, ravaged our coasts, burnt our towns, and destroyed the lives of our people." Jefferson's words did not deter the redcoats. In fall 1777, the British set fire to every house in Kingston, New York, as punishment for the citizens' support of the Revolution. In late September 1776, less than a week after the British occupied Manhattan, fire originating in the Fighting Cocks Tavern on Whitehall Street and several other locations in the lower west side of the island ultimately destroyed almost 500 buildings, a quarter of the city. Revolutionary sympathizers, including, as many believe, Nathan Hale ("I have but one life to lose for my country . . ."), are suspected of torching the Great Fire of 1776. At this point, New York City emptied, becoming a virtual ghost town for the remainder of the war. Historians are uncertain whether Jacob Stoutenburgh, the chief of department, and the rest of his volunteer firemen in New York left the city to join Washington's forces.

In 1778, a second Great Fire in Manhattan consumed another fifty buildings. Remaining Tory sympathizers and British naval personnel fought the fire. A year later, the British captured and burned Norfolk. Wherever they went, the Brits were ruthless adversaries. Mel Gibson's film *The Patriot* gets pretty close to the reality of the Revolution, as backcountry Americans were subject to terrifying experiences throughout the war. Frontier farms and communities all along the ridgeline of the Appalachians from the Mohawk Valley in New York to the Wyoming Valley in Pennsylvania, down through the Carolinas were lit up as Tories and their American Indian allies burned more than 1,000 homes and slew 300 settlers.

Finally, it was over. The Treaty of Paris recognized American independence in 1783. The Continental Army marched back into previously occupied territory, survivors staggered out of their prison ships, citizens returned to the cities from their rural refuges, and local fire departments began to reorganize themselves under the charters of their newly independent states.

In the early years following independence, towns in the new West were commonly overcrowded with shoddily built housing and mercantile facilities. Seven-eighths of New Orleans, the export point for everything being sent down the Mississippi River, was destroyed by fire on Good Friday 1788. A second conflagration seven years later burned out an additional 200 structures in New Orleans's French Quarter. In 1805, the entire village of Detroit was virtually wiped out, save for one building. Older towns were being transformed into industrial centers and as a result experienced ever-larger fires. Paterson, New Jersey, America's first planned industrial city, saw its first mill destroyed by fire in 1807. Philadelphia was particularly hard hit in this period but soon undertook a massive water-supply project that became the model for other cities.

19TH CENTURY

During this period, efforts were made to make fire ground operations somewhat more organized as officers using **speaking trumpets** attempted to direct ladder companies, hand-pumped engines, and informal salvage operations. Hundreds of new volunteer fire companies were formed, many including hose companies (the first was introduced in Philadelphia in 1803) using American-designed **"gooseneck"-style, hand-pumped fire engines** with solid-metal play pipes much like modern-day deck guns. Some engine companies were equipped with more maneuverable leather fire hoses held together by copper rivets. In New York, the first primitive American fireboat, a hand-rowed barge on which hand-pumped Engine 42 was mounted, went into operation. During this period, Philadelphia and New York insurance companies organized the first paid fire patrol units to perform salvage work. Other cities followed. In 2006, following 203 years of service, the New York Fire Patrol became the last of all the insurance-supported salvage corps to operate in the United States.

Once again, during the War of 1812, America's War for Economic Independence, periodic raids caught border towns such as Buffalo in the crossfire. Early in the war, a dozen suspicious fires broke out in Washington, D.C., and American forces burned York, now Toronto, Canada. In retaliation, the British burned government buildings in Washington, D.C., and Baltimore in a campaign commemorated in our national anthem.

Following the war, the nation embarked on a period of explosive growth in the cities and across the continent. Augmented by the Erie Canal, which connected the interior of the country to the sea, the port of New York became the hub of the Atlantic trade, undergoing a period of frenzied building. **New York City's Great Fire of December 1835** consumed more than 650 buildings, including most of the Wall Street financial area and the lower east side wharf and dock district (fig. 2–4). The flames were so bright that mutual aid companies responded from as far as Philadelphia, 90 miles away. The 1776 and 1835 blazes wiped out most of old New York, making room for new construction. Unfortunately, completion of New York's Croton water project proved too late to contain the conflagration of 1835. Across the East River, Brooklyn had its great fire in 1848.

Fig. 2–4. This is a scene near Wall Street in New York City after the Great Fire of 1835. Although this fire wiped out much of New York's financial district, the area was quickly rebuilt.

New York Common Councilmen attempted to blame effective volunteer Chief James Gulick for the extent of the Great Fire and replaced him with a political appointee. In response, a significant number of volunteers simply quit and formed the **Resigned Firemen's Association**. This was the first time any American firefighter walked off the job. With Gulick's encouragement, however, most were convinced to return shortly thereafter. They ousted the anti-Gulick members of the Council and assured their own candidate, Cornelius Anderson, the position of chief of department.

Two years after the 1835 fire in New York, the entire nation fell into a deep financial depression. As was, and remains the case today, unemployment and idleness converted into civic unrest and a significant increase in runs and workers for firemen.

The frontier West went through its own growth pangs as settlements extended from the Mississippi Valley to the Pacific Slope. St. Louis, Missouri, lost 3 lives, 430 buildings, 23 steamers, 9 flat boats, and several barges in one of a series of major fires during the 1840s. Out on California's Gold Coast, a series of seven major fires swept San Francisco between 1849 and 1851, including one that destroyed 3,000 buildings. On April 19, 1863, only five years after its founding, much of Denver was destroyed. The day after, a **brick ordinance** was enacted requiring all new buildings be constructed of brick or stone.

The 1830s through the 1850s marked the golden years of the traditional pre-modern volunteer fire system. Coast to coast, from San Francisco's Pacific Fire Company to Chicago's Washington Volunteers, Boston's Cataract Engine, New York's Hibernia Hook and Ladder, to Protection Engine in Yonkers, New York, firehouses became social centers for working- and middle-class members. Parades, civic celebrations, balls, festivals, competitive hand-pumping contests, and a cycle of visits and conventions offered countless opportunities to showcase the enthusiasm, joy, pride, and devotion of America's volunteer fire companies before an adoring public. In most places, any person having served seven years of duty as a volunteer fireman was rewarded most tangibly by being made an **exempt fireman**, meaning he was forever excused from jury and militia duty. Such older life members of fire companies often banded together to form an exempt fire company, expected only to show up for parades and civic functions or at the scenes of general-alarm incidents. The iconic image of **Mose the Fireman,** the somewhat crude but big-hearted and brave fireman, and Bowery B'hoy, the urban hero of his day, and his girlfriend Lizzie became standard features of the American theater for the next half century.

Through this period, buildings grew taller and bigger. The introduction of iron-fronted structures by James Bogardus, heavy mill construction made possible by the increased use of iron interior beams, and the introduction of the Otis elevator changed the face of urban America. Warehouses, mills, lofts, foundries, and increasingly tall office buildings became common. Their heavy fire loads substantially increased the burdens on firemen in the number of responses, severity of fires, and threats to civilian and line-of-duty personnel. At the same time, balloon-constructed housing and shoddily built, multiple-occupancy housing turned many neighborhoods into tinderboxes. Tenement fires became frequent and killed hundreds. Complicating those threats was the uncontrolled storage of combustibles in residential-area warehouses. A New York City sperm oil storage warehouse destroyed 300 buildings in 1845. The Jennings warehouse fire and collapse claimed the lives of 11 New York City volunteers in 1854. The Pemberton Mills fire in Lawrence, Massachusetts, killed 115 occupants. Nonetheless, in the absence of effective training cycles and multi-unit coordination, volunteer operations generally remained chaotic.

As fiercely held ethnic, religious, and neighborhood loyalties pitted members of fire companies against one another, traditionally healthy competition got out of hand as some companies fought each other. In the 1830s, native-born Philadelphia firemen fought Irish newcomers. In 1834, firefighters responded to the Charlestown, Massachusetts, Convent and elite boarding school that had been set afire by an anti-immigrant mob. In the 1840s, mobs in the City of Brotherly Love destroyed the Hibernia fire station, Catholic churches, a market, and many Irish homes. Nativist and anti-immigrant riots in Baltimore (1856) and Washington (1857) divided the firefighting community.

Some departments became entangled in party politics, notably in New York City. Organized on a bottom-up, democratic basis, elections allowed popular but unskilled officers to hold rank. By the late 1840s, the controversial Tammany leader, **William M. "Boss" Tweed**, began his rise to political power as foreman of Americus Engine 6 on Henry Street in lower Manhattan (fig. 2–5). Many of the more than 4,500 volunteers in the city were among his ardent supporters.

In the larger cities, it seemed that the fire bells were ringing all the time and that the scale of fires was growing enormously. Suburban flight of older, middle-class volunteers forced a lowering of recruiting standards in the companies they left behind. Active members found it difficult to run their businesses or keep full-time jobs and respond to fires at the same time. Line-of-duty deaths and fire losses rose rapidly. Under these circumstances, it became increasingly difficult for volunteers to keep pace with the growing fire challenges of the big cities. There were no formal training cycles or multi-unit drills.

Fig. 2–5. This is a helmet frontispiece from Americus Engine Company 6 of New York, made famous by its Foreman (Captain), William "Boss" Tweed. A tiger was their symbol—they even tied a real one to their hand pumper during a parade!

On the other hand, the fire service, inventors, and civic leaders were not idle. In Great Britain, **James Braidwood**, credited with organizing the first effective paid fire department when he was appointed superintendent of the London Fire Brigade in 1833, offered a model for an effective urban fire department. In America by the early 1840s, a number of circumstances began to cast doubt on the traditional volunteer system as inventor and philanthropist Peter Cooper proposed a paid fire service for New York City.

During the 1850s, New York insurance companies began pressuring the traditional volunteer system to modernize by urging the appointment of new assistant engineers to cover newly settled uptown districts. They hired Alfred E. Baker, a former reporter for the *New York Herald*, as fire marshal in spring 1854. He was tasked "to examine into the origin of and other matters connected with fires" and to continue supporting the fire patrol. Nonetheless, in the face of legitimate appeals to change over to horse-drawn steamers made by progressive fire service leaders, insurance companies, and urban reformers, a majority of traditionalists within many departments resisted.

Real modernization began as the American industrial revolution gained traction. In 1852, Boston installed and employed a central telegraph office and street box fire-alarm telegraph system invented by **William F. Channing**. At the same time, patents were issued for the first sprinkler-perforated pipe systems, which were installed shortly thereafter. Early in 1853, advocates of theories of professional, business, and military models of organization convinced Cincinnati to introduce the horse-drawn Latta brothers' steam fire engine, **Uncle Joe Ross**, and to become the first city to employ a top-down, centralized, paid department in 1853. Six years later, New York insurance companies purchased the first two steamers put into service by the volunteers (fig. 2–6). Soon, every major city began to switch to the horse-drawn steamer. The spirit of that moment was captured most vividly by the Currier and Ives lithograph, *The Life of a Fireman. The New Era. Steam and Muscle* (fig. 2–7).

On April 12, 1861, Fort Sumter in Charleston Harbor was shelled by supporters of secession, and the Civil War began. Southern fire departments were at a profound disadvantage because all their hand-drawn and steam fire apparatus and much of their equipment were manufactured in the North. Thus Southern departments, unable to replace worn-out and destroyed equipment, found themselves unable to protect their towns from fire. By Christmas 1861, much of Charleston had been destroyed by relentless fire from Union gunboats. Over the duration of the war, coastal communities of the South as well as Mississippi Valley cities, such as Vicksburg and New Orleans, were severely damaged and their fire departments disabled. In retaliation late in the war, several arson-related fires struck the lower Manhattan hotel district, part of a "Southern conspiracy" *to burn New York City.*

The involvement of firemen in the Civil War was complicated. Within days of the shelling of Fort Sumter, large numbers of New York City, Boston, and Philadelphia firefighters enlisted in the Union Army. The members of so-called **Fire Zouave** regiments wore red firemen's shirts, colorful jackets, baggy trousers, reddish-brown boots, and red caps known as "fezzes." At the same time, great numbers of firemen from Savannah, Georgia, Charleston, and other Southern towns enlisted in various Confederate units. Atlanta recruited its own Fire Zouaves. Most Zouave units took heavy casualties during the conflict and soon returned. Younger men, in many cases marginally employed, filled the ranks (fig. 2–8).

Fig. 2–6. A beautiful steam fire engine of the Passaic Engine Company Number One of Paterson, New Jersey. This heavy, hand-drawn "steamer" was built in 1874.

Fig. 2–7. Nathaniel Currier of the famed lithography firm, *Currier and Ives*, created this image called "Steam and Muscle." It portrays the transition from hand-pumped engines to steam fire engines in New York City.

On the home front, firefighting became even more difficult than it had been prior to the war. When heavy losses forced the Union to draft young men for the army, riots broke out in many northern cities. Opposition to the draft was expressed in dozens of other cities, from Brooklyn to Staten Island, Bloomfield, New Jersey, Detroit, and as far away as Wisconsin. The most serious **draft riots** occurred in July 1863 in New York City, where pre-existing tensions between Irish and black workers over jobs and housing had precipitated conflict long before the war. Historians disagree on the level of involvement of members of Black Joke Engine 33 in carrying the riots forward once they began, but they agree that individual volunteers were on every side of the incident. Chief of Department John Decker was almost hanged by rioters when he ordered fire companies to put out fires. Many firemen and their companies were praised for their courageous actions in turning back mobs, rescuing people, and fighting fires. Martin Scorsese's film *Gangs of New York* contains many historical inaccuracies, not the least of which is its overemphasis of the role of New York City's volunteer firemen as mob participants (fig. 2–9).

Fig. 2–8. Gettysburg monument to firefighters

In the final days of the conflict, General William T. Sherman captured and burned the city of Atlanta, portrayed so dramatically in the film *Gone With the Wind*. He then commenced his March to the Sea, torching everything in his path and leaving a swath of total destruction from Savannah to Columbia, South Carolina. When Richmond, Virginia, burned in the chaotic final days shortly before General Robert E. Lee's surrender, many Confederate records were lost. In spring 1867, New York City's Volunteer Association sent a **hose reel** to their colleagues in war-torn Columbia. The first was lost in a hurricane on its way. The New Yorkers then took up a second collection, which enabled the South Carolinians to purchase their own piece of apparatus.

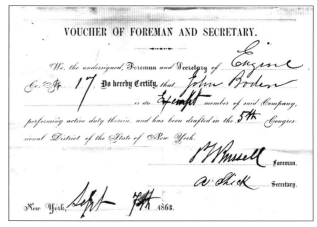

Fig. 2–9. In order to keep New York City's firemen from having to serve in the military as a result of the draft (many of whom were already "exempted" from militia duty), the city paid "substitutes" to take the firefighters place. This firefighter, John Boden of Engine 17, was replaced by a man named John Wiilliams, as seen in this certificate.

With generational continuity broken by the loss of a substantial number of older and experienced members, the Civil War put an end to New York City's neighborhood-based, volunteer, locally controlled fire department. Amidst bitterness and controversy, New York's volunteers were dismissed in 1865. They were replaced with a paid **Metropolitan Fire Department** under the direction of commissioners appointed by the insurance-influenced, rural-based, state legislature. Hand-drawn apparatus was replaced by horse-drawn and steam-powered. **Alexander T. Shaler**, appointed as New York's fire commissioner in 1866, is credited with creating New York's paid department. In 1870 under the terms of the Tweed Charter, the **Fire Department of the City of New York** was established, thus restoring home rule to the City of New York. Departments across the country quickly followed the Cincinnati and New York models. Philadelphia went paid at year's end in 1870, and Los Angeles followed the same route in 1886.

Between the end of the Civil War and the First World War, the population of the United States more than doubled. In that environment, the American fire service coped with fires of increasing magnitude and deadliness. During this period, major technological and managerial innovations were introduced to cut response time, improve firefighting capacity, and strengthen fire-safety laws.

Cincinnati, Philadelphia, New York, and other cities established fire department and hospital-related ambulance services based upon the military model that emerged from the carnage of the Civil War. (During the Civil War, volunteer fire companies in Philadelphia built their own ambulances to transport wounded members coming back from the war on the railroad to city hospitals.) In that same era, the Boston Fire Department commissioned into service the **William F. Flanders** (1873), the first American steam-powered fireboat, followed in 1875 by FDNY's **William F. Havemeyer**. In 1868, **Daniel Hayes** of the San Francisco Fire Department developed the first successful aerial extension ladder truck (all ladders up to that point were individual ground ladders) that allowed firefighters to reach the upper portions of many of the newest, tallest buildings. Additional improvements saved time in hitching up fire horses. Sliding poles were installed in some New York firehouses. Cotton-covered, rubber-lined, more flexible fire hose replaced traditional, awkward, riveted-leather hoses. One of the first medals for bravery, the **James Gordon Bennett Medal**, was introduced in New York City in 1869.

Despite the efforts of inventors, fire department managers, and firefighters, a series of conflagrations swept Portland, Maine (1866), Boston (1872), Seattle (1889), and Paterson (1902). The most serious late-19th-century fires occurred in fall 1871. The **Chicago Fire** raged for four days in early October 1871, destroyed almost 20,000 buildings in a four-square-mile area in the city center, and left 100,000 people homeless (fig. 2–10). Chicago's recovery was so swift that it became known as one of the most dynamic urban communities in the country. Years after the blaze, a news reporter confessed that he had made up the story blaming Mrs. O'Leary's cow for starting the blaze. Chicago's Fire Department Training Academy is now located on the former O'Leary property. Early October continues to be celebrated as Fire Prevention Week. A prairie fire in northeastern Wisconsin and upper Michigan swept more than 1.5 million acres. The town of Peshtigo was destroyed, and between 1,500 and 2,500 people were killed. The event drew little media attention, overshadowed as it was by the Chicago conflagration.

In the light of common problems facing the firefighting profession in the late 19th century, a number of organizations were established to coordinate fire prevention and operations across the nation. The **National Board of Fire Underwriters** was established by a consortium of insurance companies in 1866 and began to urge communities to upgrade their firefighting forces and building regulations. The **National Association of Fire Engineers**, later known as the International Association of Fire Chiefs, was formed in 1873. Founded by William H. Merrill in

the spring of 1894, the Underwriters' Electrical Bureau, later known as the **Underwriters' Laboratories**, began laboratory testing of materials for combustibility in the upper floors of a Chicago Fire Patrol house. The **National Fire Protection Association** was established in 1896 with the original intention of standardizing codes for sprinkler and electrical systems.

Fig. 2–10. The Great Fire of Chicago was one of the largest conflagrations in American history (second only to the San Francisco Earthquake and Fire of 1906). These are the ruins at Dearborn and Madison Streets.

20TH CENTURY

As the 20th century dawned, the **Baltimore fire of 1904** raged for more than two days with mutual aid companies responding from as far away as Philadelphia, Washington, New York City, Wilmington, and Atlantic City. Tragically, most mutual aid companies found that the lack of standard fire hose couplings and threads and the absence of adaptors limited their usefulness. The Baltimore conflagration was the precipitating event for the creation of a new **model building code** (a generically written code that could be adopted by any city in the United States) known as the **National Building Code** (fig 2–11).

Fig. 2–11. The Great Baltimore Fire of 1904 led to creation of the first comprehensive standardized building code. Firefighters were not successful in standardizing hose threads; many responding mutual aid fire departments, including New York City, were unable to attach their hoses to Baltimore's hydrants. There are still a multiplicity of hose threads across the United States today.

Individual catastrophes such as the **Brooklyn Theater fire** (1876), the **Iroquois Theater fire** (fig. 2–12) in Chicago (1903), and the **Triangle Shirtwaist Factory fire** in lower Manhattan (1911) led to improved laws for high-occupancy structures. A series of marine disasters were led by one in Hoboken, New Jersey (1900), followed by another on the excursion boat *General Slocum* in the East River in New York (1904), and a third on Chicago's excursion boat *Eastland* (1915). Several "high-rise" fires in New York City, one in the Home Insurance building (1898) and the other in the Equitable Life building (1912), pointed out the need for better fire-prevention regulations in office buildings. **San Francisco's Great Earthquake and Fire of 1906** destroyed more than 28,000 buildings and caused the death of Chief of Department Dennis T. Sullivan (fig. 2–13). Originally reported to have cost fewer than 400 lives, researchers now suspect the loss of life to be in excess of 3,000 after revealing a great cover-up by the city after the event. It was the largest fire in American history.

At the same time, a generation of experienced fire service leaders introduced revolutionary changes in apparatus, fire prevention laws, and technology. In 1901, New York City's chief of department was assigned a gasoline-driven **Locomobile** (fig. 2–14). By 1922, the last horse-drawn apparatus made its final run. **Rescue companies** were established in major cities, and **high-pressure water systems** aided central business district fire companies. Following the Triangle

Shirtwaist fire that cost 146 workers' lives, political leaders from the Progressive Movement, advised by fire department personnel, introduced factory legislation intended to guarantee greater safety in industrial workplaces. The **International Association of Firefighters** was established (1918), followed by the founding of fire officer associations intended to support their professional interests.

Fig. 2–12. The Iroquois Theater was supposedly "fireproof" (this is never an accurate term). 602 people died in a fire during a performance of "Mr. Bluebeard" soon after the new theater opened in 1903. It still stands today as our country's worst theater disaster. This image shows victims' bodies being removed in a hose wagon.

Fig. 2–13. The San Francisco Earthquake and Fire of 1906 was America's largest conflagration. It destroyed nearly 28,000 buildings, including City Hall as seen in this photograph.

Fig. 2–14. The transition to motorized apparatus was a major turning point in the fire service. This image shows the brand new "motor" Fire Engine Company One of San Antonio, Texas. The term "motor" is still with us today in many parts of the United States where the operators of fire engines are called motor pump operators (m.p.o.).

Along with the rest of the country, the firefighting community was swept into the vortex of each of America's 20th-century wars. Before and after America's entry into the first World War, German saboteurs created numerous problems for firefighters from coast to coast as explosions lit secondary fires. In July 1916 on **Black Tom Island**, a major munitions depot situated in the Hudson River near Jersey City, two million pounds of explosives were detonated with such force that it could be felt 90 miles away. In January 1917, another explosion at the Canadian Car and Foundry in the New Jersey Meadowlands near Lyndhurst set off more than a half million, high-explosive shells. There were no deaths among the 1,400 people in the facility, who were warned building by building by company switchboard operator Tessie McNamara, to flee for their lives. In April 1917, the same month that the United States entered World War I, the Eddystone Ammunition Corporation in Pennsylvania blew up with the loss of 133 lives. In May 1918, six months before the Armistice that ended World War I, a TNT explosion in an Oakdale, Pennsylvania, chemical factory killed 200.

The war accelerated the migrations of hundreds of thousands of immigrants and rural black Americans seeking jobs in northern heavy industry. Auto plants in the Detroit area and steel mills in western Pennsylvania and Indiana began hiring workers without regard to race or ethnicity. Competition for jobs and housing exploded into race riots in dozens of cities including Atlanta, Omaha, Nebraska, and Tulsa, Oklahoma. Peaking in 1919, the Chicago Race Riots caused 38 deaths and left a thousand people homeless. The Tulsa Race Riots burned

more than 35 city blocks with almost 1,300 buildings and, depending on the source, killed anywhere from 75 to 300. As usual, firefighters in each affected city were caught in the middle.

The period between the Great Depression and WWII was marked as an era of lean budgets, the extended use of older equipment, deferred apparatus acquisition, manpower shortages, and little or no increases in salaries. New York Mayor Fiorello LaGuardia, a fire buff himself, attempted to keep the department together by promising better pensions if members put up with the lean years of the 1930s. At the same time, the first two-way radios were making their way into many departments. Most were assigned to rescue companies, marine units, and senior command officers. In one unanticipated side effect of the Depression, many who might have gone into other lines of work or professions entered the fire service seeking security. Thus potential doctors, dentists, and teachers, and others, found themselves in the ranks.

In March 1937, a natural gas explosion leveled the **New London, Texas, Junior-Senior High School** and killed 298 students and teachers. Because natural gas is odorless, this explosion led to the requirement of using mercaptan as an odorant so leaks can be detected quickly. It was flammable hydrogen gas (used for buoyancy) and a highly combustible outer surface that spelled disaster for the airship *Hindenburg* when it caught fire at Naval Air Station Lakehurst in New Jersey, killing 36 people in May of 1937. On December 1, 1958, a fire in Chicago's Our Lady of the Angels parochial school killed 92 children and three nuns. An open stairwell allowed fire to rapidly spread from the basement of the second floor where the fatalities occurred.

When the Japanese attacked the naval base at Pearl Harbor, three civilian firefighters from the Honolulu Fire Department were among the 2,400 people killed. In New York in February 1942, a welding accident burned and sank the *USS Lafayette*, a former French luxury liner named the SS *Normandie*. In 1943, the Liberty ship *El Estero*, loaded with munitions, took fire while loading at Bayonne, New Jersey. With a cargo capable of devastating the entire lower harbor, the ship was towed to deeper water and scuttled by the heroic intervention of FDNY fireboats and Coast Guard vessels. On the West Coast, 328 ammunition loaders were killed when the Port Chicago Naval Magazine, 35 miles (56 km) north of San Francisco, blew up. On the civilian front, a fire in the **Cocoanut Grove Night Club** in Boston resulted in 492 deaths and injuries to hundreds in November 1942. Late in the war, the **Ringling Bros. and Barnum**

& Bailey circus tent caught fire in Hartford, Connecticut, killing 167 and injuring nearly 500 in early summer 1944 (fig. 2–15). Just before V-J Day in 1945, FDNY responded when a B-25 bomber lost in fog crashed into the 79th floor of the **Empire State Building**. The crew and at least 11 office workers died.

Fig. 2–15. As the band played the *Stars and Stripes* to signal a fire to circus workers, attendees scrambled to get out from under the big tent and away from the quickly spreading fire. The July, 1944 fire in Hartford cost many lives. Here firefighters wet down the ruins of the tent which had been soaked with paraffin and kerosene to prevent rotting of the canvas.

After the end of World War II, American manufacturers and Boeing Airplane Co. dominated the airways. The incredible growth of private aviation, the introduction of jet aircraft, and reasonable ticket pricing, enabled tourists to travel in relative comfort and ease. As the industry grew, the number of fires related to air crashes rose, commencing in 1947 with the loss of 52 when a United Airlines DC-6 went down near Bryce Canyon, Utah. The collision of two aircraft in the crowded airspace approaching LaGuardia and Idelwild International (now known as JFK) airports in December 1960 resulted in more than 130 deaths when one plane came down in Staten Island and the other in a crowded Brooklyn neighborhood. Prior to the World Trade Center attacks, the deadliest crash was an American Airlines flight at O'Hare International Airport in Chicago, which killed all 271 people on board (1979). More reliable equipment, effective inspections and maintenance, and rapid, advance firefighting tactics when aircraft hit the ground have reduced crash and death tolls for American flights.

On December 7, 1946, a fire moved quickly through Atlanta's Winecoff Hotel, killing 119 people. Starting on the third floor and moving rapidly up through the structure because of a lack of fire doors and other fire containment features, it became America's worst hotel fire. Other significant hotel fires include the MGM Grand Hotel-Casino fire in Las Vegas (1980), where 87 died, and the Hotel Dupont Plaza fire in Puerto Rico where 97 were killed in an arson fire on New Year's Eve in 1986.

In April 1947, an explosion rocked the port of Texas City. The French Liberty ship *Grandcamp*, loaded with ammonium nitrate fertilizer, caught fire and blew up, killing 26 Texas City volunteer firefighters (fig. 2–16). It was the largest loss of firefighters prior to the attack at the World Trade Center on September 11, 2001.

Fig. 2–16 A large group of vehicles damaged in the 1947 Texas City explosion. 576 people, including 26 Texas City volunteer firefighters, were killed in a series of explosions over two days. The disaster began with an initial explosion of ammonium nitrate in the ship Grandcamp on April 16, 1947.

Throughout the century, San Francisco continued to be battered by earthquakes. One in spring 1957 registered 5.3 on the Richter scale. In October 1989, Americans watched the developing tragedy on television as the most severe earthquake since 1906 hit the City by the Bay just before the beginning of the third game of the World Series at Candlestick Park. Quickly, San Francisco's *Fireboat Phoenix* went into operation, supplying saltwater through large-diameter hoses. Hundreds of civilian volunteers stretched lines to land companies fighting the ensuing Marina District fire.

The 1960s was an era of confusing and often violent social, racial, and economic confrontation. Beginning in the early 1960s, the fire service entered what is commonly known as **The War Years**, or the Long Hot Summers. A complicated set of factors, including frustration over poor living conditions, the emptying of some neighborhoods to the suburbs, arson, and bitterness, led to riots, burning, and looting in more than 100 American inner cities from Watts in Los Angeles to Newark, Detroit, East New York, and the South Bronx in New York City. In 1950, the number of alarms in New York had been only 62,021, rising to 261,131 annually by 1970. As portrayed by Dennis Smith in *Report From Engine Company 82*, some companies made 7,000 to 8,000 runs per year. Canopies were constructed over apparatus cabs, and members rode inside for fear of "air mail" and shooting. The orgy of destruction eventually diminished in the 1980s, and now, in many of those same neighborhoods, firefighters are viewed much more favorably.

Several reports emanated from the period. The first was from the National Advisory Commission on Civil Disorders, also known as the Kerner Commission (1968), which assessed the underlying causes for the period's civil unrest. The second, the National Commission on Fire Prevention and Control summary report on the period, ***America Burning*** (1973), noted that the mission of the American fire service had expanded rapidly beyond fire prevention, suppression, and investigation. Recognizing that firefighters are the first line of defense for citizens facing any type of disaster or emergency, the report presented an agenda for improving firefighters' ability to deal with such situations in the future.

In the words of author Terry Golway, the period after the 1960s was dominated by a "Search for Equity" in recruiting, promoting, and retaining personnel in the fire service. Since the 1970s there has been some progress toward gender, ethnic, and racial equity in recruiting, holding, and promoting firefighters from every dimension of American society. In 1973, Arlington County, Virginia, made headlines by hiring its first woman career firefighter. By the opening years of the 21st century, the number of women holding career-firefighter and officer positions exceeded 7,000. During the same time, it is estimated that there were more than 40,000 women volunteer firefighters. The 100th anniversary celebration of the San Francisco Earthquake and Fire was hosted by Chief of Department Joanne Hayes-White, a 14-year veteran and married mother to three sons. Rochelle "Rocky" Jones, whose career spans more than 20 years and whose company was part of the first alarm assignment for the Twin Towers, later earned the rank of FDNY battalion commander. Nonetheless, there were still fewer than 50 women in FDNY at the opening of the 21st century.

The situation facing black Americans is equally challenging. FDNY remains 90% white, while the Boston, Philadelphia, and Chicago departments are between 70% and 75% white. Tensions over promotions in the Saint Louis Department, led by a black chief of department, remain high, a common situation in many cities. Van Davis Jr., the first black appointment to Los Angeles County Fire Department in 1953, served 20 years, during which time no blacks were promoted to upper rank. Many fire departments in large and small communities across the nation still struggle to resolve challenges relating to gender and racial staffing, recruiting, and promotion standards.

Beginning in the 1960s, some firefighters underpaid, overworked, and convinced that they were getting little respect from politicians and residents, grew frustrated and angry. In the face of no-strike laws but encouraged by their national union, the International Association of Firefighters (IAFF), uniformed personnel went on strike in New York City, Yonkers, Chicago, New Hampshire, California, and elsewhere. Improved working conditions, binding arbitration agreements, better equipment, and some improvement in contracts diminished the number of similar job actions over time.

In the 1970s, the completion of the interstate highway system and the return of Vietnam veterans willing to serve made it possible to establish a standardized, national **Emergency Medical System** staffed by paramedics and emergency medical technicians. The onset of the high-rise and highway strip mall era in the 1950s was accompanied by cost efficiencies in architectural design and construction, as well as by major deficiencies in fire safety. In such manner, the lives of firefighters trying to effect rescues of workers and residents were placed at risk. Major blazes occurred in the **McCormick Place Exhibition Hall** in Chicago (1967) and **1 New York Plaza** (1970). Philadelphia officials described the 38-story **Meridian Plaza blaze** (1991) as the "most significant fire of the 20th century." Two significant hazardous materials incidents: propane BLEVEs (boiling liquid expanding vapor explosion, described in chapter 23, Analyzing the Hazmat/WMD Incident) occurred in the 1970s. In 1973, a rail tank car of propane BLEVEd in Kingman, Arizona, killed 12, including 11 firefighters. A few years later in 1978 at Waverly, Tennessee, another propane rail tank car exploded and killed 16. These incidents and others led to changes in rail tank cars: there have not been any rail tank car BLEVEs in the last several years.

Three notable fires in nightclubs ("places of public assembly") occurred around the last quarter of the 20th century. On May 28th, 1977, a fire erupted in the Zebra Room of the **Beverly Hills Supper Club** in Southgate, Kentucky. One hundred sixty-five people were killed, many of the victims caught in a crowd crush (jam of people) at exits as fire and smoke moved into the Cabaret Room where a large audience was waiting to hear 1970s singing sensation, John Davidson. On March

25th, 1990, an arson fire in the **Happyland Social Club** in the Bronx, New York, killed 87 people. Polyurethane foam lining the walls of **The Station nightclub** in West Warwick, Rhode Island, was ignited by indoor pyrotechnics used during a performance of the band, Great White, on February 20, 2003. One hundred people eventually died as a result of the Station fire; lethal conditions in the nightclub developed in about 90 seconds.

21ˢᵀ CENTURY AND BEYOND

With increasingly intrusive human use of naturally forested areas, wildfires are a growing hazard in most regions of the United States, posing a threat to life and property. Thus, **wildland firefighting** is a major and most significant professional specialty, particularly in western states. The **Mann Gulch Fire** in the Helena Forest in Montana killed 16 smoke jumpers (1949); the **Rattlesnake Fire** in the Mendocino Forest took 15 firefighters (1953); and in the summer of 1994, 14 wildland firefighters died when shifting 70-mile-per-hour winds trapped them and fire swept over their position in **South Canyon Glenwood Springs, Colorado**. In fall 2007, out-of-hand wildfires destroyed thousands of homes and dislocated hundreds of thousands, resulting in major economic losses in Southern California.

Recurrent and more frequent fires involving major commitments of personnel and equipment spurred many incident command models in the late 20th century. **Firefighting Resources of Southern California Organized for Potential Emergencies (FIRESCOPE)** initiated a version of ICS for wildfire operations that was a major improvement over previous systems. Under the leadership of Alan Brunacini, FIRESCOPE evolved into the **Incident Management System**. Inspired by Capt. Ron Gore, the first **hazmat** team formally went online in Jacksonville in January 1977, inspiring the introduction of such units all over the nation. In 1989, the **National Urban Search and Rescue System** established regional task forces under the jurisdiction of the **Federal Emergency Management Agency (FEMA)** designed to coordinate emergency services during major disasters.

The attacks on the World Trade Center **Twin Towers** (1993 and 2001) were not the first terrorist events American firefighters faced. Left-wing extremists include those who destroyed the Los Angeles Times building (1910), anarchists who bombed Wall Street (1920) (fig. 2–17), and revolutionary Weathermen (1960s) whose bomb factory exploded in New York's Greenwich

Village in 1970. Racists bombed homes, schools, and churches from the post-Civil War KKK years throughout the Civil Rights era of the 1960s and later. During the long, hot summer of 1964, Mt. Zion Church was burned to the ground, one of 20 black Mississippi churches to be firebombed that year. The FBI initiated the MIBURN (Mississippi Burning) investigation. Violent nationalists from Croatia and Puerto Rico (FALN) were active in the 1970s. Anti-government, right-wing radicals bombed the **Alfred P. Murrah Building** in Oklahoma City (1995). The firefighting community was on the front line in each case.

Fig. 2–17. Many Americans think that the terrorist attacks of September 11, 2001, were the first on American soil. There have been many attacks through the country's history, including this one on Wall Street in 1920. Damage to this building's (the J.P. Morgan bank) exterior wall, near the corner of Wall and Broad Streets, is still visible.

Fires in aging commercial buildings, some occupied, others abandoned and deteriorated, continue to take an increasingly heavy toll. A fire in the basement of a lower Manhattan loft killed 12 in 1966. Warehouse fires killed four firefighters in Seattle (1995) and six in Worcester, Massachusetts (1999). After nine of their members died in a collapsing furniture store in June 2007, the Charleston Fire Department requested FDNY's Emerald Society Pipes & Drums to play at the memorial service.

The destruction of the World Trade Center Towers and the Pentagon on September 11, 2001, was the most despicable act of mass murder ever perpetrated in the United States (fig. 2–18). At the Towers, it is estimated that nearly 15,000 were led to safety prior to the collapse. The retired FDNY Fireboat John Jay Harvey, which was maintained by a historical association of private citizens and retired firefighters, responded immediately and supplied the only water at the scene for more than 96 hours. Hundreds of ambulances from New

Jersey were summoned to staging areas in the region, with many being sent into **Ground Zero**. Fire, police, and emergency medical service units and personnel began to respond from as far away as New Brunswick, Canada, Florida, and Oregon. Ultimately, four FEMA Urban Search and Rescue Task Forces were sent to Washington and six to New York. Among the approximately 3,000 dead were 343 FDNY members, 1 fire patrolman, 23 New York Police Department officers, and 37 Port Authority Police Department personnel. FDNY losses included First Deputy Commissioner and former Chief of Department William M. Feehan, Chief of Department Peter Ganci, FDNY Chaplain Mychal Judge, as well as officers and firefighters of every rank, amounting to a loss of more than 4,400 years of formal and intuitive knowledge.

The outpouring of sympathy and tangible support from around the world for the city in general and for FDNY in particular was astounding. Among dozens of fund-raising efforts around the world, the citizens of Columbia, South Carolina, presented FDNY with a tiller aerial now operating as Ladder 101 in Brooklyn, a grateful thank you for the support sent to that city in 1867. The Spirit of Louisiana, donated by citizens of that state, was assigned to Engine 283 in Brownsville. In the early stages of the Hurricane Katrina disaster, FDNY sent The Spirit of Louisiana to New Orleans, where it remains a part of that city's reviving department.

What remains and what has changed? Today's **first responders** are aware that they are primary targets of terrorists. And yet the roles of firefighters, police, and EMS personnel, both career and volunteer, remain to rescue those at risk, to contain disasters, and to comfort survivors.

Fig. 2–18. This image shows the initial response of the New York City Fire Department on 9/11. It shows the Marriott Hotel on the left along West Street. The north tower of the World Trade Center is out of view to the far left. (Courtesy of FDNY Photo Unit)

QUESTIONS

1. As early as 1648, Peter Stuyvesant, the governor of New Amsterdam, implemented the use of fire wardens and strong fire prevention techniques and imposed requirements for homeowners. Nearly 360 years later and following countless large loss fires, is American society more conscious of the effects of fire or better prepared to prevent them?

2. Around 1852 the first patents were issued for the first sprinkler-perforated pipe systems. Almost 156 years after the first patents were issued, the American fire service still battles to educate politicians, model code developers, builders, businesses, and homeowners to adopt requirements to protect all structures. Discuss why the efforts to do so have been and continue to be difficult.

3. Name four professional organizations that were developed in the late 19th century. What positive effects have these organizations had on the fire service?

4. A document titled _____ was first published in 1973 in an attempt to focus attention on the nation's fire problem.

5. Two national programs were created from this document. What are they and what are their current responsibilities?

6. George Santayana, the author of "Reason in Common Sense" is quoted as saying, "Those who cannot learn from the past are doomed to repeat it." The history of the American fire service is riddled with accounts of large fires resulting in property loss, and loss of life to civilians and firefighters. Many of the circumstances surrounding those events mirror one another. Why does it appear that the American fire service has failed to take heed of our past and take the necessary steps to prevent such losses in the future?

Fire Department Organization

by John Best

This chapter provides required knowledge items for the following NFPA Standard 1001 Job Performance Requirements:

FFI 5.1.1

OBJECTIVES

Upon completion of this chapter, you should be able to do the following:

- Describe the organizational structures of small, medium, and large departments
- Identify the six types of fire department units, and the roles they play within the department
- Identify and describe the roles and responsibilities of the firefighter and fire officer positions
- Identify additional functions the fire department performs
- Identify fire department member assistance programs
- Identify the policies, procedures, regulations, and by-laws under which fire departments operate
- List and describe the roles of other agencies that impact the operation of the local fire department

INTRODUCTION

Over the last 400 years, the fire service has evolved to the point where the fire suppression function has become but one of many important missions of the fire department organization. The modern fire department responds to numerous all-hazard responsibilities including but not limited to fire suppression; **emergency medical services (EMS)**; specialty rescue operations; hazardous materials mitigation; life- and fire-safety education; the administration and enforcement of codes and standards; and emergency communications.

This evolution continues to enhance the fire service's relationship with a number of allied organizations representing the ever-increasing spectrum of responsibilities addressed by fire departments and other emergency organizations. The following organizations represent a sampling of the major organizations closely associated with the fire service:

- *National Fire Protection Association (NFPA)*, a nonprofit organization whose purpose is to reduce the worldwide burden of fire and other hazards on the quality of life by providing and advocating consensus codes, standards, research, training, and education

- *International Association of Fire Chiefs (IAFC),* composed of members considered the leading experts in firefighting, emergency medical services, terrorism response, hazardous materials, natural disasters, search and rescue, and public safety legislation.

- *International Association of Fire Fighters (IAFF),* working to promote a safe and healthy work environment, reasonable working conditions, the research and treatment of burns and other related health problems common to career firefighters.

- *National Volunteer Fire Council (NVFC),* composed of state volunteer firefighter organizations involved in providing training programs, public education, conferences, and the compilation of pertinent statistics.

Additional allied organizations and more in-depth descriptions appear later in this chapter.

The fire service addresses operational all-hazard responsibilities through a basic fire company–firefighter organization overseen by a quasi-military leadership system. The companies are assigned to the number of stations needed to meet the community's response time or **standard of cover** requirements.

Companies are generally organized by function such as an engine, ladder truck, emergency medical, rescue, or specialty service. These companies and other fire department functions are supervised and staffed by the appropriate complement of officers and firefighters.

This chapter describes the firefighter as the basic staffing unit of the fire department and the many roles that firefighters have in the modern fire department organization.

FIRE DEPARTMENT ORGANIZATION

The fire department must organize in a manner to provide the oversight and resources required to exercise its authority to meet its responsibilities to the community.

Mission

FFI 5.1.1 A fire department should develop its mission statement commensurate with the expectations and requirements of the community it serves. Elements typically included in a fire department mission statement are summarized by the NFPA 1201, *Standard for Providing Emergency Services to the Public,* as follows:

- Save lives
- Prevent or mitigate fires, injuries, and emergencies
- Work through a system of emergency management
- Extinguish fires
- Minimize damage to property and the environment
- Protect critical infrastructure
- Perform emergency medical services
- Protect the community from hazardous situations
- Perform response to and mitigation of events of terrorism
- Perform rescue services
- Perform other community-related services

A fire department mission statement is usually part of a master plan that also includes the department's vision, values, goals, and objectives. This plan should clearly communicate these factors to the organization's members and customers.

Organizational structure

FFI 5.1.1 The organizational structure of a fire department is influenced by a multitude of factors. These factors include, but are not limited to, its mission, the communities it serves and their expectations, the size and workload of the organization, available funding, and the political landscape.

This organizational structure ranges from large and complex, as in a major municipality or county; to moderate, as in a medium-size borough or city; to small, as in a single-station, small-town, all-volunteer fire company.

Generally, fire departments are organized as full-time paid, part-time paid, volunteer, volunteer-paid-on-call, or a combination of the four. They may be operated by a federal entity, a municipal entity, a special taxing district, a not-for-profit corporation, or a for-profit corporation.

The various demands placed on the majority of fire departments have made fire-suppression activity one of the smallest percentages of their workload: less than 10% for most departments. For example, fire departments that provide EMS, including advanced life support, patient transport, or both, find their EMS workload ranging from 60% to 75%.

Most fire departments deploy their resources to effectively address their community's **fire problem**. This involves organizing a cycle of resources, including the following:

- *Public education*, so that citizens are aware of hazards, how to prevent them, and what to do should the peril occur

- *Engineering and code enforcement*, so that fire and life safety is an inherent part of the community's infrastructure, and where there is a violation, compliance is achieved

- *Fire suppression*, needed when there is a failure in the education and engineering and code enforcement parts of the cycle, so that the emergency can be resolved

- *Fire investigation*, in which the incident is documented, the cause determined accidental or intentional, and steps are taken so it will not happen again

The results of fire investigation suggest new needs and goals for public education; code modifications and changes; fire department training, resources, and deployment; and identification of the community's fire problem.

According to the NFPA, there were 1,557,500 fires reported during 2007 involving $14.6 billion in property damage. Figure 3–1 provides an overview of these fire types:

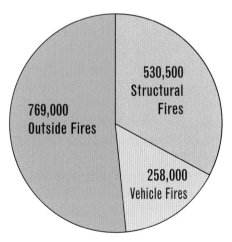

Fig. 3–1. Nearly 1.6 million fires were reported to the National Fire Protection Association in 2007. Fires are typically less then 10% of the workload for any fire department.

Whether the fire department is career or volunteer; a large, complex entity; or a small, municipal, single-station organization, the firefighter is the primary position and resource in the fulfillment of the associated missions (figs. 3–2, 3–3, 3–4).

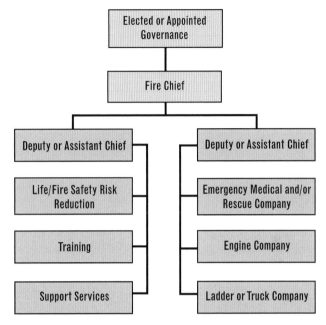

Fig. 3–2. Typical organizational structure of a small fire department

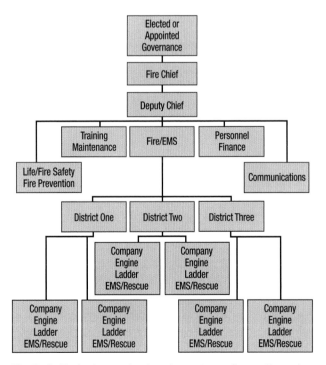

Fig. 3–3. Typical organizational structure of a medium-size fire department

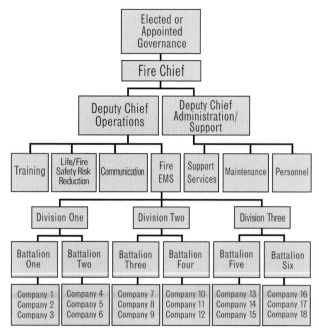

Fig. 3–4. Typical organizational structure of large fire department

THE COMPANY

As defined by NFPA 1201, *Standard for Providing Emergency Services to the Public*, the company is a group of members that is the following:

1. Under the direct supervision of an officer or leader

2. Trained and equipped to perform assigned tasks

3. Usually organized and identified as engine companies, ladder companies, rescue companies, or squad companies

4. Usually operates with one piece of fire apparatus (pumper, ladder truck, elevating platform, rescue, squad, or ambulance)

5. Arrives at the incident scene on fire apparatus or assembles at the scene prior to assignment

Engine company

An **engine company** is composed of an apparatus or vehicle, generally referred to as an engine or pumper, staffed by firefighters and a supervisor (officer) trained and assigned to deliver water, deploy hoselines, and execute other associated tactics to extinguish fires.

The engine company (pumper) vehicle, as seen in figure 3–5, is defined by NFPA 1901, *Standard for Automotive Fire Apparatus*, as fire apparatus with a permanently mounted pump of at least 750 gpm (2,839 L/min) capacity, a tank carrying at least 300 gal (1,136 L) of water, and a hose body, whose primary purpose is to combat structure and associated fires.

Fig. 3–5. The engine company is a common unit found at almost every fire station in the United States.

Many engine companies are assigned, equipped, and trained to perform rescue, extrication, and/or emergency medical services.

Ladder or truck company

A **ladder** or **truck company** is composed of an aerial apparatus or vehicle, staffed by firefighters and a supervisor (officer) trained and assigned to place ladders, accomplish search and rescue, perform ventilation and forcible-entry operations, secure utilities, and perform salvage or overhaul at fire and other emergency scenes.

The ladder or truck company aerial fire apparatus, as seen in figure 3–6, is defined by NFPA 1901, *Standard for Automotive Fire Apparatus*, as a vehicle equipped with an **aerial ladder**, **elevating platform**, **aerial ladder platform**, or **water tower** that is designed and equipped to support firefighting and rescue operations by positioning personnel, handling materials, providing continuous egress, or discharging water at positions elevated from the ground. This vehicle, as defined, must have an extensive complement of hand and power tools and should have a minimum of 115 ft (35 m) of ground ladders, including two extension ladders, two straight ladders with folding roof hooks, and an attic ladder.

Fig. 3–6. A ladder or truck company. These units can come with a wide variety of fixed aerial devices.

As with the engine company, ladder or truck companies may be assigned, equipped, and trained to perform rescue, extrication, and/or EMS.

Rescue or squad company

A **rescue** or **squad company** is composed of a vehicle carrying specialized equipment, as seen in figure 3–7, staffed by firefighters and a supervisor (officer) trained and assigned to perform forcible entry, search and rescue, and other specialized **tasks** at fire scenes. Most communities hold their rescue or squad companies responsible for confined space and **rope rescues**, vehicle accident extrications, and other technical rescue evolutions, although these tasks may be assigned to ladder companies.

Rescue or squad companies may also provide emergency medical services.

Fig. 3–7. Rescue companies can come in many shapes and sizes; however, large rescue units like this are regularly found in urban environments.

Ambulance or emergency medical services company

Many fire-service-based ambulance or EMS companies are composed of a transport vehicle, as seen in figure 3–8, carrying specialized medical equipment, and staffed by firefighters trained and assigned to provide treatment to patients, including first aid, cardiopulmonary resuscitation, basic life support (BLS) or advanced life support (ALS), and other medical procedures prior to arrival at a health care facility.

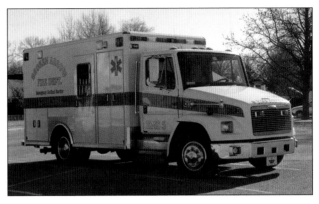

Fig. 3–8. Ambulances, or EMS units, may be staffed by firefighters or paramedics from private businesses.

Although there are numerous emergency medical staffing and response models depending on the community served, many fire departments utilize EMS-trained firefighters to staff their ambulance or EMS companies. These firefighters may be assigned to medical or firefighting duties.

Combination or specialty companies

The fire department is responsible for providing a wide spectrum of services to their respective communities. This diversity of services can mandate a variety of unique approaches, including the use of quints, **mobile water supply apparatus (water tenders)**, wildland firefighting apparatus, hazardous materials units, light and breathing air vehicles, aircraft rescue and firefighting companies, and other resources tailored to a specific community's needs.

The quint. The **quint** is defined by the NFPA 1901, *Standard for Automotive Fire Apparatus*, as fire apparatus with a permanently mounted fire pump, a water tank, a hose storage area, an aerial ladder or elevating platform with a permanently mounted waterway, and a complement of ground ladders (fig. 3–9). Basically, it combines a pumper and a ladder truck. This vehicle is staffed with firefighters and an officer trained and assigned to perform engine company and truck company evolutions.

Fig. 3–9. Quints are combination units that can do the work of both engine and ladder companies since they have a fire pump, a water tank, hose storage area, aerial ladder, and ground ladders.

Mobile water supply apparatus. NFPA 1901, *Standard for Automotive Fire Apparatus*, defines a mobile water supply apparatus (**water tender**) as a vehicle designed primarily for transporting (pickup, transporting, and delivering) water to fire emergency scenes to be applied by other vehicles or pumping equipment (fig. 3–10). This company is staffed and operated by firefighters.

Fig. 3–10. Mobile water supply apparatus, commonly referred to as tenders, help fire departments fight fires in areas without fire hydrants.

THE FIREFIGHTER

FFI 5.1.1 A firefighter, as defined by NFPA 1001, *Standard for Fire Fighter Professional Qualifications*, is an individual possessing the knowledge and skills to function as an integral member of a firefighting team, under supervision, in hazardous conditions.

In addition, firefighters should be knowledgeable of their fire department organization, its mission, standard operating procedures, and rules and regulations. They

should understand the importance of physical fitness and a healthy lifestyle as it relates to the performance of their duties.

As the mission of a fire department evolves in its community, firefighter roles may be expanded upon. These roles may include but are not limited to emergency medical first responder, paramedic, rescue specialist, driver/operator, fire investigation or prevention officer, and fire rescue communicator/dispatcher.

Many state, county, and local entities have established minimum qualifications for firefighters within their jurisdictions. The NFPA, through its various technical committees and associated consensus processes, has established numerous training and qualification standards addressing firefighter duties and responsibilities. These standards are widely accepted by fire department and emergency services organizations worldwide and are adopted as the basis for the firefighter minimum qualifications.

NFPA 1001, *Standard for Fire Fighter Professional Qualifications*, addresses firefighter minimum knowledge, skills, and abilities. These minimum qualifications are divided into **Firefighter I** and **Firefighter II** designations, generally based on the level of supervision required and the ability to operate independently.

The following list identifies examples of typical minimum skills and abilities required of a Firefighter I (fig. 3–11):

The Firefighter I has the ability to do the following:

- Don and use personal protective clothing

- Hoist tools and equipment using ropes

- Locate information in department documents, standards, and codes

- Operate fire department communications, telephone, and intercom equipment

- Control breathing, use self-contained breathing apparatus, and replace air cylinders

- Use provided safety equipment

- Transport and operate hand and power tools to force entry and ventilate

- Operate as a team member in vision-obscured conditions

- Carry, raise, and extend ladders

- Identify automobile fuel types; assess and control fuel leaks

- Operate fire attack hoses; open, close, and adjust the flow and pattern on nozzles

- Apply water for maximum effectiveness

- Hand lay and connect water supply hose and appliances

- Recognize inherent hazards related to a material's configuration

- Search for and expose hidden fires; assess patterns for origin determination

- Evaluate for complete fire extinguishment

- Conduct property conservation, protection, and salvage evolutions

- Recognize obvious signs of arson and area of fire origin

- Stop fire sprinkler system water flow and operate main control valves

- Select and operate correct portable fire extinguishers based on fire classification

- Operate fire department power supply and lighting equipment

- Identify and operate building utility-control devices

- Suppress ground cover fires; determine exposure threat based on fire spread potential

- Clean, inspect, and maintain fire department tools and equipment

Fig. 3–11. A firefighter must be able to perform a wide variety of skills in order to be successful. The skills that a firefighter may be called to do can be found in NFPA 1001.

Firefighter I may be required to drive and operate fire department vehicles and apparatus. This may include fire department vehicles equipped with a fire pump, an aerial device, a **tiller**, and a mobile water supply, including wildland fire apparatus and aircraft firefighting and rescue apparatus.

Driving and operating fire department vehicles, whether on a nonemergency basis or in response to an emergency, requires significant knowledge, skill, and ability, including the following:

- Perform and document routine tests, inspections, and servicing function

- Drive, operate, and position fire apparatus in adverse conditions

- Deploy, energize, and monitor all systems associated with the vehicle

- Position a pumper to do the following: operate at a fire hydrant and at a static water source; power transfer from vehicle engine to pump, draft, operate pumper pressure-control systems; operate auxiliary cooling systems; make the transition between internal and external water sources; and assemble hoseline, nozzles, valves, and appliances

- Maneuver and position an aerial apparatus so that the apparatus is positioned for correct aerial device deployment

- Connect a water supply to a master stream device and control an elevated nozzle manually or remotely

- Apply the principles of tiller operation; methods of communication with the driver; and effects of general steering reactions, night driving, negotiating intersections, and manufacturer operation limitations

- Apply procedures for establishing a water shuttle dump site and principles of water transfer between multiple portable water tanks

NFPA 1002, *Standard on Fire Apparatus Driver/ Operator Professional Qualifications*, provides the minimum requirements for the Firefighter I assigned to drive and operate fire department vehicles.

In addition to the typical minimum skills and abilities required of a Firefighter I, a Firefighter II must have the ability to do the following (fig. 3–12):

- Determine the need for command, and organize and coordinate incident management

- Complete basic incident reports including the operation of fire department computers

- Determine necessary applicable codes and standards

- Operate fire department communications equipment

- Extinguish an ignitable liquid fire, including through the application of firefighting foam

- Assemble a team and choose an effective fire attack technique

- Coordinate a structural interior attack hoseline as part of a team

- Execute effective fire attack advances and retreats based on condition changes

- Locate a fire's area of origin, recognize possible causes, and protect evidence

- Extricate a victim entrapped in a motor vehicle accident

- Operate hand and power tools for forcible entry and rescue

- Perform fire-safety surveys including completion of appropriate forms and reports

- Conduct life and fire-safety presentations and tours

- Identify the components of fire suppression and detection systems

- Safely conduct hose service testing

- Support technical rescue teams

Fig. 3–12. To meet the requirements of NFPA 1001 for Firefighter II, a firefighter must be willing and able to take on additional challenges and roles. Here two firefighters perform vehicle extrication.

FIRE DEPARTMENT OFFICERS

Fire departments are comprised of multiple levels of supervision depending on the size, authority, and responsibility of the organization. Although there are many variations, these supervisor levels range from company officer to chief officer.

Company officer

The **company officer** is responsible for the supervision of the personnel and resources assigned to a single or multiunit engine, ladder, or squad company. The quasi-military ranks of sergeant, lieutenant, and captain are typically associated with the company officer or the **NFPA Fire Officer I** designation.

The company officer must have an understanding of the organizational structure of the fire department, including its geographical characteristics and response districts. This station-level supervisor must be familiar with departmental operations, as well as safety and administrative procedures.

The company officer must be able do the following:

- Effectively communicate in writing, operate in an information management system, and effectively operate at all levels in the applicable incident-management system

- Assign tasks or responsibilities to unit members so that the instructions are complete, clear, and concise, with safety considerations addressed and the desired outcomes communicated

- Address community inquiries, project the role of the department, and deliver "all- hazards" education programs

- Recommend changes to existing departmental policies and/or implement new departmental policies at the unit level

- Perform a fire investigation to determine preliminary causes, secure incident scenes, and preserve evidence, as well as provide pertinent information to a fire investigator

- Supervise emergency operations, conduct pre-incident planning, and deploy assigned resources as required

- Integrate safety plans, policies, and procedures into daily and emergency activities. Don appropriate levels of personal protective equipment to ensure a safe work environment for all assigned members

Battalion or district chief

The **battalion** or **district chief** (typically **NFPA Fire Officer II**) is responsible for the supervision of the personnel and resources associated with multiple units/ stations or organizational disciplines within the fire department. This supervisor must be familiar with the organization of all applicable levels of government; their enabling and regulatory legislation; and the functions of other bureaus, divisions, agencies, organizations, and entities as they relate to the fire department.

The battalion or district chief must do the following:

- Initiate actions to enhance or correct member performance within department policies and procedures

- Develop policies and procedures identifying challenges and providing solutions

- Prepare organizational unit budgets and news releases

- Conduct inspections to identify hazards and address code violations

- Conduct fire investigations to determine origin and preliminary cause

- Supervise multiunit emergency operations, conduct pre-incident planning, and deploy assigned resources

- Produce operational plans so that required resources and their assignments are obtained and plans are carried out in compliance with approved safety procedures, resulting in the mitigation of an incident

- Review injury, accident, and health exposure reports to identify unsafe work conditions to prevent reoccurrence

Deputy or assistant chief

The **deputy** or **assistant fire chief** (typically **NFPA Fire Officer III**) is responsible for the supervision of the personnel and resources associated with a major functional discipline (training, emergency medical services, community risk reduction, etc.) within the fire department. This supervisor must keep current with national and international trends and developments related to the fire service and be familiar with public and private organizations that interact with the fire and emergency services.

The deputy or assistant fire chief must do the following:

- Have the ability to research, use evaluative methods, analyze data, communicate orally and in writing, and motivate members

- Establish procedures for hiring, assigning, promoting, and encouraging development of members

- Establish member assignments to maximize efficiency in accordance with policies and procedures

- Prepare community awareness programs

- Prepare divisional or departmental budgets, solicit bids, plan for resource allocation, and work with information management systems

- Evaluate inspection programs to determine effectiveness and develop public safety plans

- Evaluate and identify construction, alarm, detection, and suppression features that contribute to or prevent the spread of fire, heat, and smoke

- Develop pre-incident plans

- Manage multiagency planning, deployment, and operations so that the required resources are determined and the resources are assigned to mitigate an incident

- Develop, manage, and evaluate a departmental safety program

- Develop a measurable accident and injury prevention program

Fire chief (chief engineer, fire commissioner)

The **fire chief** (also known as **chief engineer** or **commissioner** in some jurisdictions) (**NFPA Fire Officer IV**) must serve as a department head and must possess advanced administrative, financial, communications, political, legal, managerial, analytical, and information management skills and abilities.

The fire commissioner or fire chief must do the following:

- Administer and evaluate job performance requirements

Fire Department Organization

FIREFIGHTER I

Chapter 3

- Appraise the fire department's human resource demographics

- Organize and implement recruitment, selection, and placement processes consistent with law and current best practices

- Project a positive image of the fire department to the community

- Attend, participate in, and assume a leadership role in community events to enhance the image of the fire department

- Accomplish long-range planning and fiscal projections

- Develop a comprehensive disaster plan that integrates other agencies' resources to effectively mitigate the impact on a community

- Maintain, develop, and provide leadership for a risk-management program to reduce department injuries and property damage

- Interface with other department heads, a city manager (in some jurisdictions), and elected officials

ADDITIONAL FIRE DEPARTMENT FUNCTIONS

As discussed under fire department organizational structure above, modern fire and emergency service organizations provide numerous functions and services in addition to their typical fire suppression responsibilities. These "additional" functions, depending on jurisdictional needs, may include EMS, community risk reduction (fire-prevention and life-safety education, code enforcement, fire investigation), training, fleet and equipment maintenance, special operations, and administrative or logistical support (fig. 3–13).

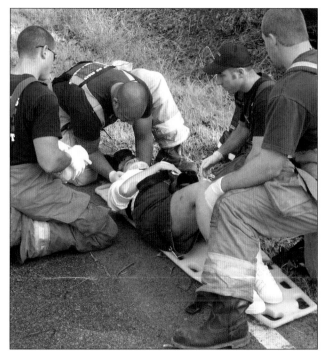

Fig. 3–13. For the average firefighter, over 50% of responses will be to emergency medical incidents. Firefighters must realize that they have responsibilities to both fire suppression and emergency medicine.

Emergency medical services

Many fire departments provide EMS to their community. This evolution to a fire-department-based EMS generally depends on the department having the required infrastructure to provide this service, an existing central dispatch resource, strategically placed stations, a centralized training resource, and a 24-hour career and/or volunteer staff.

Most fire-department-based EMS systems are staffed with firefighters with specialized EMS training, skills, knowledge, and certification, depending on community and jurisdiction needs and provider-level requirements. These provider levels are typically categorized as follows:

- **Emergency medical responder** (formerly first responder)—Provision of first aid and cardiopulmonary resuscitation (CPR)

- **Emergency medical technician** (formerly EMT Basic, EMT-B)—Considered to be the minimum level of certification required to function on an ambulance. For fire-department-based EMS systems, EMT certification is typically required during Fire Fighter I and II training.

- **Advanced medical technician** (AMT, formerly EMT-Intermediate/85, EMT-I/85)—This provider level serves to bridge the practical skills and capabilities of EMTs and paramedics. AMTs are frequently found where the paramedic provider level is not provided.

- **Paramedic** (formerly EMT-Intermediate/99, EMT-I/99, EMT paramedic)—The care and skill capability of this certification level provides for the administration of various medications and invasive EMS procedures under medical direction.

These personnel operate under the auspices of a medical director within state and/or jurisdictional performance protocols. The emergency medical responder, EMT and AMT provider levels are usually components of a basic life support (BLS) system. The paramedic provider level is part of an advanced life support (ALS) system.

Other major considerations for communities and jurisdictions receiving fire department-based EMS is whether the patient transport function should be handled by the fire department or another service or contractor, and whether the fire department should provide BLS or ALS services. Although there are numerous variations of fire department EMS delivery systems, the major options are responding with the appropriate level of service:

- BLS staff and resources to stabilize the patient and transport to a medical facility as required

- ALS staff and resources to stabilize the patient and transport to a medical facility as required

- BLS or ALS staff and resources to stabilize the patient, and another agency transporting the patient to a medical facility. The fire department response in this variation may be accomplished by the closest company staffed with the appropriately certified personnel including an engine company, a ladder company, a squad company, or a vehicle specially designed for this purpose.

NFPA 450, *Guide for Emergency Medical Services and Systems*, provides an excellent reference for community or jurisdictional EMS programs.

Community risk reduction

The transition of fire department responsibilities to an all-hazard approach necessitates the need for progressive fire service organizations to reassign their life- and fire-safety efforts from the traditional fire-prevention program to **community risk reduction**. This reassignment more accurately addresses the contemporary educational, regulatory, and enforcement requirements of a modern fire department involved in such activities as life- and fire-safety education, hazardous materials, EMS, technical rescue, homeland security, code application and enforcement, fire investigation, and **special operations**.

Firefighters may be assigned significant roles in a fire department's community risk-reduction program commensurate with their training, experience, and certification (fig. 3–14). The following standards identify the minimum knowledge, skills, and abilities required of firefighters assigned to community risk-reduction responsibilities:

NFPA 1031, *Standard for Professional Qualifications for Fire Inspector and Plan Examiner*

NFPA 1033, *Standard for Professional Qualifications for Fire Investigator*

NFPA 1035, *Standard for Professional Qualifications for Public Fire and Life Safety Educator*

Fig. 3–14. Although many fire departments have dedicated community risk reduction personnel, it is the responsibility of each firefighter to preach fire prevention and risk reduction.

Special operations

Fire departments organize specialized operational response units to address unique challenges within their respective communities or jurisdictions (fig. 3–15). These specialized units may include hazardous materials mitigation, swift water rescue, ice rescue, confined space, technical rescue, rapid intervention teams, and explosives disposal. Firefighters assigned to these units must have specialized knowledge, skills, and abilities.

Fig. 3–15. Firefighters are responsible for a wide variety of skills involving technical rescue and hazardous materials. Here firefighters operate a boat to perform a water rescue.

Training

FFI 5.1.1 A fire department, regardless of size and mission, provides a training resource in its organizational structure. This resource ranges from an individual in a small single-station department or volunteer organization to a complete organizational division headed by a chief officer in a large metropolitan fire department.

The responsibility is the same, however: administering and documenting all training activities. The department's training officer frequently serves as the organization's safety officer. This assists the department in complying with applicable state or federal Occupational Safety and Health Administration (OSHA) requirements and addresses NFPA 1500, *Fire Department Occupational Safety and Health Program*.

The fire department training function administers and documents the training and continuing education programs for all members of the organization including recruits, probationary firefighters, company officers, and chief officers (see fig. 3–16). Ongoing training for updating firefighter skills and providing specialized training such as fire investigation, specialized rescue techniques, and code enforcement are all part of a fire academy's training responsibilities.

Fig. 3–16. In order to keep skills and knowledge accurate and up to date, firefighters must receive continuing education and training on all the different types of responses they may be responsible for. Here a firefighter trains on a circular saw under the supervision of a senior firefighter.

Communication/dispatch

A number of fire departments provide a 9-1-1 communications/dispatch resource for their community or jurisdiction (fig. 3–17). Most **public safety answering points (PSAP)** are facilitated by local law enforcement where calls for assistance are initially received and then transferred to the fire department for dispatch. There are variations to this process that include the fire department providing the initial answering point.

Fig. 3–17. 9-1-1 Centers are responsible for receiving emergency calls and dispatching the appropriate agencies and units to the emergencies.

A PSAP may be staffed with civilian personnel, law enforcement personnel, uniformed firefighters, or an appropriate combination as determined by the local community or jurisdiction. NFPA 1061, *Standard for*

Professional Qualifications for Public Safety Telecommunicator, provides the minimum qualifications required of individuals assigned to a 9-1-1 communications/dispatch center.

Apparatus and equipment acquisition and maintenance

Ensuring that apparatus and equipment are in good working order for emergency response and use is an obvious priority for a fire department. The resource and organization provided by a fire department for this program depends on the size and service demands of the community or jurisdiction and local policy.

Operational fire department personnel work closely with qualified fire apparatus- and equipment-maintenance personnel to formulate specifications for acquisition of new vehicles, tools, and appliances.

Maintenance facilities and personnel for fire department apparatus and equipment may be shared with other municipal organizations in larger communities or outsourced by smaller organizations. NFPA 1071, *Standard for Emergency Vehicle Technician Professional Qualifications*, is the generally accepted standard for the minimum qualifications for fire apparatus-maintenance personnel.

WELLNESS, RISK-MANAGEMENT, AND RECRUITMENT PROGRAMS

FFI 5.1.1 The most valuable resource of a fire department is its staff. Commensurate with local, state, and federal requirements, fire departments or their human resources offices typically provide programs for health and wellness, risk management, employee assistance and recruitment/retention, as well as other ongoing member support efforts.

Physical fitness and a healthy lifestyle

Firefighters must recognize the importance of physical fitness and a healthy lifestyle as it relates to their duties and responsibilities. Routine participation in a prescribed physical fitness program coupled with a healthy lifestyle can enhance firefighters' ability to perform required

tasks and activities safely and reduce their risk of injury and premature death.

Progressive fire departments require an exercise program that includes an annual fitness assessment. The focus of this assessment is typically aerobic capacity, body composition, strength, endurance, and flexibility (fig. 3–18).

Fig. 3–18. Regular exercise, proper diet, and medical checkups are essential to all firefighters. Firefighters must have the discipline to follow a healthy lifestyle that provides for a long career and healthy retirement. (Courtesy of Frank Ricci)

Maintaining a healthy lifestyle and level of fitness is not only a benefit to firefighters but also encourages the confidence of fire department team members and the individuals the firefighters are called on to serve.

The National Fire Protection Association, through its NFPA 1582, *Standard on Comprehensive Occupational Medical Program for Fire Departments*, and 1583, *Standard on Health-Related Fitness Programs for Fire Department Members*, provides excellent job-related, references for firefighters. Additionally, the Joint Labor Management Wellness-Fitness Initiative, developed by the IAFF and the IAFC, provides a tool to be used in conjunction with NFPA 1583.

Risk management

Whether a fire department is an independent corporation, a municipal body, or a federal entity, risk management for members and employees is a high priority. Risk-management programs, for example, may encompass defining an emergency incident safety culture, establishing a departmental safety committee and safety officer, medical and workers' compensation insurance, substance abuse programs, and an **employee assistance program (EAP)**. Many of these programs are addressed in NFPA 1500, *Standard on Fire Department Occupational Safety and Health Program*.

Recruitment and retention

Fire department entities are finding it more and more difficult to attract and retain volunteer members. This phenomenon is the result of a number of factors, including increased time and training requirements, increased incident call volume, and aging communities, to name a few. The U.S. Fire Administration (USFA), the Department of Homeland Security (DHS), and the National Volunteer Fire Council (NVFC) recently published a comprehensive study addressing the decline in volunteer participation in the fire service (*Retention and Recruitment for the Volunteer Emergency Services: Challenges and Solutions*. U.S. Fire Administration, #FA-310, May 2007).

This study outlines a number of incentives designed to attract and retain volunteer firefighter candidates, many of which could be applied to career candidates. These incentives, depending on the jurisdiction, might include a **length of service award program** (**LOSAP**), pay per call or per hour, tax exemptions or deductions, health insurance, tuition assistance, and low-interest housing loans.

POLICIES, PROCEDURES, REGULATIONS, AND BYLAWS

As with any organization or business, the fire department must operate within applicable policies, procedures, regulations, or bylaws. These documents may be promulgated from within the fire department or adopted by an outside entity with application to the fire department. They may be operational or administrative in nature.

Policies and procedures

FFI 5.1.1 Policies and procedures are typically used by the fire department to document the "how-to" in a consistent manner so that all involved understand what is expected of them and their coworkers and how to accomplish it. These documents may be used to communicate administrative or operational matters, are usually codified for easy filing, retrieval and access, and provide for easy updating.

Standard operating procedures (**SOPs**) or **standard operating guidelines** (**SOGs**) typically address operational matters such as hose loads, water supply, high-rise operations, and safety requirements. Policies are more often associated with administrative matters such as time and attendance and personnel matters, and are generally promulgated from management or senior staff.

Regulations

Regulations are legal requirements and generally have enforcement or compliance requirements. OSHA and the Department of Labor (DOL), for example, use regulations to communicate their legal requirements.

INCIDENT COMMAND SYSTEM

For most functions performed by the fire service, the typical organizational model does fine. Recent events have caused the fire service to adopt organizational systems that conform to many federal and state regulations when responding to emergency incidents. The **incident command system** (**ICS**) is an organizational system that provides command and control at these emergency incidents and meets the requirements of government regulations.

The ICS has been used in various styles by the fire service since the early 1970s. The latest method allows the fire service to operate at any type of incident, natural or man-made, and coordinate operations with many other organizations not directly connected to the fire service. ICS provides for improved communications, management of resources, effective span of control, unity of command, effective division of labor, and a coordinated action plan. How ICS works with structural firefighting and hazardous materials incidents will be covered in later chapters and a more detailed explanation of ICS will be covered in Firefighter II.

A discussion of ICS typically covers command staff, general staff, functional areas, and facilities.

The command staff consists of the incident commander, safety officer, information officer, and liaison officer.

- The **incident commander** is the individual responsible for the management of all incident operations at the incident site.

- The **safety officer** is a member of the command staff responsible for monitoring and assessing safety hazards or unsafe situations and for developing measures for ensuring personnel safety.

- The **information officer** is a member of the command staff responsible for interfacing with the public and media or with other agencies that require information directly from the incident.

- The **liaison officer** is a member of the command staff responsible for coordinating with representatives from cooperating and assisting agencies.

The general staff is a group of incident management personnel reporting to the incident commander. The **general staff** consists of the operations section, planning section, logistics section, and finance/administration section.

- The **operations section** is responsible for all tactical operations at the incident. Includes branches, divisions and/or groups, task forces, strike teams, single resources, and staging areas (fig. 3–19).

- The **planning section** is responsible for the collection, evaluation, and dissemination of tactical information related to the incident, and for the preparation and documentation of incident action plans. This section also maintains information on the current and forecasted situation as well as the status of resources assigned to the incident. This includes the situation, resource, documentation, and demobilization units, as well as technical specialists.

- The **logistics section** is responsible for providing facilities, services, and materials for the incident.

- The **finance/administration section** chief is responsible for all incident costs and financial considerations. This includes the time unit, procurement unit, compensation/claims unit, and cost unit.

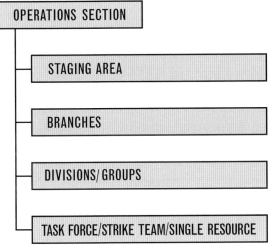

Fig. 3–19. Operations section positions

Common incident facilities include the following:

- The **incident command post** (ICP) is the location where the primary command functions are executed. The ICP may be located within the incident base or other incident facilities.

- The **staging area** is a location set up at an incident where resources can be placed while awaiting a tactical assignment. Staging areas are managed by the operations section.

- **Base** is the location where primary logistics functions for an incident are coordinated and administered. There is only one base per incident.

- **Camp** is a geographical site within the general incident area but separate from the incident base. It is equipped and staffed to provide sleeping, food, water, and sanitary services to incident personnel.

ALLIED ORGANIZATIONS AND THE FIREFIGHTER

FFI 5.1.1 The firefighter's duties and responsibilities interface with and are influenced by a number of external agencies and organizations. These entities range from neighboring fire departments to international regulatory organizations.

Mutual aid plans and automatic aid agreements

Because no single fire department can be expected to possess the resources required to resolve every possible emergency that may occur in their jurisdiction, or because the resources of a neighboring fire department may be geographically closer to an emergency, a fire department may enter into **automatic aid** or **mutual aid** agreements with neighboring organizations.

Mutual aid agreements between fire departments involve reciprocal assistance under a prearranged plan. As an example, when a target hazard or specialized hazard exists in one fire department's responsible jurisdiction that potentially exceeds that fire department's resources, a reciprocal agreement is prearranged, and the neighboring fire department responds for assistance. This type of agreement is also used in the event the closest fire department to a particular incident is committed to another response.

Automatic aid is a plan developed by two or more fire departments for the immediate, joint response to incidents. Automatic aid plans are typically developed when resources required for an initial response or fire attack are not available from the responsible or closest fire department, or neighboring fire departments are geographically closer than the responsible fire department.

These aid plans and agreements delineate requirements and expectations of each of the participating organizations, ranging from indemnity, training levels, and the number of personnel that will respond, to incident command responsibilities. Compensation arrangements are typically addressed when there is a disparity in the frequency and resources routinely responding from one fire department to another.

National Fire Protection Association (NFPA)

The NFPA was established in 1896 as a nonprofit organization to reduce the worldwide burden of fire and other hazards on the quality of life by providing and advocating consensus codes, standards, research, training, and education. The NFPA currently has more than 81,000 members, representing more than 80 national trade and professional organizations. The NFPA's 300 codes and standards influence every building, process, service, design, and installation in the United States and many other countries.

NFPA standards that have an influence on the firefighter, depending on their duties and responsibilities, include, but are not limited to, the following:

- NFPA 1001, *Standard for Fire Fighter Professional Qualifications*
- NFPA 1002, *Standard on Fire Apparatus Driver/Operator Professional Qualifications*
- NFPA 1003, *Standard for Airport Fire Fighter Professional Qualifications*
- NFPA 1005, *Standard for Professional Qualifications for Marine Fire Fighting for Land-Based Fire Fighters*
- NFPA 1006, *Standard for Rescue Technician Professional Qualifications*
- NFPA 1031, *Standard for Professional Qualifications for Fire Inspector and Plan Examiner*
- NFPA 1033, *Standard for Professional Qualifications for Fire Investigator*

- NFPA 1035, *Standard for Professional Qualifications for Public Fire and Life Safety Educator*
- NFPA 1051, *Standard for Wildland Fire Fighter Professional Qualifications*
- NFPA 1061, *Standard for Professional Qualifications for Public Safety Telecommunicator*
- NFPA 1081, *Standard for Industrial Fire Brigade Member Professional Qualifications*
- NFPA 1500, *Standard on Fire Department Occupational Safety and Health Program*
- NFPA 1581, *Standard on Fire Department Infection Control Program*
- NFPA 1582, *Standard on Comprehensive Occupational Medical Program for Fire Departments*
- NFPA 1583, *Standard on Health-Related Fitness Programs for Fire Department Members*

International Association of Fire Chiefs (IAFC)

The IAFC was established in 1873 to represent the leadership of more than 1.2 million firefighters. Members of the IAFC are considered the leading experts in firefighting, EMS, terrorism response, hazardous materials, natural disasters, search and rescue, and public safety legislation.

Some of the IAFC programs having direct interface with firefighters include the following:

- National Fire Fighter Near-Miss Reporting System
- Vehicle Safety
- Wellness Fitness
- Hazardous Materials

International Association of Fire Fighters (IAFF)

The IAFF was officially established in 1918 and is a labor union representing more than 287,000 career firefighters and emergency medical personnel. With its headquarters in Washington, DC, the IAFF works to promote a safe and healthy work environment, reasonable working conditions, the research and treatment of burns and other related health problems common to firefighters, and the establishment of schools for imparting knowledge of modern and improved methods of firefighting and prevention.

National Volunteer Fire Council (NVFC)

The NVFC pursues the interests of volunteer firefighters and volunteer fire departments. It is an organization comprising state firefighter organizations involved in providing training programs, public education, conferences, and the compilation of pertinent statistics. The NVFC represents its members' interests to the U.S. Congress and federal agencies.

Department of Homeland Security (DHS)

DHS was established after the September 11, 2001, terrorist attack, when duplications and gaps were exploited in federal, state, and local government resources. DHS integrates these resources to protect the American homeland, including the Federal Emergency Management Agency (FEMA), the USFA, and the National Fire Academy. The primary benefit to firefighters and fire departments is grant funding, incident preplanning and coordination, equipment, and training.

Occupational Safety and Health Administration (OSHA)

OSHA, part of the U.S. Department of Labor, was established to ensure safe working conditions. Many states have established a local OSHA entity to enforce the federal regulations. Whether enforced at the state or federal level, OSHA workplace requirements apply to volunteer and career fire departments.

National Institute for Occupational Safety and Health (NIOSH)

NIOSH supports the OSHA through research and educational training. The Institute recommends occupational safety and health standards and undertakes investigations of firefighter and other occupational incidents when requested.

Insurance Services Office (ISO)

ISO is a nonprofit voluntary association of insurers that gathers data for the purpose of setting fire insurance rates. Using its *Grading Schedule for Municipal Fire Protection*, ISO provides an analysis of public fire services and their ability to defend the community against a major fire. The analysis includes a review of the fire department, available water supply, the fire service communication system, and the fire-safety control capabilities.

STATISTICAL OVERVIEW

The NFPA reported that there were 30,185 fire departments in 2007. These departments were staffed as follows:

All career	2,263
Mostly career	1,765
Mostly volunteer	4,989
All volunteer	21,168

Tables 3–1, 3–2, and 3–3 provide a 5-year presentation of pertinent fire department and firefighter data, including the number of career and volunteer firefighters, the number of fire departments, the number of fire and nonfire incidents firefighters responded to, firefighter injuries, and firefighter deaths. Career firefighters include full-time, uniformed firefighters regardless of assignment, but do not include state, federal, or private fire-brigade personnel. Volunteer firefighters include active part-time and paid on-call.

Table. 3–1. Firefighter and fire department statistics

Year	Career firefighters	Volunteer firefighters	Total firefighters	Number of fire departments
2003	296,850	800,050	1,096,900	30,542
2004	305,150	795,600	1,100,750	30,400
2005	313,300	823,650	1,136,950	30,300
2006	316,950	823,950	1,140,900	30,635
2007	323,350	825,450	1,148,800	30,185

Source: NFPA

Table. 3–2. Incidents and firefighter injuries

Year	Fire incidents	Fire incident injuries	Nonfire incidents	Nonfire incident injuries
2003	1,584,500	38,045	20,821,500	14,550
2004	1,550,500	36,880	21,066,000	13,150
2005	1,602,000	41,950	21,649,500	12,250
2006	1,642,500	44,210	22,827,500	13,090
2007	1,557,500	38,340	23,777,000	15,435

Source: NFPA

Fire Department Organization

FIREFIGHTER I

Chapter 3

Table. 3–3. Career and volunteer firefighter fatalities

Year	Total	Career firefighters	Volunteer firefighters	Nonmunicipal
2003	106	26	58	22
2004	105	29	65	11
2005	87	25	54	8
2006	89	23	46	20
2007	103	42	53	8

Source: NFPA

Most career firefighters (74%) protect communities of 25,000 or more people, while 95% of volunteer firefighters protect communities with fewer than 25,000 people. More than half of volunteer firefighters are located in rural fire departments protecting fewer than 2,500 people.

The number of fire and nonfire incidents continues to increase annually, as does the number of injuries.

QUESTIONS

1. Discuss the differences between policies and procedures, operating guidelines, and regulations.

2. What are the differences between mutual aid agreements and automatic aid agreements? In what instances would one or both be used?

3. Explain the different levels of officers and their responsibilities (for example, fire chief, deputy chief, battalion chief, company officer).

4. A _____ is a type of apparatus with a permanently mounted fire pump, a water tank, a hose storage area, an aerial ladder or elevating platform with a permanently mounted waterway, and a complement of ground ladders.

5. Hazardous materials, swift water rescue, confined space, and rope rescue are all examples of _____ operations.

6. Name the different EMS certification levels and what general level of care each can provide.

7. The most valuable resource a fire department has is its _____.

8. What levels of firefighting certifications exist, and what skills are taught to each level?

Fire Department Communications

by Alan R. Young with Susan Bartlett and Penny Adams

This chapter provides required knowledge items for the following NFPA Standard 1001 Job Performance Requirements:

FFI 5.2.1

FFI 5.2.3

FFI 5.2.4

This chapter contains Skill Drills. When you see this icon, refer to your Skill Drill book for step-by-step instructions.

OBJECTIVES

Upon completion of this chapter, you will be able to do the following:

- Identify the procedures to follow when receiving an alarm or reporting an emergency
- Identify how calls are received and recorded
- Identify how emergency equipment is dispatched
- Identify emergency communication procedures to be used at an emergency incident
- Describe the policy and procedures for ordering and transmitting multiple alarms
- Define the purpose and function of all alarm receiving instruments and personnel alerting equipment provided in the fire department
- Identify and describe personnel accountability systems (PAS)
- Identify the types of communications codes and languages

INTRODUCTION

Communication within a fire department, its community, or field of service appears at a glance to be a simple matter of picking up the phone, and then all is well. In reality, it is a complex system designed to meet any and all criteria for a limitless number of circumstances and scenarios. Communications centers of all sizes must conform to standards required by the National Fire Protection Association (NFPA).[1] The system must work when all else does not. Accurate reporting, dispatching, and effective responses by fire companies and other agencies are essential to save both lives and property. In addition to this daunting task, security, which has always been a concern, is now a greater issue since the terrorist attacks of September 11, 2001. With all of these elements—24-hour service, meeting industry standards, and ensuring the security of resources—the business of public safety communications is indeed an intricate one. The information in this chapter shows how the multifaceted fire communications systems work and interact to provide the public a greater degree of safety.

Communication Facilities

What is a public safety communications center? A communications center facility is a unique and complex operation. A public safety communications center is referred to as a public safety answering point (PSAP). It is a stand-alone facility that operates 24 hours a day, 7 days a week, under all conditions, and during any circumstances. It must be built to conform to NFPA standards, specifically NFPA 1221, *Standard for the Installation, Maintenance, and Use of Emergency Communications Systems,* pertaining to how buildings are designed and how notifications are to be sent.[2] During an emergency, the center is responsible for taking the information of the emergency, including type of incident, location, and information about the person reporting the incident. That information is then used to alert the appropriate resources to respond to and mitigate the emergency. The communications center functions much as a quarterback who leads the team, provides the necessary plan or resources, and makes adjustments as needed to achieve the desired outcome.

Fig. 4–1. Communications centers come in different shapes and sizes.

Communications centers (fig. 4–1) come in many shapes and sizes. In small towns with small populations, it is not uncommon to find a one-room work area with a few dispatch positions and a small staff to handle the workload. In larger areas, the communications center may be a multistory building with 20 or more positions, requiring a large staff and training facilities. A communications center often covers only a local area of jurisdiction. However, some communications centers provide service for multiple agencies and jurisdictions under what is referred to as a **joint powers agreement** (JPA; a contract between a city, county, and/or special district in which the city or county agrees to perform services, cooperate with, or lend its powers to). Under this type of arrangement, agencies are still afforded the opportu-nity to operate independently of each other, yet during large or complex events the best outcomes are arrived at by sharing resources.

MANAGEMENT

Administrative staff

Communications centers can effectively function under a variety of organizational models depending on the configuration of their area and the populations they serve. A typical center consists of a management and operational staff of varying levels. Often administrative support staff does not report to the same supervisors as the operational staff. Each staff member would, however, report to the center manager who oversees the center's entire operation staff.

The manager (or in the case of sworn personnel, the chief) oversees the entire operation of the center. The job responsibilities are the following:

- Ensure the budgetary needs of the center's operation are met

- Make policy decisions

- Identify future needs of the center

- Ensure the center is adequately staffed with trained personnel

- Maintain the day-to-day operations

To accomplish those tasks, the manager has assistant managers (or in the case of sworn personnel, deputy chiefs) to assist in handling the responsibilities and workload. The assistant managers or deputy chiefs each have an area of the center's day-to-day operations for which they are responsible. One manager might be in charge of operations, and another manager will oversee the administrative side. The size of the agency determines how these positions are utilized and how many positions are needed to operate with an appropriate span of control, providing unity of command throughout the organization.

The administrative support staff of the communications center is vital to maintaining and supporting the operation of the communications center. This may include the information technology staff, a payroll and accounting department, and a hiring and recruitment department. At times, staff must deal with the press and public, especially with large and complex events affecting residents and property. Depending on the size of the agency, the administrative staff can report either to an immediate supervisor or directly to an assistant manager or deputy chief.

The operations side of the communications center is where all of the action takes place. It is here that the critical business of fire communications happens. The telecommunicators, also known as dispatchers, take the incoming emergency and nonemergency calls and dispatch the appropriate equipment (fig. 4–2). (A telecommunicator is a person trained and responsible for receiving and dispatching all nonemergency and emergency calls for service.) The dispatchers report to a direct supervisor, who then reports to one of the assistant managers or deputy chiefs.

Fig. 4–2. Telecommunicator takes the incoming emergency and nonemergency calls and dispatches the appropriate equipment. Photo courtesy of J. Rains.

Telecommunicators

Telecommunicators are unique, highly skilled individuals who have the ability to multitask. The position of dispatcher has evolved from an individual on light duty who was assigned to the communications center until medically cleared to resume firefighting duties. Or perhaps it was a reserve firefighter who wanted to gain full employment with the department and used dispatch as a way to obtain a permanent firefighter's position and access to the specialized career field of firefighting. Today, a telecommunicator must be able to use a **computer-aided dispatch (CAD)** system, operate an extensive telephone system, obtain information from citizens, and alert the appropriate resources. Whether an agency is large or small, high-tech or paper-based, the field units must rely on the professional telecommunicator, not only for incident information and updates but also for their actual safety.[3]

COMMUNICATION SYSTEMS

The use of highly advanced radio and computer equipment has changed the face of information technology (fig. 4–3) and, for the most part, has taken the place of most handwritten or **card systems** (fig. 4–4). Cards are used to determine a predesignated response to an emergency. Some of the card systems still exist in smaller agencies, because it works for them. In jurisdictions with a lower volume of service calls, the card system is able to initiate timely responses to calls. However, in communications centers that provide service for large or multiple jurisdictions and/or agencies with events or incidents often overlapping each other, the new information technology is vital for timely responses and efficient, effective use of personnel and equipment.

Fig. 4–3. Highly advanced radio and computer equipment have changed the face of information technology and, for the most part, have taken the place of most handwritten or card systems. Photo courtesy of J. Rains.

House Numbers	Cross Streets	Box # Map #	Fourth Alarm		
			Engine Co.	Truck	Fill
140-320 Greenfield Ave.	Foresthill Ave.	11446	Mutual Aid Engine 20	Mutual Aid 20	WT 40
320-650 Greenfield Ave.	Ida Street	11447	Third Alarm		
			Engine Co.	Truck	Fill
			Mutual Aid Eng. 8, 15	5	WT 60
			Second Alarm		
			Engine Co.	Truck	Fill
			3, 4	2	Medic 1
			First Alarm		
			Engine Co.	Squad	Truck
			1, 2	1	2
N to nn blk	Street				

Fig. 4–4. Handwritten or typed "run cards" were used to determine a predesignated response to an emergency.

Computer-aided dispatch (CAD) systems

New technology has taken over the once manual system and replaced it with CAD, an automated, integral part of the dispatching process. The purpose of a CAD system is to have the ability to enter a call location, identify the type of incident the units will be responding to, and recommend the appropriate equipment for response to the identified incident type. Once the appropriate recommendation and the identified units are available for response, the telecommunicator then uses the CAD system to send out station notification and alert tones to the recommended equipment for the response. The CAD system will then track each incident and log the time and information related to the incident, such as unit arrivals, updates of what is occurring with the incident, and any further requests for equipment. When a unit is not on a call, the CAD system is still tracking their status changes. Examples of this would be when a piece of equipment goes out of service for maintenance or when a unit is participating in a drill. The CAD system tracks every unit that is logged on to the system 24 hours a day.

The CAD system also has other functions. The system has the ability to become a vital reference for telecommunicators to use for contact information, duty rosters, and a paging system for mass notifications. As the CAD system is generally linked to the station-alerting and printer mechanism (fig. 4–5), messages can be sent instantaneously to a printer housed at the station where the responders will receive an alert notification that a message has come to the printer and then the written copy of the message is printed for future reference.

Depending on a fire department's budget and desire to be as automated, fire stations can utilize the same computer systems to automate a lot of features that would not be typically found in older fire stations. Some fire stations now have the ability, when an alarm is received, to use their computerized dispatch system to automatically turn on lights, open apparatus doors, and even turn off stoves and ovens.

CAD systems are unique in that no two are ever programmed exactly the same way. In addition, there are many different brands that offer varying features for all types of agencies, large and small. The ability to customize a CAD system is only limited to the needs of the users and the complexity of the citizenship it needs to cover. A town with minimal staffing may want to keep the system simple and less cumbersome. An agency that is providing service to larger populations or jurisdictions and multiple disciplines may want a CAD system with

multiple layers and varying levels of responses. The possibilities are endless.

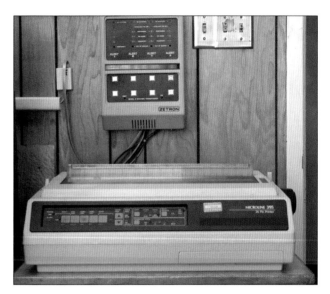

Fig. 4–5. Typical printer and alerting station located in a fire station

9-1-1

The 9-1-1 network is a vital part of our nation's emergency response and disaster preparedness system. In October 1999, the Wireless Communications and Public Safety Act of 1999 (9-1-1 Act) took effect.[4] Its purpose is to improve public safety by encouraging and facilitating the prompt deployment of a nationwide, seamless communications infrastructure for emergency services. One provision of the 9-1-1 Act directs the **Federal Communications Commission (FCC)** to make 9-1-1 the universal emergency number for all telephone services.

9-1-1 is the number that has been established in the United States to give people a quick and easy number to remember when they need help in an emergency. By law, 9-1-1 service is provided to everyone that needs it, without cost, from any hardwired or wireless telephone. It has proven to be the best and fastest way to get help in emergencies. According to the National Emergency Number Association (NENA), it is estimated that over 200 million calls are made to 9-1-1 every year in this country. A local 9-1-1 call can either put the caller in touch with the appropriate agency or, in most areas, a consolidated 9-1-1 communications center that can directly dispatch the help that is needed.

Conventional hardwired 9-1-1 systems. With conventional hardwired phones, there are two versions of 9-1-1: basic and enhanced. Basic 9-1-1 service provides a single answering point for all emergency calls. Callers must provide information about their location and phone number. **Enhanced 9-1-1 (E9-1-1)** provides enhanced equipment and database information that allows the telecommunicator to see the phone number and address of the caller on a display screen at the communications center. In the event that the caller is unable to speak or is disconnected, E9-1-1 can still send emergency units to the location and call back for further information. This also reduces the risk of lost calls. This emergency response system works from the caller's hardwired phone and is accessible from the caller's home or workplace.

Wireless 9-1-1 systems. Since a very large segment of our population is using wireless technology for their everyday communication, there is a great demand for wireless services, including 9-1-1 emergency contact capability. The service needs to be as seamless and have the same format as that used for hardwired telephone calls for assistance. Currently, calls made from a wireless phone may not go to the closest answering point. Even then, the telecommunicator does not have the caller's number or the location of the call. This may cause life-threatening delays in the 9-1-1 system's ability to dispatch the appropriate emergency personnel to the location of the emergency. This deficiency in the cellular phone system can be devastating. Currently, when a call is placed by a cellular caller using the 9-1-1 service, the call taker may be a state highway patrol dispatcher at a PSAP in a remote area far from the caller, or it could be a local agency, depending on how the wireless call is routed. (The **call taker** is the first person to receive the information into a communications center, who then passes it on to the telecommunicator.) Most of the cellular calls that are lost because of hang-ups or poor connections are lost forever. Either the caller has to try again, or others must call to report the same emergency. With the technology improvements being developed, hopefully this will soon change.

According to NENA, there are three phases of the wireless implementation process. Phase 0 is when you dial 9-1-1 from your cellular phone, and a call taker at a PSAP answers (maybe not close to you but still a PSAP). Phase 1 is the first step in providing better emergency response service to wireless 9-1-1 callers. When this phase is implemented, a wireless 9-1-1 call will come into the PSAP with the wireless phone backup number. This process is important in the event the call is dropped. However, this phase does not speak to the issue of caller location. Phase 2 allows the call takers to receive both the caller's wireless phone number and their location information.[6]

The process of implementing a wireless 9-1-1 system that will meet all the requirements is still in varying stages of development throughout the United States. There is constant improvement in the system. At some point in the near future, call takers will receive a call from a wireless phone, with the phone number and location of that phone available to emergency personnel as a matter of course.

Answering points. So what actually happens when you dial 9-1-1 from a hardwired telephone? When 9-1-1 is dialed from a conventional telephone, the call is immediately routed to a PSAP, which is a facility that is responsible for answering 9-1-1 calls for emergency assistance for police, fire, and medical services. PSAPs are generally controlled by city or county agencies; however, some communications centers are governed by a JPA and fall under the authority of a special district.

In the United States there are approximately 6,100 primary and secondary PSAPs.[7] Typically, the difference between a primary and secondary PSAP is the ability to handle law enforcement events or incidents. For example, a citizen dials 9-1-1 from a residential telephone, reporting a grass fire or a person needing medical attention. The call is initially routed to the primary PSAP which, in most instances, will be a law enforcement agency. The law enforcement agency determines what the emergency is. If the event does not require a police presence, the primary PSAP will then transfer the call to a secondary PSAP, which handles the dispatching responsibilities for fires and medical-related incidents. If the call requires law enforcement, the police will respond while transferring the other segments of the incident to fire and/or medical services.

Each communications center ensures that the information has been appropriately transferred to the respective agency and that the telecommunicator receives the information of the reported emergency. The telecommunicator then takes the reporting party's information and initiates an incident case file to track the history of the emergency and determines the resources to respond to the incident. Units are then alerted and dispatched to the emergency scene.

Walk-ins

Direct notification to a fire station of some type of incident still occurs every day in every community and will continue to be a reporting method. Firefighters need to understand that this vital information must be obtained from the person relaying the event and transferred to the communications center as rapidly and efficiently as possible. Firefighters must follow standard operating guidelines for information gathering for an event and use the proper procedure to transfer that information. Whatever the means of transferring that information—by radio, direct-dial hardwired telephone, or a computer application—the process must be always thorough and precise (fig. 4–6).

Fig. 4–6. Firefighters must be able to gather the information reported directly to them.

FIRE ALARM SYSTEMS

Municipal Fire Alarm Systems

Some communities throughout the United States use **municipal fire alarm systems (street boxes)** for notification of emergencies within their community (fig. 4–7). These systems transmit a coded signal generally to the communications center, but they can be hardwired by networks of cables to fire stations and other monitoring buildings. This coded signal indicates a physical location or vicinity. Every street box location has a different coded signal representing the location of that particular street box. These municipal fire alarm system boxes can be either a vicinity box indicating a geographical location (e.g., 8th and Broadway) without a specific address, or it can be a street box with an auxiliary protection system for a particular building. Those buildings are also monitored by a communications center. If something were to trip the alarm system inside the building, it would also activate the signal in the street box. These types of municipal fire alarm systems boxes are sometimes called **auxiliary boxes** and are still used

throughout the country. They are often identified with a white diagonal stripe on top of the box running from one corner to the other. Some of these street boxes may also have a signaling device on top, indicating activation. The problem with this type of alerting system is that they are very prone to false alarms. Many communities have elected to remove this form of alerting device because of the high false alarm rate, the high cost of maintenance, and the development of alternative reporting systems.

Fig. 4–7. Municipal fire alarm box. These systems transmit a coded signal to the communication center, but they can also be hardwired by networks of cables to fire stations and other monitoring buildings.

Private fire alarm systems

These systems employ various devices to signal potential danger. Automatic detection devices such as heat and smoke detectors are used to monitor increases in heat and smoke in the protected area. Some of these systems, along with water sprinkler systems, activate an electrical signal to the monitoring company indicating a water flow problem. Still other alerting or monitoring systems will activate only a local audible alarm but not transmit a signal beyond the location of the emergency. Those alarm systems that are monitoring a private residence or commercial building will alert a monitoring station (often what is known as a **central station**, which is described in chapter 30, Fire Protection Systems) that, in turn, notifies the local public safety jurisdiction as to the type of the emergency.

Call boxes

Call boxes put the caller and the telecommunicator in direct voice contact and are usually recorded. This form of direct communication enables the caller to request a particular type of assistance. The telecommunicator can ask specific questions about the type of emergency and the correct location. Then the telecommunicator can determine the resource requirements based on the information acquired from the caller. In many cities these call boxes are replacing municipal fire system boxes. Still others have been updated to allow the caller to push a button for the type emergency such as fire, medical, or law enforcement. Many of these call box stations are solar powered and in remote sites. They can be found along roadways, and on bridges, parkways, and footpaths (fig. 4–8).

Fig. 4–8. Call box located on a freeway, putting the caller in direct contact with a telecommunicator

REDUNDANT SYSTEMS

Single point of failure is the last phrase a communications center wants to hear or experience. Although there is no way to determine where or when failure is going to occur, it is imperative to have a backup system or redundancies of the equipment, people, and structures of communications centers. If either side of the communications link fails, the whole communication is disrupted. This same principle holds for all aspects of the fire department and related services, thus ensuring a seamless delivery of emergency notifications and resource response. Fortunately, the fire service has adopted the National Fire Protection Association (NFPA) standards, specifically NFPA 1221[10], which sets the standards for the installation, maintenance, and use of emergency systems. These standards provide a road map for communications centers, which covers everything from the construction of the building to the circuitry, staffing, and operating procedures.

Redundancy in communications centers can be as simple as a secondary device in place in case the primary methods of operation fail, or as complex as multiple, layered operating systems in place to take over in case of multiple system failures. A simple form of redundancy uses a telephone as a backup to a station-alerting system. For example, station resources are notified over a station-alerting system of an incoming event. If there is a problem with the station-alerting system, the telephone can be used to notify the needed resources and relay the incident information. If a unit is not in the station, the radio system can be used to notify the resources and relay the information. To add an additional layer of redundancy to that example, the station-alerting system can also be set up to broadcast over the radio system network. If the station-alerting system fails, the radio system could be used to alert the station. In the event the radio system failed, the telephone would then be used to notify the station to respond to the incident. Multiple layers of redundancy reduce the risk of failure.

In addition to regular preventive maintenance of the equipment, there is an operational and personnel need for redundancy as well. If all of the equipment is working, but there is no one trained to operate the facility and take the emergency call, the outcome would be some degree of failure. It is necessary for a communications center to have enough trained personnel on duty to handle service for both emergency and nonemergency calls. There must be at least two telecommunicators on duty at all times, and they must be knowledgeable of the operating standards of the communications center and able to perform their duties and responsibilities within the adopted standards. The need for redundancy in all areas of emergency response can not be overlooked or overemphasized.

METHODS OF CALL RECEIPT

Agency-to-agency contact

Direct-dial phones are used for point-to-point contact with two or more predetermined points (fig. 4–9). From one communications center to another, fire station to fire station, or communications centers to one or more fire stations, direct contact is as simple as picking up the telephone. Direct-line capabilities are a very common method of communication for dispatch centers because they provide immediate contact with other communications centers. Often, other public service facilities, such as police departments, fire departments, and emergency medical service (EMS) communications centers, use this form of communication to expedite contact with each other. Another advantage of direct-line phone communication is that a phone can be mounted on the exterior wall of a fire station (fig. 4–10). In the event the station is closed or the fire company is out of the station for other calls or training, there should be signs prominently displayed with instructions to open the door and pick up the phone, and the person would be immediately connected to a telecommunicator.

Fig. 4–9. Direct-dial telephone in a fire station

Fig. 4–10. Direct-dial telephone mounted to the exterior of a fire station for public use while the fire station personnel are out

Conventional residential and business telephones

The conventional phone is still the most common method of reporting calls for assistance. In 2009, nearly 96% of the population of the United States was covered by some type of 9-1-1 service.[8] There are advantages to using conventional telephones when requesting assistance. When using 9-1-1 systems, your conventional telephone number will be displayed for verification. By using enhanced 9-1-1 services, not only will the telephone number be displayed but also the caller's physical address. This may not be the incident address, but it is the location of the caller.

Cellular telephones

Cellular phones are becoming the norm in the field of communication. The popularity and availability of cellular service throughout most of the United States have made cell phones the new trend in communication. A growing number of people use cellular phones as their primary phone service with no conventional residential telephone service. This makes the need to complete the capability of location identification even more urgent. Currently, the wireless system has development and technology issues that are being addressed to overcome the inability of the cellular phones to act in the same manner as conventional hardwired phones. The accomplishments over the past few years have been tremendous and the ability to use global positioning system (GPS) technology has made identification of caller's location to a geographical area possible, but not with the pinpoint precision that is possible with conventional phones.

Nonemergency phone numbers

Nonemergency telephone numbers are generally used for daily business operations or telephone numbers that are assigned a specific task, such as for general information. 2-1-1 is the nationwide abbreviated dialing code for free access to health and human service agencies' information. The 2-1-1 center's referral specialists answer questions for callers. They can access databases of resources available from both private and public health and human service agencies. They match the callers' needs to the available resources. These specialists can link or refer them to an agency or organization that can help. 3-1-1 is the nationwide abbreviated dialing code for nonemergency police and government agencies. 5-1-1 is designated for road and traffic conditions. Other public-use numbers are 7-1-1, which is for the telecommunications relay service (TRS) for the speech and hearing impaired, and 8-1-1.[9] 8-1-1 is the number you call before you excavate the backyard. It arranges for utilities to be located and marked. These calls are answered by the local municipality or governmental agency. Residents who have lived in a community since before emergency numbers were available may still dial the general information phone numbers for emergency assistance. Communications centers need to be prepared to handle emergency requests for service from any of the numbers dialed.

Fire departments also maintain phone numbers that are used for business information only. These phone numbers are used by fire department personnel and the general public to reach the divisions of the fire department. Such telephone phone numbers would include the numbers for the Fire Prevention, Fire Inspections, and Report Divisions, along with the administrative sections of the fire department including the Human Resources Department and the fire chief's office.

Text phones: alternative methods of reporting

Today it is not uncommon to send a text message using a cellular telephone or an instant message via the Internet to communicate with another person. Although the technology of text messaging has advanced rapidly in recent years, the concept has actually been around for many years in the form of **text telephones** or **teletypes** (**TTYs**). Text telephone is a generic term for a device that assists people with speech or hearing impairments to communicate using a telephone. TTY is also known as TDD, for telecommunication device for the deaf.

During an emergency it is vital to have alternative methods for individuals to report their emergency. Like computers with modems, text telephones have special acoustic cups that connect to a telephone handset. The TTY provides a keyboard and visual display for the caller to type and receive messages. This is done over standard telephone lines and networks, just as anyone's calls would be. However, to communicate using a text phone, a call from one device can only be received by another compatible device. TTY is typically used by deaf, hard of hearing, or hearing-impaired individuals; the device can be used between both hearing and nonhearing individuals.

In the case of an emergency, TTY can be used for a speech- or hearing-impaired individual to report the incident. Upon receiving a call over the teletype, the dispatcher can obtain the needed information from the caller by simply typing a message over the computer. The reporting party then types back the information of the emergency. In most instances, the text telephone has a scroll of paper attached, so a copy of the conversation is printed out, not only on the visual display but on paper as well.

There are special abbreviations used when communicating over TTYs to allow the parties to know when to stop or start to speak. For example, to stop "speaking," type **SK** at the end of the sentence. The other party then knows it is their turn to respond. To let the other person know you will be hanging up, it is necessary to type **SKSK.** Once the dispatcher has the necessary information from a caller, the dispatcher advises the caller that the units are responding, and the dispatcher will end the call with *SKSK.* If a communications center does not have text phones or teletypes available, it can use a center called a telecommunications relay service (TRS). TRS is a toll-free, 24-hour, year-round facility that provides an operator to relay the information between the two parties. For example, the hearing-impaired individual with the TTY device calls into the TRS where an operator answers and relays the information. In the case of reporting an emergency, this information would go to the telecommunicator at the communications center. The TRS operator then takes the dispatcher's information over the regular telephone and types it back to the caller using the TTY service.

CALL CLASSIFICATION

FFI 5.2.2 Calls for assistance are generally received at a communications center. They can also be received while fire companies are in the firehouse by a citizen knocking on their door or while the fire company is working in the district performing fire-prevention activities, training or doing inspections. Calls for assistance are generally classified as *nonemergency* or *emergency*.

Nonemergency calls

Nonemergency calls are general-assistance calls, typically not life or property threatening. Fire companies are dispatched to incidents requiring them to perform activities: assist people with animal rescues, help individuals off a floor, or string a halyard on a school flag pole. (A **halyard** is a rope used to raise and lower a flag as well as ground ladders.) Calls of this nature are referred to as **still alarms.** They require a less urgent response and are usually handled by one company. These types of responses are quite common and help continue the good name of the fire department organization and their role in the community they serve.

When answering nonemergency calls, you should answer the phone promptly and professionally, following your department's guidelines for identifying emergency and nonemergency calls. You should be immediately prepared to take messages and record all pertinent information, including date, time, name of caller, caller's contact information, and the message.

Always record your name with the message and transfer the information promptly to the person or department it is intended for. It is sometimes appropriate to refer a caller to the appropriate authority or agency, according to your department's referral guidelines.

Emergency calls

FFI 5.2.1 Calls for service classified as emergency are generally life threatening and may also have a potential for property loss. These requests for service bring the person receiving the information, the telecommunicator, into the incident dynamics as the first line of communication with the caller. Whether the call for service is initiated at the communications center or is requested directly of fire personnel, the information gathered is critical to dispatching and arriving on scene with the right information and resources to provide the necessary aid.

Most calls or individuals requesting assistance are generally received through a communications center. The callers may be stressed and not know what information is needed. It is important for the telecommunicator receiving the call to take charge of the information flow. This person must demonstrate confidence and leadership in their approach toward processing the information received and know what additional information is needed.

A dispatcher must obtain the following pieces of information during any emergency call:

- Location
- Nature of the problem
- Caller's name
- Contact phone number
- Condition at caller's location

While additional information is still being collected by the telecommunicator regarding the incident information history, emergency resources are being dispatched to the incident location. As the telecommunicator is completing triage, determining whether additional resources will be needed, fire department personnel and apparatus are arriving on scene to assess actual incident requirements and updating that information to the communications center. This could include medical services, law enforcement, and other agencies to stabilize the incident.

A common scenario: Engine 1 is on scene of an automobile accident with extrication needed; they request the communications center to dispatch a rescue company to assist with extrication and request law enforcement for traffic control. At this point, telecommunicators would initiate requests for additional resources.

EVALUATION AND MONITORING

As the incident unfolds, the communications center actively monitors radio transmissions and supports operational requests for greater alarms or individual resource requests. The communications center and telecommunicators play a critical role in the flow of vital information from the moment of event notification to the call from incident commanders for event shutdown. Some agencies have the staffing to devote a telecommunicator solely to one event. For an agency to devote a telecommunicator solely to one event, the incident must be large enough, involving multiple resources, or so complex that it requires the concentrated effort of one or more persons handling the communications activity for that one event. Most communications are transmitted by mobile or portable radios at the scene of an event. Telecommunicators must be prepared to receive information from other sources such as telephones, both hardwired and cellular. The information that is transmitted between responding apparatus and the communications center is essential, because it acknowledges the fact that the dispatched equipment is responding. Any additional information about the event that is acquired after the resources were dispatched is relayed to the responding units, and they will acknowledge the receipt of that information.

During the response of emergency equipment to one location, sometimes additional resources are required to respond to a separate location.

For example, Engine 1 responds to a reported building fire and witnesses a vehicle accident just occurring at an intersection. The fire officer would contact the dispatch center and advise the dispatcher of the situation. The officer would conduct a **size-up** to assess the incident, determining what resources to dispatch and whether the engine company should remain on the vehicle accident scene or proceed on the original call. This decision would depend on the severity of the incident, the policy of the local fire organization, and availability of additional resources to respond. The following is a typical communication:

- "Fire Dispatch, Engine 1 is on the scene of a two-car accident at the intersection of 9th Street and Elm Avenue. Engine 1 is not involved, and we are investigating for injuries. Respond another engine company to the building fire."

- "Engine Company 1, Fire Dispatch, copy. You are on the scene of a vehicle accident checking for injuries, and we are dispatching a different engine to the building fire."

- "Fire Dispatch, Engine 1, respond an ambulance company and P.D. to the scene of this accident. We have two injuries requiring medical assistance and transport to a hospital. Require P.D. for traffic control and investigation. Engine 1 will remain on scene to assist with injuries and possible car fire."

- "Engine 1, Fire Communication copies and will dispatch ambulance and P.D. to your incident."

- "Fire Dispatch, Engine 1: Notify Battalion 1 of our reassignment."

- "Engine 1, Fire Dispatch, copy."

Status reports from the scene of an incident may include building type, exposure (areas threatened by fire or other dangers) issues, fire conditions, progress of the firefighting efforts, additional resource requests and rescue efforts. First officer in the company may respond back to the communications center with an arrival report: "Fire Dispatch, Engine 3 on scene of a single-family single-story dwelling with smoke and fire showing out front windows. Continue the assignment. Engine 3 is preparing to make entry." Engine 3 officer is Maple Street command. The telecommunicator then continues to monitor event activities and fulfills resource requests. Any status changes of on-scene resources are immediately noted and acted on. Since some fire departments have the ability to change incident status with the push of a computer button, telecommunicators have to be vigilant when monitoring the computer screens so that the status changes they are observing are appropriate for the event's status.

Many communications centers are also required by department policies or standard operating procedures to monitor additional scene activities such as incident time sequence, company accountability, and rescue notifications. This includes notifications for primary and secondary search activities, all-clears, emergency traffic requests, and evacuation requests.

In addition to monitoring and supporting activities at an incident scene, the communications center is also responsible for the fire protection requirements throughout the city, district, or county. They are responsible for the deployment of resources to safeguard the jurisdiction in question. That may mean reassigning resources for coverage responsibility. This coverage process can be monitored simply by using a map of the district with magnetic symbols for resources and fire station locations. It can also be as elaborate as the GPS surveillance of the resources, which shows automatically where the coverage requirements are needed. Whatever the agencies procedures are, they must be monitored for accuracy to ensure that they are within the guidelines of the jurisdiction's protocols.

EMERGENCY COMMUNICATIONS

FFI 5.3.5 Radio communication by fire departments is an everyday occurrence and is normally completed on a routine basis with nonemergency traffic filtering through the airways. Everyday business activities include training, fire prevention, and inspections, along with other miscellaneous information transmitted among fire companies, fire inspectors, and administrative staff.

Routine message transmission makes up the highest proportion of daily communication activity across the radio airways. "Fire Dispatch, Engine 1 is available on radio businesses inspecting." Or you may hear "Fire Dispatch, Battalion 1 is available at Station 2 conducting a vehicle inspection." The situation changes when emergency traffic is required. When communications centers are dispatching apparatus and staffing to emergency incidents, then all normal communications must cease, and emergency traffic procedures take precedence. If you were listening to a fire department radio at this time, you might hear something like this:

- "Fire Dispatch: Engine 5, Medic 1, respond to a reported vehicle fire at the intersection of 24th and Maple Street. Reported vehicle accident with injuries."

- The next transmission would be by the first-arriving unit to the scene with a transmission back to the communications center, saying.

- "Engine 5 on scene; we have a two-vehicle accident, no fire, and checking for injuries; will advise further."

- As the incident progresses, additional communication between the units on the scene and communications center will continue until the incident is shut down by the officer in charge.

- "Fire Dispatch, Engine 5 is available on radio."

These everyday communications of the dispatch center and the units responding to calls are very similar. Telecommunicators assigned to communications centers dispatch fire units from the district to any request for service. This communication process consists of the following:

- Receipt of a request for service

- Dispatch

- Information delivery to the responding units

- Delivery of any supplemental information while en route

- Arrival information of the first company (size-up)

- Additional resource request based on needs

- Progress reports during the incident

- Shutdown or termination of the incident

- Availability of unit

EMERGENCY CALLOUT COMMUNICATIONS

FFI 5.2.4 There are times when the communications between the telecommunicators and firefighters can literally mean the difference between life and death. Both ends of the communication link must be aware of the protocols and procedures to expedite all information required to stabilize the incident and assist those in distress. Firefighters at the scene of the emergency must be aware of the conditions surrounding them and know how to request assistance, especially emergency assistance. The everyday emergency call that is handled with the utmost efficiency and professionalism is not the most stressful for firefighters. It is the crisis that may occur in the middle of one of the "everyday emergency calls." Emergency announcements that put firefighters on highest alert are the "emergency traffic" callout and, for some fire departments, the callouts "urgent traffic" and "Mayday."

All three of these callouts are used for assorted reasons, but all three are designed for the same function: to signal the immediate need to clear the radio and transmit critical information. Some departments use only the emergency traffic callout. Other departments or jurisdictions may use at least two of the callouts or a combination of all three.

For fire departments using emergency traffic, the radio transmission would be:

- "Incident Command Division 2, emergency traffic."

- Normal radio traffic immediately stops, and Division 2 will proceed with their traffic.

- "Incident Command Division 2, we have a firefighter down inside the building requesting assistance on the second floor east side."

The fire department with the same scenario utilizing the Mayday callout would ask for emergency traffic to clear the airways and then declare a Mayday for a firefighter down and in life-threatening danger. The only time the Mayday callout is used is in a situation in which there is an immediate threat to the lives of firefighters.

The last callout is "urgent transmissions." This type of callout is used in the following situations:

- A fire department member suffers an injury that is not life threatening but requires medical attention and hospital care.

- There is a change in operations.

- A structural problem is discovered, indicating the danger of collapse.

- There is a loss of water, which would endanger members.

- Fire is discovered by firefighters entering an exposure.

- Any delay occurs that would increase the fire problem.

An urgent transmission might sound like this:

- "Incident Command: Urgent traffic, Division B, be advised, fire is extending to the exposure attic east of the building."

Whatever the method used by the various fire organizations, the callouts are a valuable tool to quickly clear the airways and broadcast notification of the emergency information to all involved.

Personnel accountability system (PAS)

FFI 5.2.4 As part of the evaluating and monitoring process, NFPA 1561, the *Standard on Emergency Services Incident Management System*, requires that all fire departments establish standard operating procedures for a **personnel accountability system (PAS)**. It must also provide for the tracking and inventory of all members operating at an emergency incident.

The PAS sometimes uses Velcro®-backed plastic cards attached to various apparatus. They hold the name tags that identify and account for each member (fig. 4–11). Name tags and status boards are used to track the assignments of the divisions, groups, companies, teams, and individuals at an emergency incident. Fire department personnel must be familiar with the procedures to be implemented and the steps required to ensure an accurate accounting of personnel.

Fig. 4–11. Passports hold name tags that identify and account for each member.

The PAS is designed to be flexible and allows for expansion or contraction as the events or incidents dictate. There are different levels at which the system activates. Level 1, the most basic activation, takes place at shift change. It is then that each firefighter attaches his personal ID tag to the apparatus accountability passport. At Level 2, activation is in place for all working fires, where more than one piece of apparatus is responding, as well as in hazardous situations. Often a department will assign one of the apparatus officers to document the tracking of the personnel. In extreme situations or incidents involving multiple companies, at Level 3, an accountability officer will take over the passport system. This officer will set collection points for the passports. The officer will also assess personnel entering hazardous areas to ensure proper protective clothing and proper use of the firefighters' personal alert safety system (PASS).

PASS is a personal device worn by every firefighter that when activated sounds an audible tone that alerts others that a firefighter is in distress.

The easiest way to understand the use of a PAS is to be aware that all firefighters are issued a set of identification name tags that they retain with their protection equipment. As they report for duty, one of these tags with their personal identification is removed from their personal protective equipment and placed with other crew members' identifiers on a status board on the apparatus. A firefighter's identifier is not to be removed until the individual is no longer with the apparatus. If a firefighter leaves the fire station (or apparatus at the scene) for any reason, he or she must remove the identifier from the status board. If the firefighter does not remove his or her identifier and the company responds to a fire, the firefighter would be assumed lost, and a search would be initiated. Rescue companies would be put at risk because a firefighter did not remove his or her identifier tag from the apparatus. The PAS is a life-saving tool that must be used correctly. Misuse or noncompliance is not an option.

Personnel accountability report (PAR)

Personnel accountability report (PAR) is a polling system used by the incident commander or accountability officer to ascertain that all personnel operating at an emergency incident are safe and accounted for. The following trigger points are generally used to determine the need to conduct a PAR:

- There is a report of missing or trapped firefighters.

- Operating modes are altered: offensive to defensive.

- Dramatic changes have occurred at the incident scene.

- Emergency traffic has been requested due to fireground evacuations, building collapse, or Maydays signaled for lost or trapped firefighters.

- Replacing companies are on the scene.

- At a prearranged time during an active event: Some organizations have a built-in PAR every 20–30 minutes into an event.

- Any time the incident commander deems one necessary.

Personnel accountability is accomplished by an accounting of each firefighter or other personnel to the accountability officer on scene. Company officers must verify that the personnel assigned to them are visually accounted for. The last step in the process is for all division and group officers to confirm that all crew members attached to those companies are accounted for. If during the accounting process an individual or company is not responding, an emergency traffic or Mayday will be requested, and emergency traffic procedures implemented, along with departmental operational strategy and tactics for the missing firefighters.

Building or scene evacuation signal

There are times when the decision is made to evacuate the firefighting or rescue operations inside a building because of excessive danger to the firefighters, or the scene has become too dangerous to continue any tactical operations. Throughout the country, fire departments have worked and trained for the time when it is necessary for the emergency **evacuation signal** to be broadcast. The training ensures that everyone who hears the signal will understand what needs to be done. The following example of an evacuation signal is the one used in California by all the fire agencies throughout the state. The advantage is that during emergency incidents using mutual aid, all the agencies have been trained using one evacuation signal.

> *The evacuation signal will consist of repeated short blasts of the air horn for approximately 10 seconds, followed by 10 seconds of silence. This sequence of air horn blasts for 10 seconds followed by a 10-second period of silence will be done three times; total air horn evacuation signal including periods of silence will last 50 seconds. The incident commander shall designate specific apparatus to sound the evacuation signal using air horns. This should be done in conjunction with the radio announcement of "emergency traffic," with direction for emergency scene personnel to evacuate the hazard area. The dispatch center should continue to advise the Incident Commander of the elapsed time at each additional 15-minute interval, or until canceled by the IC, or until the incident is declared under control, i.e., knockdown.*[8]

The important thing to understand is that the type of emergency traffic communications used by fire departments must be thoroughly understood by all personnel,

and procedures constantly trained for, so that when the need arises, they can be used to save lives.

RADIO OPERATIONS

Radio operations for the fire service are regulated by the FCC. The FCC regulates the design, installation, and operation of the typical two-way radio systems used by fire departments throughout the United States. The FCC has developed regulations and guidelines governing the assignments of radio frequencies in order that all fire departments will have adequate access to needed transmission capabilities. The FCC is the assigning agency and licenses fire departments on one or multiple specific frequencies.

Radio frequencies

The fire service uses several frequencies. VHF radio systems are assigned in 100 MHz (megahertz) span of the radio spectrum, whereas the UHF system is assigned in the 1 GHz (gigahertz) span of the spectrum. On the radio spectrum, the VHF system frequency is transmitting its radio signal in the megahertz range. This is equal to one million cycles per second. The UHF system frequency is transmitted in the gigahertz range, which is one billion cycles per second. Public safety radio systems generally transmit frequencies of between 30 and 900 MHz, since they are dedicated in the radio spectrum for public service.

Another system that is used by the fire service is the 800 MHz radio system: a combination of traditional two-way radio technology and computer-controlled transmitters. The main advantage to this type of system is that the radio transmitters can be shared among several agencies with the aid of computer programming. Using this type of system allows conversation utilizing only a few frequencies. Once frequencies become available, they are quickly reassigned.

Radio signals themselves are one of two types, **analog** or **digital**. While radios that use analog signals have been around for quite some time, digital signal radios are a newer technology. Analog signals are continuous pulses that are uniform in intensity and that use computer chips to create the communications you hear. There are pros and cons to each type of signal: while digital signals can provide crystal-clear communications, the signal can be corrupted by close background noise, such as a saw cutting a roof, making radio transmissions impossible to understand (the computer chip cannot distinguish between a voice and the saw). Analog radio signals, on the other hand, while perhaps not as clear as a digital signal, allow the receiver of a communications signal to hear all of the signal, including background noise (the human ear can then filter out extraneous noise such as a saw and listen for what is important.)

Radio systems

Radio systems can be as simple or complex as an agency deems necessary to accommodate the workload. Conventional radio systems provide radio communications for designated users in a geographical area. As long as the frequencies are programmed into a user's radio, the brand of radio does not have to be the same to operate on the radio system.

The simplest form of a conventional radio system is called just that, **simplex** or **direct**. The simplex system has one channel both for initiating and receiving traffic (fig. 4–12). Using this system, only one person can talk at a time. If a unit is transmitting, all other units have to wait until the traffic is clear. For smaller agencies, this may not be a problem, but for larger agencies, a half-duplex or duplex conventional radio system may better serve their needs.

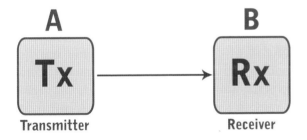

Fig. 4–12. Simplest form of radio communication is a simplex system using only one frequency to transmit and receive messages.

A **semiduplex** system allows for multiple users to transmit at the same time. The base station, which is usually a dispatch center, can transmit and receive at the same time. However, this type of system does not allow for simultaneous transmission or receipt. Only one user can be on a frequency. The half-duplex system allows for repeaters, which receive input on one frequency and provide output on a separate frequency. Repeaters can be used throughout the radio system to provide a stronger signal. This system is comparable to a two-frequency simplex system.

Full **duplex** conventional radio systems allow all users to transmit and receive simultaneously. This system uses

two frequencies that can be active all the time (fig. 4–13). This allows units to transmit and receive anytime. Repeater systems, usually placed on high elevations such as high mountain peaks, are also used in the full duplex system to strengthen the signal.

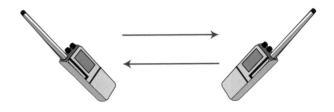

Fig. 4–13. Full duplex conventional radio systems allow all users to transmit and receive simultaneously. This system uses two frequencies that can be active all the time.

Radio **repeaters** are a combination of a radio receiver and a radio transmitter that receives a weak or low-level signal and retransmits it at a higher level or power. This allows the signal to cover longer distances without degradation.

In dispatching, amateur radio, and emergency services communications, repeaters are used extensively to relay radio signals across a wider area. With most emergency dispatching systems, the repeater is synonymous with the base stations, which perform both functions: transmitting and receiving. This includes police, fire, and ambulance systems. Repeaters are placed throughout geographical service areas. As long as these low-powered systems are able to reach a repeater, the transmission can be forwarded. This extends the range of the radio system used by the service area. When the radio transmission is unable to be detected by a repeater station, the signal is lost. The difficulty with the lost signal is that it can mean the difference between life and death for those involved in the incident.

Trunked radio systems are a better use of the radio frequencies and channels available. They constantly readjust the frequencies used for conversations. This allows for a more efficient use of the limited frequencies because each conversation does not require a **dedicated channel.** However, it also makes it very difficult to scan trunked conversations because you do not usually know what frequency the next portion of the conversation will appear on. Trunked radio systems use a data or control channel system. When incoming data passes through a control channel, it will instruct each radio using the system which frequency to use to continue to operate and remain on the selected channel. In a trunked system, predefined users are called **talk groups**. When referring to talk groups associated with radio systems, it is best to think of talk groups as being synonymous with individual radio channels. Radio systems, talk groups, and radio channels have individual frequencies. However, in a trunked radio system environment, the talk groups are not assigned an individual frequency. The talk group is assigned a frequency by the controller at the time the push-to-talk requests a channel. Essentially, any user that is on the same radio channel is considered part of that talk group. For example, if a fire company is working an incident on a defined channel and the police department wants to interact with the fire companies on scene, as long as the police department has the defined tactical channel programmed in their radio, they can go to that channel to become part of the talk group and interact with the units (fig. 4–14).

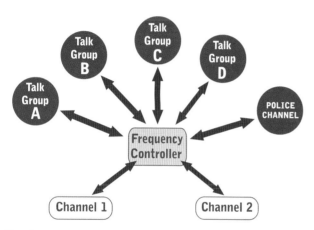

Fig. 4–14. Talk groups that have the proper talk group channel can have communications with any radio within another talk group, including those from different agencies.

A trunked radio system may be the answer to the limited frequencies assigned to each group. With a trunking radio system in place, all users have access to all frequencies, not just their one or two. Fire service personnel may know these talk groups as *fireground channels, tactical channels,* or *talk-around* channels. These types of trunking radio systems can be incorporated into a computer alerting and signaling system. For any organization changing to a trunked radio system, training in its correct use is essential. Even though for the firefighters it might seem a relatively seamless event, it is imperative for them to change their normal approach to radio use. Changing channels or frequencies in the heat of a fire or under the stress of a rescue requires intensive training. There can be no delay or confusion in the exchange of information during an incident. Planning ahead for the future use of trunking radio systems by the fire service, either for administrative, training, or emergency operations, is the process of sound communication responsibility.

FIRE DEPARTMENT COMMUNICATION DEVICES

Radios

Fire departments use three different radios for service-related activities. The radio used by fire company officers and individual fire personnel to communicate is a fire department–issued portable radio. This **handheld radio** is powered by a battery that has a limited capacity, depending on its use time. At intervals, the radio's battery must be recharged or replaced with a fully charged battery. Most portable radios have the capability of changing channels and even the capability to change talk groups. Most radios have a built-in function to eliminate **squelch,** which is high noise level when no or very weak signal is present. By manipulating a built-in function knob, any weak signals that may be interfering with radio reception are eliminated. These radios provide the users with the ability not only to talk to each other and their communications centers but also to communicate with other agencies.

The portable radio is designed to be carried in the hand or stored in a radio pocket of personal protection equipment (PPE) or even in a holster secured to the belt or on a radio strap around the neck.

FFI 5.2.3 When communicating via radio, you should be familiar with your department's equipment. Components of the radio itself may include an antenna to receive and transmit radio signals, a push-to-talk switch, and a built-in speaker and microphone. There are also control knobs for volume, channel selection, squelch control, and a personal emergency button.

The best position for a handheld portable radio is out of its storage device and held in the vertical position with the antenna pointing in upright direction (fig. 4–15). Hold the radio at a 45-degree angle, 1-2 inches from your mouth, and speak clearly and calmly. Do not shout or use profanity. Wait until the air is clear before your next transmission, and avoid unnecessary transmission that can clutter the channel.

Fig. 4–15. Firefighters must hold the portable radio in the proper position to be effective.

Follow your department's operating procedures for emergency traffic and emergency evacuation signals and communications.

Mobile radios are more powerful units that are permanently mounted on fire department apparatus (fig. 4–16). They do not require the use of external batteries because they are powered by the electrical system of the apparatus. This type of radio is equipped with at least the same features as a firefighter's handheld portable radio. An added feature of the mobile radio is that the radio speakers are mounted outside the mobile radio in a convenient location inside the apparatus. There may also be a speaker located on the outside of the vehicle. This allows the firefighting personnel to be in radio contact while outside the vehicle (fig. 4–17). A microphone is attached to the mobile radio by a coil cord and can be held away from the mobile unit while transmitting information. Many fire departments are now using a tool that incorporates the speaker and microphone into one headset (fig. 4–18); the external microphone attached to the headset allows the person wearing it to simply push an attached button to talk. The advantage of using a **radio headset** is that the captain and crew always have direct verbal contact with one another. Noise reduction with the headset ensures better communication and a better incident outcome. This headset also provides hearing protection as required by NFPA and OSHA (Occupational Safety and Health Administration). Each fire department must provide adequate hearing protection when firefighters are exposed to noise levels in excess of 90 decibels. The only exception to these regulations is when the use of the headset would cause an additional hazard to the user.[11]

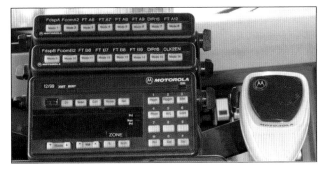

Fig. 4–16. Mobile radios are more powerful units permanently mounted on fire department apparatus.

Fig. 4–17. Firefighting personnel in radio contact while outside the vehicle

Fig. 4–18. Fire officer is able to remain in communication with the use of a headset with earpieces and microphone built-in.

Fire Department Communications

FIREFIGHTER I

Chapter 4

Base station radios (fig. 4–19) are more powerful than both the portable and mobile radios. They are usually mounted inside a communications center or fire station, or in remote locations. The base station radios, with their antennas mounted to a radio tower, enable the radios to have a wide area of coverage (fig. 4–20). There can be multiple base radio stations located in remote locations to help support large numbers of mobile and portable radios. As more channels are added to the system, it is essential that the number of radio structures increases to support the increased radio traffic. Improved base station technology is an absolute must to ensure fast, accurate communications between the various agencies for a good event outcome.

Fig. 4–20. Radio tower enables the radios to have a wider range of cover.

Computers

Fire departments are required to maintain all records related to their daily operations. This includes the safeguarding of all fire and medical emergency reports along with daily activity logs. The use of computers in fire departments has made the data collection, storage, and retrieval process and the transfer of information much faster and more accurate. At a time when multiple copies of the same incident information must be filed with fire department headquarters, the station house, and other involved agencies, computer programs and applications have made compliance easier. The fire department not only retains records and information concerning emergency incidents for collection later, if needed, but also has the ability to store information concerning other business interests such has fire-prevention information and fire-investigation reports. The fire department also retains department personnel records, inventory information, and infrastructure requirements as needed by the fire agency.

Fig. 4–19. Base station radios are more powerful than portable and mobile radios, and must be located in a communications center.

Mobile data terminal (MDT) and mobile computer terminal (MCT)

Mobile data terminals (MDTs) and **mobile computer terminals (MCTs)** are the newer generation of fire department communication devices. Their modern technology helps meet the need for better communication during an incident. This is especially true with the information flow from the communications center to personnel in the field. Better communication means a better outcome. The MDT and MCT help meet the need for a fast and accurate flow of information between all responders and the communications center.

MDTs are computer-like devices that can provide communication and transmit information such as company status, emergency notification, and event information (fig. 4–21). Developed in the 1980s to aid in the communication and management of dispatched vehicles, fire departments incorporated the use of MDTs to expedite information flow while operating from the vehicle. With the advancement of computer technology and the ability of storage and processing systems to capture and retain so much more information, fire departments' original MDTs have been replaced by more powerful ones: computer laptop models with large storage capacities. Whatever the type of information, the MDT device is used to transmit information from one point to another. The information transmitted must be clear, concise, and accurate. The transmission devices must be monitored, and the department's standard operating procedures and protocols must be adhered to.

The MCT is the latest step in the information process for fire department communications (fig. 4–22). This next phase of mobile data communications will enable increased data collection and information retrieval, along with fast service and up-to-the-minute availability. These computers have speed and storage abilities comparable to stationary computers in an office setting.

As fire service members face the challenges of new and larger crises, they must have timely access to vital information to make decisions in critical and complex situations. The MCT is a tool that has been designed to be rugged, portable, and reliable. It is able to store information, unlike the earlier versions of MDT. Fire officers are now able to retrieve, process, and store information that will enable them to make mission-critical decisions that will enhance their ability to save lives and protect property.

Fig. 4–21. The mobile data terminal (MDT) is a computer-like device that can provide communication and transmit information.

Fig. 4–22. The mobile computer terminal (MCT) is the next step in the information process for fire department communication.

METHODS OF NOTIFICATION

Pagers

These devices are telecommunications tools generally used to notify fire volunteers, paid-on-call and career, to respond to or make them aware of an emergency. They can also be used to notify others within the organization of any requests for them to respond to an event or to make contact with another person (fig. 4–23). Some pagers are activated by dialing a phone number. Other pagers are activated by an **encoder**, typically from the dispatch center. Following an alert tone, pagers send information in one of two methods: a voice message or a written display (text) message. As opposed to one-time message delivery, there are some fire departments that use pagers that have the ability to monitor radio traffic on their dispatch frequencies at all times. These same pagers are used to dispatch volunteer, on-call personnel, and on-duty staff. These pagers can be used 24 hours a day, so that personnel can be in constant contact with fire administration, operations, and communications.

Fig. 4–23. Firefighter pagers are used to notify firefighting personnel of emergency and non-emergency events.

With the increase of cellular telephone service on the rise, most pagers have been replaced or are used in conjunction with the cellular phones. There is still a need for pagers, especially for those organizations that have minimal budgets and where the pager could also be used as a dispatching tool.

Personal digital assistant (PDA)

With the advances being made in technology and the demand for faster information flow, the use of personal digital assistants (PDAs) is becoming a common practice in the fire service. They have multiple capabilities, from cellular phone and e-mail service to calendars and Web access. It provides the user with instantaneous information. Fire-prevention, fire-investigation, and fire-operational information is available at the push of a button. These devices are being used by both chief officers and company officers to aid in the daily operational needs.

Cellular phones

Major technological advances in the cellular service and availability have brought the cellular phone market into the public safety sector at a rapid pace. The convenience of having a phone in your pocket for instant communications with anyone is hard to ignore. New cellular phones, besides being able to receive and send calls, also have the ability to receive and send e-mail, take pictures, and surf the Internet.

Cellular phone systems have many advantages, but there are some limitations that users should be aware of. Users may find that their location does not have a cell site, which creates a "dead area." Within that zone there is no signal for cellular service. In a disaster area, cellular phone systems may be damaged. The massive amount of cellular usage by first responders and citizens alike will overwhelm systems that cannot meet the demand.

LAN-based telephones

Local area network (LAN) telephones are conventional telephones that are hardwired and used at the fire stations and communications centers just as they are used for standard conventional use in residential and business environments. They are used to conduct everyday business.

Direct-connect telephones

Direct-dial hardwired telephones are used for point-to-point contact with two or more predetermined locations. Whether that is from one communications center to another, fire station to fire station, or communications centers to one or more fire stations, direct contact is as simple as picking up a telephone.

Direct-line contact is a very common method of communication for dispatch centers. It provides immediate contact with other centers by simply picking up the telephone handset. Often, communication facilities such as police departments, fire departments, and EMS communications centers use this form of communication to expedite contact with each other.

SPECIAL CODES AND CLEAR LANGUAGE COMMUNICATIONS

FFI 5.2.1 Communications centers may use what is referred to as plain language dispatching, clear text, or clear speech as opposed to a numeric code like a **10-code** system (numeric codes used to assign messages to represent common phrases). In voice communication, instead of saying in clear language what is meant, a special code is used, such a 10–7 for "out of service." This type of code, along with other numeric coding systems, has been used for many years in the public safety arena. As with any form of communication, there are both advantages and disadvantages. Numeric codes of communication are brief and so use less air time and free up the radio channel for other transmissions. The clear speech or clear text type of communication eliminates the need to remember special codes, which can have multiple meanings. Clear language enables the speaker to say exactly what is meant.

Even though the U.S. Department of Homeland Security's **National Incident Management System (NIMS)**, due in part to the incident command structure and widespread exchange of information, states that the recommended language should be in a clear language format[12]; there are issues with this form of communication that all users need to be aware of. There are many words that sound alike. "Can" and "can't" are often confused, so "unable" is recommended. There are preferred words to be used for clear language communications. Some choices are affirmative instead of yes, negative instead of no, and standby instead of wait.

Events throughout the United States now necessitate the management of effective communication between several different agencies, from local resources to state and federal agency involvement. The use of resources from the different departments and agencies requires cooperation by all involved. Effective communication and the sharing of resources is more important now than any time in history. When clear language is used by all agencies and entities, there is no excuse for confusion or misinformation. Clear language is the only means of information transfer authorized by the Department of Homeland Security. If a fire department is using any special codes that are unique to that department, then care must be taken when working with other agencies who may have their own numeric codes but with different meanings. The easiest form of communication is simply to say what you mean.

RECORDS AND REPORTS

One of the last communications processes to be completed for any incident is to document the complete event. For the communications center, this documentation includes times of occurrences of event activities, such as the times of the notification of the event, resources dispatched, and arrival times of the resources. It also includes activities occurring during the event that affected the assigned personnel and equipment. These times also reflect their release times and reassignments. Communications centers should have the taped conversations with the reporting parties and the taped transmissions of all radio traffic between the communications center and the units on scene of the incident.

Fire companies are required to generate incident reports that reflect the actions of the companies on scene along with a completed incident report. These fire reports typically include type of structure, fire origin, cause of ignition, and extent of damage, the fire company's participation, and reports of any injuries or fatalities. In addition to any fire reports, there may also be medical treatment reports for injuries or treatment to anyone on the scene. With incidents that are medical-only service calls, only the communications center and the fire department are responsible for creating reports on actions taken. Incident reports are submitted by hard copy, and agencies that have the ability to submit electronic copies by computer may do so. With each method, the information must be stored for retrieval at a later time.

Information generated from incident reports is used to determine local, state, and national reporting information. Examples are the leading causes of fire, ignition sources, and types of material being ignited most frequently. This information, along with hundreds of other pieces of data, is used to determine the status of the fire service and its efforts to reduce the fire deaths, injuries, and property loss. The **National Fire Incident Reporting System (NFIRS)** is used to compile and analyze incident reports. There are numerous computer-generated programs and software available that can assist with the creation of the required reports.

From the legal standpoint, all the records and reports generated by fire communications centers and fire departments are very important components of the complete communications package generated for each incident dispatched, whether an emergency or nonemergency event. If the fire reports are not stored appropriately or are damaged, lost, or misplaced, it could cause long-term negative effects to the agencies involved. Fire reports that are incomplete or inaccurate, with only vague references to the actions taken, cannot provide useful information about what did or did not occur. Fire reports, including communications center event information, are considered public records under the Freedom of Information Act.[13] They may be viewed by attorneys, insurance companies, media sources, and the general public. Communications centers and fire departments can be held accountable for actions taken or not taken at the scene of an incident. Any incomplete reports submitted may be used to prove a lack of appropriate action by the fire communications center or fire department.

ADVANCING IN TECHNOLOGY

The field of communications technology is ever changing and advancing. Whether it is upgrading a radio system from analog to digital or adapting computer-aided dispatch systems to interface with other agencies systems, the communications center must have the latest technology. It needs to obtain real-time incident data, adapt telephone systems to receive callers' cellular telephone information or access **Voice over Internet Protocol (VoIP)** information. The communications centers have to able to change and adapt to the latest technology as quickly it is developed.

One of the major changes communications centers have had to adapt to is VoIP reporting of emergencies by individuals. Who would have ever thought someone would be able to report an emergency utilizing a computer? With VoIP, people have the ability to report an emergency using the Internet instead of a regular telephone line. The most common way to access VoIP is utilizing an analog telephone adaptor (ATA), an analog-to-digital converter that allows a standard telephone line to be connected to a computer or Internet connection. The ATA takes the analog signal from the telephone and converts to a digital signal over the Internet.

The challenge for communications centers is that some VoIP providers only offer this service to people who have the same service as the person initiating the calls. VoIP is a paid service, and each provider has different services to offer. Therefore, reporting an emergency over 9-1-1 can be problematic if the right technology is not in place on both ends of the system. Emergency calls cannot always be easily routed to a nearby communications center, and it is impossible on some VoIP systems. However, the FCC has acted to ensure that VoIP providers comply with important public safety requirements. They must serve speech- and hearing-impaired people and are

offering an abbreviated 7-1-1 dialing for access to relay service, if that is available. This technology is amazing and is continually changing on a regular basis.

NOTES

1. National Fire Protection Association Standards, 1 Batterymarch Park, P.O. Box 9101, Quincy, MA 02269-9101.

2. NFPA 1221, *Standard for the Installation, Maintenance, and Use of Emergency Services Communication Systems* (2007 edition).

3. NFPA 1061, *Standard for Professional Qualifications for Public Safety Telecommunicator* (2007 edition).

4. Public Law 106-81, 113 Stat. 1286-1290, enacted October 26, 1999.

5. National Emergency Number Association Fast Facts, *http://www.nena.org.*

6. National Emergency Number Association Fast Facts, *http://www.nena.org.*

7. Firescope California. *Field Officers Guide ICS 420–1.* Incident Command System Publication, June 2004, pp. 18–5, 6. Retrieved April 14, 2008, from *http://www2.bakersfieldcollege.edu/erp/ICS420-1FOG8x11Cmplt.pdf.*

8. National Emergency Number Association E9-1-1 Fact Sheet, *http://www.nena.org.*

9. National Emergency Number Association, *http://www.nena.org.*

10. NFPA 1221, *Standard for the Installation, Maintenance, and Use of Emergency Services Communications Systems* (2007 edition).

11. Title 26: *Labor and Industry,* chapter 28: Minimum Safety Standards for Firefighters (heading: PL 1987, c. 769, Pt. A, §109 (rpr)); NFPA 1500 (2007 edition). Retrieved April 14, 2008, from *http://janus.state.me.us/legis/statutes/26/title26sec2103.html.*s

12. The NIMS Integration Center DHS/FEMA.

13. Freedom of Information Act, U.S. Department of Justice, *http://www.usdoj.gov/oip/index.html.*

LESSON FROM THE FIREGROUND

Here is an example of a callout that is a great learning lesson for anyone communicating over the radio:

Several years ago an alarm was sounded for a commercial building fire in a section of town that was heavily commercial without very much traffic. As the units were responding, you heard a Captain from one of the units come over the radio and say, "Fire dispatch, be advised we have heavy smoke and fire in the direction of the reported building fire." Fire dispatch acknowledged the transmission as did Battalion 2 who was responding to the same incident.

As the first unit arrived on scene (Engine 9), his size-up went as follows:

Engine 9: Fire dispatch, be advised we have a large commercial car dismantling yard with many vehicles on fire.

Fire Dispatch: Copy. Large commercial car dismantling yard.

The captain of Engine 9 proceeded to give orders to the first alarm assignment and followed protocol for this type of incident, including establishing command. Battalion 2 was still responding and monitoring the communications.

The next radio transmission after the assignments for the companies was:

Engine 9: Fire dispatch, respond a second alarm assignment and he announced a staging location.

Engine 9 then continued on running the incident for several minutes. The next series of transmissions went something like this:

Incident Command (IC): Fire dispatch, who is my first-in company from the second alarm?

Fire Dispatch: IC, the first-in company would be Engine 50.

IC: Engine 50, upon your arrival report to Division C.

NO RESPONSE!

This communication between the IC and Engine 50 was repeated three or four times before Battalion 2, still responding, came on the radio to fire dispatch.

Battalion 2: Fire dispatch, did you dispatch a second alarm assignment for this incident?

Fire Dispatch: Battalion 2, negative. Do you want one?

Battalion 2: Fire dispatch, Engine 9 DID request a second alarm several minutes ago.

Fire Dispatch: Negative Battalion 2. Engine 9 only wanted to know who would be the first engine on a second alarm. Battalion 2, do you want a second alarm dispatched now?

The call continued with the Chief of Battalion 2 advising the Incident Commander of the missed communications and that he would order a second alarm. The Incident Commander came back on the radio, thanked the responding Battalion Chief and requested that he ask for a third alarm.

Within two minutes of this transmission, Battalion 2 arrived on the scene. Before the incident was over, there was a request for a 4th alarm dispatched for staffing.

THE POINT

Make sure that when you are communicating information, the people on the other end are really listening. When you make a request for resources, you need to wait for a response to ensure that the request has been correctly received.

As a result of this incident, whenever I have anything to report or request that requires action by the telecommunications, my first transmission is always:

Battalion 2: Fire dispatch, Battalion 2.

I wait for their response, then give them the information that I want acted on. It sometimes takes an extra few seconds, but a few seconds in an emergency that can make all the difference in the outcome.

QUESTIONS

1. The National Fire Protection Association (NFPA) *Standard for the Installation, Maintenance, and Use of Emergency Communications Systems* is known as _____.

2. Another name for a telecommunicator is _____.

3. What is the NENA? What is their function and responsibility?

4. The E in E9-1-1 stands for _____.

5. What is the first step in the dispatch process?

6. What critical information needs to be gathered by an emergency operator or 9-1-1 dispatcher?

7. The deaf and the speaking worlds use what types of devices to communicate with each other?

8. What federal agency regulates public safety radio communications in the United States?

9. In a simplex radio system, how many parties may speak at one time on one channel?

10. A repeater device is used to do what to a radio system?

11. How should you speak when communicating with a radio system?

12. What are the three callouts used in the chapter and explain their use.

13. What is the importance of redundancy?

14. Explain how PAS works in firefighter safety.

15. What does NFPA standard 1561 require of all fire departments?

16. Passports are used to identify and _____ for each member.

Fire Behavior

by Jerry Naylis

This chapter provides required knowledge items for the following
NFPA Standard 1001 Job Performance Requirements:

FFI: 5.3.11

FFI: 5.3.12

5

OBJECTIVES

Upon completion of this chapter, you should be able to do the following:

- Describe the parts of the fire triangle and fire tetrahedron
- Identify basic measurements of heat and temperature
- Identify the characteristics of the three physical states of fuel
- Describe the combustion process
- Define the term *flammable* (or *explosive) limits*
- Identify four types of heat sources
- Describe three types of heat transfer
- Identify the three methods of heat transfer
- Describe heat release rate
- Define the term *thermal conductivity*
- Identify the three components of smoke
- Identify the four stages of fire development
- Define the terms *thermal layering* and *thermal balance*
- Describe the three phenomena of a fully-developed fire
- Describe the two general types of explosions

INTRODUCTION

Fire has sometimes been heralded as the most important discovery known to humankind. We have learned to harness the power and energy of fire to provide warmth to heat our homes and other buildings; to create power to move vehicles such as cars, trucks, and trains; and to cook food. We have also put fire to work for us in tasks like cutting metal with a torch, burning trash to boil water to turn a steam turbine in order to generate electricity, and melting metal so that it can be formed into products. The uses of fire are indeed plentiful and beneficial, so long as fire is controlled.

Unfortunately, fire can escape the confines created by its masters and unleash a fury that can leave a wake of death and destruction that is almost unimaginable. It is at these times that the fire service is called to control what some describe as a beast. To attack and control a fire, firefighters need to have an understanding of fire including how fire occurs, how a fire grows and spreads, and how a fire can be controlled and ultimately extinguished. For this to be accomplished, a firefighter needs to have a working knowledge of combustion dynamics, chemistry, physics, and basic engineering principles.

A good start would be to have a working definition of fire. We know that fire is a chemical reaction sometimes referred to as a process, and that fire creates heat and light in varying intensities, most of which can be seen by the naked eye. A fire requires oxygen to burn. The oxygen may come from the atmosphere or may come from an **oxidizer** (such as hydrogen peroxide), a material that readily gives off oxygen or, in some cases, another gas that takes the place of oxygen (such as chlorine or fluorine). For these reasons, we will use the definition of fire taken from **NFPA 921:** *Guide for Fire and Explosion Investigations*, which defines fire as "a rapid oxidation process with the evolution of light and heat in varying intensities."

All matter exists in one of three states or categories: solids, liquids, or gases. Matter can also change from one state to another by heating or cooling, applying pressure, or releasing pressure. When matter changes phases directly from a solid to a gas, this process is called **sublimation**. Matter is further classified as organic or inorganic. Organic matter, by definition, consists of those substances that contain carbon. Inorganic matter refers to matter that does not contain carbon. Since all life on earth is based on carbon, generally speaking everything that was living or was once living will burn. Lumber in a house comes from what was once a living tree. The tree has been cut down and the wood has been shaped into varying dimensions. Even though the tree is no longer alive, the wood from the tree will still burn.

This chapter focuses on what fire is, what causes fire to start, how fires grow and spread, and, using that knowledge, what methods can be used to control and extinguish fires.

THE FIRE TRIANGLE AND THE FIRE TETRAHEDRON

Early texts used a simple three-sided **fire triangle** to shape a person's understanding of fire. Each side of the triangle represented what was needed for a fire to start. The three sides were identified as fuel, heat, and oxygen. These would be better stated as fuel, heat of ignition, and oxygen in sufficient quantity to support combustion (fig. 5–1). Once a fire was burning, the belief was that by removing one of the three sides, the fire would go out. If you removed the fuel, there would be nothing to burn, and the fire would be extinguished. If you cut off the supply of oxygen by smothering the fire, burning would stop. And if we removed the heat by cooling and quenching a fire with water, combustion would cease.

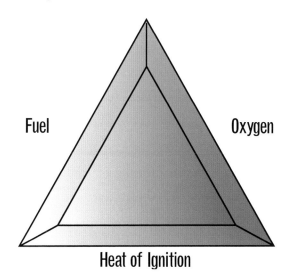

Fig. 5–1. The fire triangle

In the early 1960s, Walter M. Haessler conducted a series of tests to better explain how fires burned and how fire could be put out. His concepts were published in his seminal work, *Extinguishment of Fire*. Haessler put a new look on the old fire triangle by explaining that the fire triangle was in fact three-dimensional. The added dimension was the concept of free **radicals** being given off during a fire, which allowed a continuous chemical chain reaction to occur allowing the fire to continue to burn. Haessler used dry chemical fire-extinguishing agents to demonstrate that by arresting the fire radicals, the fire would be extinguished. After the fire was out, Haessler collected the dry chemical extinguishing agent and found that none of the agent had been consumed. With that, the three-dimensional fire triangle, known as the **fire tetrahedron**, was born (fig. 5–2).

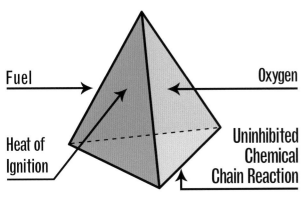

Fuel

Oxygen

Heat of Ignition

Uninhibited Chemical Chain Reaction

Fig. 5–2. A four-sided tetrahedron, the three-dimensional fire triangle illustrating the interrelationship of the chemical chain reaction in the combustion process

Measurements

Throughout any discussion of firefighting, firefighters will find it necessary to use a variety of terms alluding to a measurement. Therefore, every firefighter needs to be acquainted with the basic methods of measurements that relate to firefighting.

Not unlike what a person learns in elementary and secondary school, firefighting uses either the English system or metric system of measurements. While we use a number of measurement terms in our everyday lives, it is important to recognize that there are some measurement terms that are extremely important to firefighters because of the part these terms play in firefighting.

One example is temperature. Temperature is most commonly expressed in degrees. Different scales that have been developed over time to identify the measure of heat. These include **Rankine**, **Kelvin**, and the two most common scales, **Fahrenheit** and **Celsius** (fig. 5–3).

Heat is yet another measurement that firefighters need to be keenly aware of. Heat is a form of energy characterized by the vibration of molecules and is capable of starting and supporting chemical changes and changes of state (for example, changing a liquid to a gas). Heat is measured in BTUs in the English system and Joules in the metric system.

Firefighters need to know how much heat is being generated over time, known as **heat release rate (HRR)** so they can apply the correct volume of extinguishing agent to combat and extinguish the fire. The heat generation of a fuel is usually discussed in BTU/s, or joules/second (usually called watts). Heat release rates are established through laboratory tests where the heat release rate is measured over a period of time.

It is important for firefighters to realize that, while related, heat and temperature are two different things.

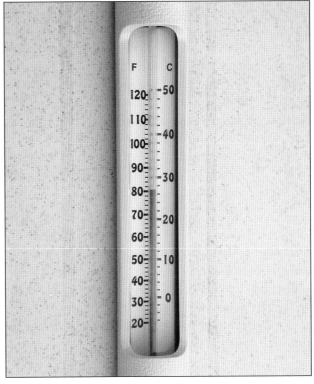

Fig. 5–3. The Fahrenheit scale and the Celsius scale

FUEL CHARACTERISTICS

FFI 5.3.10 All matter exists in one of three physical states: solids, liquids, and gases. Most matter can exist in any of the three states, with some only known to exist in two states, such as oxygen and helium. Additionally, matter can also be divided into things that burn (organic) and things that typically don't burn (inorganic). Those items that burn are usually organic, and those that will not burn are usually inorganic.

In most cases, a fuel must be in a gaseous or vaporous state in order for it to burn. As stated in the introduction, fires almost always involve reactions between various combustibles and oxygen in the air. These reactions release heat, and reactions that release heat are called **exothermic** reactions. When liquids or solids are involved in a fire, the liquids vaporize first. However, the solids usually decompose or **pyrolyze** first. This produces vapors (pyrolysates) that will react with oxygen. The vaporization and pyrolysis actually absorb some heat, and reactions that absorb heat are called **endothermic reactions**.

Fire Behavior

FIREFIGHTER I

Chapter 5

Solid

When matter exists in a solid physical state, the molecules of the substance are thought to be closely or tightly arranged. The tighter arrangement and greater quantity of molecules relates to the density and the mass of a substance. For a solid fuel to ignite and burn, the solid must go through a transformation into a gaseous state. This transformation requires the solid substance to be heated to its **ignition temperature.** Ignition temperature is the minimum temperature at which combustion can be initiated under specified test condition. The ability of a solid to absorb heat is often dependent on the physical arrangement of the substance.

An issue that has a direct impact on the time to ignition of a solid is whether the substance is considered **thermally thin** or **thermally thick.** Thermally thick means that when a material is exposed to a heat flux on its front face, appreciable temperature rise has not yet occurred on its back face. On the other hand, thermally thin means that at a given instant the material's back face is at a temperature close to that of the front face.[1]

The greater the **surface-area-to-mass ratio,** the easier it is for the solid to absorb the heat, reach its ignition temperature and ignite. As an example, take a block of wood. If a heat source such as a candle is applied to the block of wood, a considerable period of time will pass before the block absorbs enough heat to ignite. If the same block of wood is converted to wood shavings, the substance is still a solid but has a greater surface area to mass ratio, allowing the wood shavings to reach the wood's ignition temperature and ignite. Finally, if the block of wood is converted into wood dust, the substance now has an even greater surface-to-mass ratio, and the ability of the dust to absorb heat has increased dramatically (fig. 5–4). And if the dust becomes suspended in air, the ignition process can occur so quickly that an explosion takes place. Yet in all three cases, the substance was a solid at the beginning of the process. From this we learn that not only is knowing the physical state important, but knowing the physical arrangement of the substance is equally important with respect to ignition.

Fig. 5–4. Each of these items is wood: the block, the shavings, and the sawdust. But they each have a different physical configuration and a different surface-area-to-mass ratio that will make ignition easier or more difficult.

Liquid

Some liquids are capable of burning under normal temperatures and pressures while others are not. The liquids that will not burn can absorb heat, boil, and evaporate but never burn. Sometimes, these liquids can be used as extinguishing agents, such as water. The liquids that burn are referred to as **flammable** and/or **combustible** depending on the flash point of the liquid and the naming convention followed by certain entities. The NFPA uses a break point of 100°F (38°C) to differentiate between flammable liquids (liquids with a flash point below 100°F [38°C]) and **combustible liquids** (liquids with a flash point at or above 100°F [38°C]). NFPA further breaks liquids into classes and sub-classes. In Europe, the differentiation point is 140°F (60°C). To avoid confusion, the more commonly accepted term for all liquids that burn is **ignitable liquids.** Flash point is the minimum temperature at which an ignitable liquid gives off sufficient vapor to form an ignitable mixture with air near the surface of the liquid or within a test vessel.

For an ignitable liquid to burn, the liquid must be at its flash point so that when fuel vapors are mixed with it, air will burn. There is a mistaken belief that an ignitable liquid must be suspended in air, or atomized, to burn. **Atomization** is a process that breaks a liquid into a mist; yet its physical state is still a liquid even though the liquid is in finely divided particles. However, when an ignitable liquid is atomized, there is maximum surface-to-mass ratio that permits rapid vaporization as the liquid is heated. All that is now needed is for an ignition source to be introduced to the ignitable liquids (fig. 5–5).

Fig. 5–5. When an ignitable liquid is atomized it becomes easier to vaporize and ignite.

The fire point of an ignitable liquid is that temperature at which sufficient vapors are present to ignite and have sustained combustion.

Gas

Just as there are liquids that burn or don't burn, the same holds true for gases. When subjected to cooling and pressurizing, many gases become liquids. What is key to remember is that by their nature flammable gases in most ambient temperatures and pressures have already vaporized and only need the introduction of an ignition source to burn if they are within their flammable limits. If there is too little gas, the mixture is too lean and ignition will not occur. If there is too much gas, the mixture will be too rich and will not ignite.

Flammable and explosive limits

FFI 5.3.11 In order for ignition of a vaporized fuel to occur, the mixture of oxygen and fuel vapor must fall into a range commonly called the **flammable or explosive limits**. While some texts refer to an air/fuel vapor mixture, firefighters need to remember that if the ambient atmosphere is oxygen-depleted, no ignition can occur. Generally speaking, the air at sea level has approximately 20.8% oxygen, which is more than enough to support ignition and combustion.

The flammable or explosive limits have a lower point and an upper point that represent the percentage of fuel vapor. If the amount of fuel vapor is below the lower explosive limit (LEL), the mixture is classified as too lean and will not ignite. If the amount of fuel vapor is above the upper explosive limit (UEL), the mixture is classi-

fied as too rich and will not ignite. When the fuel vapor percentage is between the lower and upper flammable or explosive limits, ignition will occur. And if the volume of fuel is significant (as in a house filled with natural gas) the ensuing ignition will have explosive consequences.

The difficulty in dealing with flammable limits is that each fuel gas has a distinctly different range. Additionally, while some gases have a narrow range, such as gasoline (LEL = 1.5%, UEL = 7.6%), others have a very wide range, such as carbon monoxide (LEL = 12.4%, UEL = 74%).

When a flammable mixture is present but below the lower explosive limit, the easiest way to prevent ignition is to ventilate and supply large quantities of fresh air to further dilute the mixture and keep it from reaching the lower explosive limit threshold point. However, if a mixture is encountered where the mixture is fuel rich, then the introduction of fresh air with adequate oxygen may dilute the mixture enough to cause it to fall into the mixture's flammable range. If this occurs, the slightest spark may be enough of an ignition source to wreak catastrophic results. In such cases, ventilation and ignition source suppression must occur simultaneously to avoid endangering firefighters.

Technology has advanced to the point where many departments now carry meters and instruments to take air samples to tell them if specific flammable gases are present and, if so, at what percentage. All firefighters would be well advised to learn how to use these devices to protect them from the inadvertent ignition of a flammable gas mixture.

The danger to firefighters is when additional air is introduced to a rich mixture that results in a mixture that falls within the flammable limits. It is also important to remember that even an arc from an electric switch opening or the striking of a match has sufficient temperature to ignite a fuel/air mixture within its flammable limits.

CHEMISTRY AND PHYSICS RELATED TO FIRE

A fire is a complex process with a combination of chemical and physical events. To understand how a fire burns requires knowing some basic principles of chemistry and physics. Firefighters need to understand these basic principles in the course of their careers in the fire service, so the following terms are defined to provide a knowledge baseline.

Specific heat. **Specific heat** is that amount of heat that a substance absorbs as the temperature of the substance increases. Specific heat is expressed as "the amount of thermal energy required to raise unit mass of a substance by one degree, and its units are J/kg·K"[2] (Joules per kilogram-Kelvin) in the metric system and BTU/lbm-°F in the English system.

Latent heat. The thermal energy absorbed when a substance is converted from a solid to a liquid or from a liquid to a gas is known as **latent heat**. The amount of heat absorbed by a liquid that passes to a gaseous form is called the *latent heat of vaporization*. Water has an extremely high heat of vaporization, which makes it an ideal extinguishing agent.

When heat is absorbed by water as it converts to steam it causes the surface of the burning solid object to cool. The word latent means "hidden," and in a way the heat of vaporization is hidden. Water absorbs a great deal of heat, but upon reaching its boiling point of 212°F (100 °C), it turns to vapor (steam). In reverse, when a gas changes to a liquid or a liquid changes to a solid, heat is released and the temperature drops. When its temperature reaches the freezing point of 32°F (0°C), water becomes ice.

More information on the latent heat of vaporized water when it is used to extinguish fire is provided in chapter 16, Fire Streams.

Density. The ratio of mass to volume of an object or substance is known as **density**. The greater the density of an object or substance, the more heat energy is needed to cause ignition.

Specific gravity and vapor density. The **specific gravity** of a substance is the ratio of the weight density of the substance to the weight density of another substance, usually water. All liquid substances have different specific gravities. Water is the benchmark that other liquids are measured against to determine if a liquid is heavier (which will sink) or lighter (which will rise), Assigning water a value of 1, all liquids with a specific gravity of less than 1 will float on water. All liquids with a value greater than 1 will sink below water. Table 5–1 provides the specific gravities of common liquids.

Vapor density is the term for comparing the weights of vapors and gases with the weight of air. The terms *vapor density* and *specific gravity* should not be used interchangeably, as one measures vapors and gases and the other measures liquids. Some substances will

actually have different values for vapor density and specific gravity, depending upon the physical state of the substance (solid, liquid, or gas). Be careful to use the proper terminology when researching a substance.

Table 5–1. Specific gravities of common liquids

Liquid	Specific gravity
Acetone	0.787
Alcohol, ethyl (ethanol)	0.787
Alcohol, methyl (methanol)	0.789
Alcohol, propyl	0.802
Carbon disulfide	1.265
Carbon tetrachloride	1.589
Castor oil	0.959
Coconut oil	0.927
Cottonseed oil	0.929
Crude oil	0.876
Formaldehyde	0.815
Fuel oil	0.893
Gasoline	0.739
Hexane	0.657
Kerosene	0.820
Linseed oil	0.932
Mercury	13.633
Milk	1.035
Napthalene	0.963
Olive oil	0.703
Toluene	0.865
Turpentine	0.871

Air is the standard against which all other vapors and gases are compared and is assigned a vapor density value of 1. Vapors and gases with vapor densities greater than 1 will tend to drop to the ground. Gases and vapors with vapor densities less than 1 are lighter than air. There are only 13 gases known to be lighter than air. All other gases and vapors are heavier than air. The 13 gases lighter than air and their respective vapor densities are listed in table 5–2.

Table 5–2. Vapor densities of gases lighter than air

Gas	Vapor density
Hydrogen	0.070
Helium	0.140
Hydrogen cyanide	0.930
Hydrogen fluoride	0.901
Methane	0.550
Ethylene	0.968
Diborane	0.960
Natural gas (composed primarily of methane)	0.600
Carbon monoxide	0.970
Acetylene	0.900
Neon	0.967
Nitrogen	0.970
Ammonia	0.590

Types of heat

Heat energy comes in different forms, usually from a specific object or source. The heat of ignition is generally divided into the equipment involved in ignition and the form of the heat of ignition. It is important for firefighters to recognize and understand the sources or means of this heat generation. The four commonly accepted sources of heat are chemical, electrical, mechanical, and nuclear.

Chemical heat sources. As described earlier, fire itself is a chemical reaction, and one of the products of a fire is heat. So, the heat generated from a fire is often the heat of ignition that causes an uncontrolled fire to occur. As such, combustion is a form of chemical heat energy.

Spontaneous ignition is the initiation of combustion of a material by an internal chemical or biological reaction that has produced sufficient heat to ignite the material. This is observed by firefighters when rags and clothes made of natural fibers such as cotton become soaked with oils (such as linseed oil). The oil attacks the natural fibers breaking them down. As the fibers break down, a process takes place where heat is generated. The piles themselves allow the generated heat to be contained inside, sometimes causing them to ignite. This is the reason fire code regulations call for such oil-soaked rags to be stored in metal containers.

Electrical heat sources. Electricity is an extremely common energy source that is used by most people in everyday life. Electricity is used in residential, commer-

cial, industrial, and institutional applications. A building or area without electricity is an anomaly.

Electricity is used to provide light, power appliances, cook food, and provide heat and air conditioning. Electric power flows from a generating facility, usually called a power plant, through transmission and distribution conductors, usually called power lines, to a service cable and into a distribution panel. This panel is generally equipped with a main or service disconnect and either fuses or circuit breakers that function as overcurrent protection devices.

From the distribution panel, electric current flows out to circuits where the electricity is used. Some circuits are **switch-controlled**, meaning that power will not flow to the outlet or electric device unless a switch is turned on. A common example is a switch-controlled light. Other circuits have electricity that is at the receptacle or outlet. As soon as a plug is inserted, electrical power flows into the appliance or device.

The flow of electrical current can generate heat. In the simplest of terms, electricity is a flow of electrons from a negatively charged location where electrons are abundant to a location where electrons are less abundant, known as a positively charged location. This flow of electrons usually occurs along a **conductor**. The flow of electrons occurs as these electrons move from one atom to another along the conductor. As this occurs, electrons collide with molecules, causing the molecules to break apart, which then results in the liberation of heat energy. The quantity of heat generated depends on a number of variables, including the amount of electricity moving along the conductor and the density of the conductor. Typically, the denser a substance is, the better conductor it is. For example, **metals** are generally good conductors of electricity. Aluminum conducts electrical current (a good reason to be very careful with aluminum ground ladders around any wires), and copper is a better conductor. This is why copper is preferred for household wiring. However, silver is even better than copper as a conductor of electricity. But the cost of wiring a house using silver wire would be prohibitive! Other, less dense substances are not good conductors. Two examples are wood and cotton. Both of these are extremely poor conductors.

As the quantity or volume of electrical current (measured in amperes, or amps) flowing along a conductor increases, the potential for molecular collisions increase. This difficulty is sometimes referred to as **resistance** and is expressed in **ohms**. As resistance and quantity of electrical flow increase, the amount of heat generated increases. This is why electrically powered appliances that require large amounts of electricity to run need to have larger wires for the circuits. Specific wire diameters (wire gauges) are rated for maximum number of amps it can carry safely; the smaller the diameter, the smaller the amps it can carry without overheating. Toasters with very small diameter wires inside that glow when energized are a good example of this phenomenon.

Electrical heat energy can also be generated when a flow of electricity is suddenly interrupted by the separation of the conductor. A common example is when a switch that is closed (in the on position) is opened up (put in the off position) as current flows. The resulting arc is a release of electrical heat energy. Although these arcs are typically small in size, as is the amount of heat generated, the temperature that is generated can be substantial. Some arcs have been recorded at 2,000°F (1,093°C). Obviously, a sustained arc from a downed overhead wire can generate a continuous high-temperature, high-heat release event capable of igniting a building on fire.

Lightning is another example of electrical heat energy release. Clouds in the sky may be at differing levels of electron charging. As these clouds connect, allowing electrons to flow, one can observe what some people term **cloud-to-cloud lightning**. When a cloud and the earth have differing charges, we witness a discharge between the earth and the cloud.

Static electricity exists as the name implies, statically. Electric charges collect on the surface of an object. They are not flowing. There are a number of situations or conditions that will cause a static electricity discharge. The more common are the following:

1. Contact and separation between dissimilar solids

2. Flowing powders

3. Flowing liquids or gases

An example that many people can relate to is sliding a foot across a carpet and then touching a metal object. The resulting shock that is received is a static electricity discharge. Another example is the electric charge created when certain flammable liquids or gases flow, particularly at an elevated pressure. The static electric charge can become the ignition source, such as when acetylene gas escapes rapidly from a pressurized gas cylinder. The gas can be ignited as it flows forth from the cylinder without the introduction of any other ignition source.

Induction heating is the process of heating an electrically conducting object (usually a metal) by electromagnetic induction, where currents are generated within the metal and resistance leads to heating of the metal.

A microwave oven appliance cooks or heat food by dielectric heating, a method of heating non-conductive materials. A microwave is a radio wave that is between one millimeter and one meter in wave length. Microwave radiation is used to heat water and other polarized molecules within the food.

Mechanical heat sources. Heat of ignition can also come from mechanical actions that, developed at a sufficient temperature, will ignite flammables or combustibles. Mechanical heat is usually developed by friction when two items are rubbed together. The easiest example that demonstrates this is to rub your hands together. The faster you rub, the greater the heat produced. In that same vein, metals that rub together will also generate heat. Often, some form of lubricant is used to absorb the heat, particularly if the two metals rubbing together are part of a piece of machinery or a process. If the lubricant is insufficient or breaks down, the potential exists for enough heat to be generated to ignite surrounding combustibles, including the residual lubricant.

Friction can also create sparks where there is a lack of any lubricant. Visualize the metal edge of an axe coming in contact with a grinding wheel used to sharpen the axe head. As the edge of the metal touches the wheel, a shower of sparks flies out. Although seemingly small and insignificant, these sparks carry enough heat to ignite flammable vapors, finely divided dust particles, or wood shavings.

Compression can also generate heat, particularly if the compression is done under pressure and at a rapid pace. If a compressed gas cylinder, such as a self-contained breathing apparatus, bottle is filled too rapidly, the bottle itself will heat up as the bottle absorbs the mechanical heat energy created by the rapid compression of the breathing air. As the bottle cools off, the compressed gas, in this case air, will be subject to a lowering of the available pressure and thus the volume of air in the bottle. This is why all compressed gas cylinders should be filled slowly.

Nuclear heat sources. The two forms of nuclear heat energy are **fusion** and **fission**. Nuclear heat energy is generated when atoms are either split apart, which is called fission, or combined, which is called fusion.

Nuclear material is radioactive and unstable. These materials are constantly breaking down during a molecular process where they seek to become stable. During this process, energetic particles are spontaneously emitted by the disintegration of the radioactive material's atomic nuclei. As this fission process occurs, heat energy is released. In a controlled setting, fission is used to heat water to drive turbines and produce electricity. It should be noted that at the current time nuclear fusion cannot be controlled and has no commercial use, although its use is being explored in some experimental environments.

Regardless of how or why radioactive material is released, fires involving radiation emitting elements should only be fought by individuals specially trained and properly protected against radiation exposure. Regular firefighting personal protective equipment (PPE) offers absolutely no protection to the firefighter from any radiation that may be released. Under no circumstance should firefighters in structural PPE attempt to fight a fire involving radioactive material, no matter how small the quantity, until the radiation exposure hazard has been abated.

Heat release rate

The previous section discussed common sources of heat: chemical, electrical, mechanical, and nuclear. When we are discussing a fire's heat release rates (HRR), we are referring to the amount of energy or heat released *over a period of time*. We commonly discuss a 100 watt (100 joules-per-second) light bulb, a 100 megawatt nuclear reactor, or a 10,000 BTU/hr air conditioner. All are examples of energy being released or used over time (fig. 5–6).

When we discuss the heat release rate of a fire, we commonly use units of BTU/second in English units or watts in metric units. For example, a 1 meter by 1 meter (about a square yard) diesel fuel fire will have about a 2 megawatt heat release rate. As long as diesel fuel keeps pouring into that one square meter area, the fire will keep burning at a steady heat release rate (the fire would burn out in a short time if only a thin layer of oil was ignited and the fuel was not replenished).

Heat Release Rates (HRRs) for Common Items		
	Weight, lbs (kg)	kW
Chairs		
Upholstered, polyurethane foam	62.3 (28.3)	2,100
PVC waiting room with metal frame	34 (15.4)	270
Metal frame with polyurethane foam padding	16.5 (7.5)	40
Cotton easy chair	39.70 (18)	290–370
Mattress		
Cotton	26–29 (12–13)	40–970
Polyurethane foam	7–31 (3.2–14.1)	810–2,630
Mattress and box spring (cotton and Polyurethane foam)	137.45 (62.3)	660
Sofa, upholstered polyurethane	113 (51.3)	3,120
Christmas tree	14–16 (6.4–7.3)	500–650
Gasoline – 2 sq ft (0.2 sq m) pool		400

Sources: NFPA 921, *Guide for Fire and Explosion Investigations*; Quincy, MA, 2001; *Fire Investigation*, IFSTA, Stillwater, OK, 2000

Fig. 5–6. An example of the heat release rates of different types of common objects

Heat transfer

FFI 5.3.12 When anything burns, there are several by-products that are released. As discussed in the previous section, one of those by-products is heat. The heat that is generated is transferred to other objects. Depending on a number of factors, the heat that is transferred can cause the fire to spread and grow. These factors include the amount of heat being generated over a particular period of time, the item or substance being heated (combustibility and physical state), the distance between the fire and the item being heated, and the ability of the item being heated to retain the heat and reach its ignition temperature.

There are three modes by which heat is transferred from one substance to another. They are **conduction**, **convection**, and **radiation**.

Conduction. Conduction occurs when heat is transferred by direct contact between solid objects. One example is a steam pipe from a building's heating system that comes into contact with wooden structural members. The heat from the steam is transferred to the metal pipe that carries the steam to the heating system, providing heat for the building. The metal pipe absorbs this heat and transfers it to the wooden structural member, such as a ceiling joist in a basement that the steam pipe is in contact with. The constant heat being applied to the wood does several things. The heat dries the wood and causes the cellulose in the wood to break down. When the wood has been subject to enough heat and the wood has reached its ignition temperature, the wood will ignite and begin to smolder. This decomposition—breaking down of the wood under heat—is also known as **pyrolysis**.

There are several important points to remember regarding conduction. The heavier and denser a material is, the better conductor of heat it is. So metals are excellent conductors of heat. The second point is that ability to transfer heat by conduction is directly related to the mass of the object and the quantity of heat being released. A single candle burning will not generate the same amount of heat as a large bonfire. If you put the end of a six-inch deep metal I-beam into both fires, the I-beam exposed to the candle would barely warm up whereas the I-beam exposed to the bonfire would quickly heat up and could—through conduction from the end immersed in the fire to the other end—ignite combustibles away from the initial source of the fire, in this example the bonfire. This happens in real building fires when a steel beam passing through a wall between two rooms is heated by a fire in one room and ignites objects in the other room through conduction (fig. 5–7).

All matter is thermally conductive and will absorb, hold, and transmit heat. This ability is generally dependant on the density of a substance, which is the ratio of its mass to volume. If the substance is very dense, its thermal conductivity is high, whereas if the substance has low density, its thermal conductivity is low. Substances that have low thermal conductivity are good insulators since they inhibit the transfer of heat. Examples would include fiberglass and mineral wool. Substances that have high thermal conductivity are thought of as poor insulators and will allow the transfer of heat, such as metals.

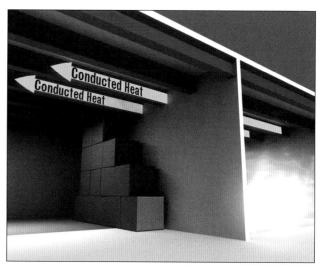

Fig. 5–7. A steel beam exposed to fire in one room can ignite materials in an adjacent room.

Convection. Convection is the transfer of heat via a fluid medium, either liquid or air. Flames and heated gases/smoke passing over a material's surface will transfer heat through convection. Many objects are ignited in this way (fig. 5–8).

Fig. 5–8. As flame passes over the surface of a material, it can ignite the material.

An accepted principle of physics is that warm air will rise and cooler air will fall. This is because, as air is warmed, the density of the air is reduced making the air lighter and allowing it to rise. As the air rises in the atmosphere, heat is given off to the surrounding air. When the heated air reaches the same temperature and density as the surrounding air, upward movement stops since equilibrium has been achieved. As the air's density begins to increase, it now begins to fall back down to the surface. This can sometimes be seen when smoke rises out of a smoke stack. It may eventually stop rising at a certain level, when it reaches the temperature of the surrounding air.

The same principle applies to liquids. When a liquid absorbs heat, the volume of the space occupied by the liquid expands. When the liquid reaches its boiling point, vapor is given off. Since the density of this vapor is lower than that of the surrounding air, the vapor rises just as heated air rises. If the heated liquid is in a closed container, then pressure will build up inside of the closed container until that pressure is released. Sometimes this pressure release is planned and regulated, such as when boiling water in a tea pot is poured out and the external heat source is removed. However, sometimes the release is not planned or regulated and the release is violent. An example would be a fire impinging on a cylinder or container containing liquefied flammable gases such as propane. A failure of any portion of the cylinder/container would be followed by a violent rupture and along with it the release and ignition of the now-boiling liquefied flammable gas. This type of event is commonly known as a **boiling liquid expanding vapor explosion** or **BLEVE**.

Radiation. Radiation is the transfer of heat through space by light waves. These light waves range from ultraviolet to infrared and contain electromagnetic energy that travels outward in all directions. This energy is absorbed by objects that are remote from and in a direct line with a fire.

Radiation is able to travel through space, including vacuums, as well as through transparent items such as clear glass and water curtains. As the target objects absorb the radiated heat, they in turn begin to give off radiated heat. This is why radiation is now viewed as even more of a hazard than conduction or convection with respect to fire spread (fig. 5–9).

The most common example of radiation heat transfer is the sun warming the earth's surface. Another example would be the warmth felt on a person's face while looking at a fire in a fireplace. If you turn and look away, your face feels cooler immediately because it is no longer exposed to the direct electromagnetic energy being given off by the fire.

When there is a fire in a building, radiated heat energy is emitted from the fire in a direct line to all objects surrounding the fire. As the items heat up, they in turn re-radiate to other objects. The heat release of the original fire and the ability of the target object to absorb and retain this heat will dictate how quickly or how slowly the fire may spread. One thing is certain: this mode of heat transfer will facilitate flashover more than the other two.

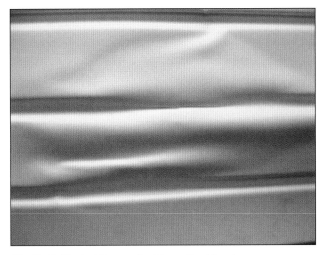

Fig. 5–9. Vinyl siding melted by radiant heat

Smoke

As identified earlier in the chapter, smoke is a product of combustion. According to NFPA 921, smoke is defined as "the airborne solid and liquid particulates and gases evolved when a material undergoes pyrolysis or combustion, together with the quantity of air that is entrained or otherwise mixed into the mass." Carbon particles ("soot," which gives smoke its distinctive range of colors) are the predominant solid particulate. Liquid particulates include condensed tars and even water vapor. A multitude of gases are produced including carbon monoxide and hydrogen cyanide (the predominant substances that cause the most deaths in a fire).

While the specific health hazards of smoke are discussed in greater detail in chapter 10, Self-Contained Breathing Apparatus, and chapter 14, Ventilation, it is important to understand the role that smoke plays in the development of a fire in a compartment. As will be seen later in this chapter, the hot smoke at the ceiling of a room will play a crucial role in the development of flashover. Smoke may also become explosive under the right conditions, resulting in a backdraft (smoke explosion).

COMPARTMENT FIRE DEVELOPMENT

FFI 5.3.11 All fires follow a distinct pattern in their development. The four stages of fire development are ignition, growth, full development, and decay (fig. 5–10). And before any fuel can be ignited, the fuel must be heated to a point where the fuel emits ignitable vapors. Obviously these vapors exist if the fuel's state is gaseous, and in some cases, ignitable liquids vaporize at low temperatures (gasoline's flash point is –45°F [–43°C]) while others have to be heated, such as fuel oil, motor oil, or vegetable oil. Solids must also be heated to point where ignitable vapors (pyrolysates) are emitted.

Ignition

Ignition occurs at the instant when an ignition source unites with an ignitable vapor in an oxygen-sufficient environment, resulting in a chemical chain reaction, and a fire begins to burn. If the ignitable vapor is already present, ignition occurs almost instantaneously. If the fuel is a solid, it may take a few seconds or longer to produce the ignitable vapor. But once the vapor starts to burn, ignition has taken place. In most cases, the fire is small and limited, sometimes called an **incipient fire**. The exception, of course, is where there are massive amounts of flammable gas capable of being ignited simultaneously.

Growth

Once ignition occurs, the fire must grow or it will die. The heat generated from the ignition now begins to cause heat transfer to spread to surrounding combustibles. Once these surrounding combustibles emit sufficient ignitable vapors, they in turn ignite, causing the fire to grow in size and spread. There are several factors that will affect the fire's ability to grow and spread.

The first factor is the amount of available oxygen. Once a fire begins to burn, available oxygen is consumed in the combustion process. If the amount of available oxygen falls below 16% of the atmosphere, the fire has a more difficult time burning. The fire will create even more carbon monoxide when the oxygen level is below 16%. If the oxygen level drops below 8%, the fire will not be able to sustain itself. Air (oxygen) is drawn into a fire through a process called **entrainment** (fig. 5–11).

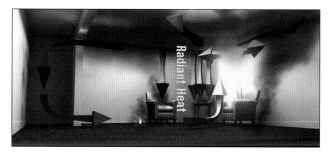

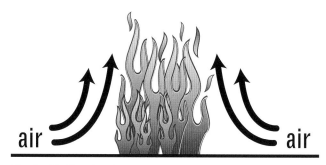

Fig. 5–10. The four stages of fire development: ignition, growth (pre-flashover), fully developed (flashover), and decay (post-flashover)

Fig. 5–11. Fire development showing air entrainment

The second factor is the amount of fuel that is available to burn. A good example is a fire in a fireplace. Once the logs are consumed, the fire goes out for lack of fuel. Conversely, if there is an ample volume of fuel such as a structure full of combustibles, the fire will grow substantially. The physical state of the fuel package and its HRR will determine how fast the fire will grow and spread.

The third factor is the relative size of the space where the fire is to the involved fuel and its distance from other surrounding combustibles. If the space is large and high, the heat generated by the fire will be distributed throughout the space and make it difficult for other combustibles to be preheated. On the other hand, if the space to the ceiling and walls is small, the heat that is absorbed by the ceiling and walls can be radiated back to the fire, allowing it to intensify, which means that the fire can grow larger and faster.

The fourth factor is the insulating value of the ceiling and walls. The better the insulating value, the less heat will pass through. This heat will be radiated back to the fire and the surrounding combustibles. If the insulating value is low and allows heat to pass through easily, that heat will not help the fire to grow.

Thermal layering and thermal balance. **FFI 5.3.12**
As a fire grows, the hot gases generated by the fire rise until they become obstructed, usually at first by the ceiling. The hot gases will spread out in all directions seeking a new path to rise. Once the hot gases reach this path, they will continue to rise. Conversely, if the gases meet a vertical obstruction such as a wall, the hot gases will begin to bank down until the hot gases find an opening that will allow them to rise again, such as a doorway, open window, or stairway. Some of the heat energy from the heated gases is transferred to the ceiling and walls in a room fire, allowing some of the heated gases to cool slightly. These cooler gases are pushed down in the room's atmosphere as the hot gases that continue to generate rise above the cooler gases. This phenomenon is known as **thermal layering**, because each portion of heated gases stratifies as equilibrium is achieved. The hottest point will be at the ceiling, while the coolest layer will be near the floor. The temperatures between the ceiling and floor will be layered. Firefighters sometimes refer to this as **thermal balance**.

The heated gases at the ceiling will be distributed throughout the room or compartment causing the temperature at the floor level to rise quickly. Any firefighters or trapped occupants will be rapidly exposed to excessively high temperatures. This is why it is critical for ventilation to be closely coordinated with fire attack and the application of fire streams.

Fully developed compartment fire

Once the fire has involved an entire compartment or space, the fire is considered to be fully developed. If this is an outside fire, all of the combustibles in a given area would be on fire. The fire would be free burning and has plenty of oxygen to continue burning. A compartment or space fire could be a room, an apartment, a floor, or an entire building. One of the hallmarks of a fully developed compartment fire is that the rate of burning inside the compartment is limited by the amount of ventilation that the room is receiving. This type of fully developed fire is sometimes called a **ventilation-controlled fire** (fig. 5–12a). Fires that have plenty of oxygen (ventilation) but have limited access to fuel are termed **fuel-controlled** fires (fig. 5–12b).

Fig. 5–12. a) Ventilation-controlled fire and b) fuel-controlled fire. (Courtesy of Dustin Hughes)

Rollover. As a fire burns and consumes a room's contents, the heated fire gases rise up to the ceiling. These heated gases and smoke are fuel and under the right circumstances will ignite. Flames will appear at the ceiling level and will travel over the heads of anyone in the room who is staying low. This is known as **rollover** (also sometimes called **flameover**[4]). The danger associated with a rollover is that a fire can travel overhead and get behind firefighters, blocking their egress path, allowing the fire to spread, and making subsequent investigation into a fire's origin more difficult by making it appear that there is more than one point of origin. In large rooms with large fuel loads this can be a particularly difficult issue.

As stated before, once a room has flashed over, a fire changes from a fuel-controlled fire to a ventilation-controlled fire. In this case pyrolysates that are hot enough to ignite will not be able to burn until they "find" enough oxygen. Usually this occurs when the gases exit (roll) through a window or a door.

Flashover. During the development of a fire, heat is generated. Some of this heat is in heated gases and fills the atmosphere of the involved room or compartment, while heat is also transferred to the structural elements and contents. The temperature of the contents rises as the heat is transferred. If the contents are ignitable liquids, the liquid will change to vapor once the liquid's flashpoint is reached. If the contents are solids, ignitable vapors will be given off when the ignition temperature is reached.

Obviously, all contents have different ignition temperatures and different physical states, and their ability to absorb the transferred heat is determined by numerous factors. However, because a fire in a confined area such as a room or compartment can result in the generation of significant heat levels, it is possible for all of the contents to quickly reach their ignition temperature. At this point, all of the contents are giving off ignitable vapors (pyrolysates). As these vapors ignite, all of the contents of the entire room or compartment become involved. This is known as **flashover** (fig. 5–13).

There are a number of ways to define flashover, the most deadly of fire "events" (building occupants will not survive the effects of a flashover; firefighters wearing full protective equipment have a only a few seconds to reach safety outside the flashover environment before they will succumb—even then, they will likely suffer injuries). One is that flashover occurs when a fire changes from becoming a fuel-controlled fire to a ventilation-controlled fire. Another is that flashover occurs when the upper thermal layer reaches a temperature of about 500–600°C (about 900–1100°F). However you define it, this sudden change can take place in a matter of seconds and create a life-and-death situation for firefighters. It is critical that all firefighters learn to identify the warning signs of an impending flashover and take immediate measures to reduce or eliminate the potential for flashover.

FLASHOVER WARNING SIGNS

- Flames licking overhead (rollover)
- *Rapid* buildup of heat in a room or compartment
- Appearance of smoke or gases coming off all contents, including carpet
- Flames emerging from doors and windows as these are the places where gaseous fuel can find a lot of oxygen.

BACKDRAFT WARNING SIGNS

- Smoke puffing from the building; sometimes the building appears to be "breathing"
- Smoke churning in window glass
- Window glass appears as if it is being pulled in
- Lack of any visible flame
- Air rushes in when any opening or vent is created

FIREGROUND NOTE

When a stream of water is introduced into a room or compartment where thermal layering is taking place, the thermal balance will be upset.

Fig. 5–13. Flashover

Backdraft. **FFI 5.3.11** A fire needs oxygen (or an oxidizing agent) in order to burn. Normally, this is not a problem since the atmosphere contains sufficient oxygen to allow a fire to burn (approximately 20.8%). However, if the fire is burning in a closed or confined area or space, the fire will consume the available oxygen and generate large amounts of carbon monoxide along with an assortment of other fire gases.

As the oxygen level drops below 16%, visible flames start to diminish because the fire is being starved of oxygen. The danger is that the compartment is charged with super heated gases and smoke. The sudden reintroduction of oxygen to the compartment or space will literally breathe new life into the fire. There will be a rapid influx of outside air as if the fire is sucking the oxygen in. This will be followed by an even faster reappearance of flames

in an *explosive manner* that has the power to blow out windows and doors and even push out walls.

This is known as **backdraft,** sometimes called a **smoke explosion** (fig. 5–14). The violent explosive force of a backdraft has been known to lift buildings off of their foundations and hurl people across streets.

Vertical ventilation at the highest point over the fire can reduce the buildup of superheated gases and minimize or prevent the possibility of backdraft.

Decay

Once the fuel package has been mostly consumed and the HRR drops significantly, the fire will diminish in size. This is the point at which the fire is in the decay stage. Small pockets of fire may still exist as the fuel

Fig. 5–14. Backdraft

slowly moves to the point of total consumption. Glowing embers will be the final indicator that the fire is about to cease because all of the available combustibles have been consumed by the fire.

During a fire, all four phases may be seen simultaneously, albeit in different locations. A unique example is a high-rise building fire, especially when the involved area is above the reach of fire department hose streams. As the fire burns a floor, the floor above is pre-heated. When sufficient ignitable vapors are emitted, ignition occurs on the floor above while the fire is burning. The fire in the floor above, grows until the entire floor becomes involved, which is now pre-heating the floor above. Concurrently, as the fire now consumes all available combustibles on the original floor of involvement, the fire in that floor enters the decay stage until the fire ultimately dies out from a total lack of fuel.

EXPLOSIONS

During your firefighting career, you will likely respond to the scene of an **explosion** after it has occurred. You may even be a witness to an explosion taking place. Explosions are not common events, but is important to understand the basics of these potentially deadly events. According to NFPA 921, an explosion is "the sudden conversion of **potential energy** (chemical or mechanical) into **kinetic energy** with the production and release of gases under pressure, or the release of gas under pressure. These high-pressure gases then do mechanical work such as moving, changing, or shattering nearby materials." Explosions occur very quickly and usually have devastating results. Explosions will be covered in some subsequent chapters.

There are two types of explosions: **deflagrations** and **detonations**. The difference is the speed in which they occur: the "combustion zone" (blast wave) moves slower than the speed of sound in a deflagration, while the combustion zone in a detonation moves faster than the speed of sound.

Natural gas explosions and many dust explosions are examples of a deflagration (fig. 5–15a). The use of an explosive such as TNT (trinitrotoluene) results in a detonation (fig. 5–15b). Generally speaking, deflagrations, while destructive and potentially deadly, do not have the same "shattering effect" of the more powerful detonation.

Fig. 5–15. Results of a) gas explosion and b) TNT explosion. (Courtesy of David Forward)

NOTES

1. Drysdale, Dougal. *An Introduction to Fire Dynamics*, 2nd ed. Chichester, UK: Wiley, 1999.

2. Babrauskas, Vytenis. *Ignition Handbook*. Issaquah, WA: Fire Science, 2003.

3. www.nafed.org/resources/library/UL300.cfm

4. NFPA 921: *Guide for Fire and Explosion Investigations*, 2004 Ed.

QUESTIONS

1. Describe two ways fire can obtain oxygen in order to support combustion.

2. What is the definition of fire?

3. What is the process of sublimation?

4. What is specific heat and its unit measurement?

5. Describe the process of latent heat of vaporization.

6. What effect does density play when it comes to ignition of an object or substance?

7. List the four common acceptable sources of heat and energy. Give examples of each.

8. Two types of reactions are _____ and _____.

9. List three physical states of a fuel.

10. Define ignition temperature.

11. Describe surface to mass ratio and its effects on fuel characteristics.

12. What is flash point?

13. What is fire point?

14. The four stages of fire development are _____, _____, _____, and _____.

15. List four factors that affect a fire's ability to grow.

16. Can all four stages of a fire be seen at once? If so, describe how this can occur.

17. List the warning signs of a potential backdraft.

Fire Extinguishers

by W. Jack Miller

This chapter provides required knowledge items for the following
NFPA Standard 1001 Job Performance Requirements:

FFI: 5.3.8

FFI: 5.3.16

This chapter contains Skill Drills. When you see this icon, refer to your Skill Drill book for step-by-step instructions.

SKILL DRILL

OBJECTIVES

Upon completion of this chapter, you should be able to do the following:

- Define the five classes of fires
- Describe fire extinguisher design and operation
- Describe the different extinguishing agents
- Explain the fire extinguisher rating system
- Have a general knowledge of inspection, maintenance, hydrostatic testing, and recharging of fire extinguishers

INTRODUCTION

Even small fires endanger lives and property. Building owners and managers have a responsibility to protect their tenants and the public by maintaining a fire-safe environment. All public buildings and workplaces need an effective fire protection program that includes strategically-placed portable fire extinguishers.

Portable fire extinguishers, when handled properly by trained and confident personnel, are useful for fighting fires before they spread—provided they are appropriate for the fire being fought and in proper working condition. To choose the right portable fire extinguisher you need to match the extinguisher to the job. This chapter provides the information to help you do just that. It covers the five classes of fire (A, B, C, D, and K) as well as the numbering system that determines the firefighting effectiveness of the different extinguishers. This chapter also reviews the classification of hazards, extinguishing agents, extinguisher design, and operating procedures.

FIRE CLASSIFICATIONS: WHAT IS BURNING?

FFI 5.3.16 The first question to ask is, "What type of fire is most likely to occur?" Fires are classified according to their fuel—that is, what is burning. Some fire extinguishers are more appropriate than others for fighting certain classes of fires. To be effective and safe, the extinguisher being used must match the class of fire to be extinguished. The proper extinguishing agent will put the fire out more efficiently. In some cases, it is dangerous to apply an incorrect extinguishing agent to a fire. The two best examples involve common water extinguishers, which should never be used to fight a fire involving combustible cooking media because water splatters grease and spreads the fire. Also, if you discharge a stream of water on live electrical equipment, you risk electric shock and establishing a short circuit that could damage equipment.

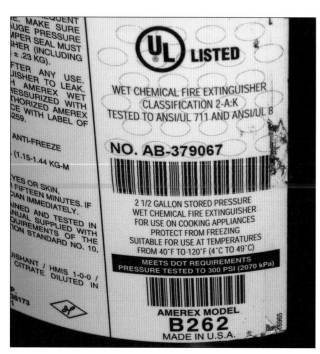

Fig. 6–1. This label from Underwriters Laboratories (UL) certifies that this fire extinguisher has been tested to their rigid standards.

Underwriter Laboratories Inc. or other independent testing laboratories rate fire extinguishers according to the type of fires they can extinguish safely. All fire tests are conducted by trained and experienced personnel in a controlled environment. Extinguishers that are tested and have been found to meet test standards are said to be listed and bear a label from the lab that conducted the testing (fig. 6–1).

Classes of fires

Class A: Ordinary combustibles such as wood, paper, rubber, fabrics, and many plastics.

Class B: Flammable liquids and gases such as gasoline, oils, paint, lacquer, and tar.

Class C: Fires involving live electrical equipment.

Class D: Combustible metals or metal alloys.

Class K: Fires in cooking appliances that involve combustible cooking media such as vegetable or animal oils and fats.

Figure 6–2 lists the classes of fire and their picture symbols.

CLASSES OF FIRES	TYPES OF FIRES	PICTURE SYMBOL
A	Wood, paper, cloth, trash, & other ordinary materials.	
B	Gasoline, oil, paint, and other flammable liquids.	
C	May be used on fires involving live electrical equipment without danger to the operator.	
D	Combustible metals and cumbustible metal alloys	
K	Cooking media (Vegetable or Animal Oils and Fats)	

Fig. 6–2. The five major classes of fire are represented with pictures so that inexperienced users can quickly identify the correct fire extinguisher to use.

TYPES OF EXTINGUISHERS

Fire extinguishers are rated for, among other things, the classes of fire they can extinguish. Note that in the following list of extinguisher types, some extinguishers can be used on more than one class of fire. Do not attempt to use an extinguisher on a class of fire that it is not rated for.

Class A (fig. 6–3)

Class A:B

Class A:B:C (fig. 6–4)

Class A:C

Class B:C (fig. 6–5)

Class D

Class K (fig. 6–6)

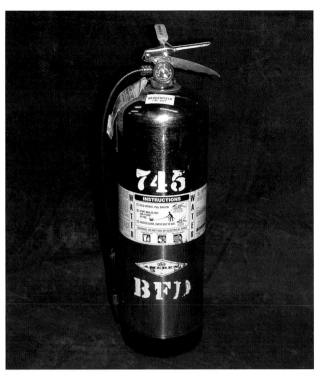

Fig. 6–3. A pressured water extinguisher can be used on Class A fires only.

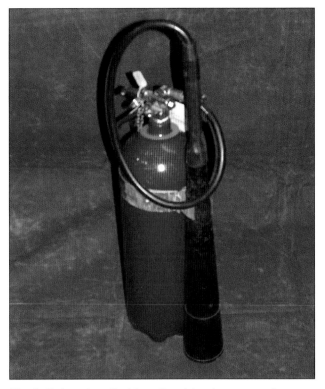

Fig. 6–5. A carbon dioxide extinguisher is common for use against Class B and C fires.

Fig. 6–4. Some dry chemical extinguishers are rated for fire classes A, B, and C. These extinguishers are commonly found in homes and commercial properties.

Fig. 6–6. A Class K fire extinguisher can resemble a Class A pressurized water extinguisher, however, has a special nozzle and water solution designed for cooking oils and greases.

Fire Extinguishers

FIREFIGHTER I

Chapter 6

Fire extinguisher design and types

All portable fire extinguishers use pressure to expel their extinguishing agents, but there are a few different designs (fig. 6–7). Many extinguishers rely on a pressurizing gas to expel their agents. Some models store the pressurizing gas with the agent in the cylinder and others store the pressurizing gas externally in a separate cartridge. Some extinguishing agents, such as carbon dioxide, create their own pressure and do not require the addition of a pressurizing gas to expel. Other extinguishers rely on pressure from a hand-operated pump.

The majority of extinguishers in use consist of six basic parts: cylinder, handle, lever, nozzle or horn, locking mechanism, and a pressure indicator (gauge).

The **cylinder** contains the extinguishing agent. Stored-pressure extinguishers store their extinguishing agent in a cylinder with a gas that provides the pressure to operate the unit. Cartridge- and cylinder-operated extinguishers use an external cartridge of a pressurizing gas that feeds pressure into the agent cylinder to expel the extinguishing agent.

Fig. 6–7. Pressure can be generated for fire extinguishers through storing the pressure in the main cylinder, having an outside cartridge, or through a manual pump.

The **handle** is the means by which an extinguisher is carried. The actual design of the handle varies from model to model. In most cases, the handle is located just below the lever that you squeeze for discharge.

The **lever** is what is squeezed or depressed to discharge the fire extinguisher's agent. In cartridge-operated extinguishers, the discharge is accomplished by releasing the pressurizing gas into the cylinder. On most extinguishers, the lever is located above the handle.

The **nozzle** or **hose/horn** is the device through which the agent is expelled.

The **locking mechanism** is a simple, quick-release device that secures an extinguisher's lever to prevent accidental discharge.

The **pressure indicator**, more commonly known as the **gauge**, indicates whether the extinguisher has adequate pressure to operate properly.

TYPES OF EXTINGUISHING AGENTS

FFI 5.3.8 The following extinguishing agents are the most often used in firefighting operations.

Water

Water is an excellent extinguishing agent suitable for use only on Class A (ordinary combustibles) fires. It extinguishes a fire by cooling fuel to below its kindling temperature. Never use water-type extinguishers on fires involving live electrical equipment or for fires in cooking media. The water could flash to steam as a result of high temperatures and cause serious burns.

Foam

Aqueous film-forming foam (AFFF) is made mostly of fluorochemical **surfactants**. As the bubbles break, drain, and lose their water, they form a film on the surface of the fuel that moves easily across the surface and prevents vapors from escaping.

Alcohol type AFFF is similar in base to AFFF with the addition of a **copolymer**. The copolymer reacts with **water miscible** fuels (**polar solvents** and hydrocarbon/polar-solvent mixtures containing 10% or more polar solvents) and reacts with the polar solvents to create a polymeric membrane.

Film-forming fluoroprotein foam forms a film over a flammable liquid surface much like AFFFs. (See fig. 6–8.)

Wet chemical

Wet chemical agents are solutions of water mixed with potassium acetate, potassium carbonate, potassium citrate, or combinations thereof. They are specifically designed for Class K fires, but they have demonstrated superior effectiveness on Class A fires when compared with plain water. They have limited capabilities on Class B fires and can be used in extinguishers with special wand applicators that achieve a Class C listing, verifying that electricity cannot be conducted back to the operator.

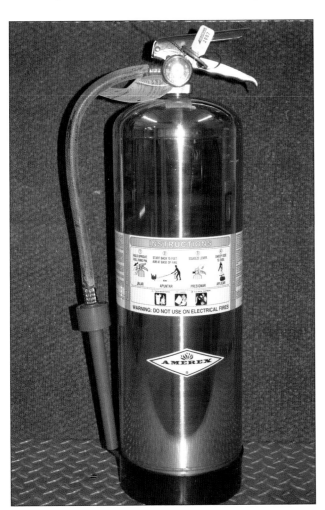

Fig. 6–8. A foam extinguisher

Wet chemical extinguishers work on Class K fires through two methods. The solution is alkaline in nature and therefore reacts with the fatty acids in the cooking medium to form a soapy foam on top of the burning material. This secures the vapors and cools the cooking medium as the foam drains and converts to steam. This reaction is known as **saponification**. In addition to saponification, the agent is discharged as a fine mist that does not submerge below the surface of the cooking medium (preventing a steam explosion), but rather it

converts to steam on the surface pulling heat out of the material. Cooking-medium fires must be cooled below their **autoignition temperature** to be successfully extinguished.

Water mist

The **water mist extinguisher** uses deionized water that is discharged as a fine spray onto the burning material. It is designed as an alternative to halon in areas where contamination must be kept to a minimum without the expense of halon substitutes. Using deionized water causes little damage to most electronic circuits and is the safest agent available for use on humans (such as in operating rooms). The wand and wide spray with fine droplets gives a soft and controlled discharge pattern. This extinguisher has passed the Underwriters Laboratories Inc. test for electrical conductivity, allowing it to be listed for Class C applications (fig. 6–9).

Fig. 6–9. Water mist extinguisher

Dry chemical

Dry chemical extinguishing agents have been used since the early 1900s. Early in the development of these agents, sodium bicarbonate was found to have greater effectiveness on flammable liquid fires compared to other chemicals being used at the time. They are still widely used. In the 1960s, major developments in dry chemical agents led to the introduction of potassium bicarbonate (Purple K), monoammonium phosphate (ABC), potassium chloride (Super K), and urea potassium (Monnex). Potassium chloride and urea potassium-based dry chemicals are not common in the U.S. market. Dry chemicals are nonpoisonous, but either the acidic-based (ABC) or alkaline-based (Regular or Purple K) chemicals could be an irritant if inhaled. Dry chemical is not recommended for fires in delicate electrical equipment or aircraft because use of these agents may extinguish the fire but damage the equipment beyond repair.

Sodium bicarbonate

Sodium bicarbonate, or **BC**, is also known as regular dry chemical. In addition to its effectiveness on Class B and C fires, it has some effect on the flaming stages of a Class A fire but no effect on the embers or deep-seated Class A fire. When used on common cooking greases, it reacts with hot grease to form a thick foam through the saponification process. The foam created by saponification acts much like other firefighting foams and extinguishes the fire through vapor securement, flame separation, and generation of steam. Sodium bicarbonate is alkaline in nature and will not cause corrosion during normal use.

Potassium bicarbonate

Potassium bicarbonate, or **Purple K** dry chemical, was developed by the U.S. Naval Research Lab precluding the use of the term "Purple K" as a trade name. It was discovered that potassium salts are far more effective on flammable liquid fires compared to sodium salts. Potassium bicarbonate is also alkaline in nature, has similar abilities to saponify when used on hot cooking grease, and does not cause corrosion in most cases.

Monoammonium phosphate

Monoammonium phosphate, **ABC**, or multi-purpose dry chemical differs from potassium bicarbonate and sodium bicarbonate in its acidic nature. In addition to similar effectiveness on Class B and C fires when compared to sodium bicarbonate, monoammonium phosphate has unique effectiveness on Class A fires. When it contacts the burning surface of an ordinary combustible, a molten residue (metaphosphoric acid) is formed. This residue coats the burning ember and excludes oxygen. Monammonium phosphate does not saponify when used on hot cooking grease and causes corrosion if not thoroughly removed from most hot surfaces.

Dry chemicals are nonpoisonous, but either the acidic-based (ABC) or alkaline-based (Regular or Purple K) chemicals could be an irritant if inhaled. If any physical discomfort is experienced, contact a physician immediately.

Dry powders for Class D fires

Combustible metal fires represent a special hazard unlike Class A, B, and C fires. Extinguishing agents used on all other classes of fires have no success when used on Class D fires. In fact, some agents, such as water, react violently with the burning metal. Most agents used in extinguishers for these fires are proprietary in nature and are classified according to the manufacturer of the dry powder or the brand name of the agent. Each agent has different limitations regarding the type of metal (magnesium, titanium, lithium, etc.,) that it may be used on and the form the metal is in (molten, casting, turnings, or fines). The following NFPA codes, standards, and recommended practices should be consulted:

1. NFPA 49: *Hazardous Chemicals Data*

2. NFPA 48: *Storage and Handling of Magnesium*

3. NFPA 481: *Production, Processing, Handling and Storage of Titanium*

4. NFPA 482: *Production, Processing, Handling and Storage of Zirconium*

5. NFPA Hazardous Materials Handbook

Most Class D agents are applied generously to the burning material, often requiring up to 15 pounds of agent per pound of burning material. The extinguishing agent usually excludes oxygen and performs as a "heat sink" to absorb the thermal energy and cool the material. Caution must always be used when applying special agents to combustible metal fires because these fires react with any moisture in the ground and surrounding materials.

Class D agents

Graphite (carbon) is a finely divided powder that must be applied with a dry scoop or shovel. The powder conducts heat away from the material, reducing its temperature below the point that combustion may be sustained.

Sodium chloride-based powder forms a crust on the burning material, excluding oxygen is available in a 30-pound extinguisher. It also helps dissipate heat from the burning material.

Pure copper powder was specifically developed for use on lithium fires.

Halogenated agents

Halogenated agents have been used for firefighting since the early 1900s. Of the 10 halogenated agents that have been used, two have been the most common since the early 1970s: Halon 1211 and Halon 1301. Halogenated agents suppress fire by interrupting the chemical chain reaction in the combustion process, working in the fire chemically instead of physically. Exactly how this chain-breaking process works is not completely understood. It is generally agreed that bromine is released from the agent as it decomposes in the fire, carrying away the free radicals that cause the combustion and releasing more bromine to continue the chain-breaking process. Halon 1211 and Halon 1301 are ozone-depleting agents subject to control under the *Montreal Protocol on Substances That Deplete the Ozone Layer* and other federal requirements. The primary advantage of halogenated agents has been the lack of cleanup required after using the agent. In some environments (such as electronics, data processing, jet engines, and high-tech equipment), discharging other extinguishing agents such as water or dry chemical could damage more property than the fire itself.

Halon alternatives

Since the ratification of the Montreal Protocol, alternatives to Halon 1211 have been sought. Various proprietary blends of gases are available. For streaming agents (those used in portable fire extinguishers), there are two popular agents in use: FE-36 and Halotron I. Both agents extinguish fires primarily through cooling.

Neither Halotron I nor Halon 1211 should be used in confined areas smaller than indicated on the extinguisher nameplate, food-preparation areas, or the presence of people with cardiac problems. If problems occur, quickly remove the person from the area where the gas is present, apply artificial respiration, and transport to a medical facility.

Carbon dioxide

Carbon dioxide, also known as CO_2, is an odorless and colorless gas that does not conduct electricity. It is stored in extinguishers as a liquid under pressure and when expelled turns into a snow (dry ice) on contact with atmospheric moisture. Carbon dioxide displaces oxygen and care should be exercised in confined spaces. Avoid skin contact, which can cause cold burns.

Things to remember

Never discharge a fire extinguisher into anyone's face. Never throw an extinguisher into a fire or leave it unattended if the fire is not out. (Pressure build-up from even a partially full extinguisher can cause an explosion.)

UNDERWRITERS LABORATORIES FIRE-EXTINGUISHING RATING SYSTEM

FFI 5.3.16 The numerical portion of Class A ratings of extinguishers is based on comparative fire tests using various sizes of wood-crib, wood-panel, and excelsior fires (table 6–1).

The numerical portion of Class B ratings of extinguishers is based on fire tests using square steel pans in specific size increments and a flammable, liquid test fuel similar to unleaded gasoline. The fire extinguisher classification is equivalent to 40% of the area of fire extinguished twice by an expert operator.

Class A fire tests

For ratings Class 1A through 6A, the extinguisher shall be tested on the appropriate wood-panel, wood-crib, and excelsior fires. For a 10A rating, the extinguisher shall successfully extinguish the 6A wood-panel fire plus the appropriate 10A wood-crib fire test. For a 20A rating or higher, only the appropriate size wood-crib fire is required (fig. 6–10).

The minimum allowable discharge time for extinguishers rated 2A and higher is 13 seconds. During the test, the extinguisher must be in the full open position under continuous discharge.

Fire Extinguishers

FIREFIGHTER I

Chapter 6

Fig. 6–10. Establishing the rating of an extinguisher often involves the use of wood crib test fires. (**Courtesy of Tom Jenkins**)

A pan containing commercial-grade heptane is placed beneath the wood crib and is used to ignite the wood members. The heptane is allowed to burn between 2 and 4 minutes, after which it is removed and the crib is allowed to burn an additional 8 to 10 minutes. After the pre-burn period, the operator attacks the fire from the front at a distance of at least 6 ft (2 m). The operator may then shorten the distance and attack the fire from all sides except the back of the crib.

For wood-panel test fires, the panel is first placed in a horizontal position, and a pre-determined volume of No. 2 fuel oil is applied to the panel, which is then mounted vertically on a steel frame. A row of excelsior is placed at the base of the panel. Three additional rows of excelsior are placed at the base of the panel. Three additional rows of excelsior are strategically spaced on the floor of the test room. Using heptane, the first row of excelsior at the foot of the panel is ignited. At 45-second intervals, the three remaining rows are pushed to the base of the panel. At 3 minutes and 20 seconds after ignition, all remaining excelsior is cleared from the base of the panel. The fire then burns vigorously for 4 to 5 minutes, at which time the horizontal furring strips located between 6 and 30 in. (150 and 760 mm) above the floor, burn through and begin to fall away from the panel. Within 5 seconds of this observation, the initial

Table 6–1. Class A Fire Tests

CLASS A FIRES Ordinary Combustible: Wood, Paper, Textiles					
Numerical rating	Excelsior fire test	Wood-panel fire test	Wood-crib fire test Overall dimension, quantity, and size		
1A	6 lb/34×68 in. (2.7 kg/86×172 cm)	8×8 ft (2.4×2.4 m)	20×20×15 in. (51×51×38 cm)	50 pcs	2×2×20 in. (5×5×51 cm)
2A	12 lb/48×96 in. (5.4 kg/122×244 cm)	10×10 ft (3×3 m)	25⅝×25⅝×19½ in. (65×65×50 cm)	78 pcs	2×2×25⅝ in. (5×5×65 cm)
3A	18 lb/59×117½ in. (8.2 kg/150×298 cm)	12×12 ft (3.7×3.7 m)	30¾×30¾×21 in. (78×78×53 cm)	98 pcs	2×2×25⅝ in. (5×5×65 cm)
4A	24 lb/72×128 in. (10.9 kg/183×325 cm)	14×14 ft (4.3×4.3 m)	33⅜×33⅜×22½ in. (85×85×57 cm)	120 pcs	2×2×33⅛ in. (5×5×84 cm)
6A	36 lb/83×167 in. (16.3 kg/211×424 cm)	17×17 ft (5.2×5.2 m)	33⅜×33 ⅜×25½ in. (85×85×57 cm)	153 pcs	2×2×33⅜ in. (5×5×121 cm)
10A	N/A	17×17 ft (5.2×5.2 m)	47½×47½×28½ in. (121×121×72 cm)	209 pcs	2×2×47½ in. (5×5×121 cm)
20A	N/A	N/A	62¼×62¼×36½ in. (158×158×93 cm)	160 pcs	2×4×62¼ in. (5×5×158 cm)
30A	N/A	N/A	74⅝×74⅝×36½ in. (190×190×93 cm)	192 pcs	2×4×75⅝ in. (5×5×192 cm)
40A	N/A	N/A	87⅛×87⅛ in. (221×221 cm)	224 pcs	2×4×87⅛ in. (5×5×221 cm)

attack with the fire extinguisher is made from at least 10 ft (3 m) from the face of panel. The operator must attack this fire using two horizontal sweeps across the bottom of the panel and then may use the technique of his or her choice, provided the extinguisher remains under continuous discharge in the full open position until emptied.

Class B fire tests

Class B fire tests are conducted using a square steel pan at least 8 inches in depth. The test fuel is to consist of at least a 2-in. (51-mm) layer of Heptane, the surface of which is to be located 6 in. (152 mm) below the top edge of the pan. Water may be added to establish the required 6-in. (152-mm) freeboard (table 6–2).

For B ratings up to and including 20B, the fire test is conducted indoors in a large–volume, draft-free room. For B ratings in excess of 20B, outdoor fire tests are conducted under conditions of essentially still air: steady between 3 to 8 miles (4.8 to 12.9 km) per hour with gusts not greater than 10 miles (16 km) per hour and no precipitation. After a 1-minute pre-burn, the operator attacks the fire but is permitted to do so only from one side. The operator is prohibited from extending any part of his or her body past the edge of the test pan while fighting the fire.

FIREGROUND NOTE

Never use ABC dry chemical, Halon 1211, or Halotron I fire extinguishers on fires involving oxidizers (pool chemicals). A violent explosive reaction could occur with the mixture of chemicals.

Table 6–2. Class B Fire Tests

CLASS B FIRES Flammable Liquids: Oils - Greases - Paints			
Flammable liquids and gas rating	Minimum effective discharge time (seconds)	Pan size (inside) sq ft	Heptane used (approximate) U.S. gallons
Indoor Tests:			
1B	8	2½	3¼
2B	8	5	6¼
5B	8	12½	15½
10B	8	25	31
20B	8	50	65
Outdoor Tests:			
30B	11	75	95
40B	13	100	125
60B	17	150	190
80B	20	200	250
120B	26	300	375
160B	31	400	500
240B	40	600	750
320B	48	800	1,000
480B	63	1,200	1,500
640B	75	1,600	2,000

CLASS C FIRES Electrical Equipment	
No fire test	Extinguishing agent is tested for electrical non-conductivity. If acceptable, "C" Symbol is added.

FLOW RATES/APPLICATION RATES

Every agent, regardless of the mechanism it uses to extinguish a fire, has a critical application rate. The **critical application rate** is the minimum rate at which the agent must be applied to the fire and is usually expressed as a ratio of quantity of agent (in pounds or gallons) per area unit (usually square foot) per time unit (either seconds or minutes).

Under most circumstances, particularly when using equipment that does not involve a fixed system (hand hose lines or extinguishers), a rate of application in excess of the critical rate must be used. Other factors involving the fire and extinguishment may cause problems. Wind direction and speed, weather conditions, length of pre-burn, application technique, and fuel sources all affect the critical application rate. Using a higher application rate will help negate some of these factors and decrease the time required for extinguishment. There is a point at which a further increase in the application rate will not result in a further decrease of the time to extinguishment.

Application rates for dry chemicals are theoretical and often expressed in pounds of chemical per square foot per second. Tests done in the 1960s involving flammable liquid in depth and spill fires using a variety of fuels established an average critical application rate of less than 0.01 lb of chemical per second per sq ft. These tests used fixed systems, thus eliminating any operator error. They are not intended for use in the designing systems or choosing hand-operated equipment.

Flammable liquid fires involving fuel escaping under pressure, **three-dimensional**, running, or gravity-fed fuel generally require higher application rates than spill or fuel-in-depth fires. Listed hand-portable dry chemical fire extinguishers may have a flow rate ranging from 0.31 lb (0.14 kg) per second to 2.5 lb (1.13 kg) per second. The flow rate of different fire extinguishers may be established as a requirement for a higher UL listing (to meet minimum discharge times) or to meet a special purpose.

In practical applications using hand-portable or wheeled fire extinguishers, it is not possible to determine the critical application of the dry chemical for every set of circumstances. The advantages in using higher application rates (extinguishers with faster flow rates or multiple extinguishers in unison) are faster knockdown, greater protection from radiant heat (heat shield), faster extinguishment on fuel in depth fires, and greater chances of extinguishing pressure, obstacle, and three-dimensional fires. Disadvantages of using higher flow rates are wasting chemical and having less discharge time.

Personnel trained during live-fire exercises with dry chemical extinguishers are often able to put out larger and more complex fires with extinguishers that have a faster flow rate (and a lower UL rating). This is partly because their application technique wastes less chemical (negating the need for a longer discharge time), has better protection against radiant heat, and allows firefighters to use the faster knockdown to their best advantage. A

20-lb (9 kg) fire extinguisher with a rating of 40 B:C and a flow rate of 1.33 lb (0.6 kg) per second is likely to have far greater extinguishing capabilities in the hands of even a moderately trained operator than a 20-lb (9 kg) fire extinguisher with a rating of 120 B:C and a flow rate of 0.69 lb (0.31kg) per second. The faster–flow, 20-lb (9 kg) extinguisher can easily extinguish a larger UL test fire than its rating implies, but the required discharge time is insufficient to meet the UL standard.

Two operators applying dry chemical to the fire at the same time can theoretically double the flow rate of each of their extinguishers, thereby decreasing the time to extinguishment and providing better safety to the operators and greater chances of success. These are reasons to train personnel to fight fires as a team rather than as individuals.

When conducting training sessions, it is important that the same flow rates are used in training that are available "on line" in the facility. If personnel are trained with extinguishers flowing chemical at 1.77 lb (0.8 kg) per second, and the extinguishers in the facility have a flow rate of 0.68 lb (0.31 kg) per second, then training will not help personnel learn application techniques for their equipment. Application techniques for fast-flow equipment are different from those used with extinguishers having low flow rates and long discharge times. Using old extinguishers for training may have the same result. Many older fire extinguishers have much lower ratings (and faster flow rates) than newer extinguishers of the same agent capacity. For example, a 20-lb (9 kg) extinguisher made in 1972 may have a UL rating of 60B:C, while the same model made in 1992 has a UL rating of 120B:C.

Higher UL ratings do not equate to greater firefighting capability. Many factors, including training, type of fire incident, fuel, and application technique affect any attempt to extinguish a fire. NFPA 10, *Standard for Portable Fire Extinguishers* recognizes this issue and provides the local agency having jurisdiction (AHJ) with the flexibility to use fast-flow equipment based on customers' needs and sound fire protection practices.

FIRE EXTINGUISHER OPERATION

FFI 5.3.16 These general instructions are intended to familiarize you with the basic operating techniques of a stored-pressure, hand-portable fire extinguisher. Because there are a variety of extinguishers, the nameplate must be consulted for specific procedures and starting distances.

1. Hold the extinguisher upright and pull the safety pin to break the plastic seal.

2. Stand back from the fire (minimum distance is stated on the nameplate) and aim at the base of the fire.

3. Keeping the extinguisher upright, squeeze the handle and lever together to discharge and sweep from side to side. Move closer as the fire is extinguished, but not so close as to scatter the burning material or liquid.

4. When the fire is out, back away while checking for possible re-ignition.

5. Evacuate and ventilate the area immediately after use. The smoke and fumes from any fire may be hazardous and deadly.

Remember the acronym **PASS** (fig. 6–11):

- **P**ull
- **A**im
- **S**queeze
- **S**weep

Any firefighting effort, first and initial response, or organized attack should minimize risk of injury and death. Once a decision has been made to fight a fire, it is important to remain calm and keep a clear perspective concerning safety. All things of a material nature can be replaced or rebuilt, but human life and health cannot.

Humans, like other animals, will react with either "fight" or "flight" when scared. Fire will cause one of these reactions to occur, sometimes involuntarily. No two people react exactly the same way, and no person is consistent from one fire to the next. Even the most experienced and trained firefighter makes bad decisions regarding safety in the heat of the battle.

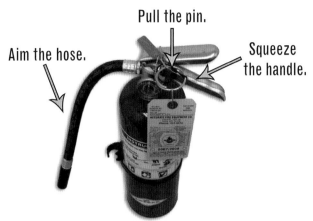

Fig. 6–11. The acronym PASS is used to remind untrained users of fire extinguishers to pull, aim, squeeze, and sweep the hose back and forth.

Application techniques

The most important aspect of any fire extinguisher application technique is operator safety. Techniques that needlessly jeopardize the safety of the operator are unnecessary and should never be taught or demonstrated.

It is advisable that all fires should be fought from the upwind side in order to stay out of the smoke, flames, and radiant heat. While this is preferable, it is not always practical. Regardless of wind direction, fires should only be fought from a side that allows a clear path of escape. Never place yourself on the opposite side of a fire from the path of escape in order to take advantage of the wind direction.

Foam application techniques. When applying foam to a fire, it is important to stay back during the initial attack. Unlike dry chemical or water fog patterns, foam streams do not give good protection against radiant heat. Once control of the fire starts to be established, the operator can safely move closer.

Care should always be taken to ensure that the foam is not submerged into the fuel and is applied gently with minimal disturbance to the fuel surface. Methods to do this include deflecting the stream off the back edge, bouncing the stream off of the front edge, deflecting it off an object in the center, or allowing the foam to gently fall down on the surface (known as the "rain down" or "snowfall" technique).

Faster extinguishment can be accomplished if the stream is moved about the surface rather than holding at one application point and waiting for the foam to move across the fuel surface. Once control has been established, shut down the nozzle and see if the foam will seal up, completing extinguishment. As long as the stream is disturbing the fuel surface, the foam cannot seal across the surface and complete extinguishment.

If water-miscible (polar solvent) fuels are involved, even in a small percentage, an alcohol-type foam must be used. When using an alcohol-type foam, it is important that the fuel surface not be disturbed so that the polymeric membrane can form on the surface.

No firefighting foam will secure a fuel surface indefinitely. Reapplication is necessary over a period of time to prevent reignition. Firefighters should never drag hoses through a **foam blanket** or step into a fuel source with a foam blanket on it without having specific equipment and protection on to do so. Water-miscible (polar solvent) fuels such as alcohol are particularly dangerous since they burn so cleanly that the flames may not be visible.

Dry chemical application. Unlike foam on a Class B fire, dry chemical has no securement capabilities. All of the fire must be extinguished or none of it will be extinguished. Because dry chemical uses a chain-breaking action to extinguish a Class B fire, no physical properties of the fire are affected. Oxygen is not displaced, little cooling is accomplished, and the fuel is not removed. Depending on the type of materials exposed to the fire (such as steel, gravel, combustibles), the chances for a reflash usually are present. The operator should anticipate the possibility of a reflash and never turn his or her back on a fire. There is never a reason to step into a flammable liquid source when using only fire extinguishers.

With the exception of fighting fires inside structures or underground mining operations, the operator should remain upright for the best and safest mobility. Bending over or running may cause the operator to trip.

Always start the approach at a safe distance. Humans were made to walk forward well, but running backwards is never safe.

Be aware of what is on the side of the fire opposite the operator discharging. The flare-up phenomenon can catch other fuels or combustibles on fire at a great distance from the dry chemical discharge.

Whether one operator is involved or several, keep alert, communicate loudly, and always have an open escape route in case you are not successful.

Dry chemical and fuel in depth. Class B fires involving fuel in depth present unique problems for the application of dry chemical. **Fuel in depth** implies that the flammable liquid is confined to a certain area either by a vessel, berm, or dike. Only the surface is of concern. It does not make a difference from an application standpoint whether the surface area encloses 5 gal or 500 gal of fuel. Because the fuel is contained to a specific surface area, it is important that the operator does not get too close and splash fuel, causing the area to increase.

Ideally, this fire should be fought upwind, but if the upwind approach would cut off a safe escape route, it can be fought with a crosswind or diagonal wind. The operator should start discharging the extinguisher from a comfortable distance using the dry chemical stream to "lay down" the fire and push it back before stepping closer.

If the fire surface is rectangular in shape, a slow, deliberate cut across the leading edge will get chemical into the **freeboard** area between the lip of the containment and the fuel surface. This is best accomplished by splitting the stream of dry chemical on the lead edge. Generally, the stream should be placed at least 6 in. (152 mm) in front of the lead edge and the sweep or cut should begin at least 6 in. (152 mm) beyond the side of the fire and continue past 6 in. (152 mm) beyond the other side of the fire.

If, after the initial cut has been made, fire is seen rising immediately on the lead edge right after the dry chemical stream moves away, the aim is too high, or in the case of a deep freeboard area, the angle is too flat. If fire immediately reappears on one side or the other, the cut or sweep is not being extended far enough to that side.

If the fire surface is in the shape of a circle, as in a round pan, start the discharge at the closest point, splitting the stream on the lead edge. Hold for a count of one to two, then begin sweeping side to side. As with a rectangular pan, each sweep must extend beyond the edges on both sides.

Once the fire is moving backwards, the operator can take slow steps forward, sweeping side to side until the fire is completely out. During these sweeps side to side, each sweep must extend at least 6 in. (152 mm) past each side. Unless it is necessary because of nozzle range, it is advisable to always back away from the fuel source. Should a sudden wind shift occur, the attempt at extinguishment fail, or a new source of ignition be introduced, the entire surface area of fuel will quickly ignite.

If for any reason it is necessary to be close to the fuel source, the speed of the sweep action must be increased in order to keep from splashing fuel.

Do not chase the flare-up. Keep the stream down on the surface of the fuel. The flare-up will burn out quickly.

Once extinguishment has been accomplished, stand by waiting for reflash, and then back carefully towards the escape route.

Spill fires. Spill fires by themselves are most likely the easiest of all flammable liquid fires to extinguish with dry chemical. There is no "lead edge" or freeboard area to conceal burning vapors. The same basic technique that is used for fuel in depth applies to spill fires, with one extra caution. With a lot of dry chemical flying about, the exact spill area may be hard to define, so it is important that the operator must stay back as far as possible to avoid inadvertently stepping into the fuel source.

Three-dimensional fire (gravity fed). This type of fire involves flammable liquids in motion, usually running from a source through several levels and pooling on the ground and other areas. Often, obstacles are involved, and, at the least, areas where fuel will flow around structures are involved. For these reasons, more than one dry chemical extinguisher operator should be present at the same time.

Initial approach and application are the same as for a spill fire. The operator(s) should open up the stream(s) at a safe distance, keep a clear exit path, and then, once the fire is moving, move forward and take care to stay out of the fuel spill.

Application must begin with the ground fire and then systematically continue extinguishment up to the source. Everywhere that fuel is flowing over hot metal surfaces or wrapping around an obstacle, the dry chemical stream should be held briefly to allow chemical to build up at that spot before continuing.

If ground fire re-ignites at any point during the application, the dry chemical stream must be brought back to the ground fire in order to be successful.

Applications with more than one operator. Using extinguishers in teams can be the safest and most successful way of extinguishing fires in their incipient or early stages. Communication is the key to having a safe, coordinated effort. All other basic rules apply regarding safe exit, distance, staying clear of the fuel source, and individual application technique. Each operator must speak loudly and clearly to each other. Dry chemical streams must be opened at the same time, and each operator should know what the other's plan is going to be prior to the attack.

At no time should the operators be at direct opposite sides of the fire. This will obscure vision and spray fuel and dry chemical on each other. Each operator should be able to see the other at all times and know where each team member is located.

If one operator runs out of dry chemical before the other, that person should say loudly and clearly, "I'm out," and then back away to safety along the predetermined path. This will let the other operator know that it is time to back away and cover both of their exits by discharging dry chemical between them and the fire and creating a heat barrier.

If one operator spots fire that is being missed by the other operator, that person must point it out immediately to the other. While each person may have a specific task to do, or a specific part of the fire to handle, it is important for each person to keep looking at all aspects of the fire. Other operators may be unable to see fire lingering in a small area because their vision is obscured by the dry chemical discharge.

If the fire is successfully extinguished, one of the operators must call the fire out. Both operators should then stop discharging, stand by, look for a reflash, and then back away to safety following the same route used to advance on the fire.

Spill or fuel in depth with an obstacle. An obstacle inside a fuel in depth or spill fire will shield the dry chemical stream from covering the entire liquid surface. At least two operators must be used when obstacles are present.

First, operators must agree on a plan of attack. (Who goes which way and covers what part?) Standing side-by-side, start discharging dry chemical together with each covering two-thirds of the surface area. Once the fire is moving, they then advance and split to each side until they can reach the back of the obstacle from an approximate 45-degree angle. When the fire is out behind the obstacle, they sweep the rest of the surface fire out. Once extinguishment is accomplished, they stand by looking for reflash, and then back away along the same path used to advance.

Fires with flammable liquids under pressure. Generally, the best way to extinguish flammable liquids under pressure is to shut off the source of supply. This is not always practical and dry chemical can be very effective on these types of fires. Usually it is necessary to place the dry chemical stream right at the point of escape and hold at that spot until the fire goes out. Then, continue to put out any ground fire that is burning. Fast-flow equipment with high flow rates must be used on this type of fire since the dry chemical flow rate must match the flow of fuel escaping.

Using dry chemical with handlines. Dry chemical can be applied to fires from behind fog patterns with great success. The fog pattern protects the fire fighters and aids in cooling the fire. The dry chemical can be directed from behind through the pattern without allowing the fire to come back on the operator. When using this technique, it is still necessary to apply the dry chemical using the same application techniques that are used without a fog pattern. Common mistakes with a combined water and dry chemical attack involve just directing the dry chemical into the water stream (this will have little effect on the fire) or sticking the dry chemical nozzle into the fog pattern (thus breaking the pattern and allowing flame to come back onto the hose team).

Dry powder on Class D fires. Applying dry powder to class D fires generally involves a soft discharge pattern that will completely cover the burning material under a mound of dry powder. The operator should be careful that no moisture is present in the surrounding area that may contact the burning metal. Once the material is completely covered, the operator should stand by and watch for "hot spots" that start to burn through the powder and reapply as necessary (fig. 6–12).

Inspection, maintenance, recharge, hydrostatic testing, and obsolete extinguishers.

Fire extinguishers are to be inspected at a minimum of 30-day intervals. They should be inspected more frequently when circumstances require. Per NFPA 10, 7.2.2 Procedures, the following shall be checked:

1. Pressure gauge reading or indicator in the operable range or position

2. Fullness determined by weighing or hefting for self-expelling extinguishers, cartridge-operated extinguishers, and pump tanks

3. The discharge outlet is not blocked

4. The seal is not broken

5. The operating instructions are clearly visible

Fig. 6–12. Applying dry powder to a Class D fire is risky and requires the fire extinguisher operator to monitor the situation for "hot spots" that might flare up.

When an extinguisher reveals a deficiency, it shall be subjected to applicable maintenance procedures.

- **Annual Maintenance.** A more complete inspection of the extinguisher that shall be done by trained, certified persons having the appropriate service manuals, tools, manufacturer replacement parts, and recharge agents specifically listed for use in the extinguisher.

- **6-Year Maintenance.** Every six years, extinguishers requiring a 12-year hydrostatic test shall be emptied and subject to thorough examination of mechanical parts, extinguishing agent, and expelling means. When applicable maintenance procedures are being done during periodic recharging or hydrostatic testing, the six-year requirement will begin from that date.

- **Hydrostatic Testing.** This involves subjecting the cylinder (known as the pressure vessel) to water pressure or pressure applied by some other noncompressible fluid, usually through the cylinder's valve opening, using a specially designed test coupling. This testing should not be performed using compressed air or any compressed gas, and all air and other gases must be vented from the cylinder before you apply any fluid pressure. Hydrostatic testing should be done by trained, certified personnel using suitably equipped testing facilities. How often hyrdotesting should be conducted depends on the type of extinguishing agent used. Examples are water, foam, wet chemical, and carbon dioxide, which require a 5-year test. Dry chemical, whether stored-pressure or cartridge-operated with mild steel cylinders, require 12-year testing.

- **Recharge.** Recharge shall be done by trained, certified personnel immediately after use. The extinguisher must be recharged with the extinguishing agent listed on the nameplate. Substitutions could cause damage or injury. *WARNING: Always use a regulated pressurizing source set to no more than 25 psi above extinguisher operating pressure.*

- **Obsolete Fire Extinguishers.** Per NFPA 10 section 4.4, the following types of extinguishers are considered obsolete and shall be removed from service:

  1. Soda acid

  2. Chemical foam (excluding film-forming agents)

  3. Vaporizing liquid (e.g., carbon tetrachloride)

  4. Cartridge-operated water

  5. Cartridge-operated loaded stream

  6. Copper or brass shell (excluding pump tanks) joined by soft solder or rivets

  7. Carbon dioxide extinguishers with metal horns

  8. Solid charge-type AFFF extinguishers (paper cartridge)

  9. Pressurized-water fire extinguishers manufactured prior to 1971

  10. Any extinguisher that needs to be inverted to operate

  11. Any stored-pressure extinguisher manufactured prior to 1955

  12. Any extinguishers with 4B, 6B, 8B, 12B, or 16B fire ratings

  13. Stored-pressure water extinguishers with fiberglass shells (pre-1976)

Further, 4.4.1 states: Dry chemical, stored-pressure extinguishers manufactured prior to October 1984 shall be removed from service at the next six-year maintenance interval or the next hydrotest interval, whichever comes first.

Section 4.4.2 adds: Any fire extinguisher that can no longer be serviced in accordance with the manufacturer's maintenance manual is considered obsolete and shall be removed from service.

NOTES

NFPA 10 *Standard for Portable Fire Extinguishers*

Fire Extinguishers

FIREFIGHTER I

Chapter 6

LESSON FROM THE FIREGROUND

On arrival the fire in the basement of the 2½-story single family colonial style house was lapping up the wall and starting to spread across the ceiling to the stairway. A firefighter in full personal protective equipment and wearing self-contained breathing apparatus positioned himself at the exterior doorway on the side of the house by the stairway. There he used a 2½-gal (9.5-L) water extinguisher from a fire chief's car to hold the fire in check by placing a fingertip over the discharge point of the nozzle and spraying intermittent bursts of water. The judicious application of water prevented the fire from extending up the stairway and into the house. Shortly thereafter, the attack hoseline was in place and quickly extinguished the fire in the basement. The deployment of the 2½-gal (9.5-L) water extinguisher was a crucial factor in minimizing the damage to the house.

QUESTIONS

1. Explain the differences between applying an extinguisher to a fuel-in-depth fire in a rectangular and a circular container.

2. The rating system for a Class A fire extinguisher is based on what?

3. Explain the difference between dry chemical and dry powder extinguishers.

4. Describe the two ways that wet chemical fire extinguishers work on Class K fires.

5. List examples of the types of fires that halogenated extinguishing agents would be more beneficial than other agents.

6. List the criteria for selecting the proper fire extinguisher.

7. What is the best way to extinguish a fire involving a flammable liquid under pressure?

8. List four fire extinguisher types that are considered obsolete by NFPA 10.

Building Construction

by Paul T. Dansbach

This chapter provides required knowledge items for the following NFPA Standard 1001 Job Performance Requirements:

FFI: 5.3.4

FFI: 5.3.10

FFI: 5.3.12

OBJECTIVES

Upon completion of this chapter, you should be able to do the following:

- Identify the types of forces and loads that impact building construction materials
- Identify and describe the basic types of building materials
- Identify and describe the five common types of building construction
- Identify the basic structural components in a building
- Identify factors affecting structural stability of a building
- Describe the hazards associated with light-weight and truss construction
- Identify the indicators of collapse
- Describe the impact of new building construction technology on the fire service
- List actions to take to limit injury or death to personnel in the event of a structural collapse

INTRODUCTION

This chapter begins your study of building construction (fig. 7–1). By the end of this chapter, you will understand the basic concepts of building construction as they relate to firefighting. To be successful as a firefighter or fire officer, the study of building construction must be an ongoing and perpetual learning experience. From the beginning of firefighting, firefighters have been called on to extinguish fires in buildings. Much of what you learn in your formal Firefighter I and II training programs centers on safe and efficient fireground operations. Fighting a fire in a building is inherently dangerous: The building and its structural integrity is attacked and weakened as the fire burns. Much has changed in firefighting since the beginning of organized firefighting, but one aspect remains the same: To successfully extinguish most struc-

Fig. 7–1. A wood frame building

ture fires, a crew of firefighters must enter the building, locate the fire, and extinguish the fire by directing a stream of water from the nozzle onto the burning material. Your success and safety largely depend on your knowledge and understanding of building construction.

FORCES AND LOADS ACTING ON A BUILDING

Forces and how they apply to a building

A **force** is any action that maintains or alters the position of a structure or a part of a structure. Essentially, it is a push, pull, twist, or a combination of these exerted on an object or a structural member. Generally, there are four types of forces that can be applied to a building or its components:

1. **Compression**: the action of squeezing or pushing of a component, a **load** or weight imposed on a structural column that result in a compressive force when applied to the column (fig. 7–2). A compressive force may shorten the structural component.

Fig. 7–2. The studs supporting the floor joists in this wood-frame wall are in compression.

2. **Tension**: the action of stretching or pulling of a component. The threaded rod in fig. 7–3, which supports the stairway's intermediate landing, is in tension. Many members, which are in tension, are supported by attachment to a structural member above (fig. 7–4). A **tensile** force applied to a structural member may lengthen or stretch the member in tension; members in tension often fail by breaking apart or failing at the connection points.

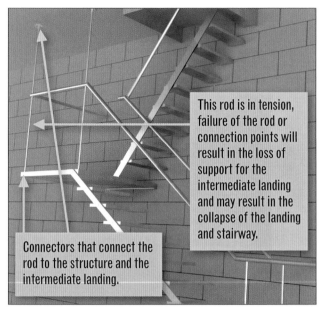

This rod is in tension, failure of the rod or connection points will result in the loss of support for the intermediate landing and may result in the collapse of the landing and stairway.

Connectors that connect the rod to the structure and the intermediate landing.

Fig. 7–3. Tensile force applied to a structural component

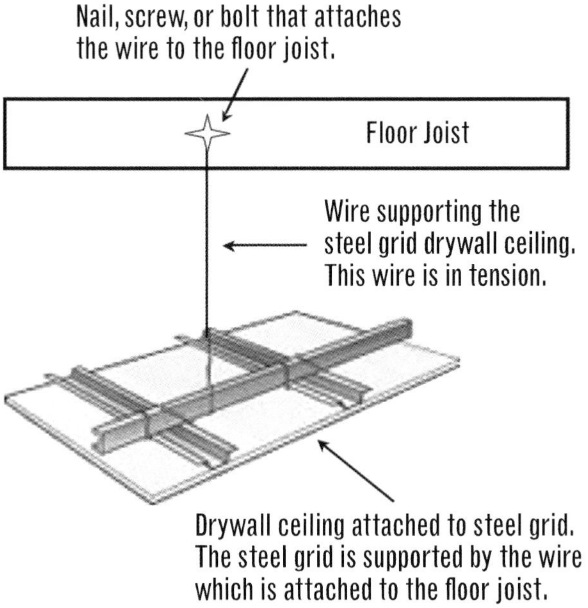

Nail, screw, or bolt that attaches the wire to the floor joist.

Floor Joist

Wire supporting the steel grid drywall ceiling. This wire is in tension.

Drywall ceiling attached to steel grid. The steel grid is supported by the wire which is attached to the floor joist.

Fig. 7–4. The wire that supports the drywall steel grid is in tension and is attached to the floor joist above.

3. **Torsion**: the action of twisting a building component such as a nut on a bolt. Torsional force is commonly expressed in terms of **torque**.

4. **Shear**: a condition or force causing two structural members to slide past each other in opposite directions (away from or toward each other). Significant shear forces can cause structural members to fail at their connection points (fig. 7–5).

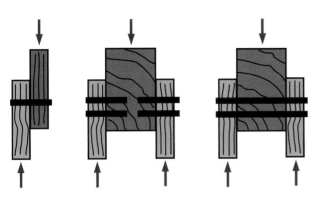

Fig. 7–5. These connections are typical connections in a wood-frame building: a shear force is applied to the connection. If the connection fails, the parts of the connection will slide past each other.

Loads applied to a building

Loads are basically the forces applied to a building from a variety of sources, such as the weight of the contents of a building (occupants, their possessions, and equipment), as well as **external forces** such as environmental effects (weather, earthquakes, etc.).

Loads may be imposed on a building's structural members in one of three different ways: axially, eccentrically, or torsionally. **Axial loads** pass through the center of a particular section or supporting member at a right angle to the cross section of the supporting member (fig. 7–6).

Fig. 7–6. An axial load is imposed on the column as the load passes through the center of the column.

Eccentric loads are imposed on a structural member at some point other than the center section of the supporting member (fig. 7–7).

Finally, **torsional loads** are parallel to the cross section of the supporting member, typically a column that does not pass through the long axis of the structural member (fig. 7–8).

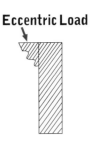

Fig. 7–7. The parapet wall is eccentrically loaded with a cornice (a decorative wall projection attached to the top of many apartment buildings.) This load does not pass through the center of the wall.

Fig. 7–8. Torsional loads are delivered at a right angle to the supporting member and usually result in a twisting of the member. Torsional loads are common in collapses when the designed structural function of the structural members is upset.

The following terms are also used to describe specific types of loads:

A **designed load** is a load that the building designer or structural engineer has calculated into the building based on sound engineering principles. The structure can carry or withstand all the design loads that are applied to a given building or structure. Several of the loads explained in the following text are easily calculated and required by code to be calculated to ensure the building can withstand the various loads.

Design loads vary based on geographic regions. For example, a roof structure designed for a building in a New England state should be able to carry a much greater load, to support the weight of snow, than a roof structure in southern California, where it does not snow. A building in Florida is designed to withstand a much greater wind load, to endure hurricanes and tropical storms, than a building in a northwestern state, where such weather events are unlikely. A building in San Francisco is designed to withstand an earthquake; however, a building in Washington, DC, is not designed to the same standards, where the threat of an earthquake is much less.

Undesigned loads are loads that a designer or structural engineer did not anticipate or calculate. Undesigned loads are often the result of unauthorized construction, such as when a building owner fails to obtain the necessary approval and permits, or work performed by untrained or unscrupulous contractors. Through the history of fire service, firefighters have been injured and killed in buildings that were renovated or altered in this manner. An undesigned load could be the placement of heating, ventilation, and air conditioning (HVAC) units on the roof of an older building without considering the additional load on the roof support structure (fig. 7–9).

Fig. 7–9. The installation of air conditioning units on a roof without consideration of the extra weight being added to the roof is an example of an undesigned load.

A **live load** is a nonfixed (sometimes moving) variable load that is added to the structure, including people, materials, and other transportable items.

A **dead load** is the load of the building itself—the structural components, building utilities, interior finishes, and any other components that are built in or permanently attached to the structure. The dead load may change through the life of the building as the result of renovations and alterations to the structure.

Environmental loads include snow, rain, wind, and earthquakes. Code requirements for these loads vary based on geographic region (fig. 7–10).

An **impact load** is a force delivered in motion such as a blow or force delivered by an object in motion striking a fixed object (e.g., an axe striking a roof). Impact loads are the opposite of a force applied slowly and maintained over an extended period of time.

A **static load** is a relatively unchanging load, which may be delivered over an extended period.

Dynamic loads display significant dynamic effects or are in motion when applied to a building, including strong earthquakes, gusting winds, and loads applied by the fast movement of water or waves.

A **concentrated load** is applied to a relatively small area, such as a steel column bearing on the building's **footing** or an air conditioning unit on the roof of a building.

Fig. 7–10. An unusually heavy snow load caused the collapse of this bowstring truss roof. The fire department was dispatched to this collapse as an activated fire alarm. When the collapse occurred, the building's automatic sprinkler piping was broken and the resulting water flow tripped the fire alarm system. Note the large area of collapse as the result of the failure of only one of the bowstring trusses.

A **distributed load** is a load distributed over a large area of the supporting surface, supporting a uniform load over the area (e.g., ballast stone applied on a rubber **membrane roof**).

A **fire load** is the total amount or quantity of combustible material stored or used in a building, including combustible building contents and furnishings not built into the building (fig. 7–11). Previously, this load was expressed in pounds per square foot of combustibles or in the combustible's heat energy potential by British thermal units (Btu). Today, however, fire load is more commonly measured in terms of the heat release rate of the building's furnishings and contents (refer to chapter 5, Fire Behavior for a description of heat release rate).

Fig. 7–11. Fire loads will vary from building to building. Flammable liquids, which are used or stored in the building, will present a higher fire load. The wooden structural members of the building also contribute to the fire load.

HOW COMMON BUILDING MATERIALS ARE AFFECTED BY FIRE

The various building materials used to construct a building are affected by fire in various ways. Some materials burn and lose mass as they burn, and others, which are noncombustible, lose their strength as they are heated. Table 7–1 details how common building materials are affected and how the materials react to the heat from the fire.

UNDERSTANDING STRUCTURAL COMPONENTS

FFI 5.3.4, 5.3.10 To understand building construction features and hazards, the firefighter must understand the buildings components, the names given to the components, and what function each component serves in the structure. The following text reviews some of the most common building components and their function.

Arch

Arches are constructed in two basic shapes: round or curved arches and flat arches. The most common arches are round or curved and usually carry forces in compression in one direction only. Arches can fail when the adjoining wall, which helps the arch resist horizontal forces, fails and flattens out. Wooden arches may fail when they cannot support the imposed load because of the loss of mass or the burning away of the arch.

Beam

A **beam** is a horizontal supporting member that transfers weight from one location to another and from one structural component to another. A beam may support floor joists and transfer the weight of the floor joists in a horizontal direction to an exterior wall. A simple beam is supported at two points, whereas a continuous beam is supported at three or more points. Wood beams fail as the result of loss of mass; the beam burns away to a point where the beam can no longer support the load imposed on the beam and a collapse occurs. Steel beams fail because of the loss of strength from the exposure of the fire's heat, and they may sag or warp and drop the

beam's load. Steel beams elongate from exposure to the fire's heat. When the steel beam is restrained in a supporting wall, the elongation may push the supporting walls out of plumb and cause the outward collapse of the supporting wall; then the load supported by the beam collapses. A 100-ft-long (30.5-m) steel beam heated evenly to 1,000°F (538°C) elongates 9 in. (229 mm).

Cantilever beam. A **cantilever beam** is supported at one end only (e.g., a balcony, which is supported by attachment to the structure at one end). A wood-cantilevered beam may fail because of loss of mass after being exposed to the fire, or the connections may fail, releasing the cantilevered beam from its support.

I-beam. An **I-beam** gets its name from the cross section of the beam, which is shaped like an I. Today, I-beams are known as **wide flange beams**, because the dimensions of the top and bottom flanges have increased in horizontal dimension; however, it is still called an I-beam in the fire service. The I-beam consists of a top and bottom flange separated by a vertical component called the **web**. I-beams are most commonly found in the form of steel and are used in steel frame buildings to support floors and roofs of these buildings. Lightweight wood floor joists are also manufactured in the shape of an I-beam and are often referred to as engineered wooden I-beams.

Girder

A **girder** is a structural support member usually found in the horizontal position. A girder is supported by a wall and/or columns and supports beams or joists.

Lintel

A **lintel** or **header** is a horizontal beam that usually supports the wall above an opening in a wall such as a window or door. It may be wood, steel, or masonry.

Column

A **column** is a vertical structural element that transmits the load imposed on the top or side of the column to another structural element at the base of the column. The load imposed on the column causes a compressive force on the column. The column may impose a concentrated load on the member supporting the column. Shorter columns tend to fail by crushing, whereas long, slender columns tend to fail by buckling. If connections are made to the column along the vertical length of the column, the connections increase the load-carrying ability of the column and reduce the potential for the column to fail.

Table 7–1. Effect of heat and fire on common building materials [FFI 5.3.12] [FFII 6.3.2]

Material	Common uses in buildings	Reaction when exposed to fire and heat
Wood	Often used in wood frame buildings as the primary structural elements (exterior and interior wall studs, floor joists, and roof rafters), ordinary-constructed buildings (interior wood studs, floor joists, and roof rafters), and buildings constructed using mortise and tenon connections (post and beam buildings).	Wood loses mass as the material burns, and the loss of mass weakens the wood member until it fails. The mass of the wood member is reduced to make the connection, when these connections are attacked by fire, they are usually the point of failure.
Structural steel	Structural steel is used in many forms. The common structural elements include columns, beams, and bar joists. It is the primary structural element in noncombustible buildings. When used as a structural element in fire-resistive buildings, the steel must be protected from the fire's heat. Structural steel may also be found in different forms in wood frame and ordinary construction.	As structural steel is heated, the steel loses strength and expands (lengthens). Once the structural member reaches the yield point (because of high temperature and resultant loss of strength), the structural element fails. The strength of structural steel varies from piece to piece, depending on the age of the steel and the ingredients added to the steel. Steel manufactured early on in the steel age is weaker than steel used today. Industry advances have lead to the development of stronger steel by using different compounds in the manufacture of the steel.
Cast-in-place concrete	Cast-in-place concrete is used in footings, foundations, and grade beams, as well as cast-in-place floors, walls, and columns.	Cast-in-place concrete is a great insulating material, because it is a dense noncombustible material. As with other masonry materials, the cast-in-place concrete is subject to spalling when exposed to high temperatures. If the cast-in-place concrete is a reinforced concrete element, and the spalling exposes the steel reinforcing bars or cables, the steel loses strength and the entire slab of concrete may be in danger of collapse.
Concrete block	Concrete block is found in foundation walls, interior and exterior bearing walls, and interior nonbearing walls.	A great insulating material, it is often used in building to construct fire walls or fire separation wall assemblies, because concrete block resists the passage of fire. As with other masonry materials, the concrete block is subject to *spalling* (fragments of concrete dislodged under the heat of a fire) when exposed to high temperatures.
Cast iron	Structural columns that support floors and roofs are made of cast iron, as are building facades. Cast iron is found in buildings constructed in the late 1800s through the 1920s.	Cast iron may fracture or spall when exposed to high temperatures or when heated and cooled rapidly, such as if cooled by a hoseline operating on the fire.

Truss

A **truss** is a structural component using one or more triangular units to attain stability. The truss consists of **top** and **bottom chords** and **intermediate web members** that connect the top and bottom chords of the truss. Three common types of trusses are available: heavy timber wood truss, lightweight wood parallel-chord or peaked truss, and steel **bar joist** truss (figs. 7–12 and 7–13). Trusses are used to create large open floor areas where the use of columns or interior walls is undesirable. All trusses have large **surface-area-to-mass ratio** that leads to poor performance and early failure of the truss under fire conditions. When a truss fails, the resulting collapse area is large because of the span between the walls supporting the trusses and spacing between the trusses.

Floor truss. A **floor truss** is a lightweight wood parallel-chord truss used in wood-frame construction (fig. 7–14). Trusses are manufactured using 2 × 4-in. (51 × 102–mm) lumber as the top and bottom chord of the trusses. The chord may be spliced from smaller lengths of 2 × 4-in. (51 × 102–mm) lumber and spliced together using a splice plate or finger joint to piece the chord together.

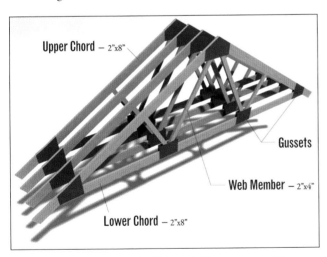

Fig. 7–12. Components of a lightweight peaked-roof truss.

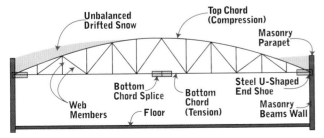

Fig. 7–13. Components of a heavy-timber bowstring roof truss.

Fig. 7–14. Use of lightweight wood parallel-chord truss members in a floor system. The use of floor trusses creates a large combustible void space. Buildings framed with dimensional lumber, which use 2 in. x 10 in. (51 mm x 254 mm) floor joists, will not have this combustible void space.

The web members of the truss are also made from 2 × 4-in. (51 × 102–mm) lumber that separates the top and bottom chord with geometric shapes; web members are connected to the top and bottom chord with gusset plate connectors or finger-joint glue connections. Theses members are used in a series to support floors and ceiling loads.

Wooden I-beam

Wooden I-beams, sometimes referred to as **engineered wood joists**, are engineered floor joists manufactured with a top and bottom chord and a web member between the chords, separating them. The top and bottom chords are made of laminated lumber and are typically 2 in. × 3 in. (51 mm × 76 mm) or 2 in. × 4 in. (51 mm × 102 mm) in dimension. A **dado** or groove is located in the center of the long axis of the top and bottom chord, and the web member is glued in place between the top and bottom chords (fig. 7–15).

Building Construction

FIREFIGHTER I

Chapter 7

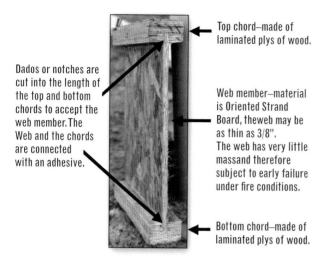

Top chord–made of laminated plys of wood.

Dados or notches are cut into the length of the top and bottom chords to accept the web member. The Web and the chords are connected with an adhesive.

Web member–material is Oriented Strand Board, the web may be as thin as 3/8". The web has very little mass and therefore subject to early failure under fire conditions.

Bottom chord–made of laminated plys of wood.

Fig. 7–15. The components of a wooden "I" beam. Math has replaced mass in the manufacture and use of engineered wood structural components. The 3/8" web on a wooden I-beam has greatly reduced the burn time for this component before collapse occurs. The fire service is experiencing a greater number of floor collapses that are injuring and killing firefighters.

The web member is a piece of **oriented strand board (OSB)**, which is typically between ⅜ and ½ in. (10 and 13 mm) thick. Theses members are used in a series to support floor and ceiling loads.

Joist

A **joist** is a parallel framing member used in a series to support floor and ceiling loads. Joists span between and are supported by bearing walls or **girders** or beams.

Rafter

Rafters are a series of sloping roof framing members that support the roof sheathing and roof covering. A rafter is supported by the outside walls at the low point of the roof and is connected to the ridgepole at the uppermost point of the roof. Rafters in buildings constructed with a flat roof may also be referred to as **roof joists**.

Ridge beam or ridgepole

A **ridge beam** or **ridgepole** is the uppermost horizontal framing member of a roof system located at the peak or uppermost point of the roof. Rafters are connected to the ridge beam or ridgepole on opposing sides.

Wall types

Load-bearing wall. Load-bearing walls are commonly constructed of wood, brick, structural steel studs, concrete block, and poured-in-place concrete. A load-bearing wall supports its own weight, the floors above it, and the walls or floors above, and sometimes the roof of the building. Load bearing walls can be exterior and interior walls.

Non–load-bearing wall. A **non–load-bearing wall** may be used to separate an area of a building into smaller rooms or individual spaces. A non–load-bearing wall supports no load other than itself and the weight of the finish materials attached to the wall. Non–load-bearing walls may be constructed from common materials including but not limited to wood-frame members and steel studs with an interior finish of drywall or concrete.

Curtain wall. A **curtain wall** is an exterior non-load-bearing wall of a building. The curtain wall is attached to the building or structure by its floors or columns. Curtain walls pass in front of the building **floor slab**. The space between the curtain wall and the floor slab may be a path for fire extension if the space is not properly **fire-stopped** (sealed with a fire-resistant barrier). Curtain walls are constructed of different materials; lightweight curtain wall panels are constructed of **heavy gauge steel stud** with a form of gypsum board attached to the steel stud and finished with a cementitious exterior finish material. These wall panels may contain some form of combustible foam insulating material.

Another form of a curtain wall panel is the large precast concrete wall panel with a decorative finish on the exterior exposed surface. Aluminum frame window systems are usually installed between the curtain walls. These **precast panels** may be attached to the steel frame of the structure by mechanical fasteners such as bolts or may be welded in place. The alternating horizontal bands of curtain wall and window systems that wrap around buildings usually identify office buildings. Residential and hotel occupancies usually have less window area than office buildings.

Parapet wall. The parapet wall is the part of an exterior wall that extends above the roofline of the building. It may or may not be on all sides of the building. Typically, if the parapet walls are part of the original construction, they are constructed of the same materials as the exterior walls of the building. A common alteration to change the façade of a building is to add a parapet wall on the front of the building. Often, the addition of a parapet wall on an existing building with exterior masonry walls uses wood or steel studs. The most dangerous type of parapet wall is a freestanding parapet on only one side of the building that is constructed of masonry (fig. 7–16). Masonry firewalls that separate buildings or parts of buildings that extend through the roof of a building are also parapet walls. Identifying this wall on the roof is a way of locating firewalls in the building.

Fig. 7–16. Freestanding parapet walls are the most dangerous parapet walls, as they do not intersect at any corner. If the roof of the building were to collapse during a fire, the freestanding portion of the wall may become greater and therefore less stable.

Roof types

Roof shapes are known by common names, with which firefighters should become familiar. More importantly, firefighters should learn the operational and collapse hazards as well as the fire spread potential of each roof type (fig. 7–17).

Flat. On a **flat roof** the members supporting the roof decking are horizontal or have a slight pitch. The building may have a cockloft, which is the space between the ceiling and the underside of the roof deck, or the ceiling interior finish material may be directly attached to the roof rafters. In buildings where an interior finish was unnecessary, the roof structure is open to the interior of the building.

Shed or single pitch. A **shed** or **single-pitched roof** is built in a single sloped plane that slopes from between parallel walls of different heights. The interior features of the roof are very similar to those found with a flat roof.

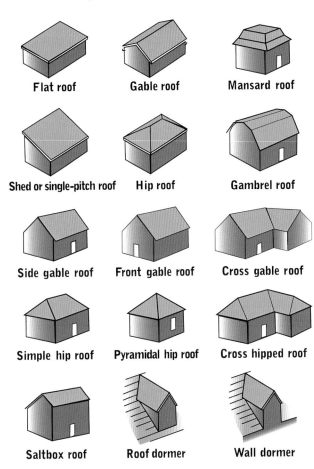

Fig. 7–17. Different types of roofs

Gable. Gabled roofs are identified by the straight slope falling from ridgepole at the highest horizontal point on the roof to opposite sides or walls of the structure. The roof rafters rest at the low end of the roof on an **exterior bearing wall**; the point at which the roof lands on and extends past the exterior bearing wall is known as the **eave**. Gable roofs are most commonly found on wood-frame buildings or ordinary-constructed buildings. The roofing material is typically some form of asphalt or fiberglass shingle. The roof shape creates a peak or triangle on the side walls or the front and rear walls of the building. Wall areas between the slope of the roof are known as the gable walls.

Hip. **Hip roofs** have three or more sides that slope to the exterior walls of the building. The hip roof may or may not have a ridgepole, depending on the size and shape of the building. Most commonly, hip roofs have sloping roof sections on all four sides of the roof. Any side of the building that has a sloping roof and an eve around the roofline is a bearing wall that supports the roof structure. Hip roofs have hips and maybe valleys. The hip is formed where two sides or parts of the roof meet and form an outside or external corner. The intersection where the sides of the sloping roof meet at an inside corner is known as the **valley**. Both hips and valleys typically start at the roof eve and continue up to their ridgepole.

Gambrel. A **gambrel roof** is similar to a gabled roof in that it is made up of two sides that slope away from the ridgepole; however, a gambrel roof begins at the ridgepole with a slight pitch and changes to a steeper pitch. The point where the roof changes slope is parallel to and lower in elevation from the ridgepole. The gambrel roof design allows for greater habitable space or floor area in the story directly below the roof structure. It is commonly found on barns and is sometimes called a **barn roof**. The walls to which the roof slopes are bearing walls that support the roof.

Mansard. A **mansard roof** is similar to a hipped roof in that the roof structure has at least three sides that slope to the exterior walls of the building. A mansard roof has two separate and distinct pitches. The slope or roof pitch that starts at the ridgepole or the flat part of a roof has a low or slight slope. Where the roofline intersects the exterior wall, the roof slope changes to a steep slope and vertically extends down along the exterior wall of the building, perhaps as much as two stories. The construction of a mansard roof may create a combustible void space where fire may extend to spread rapidly both vertically and horizontally. This roof style can also create a tremendous collapse potential because of how the roof structure is attached to the exterior walls of the building.

Saltbox. A **saltbox roof** is a form of a gabled roof where the sloping sides of the roof are asymmetrical. This roof style is used in buildings when the roof must end at two different stories of the building. For example, on a two-story building, one side of the roof slopes to and is supported by the two-story side of the building, and the opposite slope of the roof slopes to and is supported at the first story. The ridgepole on a saltbox roof is parallel to the supporting walls but may not be centered on the building. The walls to which the roof slopes are the bearing walls that support the roof structure.

Dormers. **Dormers** are small structures that rise up out of the roof to provide light, ventilation, and increased usable floor space on the story directly below the roof. Dormers are classified by their roof shape (shed, hipped, gabled, flat, etc.). Dormers are further classified into two classes based on their locations and means of support. A roof dormer extends up from the main roofline, like a small house with its own walls, roof, and window. Only the rafters or other roof structures such as lightweight wood roof trusses support the roof dormer. A wall dormer extends up from the roofline at the roof-to-wall junction and is supported partly by the exterior wall of the building, the same exterior wall supporting the main roof structure.

STRUCTURAL HIERARCHY AND FIREFIGHTER SAFETY

Certain structural components are more important than others. The term **structural hierarchy** determines which structural components are most important, factored with locations of the structural members within the building (fig. 7–18). Columns are some of the most important structural members in a building, and the column's vertical location in the building is also a factor. For example, in a four-story building, a column that fails in the basement affects the entire column line up through the building. In turn, this affects the beams on each floor supported by the column line, so the resulting area of collapse is likely to be extensive. In the same building, if a column fails on the uppermost floor of the building, the resulting area of collapse is likely to be contained to the top floor and the roof area, resulting in a much smaller area of collapse. These principles do not apply to buildings constructed with any form of trusses, because the collapse hazard associated with trusses is more severe.

Firefighters should study the collapse of Boston's Vendome Hotel, which occurred on June 17, 1972, causing the deaths of nine firefighters. The Vendome Hotel was under renovation to change the hotel into a multifamily dwelling when the fire occurred. The fire was under control and firefighters were overhauling and securing equipment when several floors and walls of the seven-story hotel collapsed without warning.

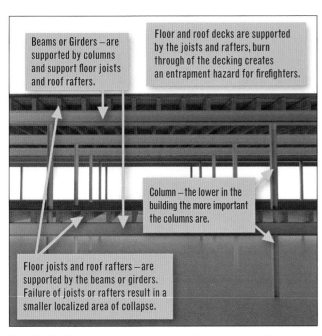

Beams or Girders—are supported by columns and support floor joists and roof rafters.

Floor and roof decks are supported by the joists and rafters, burn through of the decking creates an entrapment hazard for firefighters.

Column—the lower in the building the more important the columns are.

Floor joists and roof rafters—are supported by the beams or girders. Failure of joists or rafters result in a smaller localized area of collapse.

Fig. 7–18. The components and the importance of the components in terms of structural hierarchy

Factors affecting structural stability

FFII 6.3.2 Several factors affect the structural stability of the building. The building's structural stability is the building's ability to resist collapse. Remember, a collapse event may be a minor collapse caused by the loss of structural stability of one or more structural members.

The condition of the structural components of a building may vary and are sometimes deteriorated due to exposure to weather, lack of maintenance, or a combination of factors. For example, deterioration can be found when the ends of a wood timber truss rot because of water leaks in the roof system over the years. The wood slowly deteriorates, and this condition goes unnoticed. When a fire occurs in the building, the truss ends fail quickly as the fire burns through the deteriorated wood.

The mass of the structural elements will also be a significant factor in the structure's ability to resist collapse. Older buildings, especially wood-frame buildings and mill buildings, were constructed with many wooden structural parts. The beams, studs, and joists in the buildings had a fair amount of mass or cross-section value. In other words, there was some **fat** built into these buildings, and the fat of the **dimensional lumber** (2–4 in. nominal thickness) allowed for a certain amount of burn time before the building sustained a structural failure. In today's buildings, especially the lightweight wood-frame buildings that employ floor and roof trusses and engineered lumber such as plywood I-beams, the fat has been removed, resulting in the elimination of any

burn time for the building. Another way of looking at the issue is that through engineering and mathematical calculations, the building industry has been able to eliminate the mass of the structural components. Math has replaced mass, making lightweight wood-frame buildings much more dangerous for firefighters. If anyone describes a building to you as a safe building for firefighters because the building is constructed using engineered structural components, disregard those comments as pure myth. Engineered structural components use the least amount of material to carry a predetermined load over a maximum specified span or at the least expense to the developer or property owner. Many firefighters have lost their lives in buildings constructed of engineered structural components.

Another factor affecting structural stability is the fire loading of the building. A rapidly developing fire with high heat output damages the structural components faster than a small fire with a lower heat output. The type of construction plays a major role in this equation. For example, consider two fires in a noncombustible constructed building with a steel bar joist roof. The first fire occurs in an occupancy involving the storage of baled rags and cardboard. The bales are tightly bound, and the fire has a slow rate of heat release that produces a considerable smoke condition. The low rate of heat release prevents the bar joist roof system from collapsing or failing as quickly as a fire in the same building involving the ignition of flammable liquids. The fire involving the flammable liquids rapidly develops and releases a significant amount of heat that causes early failure of a bar joist roof system. Determining the fire load and fire behavior at all fire incidents is an important part of an ongoing size-up.

CONSTRUCTION CLASSIFICATIONS

NFPA Standard #220, *Standard on Types of Building Construction* and the *International Building Code,* classifies buildings into five classes based on the materials used in a given building and the fire-resistiveness of the structural members of the building. The following text details the five construction classifications, materials used to construct these buildings, common occupancies found in the construction classes, and hazards associated with

Building Construction

FIREFIGHTER I

Chapter 7

the construction classification. The classifications are as follows:

Type I: Fire-resistive construction

Type II: Non-combustible construction

Type III: Ordinary construction

Type IV: Mill or heavy timber construction

Type V: Wood-frame construction

Fire-resistive construction

In **fire-resistive construction**, the structural members including columns, beams, and sometimes floor slabs are protected from the fire's heat to prevent the loss of the structural element's integrity. The level of fire resistance, measured in an **hourly fire rating**, is high compared to Type II noncombustible construction (described in the following text), which has little or no fire resistance.

Early fire-resistive buildings were constructed primarily of masonry materials, most commonly poured or cast-in-place concrete. Buildings constructed of **steel skeleton frame** used a variety of materials to encase or protect the structural steel from the heat of the fire. These materials include cement plaster, clay tile, **asbestos**, layers of **gypsum board**, and spray-on fireproofing materials (fig. 7–19).

Buildings or occupancies constructed of fire-resistive materials include high-rise buildings, mid-rise residential structures, hospitals, old-style warehouses, or cold storage buildings (fig. 7–20).

Pre–World War II buildings of fire-resistive construction tended to have smaller floor areas compared to modern high-rise buildings. These buildings relied on openable windows for ventilation and had fewer accommodations for heating, ventilating, air conditioning (HVAC), and technology. Many pre–World War II high-rise buildings were constructed with true fire tower stairs that vented to the exterior of the building, which effectively prevented smoke from entering the stair towers. The floor areas were smaller and there was greater **compartmentation** of the floor areas in the forms of rooms and offices. This resulted in slower fire spread and smaller fire areas. Pre–World War II high-rise buildings were constructed with heavier materials, which created mass within the structure.

Fig. 7–19. This photo details the use of a spray on fireproofing material on structural steel columns and bar joists. The material is a mixture of an insulating material and cement. The cement binds the insulation together and ensures that the fireproofing adheres to the building component. This material is easily removed by other construction trades and results in a lapse of protection.

Fig. 7–20. A poured-in-place fire-resistive constructed building. This construction is also sometime called monolithic construction as the poured concrete forms into one piece. Detailed here are the building columns and floor assemblies, poured into the concrete columns and floor steel reinforcing bars. (Courtesy of Glenn Taldelore)

Post–World War II high-rise buildings started using more modern, often lighter building materials. This in effect reduced the mass of the structure. More modern high-rise buildings are often constructed with the lightest weight materials available. The features of modern high-rise buildings include the use of steel bar joist floor systems and curtain wall systems (fig. 7–21).

The buildings are constructed with tremendous accommodations for technology-based business systems and rely on the building's HVAC systems to heat and cool the building, because the buildings do not have any openable windows. Eliminating the need for openable windows allowed the size of the floor area to increase tremendously.

Fig. 7–21. A curtain wall system being installed on a building. The wall panel passes in front of the floor slab and does not support any part of the building other than itself. Curtain walls may be responsible for fire extension between floors if the wall space is not properly fire-stopped at each floor level.

Modern high-rise office buildings are typically constructed using a **center core floor plan**, in which utilities, elevators, bathrooms, and exit stairways are built near the center of the building and are typical on every floor. This method of construction provides the greatest flexibility for the building owner in terms of making the floors available for lease. The floor areas of modern high-rise buildings have much less compartmentation than pre–World War II high-rise buildings (fig. 7–22).

Open office plans using **low-rise** office partitions or cubes create large mazelike fire areas on the floors of these buildings. The open floor plan also allows for faster fire development and a much larger fire area. There have been several notable fires in modern high-rise buildings such as the First Interstate Bank in Los Angeles, California, and the One Meridian Plaza building in

Philadelphia, Pennsylvania. As a student of the fire service, take the time to research some of these fires; the articles, reports, and other documents are invaluable to you in your studies. See table 7–2.

Fig. 7–22. Fire-resistive constructed hotels will have the greatest amount of compartmentation because the size of the hotel room will limit the fire area. In this photo the space between the block walls will be further reduced by a non-bearing wall sub-dividing the space into two hotel rooms between the block walls.

Noncombustible construction

In **noncombustible construction**, the structural members are of **noncombustible materials** and have little or no fire resistance. The materials are typically structural steel, concrete block, poured concrete, and cold-formed steel structural elements. This class of construction may also be known as **limited combustible construction**. A major difference between fire-resistive construction and noncombustible construction is that in fire-resistive construction the structural steel must always be protected from the fire's heat. During the early stages of construction, you may be unable to determine the class of construction until the fireproofing material is applied to the steel. The collapse hazard of these buildings is due to the lack of structural steel protection. As the structural steel is heated, the steel loses strength; and when the steel member reaches the yield point, it cannot support its load and a collapse occurs (fig. 7–23).

Building Construction

FIREFIGHTER I

Chapter 7

Table 7–2. Fire spread potential of fire-resistive buildings

Fire-resistive buildings' fire spread potential based on occupancy and construction features (by increasing fire spread potential)

1	High-rise hotels	These occupancies have the least fire spread potential. The rooms are typically the smallest fire areas found in any high-rise residential occupancy (fig. 7–22). The wall that separates the hotel room from the corridor and the adjoining rooms usually is a fire separation wall that contains the fire to the hotel room of origin.
2	Mid- and high-rise age-restricted and public housing multiple dwellings	These occupancies contain the smallest square footage of multiple dwelling buildings. Typically, the dwelling unit or fire area is between 800 and 1,400 sq ft (74 and 130 sq m). The walls separating the dwelling unit from the corridor and the other dwelling units are usually concrete block; or they may be other fire-rated walls that create a fire separation wall, containing the fire to the dwelling unit. The greatest threat of fire extension in these buildings is the dwelling unit entry door. If the door is left open when the occupants flee, the fire extends into the corridor. This may prevent other occupants from exiting and create high heat and dense smoke conditions in the corridor, making entry onto the floor by firefighting crews more difficult.
3	Mid- and high-rise multiple dwellings	The dwelling units many range in between approximately 1,000 and 2,000 sq ft (93 and 186 sq m) The fire separations and fire spread risk is the same as described above in #2.
4	Mid- and high-rise luxury multiple dwellings	These buildings and dwelling units have the greatest fire spread potential of all multiple dwelling buildings for two reasons. First, they contain the largest square footage within the dwelling unit. The dwelling unit may be 2,000 to several thousand square feet. Additionally, the dwelling unit may also have two levels, meaning there is an interior stairway that leads to the second floor of the apartment within the apartment. The dwelling unit is separated from the corridor and other dwelling units as described in #2. The two-level dwelling units also have the potential for vertical extension to the second floor within the dwelling unit. In some cases, the only access to the second floor of these dwelling units is via the interior stairway within the dwelling unit. This type of dwelling unit presents many different operational concerns to firefighters.
5	High-rise office buildings	The office occupancy has the greatest potential for fire extension. The fire area is defined by the size of the tenant space. The stairways are separated by fire-rated walls, but the tenant separation walls and the walls that separate the tenant space from the corridor may not be fire rated. If one tenant occupies the entire floor area, the fire may spread throughout the floor.

Fig. 7–23. A one story, non-combustible warehouse under construction. The roof system is supported by unprotected steel columns and bar joist trusses. These buildings are very prone to early collapse as the heat of the fire attacks the steel and the steel reaches its yield point and fails.

Common occupancies and buildings made of noncombustible construction are office buildings up to five or six stories high, large single-story warehouse buildings, and smaller two- and three-story storage buildings, such as the self-storage buildings that have become popular over the past 20 years or so. Noncombustible buildings have a variety of exterior wall systems. The exterior walls may be concrete block. The concrete block wall is not a bearing wall; it is only used as a wall in-filled between steel columns and beams and is a nonbearing wall that supports only itself. Another wall is called a **curtain wall**, because the curtain wall panels hang by attachment to the building's steel structure (fig. 7–24). The curtain walls may be made from various materials, such as concrete slabs that may weigh several tons. Wall panels are constructed of **cold-formed steel studs** to which a gypsum material is applied, followed by a stucco-type finish. The space between the curtain walls is then in-filled with windows or glass mirror panels. Steel panels or steel siding is a common exterior wall material that is often found on warehouse buildings.

Fig. 7–24. This office building is a non-combustible constructed building with a glass curtain wall system. This wall system makes identifying the number of floors in the building extremely difficult if not impossible from the exterior.

Another common wall system on warehouse buildings is a **tilt-slab** wall system (fig. 7–25). These wall systems are dangerous under fire conditions. In most structural systems, the walls or columns support the roof of the building. When a building is constructed with tilt wall systems, a skeleton frame of structural steel is erected. The wall panels (usually equal to the full height of the building) are poured either on- or off-site and delivered to the site to be erected. The panels are supported on the bottom by the building foundation or footing and attached to the steel skeleton frame at the roof level to hold the walls in their vertical position.

If a fire occurs, the connections that attach the walls to the steel frame at the roofline may fail and release the wall panels. *The stability of the walls is dependent on the roof structural system.* These panels are then likely to fall out away from the building, but experience has shown some fall into the building. There is little predictability. These walls will always collapse at a 90° angle. Therefore, firefighters must maintain a proper collapse zone that exceeds 100% of the height of the building when operating at buildings with tilt wall panels.

Typically, the roofs of noncombustible buildings are flat with steel decking supported by steel beams or steel bar joist trusses. The roofing system consists of a rigid or semi-rigid insulating board and some form of membrane roofing material, such as built-up layers of asphalt roofing paper applied with hot tar, or a rubber membrane roof system that is sealed at the seams with an adhesive material. The roofs may be covered with small

stones known as slag that are raked into a layer of hot tar. For a rubber membrane roof, the roof covering may contain larger rounded river stones that range in size from approximately a golf ball to a baseball. The river stones provide ballast to the membrane roof and add weight to the roof.

The lightweight structural systems add steel bar joist roof systems to the collapse dangers associated with tilt wall panels. Such systems make noncombustible buildings some of the most dangerous buildings the firefighter encounters.

Fig. 7–25. Exterior tilt-slab wall of a noncombustible warehouse occupancy. In tilt slab construction, the exterior wall system relies on the roof for support. If a fire causes the roof to collapse, there is a tremendous likelihood that the walls will collapse next.

Ordinary construction

Ordinary construction consists of exterior masonry load-bearing walls and wood joist floors and roof (fig. 7–26). The interior bearing walls may be either wood frame, or, when required, a firewall constructed of masonry. This class of construction may incorporate some type of roof truss. Typically, buildings along old, downtown Main Street USA are made of ordinary construction. These buildings typically range from one to four stories in height.

Fig. 7–26. Ordinary-constructed buildings are made of masonry exterior walls, wood joist floors, and a wood roof structure. When the building has a storefront, the opening for the storefront windows is created with columns and beams. The steel columns and beams may be steel or cast iron. In the photo, the columns and beams support the total weight of the second and third floors, the roof structure, and the weight of the exterior masonry walls. (Courtesy of Christian P. Dansbach)

The term **taxpayer** has been applied to the one- and two-story buildings that line the streets of some older commercial districts; these taxpayers are cheaply constructed ordinary buildings. The "taxpayer" definition can vary among different regions. In some areas, it means a building erected on a property by the property owner for rental purposes, to generate a revenue to pay the property taxes. In others areas, taxpayers are a general classification of mixed-use buildings that contain a business on the first floor and apartments or living spaces on the upper floors.

The modern **strip mall** of retail stores has replaced its ancestor, the taxpayer (distinctive differences between the two are discussed further in chapter 31: Advanced Fire Attack). Strip malls are also often of ordinary construction with lightweight wood roof trusses and concrete block walls (other strip malls that use steel bar joists for roofs and concrete block walls are usually classified as Type II noncombustible construction).

Common uses of occupancies with this type of construction include older multiple dwellings, garden apartments, as well as commercial and manufacturing buildings. Manufacturing occupancies in ordinary-constructed buildings should not be confused with mill or heavy timber buildings. Ordinary-constructed buildings housing manufacturing occupancies usually have fewer square feet and stories than mill or heavy timber buildings.

Ordinary-constructed buildings that require large open floor areas may be constructed with timber truss roofs (fig. 7–27). This construction feature creates a combustible void space where the fire can intensify without being noticed by firefighters. A large volume of fire may be present in the void space created by the trusses, while conditions on the floor below the truss can be habitable with a light smoke condition. Firefighters must be able to recognize this construction feature and operate safely in these buildings. This construction feature may lead to conflicting reports between the interior crews and the roof crew. The roof crew is in a much better position to identify the fire conditions in the truss space; so when conflicting reports arise, the roof report is the better report to judge fire conditions.

Fig. 7–27. Common ordinary-constructed buildings that are constructed with truss roofs include bowling alleys, automobile dealerships, gymnasiums and churches. In this photo, you can identify the strong areas of support in the brick columns built into the exterior walls. (Courtesy of Christian P. Dansbach)

In multistory multiple dwellings, there are several construction features that permit rapid vertical and/or horizontal fire extension. These construction features include light and air shafts, dumbwaiter shafts and vertical openings created by plumbing waste and vent lines, and openings for steel channel rails in larger buildings.

Light and air shafts extend from the roof down through the building and terminate at the first or second floor level. The light and air shafts allow natural light and ventilation into rooms and apartments near the center. The shaft contains windows; if a fire in an apartment on one side of the shaft extends into the shaft, then due to the proximity of the windows in the shaft, the heat may cause the windows to fail and allow the fire and smoke to extend into the nearby apartments. An **open shaft** is open to one side of the building and easily identifiable from that side of the building; a **closed shaft** is enclosed on all sides and cannot be identified from street level. A fire extending in the shaft and showing above the roof may be mistaken for a fire burning through the roof. A report from the roof crew or identification of the shaft from another side of the building is necessary to determine if the fire is through the roof or extending from the light and air shaft.

Vertical fire extension in any building is always a paramount concern to firefighters. The location of the plumbing waste and vent lines in multiple dwellings creates significant potential for vertical fire extension. The buildings are constructed using typical floor plans, placing the bathrooms and kitchens on each floor in line vertically and resulting in the plumbing waste and vent lines serving all the apartments in that line. The openings created to install and maintain these lines produce a void space running the vertical distance of the building from the basement to and through the cockloft to the roof of the building (fig. 7–28).

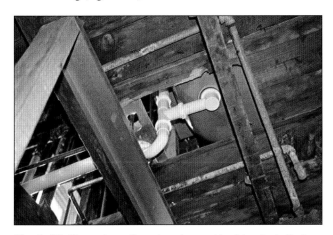

Fig. 7–28. There is no fire-stopping or blocking installed around the bathtub waste line on the floor above. From the floor below, we can see the bottom of the bathtub. Fire that starts or extends to the combustible ceiling/floor space will rapidly extend vertically through the building.

Other structural features in some ordinary-constructed buildings are channel rails, which are used in buildings requiring larger square footage. The channel rails form an interior steel frame that supports the floors of the buildings. To determine if channel rails have been used in the construction of a building, an examination of the unfinished areas of the basement of the building will reveal the channels. The steel columns and horizontal beams are often exposed. The space around the channel rails may create a void space for fire to travel, which is especially concerning if the fire originates in the basement of the building.

Dumbwaiter shafts are another means of rapid vertical fire extension that firefighters should be aware of when operating in ordinary-constructed multiple dwellings. Dumbwaiter shafts contain either a mechanical or a manual lift intended to move material from one floor to another floor so the occupants need not carry materials up and down the stairs. The dumbwaiter shafts open on each floor at varying locations. The opening in the basement or the first floor is in a common area accessible to all the tenants, whereas on the upper floors the opening may be in the public hallway or in the dwelling unit. A small enclosure housing the operating mechanism of the dumbwaiter is located on the roof directly above the shaft.

In many older buildings, dumbwaiters are no longer used and may have been sealed up, concealing the original location of the shaft. The housing on the roof is sometimes removed and the roof sealed over the top of the shaft. The abandoned dumbwaiter shafts have been used over the years to run new building utilities such as new electric wiring, telephone and cable wiring, and even new plumbing lines. The new utilities easily run the shafts because the shafts are void of any fire-stopping, making the utility run of several stories an easy task for the contractor. It is for the same reason that rapid vertical fire extension is possible through the abandoned dumbwaiter shafts. For example, the old dumbwaiter shafts landed in the kitchen of each dwelling unit. The old doors have been removed and a single layer of ½-in. drywall has been secured over the door opening. If a fire occurs in a kitchen on the lower floor and extends into the abandoned dumbwaiter shaft, the fire rapidly extends vertically to the kitchens sharing the shaft as well as the cockloft of the building.

Heavy timber or mill construction

Heavy timber or **mill buildings** were designed and used as manufacturing buildings during the industrial revolution era for the manufacturing of products and goods. These buildings may have changed in use and occupancy or have been renovated during the life of the building, but the underlying support structure remains the same (fig. 7–29). The buildings were constructed of exterior brick walls, wood joisted floors, and massive interior wood columns and beams (more than 5 in. [127 mm] in any dimension).

The buildings have large open floor areas, even up to an entire block long. If the building floor areas are subdivided, they are subdivided by firewalls that separate the floor areas of the building. Openings in the firewalls contain rolling horizontal or roll-up vertical fire doors for protection. The firewalls may be easily identified from the exterior of the building by the protruding brick wall that extends above the roof of the building (fig. 7–30).

Fig. 7–29. A typical floor of a mill or heavy timber building; notice the large cross-section dimensions of the columns and beams, the wide-open area that permitted the movement of goods and materials. This area was also the top floor of the building as evidenced by the rows of skylights that allowed natural light to enter the building. (Courtesy of William P. Dansbach)

Fig. 7–30. Mill buildings may have large open floor areas and firewalls that sub-divide the floor areas of the building. In the photo, you can see the firewalls extending above the roof of the building. Mill buildings typically had many large openable windows to allow for natural light and ventilation. (Courtesy of Courtney A. Dansbach)

The buildings contain large open areas to facilitate the movement of raw materials used in manufacturing products. Multistory buildings contain a large freight elevator used for the movement of the raw materials and finished products. The freight elevator shaft represents significant firefighting challenges. The shaft is open, allowing the rapid vertical movement of smoke and heat as well as vertical fire extension. Firefighters operating

on floors above the fire should identify the open shaft and be aware of rapidly changing conditions. The open elevator shaft also creates a fall potential for firefighters operating in the building. Even simple tasks conducted in light or limited smoke conditions in low lighting can be deadly if a firefighter falls into the shaft.

Through the years as the manufacturing operations have moved out of these buildings, the buildings have been converted to different uses. The newly established uses in these building have changed the hazards faced by firefighters. Common uses include conversion to residential occupancies, mercantile shops and restaurants, and warehousing ranging from large commercial warehouse space to self-storage facilities. In the conversion to residential occupancies, the building layout and arrangement drastically changes as many rooms are constructed and the entrances to the buildings and dwelling units are altered. Additionally, many concealed spaces are created as chase walls, and new ceilings are installed to conceal the various utilities installed to serve the residential occupancy. As with all void spaces, this alteration creates an avenue for fire and smoke to spread through the building (fig. 7–31). This concealment is not permitted by most building codes but still occurs.

Fig. 7–31. In this photo, a mill building is being renovated and a window is being added in the exterior wall. Notice the thickness of the exterior wall, the size of the interior column, beam, and floor joists. The original building had no ceiling other than the underside of the floor above. If during the renovation a ceiling is added under the floor joists (this is not permissible under most building codes), a combustible void space will be created. (Courtesy of William P. Dansbach)

Conversions to warehouse space may present challenges to the building's automatic sprinkler system if the system is not modified to meet the fire load and wall arrangement presented by the new storage occupancy. Failure of the automatic sprinkler system to control the fire requires the firefighters to manually extinguish the fire. The restaurants and mercantile shops mean higher occupant loads where the original designs did not intend occupancy by the general public. Sometimes, the conversion of a mill or heavy timber building may illegally create combustible void spaces. Modifications to such buildings often result in the rearrangement of the exits and access points to the building, and mazelike conditions from the floors of smaller tenant or occupant areas.

Wood-frame construction

This section of the chapter reviews **wood-frame construction**. Four separate and distinct classes define the features, methods, and hazards associated with each class of wood-frame construction. The four classifications of wood-frame construction are as follows: **post-and-beam** or **braced frame**, **balloon frame**, **platform frame**, and **lightweight wood frame**.

Post-and-beam. This is wood-frame construction in which the frame of the structure is formed by vertical wood posts (located at each corner of the building) connected to horizontal beams (located at each floor level) that support the floors (fig. 7–32). The walls between the beams are vertically filled in by 2 × 4 wood studs. This method of construction uses **mortise and tenon connections** to connect the beams to the posts and the floor joists to the beams.

Fig. 7–32. This photo details a post and beam building. Notice the vertical post at the corners and the horizontal beams at the floor level. (Courtesy of Tim Hetzel)

A mortise and tenon connection consists of tenon (tongue) cut onto the end of the beam that is inserted into the mortise (hole) cut into the post (figs. 7–33 and 7–34). This type of connection removes a significant amount of the cross-section value or mass of the structural members. Up to two-thirds of the beam's mass may be removed to create the tenon. As with any wood structural member, fire resistance and collapse resistance is a function of mass. Simply put, how much wood is there to burn before collapse occurs? The more wood the more burn time before collapse occurs. The mortise and tenon connection at each floor level makes post and beam construction susceptible to an **inward** or **outward collapse** when the first floor of the building is involved in fire. When the mortise and tenon connection at the first-floor ceiling level and second floor's floor is attacked by fire and can no longer support the weight of the floor or floors above, an inward or outward collapse occurs.

Fig. 7–33. This photo details the mortise and tenon connection where the post is connected to the beam, the connection is secured with dowel-like pegs called *trunnels.* The mortise and tenon connection is the weakest point in the framing system as 2/3 of the mass is removed from the beam and 1/3 of the mass is removed from the post to create the connection. (Courtesy of Tim Hetzel)

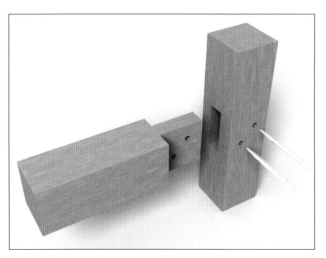

Fig. 7–34. This diagram details how a mortise and tenon connection is constructed. Notice the amount of mass removed from the beam to create the tenon. This makes this part of the connection the weak point in this connection. A wood peg or trunnel is driven into holes to secure the connection.

Fig. 7–35. In a building that is balloon framed, the exterior wall studs run from the basement to the attic without fire stopping. This photo looks up the wall as it passes the second floor joists; note the lack of fire stopping and the ease with which the duct work was run in the wall. This vertical void space becomes a chimney for the fire to travel from the basement to the attic.

Balloon-frame. Balloon-frame construction was a method employed from the mid-1880s to World War II. This type of construction employed the use of 2 × 4 wood framing members for the exterior and interior walls. The major fire problem with this type of construction is that the exterior wood stud walls are supported in the basement on the foundation plate, and the opening between the stud bays is an open vertical channel. The studs extend the full height of the exterior wall, terminating in the attic or top floor of the building (fig. 7–35). The void created by each stud bay allows for rapid vertical fire extension, especially when the fire originates in the basement (fig. 7–36). As a fire starts and continues to grow, two basic laws of physics create conditions for this rapid fire extension: The heat produced by the fire is more buoyant that the surrounding air; and whenever there is an increase in temperature in a confined room or space such as a basement, pressure increases. These factors allow the heated products of combustion, which are naturally rising to the ceiling, to be forced up through the void spaces created by the balloon framing and result in rapid vertical fire extension. Additional void spaces are found in balloon framing. Both load bearing and nonbearing interior walls may be balloon frame. Since the point in the framing system where the floor joists connect to the exterior and interior walls is not fire-stopped, this opening allows any fire running vertically in a wall to travel the horizontal concealed space created by the flooring and the interior finish applied as a ceiling.

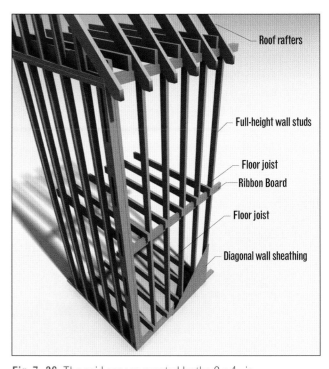

Fig. 7–36. The void spaces created by the 2 x 4–in. (51 x 102–mm) wood studs that run from the basement to the attic. These void spaces result in rapid vertical fire extension.

Platform frame. This method was introduced in the post–World War II construction boom and is still employed today. Traditional platform-frame construction used dimensional lumber such as the 2 × 4–in. (51 × 102–mm) for the interior and exterior frame walls, 2 × 8–in. (51 × 203–mm) for the floor joists, and at least 2 × 6–in. (51 × 152–mm) for the roof rafters. This construction method greatly differs from balloon frame in that the buildings are constructed one story at a time, so the construction method provides **inherent fire-stopping**. After the foundation is completed, the first floor framing is erected and the floor joists extend to the outer edge of the foundation. The subfloor is laid on top of the floor joists, completing the first-floor system. The next step constructs one story of 2 × 4–in. (51 × 102–mm) walls, a bottom 2 × 4–in. (51 × 102–mm) plate is laid horizontally on the subfloor, the walls are erected, and a double 2 × 4–in. (51 × 102–mm) top plate is run horizontally at the top of the first story of studs. This method is employed for interior and exterior walls. The floor of the next story is then constructed on the top of the first floor framing system, extending to the outer edge of the exterior wall framing. Each subsequent floor is constructed in the same manner (fig. 7–37). This framing method therefore provides inherent fire stopping because this construction method has eliminated combustible void spaces that penetrate the floors (fig. 7–38). An area of concern for firefighters is where building utilities (e.g., plumbing drain and vent pipes, HVAC ducts, and electric and communication cable) are run through the floors and walls. The installation of these utilities often results in removing parts of inherent fire stopping in the form of the top and bottom framing plates to run the various utilities. An avenue of fire extension from one floor to the floors above is created if the utility runs are not properly fire-stopped after the installation of the utilities. Experience has shown that in most instances, these penetrations are not properly fire-stopped. Firefighters may identify areas of potential vertical fire extension by locating vent pipes that penetrate the roof and subsequent vertical locations down through the building where fire extension is likely.

The interior finish of a platform-frame building is likely to be some form of drywall or gypsum material. In the beginning years of platform-frame construction, a material known as **rock lath** was used as the interior finish material. The rock lath was a gypsum board material, 16 in.- (406 mm-) to 2 ft- (0.6 m-) wide boards that had holes every couple of inches. The rock lath was installed on the walls and ceilings, and one or more coats of plaster were applied to the rock lath to complete the interior finish. This material, or a form of this material, may still be found in homes where the owner or designer prefers a plaster interior wall finish. There are many different types of drywall installed in wood-frame buildings. The most common form of drywall installed in dwellings is easily breached and removed by firefighters.

Fig. 7–37. In a building constructed of platform-frame construction, each story is built on top of the floor below. Notice the floor joists of the first and second floors extend to the outer edge of the framing, creating inherent fire stopping. (Courtesy of Robert Moran)

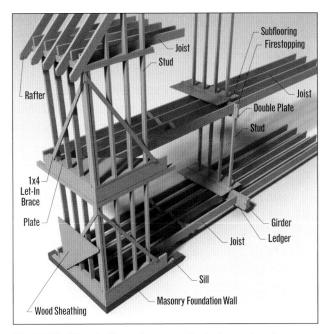

Fig. 7–38. The platform-frame method of construction. Note the inherent firestopping built into the building when one floor and one story of walls are constructed at a time.

Lightweight wood-frame construction. This is any wood-frame construction using lightweight engineered structural components, including lightweight parallel floor trusses, lightweight peaked-roof trusses, and engineered wood I-beams (fig. 7–39). These structural components have been used in the construction industry since the late 1960s; but the proliferation of townhouse and condominium construction in the 1980s saw a tremendous use of lightweight wood structural components. This will continue as the construction industry seeks ways to build more efficiently and economically (but not more fire safe), and natural resources such as wood becomes less available. These structural components have been engineered to carry the greatest load over the greatest span using the least amount of material necessary to carry the imposed load.

The connections in trusses make them dangerous under fire conditions. The trusses are connected with a steel gusset plate that only penetrates the wood between ⅜ and ½ in. The heat from the fire is conducted into the wood through the steel gusset plate and begins to decompose the wood fibers, which affect the connection's strength. Additionally, the steel gusset plate will be deformed and may warp from the heat of the fire, pulling out of the wood truss, and causing the connection and possibly the entire truss to fail (fig. 7–40).

The engineered wood I-beams are constructed of manufactured lumber; the top and bottom chord are laminated plies of lumber that create the top and bottom flange. The web of the beam is OSB, which begins to fail when exposed to the fire's heat as the resins and glues vaporize and allow chips of wood in the OSB to delaminate. From the exterior, a lightweight wood-frame building may be difficult to identify, because the exterior may appear as any other wood-frame building. Lightweight wood-frame buildings are constructed in the same manner as platform-frame buildings: one story at a time. The major difference that makes these buildings so prone to early collapse and so dangerous to firefighter is the use of lightweight wood, parallel-chord floor trusses, and peaked-roof trusses. Using these elements creates numerous combustible void spaces that can be large; there the fire can extend, grow, and destroy the structural support of the floor or roof system.

Most wood-frame buildings have an exterior siding of wood, aluminum, vinyl, composite hardboard or stucco, brick veneer, or another form of a **cementitious** finish. Many older wood-frame buildings may have **asphalt siding** (essentially, thin asphalt shingles that often look like bricks), sometime referred to as **gasoline siding** because of the combustibility and rapid fire development, which occurs over the surface of the siding. In closely built neighborhoods, fires involving this type of siding have been responsible for fire extension to the exposures. Often, the asphalt siding has been sided over with a more modern siding material. This can be a hazard when the fire extends to the siding material and the newly installed material burns away, exposing and igniting the asphalt siding.

Fig. 7–39. This photo details the many combustible void spaces that will be found in buildings constructed with lightweight parallel-chord floor trusses and peaked-roof trusses. Note the floor system in the center public corridor is a different floor system and may be dimensional lumber such as 2 x 8–in. (51 x 203–mm) floor joists which are attached to the ends of the floor trusses and separates the floor systems on each side of the public corridor. (Courtesy of Courtney A. Dansbach)

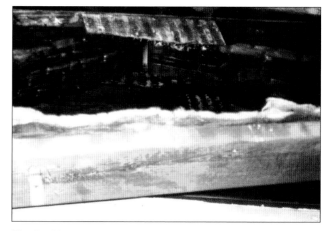

Fig. 7–40. The lack of penetration of the teeth on the gusset plate allows it to warp and twist out of the truss. Loss of strength in the connection will lead to the failure of the truss.

Building alterations

Many buildings are altered at one time or another. In many cases, buildings have been renovated more than once, and each renovation increases the potential for hazards to firefighters. Common firefighting problems created by renovations include the creation of combustible void spaces, changes to the structural hierarchy of the building, overloaded structure, and changes to the exterior of the building. A common practice during renovation is to create combustible void spaces by lowering ceilings, furring out walls to facilitate the installation of building utilities from floor to floor, and the creation of combustible void soffits to facilitate the installation of buildings utilities horizontally through the structure (figs. 7–41 and 7–42).

Changes to the structural hierarchy of the building often result when the building is renovated (fig. 7–43). The removal of bearing walls or columns and replacement of the bearing walls and columns with other load-carrying components may result in a design incapable of carrying the load brought to bear on the new structural member. A common renovation involved removing a masonry load-bearing wall from the first floor of a multistory ordinary-constructed building and replacing it with a series of columns and beams to support the load of the floors and walls above. The new columns and steel beams may not be capable of supporting the load if a fire occurs, and the steel beams and columns are affected by the heat from the fire. Failure of the columns and beams in this situation may cause the bearing wall and the floors and roof it supports to collapse.

Fig. 7–42. A dropped ceiling of 2 x 4s and drywall has been constructed below the original plaster and lathe ceiling. When checking for fire extension, firefighters must recognize this feature and continue to open the ceilings until they have exposed the underside of the floor or roof above. In this photo, the task was not completed as only the dropped ceiling has been removed leaving the plaster and lathe ceiling intact.

Fig. 7–43. A building in which the first floor exterior masonry wall has been removed and set back into the building from its original location. This renovation has changed structural support of the second floor and roof and the second-floor brick exterior wall. These components of the building had been supported by a masonry wall and are now supported by steel columns and beams. This renovation has changed the structural hierarchy of the building and has changed the collapse potential of the wall. The steel beam will be heated and may fail much sooner than the original masonry wall.

Fig. 7–41. A kitchen renovation that results in the creation of combustible void spaces when the framing for the cabinet soffit has been installed without first installing drywall on the wall and ceiling behind the soffit. Should the fire extend into the combustible void space created by the soffit, the fire will extend horizontally throughout the soffit and vertically in any non-fire-stopped void spaces in the wood framing.

NEW TECHNOLOGY IN BUILDING CONSTRUCTION

One of the greatest challenges facing the fire service is the technological advances in the construction materials. The changes are the result of less raw material being readily available such as lumber and steel; the economic desire to construct more cost-effective buildings, lighter materials, and man-made materials have reduced the cost by decreasing the time to complete a given part of the building.

The advancements in building construction and materials technology have come at great cost to the fire service (fig. 7–44). The changes in construction materials have generally resulted in use of lightweight structural elements in the construction of buildings since the mid-1970s. Materials and structural components, such as lightweight wooden floor and roof trusses, mean a developer can expend less material to support existing loads using structural members capable of spanning greater distances than standard dimensional lumber. This is an example where math, the engineering of wood trusses, has replaced mass, the amount of wood in dimensional lumber (a 2 × 10–in. [52 × 254–mm] floor joist). Using or adding engineered structural components to the buildings has resulted in a considerably reduced period of safe operating in these buildings during firefighting operations.

Fig. 7–44. The lack of quality control has lead to the truss being delivered to the construction site with one entire row of the connecting teeth of the gusset plate not being secured into any part of the wood truss. The heat from a fire will quickly attack these connections; this connection being less secure than the remaining gusset plates is likely to fail very early in the fire.

Another example of new material is the increased use of OSB (previously discussed); OSB is used in place of plywood in many applications such as exterior wall sheathing on wood-frame buildings. OSB is also used as a web member in wooden I-beams, which have replaced standard dimensional lumber in most wood-frame buildings as floor joists and roof rafters. The fire hazard of wood I-beams is again the lack of mass to the structural member. The OSB web of the wooden I-beam of at least 1½ in. (38 mm) is only ⅜ in. (10 mm) thick; compare to a 2 × 10–in. (52 × 254–mm) joist that has a nominal thickness. This results in a difference of 1⅛ in. (29 mm) in the mass of the structural member. Another factor affecting the burn time is the use of adhesive or bonding agents in the production of the OSB. These bonding agents are typically resins and wax; the greater part of the components are resins, and the wax is added to provide a degree of water resistance to the material. When the OSB that is the web of a wood I-beam is exposed to the heat, the resins and wax vaporize; as the materials vaporize, the OSB begins to degrade, delaminate, and lose structural integrity and the resins and wax add fuel to the fire. There are many documented cases where the collapse of lightweight wood floor and roof systems have killed and injured firefighters.

Another example of building designers using less and lightweight materials in Type II buildings is the replacement of steel I-beams with lightweight steel trusses (also known as **steel bar joists**). Trusses are examples of math replacing mass: geometric shapes in the truss design are mainly responsible for the support of a given load. The replacement of steel I-beams with trusses produces a building that is lighter weight. The structure's footings need not support the load of the steel I-beams, only the weight of the trusses.

Many advancements have been made in the manufacture of **gypsum board** or **drywall**. For many years, all-purpose, moisture-resistant, and fire-rated drywall were the most common types a firefighter would encounter. These types of drywall were easily opened up or removed when used in the building. Fire-rated assemblies that employ multiple layers of drywall to construct a fire-rated assembly require significant effort to breach or open up. Drywall is now available that has been reinforced with materials that make it difficult or impossible for firefighters to breach or remove the walls. **Impact-resistant drywall** is manufactured with fiberglass and other materials that make the finish of the drywall harder and therefore more difficult to open or breach. Drywall manufacturers also laminate drywall with other materials such as OSB or sheets of Lexan® plastic to make the drywall impenetrable. These different types of drywall may be found in various occupancy types. Impact-resistant drywall is found in schools and other locations, where durability of the wall is desired, and the use of impact-resistant drywall may also reduce cost by replacing a concrete block wall with a steel stud wall with impact-resistant drywall as the interior finish. **Laminated drywall** may be found on the walls of high-value occupancies such as jewelry stores in malls to prevent unauthorized entry into the occupancy by breaching the walls. Laminated drywall may be found in any location where security is a concern to the owner or occupant. Firefighters should be aware of occupancies that have been constructed with these types of drywall, because opening or breaching walls with these types may be difficult or impossible.

The exterior finishes on many recently constructed buildings appear to be a stucco or cement plaster finish, when in fact the exterior wall finish is a system known as an **exterior insulation and finish systems (EIFS)**. These appear to be typical cement plaster finishes used as an exterior finish material for many years. The EIFS is a lightweight synthetic wall cladding that includes foam plastic insulation and thin synthetic coatings that produce a finish that appears to be a stucco finish. The EIFS may be installed over a concrete block wall or over-sheathing that has been applied to wood or steel studs. The application of any stucco-like wall finish makes identifying the type of construction more difficult from the exterior of the building. The foam component in the exterior wall system is likely to be combustible; and should the fire extend to or involve the wall system, firefighters may be faced with a challenging fire because it may extend through the wall system and require significant overhauling to be controlled and extinguished.

Another part of the building that has seen changes is the roof covering. For many years, flat roofs were covered with a **built-up roof** covering. Built-up roofs employed a fiberboard insulation panel, a base sheet of roofing materials and several layers or roofing felt (paper). The roof felt is applied and lapped over each other to provide multiple plies of roofing. The roofing felt was applied by hot asphalt tar mopped out onto the roof surface and then was rolled out into the hot asphalt. More recent roofing materials include synthetic rubber membrane that provides a watertight roof covering. One form of the synthetic roof coverings is an EPDM (ethylene propylene diene M-class) rubber. The seams in the rubber membrane are sealed with a flammable adhesive.

The roof covering may be fully adhered to the roof, held in place by **mechanical fastening**, or covered with stone to act as ballast to prevent the roofing material from lifting in high winds (fig. 7–45). Firefighters may have to remove the ballast stones to access the roof covering. Additionally, the ballast stone will add a significant weight to the roof structure.

Firefighters should be constantly aware of changes in construction materials and methods. They should also know how these changes affect firefighting in the building as they conduct pre-incident inspections of buildings under construction or renovation in their jurisdiction.

Fig. 7–45. The ballast stones are placed on the roof to prevent the roof covering from lifting and are not secured to the roof. These stones make footing on these roofs difficult. The stones also add weight to the roof structure and create surface tension that slows down the drainage capability of the roof.

INDICATORS OF COLLAPSE

FFI 5.3.12 FFII 6.3.2 An important aspect of the study of building construction is to understand the indicators of collapse and the collapse potential of the various types and forms of construction. There are numerous visual indicators (identified in the following text) of an impending collapse that could cause failure of a building or part of a building. Sounds—creaking or moaning of the building—are also signs of impending collapse. In all cases, immediately report these indicators to your superior officer; rapid evacuation is usually crucial.

Major collapses at fires are uncommon, but firefighters must be aware of the smaller, more localized collapse, which can be just as deadly. Table 7–3 details some of the collapse indicators and collapse potential based on the construction type or building component.

When a building or part of a building is in danger of collapse, **collapse zones** must be established and all firefighters must remain clear of these zones. Each collapse zone has a height and width; the height of the building, or part of the building in danger of collapse, must be transferred horizontally to the ground. The collapse zone away from the building must be at least the height of the building or part of the building in danger of collapse plus a **safety factor**. The safety factor is necessary because parts of the building may bounce outward when they hit the ground (such as bricks). Because measuring the height of the building and subsequent transfer of that dimension to the ground is an estimation, always add or estimate on the high side. Policies on establishing collapse zones may vary slightly from department to department, but the policies must always include a safety factor. The safety factor should be calculated by adding several feet, an additional story, or even as much as an additional 50% to the estimated height of the building. The collapse zone must also include the width of the building or part of the building in danger of collapse; a safety factor should also be added to this distance or dimension (fig. 7–46). Firefighters should know their department's policies and procedures for the establishment of and maintaining collapse zones.

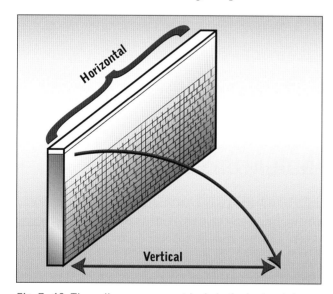

Fig. 7–46. The collapse zone must include the horizontal width of the wall and the height of the wall plus a safety factor.

There are three basic types of collapses that firefighters should understand. A **tent-type** and a **lean-to type** collapse leave void spaces in the aftermath of the collapse, where building occupants who may have survived the collapse may be located. The third type of collapse is a **pancake-type** collapse. (These types of collapses are covered in greater detail in chapter 35: Support of

Technical Rescue Teams.) The pancake-type collapse leaves little if any void space for the occupant to survive the collapse.

A paramount concern to firefighters operating at any collapse incident is the potential for **secondary collapse**. Initial fire department operations at any collapse incident should be limited to the following: size-up, removing occupants from known locations that do not require technical expertise, incident stabilization, such as securing utilities from a safe location, and evacuation of adjoining structures. Firefighters operating at collapse incidents that require structural shoring or entry into collapsed areas of the structure should only operate under the direct supervision of fire officers specifically trained in collapse rescue.

RECOMMENDED STUDIES

This chapter begins your study of building construction. Each firefighter must continue to study building construction by a variety of means. Consider continuing your education by attending formal training classes on building construction, conducting walk-through drills of buildings under construction or renovation in your jurisdiction, or in other ways. During the walk-through drill you can (with the owner's or contractor's permission) take a series of digital photos, which can be made into a PowerPoint presentation. This type of presentation can be viewed during company drills and will reveal parts of the building that are no longer visible once it is completed. This serves as a refresher to some firefighters and is an invaluable tool to future generations of firefighters serving your department.

Building construction can be somewhat geographic; firefighters should constantly be aware of new trends in construction methods and materials being used in your response area. Strive to understand how these methods and materials react under fire conditions. When you experience a fire with an unusual outcome or occurrence, share this information as soon as possible with other firefighters in your department, your surrounding departments, and throughout the country. This is one benefit of the Internet! Study fire incident reports that are published regarding major fire incidents, particularly those involving building collapse and serious firefighter injuries and deaths. These reports contain valuable information regarding construction features that may have affected the incident as well as lessons learned from the incident. Each firefighter should seek to understand these lessons learned to become a safer and better firefighter. The funny thing about building construction is that the more you learn, the more you realize there is more to learn!

Table 7–3. Indicators of collapse

Construction type, building component, or feature	Collapse indicator or collapse potential
Wood-frame buildings	Sagging roofs and leaning exterior walls are indicators of collapse.
Wood-frame buildings constructed with lightweight structural components	Fire burning in the void space created by the floor or roof assemblies presents the real potential of collapse.
Freestanding masonry parapet walls	Any masonry parapet wall that is exposed to heavy fire conditions or in which the surrounding roof has burned away or any parapet wall that is out of plumb is in danger of collapse.
Ordinary-constructed building with a heavy timber truss roof	Collapse is a danger when fire is in the truss loft or where the truss has been exposed to fire. Buildings in which the truss loft is a concealed space are dangerous because the true fire conditions are concealed from the firefighters by the ceiling material.
Noncombustible-constructed buildings with a steel bar joist roof system	Steel bar joists are susceptible to collapse even after short-term exposure to fire; they have poor surface-to-mass ratio, and the heat from the fire causes the steel to reach its yield point after short exposure to fire conditions.
Ordinary-constructed flat-roof buildings with rafters of dimensional lumber	This roof system creates a redundant support system and will sustain fire conditions for a significant period of time. When the roof does fail it may do so slowly, and the initial collapse is not easily noticed by firefighters operating on the roof. Indicators of collapse for this type of roof include plumbing vent pipes that start to grow or extend up or reveal what appears to be fresh tar or roof cement around the pipe or areas along the parapet walls that appear to have fresh tar or roof cement.
Walls, floors, and roofs of all buildings	Any wall that appears to be out of plumb is in danger of collapse. Sagging floors or roofs are also indicators of collapse.
Chimneys	A chimney where the adjoining wall or roof has burned away should be considered in danger of collapse. The adjoining wall or roof provides lateral support for the chimney; and when the adjoining wall or roof burns away, the chimney is unsupported for a greater vertical distance.
Wood-frame, ordinary, and noncombustible-constructed buildings	When these buildings become well-involved in fire and the fire has taken hold of multiple floors, they are in danger of a major collapse.

QUESTIONS

1. What are examples of undesigned loads with regards to building construction?

2. Describe the main differences between live loads and dead loads.

3. A balcony that is supported at only one end is a(n) _____.

4. Many structural columns that support roofs and floors are made of cast iron. When under a fire load, what happens to these columns?

5. In building construction, what are I-beams mostly used for?

6. Describe the factors that affect structural stability of buildings?

7. NFPA _____ groups buildings into five classes.

8. Briefly describe each of the classes of buildings.

9. What is the main reason for center core floor plans in high-rise buildings?

10. Tilt wall construction poses safety hazards for firefighters when they are under fire conditions. Describe how the construction works and the safety hazards that exist.

11. Name the four classifications of wood-frame construction and describe them.

12. What is the significance of balloon frame construction in fire suppression strategy?

Ropes and Knots

by Mark A. Sulcov

This chapter provides required knowledge items for the following
NFPA Standard 1001 Job Performance Requirements:

FFI 5.3.20

FFI 5.5.1

FFII 6.5.4

This chapter contains Skill Drills. When you see this icon, refer to your Skill Drill book for step-by-step instructions.

OBJECTIVES

Upon completion of this chapter, you should be able to do the following:

- Identify the materials fire service rope is made from
- Identify and describe the terms and parts of the rope when tying knots
- Identify the basic knots used in the fire service
- Describe and demonstrate the methods used to tie fire service knots and what their primary uses are
- Describe the inspection process of ropes, how to maintain them, and the standard methods of storing them
- Recognize the difference between life safety ropes and utility lines
- Identify methods used to secure and hoist various fire service tools and equipment
- Understand why fire service rope is downgraded and/or put out of service

INTRODUCTION

Rope work is a very important part of the fire service. The firefighter needs to understand the importance of rope selection based on construction, strength, and what it will be used for. The firefighter also needs to understand the basic elements of knots; how to tie knots for fire service use; and the proper inspection methods, storage, and maintenance procedures for ropes.

It is important to note that knots can be tied in more than one way. This chapter provides specific ways to tie knots; your instructor may show you other ways to tie a particular knot. For example, being left-handed or being right-handed affects the way people tie knots. With practice, you may be able to tie a knot with your left or right hand. In addition, people who are left-handed will take this as a personal challenge. Relate this to having more tools in your tool box. There are many tools that do the same job, but do the job differently. In your career, you will find that there is no one tool that fits all situations. Have a selection available.

ROPE MATERIALS AND CONSTRUCTION

Rope is made from either natural or synthetic material. Each has different characteristics that affect their use in the fire service (table 8–1). The first ropes used by humans, made of natural fibers such as live vines, were used to construct rope bridges. In the fire service, the natural fiber material first used was manila hemp (essentially dead vines).

Natural fiber ropes were in service in fire departments until the 1980s, when they were replaced by synthetic materials (fig. 8–1). In addition, a disastrous, fatal firefighting rope rescue failure in New York City in 1980 focused attention on fire service ropes and the need for a national standard on their design and use. In 1982, the National Fire Protection Association (NFPA) began the process of developing a standard that was first issued in 1985 and is known today as NFPA 1983, *Standard on Life Safety Rope and Equipment for Emergency Services.* It covers ropes and their uses, that is, life safety versus utility, harnesses, and hardware.

Natural materials

There are three basic natural materials that are used for rope: manila, cotton, and sisal. All of the natural ropes suffer from the same problems:

- Mildew
- Rot
- Deterioration
- Poor **abrasion** resistance
- Size-to-strength ability (natural fiber rope needs to be thicker to be stronger)
- Little predictability in terms of expected strength

Fig. 8–1. Natural fiber rope is made from organic materials and isn't generally used for fire or rescue purposes.

Manila. Manila rope is made from fibers from plants. These small fibers are twisted together (not knotted) to form longer fibers. The twisting of the fibers creates longer and longer strands that are then twisted with more strands to make the natural fiber rope. There is a definite relationship of size (diameter) to strength. The thicker the rope, the stronger it is.

Note: When looking at manila fiber rope, you can see numerous fiber ends sticking up out of the rope. These are the fiber ends that are exposed or have broken due to either stress on the rope or abrasion.

Cotton. Cotton rope is made with the same cotton seed fibers that cotton thread is spun from. Because of the very short cotton fibers, the rope is soft and pliable, but this results in very low strength and makes the rope susceptible to damage by abrasion.

Sisal. Sisal is another natural fiber that comes from plants. It is a very weak fiber that has less strength than cotton. Thus it is only used to make very small diameter rope. Cotton and sisal fiber ropes are used less today in the fire service because of the emergence and widespread acceptance of synthetic fiber ropes.

Table 8–1. Rope material characteristics

	Manila	Polypropylene	Polyethylene	Nylon	Polyester
Loss of strength, °F (°C)	180 (82)	200 (93)	230 (110)	300 (149)	300 (149)
Melting or charring temperature, °F (°C)	375 (191)	275–300 (135–149)	285 (141)	400–500 (204–260)	450–650 (232–343)
Loss of strength when wet	50%	0	0	25%	Minimal
Float	No	Yes	Yes	No	
Acid resistance	None	High	High	Low	Limited
Elongation under loads	Yes			Yes	Low

Natural material ropes are not used for *life-saving* purposes—they are never used to support a human being. When used, they are used for *utility* purposes only. Downgraded life safety rope should be labeled as utility rope.

Synthetic materials

The most widely used synthetic materials in the manufacturing of ropes are nylon, polyester, polypropylene, and polyethylene (fig. 8–2). These materials have excellent resistance to rot and mildew. Deterioration due to age is not considered a factor. Synthetic ropes are also more resistant to physical and abrasion damage, but are still susceptible to damage/destruction from the heat of a fire. The biggest advantage of synthetic materials is that, because they are manufactured, each fiber is the same and so are their properties. Each continuous fiber of the same length is just as strong as the others. In contrast, natural fiber is made up of short pieces, and thus it is weaker. This increased strength factor makes synthetic fiber rope preferable for fire service use.

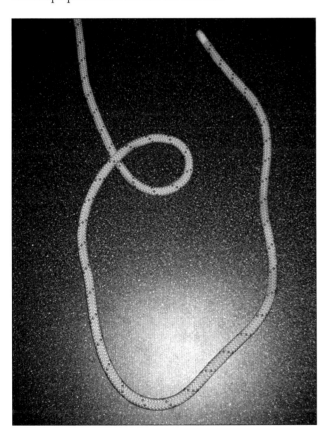

Fig. 8–2. Synthetic rope is used in a wide variety of applications in the fire service, including technical rescue.

Nylon. Nylon was invented in the 1930s by the Dupont Corporation. First used to make stockings for women, nylon was used during World War II for parachutes and

cords due to the shortage of raw materials. One nylon strand is called a **filament**. Rope is made from multifilament lines, either twisted into strands or covered with sheathing. The biggest disadvantage with nylon is that it is damaged by acids.

Polyester. Polyester material, unlike nylon, is resistant to most acids. Polyester also has relatively low stretch under a load, but does not hold up well if a shock load is encountered.

Polypropylene. **Polypropylene rope** is primarily used for water applications, that is, water rescue or any area with a high degree of moisture, because of its ability to float. Polypropylene also resists rot and mildew and has a strong tolerance to chemicals and acids. Polypropylene will break down easily from sunlight, heavy loads, and abrasion.

Polyethylene. **Polyethylene rope** is nearly identical to polypropylene, also floats, and comes in many colors. It is weaker and stiffer than polypropylene, but does have better abrasion resistance.

Construction

There are two types of rope used in life safety applications: dynamic and static. **Dynamic rope** is high stretch and very flexible. It is used mostly in rock climbing to absorb falls and put less stress on the anchoring system. **Static rope** is low stretch and is used in most fire department applications, namely, rescue, hauling, and rappelling. It has very little stretch.

Laid (twisted) rope. The laid or twisted method of construction is for natural or synthetic fiber rope. The yarn is twisted into strands, and the strands—typically three—are twisted together to make the rope (fig. 8–3).

Fig. 8–3. Laid or twisted rope construction involves the twisting of three strands of natural or synthetic rope.

Note: The quality of the fiber and the tightness of the twist determine the specific strength of a particular rope. A twisted rope leaves the three strands exposed to all the elements, leaving it open to damage, especially by abrasion. You can easily inspect twisted rope by looking at all surfaces for cuts and abrasions; chemical damage; or embedded dirt, metal, or glass pieces. **Laid rope** can be easily twisted back to expose the inside area and checked for debris that can damage the rope. If any damage is found, the rope should be taken out of service.

Braided. Braided ropes are made from natural and synthetic fibers. The most common and the only one the fire service will use is made from synthetic fibers. The rope is made by braiding the strands together uniformly, just like braiding hair. Braided rope reduces twisting when used for rappelling. The rope is very smooth to the touch, but like laid rope, the majority of the fibers are exposed and subject to damage (fig. 8–4).

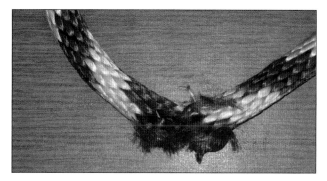

Fig. 8–4. Braided rope is commonly found in synthetic rope used by the fire service. A drawback of this type of rope is that all strands are exposed to damage from abrasion.

Braid-on-braid. Braid-on-braid is constructed by covering a braided rope with another braid (some manufacturers call this *jacketed*). The outer braid usually has a distinctive design pattern (fig. 8–5). This type of rope is very soft, and just like braided, it has the same poor characteristics. The inspection process for braided and braid-on-braid is mostly the same. We should look for cuts, abrasions, or excessive picks (fuzz) or deformities in the rope (soft spots). In braid-on-braid, we must also look for sliding of the inner and outer braid. If this is found, the rope must be taken out of service.

Fig. 8–5. Braid-on-braid rope has many of the same drawbacks as simple braided rope, except that the outer core creates a protective "jacket" for the rope.

Kernmantle. **Kernmantle rope** is composed of two sections: The *kern* is defined as the inner core of the rope, and the *mantle* is the outer cover. There are three types of kerns: twisted, braided, and continuous filament fiber. The first two types create dynamic rope, and the continuous filament fiber creates static rope. To put it simply, the mantle is a tightly woven outer shell that protects the kern. In all cases, the kern carries the majority of the load (strength), normally 75%–80%. The strength of the mantle is 20%–25%. This type of rope is primarily for life rescue (fig. 8–6).

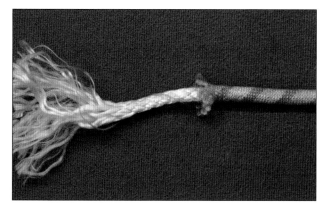

Fig. 8–6. Kernmantle rope is the most common fire service rope since it is designed for life safety operations.

Webbing. **Webbing** is not really rope, but rather woven fabric that is either flat or tubular (fig. 8–7). It is often used for slings and anchoring. Some firefighters carry small-width webbing instead of personal rope. Webbing can be used to aid in securing loads, dragging trapped people, and lowering loads. One of the advantages of webbing is that it loses very little of its strength when bent correctly around a carabiner.

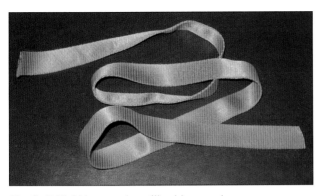

Fig. 8–7. Webbing can be utilized in complex rescue rigging arrangements or carried by firefighters to aid in maneuvering hoselines or carrying tools.

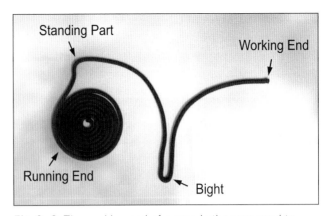

Fig. 8–8. The working end of a rope is the area used to tie a knot, while the running end is used for hoisting and pulling.

ROPE NOMENCLATURE

Primarily rope falls into two categories, utility and life safety. Utility rope is used for such tasks as hoisting and lowering of tools, securing objects, and many other nonemergency uses. Rope used for search and rescue and other non-life-threatening uses also does not fall into the life safety category. Note that these are normally **downgraded** life safety ropes and need to be marked accordingly and stored in a compartment remote from any life safety rope.

Before we can start tying knots, we must first understand what the different parts of the rope are called and what makes up a knot. First, the rope itself can be divided into three sections:

- **Working end.** This is the part of the rope that is used to tie the knot (fig. 8–8).

- **Standing part.** This part of the rope can be above or below the knot, but must be between the knot and the remainder of the rope.

- **Running end.** This is the rest of the rope used for the work of the rope such as hoisting, pulling, and so forth.

Elements of a knot

For a knot to be used in the fire service, the knot must be easy for you to tie and untie while wearing firefighter gloves. This is where repetition and practice come into play. Someone may be able to show you a knot and how to tie it. But you must practice. No one else can learn it for you.

A **bight** is made by bringing the rope back along itself side by side. A **loop** is made by placing a twist in the rope and having the standing part of the rope continue in the same direction. A **round turn** is made by making a loop and then having the standing part go back in the direction from which it came.

KNOT TYPES AND USES

FFI 5.3.20 The fire service family of knots consists of the overhand (also known as a safety), half hitch, clove hitch (open and closed), becket bend, bowline, figure eight, figure eight on a bight, figure eight follow-through, water, and handcuff. The tying instructions for these knots are located in your Skill Drill book.

Note: In the emergency services, there are numerous ways to tie various knots. The tying instructions in your Skill Drill book are only demonstrating one way. This should not stop you from learning other ways to tie knots. Try to think of it as putting another tool into your tool box, thus having a selection of ways to accomplish the same goal no matter what obstacle is in your way.

Overhand (safety) knot. This is used as a backup to the primary knot. The overhand knot prevents the loose end of the rope from walking out of the primary knot, so that it does not untie (fig. 8–9).

Fig. 8–9. An overhand safety knot is used to provide a margin of safety with other knots.

Half hitch. Always used in conjunction with another knot, the half hitch is effective at securing and hoisting long tools, such as a pike pole. The half hitch keeps the tool stabilized as it is lifted to an upper floor window (fig. 8–10).

Fig. 8–10. A half hitch being used to hoist an axe

Clove hitch (open). Basically, the clove hitch is two half hitch knots. The clove hitch secures tools or posts with the hitch, using the open end of the rope (fig. 8–11a).

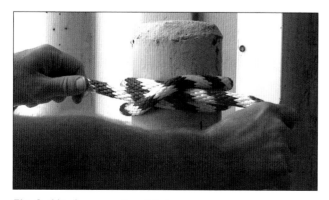

Fig. 8–11a. An open clove hitch

Clove hitch (closed) knot. This is the same as the open version, but used when there is no open end of a rope. The closed clove hitch should always be backed up with a safety knot (Fig. 8-11b).

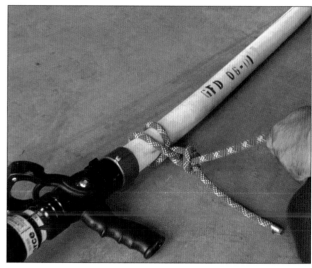

Fig. 8-11b. A closed clove hitch

Becket bend. With the becket bend, two ropes of unequal diameter are tied together. This knot places a bight in the larger-diameter rope to join to another rope or to a chain. The becket bend should not be used for life safety procedures (fig. 8–12).

Fig. 8–12. A becket bend can be used to tie two ropes together.

Bowline. Use a bowline knot to form a secure loop that will hold up to tension and not constrict the object it is placed around. This is one of the most widely used knots in the fire service (fig. 8–13).

Fig. 8–13. A bowline forms a secure knot when tension is applied to the rope.

Figure eight. This knot is used to form several other fire service knots, including the figure eight on a bight and the figure eight follow-through. A figure eight knot will effectively stop a rope from slipping through a pulley or through the grommet of a rope bag (fig. 8–14).

Fig. 8–14. A figure eight knot

Figure eight on a bight knot. This knot forms a secure loop at the open end of a rope. The figure eight on a bight is a good life-safety knot. It is also good for securing the rope to an anchored piece of equipment (fig. 8–15).

Fig. 8–15. A figure eight on a bight

Figure eight follow-through knot. This knot is for tying a figure eight on a bight through an object (fig. 8–16).

Step 1. Make a basic figure eight, leaving sufficient rope on the working end to go around the object you're securing the rope to.

Step 2. Wrap the rope around the object to be tied.

Step 3. Now follow the rope back through the knot in the opposite direction.

Fig. 8–16. A figure eight follow-through

Ropes and Knots

FIREFIGHTER I

Chapter 8

Water knot. This is the most effective knot for joining two pieces of webbing to make a longer piece, or for forming a single piece of webbing into a loop. The water knot is similar to a figure eight. Unlike a knot made with rope, the water knot must lie flat (fig. 8–17).

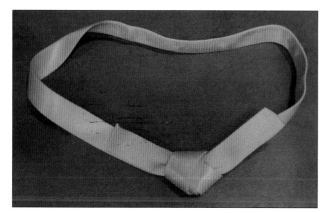

Fig. 8–17. A water knot is typically used to tie ends of webbing together.

Handcuff. This is a life safety knot with two adjusting loops that is useful for hoisting a firefighter or victim from a lower level. As the rope is pulled taut, the loops close up, forming a handcuff, which allows the person to be pulled upward. It is simple to tie, and very strong (fig. 8–18).

Fig. 8–18. A handcuff knot can be used to rescue and then drag a downed firefighter.

PROPER USE OF ROPE

There are some important points to remember when dealing with rope. A firefighter should think of these as the list of do's and don'ts with respect to rope.

1. When using a rope, always find a way to protect the rope over sharp edges. Use a rounded object such as a hose roller, ladder rung, or handle of a tool. Don't let the rope run over construction materials that have a 90° angle, like the edge of a roof or window. If possible, use **edge rollers**, which are made of metal and can be placed over edges and sharp corners to protect a rope while in use (fig. 8–19). They also reduce the amount of friction. Hose rollers are an ideal way of preventing abrasion to a hose.

2. Be aware of the effect that shock loads have on rope, and avoid creating these shock loads.

3. Regardless of the rope material, ropes and fire don't mix well. The heat from a fire can seriously damage a rope. Never let the rope pass through flames or heated gases while it is being used, regardless of the purpose. The rope could fail suddenly and without warning.

Fig. 8–19. Hose rollers can be used to protect hose and rope when drawn over sharp edges.

HOISTING TOOLS AND EQUIPMENT

One of the primary functions of rope is to hoist equipment to an elevated location. The utility rope can be used for this job. All equipment being hoisted should have a **tag line** on the ground. This line is used to keep your tools and equipment away from the structure or obstructions like branches, overhangs, or anything else it could get caught on. Remember that all knots should have safeties.

Axe or Halligan tool

Place an open clove hitch over the handle or an axe or Halligan tool and slide it all the way to the head of the tool and tighten (fig. 8–20). Remember to leave enough rope past the hitch to later tie a tag line to. Now make a bight around the head of the tool and bring the rope back up the handle, and secure with an underhanded half hitch.

Fig. 8–20. Using a clove hitch and a half hitch, along with a tag line, you can successfully raise a Halligan tool to an upper floor.

Pike pole

Like all tools, the pike pole is also tied with the heavy end down (the hook). This method will give greater control at the head of the tool to clear any obstructions. Place an open clove hitch over the handle of the tool and tighten by the hook (fig. 8–21). Remember to leave enough rope for the tag line. Take a bight around the head of the tool and bring up toward the handle. *Rule of thumb*: For every length of an axe in the handle, there should be that many half hitches.

Fig. 8–21. Usually one half hitch and a clove hitch can secure a pike pole to be hoisted.

Exhaust fan

Tie a bowline around the top two handles of an exhaust fan (fig. 8–22). Try to get all three sides of the triangle to be equal. It will look like a triangle when tension is placed on the line. The tag line is simply a closed clove hitch.

Fig. 8–22. A bowline tied around the top of an exhaust fan, along with a clove hitch for a tag line, can allow the fan to be hoisted to an upper floor.

Ropes and Knots

FIREFIGHTER I

Chapter 8

Hoselines, charged and uncharged

It is preferable to hoist both charged and uncharged hoselines the same way to keep it simple. First tie a closed clove hitch behind the first coupling. Then take a bight in the rope and pass it through the bale and over the nozzle. By pulling the rope, the bale is guaranteed to stay shut (fig. 8–23). *Note:* No tag line is necessary, so you can use the hose itself as a tag line. Also, tying the clove hitch just below the coupling eliminates stress on the coupling.

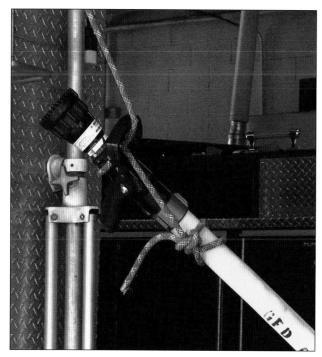

Fig. 8–23. A hose line can be hoisted by tying a clove hitch below the first coupling.

Hoisting a ladder

Using enough rope to make a 3-ft (1 m) loop, tie a bowline. Place the bowline under the top rung, over the second rung, and under the third rung. Now pull the rope toward the top of the ladder and place the loop over the beams of the ladder. Pull up on the rope to take up the slack while sliding the loop down the ladder. Attach a closed clove hitch as the tag line to the bottom rung. This will control the ladder while being hoisted (fig. 8–24). A figure eight knot may also be used to hoist the ladder instead of the bowline.

Fig. 8–24. Firefighters using a bowline and a clove hitch to hoist a ladder.

Tying a rope between objects

This is also known as a chimney or taut line hitch (fig. 8–25). Secure the rope around an upright object (closed clove hitch). Now bring the rope around the other upright object and back approximately three quarters of the way. Pass the working end under the right-hand line; this looks like the number 4. Bring the working end into the loop, pull taut, and make another number 4 with the working end. Bring this end into the loop between the first one you made and pull taut. This last time, hold the rope again as a number 4. Bring the working end into a new loop in front of the other by itself and secure tightly against the first two. If you release tension, the rope gets slack in it and people will be able to pass. Pull taut and the line will be tight again.

Fig. 8–25. Securing a rope between two objects

Using rope or webbing to secure objects

A rope or webbing can be used effectively to secure an object in place. Some firefighters carry a short length of personal rope so they can control a door that has to be forced open just in case there is a fire or severe heat condition behind the door being forced (fig. 8–26). Once opened and firefighters are advancing, the same short piece of rope can be used to hold the door open. Ropes can also be used to secure objects that are moved out of the way of firefighters, such as fencing that may be cut and rolled back, tree limbs and branches, as well as gates. In warehouses and distribution centers where most of the storage is on racks, ropes can be used to secure boxes stored on racks to prevent them from falling out of the racks and injuring firefighters. Ropes are used as a last resort for securing a motor vehicle when cribbing or blocking are not available.

Fig. 8–26. Firefighters often carry smaller lengths of rope or webbing with them to secure and control doors while performing searches.

ROPE MAINTENANCE, INSPECTION, AND STORAGE

Inspection of rope

FFI 5.5.1 FFII 6.5.4 Ropes need to be inspected just like any other piece of equipment in the fire service. In addition to a visual examination after each use, ropes should be inspected as part of the regular routine of inspection for all tools and equipment. A weekly inspection is a particularly good idea when the rope is used on

a frequent basis. For those departments that use their ropes less frequently, monthly inspections are acceptable. Regardless of the frequency, the inspection should be documented in writing (fig. 8–27). There are commercially available rope inspection forms, or a department may elect to create its own form.

The inspection report should identify what rope was used and when the rope was used. This report should also include information on how the rope was used and what type of exposure occurred to the rope. The date of the inspection, the person conducting the inspection, and the condition of the rope should also be noted.

The rope should immediately be removed from service if the rope is found to be damaged or suspected of having been damaged. Follow your department guidelines on how many picks or yarn pulls from routine wear are considered enough damage to remove from service.

When conducting an inspection, the rope should be examined along its entire length and not just the section that is thought to have been used. The person conducting the inspection should look for damage to the rope from a cut such as a laceration (cut into the rope); abrasion (cut on the surface of the rope from friction); fraying; charring; melting (especially true of synthetic fiber ropes); and damage from exposure to chemicals such as acids, corrosives, and petrochemical products.

The rope should be passed through the hands so that the person conducting the inspection can feel changes to the rope as well as examine the rope visually. These changes include finding a spot that has a different feel (hard or soft spot vs. the regular feel); a slippery feeling; or foreign objects embedded in the rope including grit, dirt, stone, wood or metal pieces. The inspection should also tell if the rope appears to be coming apart, which could indicate some type of interior damage (fig. 8–28).

The best time to conduct one of these inspections is after the rope has been cleaned and thoroughly dried out. The presence of moisture will allow mold or mildew to form, which in turn will cause the rope to rot if it is composed of natural fibers. Synthetic ropes can also disintegrate if they have been exposed to certain chemicals, and those chemicals have not been fully washed off the rope and the rope dried out.

Some people prefer to inspect a rope as they are putting it away in a rope bag or coiling it. Others prefer to tie the rope off, then slowly run their hands over the rope while the rope has some tension on it. Regardless of the method selected, the important thing to remember is that even a minor imperfection could be a tip-off of a major problem when the rope is placed under stress.

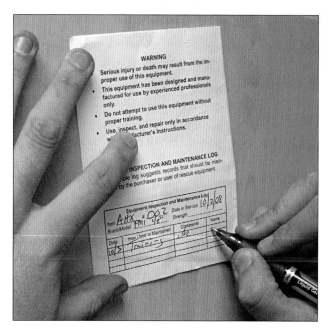

Fig. 8–27. Rope inspections must be documented and records kept in a conspicuous and accessible location.

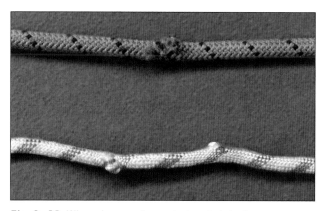

Fig. 8–28. When damaged rope is located during inspection, it should be removed from service.

Ropes that are laid or twisted together can be untwisted to reveal the inside portion of the rope during an inspection (fig. 8–29). This is not true of braided, braid-on-braid, or kernmantle type ropes, because there is really no way to twist the rope apart to reveal the inner portion of the rope. The key with inspecting these ropes is to feel for differences when running the rope through your hands. Synthetic ropes are especially good candidates for conducting a tactile inspection while putting the rope under slight stress or tension. Any irregularities in the feel should be noted, and the rope removed for more thorough inspection. Whether the situation is one braid running over the other, flat spots, bunching, stiffness, or a different feel, these ropes could be damaged and in need of replacement.

Fig. 8–29. Untwist the strands of twisted or laid rope to inspect.

Proper maintenance of life safety and utility ropes is required to ensure that they are ready for service. Most fire service ropes come with instructions on how to properly clean, dry, and store the ropes.

Cleaning

FFI 5.5.1 **FFII 6.5.4** Please follow the manufacturer's instructions. If your rope did not come with care instructions, then follow the general guidelines for cleaning, drying, and storage of ropes.

Natural fiber. A major drawback to the use of natural fiber rope is that it loses strength when it gets wet. And natural fibers do not regain lost strength. That means that using water to wash or clean a rope made of natural fibers simply cannot be done. The only way to clean a rope of natural fibers is to brush off the loose dirt and foreign material with a stiff broom or brush. This is another reason why ropes made of synthetic fibers are growing in popularity in the fire service.

Synthetic rope. Synthetic material can be cleaned in a number of ways. Again, remember that it is best to follow the manufacturer's instructions. The following is a general procedure to follow:

- Only use cold tap water, not hot water.

- Only use a mild detergent that is well-diluted. Do not use bleach or soap with bleach.

The cleaning and inspecting of kernmantle rope is difficult and time consuming because the damage might not be obvious. This inspection is done by touching all the rope as it passes through your hands. You are feeling for hard and soft spots. Note that some spots may have been made by a tight knot and are only temporary. This could indicate damage to the core, but on closer visual inspection, if the outer mantle is not damaged at that spot, then the fibers in the core may be temporarily misaligned and will relax. If there is any damage to the outer mantle, then the rope should be taken out of service. You should also look for cuts, odd shapes or weave, discoloration from chemicals, glass, metal, roughness (this may occur when a rope moves over another, stationary piece of rope), or an excessive amount of picks (fuzzies). If this or any condition presents itself, and you're not sure whether the rope is really damaged, then you should seek out someone with the training, knowledge, and experience to determine if the rope should be downgraded to another use. All ropes should be inspected after every use.

Hand washing. This is the most basic way of cleaning. Naturally, there are several methods that can be employed. One is to use a large sink or bucket and let the rope soak a few minutes, then move it around with your hands and scrub the rope with a small brush. Although some people suggest using your bare hands to wash the rope, the safer practice is to use a brush in case there are any sharp pieces of wood or metal embedded in the rope. Another method is to lay the rope out on the floor of the apparatus room. Since the apparatus bay is usually a fairly large area, the rope can be laid out in its entirety. Wet the rope with a hose and then scrub the rope with a stiff brush. If there is need to add detergent, you can place the cleaning solution in a bucket and dip the brush, then scrub.

One thing to remember regardless of the method selected to wash the rope is that if a detergent is used, the rope must be thoroughly rinsed of all detergent residue or cleaning solution (fig. 8–30). You can use a bucket of freshwater, pass the rope under a running faucet, or hose it off. However, if you use the hose, remember to turn the rope during the rinse process to get to the soap that is hidden between the rope and the floor.

Rope washer. A commercially available mini-version of a hose washer is the rope washer. The difference here is that the rope washer allows you to attach it to a threaded faucet or hose bib. You then run your rope through it, back and forth. The rope washer should have arrows that indicate the end into which the rope is placed and the end from which the rope emerges. Multiple small jets of water are directed at the rope as it is pulled through the rope washer. If connected to a faucet, the discharged water falls harmlessly into the sink. Using a hose bib may create a slip-and-fall hazard. The major downside to using a rope washer is that you cannot use any detergent in the process.

Washing machines. Only front-loading washing machines should be used. Top-loading machines should be avoided because this type of washing machine has an agitator that may damage the rope. Ideally, the rope should be placed in a mesh-type bag so that the rope does not get caught on anything inside the washing machine. If a mesh bag is not available, you can tie the rope in a **daisy chain** and place it inside the washing machine (fig. 8–31).

You may also want to select a front-loading washing machine that has a window so that you can visually check from time to time to make sure that the rope does not get snagged or damaged during the washing cycle. Add the proper detergent and make sure that all of the dirt and residue are rinsed out. One caution should be kept in mind. If the rope has been exposed to any type of chemical, you should avoid using a washing machine. The rope should be washed by hand or sent to a commercial vendor that specializes in decontamination of equipment when exposed to chemical environments.

Fig. 8–30. When washing rope, it is important to remove all detergent, if used.

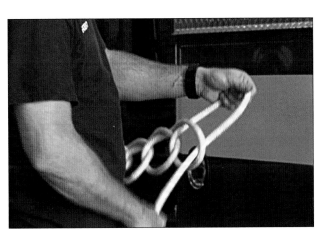

Fig. 8–31. If you don't have a mesh bag, tie the rope in a daisy chain before placing it into a washing machine. See your Skill Drill book for steps to create a daisy chain.

Drying ropes. Before the rope can be stored it must be dried. The preferred method of drying a rope is to lay it flat over a ladder so air gets all around the rope. Never expose rope to direct sunlight. Hanging rope to dry is another method. The rope can be hung in a hose tower or suspended between or below bar joists or trusses. Extra attention must be taken not to get any contaminants onto the rope.

Rope storage

It is imperative that rope be stored in a manner that keeps it clean and readily identifiable (length, size, and task), so a firefighter can quickly locate and deploy the proper rope for the task. The location on the apparatus where rope is stored needs to be a dedicated area that keeps the ropes from being buried under other equipment or being exposed to battery acid, fuel, fumes, or sunlight.

Bags. Rope storage bags will keep rope clean, neatly stored, and quickly deployable (fig. 8–32). Depending on the bag construction, some are better than others. Specially designed nylon or canvas bags are best for this purpose. A mesh bag is not. Nylon and canvas bags are best for protecting ropes from dirt, liquids, sunlight, and abrasion. A properly bagged rope is easier to deploy than a coiled rope.

Fig. 8–32. Rope bags help protect rope from abrasions and chemicals while being stored in fire apparatus.

Placing ropes into a bag. The purpose of the rope determines how the rope should be put into the bag. If placing in a **search bag**—used for carrying and deploying rope during a search—then place the rope through the grommet in the bottom of the bag, and tie a figure eight on a bight. This will give you a hand-hold to pull the rope from (bag stationary), or you can tie the bight off to the outside area and carry the bag deploying the rope behind.

If the rope is for a **drop (or life safety)** bag—used for raising tools, search or escape, and other fireground functions—then start out with a figure eight knot on both sides of the bottom grommet. This will keep the rope from being snagged and inadvertently being pulled out the bottom. Then simply load and coil the rope into the bag by starting around the inside edge and filling up the middle of the bag. You should tie a figure eight at the end of the rope and place it on the inside top of the bag.

Note: When deploying the bag, open the top of the bag drawstring and remove the figure eight, making sure that the eight has not pulled through any loops. This would cause multiple knots in the rope and a failed deployment.

Coiling and uncoiling rope

Coiling a rope using the end of a ladders is a common practice that aids in keeping rope organized and easy to deploy (Fig. 8-33). Steps for coiling and uncoiling a rope are found in your Skill Drills book.

Fig. 8–33. The end of a ladder is a useful tool for creating an organized rope coil.

OTHER EQUIPMENT

There are several tools and other pieces of equipment that are used in conjunction with a rope. It's important that you as a firefighter have at least a basic knowledge of these items should you be asked to retrieve them or provide them for technical rescue team members at a fire or other emergency incident.

Carabiner

A **carabiner** is a loop-type device with a gate-type opening on one side that opens by depressing it (fig. 8–34). This allows you to slip a rope into the carabiner or to attach the carabiner to an object. It also allows for the carabiner to be attached to a stationary object or to a piece of tubular webbing. A carabiner allows for the rope to change direction with minimal loss of strength. Carabiners are also used as part of any firefighter escape devices that you may be provided with.

Fig. 8–34. A carabiner is the most common rope tool used in the fire service. When used in conjunction with a length of rope or webbing, it can create an emergency firefighter escape system.

Figure eight plate

A **figure eight plate** is used to assist in descending (fig. 8–35). As the name implies, the plate resembles a number 8. One ring is small, and the other is larger. The smaller ring is attached to a carabiner that a firefighter wears. The larger ring is for the rope. Some figure eight plates now come with ears that stick out at the bottom of the larger ring to prevent the rope from creating a girth hitch, which would essentially stop the firefighter from descending.

Fig. 8–35. A figure eight plate assists with descending on a rope.

Single-sheave pulleys

A **single-sheave pulley** has one sheave that allows a single rope to pass through it (fig. 8–36). Single-sheave pulleys are used to change the direction of pull on a rope. Sometimes the sheave has pivoting sides that allow the rope to be placed into it without having to start from one end or the other and can be inserted anywhere along the length of the rope.

Double-sheave pulleys

As the name implies, a **double-sheave pulley** is similar to a single-sheave pulley except that this device allows for two ropes to be inserted (fig. 8–37). A double-sheave pulley can be used to help create a **mechanical advantage** for raising or lowering a load.

Fig. 8–36. A single-sheave pulley

Fig. 8–37. A double-sheave pulley

QUESTIONS

1. When should a rope be inspected?

2. What are the advantages of synthetic ropes over natural materials?

3. What do you look for when inspecting rope?

4. When should a rope be removed from service?

5. What are the differences between kernmantle, laid, and braided rope?

6. Which would you choose for life safety applications and why?

7. Describe hoisting a hoseline.

8. What is the difference between a bight, loop, and round turn?

Personal Protective Equipment

by Tim Pillsworth

This chapter provides required knowledge items for the following NFPA Standard 1001 Job Performance Requirements:

FFI 5.3.2

FFI 5.5.1

This chapter contains Skill Drills. When you see this icon, refer to your Skill Drill book for step-by-step instructions.

SKILL DRILL

OBJECTIVES

Upon completion of this chapter, you should be able to the following:

- Describe the different types of personal protective equipment (PPE) worn by firefighters
- Describe the relationship of SCBA and PPE
- Describe the purpose and operation of a personal alert safety system (PASS) used by firefighters
- Describe the six components of structural firefighting gear
- Identify the materials of which PPE is constructed
- Describe the proper method of donning PPE
- Describe the proper method of doffing PPE
- Identify the proper methods for maintaining PPE
- Identify to procedures for inspecting and cleaning PPE

INTRODUCTION

Your **personal protective equipment (PPE)** is your first line of defense when operating at alarms, but it should not be considered the last line of defense. What does this mean? Your PPE is designed to protect you from the day-to-day risks: the mechanical, thermal, and biological risks you may see at any alarm. Your PPE has limitations. The best protection that you have is to understand the fire environment and not put yourself or your partner in a position in which your lives depend solely on your PPE.

Whether a structure, vehicle, or brush fire; motor vehicle accident (MVA); medical call; or any one of the calls for help you receive each and every day, when worn correctly, your PPE offers you the best protection against harm from the forces and elements that surround you. Smoke, fire, heat, blood, sharp objects, and hazardous materials can cause injury or death if you do not respect and shield yourself from them.

Once you complete the reading, receive instruction, and train in the correct use of PPE, you will be able to protect yourself; and by protecting yourself, you protect your partners (brother and sister firefighters) and the general public. Your PPE training does not end with this chapter. You must continue to practice donning and doffing your PPE on a regular basis.

Although all PPE ensembles have some similar features and can be cross-used at times, they should only be used for their designed purpose. Structural turnout gear is the garment system or ensemble most commonly used. We will discuss this gear last because of its importance, and because it is the PPE we are all issued and use at most alarms. But the other forms of PPE must be covered to understand their use, function, and limitations.

There are several types of PPE, including the following:

1. Station wear

2. Wildland or brush

3. Proximity

4. Medical

5. Technical rescue

6. Hazardous materials

7. Ice rescue

8. Self-contained breathing apparatus (SCBA)

9. Personal alert safety system (PASS)

10. Structural

Each system/ensemble of PPE is covered under a National Fire Protection Association (NFPA) standard. As your career progresses, you should become familiar with the requirements in the regulations so you can better understand why and how the systems are designed, tested, and maintained. This knowledge will be important if one day you must specify PPE for your department. The garments, devices, and other items described show one or a limited number of manufacturers or PPE. For PPE requirements issued in your department, complete additional training with your training officer to ensure you know and understand the correct use and function of the equipment.

TYPES OF PPE ENSEMBLES

FFI 5.3.2 The following are the standard PPE ensembles worn for most department activities and incident responses.

Station wear

Station wear PPE is covered under NFPA 1975: *Standard on Station/Work Uniforms for Emergency Services*. This clothing is worn while on duty in the fire station, awaiting a response (fig. 9–1). Station wear serves as a "work" uniform and is designed to be worn under other protective clothing such as structural firefighting gear (wearing station wear alone is not appropriate for structural firefighting, as they are not considered primary protective clothing).

Fig. 9–1. Station wear

This gear, at a minimum, meets specific ignition and flame spread testing criteria to avoid injury during firefighting activities. In the past, some fire departments issued non-fire-resistant station wear made of synthetic materials. Such practices sometimes led to burn injuries of firefighters. With certified station wear, such problems have been greatly minimized.

Station wear may also be "dual certified" to meet the requirements of a variety of other specific PPE standards such as NFPA 1951, *Standard on Protective Ensembles for Technical Rescue Incidents*; NFPA 1977, *Standard on Protective Clothing and Equipment for Wildland Fire Fighting*; NFPA 1994, *Standard on Protective Ensem-*

bles for First Responders to CBRN Incidents; and NFPA 1999, *Standard on Protective Clothing for Emergency Medical Operations.*

Wildland or brush PPE

Wildland or brush PPE fall under NFPA 1977, *Standard on Protective Clothing and Equipment for Wildland Fire Fighting.* Wildland or brush gear is designed to protect the firefighters from flash fire and abrasion during wildland fires while allowing the greatest amount of mobility and heat recovery possible (fig. 9–2). Fighting a wildland fire may expose you to extended hours of operation including walking and hiking on uneven terrain, high heat and low humidity, and even the possibility of snake or other small animal bites. The wildland PPE offers limited thermal protection, which structural gear offers, but is much lighter, less restrictive to movement, and will release body heat more readily. PPE garments are constructed of material similar to that of structural gear. Materials such as Nomex® and treated cotton are used in pants and coats, shirts, or overalls (jumpsuits) with common closures, which are worn much like jeans and long-sleeved winter shirts. Often reflective stripping is added for nighttime safety and visibility. Head protection can be offered by a standard structural helmet with eye protection and earflaps or rated as a wildland fire helmet, which are similar in appearance and to construction hard hats. With the wildland fire helmets, hoods for neck and ear protection and goggles are required for full head protection. Protection for the foot, ankle, and lower leg, wildland boots are similar to hiking and construction work boots. They use regular laces or **speed laces** (laces located in the surface of the boot and tightened/secured by a **cinch** system rather than a knot). Leather boots have hardened toes and shank for protection from rocks, punctures, and tools used during wildland operations. Using steel for toe and shank protection reduces the amount of heat buildup from walking on embers. Typically, this style of PPE is only purchased and issued to departments dealing with many large and or prolonged wildland fires. Most departments with limited wildland fires will use their issued structural gear for this purpose. The level of protection offered by the structural gear will be far above the wildland gear, but it will be much heavier and can cause higher levels of heat stress for the firefighter.

Although wildland PPE offers a lighter easy breathing garment, in the event of a fire entrapment situation such as a **blow-up** (a sudden increase in fire intensity), the gear will *not* protect you from the extreme heat. With each set of wildland gear, a **personal fire shelter** should

be issued. This is a self-deployable shelter is constructed of an aluminized material to reflect the extreme heat during a fire roll over. This shelter is used as a last line of defense for survival.

Fig. 9–2. Wildland PPE. (Courtesy of Andoni Kastros)

Proximity PPE

Proximity PPE is covered under NFPA 1971, *Standard on Protective Ensembles for Structural Fire Fighting and Proximity Fire Fighting.* The proximity gear's outer shell has an aluminized surface. The outer **shell** reflects rather than adsorbs the vast radiant heat created from aircraft and petroleum based fires (fig. 9–3). With an aircraft fire, a single plane can hold 20,000 gal (75,708 L) or more of aircraft fuel. Although this form of gear offers high levels of protection from radiant heat, the outer shell is extremely expensive and cannot withstand the daily punishment from normal municipal firefighting. The thermal and moisture layers (described in detail in the structural firefighting section later in this chapter) within the proximity gear can be constructed from the same materials found in structural gear. Both the helmets and boots for the proximity gear must meet the same standards as the coat and pants. The boots will typically have an aluminized coating applied, which is similar to the material found on the coat and pants. This coating reflects the high radiant heat. The head protection comes in two forms: a standard structural helmet with elastic covers made from the same material as the outer shell as well as a full-head hood system. To protect the face and the SCBA mask, full-face shields must be incorporated. The shields have a gold tone coating to reflect the radiant heat while still offering visibility. Without the shield, the high radiant heat levels burn the firefighter's face and damage the SCBA masks.

Medical PPE

Medical PPE is covered under NFPA 1999, *Standard on Protective Clothing for Emergency Medical Operations.* The use of medical gear has been increasing over the past few years in many departments that provide medical responses in their jurisdictions. The use of dedicated medical PPE preserves body substance isolation and will greatly reduce the possibility of cross contamination (fig. 9–4). The PPE is much lighter and less cumbersome than structural gear and, in many ways, appearance; and style looks much like wildland fire gear or technical rescue gear. The reduced weight and bulk make for less fatigue

while operating at medical calls and MVAs. Where the medical gear differs is its protection from bloodborne pathogens (BBPs). BBPs are microscopic organisms that, if introduced to the body, can cause illness or even death in the most extreme cases. The medical gear has a moisture barrier, which will prevent any liquids such as blood or vomit from penetrating the PPE and reaching your body. It is important to protect your hands with single-use medical gloves that meet NFPA standards. However, because these medical gloves can be damaged under normal working conditions, it is best to carry an extra pair in your gear at all times. Be aware that some firefighters have latex glove allergies; some disposable gloves are made of this material. If you have such an allergy, ensure that you are issued non-latex gloves.

To protect your face from airborne fluids, a shield or goggles that meet the fluid-borne pathogen resistance standards must be donned. When it comes to foot protection, many departments that issue **day boots** use boots that meet the standards for slip-resistant soles, hardened toes and shank, and body fluid–borne pathogen resistance. The boots will appear and feel much like normal work boots.

Fig. 9–3. Proximity PPE

Fig. 9–4. Medical PPE. (Courtesy of Jeanette Kendall/State Line Fire and Safety)

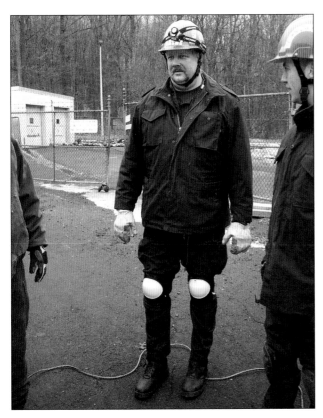

Fig. 9–5. Technical rescue PPE

Technical rescue PPE

Technical Rescue PPE is covered under NFPA 1951, *Standard on Protective Ensembles for Technical Rescue Incidents.* The ensemble incorporates lightweight flexible PPE to offer protection during special rescue operations (fig. 9–5). Whether it is a high angle, trench, or collapse rescue situation, the PPE is designed to offer protection to the head and body. The PPE can come in the form of a coat and pant or a jumpsuit. They both must offer abrasion, liquid, and flame resistance. Once again the boots are similar to medical boots with toe, foot, and general penetration protection. To protect your head, special *technical rescue* helmets are employed. They typically have no rear brim like a structural firefighting helmet; each has chinstraps, sweat bands, and an internal suspension system. In addition to the PPE, rescue harness, rope, and rope accessories can be included.

Hazardous material PPE

Hazardous material PPE is covered under NFPA 1991 and 1992, *Standard on Vapor-Protective Ensembles for Hazardous Materials Emergencies* and *Standard on Liquid Splash-Protective Ensembles and Clothing for Hazardous Materials Emergencies*, respectively. The most technical form of PPE is the equipment used at hazardous material (hazmat) incidents. With the exception of the SCBA, this equipment is vastly different from any other from of PPE. The protection during a hazmat incident can vary from Level A (the highest level of protection) to Level D (the lowest level of protection). The Level A suit is designed to protect you from liquid or vapors and requires full SCBA (fig. 9–6a). Level B will only protect you from liquids but once again requires full SCBA to be donned (fig. 9–6b). Level C has the same level of skin protection as Level B but does not require the use of a SCBA (fig. 9–6c). The lowest protection, Level D, would be covered by your issued structural PPE (fig. 9–6d). The level of required protection is governed by what materials are present, the form they are in (vapor, liquid, particle), their concentration, or if the material is even known. To use this type of PPE, numerous advanced training courses are required and will not be covered in this chapter. This equipment is discussed in further detail in chapter 25: Implementing the Planned Response to a Hazardous Materials Incident.

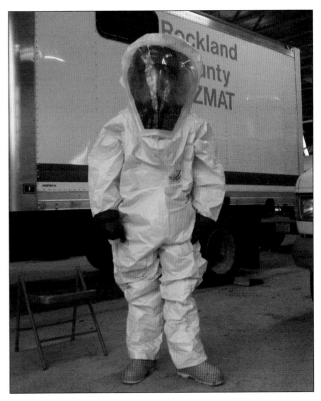

Fig. 9–6a. Level A hazardous material PPE—This is the highest level of protection, with integrated gloves and boots. They come in different materials for protection against different chemicals. SCBA is donned under the suit for respiratory protection. (Courtesy of Jerry J. Knapp)

Fig. 9–6b. Level B ensemble

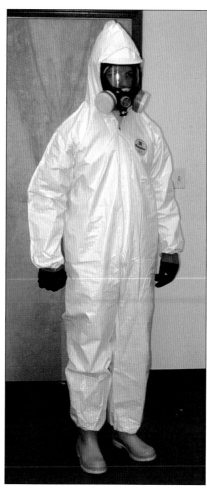

Fig. 9–6c. Level C ensemble

Fig. 9–6d. Level D clothing

Ice rescue PPE

Design of **ice rescue PPE** is not governed by a specific standard (but ice rescue and PPE is covered by NFPA 1670, *Standard on Operations and Training for Technical Search and Rescue Incidents*). Many think that ice rescue is only on ice, but it is considered a cold-water event in any water less than 70°F (21°C). Therefore, the rescuer must be protected from hypothermia. Water has the ability to remove heat from the human body 32 times faster than air. The heat transfer can be so rapid; a person can be hypothermic in only a few minutes. The ice rescue ensemble will seal your body from the water and the only area exposed is your face. The ice rescue ensemble consists of the suit, helmet, and harness (typically integrated with the suit itself). The suit is one piece, much like coveralls with attached boots, gloves, and hood (fig. 9–7). The integrated gloves and boots are formfitting and do not require the need for additional internal apparel for use. Once donned and closed, the hood creates a tight seal around the face to keep water from entering the suit.

Additional ice shoes, which are like sandals with spikes, make maneuvering on ice quicker and safer. A helmet much like the technical rescue helmet is required for protection in case of a fall; remember, ice is slippery. The chest harness is for both your safety and for recovery. It will act as you lifeline but will assist in retrieving the victim from the ground crew.

SCBA as part of PPE

SCBA use and care are covered under NFPA 1981, *Standard on Open-Circuit Self-Contained Breathing Apparatus (SCBA) for Emergency Services*. To protect your respiratory system, the use of a SCBA is required. SCBA will be covered in great detail in chapter 10 in its use, care, and procedures. This chapter will cover and show how it interfaces with your PPE garments to complete your full PPE envelope. Without both the SCBA and your PPE garments working together properly, your body will not be completely protected.

Fig. 9–7. Ice rescue PPE

PERSONAL ALERT SAFETY SYSTEM DEVICES

PASS is covered under NFPA 1982, *Standard on Personal Alert Safety Systems (PASS)*. The PASS is a device that can be either removable (clipped on a strap) or integrated as a component of an SCBA. When in alarm the PASS will notify firefighters working in and around the scene that a firefighter is down, trapped, or in some life-or-death emergency. The PASS will activate in two different modes. The first is the manual alarm activated by you. You can activate the PASS by turning a switch or pushing a button on the device. The second is by the use of the motion detector within the device. If you are motionless for 30 seconds, the PASS will alarm. In the automatic mode, the PASS will pre-alarm to warn that the full alarm is imminent if there is not motion or a button or switch is not adjusted. Once in full alarm, the only way to deactivate the alarm is to manually turn off the alarm by either a button or switch on the PASS itself. For many years the PASS was a separate unit typically attached to the waist strap of the SCBA and turned on by the firefighter for operation (fig. 9–8).

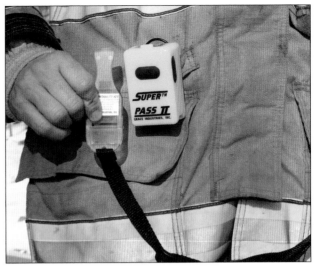

Fig. 9–8. Stand-alone PASS—The stand-alone PASS is still in compliance but must have the key or clip for activation. Many people forgot to turn on the older switch-style PASS units before entering the IDLH area. (Courtesy of A. Zytowski)

More recently, most SCBA manufacturers have designed integrated PASS alarms into their SCBAs (fig. 9–9). The PASS will operate in the same manner, but the device will be turned on automatically when the SCBA is turned on. This solved the problem of firefighters not turning on their PASS before entering an **immediately dangerous to life and health (IDLH)** area. To have the PASS taken seriously as a safety device, it must be used correctly, which requires a lower number of false activations. With its correct operation, there will be less chance of a false alarm. To ensure that no PASS is left on, practice turning it off after you doff your SCBA or return to the apparatus. Remembering this reduces the "will someone turn that off" alarm, leaving only the true emergencies.

The aforementioned ensemble of PPE and the structural gear, which will be discussed at length in the following text, will not offer any protection to your respiratory system. The products of combustion found in the smoke from all fires will cause damage to your lungs, mouth, nose, and the remainder of the respiratory track. To protect yourself, learn and understand the use and care of the SCBA. This will be covered in depth in chapter 10. But as part of the complete PPE envelope, it will be covered as it interfaces with your helmet, hood, and coat. Without all the parts of the PPE worn correctly, you will not be protected.

Personal Protective Equipment

FIREFIGHTER I

Chapter 9

Fig. 9–9. SCBA PASS—Today most newly purchased SCBAs have integrated PASS alarms to insure they are activated when the unit is turned on.

STRUCTURAL FIREFIGHTING PPE

Structural PPE is covered under NFPA 1971, *Standard on Protective Ensembles for Structural Fire Fighting and Proximity Fire Fighting*. Structural PPE is also known as **turnout** or **bunker gear**, the names given to the ensemble that we all use and know the most. All the pieces of your turnout gear working together (helmet, coat/jacket, pants, gloves, boots, hood, SCBA along with miscellaneous personal tools) create an ensemble to protect you from the dangers of all operations on the fireground. To know your total structural ensemble, you will need to understand each of its parts.

Working from the bottom to the top, the boots (most likely readied in your pant legs) will be the first donned (fig. 9–10). To meet the NFPA 1971 standard, the use of the hip boots (also known as ¾ **rubber boots**) are not allowed. However, they can serve an import role. In the event of water emergencies from the flooded basement to minor street flooding, they can be used to keep you dry and protected. The hip boots must not be worn for any rescue or fire operation, they offer little thermal protection and do not cover the waist area.

The boots used today are typically called **bunker boots**. They can be pull-on leather or rubber boots, which are typically 14–16 in. (36–41 cm) high; or they may be laced/speed laced boots, which are typically 10 in. (25 cm) high. Boots are typically placed within the pants

before use for efficient donning. Each have their own pros and cons; and depending on your department PPE specifications, you could be issued one of multiple styles. All offer toe protection by steel toe, foot bottom protection by a shank, aggressive tread, and ankle support.

Fig. 9–10. Structural firefighting boots—Boots have changed over the years. The tall rubber boots are no longer appropriate for structural firefighting, but are very good for water emergencies. Rubber and leather pull-on bunker boots are the most popular, while the leather zip-up short boots are used in some areas.

Many leather bunker boots offer additional shin guards and greater ankle support. Also, moisture barriers are now found in many boots for better water resistance and BBP protection. Even with the additional lining, with prolonged exposure to water, the boot will be penetrated. The leather and more recently designed boots of leather and high-tech materials are much lighter, offer a tighter fit, offer better foot and ankle support than traditional rubber boots, and typically are 50% or more in cost. Traditional rubber bunker boots offer the greatest protection from water, are the least expensive to purchase, and are easily donned; but they offer the lowest level of foot and ankle support.

The low-cut laced structural boots, sometimes referred to as *day boots*, offer the highest level of foot ankle support; and they look and feel much like a construction work boot. They are typically lower than the pull-on boots (10 in. vs. 14–16 in.), therefore any deep water will more readily overtop the boot.

Working up from the boots, pants are next in line. With the construction of the pants and coats being the same, the general design will be discussed together. The combination of the coat and pant creates a system designed to work together; they are constructed from three separate layers of materials, which protect you from heat, water, and abrasion (figs. 9–11 and 9–12). Mixing and matching different styles of gear, even from the same manufacturer, will place you at risk of injury and void any testing and certification the manufacturer has on the gear. The coat and pant is one system or ensemble and cannot be mixed and matched.

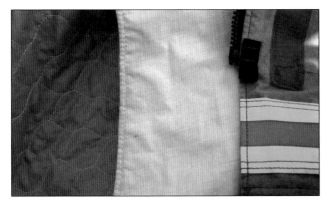

Fig. 9–11. The three layers of structural PPE—Thermal liner with the moisture barrier and outer shell of a structural coat

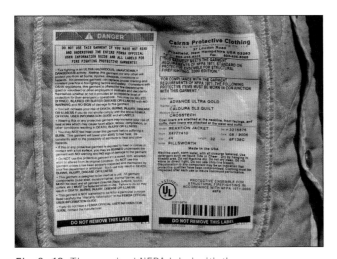

Fig. 9–12. The required NFPA label with the garment's information

The outer shell is the most durable layer and will protect you from flame and abrasion. It can be constructed of Nomex®, PBI®, or Advance Ultra®, just to name a few materials, and can be produced or dyed to a variety of colors. Each material will offer different levels of protection and cost. Many outer shell materials used today are highly heat resistant and have the ability to self-extinguish once the ignition source is removed. With the more advanced material, the ability to dye the shell is becoming limited and the only color available is its natural state. But when dyed, damage can be noticed by the removal or discoloration of the dye. Although this might not be a sign of damage, it does show a heat event happened to the coat.

The middle layer is the moisture barrier that protects you from water, common liquids (gasoline, battery acid, hydraulic fluid, and chlorine solution of 65%), and BBP; it can be constructed from Crosstech®, Gore®, and Stedair® to name a few materials. The moisture barrier will also prevent any common liquid from entering the thermal layer of the garment and reaching your body while allowing perspiration and body heat to be released. The moisture barrier is the thinnest layer of the garment and is only seen when the inner liner is removed from the outer shell. This layer can be damaged from heat and small punctures with little to no noticeable damage to the stronger outer shell.

The innermost layer is the thermal liner and will protect you from convected and conductive heat and control the moisture (sweat) that you generate. Common materials are Caldura®, Aralite®, and Synergy®. The liner is woven layers of thin materials quilted together, which trap air in between each layer to create the desired thermal protection. Air is a poor conductor of heat and the small air pockets will not allow the heat to transfer toward your body. This is one of the reasons why such a thin layer of material can protect you from such high heat. The innermost surface will typically have a smooth finish for comfort and easy donning. The thermal and moisture layers are attached to the outer shell by a combination of snaps, Velcro®, and zippers.

Structural PPE is required to meet two minimum performance criteria. The first is the **thermal protective performance (TPP)** test, which is essentially a test to measure the time it takes for convective and radiant heat to penetrate through the three layers of a the complete PPE system—the outer shell, moisture barrier, and thermal liner—and injure the wearer. A PPE must receive a minimum TPP numerical rating of 35, which is equivalent to receiving a second-degree burn after 17½ seconds under flashover conditions. Flashover, of course, is considered the worst *fire* condition that a firefighter may encounter.

The TPP is a test by which all three layers of the garment are tested at once by applying heat from a burner and a radiant heat source on one side of the test sample, and a sensor to measure the heat transfer on the other. The test results in a time and temperature graph. Therefore, if your gear has additional insulation, the TPP could increase to 40, which would only increase your time to burn by 2.5 seconds. With an increase in TPP caused by additional insulation, the garment will become heavier and will most likely reduce your body's ability to release heat generated from activity. This test does not mean you cannot get burned while your gear is donned. This is a test for use for comparison and minimum values; it is not actual fire conditions.

Personal Protective Equipment

FIREFIGHTER I

Chapter 9

The second test is the **total heat loss (THL)** test, which measures the ability of the PPE to allow heat to pass away from the body through the three layers (described earlier) that make up the garment. The minimum required heat loss is 205 W/m² (watts, a measurement of heat energy, are described in chapter 5, Fire Behavior). The three layers working together will create air gaps between the layers and have synergistic effect on the values of the tests. This means that the value of the group is higher than the sum of the individual components.

The importance of the removal of heat created from your body (reflected in the THL value) during any alarm is critical. The buildup of body heat within your gear will reduce your efficiency and the total time you are able to perform tasks. If your PPE will not dissipate body heat, the possibility of heat stress and heat stroke increases. The extreme heat stroke can cause permanent brain damage and even death.

In the vulnerable areas of your body and the garment (cuffs, knees, elbows, and shoulders), additional layers of material can be added to increase the thermal and abrasion protection as well as offer padding for comfort. The materials can vary from the outer shell and thermal liner materials as well as high abrasion-resistant materials. Over time leather has been proven to be one of the strongest material for abrasion resistance; but it is heavy, becomes stiff with age, and is prone to absorbing water and fluids, causing problems with decontamination. Many of the new high-abrasion materials such as Arshield® and Dragonhide® offer high levels of abrasion protection, will not stiffen over time, and resist absorbing water and other fluids, thereby reducing the difficulty of decontamination.

For nighttime operations, general visibility and identification NFPA 1971 requires a combination of **retro-reflective** (a characteristic in which the light received by the reflective surface is reflected *directly* back at the actual source of light, such as a car's headlight) and fluorescent surfaces on the coat and pant system. The reflective material must be placed in such a way that it is visible from 360°. The minimum requires bands around the coat and pant cuffs, on the front face of the coat at the waist and chest, and on the back at the waist and mid-back or two vertical strips at the sides of the back. This is the only the minimum. Many departments add additional bands to the arms and legs as well as letters and numbers for department and personal identification, which add to the level of protection. The color, material, and layout offer different levels of performances, but the end result is your safety.

With the general knowledge of the makeup of the layers of the coat and pants, now the properties of each can be described. The pants will offer protection from the ankle to the hips and lower back if so equipped. For comfort and protection from heat, additional padding is typically added to the knees. At the fly and waist, there will be a positive fastener system to secure the pants to your waist. With many of the newly designed pants, a belt, clip, or zipper will allow the pants to stay in place without the use of the suspenders. This is important for comfort by taking the weight of the pants off your shoulders, but the suspenders should be worn to ensure that the pants stay at the correct location for the knee pads and ensure they stay on in the event that you need to be rescued. If you go down, your bothers will use every method to pull you out, even pull you by your pants. The suspenders will keep them on.

The coat will protect your torso, chest, back, shoulders, and arms much the same way the pants protect your legs. A fastening system of zippers, Velcro®, snaps, hook and eye, or combinations form a positive seal once donned (figs. 9–13 and 9–14). The collar's neck flap works with the hood and ear flaps to protect the neck and the back of the head. At the end of each arm there are two general types of cuffs, **standard** and **wrist guard**. The difference in the cuffs allows different styles of gloves to be worn. The longer cuff with either a thumbhole and palm protection or thumb loop allow the use of **gauntlet gloves** (an **interface component** that extends from the *end of the glove itself* and provides limited protection to the area where the coat and glove meet). The standard cuff requires **wristlet** style (*interface component*, which is typically a specially designed piece of fabric that extends from the *end of a coat sleeve* that provides limited protection to the area where the glove and coat meet). One new requirement for all structural coats is the **drag rescue device (DRD)**. This was adopted by the NFPA 1971 standard in 2005 to offer a safe and efficient rescue method for a downed firefighter. The DRD is a webbing loop that wraps the back and shoulders when deployed (fig. 9–15). To deploy, lift a flap located on the top back of the coat or within the back of the collar and pull the webbing outward; and you will have 2 ft (61 cm) of a loop to pull your partner to safety. This DRD is designed to allow leverage and distance to pull a firefighter along floor or ground (fig. 9–16). It is not designed to be attached to a rope and used as a lifting or lowering harness or attached to some form of mechanical pulling device (winch). This can cause grave injury.

Fig. 9–13. Coat closure, zipper, and Velcro®

Fig. 9–14. Coat closure, hook & dee, and Velcro®

Fig. 9–15. Stowed structural coat drag rescue device (DRD) under outer shell

Personal Protective Equipment

FIREFIGHTER I

Chapter 9

Fig. 9–16. Deployed DRD—While short, it is usable for a firefighter rescue in a horizontal direction only.

The structural gloves are required to offer a minimum TPP value of 35, the same requirement as your coat and pants. Typically, the outer layer is made from some form cow or elk leather or kangaroo hide (fig. 9–17). But many gloves made with the newer materials in conjunction with the leather to create a more comfortable and user-friendly glove. Thin layers of thermal protection and a moisture barrier under the outer layer complete your protection (fig. 9–18). One of the largest complaints of fire gloves is the loss of dexterity with the gloves donned. The solution to this compliant is twofold. First, get fitted for the correct size gloves. A properly fitted set of gloves not only offers you the best protection, it allows for the greatest level of dexterity. Second, wear your gloves, all the time, at all alarms and drills. With high level of use, you will gain muscle memory making the tasks of starting saws and operating tools easier.

Fig. 9–17. Structural gloves

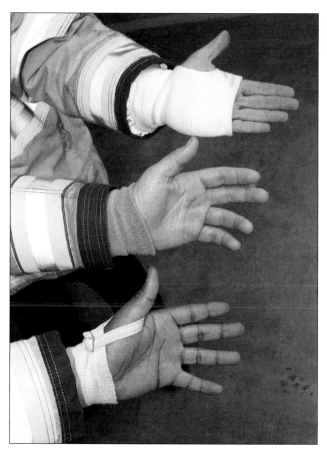

Fig. 9–18. Structural coat wristers

A structural hood is worn under your helmet and over the SCBA facepiece netting to protect your ears, neck, and any exposed skin not covered by the helmet, facepiece, or collar. The structural hoods come in various styles and are constructed of Nomex®, PBI®, and Carbon-X®, and when donned correctly with the helmet and facepiece, there will not be any exposed skin visible. The hood covers the most important and most difficult area of your body to protect. When donned correctly the hood is tucked into the coat so it will lay flat along your head, neck, and shoulders. To have it tucked into your coat it should be donned before the coat.

The interface with the SCBA facepiece is completed by sliding the hood over the back of the head, then donning the facepiece, which is covered in depth in chapter 10. Once the facepiece is in place, you can slide your thumbs around at the base of the head, hook the hood, and slide over the netting. Once complete, adjust any areas to ensure complete coverage. If correct, no visible skin will be exposed and the entire head net of the facepiece will be covered (figs. 9–19a, 9–19b, and 9–19c).

Fig. 9–19a. Hood donned and tucked under coat

Fig. 9–19c. Hood donned incorrectly—Old, stretched hoods leave open gaps that will allow the super-heated atmosphere to reach the sensitive skin of the face and ears.

Last, let's cover what protects the thing you should use the most on the fireground: your head. Helmets come in many different shapes and styles and are constructed from many different materials.

From traditional to modern styles, from leather to plastic, the structural helmet can take different forms and materials. With all their visual differences, each has the same components (eye protection, suspension system, ear flap, chin strap, identification shield, reflective material, and protective shell), which meet or exceed the same NFPA standards (figs. 9–20a, 9–20b, 9–20c, and 9–20d).

All PPE manufacturers must submit samples to undergo extensive testing, as required NFPA 1971, before it can be used by firefighters. Each PPE component is thoroughly analyzed. For example, structural firefighting helmets must undergo several rigorous tests. These tests include an impact resistance test, a corrosion resistance test, an electrical insulation test, a retention system test for chinstraps, a suspension system retention test, a shell retention test, a retroreflectivity and fluorescence test, a radiant heat resistance test, and flame resistance tests.

To have the helmet protect your head, it must be worn correctly, every time. The **ratchet adjustment** (a change-

Fig. 9–19b. Hood donned correctly

Personal Protective Equipment

FIREFIGHTER I

Chapter 9

able headband inside the helmet) will allow you to make changes to the fit, having the helmet donned with or without the SCBA facepiece and hood. Adjust the ratchet for a snug comfortable fit, and use and adjust your chinstrap every time. With both in use and adjusted correctly, your helmet will stay in place offering you the best protection. If your helmet falls off, it can be lost in a smoke-filled room and you will have lost your protection from both heat and impact. *The use of the chin strap is essential at all times; it is critical for your safety if you should fall and strike your head.*

Either a **Bourke shield**™ or face shield can offer secondary eye protection. Both styles will protect your eyes from an object from the straight-ahead direction, but not from spray or an object bouncing under the face shield. If a SCBA facepiece is not donned, to meet the primary level of eye protection, goggles or safety glasses must be used, especially when using tools.

Frontpieces, also known simply as *fronts* or shields, display your fire company identification and rank on the front of your helmet.

DONNING AND DOFFING PPE

Donning your PPE

Now with your newly gathered knowledge of what and how your structural PPE is constructed, you will need to learn how to don it correctly, and in under 1 minute. It might seem impossible to do now, but with practice and some basic tricks, it will be an easy task. But to do this, you first need to have your gear set up for donning (ready for the next alarm).

Place your boots in your pant legs and pull the pants down around the boots, leaving the tops of the boots and bootstraps exposed. Place the suspenders over the tops of the boots so they are visible and remain untangled. Place your hood in an accessible location so it can be donned before your coat; on top of the helmet or on top of the boots or pant pocket works well for many. Have your coat open when it is hanging up and your helmet in close proximity. Your gloves can be in the coat pocket or kept with a glove keeper. Many departments have gear racks, which allow the gear to be stowed in a convenient and orderly manner (fig. 9–21).

Donning is in the following order:

1. Clear the suspenders from the tops of the boots, and set in/pull boots on.

2. Pull up your pants from the waist, pull the suspenders over your shoulders, and fasten the waist closure.

3. Gather your hood and pull it over your head.

4. Don your coat and fasten the closure. Close the coat fastener system and collar.

5. Slide your hood off your head and down to your neck.

6. Don your hand light and radio if so equipped and required.

7. Don your helmet with chinstrap.

8. Don your SCBA.

9. If needed, don your facepiece, pull the hood over the netting, and replace your helmet and chin strap.

10. Gather and don your gloves.

Fig. 9–21. Gear properly stored on rack—Your gear can be stored in an open locker, apparatus compartment, or gear room.

Fig. 9–20a. Structural helmets

Fig. 9–20b. Rear of structural helmets

Fig. 9–20c. Structural helmet suspension—note all approved helmets have attached ear protection and chin straps.

Fig. 9–20d. Structural helmet eye protection

Personal Protective Equipment

FIREFIGHTER I

Chapter 9

Once complete, all your skin will be covered by one or more layers of protection (fig. 9–22). All pieces of the PPE, when sized correctly, will allow for maxim movement without being overly large or binding.

Doffing your PPE

Doffing (removing) your gear is an important task rarely talked about. Under normal circumstances, the most import thing to remember is to remove it in the order it was donned and stow your gear the same way each time. By placing your hood and gloves in the same location, and stowing your gear the same way each and every time, you will be able to don it faster at your next alarm. Stopping to search for your gloves or hood will be slow and inefficient.

Fig. 9–22. Correctly donned structural PPE

While doffing, perform a quick inspection of any component you feel you might have damaged or contaminated. Before stowing your PPE—whether in a locker, bag, or compartment on the apparatus—make sure all components are completely dry. Wet gear will not dry when packed away, which promotes mold growth. Additionally, donning wet gear is more difficult and very uncomfortable. Make sure the coat cuffs are pulled out and the

tops of the boots are clear with the handles exposed from the pants for easy donning for the next alarm.

Under most conditions, doffing your PPE will not take much attention and become a routine after every alarm, with one exception: doffing superheated gear. Injuries from superheated gear have been on the rise for the last few years. This is because of the high level of protection from your PPE. If you are operating within a superheated environment for a prolonged time, all your gear will become superheated. The temperature will be high enough to cause burns if you do not doff quickly and correctly.

A signal that your gear is superheated is the **off-gassing** your PPE exhibits; the gear is literally *smoking* when you leave the building (not to be confused with steam coming off your PPE when leaving the fire building and going into a cold environment). This process is your gear releasing heat absorbed from the fire. If this happens you will feel the heat on your body and at best are very uncomfortable or feel pain from the burning heat. This is not the time to apply water or pat down your gear in an attempt to cool off or *put out* your gear. This will cause the air pockets within the gear to be filled with steam or collapse, keeping the superheated gases closer to your body. The discomfort you were feeling will be greatly increased.

If you are in superheated gear, follow the following steps to limit any burns you might receive. This set of procedures was developed by Firefighter Patrick Brown of the Chicago Fire Department:

1. Keep your gloves on and remove your regulator from your facepiece.

2. Loosen the shoulder straps to your SCBA.

3. Open the collar tab and closure from the top down.

4. Once at your waist strap, open the strap and open the top of your pants.

5. Open your coat as wide as possible and roll the coat and SCBA out and off your shoulders and let them slide to the ground.

6. Use your feet step on your coat and help pull your arms out of the coat.

7. Undo your suspenders and let the pants fall down and step out of your boots.

This procedure can be done by yourself or with the assistance of a firefighter on the scene. If there is a member there to assist you, tell him or her that you have super-heated gear and need assistance; talk him or her through the process.

If this does happen, your gear must be removed from service and completely inspected for any damage. There will be a good chance that the gear has been damaged and will require repairs or replacement.

AUXILIARY PPE

Many items may not be required in the NFPA PPE standards, but they do offer you convenience and safety while working on the fireground. Some items may be clips, tabs, glove keepers, and pockets on your coat and pants or the personal tools and equipment you carry in them to make your work safer and easier.

Pockets will allow you to carry tools, radio, and safety equipment at all times while keeping your hands free, reducing entanglement issues, and protecting the tools from heat and loss. Typically, bellow-style pockets that expand for storage are found on each side of the coat and each pant leg. A radio pocket can be added for radio storage, protection, and convenience. Remember that all the tools you might put into your pocket will be there all the time. They are additional weight and possibly snag or become entangled. If possible, place all auxiliary PPE inside a pocket to avoid entanglement hazards. Anything on the outside of your PPE will become an entanglement hazard (e.g., hand light, radio strap, mic cord, rope).

Whenever you don your PPE, have at least one hand light, even in the middle of the day, and a radio. If the hand light or radio has a shoulder strap, wear it under the SCBA straps to reduce the chance of entanglement. Inside every structure fire, the rooms are dark; or at a MVA, additional light might be required to see under the dashboard.

Personal hand tools such as pliers, knife, wire cutters, window punch, shove knife, screw driver (combination flat/Phillips to reduce number), door wedge (two in a pocket, one on helmet), webbing, hose strap, spanner wrench, rope, and extra medical gloves are important to carry (fig. 9–23). All these tools will be helpful whether disconnecting a car battery, resetting a pull station, or cutting your way free from entanglements. Place the life safety tools (knife and wire cutters) in a place that can be easily accessed when full PPE is donned, including SCBA, working in zero visibility. Lives could depend on the life-safety tools, so keep them accessible. Your

pant pockets may offer the best location for these tools, because your SCBA straps will interfere with access to them in a coat pocket. The remaining tools can be kept in a comfortable safe location. To keep the tools from damaging your gear, try to wrap them in a tool roller or inside an old glove, or place them in an old section of hose. The sharp points and edges will damage the expensive PPE and your body if you do not protect them.

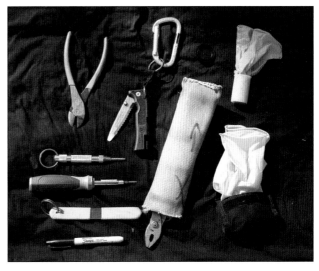

Fig. 9–23. Personal tools—your personal tools should include some combination of extra medical gloves (in a holder or even a 35 mm film case), wire cutters, screwdriver, pliers, center punch, and a knife. They can be used while performing your duties, or even to rescue yourself in an emergency.

PPE INSPECTION AND MAINTENANCE

FFI 5.5.1 Care, inspection, and maintenance of firefighting PPE is covered in NFPA 1851, *Standard on Selection, Care, and Maintenance of Protective Ensembles for Structural Fire Fighting and Proximity Fire Fighting.*

NFPA 1851 requires all PPE to be fully inspected, cleaned, and repaired (if required) a minimum of *twice* per year to prevent the buildup of containments (fig. 9–24). The contaminates your PPE holds will degrade the materials, will conduct electricity more readily, may cause illness, and may reduce your overall level of protection. By no means must the inspection and cleaning take place *only* twice per year, it can be completed more often if you see or feel there was any damage to your PPE. Remember, if it is damaged, it will not offer you full protection. The idea that having the dirtiest, most worn gear in the station makes you look seasoned or macho is long past. The contaminants found in the smoke—such as hydrocarbons, grease, and oil from MVAs, BBPs, and possibly even carcinogens such as asbestos—will penetrate the PPE and must be removed from your gear to ensure it is safe to wear.

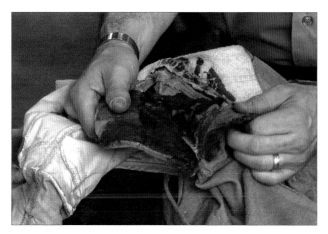

Fig. 9–24. Damaged gear being inspected

Inspections should be done to some extent after every alarm as well as prior to and after cleaning. As you are doffing your gear, look at it. Does it have a hole, burn, cut, or a seam opening? Is their any reflective striping missing or hanging? Does one area of your body get wet quickly while the remainder stays dry? These are all part of normal wear-and-tear damage that happens to all gear over time. If they are not addressed correctly, they will put you at risk.

A full inspection should be done when the gear is up for its cleaning cycle, or after any event when you feel there was the possibility of damage. Because you must remove everything from your pockets to separate the components, this would be a good time to inspect your personal tools.

Separate the outer shell and the inner liner so each component can be inspected.

The outer shell should not have any holes, cuts, separated seams, or missing reflective striping. All snaps, Velcro®, and fasteners must be in working order.

The outer shell will be able to withstand damage from heat better than the moisture barrier, and the damage to the moisture barrier might not be visible from the outside. The moisture barrier should be uniform in color. All seams should be intact. There should not be any signs of abrasion (typically in joint and pressure point areas such as the knees, shoulders, and elbows). When the moisture barrier has sustained heat damage, the area will become brown to black and can crust or char.

The thermal liner is the innermost layer and is next to your body. The sweat from your body will be absorbed into this layer, possibly causing bacterial growth. Look for signs of staining, worn seams, and quilting becoming unwoven. Some firefighters may spray air fresheners, odor removers, or other materials to remove any body odors; but this should not be done unless the materials being used are approved by your PPE manufacturer. Using non-approved sprays can result in degradation of the materials or lamination.

When any damage is found, the PPE needs to be taken out of service and either repaired by the manufacturer or certified repair facility or replaced. If you find or suspect any damage, report it to the station officer in charge of PPE.

There are two ways to properly clean your gear. You can send it to an approved cleaning facility or clean it at your station. Never bring your gear home to wash it in your own washing machine. By doing this, you will bring all the contaminants (BBP, smoke, grease, and oil) home to your family. If you clean your gear at your station, you must learn two important things. First, learn how to operate your model of washer. It might sound like something you already know, but each unit and its cleaning chemical work differently. Second, know the cleaning requirements for your gear. This information must be gathered from the manufacturers. They will be able to supply you with the correct methods, chemicals, and protocols to follow.

Never wash the outer shell together with the inner liner! The cleaning chemicals are designed differently to remove the containments from that component. Start by washing your inner liner first with the correct cleaning chemical. The reason is that the inner liner will take longer to air dry. While the outer shell is being washed, the inner liner is already drying. Do not reassemble the PPE until everything is dry. Once reassembled, everything will take longer to dry; and wet gear can grow mildew or cause steam burns. For additional information on the care and maintenance of your PPE, review manufacturer's recommendations.

If your department sends your gear to an approved cleaning facility, contact the officer in charge of PPE and follow the department protocols for sending the gear out. It will most likely be out of service for 3 to 7 days. Once it is returned, inspect it much like you would inspect your dry cleaning. Make sure it is your gear and there was no damage from the cleaning process.

NOTES

NFPA 1951 *Standard on Protective Ensemble for USAR Operations*

NFPA 1971 *Standard on Protective Ensemble for Structural Fire Fighting*

NFPA 1976 *Standard on Protective Ensemble for Proximity Fire Fighting*

NFPA 1977 *Standard on Protective Clothing and Equipment for Wildland Fire Fighting*

NFPA 1999 *Standard on Protective Clothing for Emergency Medical Operations*

NFPA 1981 *Standard on Open-Circuit Self-Contained Breathing Apparatus for Fire and Emergency Services*

NFPA 1982 *Standard on Personal Alert Safety Systems (PASS)*

NFPA 1991 *Standard on Vapor-Protective Ensembles for Hazardous Materials Emergencies*

NFPA 1992 *Standard on Liquid Splash-Protective Ensembles and Clothing for Hazardous Materials Emergencies*

Recommended additional reading material

Manufacture specifications and product information for the PPE that you are issued from your department. Include all aspects of the PPE you are issued, helmet, hood, coat, pants, boots, gloves, and eye protection. Read and understand the design and construction on the PPE that will be protecting your body at your next alarm.

Personal Protective Equipment

FIREFIGHTER I

Chapter 9

QUESTIONS

1. What is the best protection you have on the fire scene?

2. What level of hazmat protection does structural PPE provide?

3. The PASS will activate in what two modes?

4. NFPA _____ covers structural PPE.

5. What are the advantages and disadvantages of leather bunker boots?

6. What are the advantages and disadvantages of rubber bunker boots?

7. What are the three layers of structural PPE and what do they protect the wearer from?

8. What is the minimum performance criterion for thermal protective performance for structural PPE? What is this number equal to on a fire scene?

9. What is the minimum performance criterion for total heat loss for Structural PPE? What does it tell us?

10. How is the drag rescue device (DRD) designed to be used?

11. Does the face shield or flip down on a helmet provide primary eye protection? Why or why not?

12. Structural PPE should be donned within _____ minute(s).

13. NFPA requires all PPE to be formally inspected, cleaned, and repaired, if needed, a minimum of _____ times per year to prevent the buildup of contaminates.

14. What are some contaminates that can get on your PPE?

15. When should a full field inspection of your PPE take place?

16. During an inspection, what are you looking for in the outer shell? The moisture barrier? The thermal liner?

Self-Contained Breathing Apparatus

by Phil Jose, Mike Gagliano,
Casey Phillips, and Steve Bernocco

This chapter provides required knowledge items for the following
NFPA Standard 1001 Job Performance Requirements:

FFI 5.3.1   FFI 5.5.1

FFI 5.3.10

FFI 5.3.11

This chapter contains Skill Drills. When you see this icon, refer to your Skill Drill book for step-by-step instructions.

OBJECTIVES

Upon completion of this chapter, you should be able to do the following:

- List types of respiratory devices for fire and non-fire applications
- Describe how self-contained breathing apparatus (SCBA) protects the user at an emergency incident
- List the physical requirements needed by a user of SCBA
- List and describe the major components of an SCBA
- Describe and demonstrate the approved methods of donning and doffing SCBA
- Describe and demonstrate installing an SCBA regulator
- Describe and demonstrate changing SCBA cylinders and filling them
- List three activities accomplished by firefighters while wearing SCBA
- Describe how air consumption rates impact the use of SCBA at an emergency incident
- Describe the procedures for exiting a hazardous area while on emergency reserve air supply
- Describe the proper emergency measures to take when there is a failure of the SCBA
- Describe and demonstrate the proper inspection and maintenance procedures for SCBA
- Describe and demonstrate periodic inspections of SCBA unit
- Describe and demonstrate cleaning an SCBA

INTRODUCTION

This chapter introduces you to the open-circuit **self-contained breathing apparatus (SCBA)**, and includes the necessary information to meet the requirements for National Fire Protection Association (NFPA) Firefighter I and Firefighter II from NFPA 1001, *Standard for Fire Fighter Professional Qualifications*; components of NFPA 1500, *Standard on Fire Department Occupational Safety and Health*; and components of NFPA 1981, *Standard on Open-Circuit Self-Contained Breathing*

Apparatus (SCBA) for Emergency Services. These standards require firefighters to be trained in accordance with NFPA 1404, *Standard for Fire Service Respiratory Protection Training.*

OVERVIEW

Fire departments provide firefighters with many types of respiratory protection so firefighters can operate safely in all kinds of hazardous environments. Respiratory protection can include various levels of protection, from the paper dust filter-style mask to the SCBA. This chapter focuses on the SCBA as the tool of choice for respiratory protection while performing duties at a structural fire. It also provides a brief introduction to three types of respiratory protection for special applications ranging from fire investigation to confined space entry.

RESPIRATORY PROTECTION FOR NONFIRE APPLICATIONS

Fire departments often have air purifying respirators (APRs) for use by fire service personnel, like those worn by fire investigators (fig. 10–1). APRs have particulate or chemical filters that must be matched to the specific situation in which they are to be used. APRs have particulate filters, chemical filters, or combination filters to clean the air breathed by the user. Although APRs do not supply breathing air from a known source, they filter the ambient air surrounding the user. For this reason they cannot be used in oxygen-deficient atmospheres (less than 19% oxygen).

Fire departments may also use the powered air purifying respirator (PAPR), which has the same limitations as the APR (fig. 10–2). The primary advantage of the PAPR over the APR is that the PAPR unit provides a blower that supplies air to the user. This supplied air reduces the effort needed by the user to breathe, thereby reducing overall fatigue and increasing the work time of the user. Neither the APR nor the PAPR is approved for use by structural firefighters while operating at the scene of a working fire.

The supplied air respirator (SAR) is another type of respiratory protection that is available for fire department operations (fig. 10–3). The SAR provides breathable air to the user from a remote source through an air supply line. Fire departments use the SAR primarily for confined space operations. The SAR can be used safely

and effectively by trained personnel in known and properly controlled operational environments. The SAR, when used in fire department operations, includes some type of escape cylinder that is carried by the user in case of failure of the air supply line or the need for the user to immediately exit the space without time to manage the air supply line during exit. The SAR is not approved for structural firefighting and requires additional training.

Fig. 10–1. Sample of an APR often used during fire investigations. (Courtesy of Mine Safety Appliances)

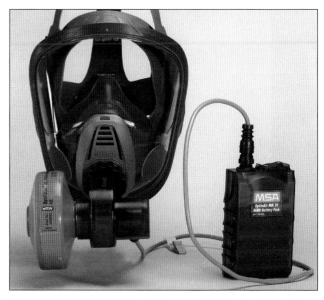

Fig. 10–2. A PAPR with the battery pack attached. (Courtesy of Mine Safety Appliances)

Fig. 10–3. This sample of a SAR shows the air supply line attached. You can also see the small escape cylinder on the waist belt. This cylinder is used for emergency egress only. (Courtesy of Mine Safety Appliances)

SELF-CONTAINED BREATHING APPARATUS

SCBA is the firefighter's tool for breathing air in structural fire environments (fig. 10–4). SCBA is a time-tested and reliable method for firefighters to have safe, breathable air while operating in the most extreme of environments. Modern SCBA are designed and stringently tested to meet the requirements of NFPA 1981 *Standard on Open-Circuit Self-Contained Breathing Apparatus (SCBA) for Emergency Services, 2006 Edition.*

Fig. 10–4. In some cases, it is necessary to use SCBA outdoors when smoke conditions dictate.

USE OF SELF-CONTAINED BREATHING APPARATUS AT EMERGENCIES

FFI 5.3.1 SCBA provides an excellent level of respiratory protection for firefighters engaged in operations at structural fires. Firefighters are provided a known quantity of breathable air for operations in immediately dangerous to life and health (IDLH) or potential IDLH environments. The IDLH environment at structural fires includes gases produced by the combustion of the building and its contents (fig. 10–5).

Fig. 10–5. This firefighter is preparing to make entry into a known IDLH environment. His respiratory protection protects him and allows him to complete his assigned duties safely and effectively. (Courtesy of Lt. John Lewis, Passaic, New Jersey, Fire Department)

FFI 5.3.10 FFI 5.3.11 The gases produced during a fire are toxic. The gases are carcinogenic. The combination of toxic and carcinogenic is IDLH for the firefighters. A common example is carbon monoxide (CO), which is present at all structural fires. CO has a much stronger affinity to red blood cells than oxygen (O) and works to displace the blood's ability to carry oxygen. The effects of CO can be seen in (table 10–1). Breathing the gases created during a fire can cause serious injury or death, even from a single exposure. The combination of toxic and carcinogenic is eventually dangerous to the firefighter's life and health. Low-level exposures to fire gases over the long term can cause serious health problems, including cancer (fig. 10–6).

Self-Contained Breathing Apparatus

FIREFIGHTER I

Chapter 10

Fig. 10–6. Before SCBA were readily available, firefighters were exposed to toxic gases while operating on the roof of the fire building. Firefighters from this era were at elevated risk for cancer because of their exposure. There is no excuse for this type of behavior on the modern fireground. (Courtesy of Seattle Firefighters Local 27)

Firefighters often underestimate the long-term damage produced by small exposures to toxic gases. There is often a cultural bias in favor of using the mask as little as possible. The reality of the modern smoke environment requires the firefighter to use the SCBA whenever any smoke is present. If you want a long and healthy career followed by a long and healthy retirement, do not breathe smoke.

The following is a brief description of a few fire gases and their effect.[1]

The deadly duo: polyvinyl chloride and hydrogen cyanide

Two of the least recognized components of the modern smoke environment are **polyvinyl chloride (PVC)** and **hydrogen cyanide (HCN)**. The former is a product present in large quantities at most fires today, whereas the latter is a deadly by-product that is the silent killer of the fireground.

PVC, a type of plastic similar to that used in plumbing piping, is likely to be found in more abundance than any other product in today's homes. It is devastating to the firefighter no matter where they are in the smoke as

its deadly fumes are emanating from materials at every level of structure. Its "emissions during fires of benzene, chlorinated dioxins, and dibenzofurans, known carcinogens, appears to explain the high frequencies of leukemia, laryngeal and colon cancer, and of rare soft tissue cancers found in many firefighters at relatively young ages."[2] PVC fires also include the presence of the highly acidic gas hydrogen chloride and other gases that impact respiratory and circulatory health.

Hydrogen cyanide is a colorless, odorless gas that emanates from both natural and synthetic sources (fig. 10–7). Unlike carbon monoxide, a common cause of death in firefighters, hydrogen cyanide is relatively unknown; but it is steadily assuming a more prominent place in the hierarchy of the causes of death at fires. It was the gas of choice for Hitler's death camps (Zyklon B) and the method the terrorists of the Aum Shynrikio religious cult attempted to use in their attack on the Shinjuku Station in Tokyo (May 5, 1995).

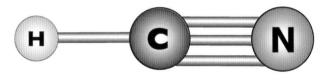

Fig. 10–7. Hydrogen cyanide molecule

A more comprehensive list of chemicals can be seen in table 10–1. Firefighters should understand that these gases are present at every fire. These gases can cause short- and long-term health problems. Furthermore, they can cause the immediate death of a firefighter from a single breath. Firefighters should not breathe smoke. The correct tool to prevent the exposure of firefighters is the SCBA. There is no better way to protect the health of the firefighter than a well-maintained, properly worn, SCBA.

Table 10–1. Toxic effects of carbon monoxide

Carbon monoxide (CO) (ppm)	Carbon monoxide in air (%)	Symptoms
100	0.01	No symptoms-no damage
200	0.02	Mild headache; few other symptoms
400	0.04	Headache after 1–2 hours
800	0.08	Headaches after 45 minutes; nausea, collapse, and unconsciousness after 2 hours
1,000	0.1	Dangerous; unconscious after 1 hour
1,600	0.16	Headache, dizziness, nausea after 20 minutes
3,200	0.32	Headache, dizziness, nausea after 5–10 minutes; unconsciousness after 30 minutes
6,400	0.64	Headache, dizziness, nausea after 1–2 minutes; unconsciousness after 10–15 minutes
12,800	1.26	Immediate unconsciousness, danger of death in 1–3 minutes

Table 10–2. Fire gases and their effect on the human body

Table of primary fire gas toxicities

Gas	Assumed LC50 (ppmv) 5 min	Assumed LC50 (ppmv) 30 min
Acetaldehyde	—	20,000
Acetic acid	—	11,000
Ammonia	20,000	9,000
Hydrogen chloride	16,000	3,700
Hydrogen bromide	—	3,000
Nitric oxide	10,000	2,500
Carbonyl sulfide	—	2,000
Hydrogen sulfide	—	2,000
Hydrogen fluoride	10,000	2,000
Acrylonitrile	—	2,000
Carbonyl fluoride		750
Nitrogen dioxide	5000	500
Acrolein	750	300
Formaldehyde	—	250
Hydrogen cyanide	280	135
Toluene diisocyanate	—	100
Phosgene	50	90
Perfluoroisobutylene	28	6

THE SCBA IN THE POSTFIRE ENVIRONMENT

In the postfire environment, the contents of the structure begin to cool. These contents continue to release toxic gases at lower concentrations. Many gases are the same as those produced during the active fire stage of the incident. Firefighters must be aware that, although a postfire environment may appear clear, toxic gases such as hydrogen cyanide and carbon monoxide and cancer-causing agents such as benzene are still released into the atmosphere (table 10–2). For this reason, firefighters should continue to wear SCBA after the fire is out and during all overhaul activities. In addition, the use of total flooding fire extinguishing system agents such as carbon dioxide (covered in chapter 30: Fire Protection Systems), an asphyxiating gas that is heavier than air, may remain after the fire has been extinguished.

Many fire departments use some type of gas detector to identify the level of CO present in the postfire environment. This is a weak attempt to identify that the air is safe enough to breathe to permit firefighters to operate without SCBA. However, this practice is strongly discouraged. There is ample evidence that low CO readings do not indicate the absence of other toxic and cancer-causing gases in the atmosphere. Keep in mind that CO readings do not provide information about particulate matter, such as asbestos, suspended in the air that will be inhaled by firefighters not wearing SCBA (fig. 10–8).

Self-Contained Breathing Apparatus

FIREFIGHTER I

Chapter 10

Fig. 10–8. Firefighters conducting overhaul operations without SCBA are exposed to toxic and cancer-causing gases. Firefighters should always wear respiratory protection in the postfire environment. (Courtesy of Seattle Firefighters Local 27)

The postfire environment, while not necessarily an IDLH environment, is a time when firefighters without SCBA are exposed to chemicals that are known to cause cancer. There is no reason to knowingly expose firefighters to these dangerous gases and chemicals when the SCBA can provide excellent protection. The SCBA provides protection for the user's respiratory tract (fig. 10–9) from toxic and superheated gases. The SCBA also provides a significant level of protection to the user's face and eyes. However, the SCBA does not protect the user from exposure to chemicals absorbed through the skin.

Many SCBA are approved by the National Institute for Occupational Safety and Health (NIOSH) to provide respiratory protection in **chemical, biological, radiological, and nuclear (CBRN)** environments. NIOSH performs extensive testing of SCBA assemblies for compliance with a variety of federal standards. As those

standards apply to firefighter and CBRN qualification, here is what NIOSH reads about their testing:

To Protect Emergency Responders Against CBRN Agents in Terrorist Attacks

The U.S. Centers for Disease Control and Prevention's (CDC) National Institute for Occupational Safety and Health (NIOSH) has a program to approve self-contained breathing apparatus (SCBA) for use by fire fighters and other first responders to terrorist attacks. NIOSH approval under the program signifies that an SCBA is expected to provide needed protection to first responders in situations where an act of terror has released harmful chemicals, pathogens, or radioactive materials into the air. Approvals are based on positive results from rigorous tests on sample units submitted to NIOSH by manufacturers, and from stringent evaluation of manufacturers' quality-control practices, technical specifications, and other documentation.

To ensure protection in CBRN environments, the firefighter should look for a CBRN-NIOSH Agent Approval label on the SCBA assembly. If there is no CBRN Agent Approval label, or it has been removed or destroyed, the SCBA is not approved for use by firefighters in the environment.

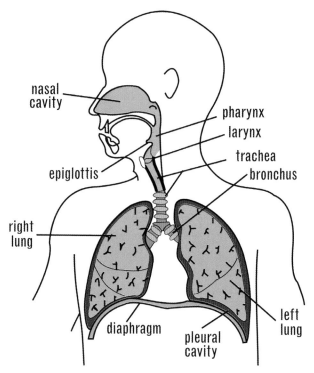

Fig. 10–9. Respiratory tract

PHYSICAL REQUIREMENTS OF THE USER

Firefighting is an extreme physical activity. Firefighters must use SCBA during all phases of firefighting operations in areas that are or could become IDLH. Fire departments should ensure that any person trained to use SCBA for emergency operations receives appropriate medical screening. Firefighting is an ultra-hazardous occupation, and the leading cause of death for firefighters is cardiac arrest. This fact alone should provide ample incentive for fire departments to ensure that all personnel engaged in emergency operations in IDLH environments receive medical screening that complies with all applicable standards. Medical screening should be performed before SCBA training and should continue to be performed annually as long as the firefighter is responding to emergency scenes.

In addition to appropriate screening, the properly trained firefighter must understand that there are multiple layers of regulations regarding the use of the SCBA in IDLH environments. These include local, state, and federal regulations. The basis for most fire department regulations related to SCBA and IDLH environments comes from the **Code of Federal Regulations (CFR)**; specifically, CFR 29 section 1910.134 sets the requirements for many parts of the respiratory protection program including the following:

- Selection of respirators for use in the workplace
- Medical evaluations of employees required to use respirators
- Fit testing procedures
- Procedures for cleaning, storing, inspecting and maintaining respirators
- Procedures to ensure adequate air quality, quantity and flow of breathing air

In addition, CFR 29 1910.134 requires fire departments to meet the minimum requirements of what is commonly referred to as the "two in—two out" rule. This rule requires that firefighters enter the IDLH as a team, the "two in." These two must be supported by at lease two firefighters outside the hazard area, the "two out", who can help if the "two in" experience an emergency. The standard reads as follows:

Procedures for interior structural firefighting.

In addition to the requirements set forth under paragraph (g)(3), in interior structural fires, the employer shall ensure that:

1910.134(g)(4)(i)

At least two employees enter the IDLH atmosphere and remain in visual or voice contact with one another at all times;

1910.134(g)(4)(ii)

At least two employees are located outside the IDLH atmosphere; and

1910.134(g)(4)(iii)

All employees engaged in interior structural firefighting use SCBAs.

As a Federal regulation, CFR 29 1910.134 applies to all fire departments. The rule above does not prevent firefighters from taking immediate action, when necessary, to save a life. This rule is also supported by other documents such as NFPA 1500, *Standard on Fire Department Occupations Safety and Health Program.*

COMPONENTS OF THE SCBA

FFI 5.3.1 The major components of the SCBA are the facepiece, regulator, harness, and cylinder (figs. 10–10 and 10–11). The cylinder holds compressed breathing air for use by the firefighter. Cylinders come in a variety of construction types and capacities. Cylinders are made of steel (not typically used today), aluminum, composites such as carbon fiber (fully wrapped), and fiberglass or Kevlar (hoop wrapped or fully wrapped). Although there are exceptions, fire service cylinders are commonly grouped into two pressure categories: low-pressure cylinders, which operate with an upper limit of 2,216 psi (15,279 kPa), and high-pressure cylinders that operate up to 4,500 psi (31,500 kPa). Regardless of the pressure rating of the cylinder, firefighters should focus on the volume of air contained within. The amount of air in the cylinder is the limiting factor for a firefighter operating in an IDLH environment.

Fig. 10–10. Components of the SCBA

Fig. 10–11. SCBA bottle valve assembly

Common terminology for fire service organizations is to refer to cylinders by their rated service time (fig. 10–12). There are three common cylinder sizes in the fire service (fig. 10–13):

- 30-minute/1,200 liter/44 cubic feet (cu ft)

- 45-minute/1,800 liter/66 cu ft

- 60-minute/2,400 liter/88 cu ft

These cylinders hold enough air for a firefighter to use at a standard rate of 40 liters per minute (lpm)/1.4 cubic feet per minute (cfm) for the rated time (table 10–3). However, firefighters must understand that air consumption rates (ACRs) during firefighting operations far exceed the 40 lpm/1.4 cfm standard and can easily reach over 100 lpm/3.5 cfm. For this reason, firefighters should not expect the air in the cylinder to last for the rated service time. The minute ratings are inaccurate for fire service applications. In a study conducted by Phoenix Fire Department, and published

in the article "Rapid Intervention Isn't Rapid" by Steve Kreis (*Fire Engineering*, December 2003), a "30-minute cylinder" will last a firefighter between 16.5 and 18.5 minutes. Firefighters should refer to cylinders by their standard volumes so there is no confusion between rated service times and actual fireground use. Air management and air consumption techniques are addressed later in this chapter.

Fig. 10–12. Cylinder label that shows capacity and minute service time

Fig. 10–13. Different types of cylinders

Before each use, the cylinder should be visually inspected to ensure that it is full, has not been damaged, and has a current hydrostatic test sticker (fig. 10–14). All cylinders have a cylinder valve and pressure gauge assembly that should be checked to ensure that the cylinder is full. Although 100% of the rated capacity is desired at all times, fire departments should establish a written policy addressing the minimum acceptable capacity for a cylinder to remain in service. The user should ensure that the cylinder is above the minimum guidelines set by department policy or the SCBA manufacturer.

Table 10–3. Standard SCBA cylinder specifications

Model	Approx. duration (min.)	PSI	Weight (lbs)	Weight (kg)
374	15	3,000	3.3	1.5
602	30	2,216	6.7	3.04
639	30	4,500	7	3.18
687	30+	3,000	8.3	3.76
603	45	4,500	9.3	4.23
695	45	4,500	9.4	4.26
604	60	4,500	12.2	5.53

Fig. 10–14. This firefighter is checking for a current hydrostatic test label before filling the cylinder at an emergency incident. (Courtesy of Seattle Firefighter Local 27)

Most manufacturers mandate exchanging a cylinder at 90% or less of the rated capacity for a cylinder. Any cylinder that does not meet the requirements must be exchanged for a full one.

Visual inspection for damage to the cylinder should also be performed by the user on a daily basis. Cylinders contain an incredible amount of stored energy, and damaged cylinders should be removed from service. There are different levels of damage (fig. 10–15). Small

nicks and scrapes from normal wear and tear are the least problematic and are considered Level 1 damage, which should be noted but does not require action by the user. Level 2 damage includes significant scraping or otherwise missing layers of the clear-coat protective cover. Level 2 damage requires that the cylinder be removed from service and repaired. Level 3 damage is anything greater than Level 2 and includes such items as damaged carbon fiber wrapping or significant damage caused by striking another object. Firefighters should be trained to recognize all three types of cylinder damage. Training should indicate the levels of damage that can be anticipated to distinguish normal wear and tear from more significant and dangerous damage. Check that the cylinder has been hydrostatically tested according to recognized national standards. Essentially, cylinders are subjected to specified high pressures using water as the pressurizing material rather than air. Cylinders require hydrostatic testing at 3- or 5-year intervals. Firefighters must be familiar with the requirements for the SCBA cylinders they are assigned to use. Cylinders that are beyond the accepted testing interval should be removed from service and identified for repair according to department standard practice.

The cylinder is held to the SCBA by the harness assembly. The backpack harness assembly has been the fire service standard for more than 50 years and has an excellent service history. Modern harness assemblies are rated to survive extreme conditions without failing. The back plate of the harness holds the cylinder in an upright position. A high-pressure line connects to the cylinder valve assembly by a threaded coupling to permit air flow from the cylinder to the regulator assembly. This connection includes an O-ring assembly and is particularly vulnerable to leaking and failure. Pay careful attention when connecting and disconnecting this fitting to ensure that the O-ring is present (fig. 10–16).

The harness assembly has waist and shoulder straps that connect the harness to the user like a backpack. These straps should be secured and appropriately adjusted whenever the SCBA is used. The harness assembly is designed to effectively transfer the load of the cylinder and backpack assembly to the body of the user. In addition, many harness assemblies, when fully connected, make excellent handholds to extricate unconscious firefighters from fire environments. Firefighters who operate without the waist belt or shoulder straps connected or properly adjusted increase the potential for negative consequences on the emergency scene (fig. 10–17). Although department policy should state that firefighters wear the SCBA properly, it is ultimately the responsibility of individual firefighters to operate safely.

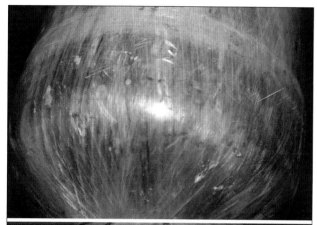

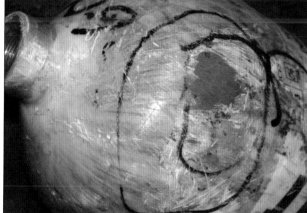

Fig. 10–15. Examples of Level 1, Level 2, and Level 3 damage

Air is provided to the user through the **regulator assembly** (fig. 10–18). First-stage regulators reduce the high pressure (4,500 psi [31,500 kPa]) from the cylinder to approximately 100 psi (700 kPa), whereas second-stage regulators reduce it to just above atmospheric pressure. Air is provided to the facepiece at slightly more than atmospheric pressure to provide a positive pressure inside the facepiece. This ensures that the firefighter is not exposed to products of combustion in case of a facepiece malfunction or inadequate seal against the face. One style regulator is belt mounted with a low-pressure tube connecting the regulator to the facepiece. The other style is a **mask-mounted regulator (MMR)**, where the regulator connects directly to the facepiece. Firefighters

should be thoroughly trained on every type of SCBA that they may be expected to use (fig. 10–19).

Fig. 10–16. Here you can see the high-pressure hose connection to the neck of the cylinder. The low-pressure alarm and the rapid intervention connection (RIC) are also visible.

Fig. 10–17. This firefighter does not have all of his SCBA straps properly connected.

Both types of regulator assemblies have **main line** and **bypass valves** attached. The main line valve allows air to flow into the regulator at a high pressure, which the regulator then reduces to just above atmospheric pressure, providing positive pressure in the facepiece. Main line valves on belt-mounted regulators are generally manually operated, while on MMRs the valve automatically opens when the regulator is placed inside the facepiece and the user inhales (fig. 10–20).

Fig. 10–18. Non-mask mounted regulator

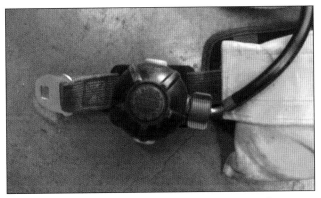

Fig. 10–19. The MMR shown here is properly stored. When placed in service, the regulator is attached to the facepiece.

Fig. 10–20. The mainline valve on this MMR is internal and operates automatically. The bypass valve is red and can be seen mounted on the left side of the MMR.

The bypass valve allows air to go around the moving parts of the regulator and flow at increased pressure directly into the facepiece assembly. Bypass valves are usually red

and are manually used only during SCBA malfunctions. Firefighters who must use the bypass valve should notify their supervisor immediately and seriously consider calling a Mayday.

The facepiece is the final component of the SCBA. The facepiece is individually sized to the user, with most manufacturers offering small, medium, or large sizes. Most facepiece assemblies offer optional equipment such as electronic voice enhancement for improved communication and **Heads-Up Display (HUD)** to assist in air management. Each firefighter must receive a fit test before initial training as well as annually to ensure proper fit. Fit testing is required by NFPA 1404 and other national standards. Fire departments should maintain a record of the annual fit test.

A **low-air alarm** is provided on all SCBA (fig. 10–21). Some take the form of a light-emitting diode (LED) lamp on an MMR and vibrating facepiece. Some SCBA manufacturers provide other types of visual and audible alarms. It is important that you determine the type of low-air alarms provided on the SCBA you will be using.

Fig. 10–21. Low air alarm on a HUD

The HUD is a great addition to the modern SCBA. The HUD allows firefighters to get information about air volume by looking at the HUD in the facepiece. While manufacturers place the HUD in different places, every HUD has a combination of lights that indicate the volume of air remaining in the cylinder by one-fourth volume increments. A full cylinder will be indicated by four green lights, 75% by three green lights, 50% by two yellow lights, and 33% by one red light. The HUD can assist firefighters in determining when they should begin to exit the IDLH environment. It is a good idea to consider beginning your exit when the 50%, or two yellow lights, marker is reached. Good air management practice will allow the entire team to exit the IDLH environment before any member reaches the 33%, or one red light, marker.

Facepiece assemblies provide air to the user from the regulator. The most common process is for fresh air to flow from the regulator through the inhalation valve across the lens to keep the lens clear of fog. The air then flows through the nose cup and is inhaled by the user. Exhaled air flows through the exhalation valve and out into the atmosphere. A properly fitted facepiece ensures that no leakage occurs around the face. The facepiece should be cleaned by the user after each use, and the lens should be inspected regularly for clarity of vision and safety. The facepiece is held to the head with a weblike harness normally consisting of three or five straps. Firefighters should be thoroughly trained to effectively and efficiently place the facepiece on the head to obtain and maintain a seal. Firefighters who use corrective lenses should consult with the SCBA manufacturer for information on placing corrective lenses inside the facepiece.

Many modern SCBA also have a built-in personal alert safety system (PASS) device, an alarm device that activates when a firefighter becomes motionless. While some firefighters still use individual PASS devices, which attach to their coat, in the past it has been shown that many firefighters failed to turn their PASS devices on. PASS devices integrated into SCBA prevent this problem: when the SCBA is turned on, so is the PASS device. PASS alarms are discussed in greater detail in chapter 9: Personal Protective Equipment.

DONNING AND DOFFING THE SCBA

FFI 5.3.1 The proper use of SCBA by a firefighter is a critical function on the fireground. If not donned properly, the unit may malfunction at a critical time. The two most common methods of donning are over-the-head and the coat methods. For both it is important that the firefighter's protective clothing be properly worn and that the SCBA be fully charged.

Over-the-head donning

The firefighter must fully open the main cylinder valve and make sure it matches the regulator gauge. With the unit being held in front of the firefighter and the cylinder valve facing away, the firefighter will lift the SCBA unit

over their head and slide the unit down their back (fig. 10–22). The shoulder and waist straps are adjusted for comfort. The firefighter will then pick up their face piece, set their chin in the chin pocket of the mask, and bring the straps/webbing over their head, adjusting the straps for proper fit and comfort. Their hood is then pulled into place and their helmet is placed on their head and secured with the chin strap. The regulator/breathing tube is then attached to the mask, the gloves are put on, and the firefighter is ready for assignment.

Fig. 10–22. Over-the-head donning

Coat method donning

The firefighter must fully open the main cylinder valve and make sure it matches the regulator gauge. With the SCBA unit in front of them, the cylinder valve facing away, and the straps to the sides, the firefighter will place their dominant hand to the opposite shoulder strap near the backplate and lift and swing the unit over their dominant shoulder (fig. 10–23). The other hand and arm will be slid between the cylinder and corresponding shoulder strap. The shoulder and waist straps are adjusted for comfort. The firefighter will then pick up their face piece, set their chin in the chin pocket of the mask, bring the straps/webbing over their head, and adjust the straps for proper fit and comfort. Their hood is then pulled into place and their helmet is placed on their head and secured with the chin strap. The regulator/breathing tube is then attached to the mask, the gloves are put on, and the firefighter is ready for assignment.

Fig. 10–23. Coat method donning

Doffing the SCBA unit

This is a reversal of how the unit was donned. The firefighter removes his gloves, disconnects the regulator from the mask, and removes their helmet and hood. The mask is removed in the following manner: Loosen head strap, if available, temple straps, chin straps, and remove the face piece. Unbuckle the waist strap and loosen the shoulder straps. While holding the shoulder strap where the regulator is attached, slide the opposite shoulder strap off your shoulder and lower the unit to the ground. Shut off the main cylinder valve and bleed of any air in the regulator by opening the purge valve. Then turn off the PASS device if it is integrated into the unit.

Installing the mask mounted regulator

To place the MMR in service, the firefighter shall pick up their face piece and set the chin in the chin pocket of the mask. They will then fit the face piece to their face and bring the straps/webbing over their head. To adjust the face piece straps the firefighter will do so in this order: First adjust the chin straps, then the temple straps and, if available, the head strap. They will make sure the straps are pulled straight back, not outwards. They will then check for proper seal. They will then pull their hood over the straps/webbing, making sure not to dislodge the face piece. Lastly, the helmet is placed on their head and secured by the chin strap. The regulator will then be attached to the face piece as per manufacturer's recommendations.

Replacing an SCBA cylinder

The firefighter will place the SCBA unit with the depleted air cylinder on the floor and turn off the cylinder valve. Any remaining air will be bled off using the purge valve. Disconnect the high-pressure hose from the cylinder valve and inspect the O-ring for damage. Release the cylinder from the backpack and remove the cylinder from the unit. Then place it by the refill station and take a full cylinder from the refill station. Make sure the cylinder is full by looking at the cylinder valve. Place the full cylinder in the unit's backpack and lock into place, and connect the high-pressure hose to the cylinder. *Hand-tighten only!* Then slowly open the cylinder valve and listen for leaks. Once the cylinder valve is fully opened, check the cylinder gauge with the regulator gauge to see that they match.

Replacing an SCBA cylinder being worn by a firefighter

Have the firefighter lean over forward and remove their helmet and hood. Disconnect the regulator from the mask. Turn off the cylinder valve on the depleted cylinder and bleed the remaining air in the hoses using the purge valve. Then disconnect the high-pressure hose from the cylinder valve and inspect the O-ring for damage. Release the cylinder from the backpack, remove the cylinder from the unit by sliding it forward and away from the backpack, and place by the refill station. Take the new full cylinder and slide into the backpack, avoiding hitting the firefighter in the head. Lock the new cylinder in place, reconnect the high pressure hose to the cylinder, and open the cylinder valve and make sure the cylinder valve matches the regulator valve. Notify the firefighter that the cylinder exchange is complete and they may return to service.

Many modern SCBA also have a built-in PASS device, which activates when a firefighter becomes motionless. While some firefighters still use individual PASS devices that attach to their coat, many firefighters in the past have failed to turn their PASS devices on. PASS devices integrated into SCBA prevent this problem—when the SCBA is turned on, so is the PASS device. PASS alarms are discussed in greater detail in chapter 9: Personal Protective Equipment.

ACTIVITIES WHILE IN SCBA

The SCBA is worn by firefighters at all structural fires and many other types of emergencies including hazardous materials, confined spaces, structural collapses, and some emergency medical alarms. It is important for firefighter trainees to have the opportunity to operate in the SCBA in enough nonemergency capacities to prepare for whatever an emergency scene may present. Thorough training includes practice in advancing hoselines, climbing ladders, crawling through windows, and many other activities that the firefighter can be expected to perform on the fireground.

Firefighters are often called on to perform a variety of tasks. To perform these tasks, the firefighter must be competent enough in the operation and use of the SCBA so that the firefighter can concentrate on the other skills. Take the example of a **primary search**. If a firefighter enters the structure from a ladder, the ladder must be taken from the apparatus, carried to the fire building, spotted and raised, and finally climbed by the firefighter to make access through a window (fig. 10–24).

Fig. 10–24. Firefighters putting up a ladder at a fire have many things to consider. Wearing the SCBA should not negatively affect the ability of a well-trained firefighter to perform basic tasks.

The firefighter then must perform a search of the fire room or fire floor, communicate within the crew, and perhaps even talk on the radio. If the firefighter is accessing the building through the front door, the firefighter may need to perform forcible-entry skills, assist with the hand line advancement, and then proceed with the search. In both examples the SCBA is expected to be a part of the firefighter's protective ensemble. The firefighter must be comfortable and confident enough with using their SCBA to safely and effectively perform the tasks. This level of SCBA comfort and confidence comes through regular and realistic training exercises. This level of SCBA comfort and confidence is maintained over a career through regular and realistic training exercises.

AIR CONSUMPTION RATES AND FACTORS THAT AFFECT THE DURATION OF THE AIR SUPPLY

Firefighters operating in an IDLH environment are limited by the amount of air they bring with them in their SCBA. Firefighters must be trained to exit the IDLH environment before the activation of the low-air warning alarm. To do this effectively, each firefighter must be aware of the amount of air they use in a given time or their **air consumption rate (ACR)**. The ACR will have a big impact on the duration of the air supply and can help firefighters and fire officers balance the needs of the incident or assignment against the ACR and other factors. Some of the factors that must be considered are outlined in the following text:

- Fitness:
  - The size, weight, and overall aerobic fitness of a firefighter affects the duration of the air supply and the ACR. As a rule, smaller firefighters use less air in a given time than larger firefighters given the same workload. Aerobically fit firefighters generally use less air than the same size firefighter who is unfit.

- Nature of the work being performed:
  - The harder the work performed, or the more physical exertion required by a firefighter, the more air the firefighter uses. This applies independent of other factors. Given an

assigned task, there are often higher workload positions within a crew. Understanding the ACR for individual members of the team can assist the company officer in making assignments to maximize team effectiveness related to the ACR.

- The environment where the work is being performed:
  - Hot, dark, smoke-filled rooms create physical and emotional stress on the human body. Although some improvement to the ACR is expected in firefighters with experience, it is important to understand the physiological and psychological stressors that apply in IDLH environments. Firefighters should be aware of their own physical reaction to environmental stressors and train themselves to control their respiratory rate and emotional state during times of high stress.

- The effects of protective clothing and repeated work cycles:
  - The modern PPE, or bunker gear, provides a great degree of protection from fire and other thermal effects. The downside to this level of protection is the encapsulation of the member within the *greenhouse* created by the sweat and heat of their own activity. Fire departments should address the ratio of work cycle to rest cycle requirements for firefighters operating in full PPE and SCBA.

- The duration of a firefighting operation inside an IDLH environment:
  - The amount of air inside the cylinder when entering the IDLH environment affects how long you can operate. The more air you start with, the longer your operating time will be. Fire department policy should address the minimum pressure, or volume, allowed before committing to an IDLH environment. In no case should this be less than 90% of the rated capacity of the cylinder. Firefighters have died after entering an IDLH environment with a cylinder that was less than the minimum required.

- How far firefighters travel inside the IDLH environment and the distance and time required to reach an area of safety:
  - Because a firefighter is required to exit the IDLH environment before activation of the low-air warning alarm (33% of the capacity of the cylinder), the firefighter must be aware of how long it takes to reach the area of safety, how much air that travel time uses, and how this affects the assigned activity. Having a clear understanding of how and when you will exit the IDLH environment allows the firefighter and the team to perform effectively in the firefight. In addition, the company officer can more easily identify whether the team can complete their assigned objective.

- Company officers coordinating the activity of the team:
  - Getting the team to complete the assigned task effectively, exit in a coordinated and safe manner, and maintain an appropriate margin for safety are necessary components of the company officer's responsibility. To do this effectively, the company officer needs information and interaction with the members of the team. The company officer also coordinates with the incident commander to arrange for a crew to relieve the team inside the IDLH environment if the team cannot meet their assigned objective and safely exit the space. This responsibility requires the company officer to know and understand the ACR for each team member and how this applies to the current team assignment. Improved understanding of the ACR as well as the factors that affect the duration of the air supply lead to improved situational awareness for all members of the team.

The ACR is a fluid factor for a given firefighter or team within an incident and over a career. For example a veteran generally experiences less stress than a rookie on the fireground. Understanding how the ACR, incident, and team members interrelate can be maintained through regular and effective training exercises with the SCBA. Well-trained firefighters, working in well-led teams, perform more safely and make their air last longer.

Self-Contained Breathing Apparatus

FIREFIGHTER I

Chapter 10

THE AIR MANAGEMENT PROGRAM

FFI 5.3.1 Fire departments are required by NFPA 1404, *The Respiratory Protection Training Standard,* to have an **air management program (AMP)**. The AMP is the foundation for understanding the relationship between the ACR, the factors that affect the duration of the air supply, effective operation of the firefighting team in an IDLH environment, and the safe exit of the team prior to the low-air warning alarm activating.

All SCBA are equipped with a low-air warning alarm. This alarm is designed to indicate to the wearer that they have used all of the air designated for operation in the IDLH environment and are now consuming the emergency reserve. Low-air warning alarms are required to activate when the cylinder reaches 33% of the rated capacity. Manufacturers have created various types of low-air warning alarms: from a ringing bell, to a vibrating alarm, to an electronic beep or whistle. Firefighters must be able to recognize the sound of the low-air warning alarm for each type of SCBA they may be required to use or hear at an incident scene. A firefighter's survival may depend on their ability to recognize, or have others recognize, the activation of the low-air warning alarm on the incident scene.

Each department is required to have an AMP that should include the following three directives for firefighters using SCBA:

1. Firefighters must exit the IDLH environment before consumption of the emergency reserve begins.

2. The low-air warning alarm indicates that the firefighter is using the emergency reserve.

3. Activation of the low-air warning alarm is an "Immediate Action Item" for the individual and the team.

Another way to look at this requirement is to simply follow the **rule of air management (ROAM)**. The ROAM states:

> "Know how much air you have, and manage that air, so that you leave the hazard area BEFORE the low-air warning alarm activates."

– Know what you have.

– Manage it as you go.

– Exit before the alarm.

The firefighter functions as a member of a team while operating in and SCBA. The team leader must understand the components of the AMP and how each applies in different situations. In all cases the team leader is required to ensure that the team follows the ROAM and exits the IDLH environment prior to the activation of the low-air warning alarm. To accomplish this, the team leader must coordinate the activity of the team in conjunction with the ACR and the air management policy. The team leader may consider assigning roles on the team based on the individual ACR (fig. 10–25).

Fig. 10–25. Company officers of the roof ventilation team quickly review assignments before going up the ladder. Understanding the high and low workload positions during a roof operation increases the effectiveness of the team. (Courtesy of Yukari Horikawa)

The team leader may rotate personnel from positions of high work to positions of low work to ensure that air use is equalized within the team. Team members should understand how to use **controlled breathing** techniques. Team leaders must have an area of safety identified (the exit out of the hazard area), estimate travel time and distance to the area of safety, and determine when the team must begin to exit to reach the area of safety before the activation of the low-air warning alarm.

IV. Controlled Breathing Techniques (1–4)

A. Breathing must be kept on a conscious level. Subconscious patterns result in breathing only through the mouth or nose

  1. Nose breathing results in
    a. Short breaths
    b. Lungs not filled to capacity

  2. Mouth breathing results in
    a. Rapid breathing
    b. Body cannot take full advantage of oxygen before exhalation

B. Suggested Patterns

  1. In through nose - out through mouth
    a. Easy to learn and remember
    b. Close to normal pattern when speaking
    c. Technique
      1) Breathe in slow and deep
      2) Hold in lungs 3–4 seconds for maximum oxygen/carbon dioxide exchange

  2. In through mouth - out through nose
    a. Allows for good air exchange without holding breath
    b. Techniques
      1) Inhale rapid and full
      2) Exhale slowly
      3) Best method for strenuous work

  3. Five-second count method
    a. Technique
      1) Inhale for 5 seconds using either of first two methods—slowly and fully
      2) Hold for 5 seconds
      3) Exhale for 5 seconds
      4) Hold for 5 seconds
      5) Repeat cycle
    b. Best for short rest breaks

  4. Skip breathing
    a. Emergency only - for conservation of air
    b. 30-minute SCBA may be extended to 2 hours
    c. Technique
      1) Inhale fully
      2) Hold breath for normal exhalation time
      3) Take additional breath before exhaling
      4) Exhale slowly
      5) Repeat cycle
    d. Important to remain mentally and physically calm

COURTESY: British Columbia Fire Training Officers Association. http://www.bcftoa.com/private/docs/training/scba.html

Exiting the hazard area prior to activation

The requirement that firefighters be trained in the AMP and exit the IDLH environment prior to the activation of the low-air warning alarm is new to the fire service and began with the adoption of the 2006 version of NFPA 1404. This practice is designed to improve the safety of firefighters wearing SCBA and provide a margin for safety in case of an accident inside the hazard area. Managing air and exiting the IDLH with a margin for safety can help prevent firefighter emergency and Mayday situations. Although rapid intervention teams (RITs) are a required and important fire scene resource, prevention of Mayday situations is always preferable to relying on intervention capabilities at the incident scene.

To exit the IDLH safely, firefighters must operate as a team. The foundation for an effective team is training before the run (event). When operating, always ensure that other members of your crew and other firefighters are not endangered by your activities. Work within the team and respond to the company officer's direction to make the team successful. Maintain your own situational awareness, including air supply and ACR. Maintain team accountability, including the location of, and distance to, your exit and the amount of air required for the team to get there safely. Complete the assigned activity and recognize when your air supply or other factors may prevent you from completing your assignment. Communicate within the team and with the incident commander whenever you have completed your task, are unable to complete your task, recognize that the fire conditions are changing, or identify fireground tasks that need to be completed. Begin exiting the hazard area so you reach the area of safety before the activation of the low-air warning alarm.

On occasion, a firefighter or team may stay too long in the hazard area and activate a low-air alarm on the way out. These situations require immediate action by the individual and the team. At a minimum, department policy should require a firefighter with a low-air alarm to contact the incident commander; identify the team; communicate the situation, the projected exit time, and location; and advise if any additional assistance is needed. Be realistic about your situation. This is no time for bravado. You may literally be betting your life on this decision. If there is any chance you will not exit before your air is exhausted, request activation of the rapid intervention team (fig. 10–26). The low-air alarm emergency should be included in fire department policies addressing firefighter emergency, urgent, or Mayday calls.

Fig. 10–26. Incident commanders can only provide assistance when they know you have a problem. Communicate the Mayday early so the appropriate resources can be sent. (Courtesy of Seattle Firefighter Local 27)

Fig. 10–27. Two SCBA temporarily stored on the ground with the regulator exposed. Improper storage can result in water or debris entering the regulator assembly and causing a malfunction. Always store the SCBA with the regulator protected.

SCBA FAILURES

The modern SCBA is a reliable piece of safety equipment when it is properly maintained. Regardless of the reliability, situations occur when the SCBA partially malfunctions or fails outright. The potential for SCBA failure is one reason firefighters must maintain a margin for error with effective air management technniques while operating in an IDLH environment.

One common cause for equipment failure is the abuse or misuse of equipment. Many photographs or video-tapes of fire scenes across America show firefighters who are abusing their SCBA by wearing it improperly. The waist belt holds the regulator assembly for most SCBA. Wearing the backpack without the waist strap attached causes the regulator to receive more abuse than with the waist belt attached. In addition, the failure to connect the SCBA's straps and belts decreases overall safety and should not be allowed. Many photographs show firefighters who have removed the MMR from the facepiece but have not stored it on the waist belt. This practice allows dirt and moisture to enter the regulator and increases the potential for failure (fig. 10–27).

Unapproved equipment attached to the SCBA can cause the device to fail. First among the list of unapproved equipment is the **cheater** that has been used by firefighters for years. The cheater is an unapproved modification to the SCBA that consists of a tube attached to the inhalation valve on the facepiece. The cheater allows a firefighter to choose between breathing the clean air provided by the SCBA or breathing the contaminated air of the fire scene. This modification violates all safety related to the SCBA and cheats only the firefighter and the firefighter's family. In this way firefighters cheat themselves out of a long life. In this way firefighters cheat their daughters out of a walk down the aisle. In this way firefighters cheat their grandchildren out of a good spoiling. Unapproved equipment should *never* be attached to the SCBA, and fire departments should deal with cheaters effectively. The firefighter should never consider attaching the cheater to their SCBA or their reputation.

The practice of **buddy breathing** is another way the user can cause the SCBA to fail. The practice of buddy breathing should not be confused with using the RIC fitting or other devices attached to the SCBA for the purpose of providing emergency assistance to a firefighter experiencing a low-air or out-of-air emergency. Buddy breathing in this context is the practice of sharing the SCBA facepiece with a civilian or other firefighter. This practice should not be condoned or practiced in any way. Firefighters must maintain their respiratory protection to ensure that they can guide an affected civilian safely from the fire building. Proper air management practices can prevent situations where another firefighter experiences a low-air or out-of-air emergency.

The best way to ensure that your SCBA provides excellent and reliable service is to ensure it is properly maintained, serviced at appropriate intervals, and checked prior to use. Training, record keeping, and effective leadership on and off the fireground prevents SCBA failure as well as the attendant urgent, Mayday, low-air, or firefighter fatality situation (figs. 10–28 and 10–29).

DAILY CHECKS – EVERY DAY

Cylinder:
-Cylinder gauge reads above 4050.
-Cylinder with less than 4050 will be replaced.
-Check condition of the cylinder.
-Damaged cylinders shall be removed from service.
-Cylinder band is fully tightened and latch locked.
-Rubber bumper is in place.

Low Pressure Audi Alarm:
-Coupling nut is hand tight at the cylinder valve.
-Bell clear of obstructions, dirt or debris.
-Quick fill cover is in place.

Pressure Hoses and First Stage Regulator:
-Check for tight fit at the bell and the regulator.
-Check for physical damage to the hose.

Second Stage, Mask Mounted Regulator:
-Follow hose checking for physical damage.
-By-pass knob closed finger tight.
-Regulator free of moisture and debris.
-Store in belt mounted holder.

ICM 2000 / Pressure Gauge:
-Open Cylinder Valve fully to charge system.
-Listen for Audi-alarm bell and ICM 2000.
-Listen for air leaks.
-Check that cylinder gauge and ICM 2000 pressure gauge read within 10% psi of each other.
-Close Cylinder Valve and bleed pressure from system using bypass until low pressure bell sounds at 1175 psi.
-Turn off alarm by pressing yellow switch twice in succession.
-Check that ICM 2000 connector nut is tight at swivel.
-Quick-fill cover is in place.

Backpack Harness and Carrier:
-Check that straps are fully extended and buckles work.
-The quick-fill hose with protective pouch in place.
-Check for cracks or deterioration in the frame.

WEEKLY – AFTER YOUR FOUR OFF

Face piece:
-Lens clean and free of cracks.
-Four adjustable head straps have not deteriorated.
-The nose cup is in place and free of debris.
-Nose cup inhalation valves installed properly.

Pass Device and ICM 2000 Check:
-Don SCBA backpack.
-Open Cylinder Valve fully to charge system.
-Stand motionless until warning tones sound, move PASS to cease tones and assure proper operation of motion sensor.
-Remain motionless and let system go into full alarm.
-Reset by pushing yellow button twice in succession.
-Manually operate ICM 2000 Alarm by depressing red emergency alarm button. Reset with yellow button.
-Check operation of backlight by pressing green button.
-Operate Bypass and listen for air flow, then close.

Operation and System Check:
-Don facepiece.
-Check facepiece seal by holding palm of hand over inlet connection. Inhale, holding breath for 10 seconds.
-Keep inlet covered, breath out to test exhalation valve.
-Connect MMR to facepiece and inhale sharply to start air flow.
-Turn on amplifier and verify operation. Turn off.
-Verify HUD operational with 4 green lights.
-Disconnect MMR.
-Close cylinder and check that the alarm pressure gauge does not show a reduction in pressure, for 30 seconds, due to leaks.
-Bleed off pressure, holding face piece close to HUD sending unit and verify that HUD and ICM 2000 low air lights flash at 1175 psi. then reset ICM 2000.
-Place backpack and facepiece on vehicle ready to respond.

SUNDAY
-Lubricate second stage regulator, belt mounted storage unit and face piece with Christo-lube lubricant.

TRAINING
Video instructions for performing the checks on this sheet are available on the in-web under Training/videos.

DATE	REMARKS – REPAIRS	DATE REPAIRED

FORM 029 Page 2 (10/2004) O:dept\forms\form029

Fig. 10–28. A sample of an SCBA maintenance document. This side of the document lists the minimum daily and weekly checks that must be performed and repair notes.

DAILY AND WEEKLY MASK CHECK

DATE	MASK NUMBER							DATE	MASK NUMBER						
1								16							
2								17							
3								18							
4								19							
5								20							
6								21							
7								22							
8								23							
9								24							
10								25							
11								26							
12								27							
13								28							
14								29							
15								30							
Company No.______ Month______ 20____								31							

Form 029 (9/2003) Indicate "OK" or "R" for repair

Fig. 10–29. This side of the document records the identity of the person who completed the daily or weekly check.

FIREGROUND NOTE

Cheating is an act of lying, deception, fraud, trickery, imposture, or imposition. Cheating characteristically is employed to create an unfair advantage, usually in one's own interest and often at the expense of others.

EMERGENCY PROCEDURES FOR SCBA FAILURE

SKILL DRILL

FFI 5.3.1 **FFI 5.3.5** Firefighters should be trained in and regularly practice for failures of the SCBA. The SCBA is a piece of mechanical equipment. No matter how well built, maintained, or checked, failure is not only possible, *it is predictable.* Although SCBA failures are rare, they do occur. Firefighter training should include the potential causes for SCBA failure and specific procedures to follow for different failure situations. Each type of SCBA should include specific emergency procedures in the owner's manual. Fire departments should ensure that each firefighter can demonstrate all emergency procedures associated with each SCBA that may be used. Although it is impossible to address all of the emergency procedures for all the manufactured styles and types of SCBA, some failure considerations are identified in the following text and a basic procedure for a cracked facepiece can be found in fig. 10–30.

One category of problems can be attributed to operating the SCBA in low temperature situations. Firefighters should be aware that low temperatures can cause freezing and icing problems. Icing can occur on the cylinder. The release of compressed air from the cylinder causes the remaining air to cool. The cooling properties of expanding air can also cause icing to occur on the hoses connecting the cylinder to the regulator assembly. In some SCBA, this icing can negatively affect the low-air warning alarm and cause a partial or complete malfunction. Such a malfunction can cause a firefighter who is not practicing air management to run completely out of air in the hazard area and may lead to significant injury or death. Mechanical failure like this is another reason firefighters must manage their air.

Low-temperature situations can also cause fogging or icing of the facepiece. The design of the positive-pressure facepiece directs the incoming air across the front of the glass lens to minimize internal fogging. The cold air causes the glass to become cold, which can increase the tendency for moisture to condensate on the outside of the facepiece obscuring the vision of the firefighter. Fogging of this type can be easily dealt with by wiping the facepiece with the gloved hand. Firefighters should be aware that this may scratch the glass or deposit debris on the lens. Anti-fogging compounds can be used to minimize the effect of internal or external fogging within manufacturers' specifications.

MINOR CRACK OR LEAK IN FACEPIECE

- Don't PANIC. The benefits of remaining calm cannot be emphasized enough when dealing with an emergency procedure.

- Leave facepiece on. The facepiece continues to provide protection to the lungs, eyes, nose, mouth, and skin. With a minor leak, leaving the facepiece on provides the best option.

- Place hand on facepiece/regulator and press against face. A leak from the facepiece from a minor crack will act similar to an inadequate fit of the facepiece seal. Due to the positive pressure of the system, excess air will leak out from within the facepiece. Pressing the facepiece against the face helps to alleviate the option that air is leaking between the skin and the seal. It helps to ensure that a leak is coming through the facepiece itself.

- Conserve air by covering crack with hand. The air coming out of the regulator is slightly above the atmospheric pressure outside of the facepiece. This helps to ensure that there is a positive pressure within the facepiece and thereby neglecting contaminated air from entering through a small hole or crack. However, if the crack/hole is not covered, the air in the cylinder is depleted at a faster rate.

- Notify officer and leave with another member. Consider your department's policy on accountability and Federal or State OSHA laws, when a member enters or leaves an IDLH.

MAJOR CRACK OR LEAK IN FACEPIECE

- Continue to cover damaged area.

- Press the manual shutoff after each breath. If air still seems to be leaking out, excess air is being lost while a hand covers the crack/hole. Engage the manual shutoff after each breath. This will thereby limit the amount of air from the cylinder that will be lost due to the positive pressure of the system.

- If manual shutoff will not release on inhalation, control air flow using purge or bypass valve. If a gloved hand over the leak does not cover enough of the crack/hole, the inhalation may not be strong enough to activate the flow of air out of the regulator. Therefore, continue to have the manual shutoff engaged and utilize the purge or bypass valve to allow enough air to enter the facepiece. A partial opening of the purge or bypass valve may be enough for a breath, then close the valve after each breath. SCBA manufactures have their purge or bypass valves on different sides. Check yours to ensure what hand will cover the leak and what hand will operate the valve.

- Notify officer and leave area immediately with a partner. Consider your department's policy on the urgency of these two emergencies in the use of your PASS and the necessity of a Mayday radio transmission.

Fig. 10–30. Cracked facepiece emergency procedure (Jarod Blake, FDNY, FDIC 2007 instructor)

Low temperatures can also cause high-pressure hose leaks with the contraction of the metal. Firefighters should take extra care to ensure hose connections are tight enough to prevent leaking during low temperatures but still loose enough to operate effectively when warm. A leaking low- or high-pressure fitting can be identified by listening carefully when charging the system with air during the daily check. Leaking SCBA that cannot be fixed should be placed out of service and identified for repair. Unexplained increases in the ACR for a firefighter may also indicate leaking. A leaking hose is cause for immediate exit from the hazard area.

High temperatures can present challenges to the firefighter using an SCBA (fig. 10–31). Although the ambient air may be hot, the breathing air supplied to the firefighter is relatively cool. This occurs because the physical properties of compressed air cause it to cool as it expands. Firefighters must be aware that the temperature around them may be quite high even though they are comfortably breathing fresh air. Training programs should include information so that firefighters can accurately identify when high temperatures exist in the IDLH environment and how to deal with them effectively when they occur. This training should include situations where rapid temperature changes can be considered indicators of extreme fire behavior, such as rollover or flashover, and the potential for serious injury or death.

Many SCBA include built-in or add-on communications devices. Communications devices often improve the ability to talk within the team or over the radio (fig. 10–32). They can present their own challenges and limitations. For example, if many devices are in the same area or the operator is in an area with thick or reinforced walls, the transmission may be compromised. It is also possible for feedback to occur if there are many communications devices within the same small area at a fire. The ability to communicate effectively is critical to fireground safety. All firefighters should be trained and familiar with any communications device that is provided for use during an emergency. Firefighters should also understand alternate techniques to improve communication through a radio microphone. Many firefighters have success by placing the microphone against the throat or against the facepiece glass while talking. One factor that will always improve communication is a calm and steady voice.

Fig. 10–31. Firefighters exposed to high-temperature fire gases while making entry or operating in an IDLH environment are well protected when they use the SCBA properly. (Courtesy of PM Brian Smith, Seattle, Washington, Fire Department)

Fig. 10–32. An example of a communication device attached to the facepiece. Firefighters should be well-trained in how to communicate effectively while operating in their SCBA. (Courtesy of Mine Safety Appliances)

Out-of-air situations, although rare, can be fatal. Firefighters should avoid out-of-air situations at all costs. It is possible to prevent out-of-air situations through good teamwork, good situational awareness, good training, and good air management practices (ROAM). Low-air situations should be considered an emergency and an urgent or Mayday should be transmitted. Firefighters' training should include methods to conserve air during low-air emergencies to maximize survival time while finding an exit or awaiting the RIT team. In all cases consider reducing physical activity to reduce respiratory demands. These can include the following:

- **Skip breathing:** Take a small breath, hold 5 seconds, take in another breath, hold 5 seconds, exhale, repeat.

- **Breath control:** Calm your mind and focus on restricting air intake while reducing physical activity.

- **Use the Reilly Breathing Technique:** Breath in slowly, exhale slowly while humming a calming song. This may also help calm your mind to help breath control.

In the rare circumstance that a firefighter runs completely out of air, the Mayday should already have been called and help should be on the way. Once you are out of air your survivability is in jeopardy. Clear thinking and calm action may make the difference. Remain calm, and do not give up. Whenever possible, leave your facepiece on. This will allow the RIT team to connect to your universal RIC connection and provide breathable air as quickly as possible.

Here is a list of last resort options for dire situations:

- Leave the facepiece on, remove the regulator, and "filter breathe" the ambient air. Use your hood or glove to filter and possibly cool the smoke. Breathe as shallow as possible. Many fire service instructors will advise you to keep low to the ground. However, this may be a bad option if the carpet has been heated to the point that it is off-gassing. If the carpet is off-gassing, the primary component will be hydrogen cyanide. One breath may be enough to incapacitate.

- Attempt to find areas where there is less contaminated air to breathe. These may include toilet tanks, wall or floor void spaces, washers and dryers, windows, ventilation shafts, and sewer vent pipes.

Use of universal rescue connection assemblies

All NFPA 1981–2002 approved SCBA come equipped with a URC assembly fitting. The **universal rescue connection (URC)** is a male quick-fill inlet found on the back of the SCBA by the cylinder valve. The URC is for use by RICs for emergency filling operations only. Some SCBA manufacturers also equip their SCBA with a shoulder-mounted quick-fill system.

Fire departments must develop and use standard operating procedures (SOPs) for URC use by RICs or RITs as well as for emergency operations. Firefighters must understand how to use the URC, under what circumstances to use the URC, and when they should not use the URC. Of course, a solid hands-on training program focusing on the URC and rapid intervention is critical to the success of firefighters using the URC correctly.

The following is a step-by-step method for using the URC in emergency situations. It should be noted that RICs must use a separate air supply (a secondary air supply), such as a **rescue air kit (RAK)**, which is a full air cylinder, a quick-fill hose, and an extra facepiece. These kits can be purchased from the SCBA manufacturers. *NIOSH does not approve the use of the URC assembly to transfer air from the cylinder of one SCBA to another SCBA. Failure to follow this warning can result in serious injury or death.*

1. To attach the quick-fill system hose of the secondary source, such as a RAK, to the URC:

   - Turn the secondary air source on, fully opening the RAK cylinder valve.

   - Remove the rubber dust cap from the male inlet fitting on the URC found on the back of the SCBA of the firefighter needing air. Be sure that the firefighter's SCBA cylinder valve is fully opened.

   - Remove the rubber dust cap from the female fitting on the quick-fill hose.

   - Push the female fitting of the quick-fill hose on the male fitting of the URC until it snaps into place. Pull on the hose to be sure the fitting snapped into place. Filling begins when the female fitting is snapped on the URC.

   - After approximately 45 to 60 seconds, pressure equalizes between the secondary air source (such as the RAK) and the SCBA of the firefighter needing air.

2. Compare the SCBA pressure gauge of the firefighter receiving air to the secondary air source cylinder gauge. If the readings are the same, the pressure is equal.

3. Disconnect the quick-fill hose after the transfill is complete.

4. Remove the firefighter who needed the emergency air outside the hazard area as quickly as possible.

INSPECTION AND MAINTENANCE

Basic maintenance on SCBA is very important. If the unit is not checked on a regular basis, there is the chance it will fail at a critical moment on the fireground. To inspect a cylinder, the following is performed. Remove the unit from its holder or container. Check the straps and backpack for any excessive wear or damage. The high-pressure hose between the regulator and the cylinder should be checked for any damage or excessive wear. Next is the cylinder. This outside should be checked for damage to the fiberglass or metal. Make sure that there is no damage around the cylinder valve. The cylinder valve should read full. Open the cylinder valve and check it against the regulator valve. If the unit is an MMR check the low pressure hose from the regulator to the pressure reducing device. Activate the integrated PASS device, if available. Connect the regulator to the face piece and take several breaths. Once this is complete close the cylinder valve, purge the air from the system and make sure the low pressure alarm activates. Close the purge valve and restore to service.

Cleaning an SCBA

FFI 5.5.1 In order for firefighting equipment to work properly, it must be maintained and cleaned on regular basis. To clean an SCBA unit, do the following. Remove the face piece from the regulator and place on the side. Then remove the cylinder from the SCBA harness. Rinse all parts of the unit with clean water to remove any debris. A soap and water solution should be used to scrub the cylinder and harness with a still bristle brush. Rinse the harness and cylinder off and set aside to dry. To clean the face piece, first mix a solution of mild soap and water in a 5-gal (19 L) bucket. Place the face piece in the solution and allow to soak. Clean the regulator using the solution and a soft-bristle brush, making sure soap doesn't get inside the regulator. Rinse the face piece and regulator with clean water and set aside to dry. When components are dry, reassemble and inspect the unit before placing back in service.

Refilling a bottle with a cascade system and a compressor system

Before any cylinder is refilled, there is certain information that needs to be obtained about the cylinder. The necessary forms to be used should be spelled out in the department SOPs. Information to be filled out will be cylinder type, required air pressure to be placed in the cylinder, cylinder serial number and identification number, the hydrostatic test date of cylinder, date of the refill. Once this is recorded, the operator needs to check the condition of the cylinder, date of cylinder manufacturer, hydrostatic test date. After these items

have been checked, the cylinder can be filled. To fill the cylinder, place the air cylinder in the shielded refill station, then fill the cylinder slowly to prevent overheating. Once you are sure the cylinder is full, but not over-pressurized, remove the cylinder from the refill station.

NOTES

1. Gagliano, Mike, Casey Phillips, Phil Jose, and Steve Bernocco. *Air Management for the Fire Service.* Tulsa, OK: PennWell, 2007.

2. Wallace, Deborah. *In the Mouth of the Dragon.* Garden City Park, NY: Avery, 1990.

LESSON FROM THE FIREGROUND

The first arriving company observes heavy smoke pushing from the first floor apartment of a two-story garden style apartment complex as they turn the corner. As the apparatus pulls to the front of the building a woman with a baby in her arms appears in the window of the second-floor apartment above the fire apartment. The officer jumps from his seat on the apparatus and races into the building to make a quick rescue. He thinks he can hold his breath long enough to make the grab and exit quickly. The unfortunate reality of this poor decision is readily apparent as the officer is seen stumbling out of the doorway gasping for air.

One of the firefighters from the first due unit has donned an SCBA while the officer ran into the building. He passes the officer who is stumbling out of the doorway and quickly makes his way to the trapped occupants. The SCBA equipped firefighter is able to quickly remove the woman and her baby to safety. Once outside, the firefighter sees the company officer on the rear tailboard sucking on an oxygen mask and being readied for a trip to the emergency room. The lesson is indelibly engraved in the firefighter's memory—always take the time to don the SCBA.

QUESTIONS

1. Firefighters are provided a known quality of breathable air for operations in IDLH or potentially IDLH. What does IDLH stands for?

2. The IDLH environment is produced by the combustion of the_____.

3. The combination of _____ and _____ substances is IDLH for firefighters.

4. What is likely to be found in abundance compared to any other product in today's homes?

5. What gas is a common cause of death to firefighters?

6. The respiratory tract is protected by SCBA use from toxic and _____ gases.

7. The leading cause of firefighter deaths is _____.

8. When should medical screening start? How often should it be done?

9. When a 2,216 psi bottle reaches _____ psi, it should be recharged. When a 4,500 psi bottle reaches _____ psi, it should be recharged.

10. How often do cylinders have to be hydrostatically tested?

11. Fit testing is required by NFPA _____.

12. Low-air alarms are required to sound when cylinders reach _____ %.

13. ROAM stands for _____ _____ _____ _____.

14. ROAM states that you should leave the hazard area _____ your low air alarm activates.

15. Skip breathing is when you take a small breath, hold for ____ seconds, take in another breath, hold for ____ seconds, exhale, and repeat.

Firefighting Basic Tools

by Rick Fritz with Michael N. Ciampo

This chapter provides required knowledge items for the following
NFPA Standard 1001 Job Performance Requirements:

FFI 5.5.1

FFII 6.5.4

This chapter contains Skill Drills. When you see this icon, refer to your Skill Drill book for step-by-step instructions.

OBJECTIVES

Upon completion of this chapter, you should be able to do the following:

- List and describe general-purpose firefighting tools and equipment
- List and describe the safety considerations for each tool
- Identify tools used during forcible entry
- Identify tools used during overhaul
- Identify tools used for ventilation
- Identify tools used in fire attack
- Identify the different types of saws used in firefighting
- Describe the maintenance requirements for each type of tool and equipment
- Describe how to clean and inspect each tool prior to and after use

INTRODUCTION

As you can see from your work in the previous 10 chapters, firefighting is a labor-intensive, tool-dependant occupation. Firefighters who master the use of firefighting tools will do well in the profession. Tools accomplish various tasks on the fireground, including cutting, cutting and striking, striking, pushing, pulling, and prying. By effectively using tools as extensions of their bodies, firefighters may multiply the force or leverage applied in a given circumstance while quickly and safely accomplishing the task.

This chapter examines the uses of basic firefighting tools during fire responses. You might not use all the tools we describe during the same fire, but chances are good that you will use at least one or more before returning to the firehouse. Subsequent chapters in this book will cover the use of these tools in greater detail.

Basic firefighting tools are categorized by what they allow firefighters to do. The first group is hand tools that cut.

TYPES OF TOOLS

Cutting tools

In the United States, engines and trucks carry two types of tools that strictly cut: one is a type of axe, the tool most recognized within the fire service, and the other is different-sized bolt cutters.

Pick-head axe. A **pick-head axe** (fig. 11–1) is a steel, single-bit axe, which means it has only one cutting blade. This blade should maintain a smooth cutting surface that is free of nicks and dings. On the opposite side of the blade is a pick. This triangular point can pierce materials such as roofing when it is necessary to create a starting point for cutting. It can also shatter materials such as glass, plastic, and fiberglass.

Fig. 11–1. Pick-head axe

FIREGROUND NOTE

These tools are as important to a firefighter as weaponry is to a soldier. Without them, the enemy is going to kill you.

An ideal axe head weighs 8 lb (3.6 kg). A heavier head will wear out the user before the task is accomplished, and a lighter head means the user must strike harder, which also will exhaust the user and make the axe hard to control.

Accuracy is the key to effectively using any axe. Swung properly, an axe will cut every time. If a user can't place an axe blade in the same place with each swing, he or she will never open a hole. If he or she continually misses the surface of the tool that needs to be driven into a door or wall, the user's firefighting effectiveness will be noticeably lessened.

To maximize your effectiveness, keep your eye on the area in which you want to drop the axe blade. Cutting with

an axe is as much hand-eye coordination as strength. Before using any axe, clear the area around you. Axes can severely injure or kill anyone they hit.

To cut using a pick-head axe, grasp the handle firmly and find a stance that is comfortable and compatible with the surface on which you are working. Try to spread your feet and center your body weight. Flex your knees a little. Hold the axe handle where it feels comfortable, but not close to its head. Your stance should feel good and give you balance. You must be able to rock back and forth on your feet while swinging to maintain your balance. Gravity, the force of the wind, bad weather conditions, a burning structure, and the weight and restrictions of your turnout gear will all work against you. Your hands should go no higher than your shoulders on the upswing. Do not let the axe head go behind your head and shoulders. The axe's weight will pull itself from your hands and create a dangerous situation. Letting the axe drop into place will allow the weight of the axe to do the work. As you swing, slide one of your hands along the shaft of the handle to meet the other hand that is grasping the bottom. Don't try to push the tool or swing with one arm stiffened because you will tire quickly. An axe swung with too much force might slip from your hands and plunge into the hole endangering crews working below you, or you could miss your mark and hit another firefighter.

Concentrate on accuracy. Swing the axe so that the blade strikes the surface you want to cut at a slight angle. A dead-on strike might cause the axe to bounce back without cutting the material. If the blade sticks in the material, don't pull because you'll fall. Work the handle of the axe up and down a few times to release the blade. For pick-head axes that are deeply stuck, release the axe by gripping the handle with one hand and grasping the pick with the other. Work the axe head back and forth to release the blade. Place a Halligan bar or piece of debris under the axe handle near the head to create a fulcrum. (A Halligan bar works better.) Push the handle down to force out the axe head.

The pick side of the pick-head axe allows a user to make a purchase point, or starting hole, in materials that are too hard or that have too much spring to allow immediate cutting. To use the pick, flip the axe over and set your stance.

The axe will swing differently because the mass of the axe head will be at the top of the axe. As you swing as though you were using the blade side, maintain a firm grip on the handle to prevent the tool from rolling to the blade side. Keep your eye on the spot you want the pick to hit, and let the weight of the tool drive the pick.

Like the blade side, the pick might get stuck. To release the pick, don't pull. Push the handle forward a little, and then pull it back toward you. If the pick still won't release, lower the handle parallel to the surface you are cutting and rotate the handle 15 degrees in either direction. The pick is self-extracting and should enlarge the hole enough to release it.

Bolt cutters. **Bolt cutters** (fig. 11–2) are another cutting tool firefighters use. They provide a quick and relatively easy method of cutting through various materials. Other tools are available to firefighters for cutting materials such as chain, lock shackles, fencing, etc., but bolt cutters are inexpensive and, when used properly, they are also fast and efficient. Most important in using bolt cutters on the fireground is having the right set for the material to be cut. Some departments keep different types of cutters on the apparatus to cut materials of various strengths. The cutting surface of the cutter may not be suitable for case-hardened material such as some chains and lock shackles, but it's better at cutting fencing, light locks, and small cable.

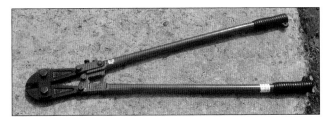

Fig. 11–2. Bolt cutters

As a firefighter, be wary of dielectric bolt cutters and wire cutters. Firefighters don't cut energized electric lines of any type, ever. Bolt cutters should be made of high-quality carbon steel with long, powerful, preferably fiberglass handles with rubber grips. Handles should be long enough to make cutting easy. The shorter the handles, the less leverage for cutting.

When using bolt cutters, evaluate the material to be cut. Ensure that you have the proper bolt cutters that will bite into and cut completely through the material. Wear eye protection because bolt cutters can launch the cut-off end of chain, bolt head, or whatever you cut. Protect yourself from flying debris. Never intentionally cut a loose end. When cutting cable or some other material, make sure of the end result before you cut. Cutting cables or cords may release an object being held up or in a tension situation, such as a garage door spring.

When performing **forcible entry**, cut lock shackles high on the shackle. Cutting too close to the lock body might jam it if you don't cut all the way through or if the cutters

twist. Cutting high on the shackle gives you another place to get a purchase if you can't get the leverage for the first cut. Bolt cutters are not designed to cut case-hardened material such as high-security padlocks and some security gates. Using a firefighter on each handle is dangerous. The bolt cutter blades might dimple or shatter, and the hinge mechanism of the bolt cutters might self-destruct under the tremendous pressure and force. If you encounter case-hardened materials, select another tool.

Bolt cutters can be used to remove wire lath or mesh during overhaul, and they can be used in conjunction with a hook. With the hook, knock the plaster loose. With the bolt cutters, cut the staple that holds the mesh to the wall. Peel back the loosened mesh with the hook.

Bolt cutters can also twist off, *not cut*, battery terminals on cars and trucks. Be extremely cautious working around the battery cells of hybrid cars. The voltage can be lethal.

Cutting and striking tools

There are many cutting tools available to firefighters. Handsaws, power saws, chain saws, hydraulic cutters, and other rescue-type tools are covered in other chapters of this book. The next category of tools is a step up from single-use tools; these tools allow firefighters to cut and strike. These tools include the flat-head axe and splitting maul.

Flat-head axe. The **flat-head axe** (fig. 11–3) is a steel, single-bit axe. Its blade should also be maintained with a smooth cutting surface that is free of nicks and dings. Unlike the pick-head axe, the opposite side of the flat-head axe is a flat striking surface that can be used as a sledgehammer.

Fig. 11–3. Flat-head axe

To use the flat-head axe as a cutting tool, see the previous directions for the pick-head axe. A slight difference exists in the way the axe handles because of the absence of a pick. Otherwise, the axes are identical in use. When using the flat-head axe as a striking tool, allow the weight of the tool to do the work. It is not necessary to swing the tool in a full arc to get the benefit as a striker. Hold the tool at waist level. Line up the flat striking surface against the tool or object you will strike. Instruct the firefighter holding the tool you will strike to stay still. Don't allow the tool being held to move. If you miss, you will certainly strike the firefighter holding the tool, and that will spoil his day.

Arrange your stance so you can effectively and strongly pivot your hips and hit your target. By putting your body weight behind the flat-head axe, you will strike and efficiently drive the tool into or through the target.

Eight-pound splitting maul. The **eight-pound splitting maul** (fig. 11–4) is another tool that will complement your cutting and striking capabilities on the fireground. The maul has a sledgehammer face on one side and a wedge-shaped splitter on the other side. The splitting maul can replace the flat-head axe in some forcible-entry situations. Its weight is effective, it provides cutting and striking surfaces, and it is inexpensive and readily available.

Fig. 11–4. Eight-pound splitting maul

The splitting maul is used primarily the same way as a flat-head axe. It is swung and used the same as a striking tool. The biggest difference is that the maul does not cut. It is designed to split wood, so it is a bit more brutal. The splitting maul makes short work of roof ventilation. Once the site for the vent hole has been selected, a firefighter can smash a hole through the roofing material, rather than cut it. The splitting maul easily splits oriented strand board (OSB) sheeting and even plywood. No shingles have to be pulled, and because of the shape of the head, a simple twist of the handle to the right or left will free the tool head.

Using this tool is much like using an axe; a proper stance must be taken to properly swing it. Hold the splitting maul as you would an axe. The head is a little more off-balance because the bulk of the weight is to the rear of the head.

When using the cutting edge, expect the tool's tendency to invert to the striking side. Hold the handle tightly and prevent it from flipping around in your hands when you swing and strike. Be prepared to shift your weight to accommodate the off-balance head.

As with every cutting or striking tool we have discussed, accuracy is key. Do not swing giant strokes. Slide one hand down the handle no more than shoulder high to meet the other hand that has a firm grip on the bottom of the handle. Allow the weight of the tool to do the work.

When the maul gets stuck, free it by twisting the handle to the right or left about 15 degrees. Pulling will cause you to lose your balance and fall. Remember, this tool is designed to split wood, not cut like an axe. A heavy, deep stroke might bury it into the material being cut and make for difficult removal.

When using the splitting maul or flat-head axe as a striking tool, allow the weight of the tool to do the work. It is not necessary to swing the tool in a full arc to get the benefit as a striker. Hold the tool at waist level. Line up the flat striking surface against the tool or object to be struck. Don't move the tool. Arrange your stance so you can effectively and strongly pivot your hips and hit the target.

Wall breaching and situations that require greater force than can be delivered with an 8-pound tool call for a sledgehammer.

Striking tools

Types of striking tools. A **sledgehammer** (fig. 11–5) is used for one purpose: to strike an object or another tool. A sledgehammer has striking surfaces on both sides of the head. It is often mistakenly called a maul, which has a striking surface on just one side of the head; there is another tool on the opposite side. The splitting maul is a true maul. The sledgehammer is a big, heavy hammer.

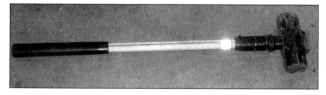

Fig. 11–5. Sledgehammer

Only four firefighter tools are engineered to strike other tools: the back of the flat-head axe, the eight-pound splitting maul, the sledgehammer, and, in certain circumstances, the Halligan bar.

When you select a sledgehammer as a striking tool, the weight of the tool is important. To drive a stake into the ground, to hold a deluge gun, or to strike a Halligan bar in breaking a lock, you must determine how hard to swing. If you have to swing too hard, get a heavier hammer. Swinging hard does not mean swinging accurately.

Weight is the key. Sledgehammers should weigh 8, 10, 12, or 16 pounds (3.6, 4.5, 5.4, 7.3 kg). The mass of the tool determines how effective it is, as well as your ability to swing and strike effectively and accurately. Special care must be taken when you swing a sledgehammer, regardless of its weight. There is no need to swing a sledgehammer over your head and out of sight. Controlling the tool is paramount for your safety and the safety of others. If you find yourself swinging the tool into a position out of your peripheral vision, use a heavier sledgehammer.

Tool safety

Swinging your tools. You should never lose sight of the tool during your swing. That means no over-the-head or way-around-sidearm, off-behind-you swinging. Keep the tool head in site and maintain good hand-eye coordination to deliver the maximum effective blows on target. Missed blows are just that many more strikes you'll have to make to accomplish the job, and too many missed blows can damage a tool.

Carrying your tools. Safety is a number-one priority at all times on the fireground. Axes, mauls, and sledgehammers are dangerous tools that can do great bodily harm if they are not handled carefully. The safest way to carry an axe, maul, or sledgehammer is to grasp the handle close to the head of the tool with the handle pointing away from you. You can use the handle to gently clear your path without hurting anyone with the steel tool head. You can also use the tool as a search tool when you carry it this way. The handle will act as a blind man's cane, allowing you to extend your reach safely during a search. An axe can be carried with the head of the tool tucked under your arm, blade facing backward, pick facing forward. Hold your hand over the pick. A flat-head axe may be carried under the arm with the blade facing backward, away from the body. If you carry either axe in a belt, always sheathe the axe. Never crawl with an axe in your belt. The weight of the axe head will cause it to slide out.

Prying tools

Next to cutting tools for getting to a fire, the most important group of tools can pry or increase your leverage. They are pry bars, claw tools, and Halligan-type bars.

Pry bars. **Pry bars** are the ultimate in simplicity because they are basic, true levers. There are two types. **Pinch-point bars** (fig. 11–6) have only one beveled side. **Wedge-point bars** (fig. 11–7) have a bevel on both sides

of the bar, forming a wedge point. Both bars are available in various sizes, dimensions, and weights. Both inexpensive pry bars are limited-use tools because many fire service tools work more efficiently. Nevertheless, these ultimate levers should not be removed from service. Learning how to use them will equip you to handle many situations. Their use in collapses, heavy rescues, and some confined-space, industrial rescues cannot be matched by any other tool.

Fig. 11–6. Pinch-point bars

Fig. 11–7. Wedge-point bars

A pinch bar and wedge bar are probably carried on at least one of your rigs. Neither will get much use, but when needed, one or the other will be the only tool that works. The pry bar can be used in conventional forcible entry to force open doors, windows, etc. These bars should not be the first choice for forcible entry. The wedge-point bar has a slight advantage over the pinch-point bar in conventional forcible entry. When combined with a striking tool, the wedge point of the bar can be driven into a door, window frame, etc. The wedge shape allows the tool to slip readily into recessed areas while spreading force is applied in both directions. Once the tool has been driven deeply into the door or window frame, force can be applied and the door or window will open.

A big advantage pry bars have over other tools is their length and narrow profile. These tools can be used with a proper fulcrum to raise collapsed material, machine parts, automobiles, trees, and other debris that has fallen or blocked a means of egress.

A firefighter may use a pry bar when stabilizing a car with cribbing by using the cribbing as a fulcrum. Firefighters can gently move or lift a vehicle by slipping cribbing materials under the frame.

During overhaul operations in plaster and lath fire buildings, firefighters can insert a pry bar into the bay of a wall and quickly open the walls. The entire length of the tool is then used, and there is no chance of snapping the tool as there is when performing the procedure with an axe handle.

Pinch-point bars are excellent tools for prying up wood floors. By inserting the tool bevel-side-up into the seam of a wood floor, a user can drive the tool in and lift the first piece of flooring. Then, using the tool as designed, the user can apply leverage and the flooring will come up. Two firefighters, each armed with a pry bar, can quickly remove many floor surfaces this way. Once the first piece is removed, the rest will follow easily.

Baseboards, moldings, and door and window frames are also easily removed with a pry bar, and, often, a firefighter will not need to bend to insert the tool. Allow the pry bar to slide along the face of the wall. Both wedge-point bars and pinch-point bars will almost always find the joint between a wall and a baseboard. Allow the weight of the tool to slide and force its way between the wall and baseboard. Pry outward, and the baseboard or molding will pop off.

Pry bars have a variety of uses, none of which has to do with using the tool as it was designed.

To make firefighting operations safer, you may use the tool as a securing post for ground monitors or deck guns. A pry bar can be driven into the ground like a fence post, and a monitor can be secured to it to prevent it from walking. The pry bar must be driven in deeply and could be difficult to remove following a fire, but it provides a secure post to which you may lash a gun.

Pry bars can also be used for securing ladders to windows. Place a long pry bar horizontally inside a window, and secure the ladder rung or beam to the pry bar. Apply sufficient pressure with the rope to pull the pry bar tightly against the interior window framing or walls. Ensure that the pry bar is substantially wider than the window.

Pry bars also make good handles for carrying basket stretchers or other heavy objects. Properly lashed, a bar provides handles for several firefighters to carry a stretcher or heavy object.

Claw tool. A **claw tool** (fig. 11–8) is a step up from a pry bar. It is a multipurpose prying tool, and although not extremely versatile, it can perform many tasks on the fireground when used correctly. Forcible-entry procedures can be performed easily with the claw tool.

Fig. 11–8. Claw tool

Its biggest disadvantage is the absence of an engineered striking surface on the hook end. When combined with a striking tool, a claw tool can be driven in and conventional, forcible-entry techniques can be used. The tool's length makes it a great lever, but at 42 in. (1,067 mm) long or more and with two sharp ends, it's a tight fit in narrow hallways and rooms. When using the fork, you must pay attention to the hook end. If the claw tool is not well set and it slips, the point of the hook end can rip skin and hook and tear face pieces.

The claw tool can also open windows. The fork can slide between the bottom rail of a window and its sill. Remember the principle of leverage and set the fork well. Once the fork is slid as far as possible, pry down on the bar. The screws holding the window lock should pull out.

The fork end can also shut off residential, light commercial, and industrial gas valves. The distance between the tines of the fork allows a good bite on gas valves.

Sliding both sides of the shackle into the fork and twisting or prying down with a sharp motion can twist off padlocks. Proper sizeup is key. If the hasp or other device to which a lock is attached is not of good, strong material, do not twist off the lock. The claw tool should be flipped over to use the hook end for easily breaking padlocks. The striking surface of the tool can be used, making this technique much safer than twisting.

The claw tool makes an excellent overhaul tool as well as a forcible-entry tool. Here, its length is an advantage because a firefighter doesn't have to bend so much when removing baseboards and flooring. The hook works well for prying up flooring and subflooring, and the curve of the hook acts as an effective fulcrum when rocking the tool back to apply force to the floorboards. The fork can also slide under floorboards to easily pull up flooring. The 42-in. (101-cm) or longer length is a mechanical advantage for heavy-duty work such as overhaul.

A firefighter wouldn't want to work with the claw tool over his or her head for long. The tool is best used at waist level or below. Fourteen pounds is a lot of weight to hold overhead when removing upper window casings and door trim.

The claw tool has some minor special uses, but they are limited. The hook end is an effective ripper for getting a firm bite into ductwork and other light-gauge, metal surfaces. You may use it to easily perforate and remove ductwork or metal. The curve of the hook end is a great handle when using the claw tool to open walls. Once a hole is created in a wall, slide the tool fork-end-down into the hole. Grasp the hook end and pull toward yourself.

The entire length of the tool will pull through the plaster and lath or wallboard, making opening much easier.

Halligan bar. If there has been one fire service-driven innovation that changed the way fire service operations are conducted, it was Chief Hugh Halligan's **Halligan bar** (fig. 11–9). Developed in the 1940s, this bar is now the preferred prying tool. It is the most efficient, effective tool available to any firefighter for tasks that require leverage (fig. 11–10).

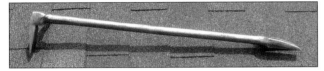

Fig. 11–9. Halligan bar

Fig. 11–10. Halligan bars

The many functions of the Halligan bar depend on leverage. The tool's design allows for multiple functions with one tool, but leverage is the key. Halligans are available from 20-in. (508 mm) lengths to 42-in. (1,067 mm) lengths. The longer the bar, the greater the amount of leverage it is capable of producing. Its use will dictate what length you need. A 30-in. (762 mm) Halligan bar is the best bar for day-to-day, conventional forcible entry, ventilation, overhaul, and other standard fireground activities. Shorter and longer bars have their places, but you can optimize your tool selection with a 30-in. (762 mm) bar. Weight is also a consideration, and the 30-in. (762 mm) bar weighs only 9 lb (4.1 kg).

The Halligan bar is a single piece of forged steel. The adz end of the tool should gently curve and flare slightly from the tool's shaft to the end of the adz. The adz should be beveled, with the bevel on the topside of the adz. At a 90-degree angle to the adz is a hook point or pick. Wide at the base where it joins the tool, the pick should also taper and curve, ending in a sharp point. The adz portion of the Halligan tool has three areas designed as striking surfaces: the top of the tool, the side opposite the pick, and the side opposite the adz. These striking surfaces are designed to receive heavy blows from a striking tool, or to be used as striking tools themselves.

The shaft of the tool is usually at least $^{15}\!/_{16}$-in. hexagonal steel. The hexagonal shape adds strength and rigidity, and the many faces improve a firefighter's grip on the tool.

The fork is broad and tapered. It should be a minimum of 6 inches long and taper into two well-beveled tines. The bevels are located on top of the tines. The spacing between the tines allows gas valves, padlock hasps, and other objects to be inserted and levered by the tool. The bottom side of the fork is called the beveled side, and the topside of the fork, or "dished" side, is the concave side. There are no engineered striking surfaces on the fork. The tool may or may not have an attached ring just above the fork to which you may snap a utility rope for hoisting and lowering, attaching a carrying strap, or throwing the tool off a roof to ventilate upper-floor windows.

There are other versions and takeoffs of the Halligan bar. Two versions are the **San Francisco bar** and the **Chicago Patrol bar**. Although both are outstanding tools, the Halligan bar is more universally used by the fire service.

Push-pull tools

Pike pole. The **pike pole** (fig. 11–11) is one of the oldest tools in our arsenal of weapons to combat fires and, next to the pick-head axe, is the most readily identified tool of our trade. Pike poles are used during most fire incidents to pull apart debris and burning materials, open walls and ceilings, remove trim, and allow engine companies to find and extinguish deep-seated fires.

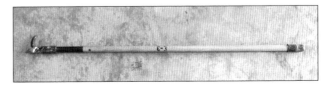

Fig. 11–11. Pike pole

There is a variety of pike poles. Your department may or may not have a selection of pike poles for you to use. Pike poles come with different pike head styles to suit different materials, different handles that make them stronger and more durable, and different lengths to accommodate working overhead or below grade.

Pike pole handles come in three basic materials: wood, metal, and fiberglass. The shape of the pole can be round, oval, or I-beam. Wooden handles can be pine, hickory, or ash. Fiberglass handles can be solid round or oval, hollow core, or solid I-beam. Metal handles can be stainless steel, plain steel, or aircraft steel.

The biggest problem is the pole's diameter. Some fiberglass pike poles are 2 in. (52 mm) or more in diameter. They are extremely difficult to work with because they don't fit in your hand, they are slippery when wet, and they are difficult to stow on the apparatus.

Pike pole length is always a hot topic in firehouses. Many departments use short pike poles: 4 ft (1.2 m) long or shorter for working in tight areas. Many firefighters prefer this set-up. Tip: you'll be much more efficient if you use a Halligan bar in place of the short hook.

Pole length should depend on the type of structure for which you use it. Consider taking the standard 6-ft (2-m) pole as the minimum-length pole carried for standard firefighting operations. A 6-ft (2-m) pole will easily reach most parts of a residential structure that you will need to reach. It can be carried into and out of structures safely and can be maneuvered easily inside.

The 8-ft (2.4-m) pole should be the minimum-length pole taken into a commercial structure or light-industrial building.

The 10-ft (3-m) pole is not suitable for a typical residential home, or is it? Do you have any mansions in your jurisdiction? Large homes often have building features that require a 10-ft (3-m) pole. The pole is a bit cumbersome in single-family dwellings and sometimes won't fit. Have one available for overhauling large houses and commercial structures and for ventilation operations. The 10-ft (3-m) pole is the most useful pole in commercial buildings and light-industrial buildings.

Some poles become extremely flexible at 10 ft (3 m) or longer, especially oval fiberglass poles. It's like trying to use a fishing pole to pull ceilings: The head end bends and wobbles. Consider solid wood or fiberglass for long poles.

Pike poles come with various head styles. The most common is the standard pike pole. You will find many

stored in compartments or on the side of the apparatus (figs. 11–12 and 11–13).

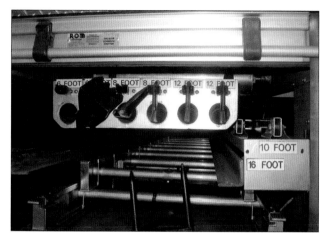

Fig. 11–12. Apparatus tool compartments

Fig. 11–13. Tools hung on the side of an apparatus

Other poles. Other styles of pike poles you might see in your department include the following (fig. 11–14 from left):

- The **Boston rake** is a great tool for older buildings with plaster and lath walls.

- The **Chicago pike pole** is a favorite tool of the CFD because the originals were made by the CFD shops.

- The **Providence hook**, a special hook with a cutting surface on the backside of the point (pike) and another on the top of the hook, pushes easily into gypsum and plaster, downside. The head is so thin that it doesn't pull a lot of material on the down stroke. It's great for light, tin ceilings.

- The **Halligan hook**, also known as the multipurpose hook, was invented by Hugh Halligan, inventor of the Halligan bar. With its engineered angles, this hook makes quick work of overhaul. Ceilings, moldings, baseboards, and other trim offer little or no resistance.

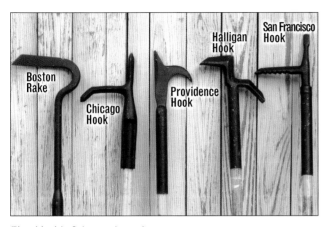

Fig. 11–14. Other pole styles

Fig. 11–15. New York hook

- The **San Francisco hook**, named because the city has many lath and plaster houses, quickly penetrates plaster and lath and pulls big holes in ceilings and walls during overhaul. The chisel point on the top of the pike allows for quick, efficient trim removal.

- The **Falcon hook**, a modified Halligan hook with broadened hooks and a curved cutting blade at the top, is a great hook for lightweight, metal buildings, tin ceilings, ductwork, and other hard-surface materials.

- The **New York hook** (fig. 11–15), official hook of the FDNY, is similar to the standard hook in configuration, but is beefier. A great hook for heavy-duty work. The head design allows more leniency when used as a prying tool.

- The **Gypsum board hook** (fig. 11–16) isn't really a hook at all, but a clawed rake that can chew and open up gypsum wallboard with little or no effort on your part. The angled jaw and cutting blade make pulling drywall easy. If you can get your hands on one of these during overhaul, it will become your favorite style of hook.

- The **L.A. trash hook** or **rubbish hook** (fig. 11–17) isn't really a hook, either; it is also a rake. Often referred to as an arson rake or trash hook, this tool is great for raking trash around in a burning dumpster to make sure you've gotten it all. It works as a tremendous lever in removing beadboard ceilings. Taken to the hook, the design of the tool head allows you to push down large sections of ceiling without getting tangled in the wiring.

Your department may or may not have any of these hooks in addition to a standard pike pole. Mutual aid departments might have them. The more you know about tools in the fire service, the better firefighter you will be.

Fig. 11–16. Gypsum board hook

Fig. 11–17. L.A. trash or rubbish hook

USED FOR WHAT?

We've looked at a lot of the basic tools you will use during most fires. When you get which tool and for what will depend on your department's operating procedures and

Firefighting Basic Tools

FIREFIGHTER I

Chapter 11

the wishes and tactics of your company officer. Basically, they are the following:

Cutting tools

1. Pick-head axe (fig. 11–1): forcible entry, overhaul, rescue, fire attack, ventilation.

2. Bolt cutters (fig. 11–2): forcible entry, rescue.

Cutting and striking tools

1. Flat-head axe: forcible entry, ventilation, fire attack, rescue, and overhaul. When married to a Halligan bar, the set of tools is known as a **set of irons**.

Prying tools

1. Pry bars (figs. 11–6 and 11–7): forcible entry, ventilation, fire attack, rescue, overhaul.

2. Claw tool (fig. 11–9): forcible entry, ventilation, fire attack, rescue, overhaul.

Striking tools

Four tools available to firefighters are engineered to strike other tools and are used for forcible entry, ventilation, fire attack, rescue, and overhaul:

1. Back of the flat-head axe (fig. 11–3)

2. Eight-pound splitting maul (fig. 11–4)

3. Sledgehammer (fig. 11–5)

4. Halligan bar (fig. 11–9 and 11–10), in certain circumstances

Push-pull tools

Pike poles (figs. 11–11, 11–14, 11–15, 11–16, 11–17) are primarily used for overhaul, although in some instances they are needed during fire attack and have been used in rescues.

TOOL MAINTENANCE

FFI 5.5.1 FFII 6.5.4 Don't be too disappointed if the tools at your department could use a little work. Basic hand tools sometimes get overlooked for simple maintenance. Maintenance does not take long and is an outward sign of great company and departmental pride.

You will also find that a little effort in the firehouse yields tremendous advantages on the fireground. Well-maintained tools look good, function well, and are safer than neglected tools.

Note: Do not perform any maintenance on your company's tools without authorization.

Cutting tools

1. **Pick-head axe:** Remove all paint from the axe head. Sand or use a wire brush until the steel is clean and shiny. Use a mill bastard file to maintain the cutting edge of the axe. Do not over sharpen. Do not use a grinder. When finished, put a thin coating of light machine or motor oil on the tool head. Do not use any lubricant that contains 1,1,1-trichloroethane.

   Handles:

   a. Wood: Sand smooth. Inspect for splintering and cracks. Wipe with a tack cloth to remove dust. Coat handle with boiled linseed oil. Work well into wood.

   b. Plastic: Clean thoroughly with mild detergent and scrub brush. Dry thoroughly.

   c. Fiberglass: Inspect for splintering and cracks. Clean with soap and water. Dry thoroughly. If needed, rough spots can be sanded with fine-grit paper and wiped with a damp cloth. If fibers are showing or if cracks develop, replace handle.

2. **Bolt cutters:** Use a mill bastard file to maintain the cutting edge on the blades of the bolt cutter jaws. When finished, wipe entire tool with light oil. Do not get oil on rubber handles.

Cutting and striking tools

1. **Flat-head axe:** Remove all paint from the axe head. Sand or use a wire brush until the steel is clean and shiny. Use a mill bastard file to maintain the cutting edge of the axe. Do not over sharpen. Do not use a grinder. When finished, put a thin coating of light machine or motor oil on the tool head. Do not use any lubricant that contains 1,1,1-trichloroethane.

   Handles:

   a. Wood: Sand smooth. Inspect for splintering and cracks. Wipe with a tack cloth to remove dust. Coat handle with boiled linseed oil. Work well into wood.

b. Plastic: Clean thoroughly with mild detergent and scrub brush. Dry thoroughly.

c. Fiberglass: Inspect for splintering and cracks. Clean with soap and water. Dry thoroughly. If needed, rough spots can be sanded with fine-grit paper and wiped with a damp cloth. If fibers are showing or if cracks develop, replace handle.

Prying tools

1. **Pry bars:** Use a mill bastard file to maintain the bevels on the adz and forks. Sharpen the pick. Use fine-grit sandpaper or a wire brush to remove all rust and debris. Wipe entire tool with light motor oil.

2. **Claw tool:** Use a mill bastard file to maintain the bevels on the point and forks. Use fine-grit sandpaper or a wire brush to remove all rust and debris. Wipe entire tool with light motor oil.

Striking tools

1. Remove all paint from the tool head. Sand or use a wire brush until the steel is clean and shiny. Use a mill bastard file to maintain the striking surface of the tool head. Do not remove too much metal or change the shape of the tool face. Do not use a grinder. When finished, prime and paint the tool head with a quick-drying, acrylic paint.

   Handles:

   a. Wood: Sand smooth. Inspect for splintering and cracks. Wipe with a tack cloth to remove dust. Coat handle with boiled linseed oil. Work well into wood.

   b. Plastic: Clean thoroughly with mild detergent and scrub brush. Dry thoroughly.

   c. Fiberglass: Inspect for splintering and cracks. Clean with soap and water. Dry thoroughly. If needed, rough spots can be sanded with fine-grit paper and wiped with a damp cloth. If fibers are showing or if cracks develop, replace handle.

Push-pull tools

Use a mill bastard file to maintain all sharp surfaces on the tool head. Using fine-grit sandpaper, remove all dirt and rough metal from the tool head. Prime and paint.

Handles:

a. Wood: Sand smooth, inspect for splintering and cracks. Wipe with a tack cloth to remove dust. Coat handle with boiled linseed oil. Work well into wood.

b. Fiberglass: Inspect for splintering and cracks. Clean with soap and water. Dry thoroughly. If needed, rough spots can be sanded with fine-grit paper and wiped with a damp cloth. If fibers are showing or if cracks develop, replace handle.

POWER SAWS, CHAIN SAW, RECIPROCAL SAW

Rotary power saws

Rotary power saws play a big part in firefighting tactics and procedures. These saws are commonly used to assist firefighters in performing forcible entry, ventilation, breaching, and demolition operations. The rotary power saw is commonly called a cut-off saw, demolition saw, or rescue saw (fig. 11–18). Some firefighters also associate a specific brand name or model number and often call the saw by that nomenclature.

Fig. 11–18. A rotary power saw

A rotary saw is a portable saw with a **two-cycle engine** that normally runs on a gas-and-oil fuel mixture. The engine's driveshaft powers a clutch assembly that operates a drive belt that is driven over two pulleys that spin the blade. As the blade spins, a specific material is cut. The speed of the saw is controlled by the firefighter as he or she applies pressure on a throttle lever in the saw handle. For the firefighter to control the saw during cutting, his or her hand that is not controlling the saw's speed must hold onto the carrying handle.

The rotary saw can be equipped with a variety of blades to cut a range of materials. **Carbide-tip blades** are normally used for roof ventilation and cutting wood flooring (fig. 11–19). These blades cut through tar-covered roofs, Lexan®, acrylic glass panels, and light-gauge metal (i.e., "**Q-decking**," metal, aluminum, and vinyl siding). These blades should not be used to cut case-hardened locks, roll-down security gates, or structural steel components because the tips could snap off the blade causing a severe injury to a firefighter.

Fig. 11–19. Carbide tipped blades

For a rotary saw to cut heavy-gauge metals, it must be equipped with the proper blade (fig. 11–20). Rotary saws equipped with **aluminum oxide abrasive blades**, sometimes referred to as discs, will cut these metals (fig. 11–21). These blades are made up of metallic and composite materials held together by an organic bonding agent. These blades may also be reinforced with a fabric or fiber base that prevents the blade from breaking apart during cutting operations. The blades cut through material by friction and heat the metal being cut, disintegrating it into sparks, chips, fragments, and dust. The life span of these blades is relatively short if a large amount of metal material must be cut. The aluminum oxide blade can also cut through wood, although it's not the blade of choice. It actually burns through or grinds up the wood as it is cut.

A rotary saw with a **silicon carbide blade** or abrasive disc can cut through concrete, mortar, brick, block, tile, and stone. The blade closely resembles the aluminum

oxide blade but is made of different composite materials that when applied to materials heats it through friction, causing the material to turn into chips and dust. To distinguish the two blades, some fire departments label or paint identification labels on them.

Another blade commonly used in the fire service is known as a multi-functional, multi-purpose blade or **diamond-cut grit blade** that will cut materials such as steel, concrete, and wood. These steel blades closely resemble carbide-tip blades. The major difference is that they are covered with industrial diamonds and grit held together by a bonding agent located toward the tips of the blade. These blades normally don't need lubricating fluids or water to assist the blade in its cutting efforts. The only minor downfalls are that these blades are expensive and once the diamonds become worn, a blade will not cut well.

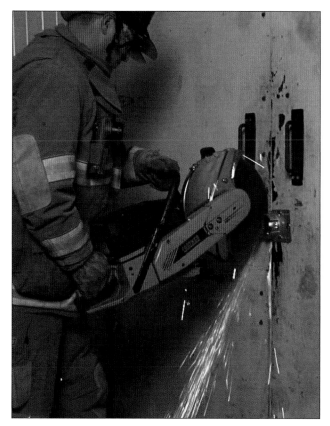

Fig. 11–20. An irons saw

Fig. 11–21. The aluminum oxide and silicone carbide abrasive blades are similar in appearance, some departments paint the blade yellow to distinguish the two.

Saw safety. Firefighters must learn to operate a power saw under adverse fire conditions to reduce the risk of a severe injury or accident. Firefighters should follow the safety items listed to operate safely and efficiently with a running saw.

- Full personal protection equipment and eye protection must be worn when operating any saw.

- Prior to beginning a cutting operation, the operator should formulate a plan of action that includes the sequence of cuts, wind direction, and travel to a safe mean of egress.

- Firefighters should make all attempts to stand clear of debris thrown from the rear of the saw. Sparks, splinters, and chipped-off teeth can fly off the blade and injure an unassuming firefighter operating toward the rear of the saw.

- All firefighters should maintain at least 10 ft (3 m) from the saw during cutting operations. This circle of danger should encompass the saw and its operator.

- Once the saw is started, the operator should lift the carrying handle and push down with the hand holding the control handle. Following this procedure allows the saw blade to rise off the ground first.

- The operator should maintain constant contact with the saw using both hands when performing

cutting operations. The saw can vibrate and move when cutting and easily slip or slide from an operator's hands if they aren't maintaining a grip on it. In addition, the saw can be awkward to operate and lift in overhead-cutting operations, so both hands should be used.

- When cutting, the operator should keep clear of the blade's path and discharging material thrown from the saw. When cutting metal overhead, the operator should hold the saw so that discharging sparks fly away from the operator and others.

- If manpower allows, a firefighter should be assigned to act as a guide person during cutting operations. This firefighter can monitor conditions around the saw operator and guide his or her movements when working in hazardous conditions and positions.

- Many times as a result of saw noise, communication between firefighters is not understandable or heard. To alleviate this, some fire departments rely on hand signals or taps/slaps on the operator's back to permit nonverbal communication. The following are the meanings of taps or slaps to the back:

  - One tap = stop cut

  - Two taps = cut

  - Three taps = shut down the saw

- Saw operations should be conducted in a well-ventilated area to prevent carbon monoxide buildup from the saw's exhaust.

- Saw should not be started or operated in suspected explosive atmospheres.

- Whenever a saw blade is removed from a cut, the operator should stop the blade on the material so it stops spinning. It's common for firefighters to mistakenly lift the saw and spin it to their side when they remove a saw blade from a cut, which could injure a nearby, unsuspecting firefighter.

- When cutting during dark hours, firefighters should provide adequate lighting to the scene.

- If manpower and conditions permit, a firefighter should be positioned away from the loud saw operations to monitor radio communications.

- If roofs covered with gravel must be cut, a path should be made in the gravel to decrease the chance of sending gravel flying like a projectile.

- When firefighters with a running saw must travel to a new location on a roof, they should stop the blade from spinning and roll the saw on its blade to the new location.

- A running saw should never be refilled with fuel. Firefighters must use caution when refueling a saw that has been running. The engine housing is hot, and any spillage of fuel mixture could ignite and cause an injury. Use a funnel in refueling operations.

Starting operations. Prior to starting any saw, a firefighter should ensure that the saw is in proper working order and equipped with the right blade for the task. There should also be sufficient room around the saw to ensure that the blade is able to rotate when started. Because most saws run on an oil-and-gasoline mixture, shaking a saw prior to starting it ensures the gas and oil in the fuel tank are properly mixed (fig. 11–22).

Fig. 11–22. Starting a cold engine

Starting a cold engine.

1. The firefighter checks that the stop or kill switch is in the off position.

2. The firefighter engages or pulls the **choke lever**, switch, or handle.

3. The firefighter then engages the **throttle handle trigger** and **throttle lock**.

4. If the saw is equipped with a **decompression button**, the firefighter presses the button to reduce the pressure in the cylinder and make the saw easier to start.

5. The firefighter places either boot into the saw handle while bending over to grab the control handle with the left hand. With the right hand, her or she grips the starter cord handle.

6. The firefighter then slowly pulls the **starter cord** until he or she feels resistance. Then, he or she pulls quickly upward with the right arm.

Note: *Do not attempt to pull the starter cord completely out of the saw or too forcefully because the chord could snap or damage the internal coil spring. Damage could also happen if a firefighter were to let the extended starter cord snap back into the starter mechanism.*

7. Once the saw starts, the firefighter applies full throttle to disengage the throttle lock. This stops the saw from running at its full **revolutions per minute (RPM)**.

8. If the saw starts and putters or runs for a few seconds, the firefighter may attempt to push in the choke lever to keep it running. Often, this doesn't happen and the saw stalls. Prior to restarting the saw, the firefighter pushes in or shuts off the choke lever. Many times, there is sufficient gas-and-oil mixture in the **carburetor** chamber to permit starting on the next pull.

9. Now that the saw is running, the firefighter ensures that the blade has stopped rotating and lifts the saw upward toward the cutting task.

For the firefighter to stop the saw, he or she must use a finger to engage the stop button, lever, or switch.

Starting a warm engine. When a saw has been running, the starting sequence may differ from starting a cold saw. Usually, there is no need to choke the saw again. The saw's engine is warm, and sufficient fuel is in the fuel lines and carburetor chamber. Firefighters should follow the same sequence as above other than choking the saw. If after two pulls the saw shows no signs of starting, then it may have to be choked.

Simple saw starting. A simple procedure to assist firefighters in saw starting was developed by Lieutenant Michael Ciampo of the Fire Department of the City of New York. All the previously mentioned mechanical procedures are followed in reference to the saw's physical positions for starting the saw. The change is in

Chapter 11 — Firefighting Basic Tools   221

the firefighter's body position. The firefighter positions himself or herself behind the saw in a balanced squatting position resembling a catcher's stance. The right knee exerts downward pressure onto the saw's air cleaner or upper housing (fig. 11–23). The firefighter extends the right arm forward and holds onto the control handle of the saw, keeping it balanced. The left arm pulls up on the starter cord to start the saw.

This method of saw starting has a few advantages:

- It puts the firefighter's hands closer to the choke and throttle levers once the saw is started.

- It shortens the pulling distance of the starter cord, which reduces the chances of damaging it or the saw's **recoil spring**.

- It allows the firefighter to lift the saw upward using leg and back muscles together, reducing the chances of an injury.

- It can be used on different types of saws.

Fig. 11–23. An alternative method for starting an engine

Traveling with a live saw

When a saw is running, it is commonly referred to as a *live saw*. Firefighters must ensure that whenever changing locations or positions, the saw blade has stopped rotating. A rotating blade can injure an unsuspecting firefighter. To combat this problem, firefighters learn to roll a live saw on its blade when traveling. Rolling a saw to its next location decreases the chances of a rotating blade injuring a firefighter (fig. 11–24). It also can assist firefighters working on a smoke-covered rooftop. Pushing a saw in front of them while moving can inform them of any holes in the roof, shafts, setbacks, or edges of the roof.

Fig. 11–24. Rolling a saw

Carrying a saw in a sling

Carrying a saw up a ladder in a sling enables a firefighter to maintain hand contact with the ladder (fig. 11–25). Most manufacturers have made renovations to their particular saws that enable **saw slings** to be attached. If a saw doesn't have specific brackets or attachment rings, the saw sling can still attached to it. Never carry a live saw up or down a ladder.

A **choker hitch** can be made around the control handle of a saw and then the other end looped around the blade and down onto the **arbor**. This permits a firefighter to place the sling around one shoulder and or over the head to carry the saw.

Firefighting Basic Tools

FIREFIGHTER I

Chapter 11

Fig. 11–25. Using a sling to carry a saw up a ladder

Operating with a saw

The work area should be as stable as possible so a firefighter can work in a balanced position while operating with a saw. Obstructions should be removed and all hazards in the cutting area identified prior to cutting operations. The firefighter operating the saw should have a plan of action and relay it to anyone operating within the vicinity of the saw.

Because firefighting is dangerous and conditions can change in a moment, saw operations are often performed in a two-person team: the saw operator and a backup, safety, or guide firefighter. The operator is responsible for the safe operation of the saw while the safety firefighter is responsible for the movement of the pair, giving hand signals, and watching and monitoring conditions around them. This procedure is normally used when performing certain types of roof ventilation. For other simple situations, such as cutting a lock off of a gate, there may be no need for a backup firefighter.

When cutting a roof for ventilation, vinyl siding with wood sheathing, or wood flooring, the saw must be run in a specific manner. Carbide-tip blades or multipurpose blades should be brought up to full rpms prior to engaging the material to be cut. If the blade were not spinning at full rpms, the blade could stop or become wedged in the material being cut.

When the saw is parallel to the material being cut, the saw's **foot bracket** should rest on the material. This will act as a pivot point. Once the saw is brought up to full rpms, the throttle handle is lifted upward and the saw pivots on the foot, bringing the blade closer to the material being cut. The firefighter must maintain control and balance of the saw while operating the throttle with one arm and holding the control arm with the other (fig. 11–26).

Fig. 11–26. One firefighter cuts a padlock while another firefighter holds the padlock with a pair of channel locks.

Once the saw is cutting, the firefighter maintains full rpms while he or she drags, pulls, or walks the saw back toward himself or herself. The saw blade spins toward the firefighter and cuts in a backward direction. Firefighters must not pull too fast because this can cause the saw to stall. They must ensure that they are cutting the material during the first attempt and monitor the cut for material being thrown. Sawdust and tar chips are tell-tale signs that the roof covering and roof boards are being cut in one operation. To assist the saw during the cutting operation, some firefighters gently rock the saw up and down by first lifting on the control handle and pushing down on the throttle handle and vise versa. This often assists the saw in throwing debris out of the blade guard and also increases the depth and width of the cut line, commonly referred to as the **kerf** of the blade.

Note: *Once the saw is removed from the cut, the firefighter should release the throttle trigger and slowly place the blade into the material being cut. This stops the blade from spinning and decreases the chance of hitting anyone with the blade.*

When cutting metal with an aluminum oxide blade or brick with a silicone carbide blade, the initial cutting operation is a little different. When the blade first comes in contact with the material to be cut, it should rotate at a slow to moderate speed. This enables the blade to start a groove in the material to be cut. Then the saw can be brought up to full rpms to complete the cut. This also works for multipurpose blades when cutting metal or concrete.

Often during firefighting operations, the saw must be operated in precarious positions and a firefighter finds it difficult to balance or operate the saw. It may be necessary for the saw to be supported in a few manners. The saw can be supported by a firefighter's boot when he or she may have to cut at a low level. The firefighter can also use the upper leg to support the saw when cuts need to be made below the waistline. If the cut is chest-level, sometimes a firefighter may be able to press his or her chest into the saw's housing to support the cut. Cutting overhead is the most difficult, and firefighters must use upper-body strength to support the saw during these cuts. When performing cuts in precarious positions, it may be necessary to move the saw's blade guard to protect the firefighter from flying debris from the cut.

Whenever cutting with any type of blade, firefighters must remember the following:

- Limit side pressure on the blade and try to cut in a straight line. Side pressure or twisting of the saw can bind the blade in the cut or damage the blade.

- Firefighters should cut only as deep as necessary through materials; cutting through structural members can weaken a structure. A firefighter must learn how to listen to the saw's cutting sound and how it feels cutting through materials.

- Firefighters should not play with the saw's throttle, commonly referred to as **gunning the saw**, while waiting to perform another cut. This can damage the saw or injure another firefighter.

- Firefighters should operate to side of the saw in a well-balanced **boxer's stance** while cutting on a flat surface. This helps keep the firefighter clear of the debris being thrown from the blade.

- When firefighters cut metal, they should stand out of the flying sparks at all times. These sparks and molten metal have burned or melted the rubber on SCBA facepieces.

- Do not start or use saw in the presence of flammable gases or vapors.

Refueling the saw

If the saw needs to be refueled during cutting operations, it must be shut down and moved to a safe location. Extreme care must be taken because the saw's exhaust is extremely hot and any spillage of the gas and oil mixture could ignite if the two come in contact. A small funnel should be used for all power saw fueling operations to prevent spillage or injury (fig. 11–27). Ensure that you use the proper type of fuel mix based on engine type (two-stroke vs. four-stroke engine, for example).

Prior to taking off the fuel cap, ensure that it and its surrounding are clean of sawdust, dust, or debris. Debris that gets into the tank can harm the saw. Also, always open the fuel cap slowly to release any over pressure that exists in the tank. After fueling, always tighten the fuel cap carefully, ensuring that the threads line up and the cap and gasket fit tightly onto the saw housing.

Fig. 11–27. Be careful when refueling a saw.

Maintenance

Saw maintenance is a large factor in determining the life expectancy of a saw. There are specific instructions set forth by the saw manufacturers for specific saws. Firefighters must read and be accustomed with their particular saw-maintenance procedures. Firefighters may perform some maintenance. Qualified technicians must perform other procedures. Firefighters must check the following items regularly and after each use:

- The saw and saw guard blade must be clean and free of debris that could affect proper operation.

- The saw's throttle components, choke, and shutoff must operate freely and correctly.

- The saw's starter cord and handle must be free from defects.

- The saw's air intake fins must be free of debris.

- All bolts and nuts must be tight and secure (fig. 11–28)

- The fuel tank must be full and the cap must be secured.

- The clutch assembly and belt must be adjusted properly.

Depending on use and maintenance requirements, saws also need firefighters to do the following:

1. Change the air filter(s).

2. Change the fuel filter.

3. Change or clean the **spark plug**.

4. Adjust the belts and clutch assembly.

5. Check all cables and electrical connections.

6. Fix any deficiency with the saw.

7. Clean the cooling fins from dust and debris.

8. Check that the muffler is securely attached.

9. Check that the carburetor functions properly.

Fig. 11–28. Make sure all nuts and bolts are secure.

Miscellaneous rotary saws

There are also many types of saws powered by hydraulic fluid, lithium batteries, electricity, and water in a rotary design (fig. 11–29). These are not commonly used in everyday firefighting operations, but firefighters use them

during collapsed-building operations and vehicle extrications. The saws run on the same principle as regular power saws but are constructed for adverse conditions. Specialized training may be required.

Fig. 11–29. Various rotary saws

Chain saws

Chain saws in the fire service are normally used for ventilation efforts at structure fires or for cutting trees to provide a fire break in wildland firefighting operations. They also assist in removing trees from structures and automobiles during weather-related emergencies. Some chain saws can cut through concrete, **reinforced concrete**, bricks, and cement block and are useful at building collapses and for breaching walls and floors (fig. 11–30).

Fig. 11–30. Different types of chain saws

A chain saw is a portable saw with a two-cycle engine that runs on a gas-and-oil fuel mixture. The engine's driveshaft powers a sprocket assembly that operates a chain that rotates over a metal alloy guide bar. As the blade rotates across the guide bar, its teeth chip and cut a specific material. A firefighter controls the saw's speed by applying pressure on a throttle lever in the handle. Some saws come equipped with a **safety brake handle** or lever that prevents the blade from rotating across the bar as the throttle lever is engaged. It also allows the operator to apply the brake, which immediately stops the blade from rotating in an emergency. To control the saw during cutting, the hand not controlling the saw's speed must hold onto the carrying handle.

A chain saw's cutting chain resembles a bicycle chain. Individual links are riveted together, and teeth on the top cut and chip the material being cut. These teeth can be carbide-tipped and can cut a multitude of materials. Some specialty blades reduce the chances that the blade will hook into the material, protect the carbide, and actually file through a material instead of cutting it. A metal finger on the underside of the chain attaches to the link, enabling the chain to ride inside the **guide bar**, carry oil to lubricate the cut, and engage in the sprocket to allow chain rotation around the bar.

The life span of a blade depends on how well it is lubricated throughout the cut and how much material there is to cut. Chain saws are equipped with a reservoir that holds bar oil. A built-in pump disperses the oil across the bar and into the bar's channel, which lubricates the chain throughout the cut. For long operations, firefighters must ensure that the reservoir always has oil. A sharp chain throws shavings and chips and requires little force to cut. A dull chain throws dust and requires a lot of pressure applied to the saw to cut.

Numerous brands and types of chain saws are used throughout the fire service. Some of the most common saws have **chain guards** and cutting **depth gauges**. A gauge set to the depth of the cut helps prevent the blade's teeth from cutting through the roof joists (fig. 11–31). These saws are normally used for roof ventilation. Some chain saws with specially designed guide bars are shaped differently than most common guide bars. Firefighters must know their departments' specific saw specifications and operating procedures.

Fig. 11–31. A chain saw with a depth gauge

Chain saw safety. Many safety items mentioned in the rotary saw material apply to chain saws, with a few additions:

- Never lean over or straddle a moving chain saw blade.

- Position yourself left of the chain line, with the left hand on the control arm and right hand on the control handle.

- When performing prolonged saw operations, wear approved hearing protection.

- Find an alternative to cutting overhead with a chain saw.

Traveling and carrying a chain saw. A running saw is a "live saw." Firefighters must ensure that the chain has stopped rotating when changing locations or positions. A rotating chain can injure an unsuspecting firefighter. To combat this, firefighters should engage the **chain brake** (if the saw has one) before moving to a new location. Firefighters can also roll a live saw on the chain when traveling.

If the saw isn't running, firefighters should carry the saw with the chain facing the rear. If they were to trip or fall forward, they would not land on the blade. In addition, it would less likely strike another firefighter on the fireground.

Chain saws can also be carried using a saw sling. Most manufacturers have procedures for carrying saws. Firefighters must be accustomed to their departments' saw procedures.

Starting a chain saw. Rotary saw starting procedures apply to the chain saw with one additional safety factor: If the chain saw is equipped with a chain brake, it should be engaged before starting the saw. This eliminates the chance of the blade's rotating around the bar once the saw is started. If the saw does not have a chain brake, the firefighter must be aware that the blade will begin to rotate around the bar once the saw is started. Firefighters must remember that a rotating chain can injure. All safety procedures must be followed.

Operating with a chain saw: ventilation. The work area should be as stable as possible so a firefighter can work in a balanced position while operating a saw. Obstructions should be removed and all hazards in the cutting area identified before cutting begins. The firefighter operating the saw should relay his or her plan to anyone operating within the saw's vicinity.

Because firefighting is dangerous and conditions can change, saw operations are often performed in two-person teams: the saw operator and a backup, safety, or guide firefighter. The operator is responsible for the safe operation of the saw while the safety firefighter is responsible for the movement of the pair, giving hand signals, and watching and monitoring conditions around them. This procedure is normally used when performing certain types of roof ventilation.

Because many chain saws used for roof ventilation lack a safety guard, the safety or guide firefighter should place himself or herself slightly behind and to the opposite side of the saw when cutting is in progress. The possibility of the saw kicking back out of the cut line or the operator lifting it up could cause the saw to kick toward the rear and cause an injury. Some fire departments do not allow a guide or safety firefighter to be near a saw with no safety guard. Firefighters must understand their fire departments' standard operating guidelines (SOGs).

When cutting a roof for ventilation, vinyl siding with wood sheathing, or wood flooring, a firefighter must run the saw in a specific manner. Normally, only the tip of the saw and a few inches of the bar are used to cut through a material. Burying the whole saw's bar and blade into the roof could cause the saw to cut right through the structural joist and cause a collapse. Saws that have depth gauges and guards should be set to cut only through the roofing material. Firefighters can cut a small inspection hole, kerf cut, or cut line to verify roof thickness and then set the depth gauge before cutting operations begin.

When saw cutting begins, the chain must be plunged into the roofing material to start the cut line. The saw should be brought up to full rpms before engaging the material to be cut. If not, the chain could stop or become wedged into the material. If a chain saw has a depth gauge or safety guard, the underside of the guard at the tip can be placed onto the roofline to assist in making the initial cut. The saw can pivot on the guard as the firefighter brings the saw up to full rpms and then rotates the tip into the roofing. Once the saw plunges through the material, the saw cuts back toward the operator and should be held almost vertical and run at full speed during the entire cut. The operator should watch the debris being thrown to judge the cut's progression.

Note: *As the saw is pulled from the cut, the operator should engage the brake lock, which will stop the chain's rotation. This prevents injuring anyone when the saw is moved. If the saw does not have a brake, the blade should be kept near the cut until it stops rotating and then be moved to the next cut.*

Chain saws assist firefighters in ventilating hurricane windows (see chapter 12, Forcible Entry, for more information on these windows). Firefighters should be equipped with proper breathing protection during cutting operations. Before beginning the cut, ensure that a purchase point for the saw's chain exists. Cutting these windows can be dangerous and all safety procedures should be followed.

Operating with a chain saw: tree cutting. Cutting trees with a chain saw is different than cutting a ventilation hole in a roof. Different procedures must be followed. Normally when firefighters cut trees or limbs, their chain saws lack a safety bar or depth gauge. The entire bar and chain is exposed during cutting, which increases the risk of injury if safety is not practiced at all times.

Prior to cutting any trees, limbs, or branches, firefighters must perform a scene size-up to ensure they are not in any contact with electrical lines. The size-up should include the position in which the tree is resting or leaning. In instances such as a crushed automobile with a trapped victim, it may be necessary to lift the tree with firefighting equipment instead of cutting it. Another danger is when a tree is leaning on a structure and firefighters begin to cut. Once a few of the larger branches are removed, sometimes the trunk may actually spring up and back into position because the weight is released, or fall farther down into the structure. Firefighters must use caution when performing these tactics. If the situation has no immediate rescue or life hazard, the area should be secured or stabilized and left for the proper attending authorities.

To begin saw operations, firefighters place the saw against the tree with the **bumper spikes** in contact with the tree. The saw is held with the bottom of the chain just off the tree. Once the throttle is fully engaged, the saw can pivot on the spikes and the chain can cut into the tree. The saw must be run at full speed during the entire cut. Once the chain has cut through the material, the throttle releases. The chain saw should not be forced downward into the cut. The firefighter should allow the saw's chain to cut the tree. The saw can be slowly rocked up and down to assist in the cut.

Firefighters must remember that any cutting with the tip of the bar and chain can cause the saw to kick back toward the operator. Using the tip is dangerous and should not be done.

There are numerous cutting variations and situations when cutting trees and dismantling limbs. Wedges and blocks assist firefighters in many of these procedures. Firefighters must follow manufacturers' guidelines when operating their departments' saws.

Maintenance. Chain saws require more labor-intensive maintenance than rotary saws because of all of its parts. Firefighters must know their departments' saws and follow specific manufacturers' procedures. The following are some of the most common post-cutting maintenance requirements for chain saws:

- Clean and inspect the guide bar for wear and damage. It is also recommended to run a narrow object around the entire channel in which the chain rides to remove debris.

- Maintain the saw with a sharp, properly adjusted chain.

- Ensure that the oil discharge ports are clear and oil flows freely through the bar.

- Ensure that the oil reservoir and fuel tanks are full.

- Clean and inspect the air intake and remove any dust or debris from the openings.

- Ensure the air cleaner is free of dust and debris.

- Clean and remove any sawdust or debris from around the sprocket and inside the saw's sprocket housing cover.

- Ensure that the depth gauge or chain guards are in good working order.

- Wipe off the saw housing and any areas that may have excess oil.

- Ensure that the chain is installed properly.

Periodic maintenance should also be conducted.

Reciprocating saw

Reciprocating saws are commonly used for vehicle extrications, machinery extrications, and building collapses. These portable saws are lightweight, small, and easy to transport (fig. 11–32). They are capable of operating on battery power with no need for an electrical cord. Some reciprocating saws operate on air supply and normal, household electrical current. They are commonly called sabre saws or by the brand, Sawzall®.

Fig. 11–32. Reciprocating saw

The reciprocating saw uses an alternating-direction motor (reciprocating motion) to move a blade back and forth to cut through material. Many of these saws offer a variable speed control option that works in conjunction with the amount of pressure applied to the trigger switch by the firefighter. The saw can be equipped with a multitude of blades that can cut wood, metal, plastic, automobile windshields, and drywall (fig. 11–33). Many of these blades are capable of cutting a few types of material and may be labeled as **bi-metal**, meaning they can cut metal and wood products. The blades are inserted into a holder and kept in place by a set screw or a manual locking device. They also can be inserted with the teeth of the blade facing either up or down to offer a different angle or plane of cutting. Lubricating some of these blades while cutting may also increase the blade's life span.

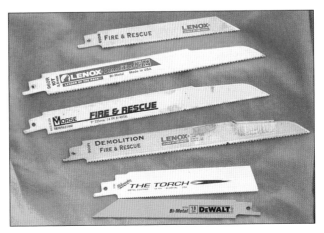

Fig. 11–33. Reciprocating saw blades

FIREFIGHTER I

Firefighting Basic Tools

Chapter 11

Maintenance. After each use, the saw should be cleaned of dust, dirt, and debris, especially around the blade holder. If the saw is cordless, it needs its batteries recharged. A new blade should also be installed even though the blade may still have some life left in it. The fire service must keep its equipment fully ready for service at all times. The old blade can be used for drill periods.

Safety

- Prior to cutting, the firefighter should be wearing all personal protective equipment and safety glasses.

- Anything being cut that has a power supply should be shut down prior to cutting.

- The area or material being cut should be surveyed to ensure other or structural members aren't cut accidentally.

- Firefighters must wear gloves. Blades are hot after cutting and can burn.

- When necessary, clamp or secure the item being cut so it doesn't move during or after cutting.

- Maintain a well-balanced position while cutting, and don't overreach with the saw.

Cutting operations. The firefighter first ensures that the saw is equipped with the proper blade for the cutting operation. He or she holds the control handle in one hand with the index finger on the speed control trigger. The other hand holds the saw near the blade around the tool's shaft or grip handle. Now, the firefighter holds the blade slightly off the material with the safety shoe against the material and slowly engages the trigger to make a cut line in the material. Once the blade bites into the material, the firefighter either operates the saw at full speed or a slower speed depending on the cutting operation.

As the saw cuts, the firefighter should watch the dust and debris thrown by the saw and the depth of the cut. He or she also listens to the saw and blade cutting through the material. If the saw sounds like it is laboring, the firefighter is placing too much pressure on the material being cut, the saw needs to run at a higher speed, the speed of the cut must be slowed to enable the blade work, or the blade may need replacing. In some cutting operations, the saw can be pivoted on the safety shoe in an up-and-down motion to assist the blade in cutting the material.

LESSON FROM THE FIREGROUND

A tool's efficiency depends on you. Size-up is critical to tool selection, and it should be made long before you respond to an alarm. Knowing the types of building construction in your response area is an absolute must. Know your town's history. By studying the history of your community, you will learn what types of buildings you may encounter and what building techniques were used. It is very important. Germans built buildings differently from the Swedish, who built differently from the French, who built totally differently from the colonists. Our own fire service history has played an important role in the way buildings are constructed. Huge conflagrations and high death tolls brought about the enactment of building and fire codes. As a firefighter, you are responsible for every structure in your community, not just those under construction today, but every building ever built and still standing.

Become familiar with what types of security devices are being sold and used. A trip to the local home-improvement store will answer a lot of questions about what types of tools you will need to bring with you to the next fire. Do prefire inspections. Don't just look for code violations. Look at how the occupant secures the building at night. How do you get in? What tools do you need?

MY POINT

Standing in front of a locked door with the most sophisticated tools in the world won't open that door. Know the capabilities and limitations of the tools you are holding in your hand.

QUESTIONS

1. Name the tools identified in chapter 11 as roof ventilation tools.

2. What type of fuel is used with rotary and chain saws?

3. Describe the maintenance needs for fire service axe heads.

4. According to the text, what four tools are available to firefighters to strike other tools?

5. Carbide-tip blades on a rotary saw are used to cut what materials?

6. Describe the most common lengths for pike poles and their uses.

7. Describe the maintenance procedures a firefighter should carry out after using a chain saw.

8. Describe the parts of a Halligan tool.

9. Describe the primary disadvantages of fiberglass poles used on pike poles and other push-pull tools.

10. Which general variety of tools is used for overhaul?

11. Describe the necessary actions to start a cut in a roof with a chain saw.

12. Describe the signal system recommended in the text for physical communication between a saw's operator and her partner during roof operations.

13. What is the recommended minimum distance other firefighters should maintain from a firefighter operating a saw?

14. What is the proper method for starting a cold engine on a rotary saw?

15. What is the most important safety factor a saw operator must do after cutting?

16. How should a saw in use be refueled?

17. When using a saw to ventilate a roof, what is the recommended method for moving to start a new hole?

18. An ideal axe head should weigh how many pounds?

19. What is considered the ideal length of a Halligan bar?

20. When using a monitor nozzle or deck gun as a master stream device, what tool can be used to safely anchor the device?

21. Discuss the safety considerations firefighters employ when using an axe.

Forcible Entry

by Dan Sheridan

This chapter provides required knowledge items for the following NFPA Standard 1001 Job Performance Requirements:

FFI: 5.3.4

FFII: 6.3.2 (Specialized forcible entry tools)

This chapter contains Skill Drills. When you see this icon, refer to your Skill Drill book for step-by-step instructions.

SKILL DRILL

OBJECTIVES

Upon completion of this chapter, you should be able to do the following:

- Identify and demonstrate in a safe manner the use of tools needed for forcible entry
- Identify the proper tool for each situation requiring forcible entry
- Identify different types of locks
- Identify different types of doors
- Describe forcible entry on different types of doors
- Describe the "through the lock" method of forcible entry
- Identify different types of windows
- Describe forcible entry on different types of windows
- Describe methods for breaching floors and walls

INTRODUCTION

On Broadway the show doesn't start until the curtain opens. It is the same in the fire service—nothing can happen on the fireground until **forcible entry** is effected. Whether it is a fire in a dwelling or just a simple emergency call, we need to gain entry to perform our duties. We need to be proficient in forcible entry, choosing the right tool for the job in every situation and operating safely.

More lives are saved by stretching a hand line to the proper location and extinguishing the fire than by any other tool we have in our arsenal. Often, it is necessary to force entry to be able to place this critical first hoseline. Forcible entry includes being able to size up the situation, and picking the right tool for the situation at hand will help facilitate the placement of that very important first line.

It is human nature to always want to improve our surroundings. We are always trying to build a better mousetrap. Technology is constantly changing on both sides of the fire service. When crime emerged as a significant issue in the early 1960s, people started putting better security systems in homes and places of business. This forced the fire service to adapt and find better ways to gain entry to fires and emergencies. The fire service has at times lagged behind the security measures and our ability to make rapid entry. Years later, as forcible-entry technologies and training improved, the fire service began gaining entry much more quickly than the hoselines were being stretched. Firefighters were able to, in some cases, outpace the stretching of hand lines.

New challenges continue to present themselves even today. One of the more recent changes, sparked by the need for energy efficiency, is the installation of **thermal pane windows**. These windows have proved to be much more difficult than single-pane windows to force entry into and ventilate. People are now installing more complicated gates on windows, particularly in high-crime areas. It is not uncommon to find whole houses in "cages." Modern office buildings often utilize **magnetic locking devices** that are very difficult to force. Forcible entry is a constantly evolving function within the fire service.

FORCING ENTRY

FFI: 5.3.4 Firefighters should be aware of the hazards involved with forcing entry. The acts of forcing through doors, windows, or walls can all have adverse effects on firefighting operations and personal safety.

The entry point for a fire attack will usually be the front door. When commencing fire operation, keep in mind that any opening we make will also affect fire behavior.

Depending on their locations, forcing doors or windows can disrupt or redirect ventilation, which can increase fire growth. In very tight buildings, the simple act of opening the front door may cause a backdraft. This makes it of utmost importance to control the door after forcible entry. Firefighters should be prepared for those changes when selecting a forcible entry target.

In multiple dwellings, for example, where the door to the apartment leads into an open interior stairwell, it is critical to control the door so that occupants who may be above the fire can safely get past the fire apartment. Some wooden doors have panels that can be easily removed, and it may seem like a good idea to just remove one of the panels and reach in and unlock the door. If you do this, though, you will not be able to **control the door**. That door is just like a lid. It is the only thing that keeps the fire in the area of origin. The only time it may be acceptable to remove a panel would be in a minor emergency or a very small fire, like a pot burning on the stove. Even then, many locks on exterior doors today are **double keyed**, that is, a key is needed to turn the lock on either

side of the lock cylinder. Removing a panel will not allow the door to open, and heat and smoke may begin to enter the hall. In addition, the occupant is faced with replacing an entire door instead of just a lock, and we have no way to secure the premises if no one is home.

As we move through this chapter, keep in mind how it will affect the fire when forcible entry is performed before a hoseline is stretched. Sometimes the easy way is not the best way, as we will see.

Forcible entry doesn't end after we force the front door. The old thinking was that after the front door was forced, an axe or another type of chock should be placed under the door so it wouldn't close behind the **forcible-entry team**. With buildings being tighter and outfitted with thermal pane windows, we are more concerned about the air supply to the fire. Today, it is recommended that we control the door by leaving a firefighter there, or making sure we throw the slide bolt so that the door can't relock and closing the door.

Once in the fire area, we may still have to perform forcible entry. It is not uncommon anymore to find a window gate with a padlock or a locked bedroom door. Many dwellings appear to be one- or two-family homes from the outside, but may in fact contain many single-room occupancies, each with their own locking devices. Some may even be padlocked from the outside with the occupant inside. In some businesses, where employers are concerned with employee theft, employers will lock some employees in the workplace overnight. It is also not uncommon to find emergency exits locked, or locks that can't be opened by hand. The **fox lock** is a lock that is sometimes found in commercial buildings. Employers have been known to remove the knobs that enable the door to be opened.

Firefighters entering any situation should always be thinking, "What is my second means of egress?" A firefighter was killed in New York City in the 1990s when a room he entered to search exploded with fire, and his only way out was a fire escape that contained a padlock. The first thing we should do when entering any room is check to see if the second way out is accessible.

SPECIALIZED FORCIBLE-ENTRY TOOLS

FFII: 6.3.2 Some forcible-entry tools, including the Halligan tool and the power saw, are used for other purposes on the fireground and are covered in chapter

11. Other tools, however, are used almost exclusively for forcible entry, including the following:

Officer's tool/A-tool

The **officer's tool** is also known as the A-tool. There are a few versions of this tool. In the New York City Fire Department (FDNY), a new generation of the A-tool has been introduced called the rex tool. It is not a front-line forcible-entry tool, but rather a tool that firefighters could carry in the event that they need to self-extricate in an emergency situation. This tool also doubles as a component of the through-the-lock kit.

Made of high-strength steel, the versatile **A-tool** pairs a pry bar at one end with an a-type lock puller and adz at the opposite end. The head is welded to the shaft and covered with a non-slip surface. The complete A-tool set includes a through-the-lock kit, a double-ended key tool, and a shove knife, all stored inside the shaft of this tool (fig. 12–1).

Fig. 12–1. A-tool

Rex tool

The **Rex tool** has been called "the A-tool on steroids." This well-designed forcible-entry instrument has a double-headed feature that includes tapered blades that can pull a variety of lock cylinders. A chisel on the opposite end drives out rim locks once the cylinder is removed (fig. 12–2).

Fig. 12–2. Rex tool

K-tool

The **K-tool** is very limited and has only one function, to go through the lock. It is made up of a lock-pulling device that needs to be used in conjunction with a Halligan tool. It is usually carried in a leather pouch, with a set of keys including a 5/32 square-head key, a key tool, and a shove knife (fig. 12–3).

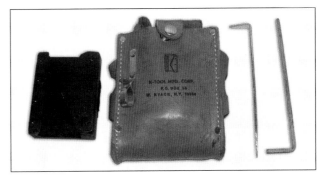

Fig. 12–3. K-tool

Duck bill

Simple, but effective, the **duck bill** incorporates basic physics to break locks. With a long, tapered end and a flat back strike zone, it fits almost any lock shackle, and an 18-in. (460-mm) handle ensures that hands are away from the strike area. The duck bill's striking surface combines well with a maul or back of an axe (fig. 12–4).

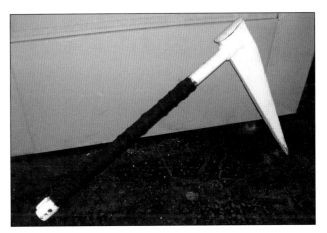

Fig. 12–4. Duck bill

Hydraulic spreading tool

There are two types of **hydraulic spreading tools**. The first is the "rabbit" tool which has spreading jaws attached to the end of a hose that, depending upon the model, can spread 4 in. (100 mm) or 9 in. (230 mm) with 8,000 lb (3,629 kg) of force. The other "integrated" tool has the spreading jaws as part of the hydraulic pump, and is commonly known by it's trade name of Hydra-Ram™. It has a spreading distance of 4 in. (100 mm). or 6 in. (150 mm) (depending upon the model) and applies 10,000 lb (4,536 kg) of force. These tools are typically employed to force inward-swinging metal doors, but they have many other applications as well.

When practicing with the tool, become familiar with the number of pumps needed to fully open them and how much the jaws spread with each pump. Check these tools frequently by placing them under a load to verify proper operation (figs. 12–5 and 12–6).

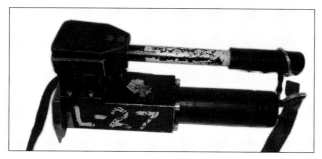
Fig. 12—5. Integrated hydraulic forcible entry tool

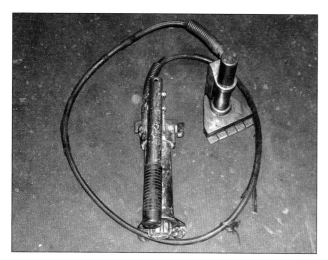
Fig. 12—6. The rabbit tool

Bolt cutters

Heavy duty **bolt cutters** are useful and effective tools for numerous cutting situations. Padlocks, bolts, chain links, rivets, and reinforcing rods are typical cutting tasks for bolt cutters. These tools come in 18, 24, 30, and 36 in. (46, 61, 76, and 91 cm) sizes. Bolt cutters will not cut **case-hardened steel** (fig. 12–7).

Battering ram

Sometimes the oldest and simplest tools are still the most effective. Case in point is the **battering ram**, a 35-in. (89-cm) 35-lb (15.9-kg) one- or two-person tool. Invaluable for reaching trapped firefighters, battering rams can breach solid doors or concrete and brick walls (fig. 12–8).

Fig. 12—7. Heavy-duty bolt cutters

Fig. 12—8. Battering ram

Keyless garage door entry tool

Firefighters needing access to garage doors can have a difficult time forcing an opening. The **keyless garage door entry tool** will unlock nearly any overhead garage door that uses an automatic opener. The firefighter slips the tool between the garage door panels to pull the emergency release rope attached to the automatic opener and manually lift the garage door (fig. 12–9).

Fig. 12–9. Keyless garage door entry tool

Choosing the right tool

It is important to choose the right tool for the job. If the situation allows, we will always try to choose the method that will do the least amount of damage. If we were responding to an emergency where there was no life hazard, such as a water leak, it would be bad public relations to destroy an expensive door, and also security would become an issue. In this situation it may be more appropriate to find a window, or if that is not an option, we may want to go through the lock using the K-tool or A-tool. On the other hand, if we are responding to a confirmed structure fire, we probably will want to use the tool that will give us the quickest access, such as hydraulic spreading tools.

In the fire service it is important not to pigeonhole our thinking into having to do certain things the same way every time. It is very easy when it comes to forcible entry to get tunnel vision. The best firefighters are the ones that can think outside the box. Although it is true that certain situations will always call for the same tools, for

example, when we are forcing residential doors, we will usually use the axe and Halligan tool, or if we are dealing with roll-down gates, we will probably need a power saw with a metal cutting blade (aluminum oxide blade).

Choosing the correct tool also means having the right blade on the saw; for example, we wouldn't want to attempt to cut a padlock with a wood-cutting blade (carbide tip). We wouldn't bring a rabbit tool to force the gates, either.

The obvious. One thing to keep in mind when approaching forcible entry is not to overlook the obvious. The old saying "try the door first" still is valid today. Many times we will find that the door is unlocked. Another scenario is when we encounter very expensive, strong locks held on by just a cheap hasp with some small wood screws or a cheap chain.

A few years back, a ladder company was working for quite some time on a very stubborn commercial door. A few minutes into the operation two firefighters came over to help, and decided that they would look for another way. Ten feet down the wall from the door, they found another door, a cheap one with a cheap rim lock. The firefighters put the Halligan tool into the door and popped it open in a few seconds.

Confidence. Forcible entry is an art, a skill to be honed by practice. It is not something that can be learned by just reading about it. It is a very hands-on skill. One of the tasks that probationary firefighters need to perform on every tour or whenever they are required to be at the station (if they are in a volunteer company) is to clean the tools, not because fire departments really like shiny tools, but because by cleaning the tools, new firefighters will actually have to handle and touch them. They will become familiar with the weight and specific characteristics of each tool. In chapter 11, tool maintenance was covered. This is the same time that we should practice swinging the axe, holding the Halligan tool the proper way, and giving the rabbit tool a few pumps. This is the start of building confidence with ourselves and our tools. One thing that is passed down to the new firefighter by senior firefighters is to have confidence in yourself and your tools. Attack every situation with vigor—like there is no door that you can't get through, no gate you can't open. This is the secret to forcible entry: self-confidence.

How else do we start building self-confidence? Of course, we have to train. We train by doing drills in the station, or we read about forcible entry. Most importantly, we start by putting theory into practice. Minor incidents are a great time to train. Emergencies and minor fires are a great time to sharpen our forcible-entry skills. Good golfers are not good because they are extremely talented and can go out once a week and break 100. They are good because they go to the driving range and practice, or they set up putting greens in their basements and practice. It is all about muscle memory and, again, self-confidence. It is the same with forcible entry; you can't expect to sit in the station and never look at he tools and still be proficient at forcible entry. The time to learn is not at 03:00 hours when you pull up to a house with smoke and fire showing and reports of people trapped inside. The golfer who doesn't break 100 may get hurt feelings, but he or she can come back another day. If we don't get the door open, and we can't get the line onto the fire, firefighters and civilians may die!

LOCKS

FFI 5.3.4 Locks are the primary reason why firefighters need to have forcible-entry skills. Locks come in a variety of types; some locks are easier to force than others. The key to getting past a lock is to understand its vulnerabilities and attack the lock at these points.

Padlocks

Padlocks can be used for either heavy-duty or regular service. They are portable devices that are made up of a **shackle** and a body that secure a door or a gate to a **hasp** or a chain (fig. 12–10).

Fig. 12–10. Locked padlock attached to a staple and hasp

When sizing up padlocks, remember to look at the whole picture, because, as always, we need to be able to keep our options open. Often we may find a very expensive lock being held on by a cheap **staple and hasp** or chain. It may

be easier to break the hasp or cut the cheap chain and save the lock for reuse.

In heavy-duty padlocks that have shackles larger than ¼ in. (6 mm) in diameter, the toe and heel both lock. They are made of hardened steel, the result of a process in which the steel is heated to give it more strength (fig. 12–11).

Fig. 12–11. Heavy-duty padlocks

Regular padlocks have a shackle of less than ¼ in. in diameter and are not case-hardened (fig. 12–12).

Fig. 12–12. Regular padlock

Heavy-duty padlocks: forcing entry. The preferred method is to use a power saw, if one is available, with a metal-cutting blade. When cutting these types of locks, it is necessary to cut both sides of the lock. (*Note:* Attach a pair of Vise-Grips to the power saw with a short chain, to hold the lock in place while cutting. This is a much safer way to operate.)

- If a saw is not available or desirable (e.g., near gasoline spills or natural gas leaks), the duck bill will work well. Insert the bill into the opening of the lock and drive it in with a maul or heavy axe. The bill will force the lock open. Be sure to put the duck bill into the lock bow so the wedge will pull the lock open, not make it wider. If put in sideways, the duck bill may get jammed and may not open the lock (fig. 12–13).

Fig. 12–13. Duck bill breaking heavy-duty padlock

- Bolt cutters are ineffective on case-hardened locks.

- A pipe wrench is quite effective, especially on American Lock™ Series 2000 locks (see later in this chapter) but also on strong conventional padlocks, as long as there is room to twist. The teeth should be kept sharp, and two people can help in setting up the tool onto the lock, as the tool can be heavy and often won't hold until torque is applied. The best grab is accomplished if the tool is adjusted so the back of the jaw just touches the lock or chain to be broken.

Regular padlocks: forcing entry. These types of locks should not present much of a problem. If there are a few locks to force, it may be faster and easier to cut them with a power saw. If one is not available, a Halligan tool and heavy flat-head axe will work fine. Insert the pike end of the Halligan in the opening and drive it through with the heavy axe (fig. 12–14). Use the fork end of the Halligan tool around the staple and twist. Another option, if available, is to use bolt cutters.

Fig. 12–14. Halligan tool breaking padlock

American Lock Series 2000 locks

American Lock Series 2000 locks, also known as "**hockey puck locks**," are made of case-hardened steel and have the locking pin inside (fig. 12–15).

Fig. 12–15. American Lock Series 2000 lock

Forcing entry. Using a power saw, if available, with a metal-cutting blade is the preferred method. Make a notch two-thirds of the way from the keyway with the blade. After the blade has a small channel, bring the saw up to full RPM, and cut the lock into two pieces, resulting in cutting the pin inside. If a saw is not available, use an 18-in. (460 mm) pipe wrench with a 36-in. (915 mm) extension. Place the pipe wrench firmly around the lock and twist off the lock. If the lock has a guard around it, this won't work, and you will need to use the saw (figs. 12–16 and 12–17).

Fig. 12–16. Firefighter cutting American Lock Series 2000 lock with power saw

Fig. 12–17. Firefighter removing American Lock Series 2000 lock with pipe wrench

Door locks

The following three general types of locks—mortise, rim, and cylindrical—are described next. Forcible-entry techniques for each lock type are described in the succeeding sections concerning different types of doors.

Mortise locks. A commonly used lock before bored cylindrical locks became prevalent, **mortise locks** have seen resurgence in recent commercial and residential construction.

Typically, a mortise lock installation includes a **lock body** (installed within the "mortise cut-out" in the door) and the **lock trim**, and includes a variety of designs, a **strike plate**, and the **keyed mortise cylinder**. This final piece operates the locking and unlocking function of the mortise lock (figs. 12–18 and 12–19).

Rim locks. **Rim locks** are locks in which the body of the lock is surface-mounted on the inside of the door. A cylinder extends through the door to the outside, where the lock is opened by a key. A vertical bolt lock is secured to its mating plate in the same fashion a door hinge is secured by its pin. To remove the lock, you must destroy it (figs. 12–20 and 12–21).

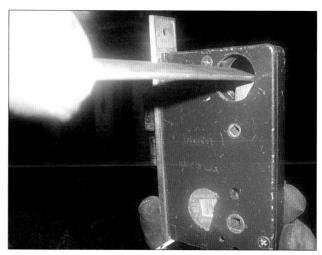

Fig. 12–18. Demonstrating the use of a key tool on a mortise lock

Fig. 12–19. Exploded view of mortise lock

Fig. 12–20. Rim lock

Fig. 12–21. An exploded view of a key-operated rim lock

Cylindrical locks. Cylindrical locks have locking mechanisms that are round in shape, hence their name. The locking mechanism itself is contained in the door's lever or knob, not in the door (unlike the mortise lock). Compared with the mortise lock, it is simpler and less formidable. **Key-in-the-knob locks** (fig. 12–22) and **deadbolt locks** are examples of a cylindrical locks.

The bolt itself on a deadbolt has a flat "squared" end, as opposed to a spring latch which is beveled. A cylinder is set into the face of the door; the bolt is moved in and out by either a key or a thumblatch by the occupants inside the building.

Fig. 12–22. Key-in-the-knob lock

Extraordinary security devices

In certain areas of the United States, people have different security needs as well as different forces of nature. In urban areas as well as the suburbs, crime is now a major concern. People are generally more concerned with crime than they are with the threat of fire. Given the choice, people are more inclined to fortify areas, regardless of the fire hazard. People are literally locking up their dwellings like fortresses. Commercial occupancies are also as well fortified as some banks. Some examples are fox locks, magnetic door locks, and electric strikes.

Fox locks. Fox locks are devices with two bars that hold the door closed from the inside. The bars are attached on a rotating plate on the door. The plate is rotated in order to move the bars. Looking from the outside, you will be presented with two sets of bolts. The lower set of bolts indicate the direction that you would turn the key to remove the bars from the keeper. From the inside, the process is reversed; the plate has a knob that needs to be pulled out before you can turn it. If you fail to pull out the knob, it will only spin and not engage the bars (figs. 12–23 and 12–24).

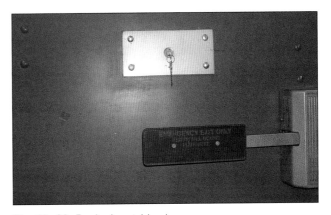

Fig. 12–23. Fox lock outside view

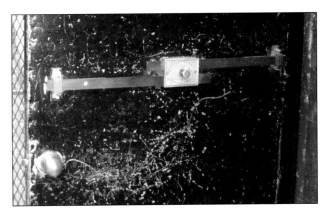

Fig. 12–24. Fox lock inside view

Forcing entry. You will normally find a plate surrounding the lock with four bolts. To force entry, shear three of the four bolts, thus exposing the cylinder. Next remove cylinder with the point of the Halligan tool. Use the 5/32 square tool to open the locking mechanism. Turn the key toward the bottom two bolts while pushing in (fig. 12–25).

Fig. 12–25. Opening a fox lock with 5/32 square tool

Magnetic and electric strike locks. These types of locks are typically found on outward-opening entrance doors, gates, and inward-opening doors to large multiple dwellings and commercial buildings.

All **magnetic locks** will work only with DC current. You may come across a magnetic lock that comes with an AC power supply, but here the AC voltage is being converted to DC in the lock. All magnetic locks are fail safe. This means that they need a constant source of current to remained locked. If power is removed the lock will open (fig. 12–26).

Electric strikes are often used for "buzz in" type of systems. Electric strikes come in many varieties. They may be fail-safe or fail-secure (fig. 12–27).

- A fail-safe electric strike needs power to keep it locked.

- A fail-secure electric strike stays locked even without power.

The most common by far is a fail-secure. When using a fail-secure electric strike even without power, it stays locked from the outside coming in. For **egress** or getting out, a door knob or lever on the lock allows for safe exit.

Forcing entry. Outward-swinging doors should be forced with conventional forcible entry using a Halligan tool and flat head axe, including doors with two magnets (top and bottom) or three magnets (top, middle, bottom) running down the side of the door frame. Start at the top and work downward. When the top magnet releases, it may be necessary to put the axe or chock into the space and let the Halligan slide down the gap to force the next magnet. When you reach the bottom magnet, you can pivot the axe so its wider width is able to hold the gap further open and assist in releasing this magnet. Some doors may only have a top magnet located about

6–8 in. (150–200 mm) away from the door frame on the handle side. These doors can be forced with the Halligan tool by prying down on the adz or popping it with a hydraulic tool if it's an inward-opening door.

Fig. 12–26. Magnetic door lock

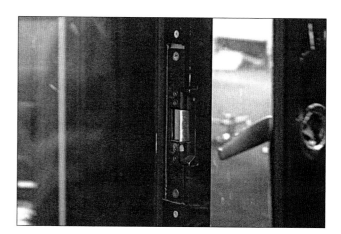

Fig. 12–27. Electric strike door lock

In some cases, firefighters can use the blunt end of the tool and strike the door near the magnet while also pulling on the door handle. The force from striking the door near the magnet and the pull on the handle will allow the magnet to be freed from its receiver. This will not always work, but offers the possibility of quickly opening the door in some cases.

Hydraulic spreading devices are the tools of choice to force inward-swinging doors with electric strike doors and magnetic door locks. When forcing an electric strike door, treat it like a normal inward-opening door. Use the Halligan tool and axe (or maul) to create a small gap between the door and the door frame, at the electric strike. Place the jaws in the gap, with the fixed jaw against the door frame. Pump the tool and push the door away from the electric strike. Magnetic locks are formidable foes. They can exert a force of 3,000 lb (1,361 kg). If accessible, you can de-energize the lock by disconnecting the DC current to the device. Alternatively, you can use your hydraulic spreading tool. As with the electric strike, create a gap next to the magnetic lock between the door and the door frame using the Halligan and a striking tool. Place the jaws in the gap and pump the tool until the magnetic hold is broken (note that you must control the door with a hose strap or the like as it may swing quickly away from you). Place a ten penny nail on the magnet to prevent it from closing once you have forced the door.

Forcing magnetic locks on ornamental entry gates. Many gates are also equipped with magnetic lock assemblies. Often these will have a large flat plate handle on them protecting the lock mechanism and magnet. To force these gates, a simple tactic can be performed by the firefighter. First they will pull on the handle and take any slack out of the gate; this usually creates a gap above and below the handle. Then the adz end of the Halligan can be inserted into this space and either pushed upward or pried downward to pop the magnet's hold onto its receiver. Normally, this is a quick and easy tactic to perform to force entry when faced with these gates.

DOORS

Types of doors

Inward-opening doors. **FFI 5.3.4** The majority of the doors that we encounter are the types that swing inward, which is away from the forcible-entry team. These doors will usually be found with more than one type of locking device. Single-family homes—the most common location of fires in the United States—typically use wood inward-opening doors with wooden frames. In some newer residential buildings, as well as commercial buildings, we will find metal doors. Metal doors (usually steel) can have a hollow core, be filled with a honeycomb cardboard, or have a wooden core (also known as **Kalamein doors**). These doors are usually set in metal frames, and together they create a very formidable door.

Looking at a door from the outside, if the hinges are not visible, we are dealing with an inward-opening door (figs. 12–28 and 12–29).

Fig. 12–28. The use of a Halligan tool on an ornamental entry gate

Fig. 12–29. Inward-opening steel door

Note: Kalamein doors are set in metal frames, as are metal doors. Sometimes you may not pick up the difference immediately. When we begin forcing entry into both these types of doors, you will notice the difference immediately. The Kalamein door is more pliable; that is, there is more "give" in the door. Because metal doors are stronger, they will not bend as much when attempting to force. The energy from the tool is more easily transferred to the lock. Think of it as the same concept as the crumple zone, which is built into cars today. Older cars were made of steel, where the force would be transferred throughout the vehicle.

Outward-opening doors. When the hinges are visible from the outside, the door will swing toward the forcible-entry team. These types of doors are usually found in commercial occupancies, including places of public assembly, which are required to have doors that swing in the direction of egress for life safety purposes (fig. 12–30). Strip mall storefronts, for example, should have outward-opening tempered glass doors with aluminum frames, known as **aluminum stile doors**. The glass is heat treated to add strength (fig. 12–31). We often find outward-opening metal doors in factories as well.

Fig. 12–31. Aluminum stile door

Fig. 12–30. Outward-opening door

Fig. 12–32. Tempered glass door

Tempered glass doors. This type of door is usually distinguishable by its lack of frame and little or no trim. The lock is usually found in the bottom stile. Its tempered glass is four times stronger than plate glass. If smashed, it will explode into little pieces (fig. 12–32).

Sliding doors. Sliding or patio doors are really door-sized windows that glide in tracks. They first appeared in the Southwest in the United States in the 1950s. Sliding doors provide wide, easy access between indoors and outdoors (fig. 12–33).

Fig. 12–33. Sliding patio door

Residential overhead garage doors. Overhead doors are normally found in garages. Garage door panels are made of fiberglass, fiberboard, steel, aluminum, or wood. Windows are optional.

There are three types of garage doors:

1. Roll-up: Doors with hinged sections that roll on a track (fig. 12–34)

2. Swing-up: One piece that arcs up (fig. 12–35)

3. Hinged: Pair of doors that open outward (fig. 12–36)

Fig. 12–34. Roll-up garage door

Fig. 12–35. Swing-up garage door

Fig. 12–36. Hinged garage door

Hurricane-resistant garage doors. In some parts of the country where hurricanes and tornados are a common occurrence, homeowners have either upgraded their garage doors or replaced them altogether with stronger reinforced garage doors (fig. 12–37). When homeowners do these types of renovations, they inadvertently make our job of forcible entry a lot tougher.

Hurricane-resistant garage doors are embedded with heavier vertical stiles and horizontal reinforcement, as well as impact-resistant steel skin and heavy-gauge sheathing. They also use heavy-gauge steel tracks supported with a high number of anchoring brackets to help maintain the door's integrity in high-wind situations.

To sum it up, tougher doors mean added delays if we are not aware of them.

Fig. 12–38. Manually operated roll down gate

Fig. 12–37. Hurricane-resistant garage doors

Fig. 12–39. Electric powered roll-down gate

Security gates or roll-down gates. Security gates are more commonly known to firefighters as **roll-down gates**. Roll-down gates are normally found in strip malls and commercial occupancies known as taxpayers. They come in a variety of thicknesses and types. Roll-down gates operate in three ways:

1. Manually operated: Often recognizable by their smaller size and wide slats with handles on the bottom. The gate is lifted up by hand with the assistance of springs (fig. 12–38).

2. Electrically powered: An electric motor raises and lowers the gate, activated by a switch on the wall (fig. 12–39).

3. Chain operated: A chain hoist mechanism lifts the gate (fig. 12–40).

Fig. 12–40. Chain-operated roll-down gate

Forcing doors

FFI: 5.3.4 Before we commence operations, we need to assess what the call is for: fire, medical, or other nonemergency. We should always strive to gain entry in the least damaging way. Sometimes we may not even wind up forcing the door if there is another means of entry. If the call is for a fire, then there should be no delays, and we need to force entry immediately, in the most efficient way. We need to attack the normal point of entry. This is the route that most people take in a fire or an emergency. Lives are depending on it. It is important for firefighters to use the tools correctly.

- A Halligan tool is held like a baseball bat, except that the hands should be spread apart. The hand at the hook end is palm up, and the hand at the fork end is held palm down. Your hands should never be anywhere but on the shaft of the Halligan tool (fig. 12–41).

- The axe is held with the upper hand 6 in. (152 mm) from the head of the axe, with the other hand near the bottom of the handle (fig. 12–42).

After forcing, doors may have to be propped open to keep from closing on hoselines, or to remain visible as exits.

Fig. 12–41. Firefighter holding Halligan tool correctly

Fig. 12–42. Firefighter holding axe correctly

Inward-opening doors. One of the more common types of doors encountered when forcing entry is the inward-opening door. To achieve entry, firefighters should work in teams of two while using a flat-head axe or maul and a Halligan tool. First and foremost, size-up the door to determine the best means possible of entry. Once this is done, the team of firefighters will insert the Halligan tool in between the door and frame near the lock. The flat-head axe or maul is then used to drive the tool in further to allow the door to be pried open. In order to increase safety, a rope or hose strap should be used to hold the door so that when it is opened it does not swing into the room prematurely and expose the firefighters to danger. This method can also be accomplished by a single firefighter if necessary.

Forcing inward-opening door with hydraulic spreading tool. While manual tools are more commonplace on the fireground and will typically be used for forcing entry, there are a number of power tools that can be used to also accomplish the job. One of these is the hydraulic spreading tool. As with any attempt at forcing entry, it is important to size-up the situation before proceeding. This method is best accomplished with a minimum of two firefighters working as a team. To open the door with a hydraulic spreading tool, it is a good idea to have hand tools like the Halligan available. First, "shock and gap" the door or loosen it on the lock side with the Halligan tool. Then place the spreaders of the tool in the opening and operate the tool with short pumping strokes to force the door open. In order to increase safety, a rope or hose strap should be used to hold the door so that when it is opened it doesn't swing into the room prematurely and expose the firefighters to danger.

Note: Some hydraulic forcible-entry tools utilize a small spring to keep the tool in *work* mode. This spring can easily get dislodged. If the tool falls to work, firefighters should know without looking at the tool which direction the lever needs to be pushed to put the tool into work mode. It's a good idea to put hydraulic tools under a load to test them, because often failures will only be apparent if the tool is under a load—so give them an operational test.

This tool will actually work best on stronger doors, given that some wooden doors that have strong locks will actually blow the door jamb. The tool is best used with the jaws placed directly on the lock. Some residential occupants add a piece of angle iron around their door locks to prevent people from forcing them open. You will need to position the jaws of the tool as close as possible to the locks in order to force the door (fig. 12–43).

Fig. 12–43. Angle iron on inward-opening door

Through-the-lock technique. When using the **through-the-lock** method, we are normally going to be dealing with two types of locks, the mortise lock and the rim lock. We are going to be using the K-tool to remove the trim ring and the face of the lock cylinder. After getting a bite into the cylinder, the tool's blades will lock onto the cylinder and then be leveraged out. In the case of aluminum stile doors with mortise pivoting dead bolts, a pair of vise grips may be used to turn the entire cylinder housing 1/4 turn clockwise to bend the two set screws that hold it in place. The cylinder can then be spun completely out of the door by turning it counter-clockwise, allowing it to be manipulated with the key tool as described below. The cylinder can be reinstalled at the conclusion of the incident.

Mortise locks. The key turns a cam that slides the bolt out of the strike. To open the lock after the cylinder has been removed, use the key tool. Before pulling the cylinder, note the position of the keyway. The keyway would normally be found at the 6 o'clock position. Use the bent end of the key tool and slide the bolt from the 5 o'clock position to the 7 o'clock position. If the slide is

found at the 7 o'clock position, then move it over to the 5 o'clock position.

Note: If the lock has a dead bolt mechanism that prevents the bolt from moving, you must depress the dead bolt mechanism with the end of the key tool while sliding the bolt. If after doing this, you still find that the latch is in the locked position, continue rotating the key until you make contact with the spring-loaded latch lever, found at the 3 or 9 o'clock position. Depress this latch to release the spring latch.

Rim locks. The key turns stem on the end of the cylinder, which fits into the back plate of the lock. We are going to insert the straight end of the key tool into the slot and turn left or right. If you cannot insert the key tool into the slot because a shutter is present, or turn it because the **night latch** is thrown, take the point of the Halligan, insert it into the opening, and drive the lock off the door.

Note: The lock may have a shutter that closes when the cylinder is withdrawn. Some firefighters carry a dental pick or a ground-down screwdriver to get at the shutter.

Forcing inward-opening doors using a Halligan tool and flat-head axe. The method we use to force these types of doors depends on the position of the door in the frame. They may be **flush fitting** or **recessed**.

Flush fitting. These doors may be forced using the adz or the fork end of the Halligan tool. When using the fork end of the tool, place the concave end of the tool facing toward the door. Slightly canted for ease of penetration, as the tool is being driven in between the door and the jamb, bring it to perpendicular to avoid being driven into the jamb. After the tool has spread the door as far as possible, push the tool away from the door. Place the adz end of the Halligan tool 6 in. (152 mm) above or below the lock. Drive it into the area between the door jamb and the door. Avoid penetrating the door stop. Pry the tool downward and out.

Recessed doors. The fork end of the Halligan tool cannot be used for these types of doors. We will only use the adz end of the Halligan tool, in the same manner as in the flush fitting doors.

Note: Realize that to force an outward-opening door, sometimes the adz needs to get behind the door. This will require the entire head of the Halligan to get in between the door and the jamb. This will take some time and effort (a minute longer than an inward-opening door operation), so persevere.

Forcing an aluminum stile glass door using a power saw. Some doors are designed so that traditional means of forcing them with hand tools will cause substantial damage to the door which flies in the face of the third incident priority, **property conservation**. To effectively perform this task, a power saw is an effective tool. This method requires at least two firefighters and the use of a Halligan tool, flat-head axe, or maul and a power saw. As with other methods, first size-up the situation before going ahead with the operation. For this method the firefighter makes a gap in the door using the hand tools, then uses the power saw to cut the slide bolt and open the door. Because they are using power tools, safety is a primary concern for this operation.

Note: Often the frame of a glass and metal store door is part of a showcase window. These frames can have quite a bit of play. You may be able to get the door somewhat easily using conventional forcible entry, even though the keeper of the lock has considerable throw. Check to see if the door is outward-opening, so that when the keeper of the lock pops out, it won't wind up on the inside of the frame. This will prevent the door from opening, even though the dead bolt is out of the strike box.

If it's a double door, this will not work because the keeper of the lock will have a hook on it to prevent the spreading of the door from unlocking the door.

Forcing sliding doors. If the occupants don't have any homemade security devices in the track, such as a cut-down broomstick or 2 × 4 or pipe, forcing the door should not present much of a problem. Place the fork of the Halligan tool with the bevel side against the door jamb and snap the lock striker out of the frame (fig. 12–44).

As a last resort, if there is a homemade device, you will have to break the glass. Remember that if you break glass, you will be adding oxygen to the fire and may increase the fire.

Forcing residential overhead garage doors. Normally these types of doors are found with glass windows or wooden panels. The best method with these types doors would be to break one of the panels and reach in and unlock the door. Break a panel near the lock, but also near where you think the cross bar may be, so if double-keyed, you can put the fork of the Halligan on the bar and beat it in by hitting the head of the Halligan tool with the maul. This should pull the bar out of its keeper in the door track, enabling the door to be opened. If the garage has an electric opener, you should break one of the panels and reach in and pull the release cord. The through-the-lock method can also work here. Use the K-tool or A-tool and pull the cylinder. If the above methods don't work, you can use the power saw and make an inverted V cut or a box cut (figs. 12–45 and 12–46).

Fig. 12–45. Inverted V cut

Fig. 12–44. Locking device on a sliding glass door

Fig. 12–46. Box cut

Note:

- After forcing the door you need to secure it, to make sure it doesn't come down behind you. A portable ladder or a 6-ft (2-m) hook propped under the door works; if these are not available, use vise grips on the track.

- Keep in mind that this may not be the best point of attack if there is a fire in the garage. If there is a front door, you must also make entry there and make sure that fire is not extending into the house through an opening between garage and house. You don't want to save the garage and lose the house.

- When overhauling garage fires with overhead doors, make sure to inspect where the door track supports pierce the ceiling. It is often not spackled, so an opening in the Sheetrock® may be present that would allow extension. This is sometimes missed because the open door hides this likely avenue of vertical extension.

Forcing entry. The primary point of attack will be the padlocks. Cutting the padlocks is usually the fastest way to gain entry. When cutting padlocks you also must remember to pull the pin that holds the lock to the hasp on the gate (fig. 12–47). After the pin is pulled, you must manually lift up the gate.

Fig. 12–47. Pin in roll-down gate

If it is not feasible to remove the locks, you should then attack the gate itself. Sometimes the gate is little used and so may resist raising even with the locks removed. Sometimes the fire may have warped the door. The idea is to cut the gates and remove the slats. Removing the slats will free up the slats and release the tension on the gate. There are two methods to do this:

1. Make an inverted V cut. When doing this, leave a small piece at the apex uncut as this will allow the gate to stay in place while finishing the cut.

2. The second style is a **slash cut**. Make two parallel cuts from top to bottom and pull out the middle slat above the highest lock. Then pull out the remaining two slats on either side. This will release the gate (fig. 12–48).

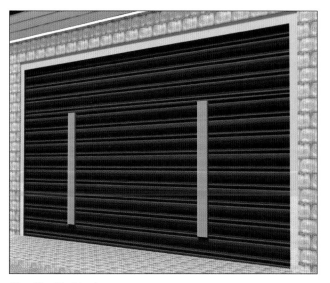

Fig. 12–48. Slash cut

Note: It is generally a good idea to open all the gates at the same time at a serious working fire. Cutting gates will also chew up a blade very quickly; so if you have a lot of cutting to do, make sure you set your priorities and get the main gate first.

Forcing hurricane-resistant garage doors. One of the more interesting doors that firefighters come up against are hurricane-resistant doors. By their nature they are designed to withstand severe forces of nature. Forcing this type of door requires a team of firefighters using hand tools, a power saw, and bolt cutters. As with previous methods of forcing doors, size-up is critical before committing firefighters to the task. Access to this door usually requires the removal of a pad lock and the cutting of the door near the lock mechanism to make it accessible.

Forcing entry to security gates or roll-down gates. In many urban areas it common to find roll down gates protecting the entrances to commercial establishments. Access to these buildings can prove to be a challenge. Forcing this type of gate requires a team of firefighters using hand tools, a power saw, and bolt cutters. As with previous methods of forcing doors, size-up is critical before committing firefighters to the task. Since this involves any incident with heavy fire, the main purpose is to allow for access to quickly attack the fire.

A cone cut allows for stream application at ceiling level prior to entry for a quick knockdown.

Forcing entry to electric powered roll-down gates.

The motor on the wall could be mounted outside or inside the building. If inside, you may have to cut an inverted V or box cut to gain entry. Be aware that often these larger gates do not have slats that are removable.

Another method is to gain entry and use the manual override cable and chain to raise the gate. In a smoke condition this can be difficult. The firefighters must coordinate their efforts. One firefighter pulls on the cable or chain that engages the gear for manual raising of the door. This may take several tries, as the gears may not be lined up and may be stiff from lack of use. The second firefighter needs to pull the chain that raises the door. This firefighter will not know if he or she is pulling the right way, as the gear ratio is usually very low to accommodate the motor. The solution is for the second firefighter to pull in both directions as the first firefighter continues to tug on the cable, and at the same time a third firefighter uses his or her hand or light to detect when the door is rising. Once the door is found to be rising, the third firefighter instructs the other two to continue doing what they are doing to raise the door. Getting a large door fully open this way will often have dramatic improvement on the fire operation.

If the motor is outside, the manual override may be up in the housing of the motor or locked in a vertical track alongside the gate. Accessing this may allow you to use the manual override. If there is a keyed switch outside, you may have two options: pulling the lock cylinder and turning the switch with a screwdriver, or you may shear the housing cover and jump the switch.

WINDOWS

FFI 5.3.4 Our normal point of entrance in a fire operation rarely involves entering through a window. There are exceptions, but for the most part we use the door. This is not to say that we don't need to know how to force entry. The reality is that in a working fire, we will not be forcing windows, but breaking them. Extreme care must be used, as there have been cases where firefighters have been killed or injured behind windows for various reasons.

Flying glass from forcing windows can be dangerous to both firefighters and interior victims, as well as the shards remaining in a window where firefighters or victims must exit.

Most of our responses today are for calls other than fires. We get calls for all sorts of emergencies. In this chapter we have discussed using less damaging methods when forcing doors, such as going through the lock. There are sometimes even better options when we are confronted with non-life-threatening emergencies. Many homeowners go through great lengths to fortify their front doors but a second-floor window may have a cheap window lock. If there is a window within reach of the street, a portable ladder or fire escape will usually provide us with the least damaging way to gain entry. For safety, always send at least two firefighters when using a window for entry.

Windows usually were single pane up until the mid-1980s. This was bad for the homeowner but good for the firefighter. Windows would fail very early in a fire and prevented firefighters from entering a potentially explosive situation.

This section will show you how to identify the various window types.

Window types

Glazing: Low-E glass. In these types of windows, a low-emissivity (low-E) coating is applied to each layer of glass in the unit. Each unit can be either double glazed or triple glazed, meaning that it has two or three vertical panels. Each panel is separated by an air gap that is normally filled with some type of inert gas such as argon or krypton.

In areas of the country where there are ultraviolet (UV) issues, most window manufacturers offer some form of "superglass" technology. The most common superglass is called low-E glass, which has a metallic film vacuum-deposited on one side. In a double-pane unit, the film is on the outside of the inner pane.

What this means to the firefighter is that we will have a very difficult time venting these windows.

Plate glass. The dictionary defines **plate glass** as "glass produced in thin sheets, used for windows and mirrors" (fig. 12–49). This is the type of glass that we see every day used as windows in storefronts. It is heavy and will shatter when you break it. Firefighters who have underestimated the weight of these windows have been injured when breaking these, and pieces of glass have landed on them.

Note: Keep in mind that when we are training to be professional firefighters, anybody can break a window. What is going to set us apart from the rest of society is our professionalism. We should treat every home or business we respond to as if a close relative owned it. This means when we have opportunities in non-life-threatening emergencies to create less damage by opening a window rather than breaking it, we should do so.

Fig. 12–49. Plate glass window

Tempered glass. **Tempered glass** has been treated either chemically or in a thermal process to add strength (fig. 12–50). In addition to the increased strength, tempered glass shatters into soft-edged tiny fragments instead of the sharp-edged shards of typical pane glass. Side and rear windows of automobiles are made of tempered glass.

Fig. 12–50. Tempered glass

Wired glass. A wire mesh fed into molten glass during manufacturing adds strength to wired glass. Usually installed for doors and roof applications, **wired glass** keeps objects from breaking through, and when the glass is broken, the wire holds pieces together. Ideal for deterring burglaries, wired glass can also inhibit the spread of a fire (fig. 12–51).

Fig. 12–51. Wired glass

Lexan®. **Lexan®** is a polycarbonate resin thermoplastic glazing that has an impact resistance 250 times greater than safety glass (fig. 12–52). It will not shatter and is half the weight of glass. It is self-extinguishing and has one-third the conductivity of glass.

It is usually found in high-crime areas or areas that are prone to vandalism. Fires where Lexan® is involved are very difficult to ventilate since Lexan® cannot be broken with conventional forcible-entry tools.

Forcing entry. The best tools to use are either a power saw with a carbide-tipped blade or a reciprocating saw (e.g., Sawzall®) with a coarse wood-tooth blade. The reciprocating saw is slower than the power saw. If neither of these tools are available, the Halligan tool and axe can be used to force the framing or mullions, thus making it possible to remove the whole pane of Lexan®. If the window is at ground level, a portable ladder can be used to push in the whole assembly.

Casement windows. **Casement windows** open sideways at the turn of a crank. The advantage is that the whole window can be cracked slightly and still (with the handle removed) prevent entry by intruders. These windows are a disadvantage for the fire service given that vent and access are limited by the way they open and their small size. They close tightly because the lock draws the sash against the frame. The handle can be removed to add additional security (fig. 12–53).

Double-hung windows. In **double-hung windows**, both sashes move up and down vertically. (A single-hung window has only the bottom sash that moves.) Some have key locks that attach to the top rail of the lower sash. They can be used to keep the window shut or partially open. The lock pins into the jamb (fig. 12–54).

Fig. 12–52. Lexan® window

Fig. 12–53. Casement window

Forcing entry. From the exterior, place the fork of the Halligan tool with the bevel side against the window-sill and pry inward and downward. This should break the weak window latch. Should the glass break, clear it completely.

From the interior, most modern double-hung windows have clips that can be moved to allow easy removal of the entire window with the glass intact. If in a heavy smoke condition, these windows can be readily forced by placing the adz of the Halligan tool between the upper and lower sash against the window jamb and prying upward. This is faster and provides a better opening than breaking a double-paned glass window.

Note: Anytime you make entry into a window at a fire, you should remove both the bottom and the top sashes, for safety reasons. The old expression is to "**make a door.**"

Fig. 12–54. Double-hung window

Sliding windows. Sliding windows are like patio doors, only smaller. The primary advantage is that the sash doesn't protrude outward when open. A problem for the fire service is that they are often too small for effective vent and entry (fig. 12–55).

Fig. 12–55. Sliding window

Forcing entry. Here is the same type of locking mechanism as on a double-hung window. The best way to force this window is to use the Halligan tool with the bevel end against the wall, placing the fork end of the tool between the edge of the window and the window jamb and pushing the tool toward the wall.

Awning windows. **Awning windows** are like casement windows, but open upward instead of sideways. They are normally used for basement windows. Like casement windows, the crank handle can be removed for added security, and like casement windows, their small size limits our vent and access capabilities (fig. 12–56).

Fig. 12–56. Awning window

Jalousie windows. Overlapping glass panes opened with a crank or turn-screw form the sections of a **jalousie window** (fig. 12–57). When opened, the sections allow air flow through a residence, but this type of window does not form a tight seal when closed. Even closed tightly, the glass louvers still allow air to pass through, and the side hinges also are difficult to seal without completely covering the window. The disadvantage for a homeowner with this type of window actually helps in a fire situation: the air leakage allows a fire to breathe and greatly diminishes the chance of a flashover.

Fig. 12–57. Jalousie window

Window security devices

Window bars. In some high-crime areas, people try to make their homes impregnable. Firefighters are finding more windows that are accessible from the ground or a ladder covered with outside bars, also called **burglar bars**.

Just as there are numerous types of windows, there are equal types of bars that can be installed (figs. 12–58, 12–59, and 12–60). From ornamental wrought iron to simple iron bars, there are many examples, as well as a variety of anchoring systems. Often these iron bars are mounted with lag screws in the exterior of the building. Firefighters also will encounter burglar bars that were set directly into the building's masonry or frame (fig. 12–61).

Note: Structure fires in buildings with strong security devices should be approached differently than fires in unsecured buildings. While security devices covering windows and doors keep unwanted people out during normal situations, these same devices can make a building unsafe for firefighters (and building occupants) who need a quick exit from an unsafe situation. Security bars on windows and doors should be addressed by the incident commander, and communicated to all personnel on the scene. Removing window bars and all barriers needs to be handled quickly, and in some instances with assistance from the rapid intervention team (RIT).

Fig. 12–58. Window bars on a house

Fig. 12–61. Burglar bars on a wooden frame

Fig. 12–59. Close-up of window bars

Fig. 12–60. Decorative window bars

Tools for window bar removal. The tools of first choice for removing burglar bars usually are common power tools such as the air chisel or rotary saw with the metal-cutting blade. However, sometimes power tools don't work or aren't available. Because removing burglar bars is such a crucial operation, always have basic hand tools such as a sledgehammer and irons (flathead ax and Halligan) as a backup.

Rotary gas-powered saw. The rotary saw can be used in a number of ways to defeat security bars. One approach is to remove the moving sections of the hinges by cutting vertically through the edge of the hinge assembly to remove it from the doorframe. Another method is to cut through the deadbolt as if you were cutting the deadbolt on metal doors. Position the blade in the gap between the gate edge and the jamb, and cut downward through the bolt. This can be more difficult if the bolt is protected by a metal cover; in this case you must cut through the cover as well as the deadbolt. If a metal cover is present, it is often better to use the saw to cut through the bar segments that support and connect the lock mechanism to the gate. Cutting these bars that support the lock will enable you to displace the lock assembly from the gate. When using the saw to remove burglar bars on windows, cut at the points where the bars are flattened into tabs and attached to the building with connectors, at the weakest link or attachment point.

Cutting through the main bars with a rotary saw should be a last resort. Working horizontally with the rotary saw can be very awkward and fatiguing. It's better to make vertical cuts through horizontal members, whenever possible—i.e., move the saw blade up and down while cutting through horizontal bar members and let the weight of the saw assist with the cutting. Older-model rotary saws can also be awkward and fatiguing to use above eye level, so if you must make higher-level cuts, work from a stable ladder or an elevated platform. Another point to remember, especially when using the rotary saw to cut metal, is to keep the revolutions per minute (rpm) high for greatest cutting efficiency.

Forcible Entry

FIREFIGHTER I

Chapter 12

Flathead axe and Halligan. In the hands of firefighters who know how to use them, the irons are the "master keys" for all-purpose forcible entry on the fireground. Use the adz end of the Halligan driven by the flathead ax as a muscle-powered version of the air chisel to shear off burglar bar hinges or connections. Use the point end of the Halligan to attack burglar bar gate hinges. Position the point on the top of the hinge, and use the ax (or maul) to pound the claw point down and split open the hinge assembly. Once again, if the lower and center connections can be broken at two or three points, very often you can bend back the bars from the loosened points and use leverage to either break the remaining connections or move the bars completely out of the way.[1]

Window gates. Instead of fixed burglar bars, some buildings actually have a gate that can be opened. The gates themselves may be may be operable by pushing a button to release them (or by the operation of a smoke detector tied directly to them), or a key may need to be turned inside. Sometimes the gates have padlocks on the inside. Note that fixed bars as well as gates that need keys to open are typically prohibited by building and fire codes; however, many people in high-crime areas install them illegally.

Note: Recently building owners have begun installing metal window enclosures on top of the window gates and window bars, while a building is undergoing renovations or foreclosures. These will have to be forced prior to attacking the window gates or window bars (fig. 12–62).

Fig. 12–62. Metal window enclosures

In multiple dwellings that have fire escapes, you will find window gates attached to the inside of the window. The upper and lower hinges are screwed into the jamb (fig. 12–63).

Fig. 12–63. Window gate

Forcing entry. You will need to open the window and attack the hinges. Attack the top hinge first with the Halligan tool, and afterward attack the bottom hinge. When both hinges have been removed, slide the gate toward the lock, and this will open the window two-thirds of the way.

Note:

- Do not kick the gate, as this could result in the gate jamming and your wasting time. Also keep in mind that you may find padlocks on the inside. When entering a room, size up the situation first, and if there is a lock, remove it.

- It's a good idea when searching a large fire area (big apartment) to establish a second means of egress. You wouldn't want to get cut off from the way you came in and only then find out that the windows had gates or bars on them. Determine early on if there are accessible windows, and make one into a second means of egress remote from where you came in, just in case.

Window guards. **Window guards**, also known as "child guards," are usually three to four horizontal bars that interlock and slide into a prescribed opening (fig. 12–64). The device is installed on the lower sash to prevent children from falling out. They are normally screwed to the outside of the lower sash of the window frame.

Forcing these window guards is normally not a problem. Striking the vertical frame of the window guard (there are two) away from the mounting frame will get the job done.

Note: Sometimes if the gate is larger than the window, the vertical frames will be too close to the side of the window frame to insert the fork of the Halligan tool. If that is the case, you will need to work on the mounting screws.

Fig. 12–65. Tap cons

Fig. 12–64. Window guard

Hurricane-resistant windows.

Security is not our only issue. In the areas of the country where hurricanes are prevalent, people are now using windows that can withstand hurricane-force winds. As a result, people who don't even live in hurricane-prone areas are now using **hurricane-resistant windows** because of the added security value. Chances are now that you may find these windows in any part of the country.

The frames are built right into homes that are constructed with concrete block walls. They are set into the openings with tap cons, which are 3 in. (76 mm) long and ⅜ in. (10 mm) in diameter. They are tapped in 8 to 12 in. (200 to 305 mm) apart (fig. 12–65). The glass rests against the frame (resistance is to the inside). Hurricane-resistant windows feature three panes of glass—two of which sandwich a protective interlayer—solar control plus low-E (metallic film), argon gas, and heavy-duty double locks (fig. 12–66).

Note: The film gives the glass the ability to stay together.

Fig. 12–66. Hurricane-resistant windows

Forcing entry. As mentioned earlier, hurricane-resistant doors provide challenges to firefighters. Hurricane resistant windows are no different. Forcing this type of door requires a team of firefighters using hand tools, chain or reciprocating saw, and pruning shears. As with previous methods of forcing doors, size-up is critical before committing firefighters to the task. Because these windows are designed to resist high winds and debris, the use of a saw is needed to cut through the window panes.

Note:

- If a saw is not available, use pruning shears. If pruning shears are used, you will have to shatter the glass to loosen it up, because the shears don't have the power to go through glass like a saw.

- Full personal protective equipment (PPE) must be used, because the cutting operation will create a dust cloud, and there will be small shards of glass thrown about while you are cutting.

Breaching walls and floors

FFI 5.3.4 FFI 5.3.9 **Breaching** walls and floors should usually be a last resort. To breach a wall or floor takes a great deal of time and energy and also damages the structure, which can be costly and dangerous.

Breaching a wall is especially dangerous, as firefighters must be very aware of the fire-related structural weaknesses and load-bearing factors, as well as any electrical, gas, or plumbing lines hidden in the walls that could be struck or cut when breaching. In some cases, cutting into a load-bearing wall could precipitate a collapse. The collapse potential must be carefully weighed against expected gains.

There are times, however, when it is the best course of action, and firefighters should be able to breach walls or floors when the need arrives.

There are a great many special tools coming into the fire service from the demolition, construction, and mining industries. Generally these tools are expensive and therefore in short supply in the fire service. They usually need to be special-called to a fire or emergency scene and require specific training on the use of the tool. The methods discussed next involve the use of tools commonly found on today's fire trucks and as so should be available for rapid use.

Breaching interior walls. Breaching interior walls is generally considered as an emergency method to exit a fire area if cut off from a normal route of egress by an unexpected fire growth. If you are put to work as part of a rapid intervention team (RIT) to breach an interior wall to help find or free a lost or downed firefighter, a good tool to bring may be a reciprocating saw. Many of these saws are now light, have quick-change blades and batteries, and will operate in heavy smoke. In some cases, interior walls are breached to create openings to attack a fire in an adjacent room that cannot be attacked from a public hallway door.

For a wood stud wall, firefighters can dismantle tough wood studs by splitting them with either the point or the adz swung or placed and hit with an axe or maul (fig. 12–67).

Some large and tough studs found in older construction or pieces installed by "wood butchers" can be rapidly removed with this method.

There are occasions when an interior wall may be breached to facilitate line placement or search, usually if an alteration to the building has sealed off the expected

access (hallway), and the new access cannot readily be found. If faced with duplex, triplex, or "sandwich" apartments, and the line has to advance down into the fire area, it may be advantageous to breach an interior wall from the level of the fire area to avoid the punishment of pushing in from above. Any breaching is a judgment call, and the firefighter or officer should try to determine if the wall is a bearing wall.

Fig. 12–67. Firefighter removing wood stud

Note: Often a valence of greater depth over a doorway or window might be a beam or double header, indicting that the wall is a bearing wall. Removing more than one stud on a bearing wall could cause a collapse.

Breaching a lath and plaster or gypsum board wall. The preferred method of access to a victim or for firefighter escape is through a door. If a door is not readily accessible or it is too difficult and time consuming to force, breaching a wall may be a necessary alternative. While this method of entry can be accomplished by a single firefighter, a team effort should be used. The tools consist of a Halligan tool, pike pole, and an axe or maul. Just as with forcing doors, size-up is a primary concern for the firefighter. It is important for the firefighter(s) to make sure that any hazards are removed or not in the area where the opening will be made. Once this is done, the firefighter will make an opening that will be large enough to move a victim or themselves through.

Breaching exterior walls. Breaching exterior walls for access or line placement is not a sound firefighting tactic. The fire probably has made good headway by the time this option is considered, and the wall is probably load bearing if the construction is common (unframed).

In some cases, cutting into a load-bearing wall could precipitate a collapse; the risks must be thoroughly understood. Some modern buildings can be supported by steel columns and beams, with the walls of glass, masonry, or metal providing covering and rigidity rather than support. This is known as framed construction, but most buildings are supported by their exterior walls. Although breaching is possible, the collapse potential must be carefully weighed against expected gains.

Breaching exterior walls for rescue, especially of firefighters, may be needed. Collapse potential and the hazards of gas or electric utilities within the wall all need to be considered. Fuel-powered saws, reciprocating saws, mauls, axes, and Halligan tools may be used to breach wood-framed walls. Power saws are versatile and powerful (*measured in horsepower*). They can do the work of several firefighters working to their full capacity, and do it continuously until out of fuel or blade. However, saws can bog down in heavy smoke and are limited to a 4-in. (100-mm) cut if using the common 12-in. (305-mm) blade on circular saws. Chain saws cut deeper but can be quite dangerous as they can kick or pull as they go through different materials.

Breaching masonry walls with a power saw usually requires a blade change, as most units run with carbide-tipped blades for general purpose and metal-cutting blades (aluminum oxide) for locks and gates. A blade change may not be desirable in a rapid intervention situation due to the time needed to change blades. A maul and a Halligan tool can be used to readily breach hollow-core concrete block. If the wall is three **wythes** thick (a wythe is a single vertical stack of brick), brick-faced concrete block, or solid filled concrete block, it can be breached with a battering ram. To do this, two firefighters would pick up the tool and swing repeatedly using the forked end of the tool to chip the masonry. Some firefighters like to start high to get the tough work done before their arms tire out. Other firefighters may choose to start low to help their arms work while making the tough initial hole, and hope gravity will assist them with making the upper blocks fail once the blocks below have been compromised. You will need to rotate members as you create a hole and then enlarge the hole into an upside down V-shaped opening. (The upside down V shape may aid in keeping wall stability.) The knob end of the tool may be used to knock out bricks or blocks once the masonry yields. The knob end might also allow rapid takedown of plastered-over plywood coverings used to seal vacant buildings. Any use of the battering ram will rapidly exhaust a crew.

Breaching floors. Floors have been breached in the fire service to do the following:

- Vent cellar fires

- Allow water application to cellar fires from the floor above

- Put water on fires in voids between flooring layers

- Rescue

- Allow for drainage and runoff

If the area is carpeted, clear it using a sharp knife. Generally power saws are used to cut the flooring, but if unable to use saw due to smoke, the old reliable axe and Halligan tool are used to dismantle wood floors. Strike close to the beam (determined by sounding or seeing nail heads), with the axe blade hitting at an angle to allow penetration into the hard wood that often makes up flooring. Cut where it will facilitate the prying tools (across the grain) (fig. 12–68). Work in teams, starting where the floorboards or plywood end if possible.

Fig. 12–68. Axe opening a floor

If you need to cut a masonry floor, you already have a very serious situation. If the fire is below the masonry floor, it is weakening the much-needed supports to the heavy floor. Serious consideration needs to be made as to the risk versus reward of this operation. Special tools such as power saws with concrete cutting blades, concrete cutting chain saws, and power hammers (jackhammers) may be needed to breach masonry floors.

NOTES

1. Crow, J. "Burglar Bar Removal: Strategies and Tactics," *Fire Engineering* magazine online, www.fireengineering.com.

I train my firefighters in every aspect of firefighting. In the fire service you never can predict what you will be doing at an operation. I think it is important that firefighters know every part of the job even if they are not assigned to it. In my station, we send firefighters to the company "across the floor" to cross train in truck work, and the ladder company sends firefighters across the floor to do engine work.

The training detail is normally 90 days. One of my firefighters, Dan, had just come back from a 90-day detail in the ladder. It was a busy detail—he went to a few good fires and worked in all the positions. Dan is a great young firefighter, and this detail just made him that much more experienced.

We also just received two new probies, Brian and John, out of the training academy. It is always a good thing to get new guys in the house because it gives the officers a chance to train them the way we want, and at the same time it refreshes the memories of some of the senior guys. You know that they are just chomping at the bit to use all that great knowledge they just learned at the training academy, and put it into action.

I was the acting battalion chief on the night tour, and it was an uneventful night. I was waiting for my relief to come in so I could get back to my engine company. Around 0800 hours, I heard on our department radio a call for a fire in a store. Usually when we get a call at that hour for a store, it means that the workers came to the store and opened the gates and discovered the fire. I knew the area, and there are lots of stores in a row, called taxpayers. The first unit came upon the scene and gave the signal: 10–75, working fire. I knew that this was going to be a big fire, and after a few minutes, they transmitted a second alarm. At that moment, as the fire was gaining headway, my relief man came in. I didn't waste much time with him; I gave him a quick rundown of the previous night, then I bolted out of there. I knew that if the fire progressed, we were going to be assigned on third alarm. I raced back to firehouse and parked the car. As I walked in the front door, the alarm went off; we were going to the fire.

Brian, my brand new probie, was working one of his first tours, and Dan was working as well. En route, the chief was asking companies to report in to the front of the fire building with their multiversals. I informed the members of my company that we were going to probably "surround and drown" this fire, now an outside, defensive operation. When we arrived, there was heavy fire in about 13 stores, and it was through the roof. Next to the fire building, there was a huge multiple dwelling, which the fire was now threatening. We reported in to the front of the building with our multiversal, expecting that we would pick a store and operate the large-caliber stream into that store. We began setting up the device, and we were ready for water. Just then the chief grabbed me and ordered me to drop what we were doing, because he needed a line in the multiple dwelling. We left the device and started out our search for a pumper from where we could stretch a hose. I found a pumper on the other street that was on a hydrant, which was close to the entrance to the multiple dwelling. We were now on our own, and we needed to stretch eight lengths of 2½-in. (65 mm) hose to the most severely exposed apartment.

I figured out which was going to be the best building entrance to stretch to: the building had five wings. I told the men to start stretching to the front of the building, and I would let them know where to go when I found the right apartment. I found the right apartment, and I was hoping someone was home, so I banged on the door, but got no answer. I now had a little problem, as this was the apartment I needed to get into. It was the perfect spot; it was right where the fire was hitting the building, and I knew that if we didn't get water on this apartment soon, we would have a fire in the entire multiple dwelling. The apartment also had a very difficult door with five locks and an angle iron. Not only did it have angle iron, but this angle iron was held together with a J channel. The men brought the line up to the fire floor, and we were ready for water.

I radioed to Dan to get the forcible-entry tools. He brought them up, and I showed him what we had. Due to the severity of the situation, I was tempted to grab the tools myself, as I knew what was needed and how to force this door. In my department it is a big "no-no" for officers to work with tools—we supervise. I trusted my men and their training, and I also had two other more senior firefighters working, but instead I grabbed the probie Brian to assist him, and we went to work on the door. I thought this would be a great opportunity for Brian to work under a pressure situation and build his confidence. Neither of them was phased by the formidability of the door (at least they didn't show it). We were on our own, all the ladder companies were heavily engaged, and there was no time to call for one. I instructed them on where to place the tool, and we began dismantling the door one lock at a time. I helped them with my officer's tool when it was needed to chock an opening. We took it a lock at a time, and we were through the door in no time. Our troubles were not over, however, as the window we needed to get to was covered by a window gate. We now needed to force the gate to get to the fire. Again we took our tools and forced the gate. We brought the line out on to the fire escape, and were able to keep the fire out of the multiple dwelling. We were in a perfect spot.

After the fire, the occupant of the apartment showed up. I asked him if he was storing gold and diamonds in his apartment, because it was like Fort Knox. He told me that he didn't have anything that valuable, but he mentioned that he was a locksmith!

QUESTIONS

1. How has technology changed forcible entry?

2. Why is it important to "control the door" when forcing entry for fire attack?

3. List the four typical door locks.

4. Explain the role of size-up in forcible entry.

5. Describe how a key tool is used to operate a locking mechanism after the cylinder has been removed.

6. What is the difference between a single hung and a double hung window?

7. Describe techniques to remove burglar bars or window grates.

8. When would firefighters breach an interior wall?

9. Describe the differences between plate and tempered glass in terms of forcible entry.

10. What are two cuts used for roll down gates?

11. What is a keyless garage door entry tool, and how is it used on residential garages?

12. List security features which complicate forcible entry present in high crime areas.

Ladders

by Michael Ciampo

This chapter provides required knowledge items for the following
NFPA Standard 1001 Job Performance Requirements:

FFI 5.3.6

FFI 5.3.10

This chapter contains Skill Drills. When you see this icon, refer to your Skill Drill book for step-by-step instructions.

OBJECTIVES

Upon completion of this chapter, you should be able to do the following:

- Describe the purpose of fire service ladders
- Describe basic ladder terminology
- Describe and identify the basic types of fire service ladders
- Describe and identify common methods of ladder construction
- Describe the basic techniques for the inspection & cleaning of ladders
- Describe the general safety specifications of using ladders
- Describe the methods used to determine the correct angle for ladder placement
- Describe the correct placement of a ladder
- Describe and demonstrate the methods of securing a ladder
- Describe safety checks that should be accomplished prior to climbing a ladder
- Describe the method for advancing dry and charged lines up a ladder
- Describe and demonstrate the methods of securing oneself to a ladder
- Describe and demonstrate the proper methods of safely working from a ladder
- Describe the proper method for assisting or rescuing victims down a ladder
- Describe ladder placement for ventilation, rescue, hose advancement
- Describe the six ladder carries
- Describe the three types of ladder raises

INTRODUCTION

Ladders have been around since the beginning of the fire service. They've been updated, but their dynamics remain unchanged. Ladders offer firefighters upper-floor access to fire buildings, and they enable firefighters to perform rescues and other actions described in this chapter.

For firefighters to be successful in portable ladder operations, they must understand ladder safety. The following pages expose firefighters to terminology and practical information. Failure to understand and learn this information before stepping on the fireground could be harmful.

TYPES OF LADDERS

Apparatus-mounted ladders

Many apparatus are equipped with permanently mounted ladders that provide firefighters elevated access for vital firefighting tactics. Most can also provide elevated master streams. To rise and operate properly, the ladders must be stabilized with hydraulic jacks and tormentors. These apparatus are commonly called aerial ladders. **Mid-ship apparatus** are aerial devices mounted just behind an apparatus's cab or mid-frame with the ladder tip extending toward the rear of the apparatus. **Rear-mount apparatus** are aerial devices mounted at the rear of an apparatus with the ladder's tip/bucket mounted over the cab of the apparatus. Firefighters use the following types of apparatus-mounted ladders:

Aerial ladder. The **aerial ladder** is a firefighting apparatus that has a permanent, mounted, telescoping ladder usually constructed of steel, aluminum, or a combination of metal alloys, and that is operated via a hydraulic fluid and lift system in conjunction with steel cables and pulleys (fig. 13–1). These ladders vary in size and reach heights of 100 ft (30 m) or more. A ladder may have a pre-piped waterway and fixed monitor nozzle or a ladder pipe system that must be attached to the tip of the ladder with the hose running down the rungs to provide an elevated master stream. Some aerial ladders, commonly called tillers, are constructed in a tractor-trailer-type design. They are recognizable with a tillerman driving the rear of the apparatus. These apparatus are commonly used in areas with narrow roadways and alleys.

Tower ladder. The **tower ladder's** original design came from the telescoping sections of a crane and is still used today. Engineers adapted this to include a bucket or basket attached to the end of the boom with a pre-piped waterway and monitor nozzle. Engineers created a heavier-duty aerial ladder with a bucket and pre-piped waterway attached to it, commonly referred to as a **ladder tower.** Today, whether it is a boom-type or ladder-type assembly, it is a tower ladder. A main difference of tower and aerial ladders is that firefighters can work out of a tower ladder bucket, and they stand on a small rung of an aerial ladder (figs. 13–2 and 13–3).

Fig. 13–1. An extended aerial ladder. (Courtesy of Bobby Saulters)

Fig. 13–2 and 13–3. Tower ladders

Articulating ladder. The **articulating ladder** may incorporate the use of boom, tube, or ladder construction with an articulating joint that allows one section to be placed above, behind, or over an object. At the end of the boom, a bucket is attached with a pre-piped monitor nozzle for master stream operations. Newer apparatus have replaced many older-type apparatus, commonly called *snorkels.* One of today's engineering marvels has equipped these articulating arms or booms to the end of an aerial ladder (fig. 13–4).

Fig. 13–4. Apparatus with an articulating boom. (Courtesy of Jeff Goldberg)

Quint. The **quint** is a fire department vehicle equipped with a permanently mounted fire pump, water tank, hose storage area, and aerial device with a permanently mounted waterway and complement of portable ladders. Many of these apparatus are constructed on a short frame assembly and resemble an engine company apparatus with a mounted aerial device. They can also be constructed on larger ladder company apparatus. In numerous fire departments with limited manpower or resources, this apparatus performs more than one function and is a fireground asset (fig. 13–5).

Fig. 13–5. Quint

Portable ladders

Straight ladder. The **straight ladder** is a lightweight, single-section ladder with a fixed length, usually 12–20 ft (3.7–6 m), commonly called a **wall ladder**. A drawback with this ladder is that its length can't be adjusted. Normally, these ladders can reach only windows and roofs on certain one- and two-story structures.

Roof ladder. The **roof ladder** is a form of a straight ladder also commonly called a **hook ladder** because of curved metal hooks permanently attached to its tip. When these spring-loaded hooks deploy, they allow the ladder to bite into the ridge of a roof, which provides a stable platform for a firefighter working on a steep roof (fig. 13–6).

Fig. 13–6. Roof ladder with hooks deployed

Extension ladder. The **extension ladder** is adjustable with two or more sections. This ladder is more practical than a straight ladder because it offers a range of heights (fig. 13–7). An extension ladder has a **bed section** and one or two **fly sections** that rise as a firefighter operates the halyard. As the fly section rises, the ladder's **locks**, also called **dogs**, travel over each rung and make clicking noises. When the ladder locks into a rung just after the "click" of the lock, the fly and bed section rungs align. In an extension ladder with one fly, the ladder rises in 14-in. (356 mm) increments. With a two-section fly, the ladder rises in 28-in. (711 mm) increments. This occurs because both flies rise as a firefighter pulls the halyard. Some larger extension ladders are equipped with **tormentor poles** to maximize stability during raising and lowering. These ladders are commonly called **Bangor ladders** or **pole ladders**.

Folding ladder. The **folding ladder** is narrow, collapsible, and folds into itself for transportation through small, narrow spaces. It is also called an **attic**, **scissor**, **suitcase**, or **closet ladder**. It provides inside access to attic hatchways, some of which are commonly inside closets. One also can be used for: removing occupants of a stalled elevator through the roof hatch and out of the hoist way shaft; confined-space rescues; and climbing to a bulkhead structure to vent a skylight (fig. 13–8).

A-frame ladder. The **A-frame ladder**, also called a **combination ladder**, that when closed resembles a small extension ladder. The main difference, however, is that it does not have any halyard or pulleys. It has two pins and two receiver brackets mounted at the ladder's tip. Most of these ladders have two stationary ladder locks that hook onto a rung to keep them closed or locked together

Fig. 13–7. An extension ladder and a roof ladder

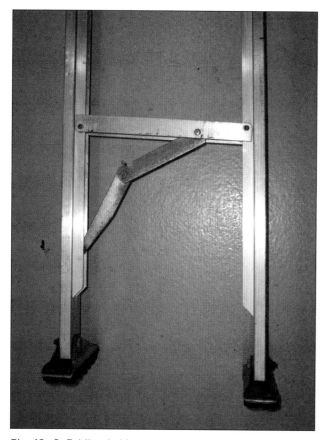

Fig. 13–8. Folding ladder

when extended manually. This ladder can be used in the A-frame position or as a small extension ladder. Because of its size, it can be transported conveniently throughout a structure (fig. 13–9).

Fig. 13–9. A-frame ladder

Fresno ladder. The **Fresno ladder** is a narrow extension ladder with no halyard or pulleys. This ladder also provides access in narrow areas. It rises manually when the fly section is pushed up and locks in position as the spring-loaded dogs pass over the rungs. It is commonly called a **two-section attic ladder**.

Pompier ladder. Also called a **scaling ladder**, the **Pompier ladder** is historic in the fire service. It is no longer recognized by the National Fire Protection Association, but some fire departments and training facilities still use it to increase a firefighter's trust in tools and equipment. In the early years of the fire service, this ladder enabled many dramatic rescues. Its construction includes one center beam with rungs attached to each side. A large, solid, forged hook at the top of the beam was used for breaking windows and then could be hooked onto a window's ledge. Then, a firefighter could climb the ladder and proceed up the side of a building floor by floor, if needed (fig. 13–10).

Miscellaneous ladders. Many fire departments carry portable ladders such as the collapsible combination ladder on their apparatus, while others carry various sizes of the common stepladder. Although a stepladder in the open position resembles an A-frame ladder, a regular stepladder cannot convert to an extension ladder. It is common to find many types of collapsible and telescoping portable ladders on ladder company apparatus (fig. 13–11).

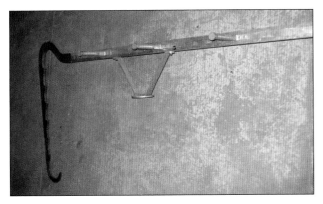

Fig. 13–10. Pompier ladder

Fig. 13–11. Combination ladder

STRUCTURAL COMPONENTS

FFI 5.3.6 The main structural components of portable fire service ladders are aluminum, fiberglass, wood, or a combination of these materials. In addition, lightweight metal assemblies and parts allow ladders to function properly. Most fire departments rely on lightweight aluminum and fiberglass ladders in lieu of heavy wooden ladders with many maintenance requirements. Wood and fiberglass ladders are often referred to as **nonconductive** ladders, meaning they do not conduct electricity. Any damp or wet ladder, however—even wood and fiberglass—can conduct electricity.

Although there are many types of ladders, almost all have the same structural components. Firefighters must know and understand ladder names and parts to operate safely and efficiently on the fireground.

- **Beam:** the main structural component of a ladder that supports a firefighter's weight and transfers it from the rungs to the ground. The beams run the long sides of the ladder and support the rungs at 14-in. (36 cm) intervals. There are a few types of beam construction used in the fire service:

  - **Trussed beam:** a trussed-beam ladder has a top and bottom rail joined together with gusset plates, usually at the rung position. It is of open construction and usually made of wood or aluminum. Most have spikes or permanent cleats mounted at the base.

  - **Solid beam:** a solid-beam ladder has side components that are solid core as in wood ladders or constructed with a rectangular tube design as in aluminum ladders.

  - **I-beam:** the beams of these ladders are shaped in an *I*-like configuration, with the rungs attached to the beams. Fiberglass and common homeowner ladders often carry this design.

- **Balance point:** the spot on a ladder where it balances evenly when lifted. It may not be the true center of the ladder's length because other mechanisms attached to the ladder may render the balance point more toward one end (figs. 13–12 and 13–13).

COMPONENTS OF A LADDER

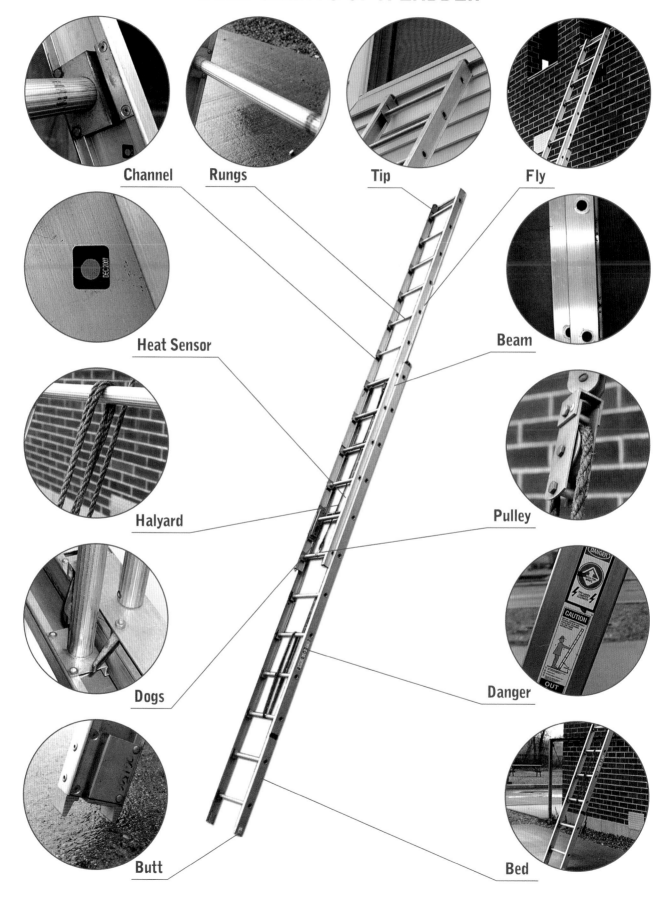

Channel

Rungs

Tip

Fly

Heat Sensor

Beam

Halyard

Pulley

Dogs

Danger

Butt

Bed

Fig. 13–12. A sticker marking the balance point

Fig. 13–14. A pivoting combination safety shoe with slip-resistant rubber

Fig. 13–13. Holding a ladder at the balance point

- **Channel guide:** a section, channel, or slot in a ladder that supports and interlocks with a corresponding section of a ladder as it is raised.

- **Dogs:** spring-loaded, mechanical locking devices at each end of the beam on the fly section that engage on each rung as an extension ladder is raised. They are also called **pawls**, **rung locks**, and **ladder locks**, and they are usually encased in a protective metal box shield (fig. 13–15).

- **Bed section:** the bottom section of a ladder that remains in touch with the ground or apparatus. The bed section is normally the widest section because upper or fly sections retract into it. The bed section is normally the only section with a designed foot or butt attached to it.

- **Butt:** also called the **heel** or **base** of the ladder, it is located at the end where it contacts the ground when positioned against a structure. In a truss-construction ladder, spurs or spikes are usually mounted onto the ladder at its base. In other types of ladders, a permanently mounted precast aluminum foot, butt, or shoe attaches to the base. Some ladders have a slip-resistant combination safety shoe, a rubber nonslip pad that attaches to the base with a pivoting hinge. Often, these devices have spurs or teeth forged into an end for use on soft surfaces (fig. 13–14).

Fig. 13–15. A locked "dog"

- **Danger/electrical/angle stickers:** stickers attached to each side of the base section of a portable ladder between the fourth and fifth rungs. They warn of electrical hazards overhead, question whether a ladder is in a correct climbing angle, and remind the user of the proper direction the fly section should face (fig. 13–16).

Ladders

FIREFIGHTER I

Chapter 13

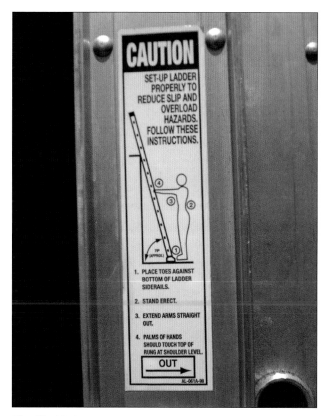

Fig. 13–16. Caution sticker

Fig. 13–17. A heat sensor sticker notifies firefighters when the ladder has been exposed to high heat.

- **Fly section:** a section of a ladder that can extend from the bed section to gain height and distance. In many applications, if a ladder has more then one fly section, both fly sections move when the ladder is raised. The fly sections are normally narrower to fit into the bed section. The fly attaches to other ladder sections by fitting inside a channel or guide section of the corresponding section of ladder.

- **Halyard:** a manila or nylon rope used to extend or retract the fly section(s) of a ladder out of the bed section. The halyard runs through pulley(s) for ease of raising and lowering. In three-section ladders, a wire cable runs in conjunction with the halyard to assist in raising and lowering the two fly sections.

- **Heat-sensor labels:** usually small, round, heat-sensitive, orange stickers with expiration dates attached below the second rung from the top of each section of a ladder and on each side of the beams. They warn users when a ladder has been exposed to enough heat to damage it. When this occurs, a sticker turns black to warn firefighters that the ladder has been subjected to more than 300°F (149°C). Ladders exposed to high heat must be placed out of service and tested prior to further use (fig. 13–17).

- **Pulley:** a small wheel with a grooved channel attached to a ladder by a bracket. The grooved channel allows the halyard to pass through it, reducing friction on the rope and allowing for easy raising of the ladder.

- **Roof hooks:** permanent curved, spring-loaded, metal hooks that secure the tip of a roof ladder to a pitched roof (fig. 13–18).

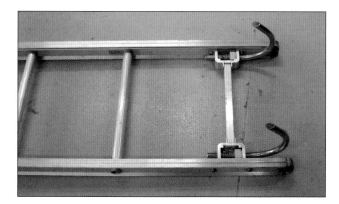

Fig. 13–18. Roof hooks

- **Rungs:** circular, horizontal cross members of a ladder that tie two beams together. The rungs serve as footrests for climbers and transfer one's weight into the beams and then into the ground. In aluminum ladders, rungs may have raised extrusions or tops of rungs may be flat to allow more traction for climbing. There are 14 in. (356 mm) between rungs.

- **Tie-rods:** normally found only on wooden ladders, these metal rods run under rungs and through both beams. They help secure both of the beams together with the rungs.

- **Tip:** the top or top few rungs of a ladder when it is propped over the roofline of a structure.

- **Tormentor poles:** metal poles attached to the bed section of a ladder with a swivel connection. These poles help stabilize the ladder as it is raised and lowered. They also have a single spur at their bottoms to assist in footing the ladder (fig. 13–19).

Figs. 13–19. Tormentor poles used to raise a ladder. (Courtesy of Jerry Naylis)

FIREGROUND NOTE

A 24-foot extension ladder in the closed position is the same length as a 14-foot straight ladder but offers additional lengths.

INSPECTION, MAINTENANCE, AND CLEANING

FFI 5.5.1 Portable ladders are subjected to harsh conditions, including the weight of several firefighters removing a victim, physically venting a window with a ladder, and using a ladder over a burned-out stairway. Firefighters must regularly clean, inspect, and maintain ladders for them to remain in service as beneficial tools.

Inspection

Portable ladders should be visually inspected monthly, after each use, and prior to being placed back on an apparatus. If they are dirty, they should be cleaned prior to inspection. Caked-on dirt and grime can hide defects on ladders. The National Fire Protection Agency has created standards on portable ladder design, use, maintenance, and testing. Knowing these standards and those of a ladder's manufacturer simplifies inspections. The following are some general guidelines for portable ladder inspection:

- Check the halyard for any fraying, kinking, and cut fibers. Ensure it operates smoothly through the pulleys. Halyards often have to be replaced during the ladder's life.

- Check the rungs to ensure none are bent, loose, cracked, or gouged. Also check their ends where they are pressed into the beams for looseness. If they are welded at the end, check the welds for cracks.

- Check that all rivets, nuts, bolts, and plates are secure.

- Check main beams for straightness or bowing, cracks, splintering, and obvious signs of excessive heat exposure.

- Check that dogs or ladder locks and spring assemblies function properly.

- Check that the ladder's feet or spurs are secure and/or pivot freely. If they have rubber cleats on the bottoms, make sure they are secure. If they are cast aluminum, check that they are not cracked and the nut and bolt are secure.

- Check that the ladder slides smoothly through the guide rails and stops at the ladder stops.

- Check that pulleys are secure in their brackets, operate freely, and are not out of round.

- Check the tips of the ladder. If they have cast aluminum rail caps, search for cracks and ensure the nut and bolt are secured.

- Check that hooks on roof ladders operate freely, ends are sharp, and the hook's shape is not distorted. Also verify that tension springs controlling the hook's movements are well-lubricated and operate properly.

- Check that heat-sensor stickers are in place and haven't been subjected to excessive heat. Also check that they are within their expiration date.

Ladders

FIREFIGHTER I

Chapter 13

- Check that wire cable halyards are taut and not fraying or kinked. Ensure their cable-tie clips are secure.

- Check all surfaces for gouges, chips, dents, and sharp edges that could injure a firefighter or place the ladder out of service.

- Check that any additional add-on or after-market items (ladder light beacons, adjustable beam legs) are in place and functional.

If any defect or deficiency is noted, a ladder must be placed out of service for repair. Trained firefighters can perform most minor repairs and regular maintenance. Major repairs to a ladder's structural components must be performed by the ladder's manufacturer or at a certified repair center.

Certification/serviceability testing

Annual service and load testing must be performed on all portable ladders to ensure structural soundness for firefighting. Any ladder that has been dropped, overloaded, exposed to high heat, repaired, structurally damaged, or if its serviceability is in question, should be tested. A **horizontal load test** determines serviceability of a ladder by placing weight on a horizontally supported ladder. The amount of deflection or bending determines the ladder's strength and serviceability. Tests are also conducted on roof hooks, ladder locks, and mechanisms of ladders.

Maintenance and cleaning

All firefighters must perform routine maintenance on portable ladders. Regular, preventive maintenance increases the lifespan of a ladder and its parts and can pinpoint a defect prior to a ladder's malfunction or failure. Following the manufacturer's recommendations is the best way to keep a ladder in service. The following are some general guidelines for ladder maintenance:

- Ladders must be cleaned regularly and after each use with water and a mild detergent. Wash ladders with a soft-bristle brush and rinse with fresh water, remembering to flush out any residue inside the rungs. If melted tar covers a ladder, a degreaser or solvent approved by the manufacturer may be necessary.

- After cleaning, lubricate the ladder locks or dogs, slide rails, and the roof hook's spring assemblies and pulleys with lubricants prescribed by the ladder's manufacturer. Normally, this consists of applying

either candle wax or paraffin to the slide rails and friction areas. Other recommended lubricants may be applied to the springs of roof hooks and spring assemblies.

- If the halyard is frayed, kinked, or has cut fibers, or if the wire cable is worn, stretched, or kinked, replacement is necessary.

- If there are any sharp edges on a rail, beam, rung, or foot, it may be necessary to file each down with light-grit sandpaper or a metal file.

- If the ends of the roof hooks become dull, they may be filed to a sharp point and painted.

- Replace any heat-sensor sticker that is falling off and any that have reached their termination date. If a sensor shows that the ladder has been exposed to high heat, place the ladder out of service for testing.

- When a ladder is being inspected, also inspect the ladder brackets that secure the ladder (figs. 13–20 and 13–21).

Fig. 13–20. Ladders must be cleaned after each use.

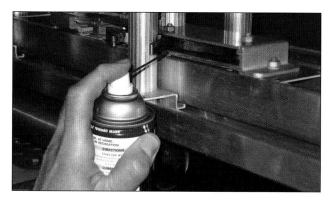

Fig. 13–21. Lubricating the dogs

Fiberglass ladders

Fiberglass ladder manufacturers recommend other maintenance requirements. After a ladder is washed in a mild soap-and-water solution with a sponge or rag, it may be waxed with regular car wax to restore the surface.

Small nicks and scratches may be lightly sanded and covered with a thin coat of clear epoxy glue. Once it has dried, the epoxy should be sanded smooth. If there are any doubts about the severity of a scratch or dent, the ladder should be placed out of service and tested.

> # FIREGROUND NOTE
>
> Keeping a maintenance log for each ladder can assist fire departments with record keeping and data.

Wood ladders

Wood ladder maintenance requirements differ from those of aluminum and fiberglass ladders. They may be cleaned with a sponge or rag in a mild soap-and-water solution, but soaking a wood ladder in water damages surface varnish and allows rungs and joints to absorb water and swell the ladder. When a wood ladder dries, it constricts. These actions damage the rungs, rails, and joints and force additional maintenance.

After cleaning the ladder, inspect it for any varnish damage. Varnish on wood ladders helps keep them nonconductive. Remember, wood ladders can conduct electricity, especially if they are wet or damp. In addition, some wood ladders have aluminum rungs, metal tie-rods, and steel roof hooks attached to their ends, all of which conduct electricity. Spot repair any minor scratch, chip, or dent with a light sanding to the bare wood and reapply varnish to the area. Wood ladders may be waxed after being cleaned and inspected.

Wood rails and rungs also expand and contract in response to humidity and temperature changes. The rungs and metal tie-rods must be checked regularly for tightness in wood ladders because they uphold structural integrity of wood ladders.

MARKING LADDERS

Ladders must be marked with their proper numerical length so firefighters can quickly identify them by size. Normally, all ladder manufacturers label both beams of a ladder near the base with permanent, size-designation labels. These labels allow for quick identification, but viewing them can be difficult when they are stored on an apparatus. To solve that problem, firefighters commonly use paint markers or self-adhesive stickers to display a ladder's size on the base of the ladder's butts for easy identification (fig. 13–22). They also label the ladder's bedded length next to the overall size. With straight ladders, manufacturers commonly attach identification labels at the base and near the tip or roof hooks on both beams.

Fig. 13–22. Stickers display each ladder's size.

Fire departments commonly color code the bases of their ladders to show their sizes. For easy identification, it is also good to put the size of the ladder with the color code. Other departments allow individual companies to color code or paint their company identification colors or numbers on ladders to reflect company ownership. Whichever manner a ladder is marked, it should be large enough to allow easy visibility.

Firefighters also mark the **balance point** of a ladder to permit ease of operations. This proves especially useful when a firefighter must remove a ladder off the back of an apparatus or lift one by himself or herself. Finding this spot is easy. A firefighter can pick up the ladder in the suitcase-carry position and find the spot where the ladder balances itself. At this location, paint a line, stick a piece of colored electrical tape, or label the beam with the company identification numbers. Some balance points on solid-beam ladders fall directly between a set of rungs, so fire departments paint the inside and outside of both beams. When they remove the ladder from a vertically stored ladder rack, firefighters easily recognize the balance point. This is referred to as **painting the box**. A ladder's rungs must never be completely painted.

The tips of many fire service ladders are often brightly painted or covered with reflective tape to enhance their visibility in smoke and low illumination. Remember, ladders should not be painted entirely to improve their appearance. Painting ladders entirely can hide dangerous defects. For instance, painting an aluminum ladder's entire rung can create a slipping hazard.

Fire departments can purchase small lighting or beaconing devices that attach to the tip of a ladder or end rung to improve the ladder's visibility. When activated, the device sends a strobe light or flashing signal that directs firefighters to the ladder.

Another application in marking straight or roof ladders after locating their balance points is to mark their **hoisting points**. Often on the fireground, a ladder needs to be raised with a piece of rope. Marking the rung two up from the center rung with a small paint mark or piece of electrical tape near the beams or in the center of the rung will assist in placing the rope for the lift.

Engine companies commonly mark their ladders' beams or rails with paint or tape to indicate where the ladders sit in holding brackets on their apparatus. This is beneficial for post-fire operations, and the ladders must be put back in their proper places. Often, ladders on these apparatus interfere with compartment openings or the stretching of hoselines if placed in a wrong position.

OPERATING SAFELY

FFI 5.3.6 Operating ladders safely and properly on the fireground is important for all firefighters. Numerous firefighters have died or have been severely injured as results of ladder mishaps during training and on the fireground. The following are some general safety guidelines for working with ladders:

- When possible, work with another firefighter to reduce the risk of straining or injuring yourself and others. Ladders are cumbersome and heavy. Moving or placing them on the fireground can be difficult.

- Most importantly, look for overhead utility wires before raising any ladder. Most departments use aluminum ladders, which are good conductors of electricity. Wood and fiberglass ladders also can conduct electricity because they have metal assemblies and get wet. Maintain a minimum distance of 10 ft (3 m) when operating near overhead power lines. Electrical arcs from overhead power lines have hit ladders operating in their vicinity.

- Prior to resting a ladder on a structure with aluminum siding, release the ladder as it makes contact with the structure to avoid being electrocuted. Electrical feed lines have shorted out and charged siding on numerous occasions.

- While making overhead visual inspections, look for tree limbs and branches, overhangs, canopies, and elevated decks and platforms that can affect the extension or placement of a ladder.

- Survey the ground where the ladder will be placed. Look for a solid, level foundation for the ladder's base.

- Resist overreaching when working on a ladder. Instead, reposition the ladder or use a longer tool. Use one of the leg-lock or arm-lock maneuvers whenever working from a ladder.

- Choose the proper ladder for the job. Extension ladders offer variable heights, whereas straight ladders do not adjust.

- Use caution in placing ladders. A ladder placed in front of a lower-floor window or door is not always advisable. Fire may or can erupt out of the window, cutting off the escape route of a firefighter. A ladder positioned by a door can be knocked off its base by a charged hoseline or unassuming firefighter.

- Always face the rungs when ascending and descending from a ladder. If you were to slip, you could grab the ladder for support. A slip while not facing the rungs could cause you to fall off the ladder and be injured.

- When lifting a portable ladder lying on the ground, use your leg muscles. Just bending over to pick the ladder off the ground could cause a back injury.

These are a few safety guidelines that must be followed to prevent injury and death. In following sections of this chapter, equally important safety guidelines are presented.

SELECTING THE PROPER LADDER

Firefighters must be familiar with the apparatus-mounted ladder and the capabilities of all portable ladders on the apparatus. Ladder selection often must be made in a split second, and choosing the wrong ladder can have severe consequences. Prior to choosing a ladder, ask yourself where the ladder must be placed, what length is needed, and what its purpose is. An upper-floor fire in an eight-story building might require an aerial ladder or tower ladder, whereas a portable ladder could be used faster than a mechanical device for second-floor fire at the same building.

Knowing a building's characteristics can also assist in choosing an appropriate ladder. Normally, most residential structures measure approximately 8–10 ft (2.4–3 m) from floor to floor, whereas a commercial structure may measure 10–12 ft (3–3.7 m). A general rule passed through the fire service is that taking the first number of a ladder's length determines what floor it will cover. (For a 24-ft (7.3 m) portable ladder, two is the first number, so the ladder will cover the second floor). Exceptions should be noted. A 28-ft (8.5-m) or 35-ft (11-m) extension ladder can reach the next higher floor's window if set up on a level surface. Again, knowing the capabilities of your apparatus' ladders and your response area characteristics will assist you in choosing the proper ladder.

Of course, other factors will influence your choosing a ladder at a fire. Often when operating short staffed, firefighters choose straight ladders because they are easy to maneuver around the fireground single-handedly. If the straight ladder were being placed only to a low porch roof for access, it might be a wise choice. If the ladder were needed later for a task at a higher elevation, it might not reach. An extension ladder offers more variables. Remember, straight ladders offer only one height and cannot be adjusted.

REMOVING LADDERS FROM THE APPARATUS

Following sections of this chapter discuss how to store and remove ladders from different fire apparatus, including apparatus positioning and effects on the removal of portable ladders. Often on the fireground, one apparatus pulls close to the rear of another apparatus and prohibits the removal of a portable ladder. Apparatus operators must leave sufficient clearance to the rear of an apparatus to permit ladder removal. Some fire departments offer apparatus operators tips in this area. If the largest ladder on a ladder apparatus with rear storage compartments is a 20-ft (6-m) roof ladder in nested position, the apparatus must leave at least a 20-ft (6-m) clearance at the rear. Other departments instruct operators to park at an angle to the fire building to expose the rear ladder compartment. If an apparatus has side-mounted ladders, allow enough side access for ladder removal.

Engine company apparatus

Because of the numerous styles and designs of fire apparatus, portable ladders are stored or mounted in many places. In years past, engine company apparatus had portable ladders mounted in shoulder-height brackets on the sides. As fire departments kept pace with society, the need for more compartments was necessary and ladder locations changed. It is common to find engine company ladders mounted on hydraulic or electric lift assemblies that lower themselves from a horizontal position over a hosebed to a vertical, shoulder-height position on the side of the apparatus. Other lift assemblies raise only the ladder over the highest compartment on the side of the apparatus. Note that the controls to lower the ladder may be in the cab of the apparatus or near the ladder itself.

Once either assembly is in the down position, the rung-locking clamps must be released for ladder removal. Normally, the engine company's extension and roof ladders are nested inside one another. It is a good rule to mount the extension ladder so it can be the first ladder off the apparatus. Once the locking clamps are released, two firefighters can lift the ladder off the rack and proceed to where it is needed.

If the roof ladder must be removed to reach the extension ladder, place it out of the way. Carrying it to the rear of the apparatus and sliding it under the apparatus could cause you to interfere with the hose when it is stretched off the back step. Plus, it puts the ladder out of the firefighter's sight, and it might be problematic to retrieve it for other uses. Laying the ladder up against the tire in the standing position can also be problematic. It could fall and strike a firefighter in the leg, or it could become heated from apparatus exhaust and suffer structural damage. Putting the ladder back on the rack and out of the way or taking both ladders with you can be solutions.

On some engine company apparatus, ladders are stored in a vertical or horizontal compartment under or alongside the hosebed. If the hose hasn't been stretched, it is easy to remove the ladders by sliding them out of the compartment. If the hose has been stretched, it might be necessary to lift loose ends back into the hosebed to prevent a tripping hazard or the ladder from snagging onto the hose. If the hose has been charged with water, it might be necessary for one firefighter to lift up on the hose as another firefighter slides the ladder from the compartment (figs. 13–23, 13–24, 13–25, and 13–26).

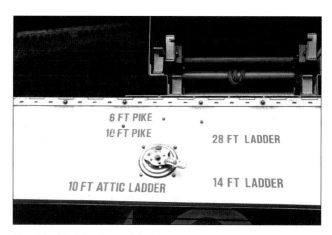

Fig. 13–25. A horizontal ladder-storage compartment

Fig. 13–23. Ladders mounted on a lift. (Courtesy of Bill Marshall)

Fig. 13–26. Side-mounted ladder

Ladder company apparatus

Normally, there are three ways to store portable ladders on ladder company apparatus. Two involve the ladders being stored in a rear compartment or trough, which permits storage under the main ladder assembly. Firefighters might have to use caution when working near the rear of some ladder apparatus. Some of these apparatus can have a rear overhead obstruction such as an aerial ladder or tower ladder bucket. Firefighters must wear head protection when working in these areas. These compartments or troughs may be an enclosed or an open-style compartment (figs. 13–27 and 13–28). The ladders in this compartment sit in a vertical or horizontal position with tips facing forward and bases toward the rear of the apparatus (figs. 13–29 and 13–30).

Fig. 13–24. A vertical ladder-storage compartment. (Courtesy of S. K. Willis)

Fig. 13–27. Ladder compartment

Fig. 13–28. Ladder trough

Fig. 13–29. Horizontal ladder storage. (Courtesy of S. K. Willis)

Fig. 13–30. Vertical ladder storage. (Courtesy of S. K. Willis)

There might be exceptions. Some fire departments place roof ladders with the butt end inside the compartment. In this manner, a roof ladder's hooks are closer to the outside of the apparatus. This way there is less chance of the roof hooks snagging the other ladder's halyards in the compartment as the ladder is removed. Plus, when the ladder is carried to the structure, the hooks and tip of the ladder are forward, ready to be raised onto the roof without spinning the ladder around (fig. 13–31). The third way portable ladders are stored on ladder company apparatus is in compartment racks on either side of the apparatus (fig. 13–32).

Removing ladders from the rear compartment is easy for two firefighters. Open the compartment door(s) and/ or release the ladder lock mechanism or stop bracket assembly. Then position yourselves on the side of the ladder that enables you to keep the fire building in sight. Often, this is referred to as **body to the building**. You will be able to remove the ladder and watch changing conditions on the fireground.

After choosing the appropriate ladder and checking that no one is in the way, one firefighter pulls the base of the ladder to slide it out of the compartment. This firefighter should maintain his or her position at the base of the ladder to prevent it from striking anyone as the ladder is removed from the apparatus. He or she should proceed slowly and steadily as the ladder nears the end of the compartment. Once the second firefighter supports the ladder at the opposite end and it is clear of the compartment, this firefighter can turn into the direction of deployment (figs. 13–33 and 13–34).

Ladders

FIREFIGHTER I

Chapter 13

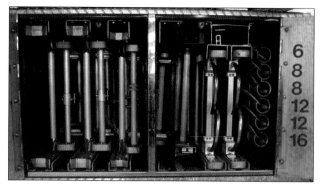

Fig. 13–31. Ladder with hooks toward the rear of the compartment

Fig. 13–32. Ladders stored on side compartment racks

Fig. 13–33. One firefighter pulls the base of the ladder from the compartment.

Fig. 13–34. The second firefighter supports the ladder at the opposite end.

The second firefighter, also facing the fire building, can now assist in removing the ladder by slowly sliding the ladder out of the compartment. As the end of the vertically stored ladder nears the end of the compartment, the second firefighter can place his or her shoulder into one of the rung spaces near its end. If the ladder is coming out horizontally, it must be grabbed with both hands and then be positioned in a shoulder- or suitcase-carry position for transport. Verbal communication between the firefighters makes this operation smooth. If a third firefighter is available, he or she may be positioned midway on the opposite or same side of the ladder to assist in the ladder's removal and transport.

One firefighter may perform this a few ways, but it is more difficult. One technique involves pulling the base of the ladder almost completely out of the compartment. As the ladder is suspended tilting toward the ground, or its base touching the ground, the firefighter may proceed to the balance point and remove the ladder from the apparatus in a well-balanced position. Another common method involves the firefighter's sliding the ladder from the compartment while maintaining a position near the back of the apparatus. As the ladder's balance point comes out of the compartment, the firefighter either steps into the rung spacing or grabs the ladder and continues walking the ladder out of the compartment. Again, the ladder is well-balanced and can be transported by a single firefighter. A safety concern when using this method is that the ladder's butt is unprotected as it slides out of the compartment and could strike an unsuspecting firefighter (fig. 13–35).

Fig. 13–35. Find the balance point and carefully remove the ladder.

Side-mounted portable ladder storage. Numerous ladder company apparatus have portable ladders mounted on sides of their apparatus. These ladders can be mounted vertically or horizontally in compartments or on mounting brackets. Tractor-trailer-type aerial ladders often have a portable ladder mounted on one or both sides of the trailer apparatus. Some rear-mount aerial ladders are constructed with the turntable mounted lower in the rear. This reduces the overall height of the apparatus and ensures it will fit through the apparatus bay doors of older fire stations. Because the turntable is mounted lower, there is reduced ladder storage in the rear and more side storage. Some rear-mounted tower ladders have a large frame and brace assembly in the rear of the apparatus with reduced ladder storage in the rear compartment. Ladders may be stored on the sides of the apparatus.

For firefighters to remove ladders off the side of fire apparatus, there must be sufficient clearance between any object and the apparatus. Removing ladders off the side of the apparatus is easy for two firefighters. The ladder securing bracket(s) or locking mechanism must first be released, and then both firefighters can position themselves evenly along the ladder. After releasing the holding mechanism, lift the ladder off the bracket or slide it off the side of the apparatus and transport it to the proper location. Sometimes sliding or lifting the ladder off the apparatus from the side is difficult because the ladders are stacked high. If they are, the shorter roof ladders are normally stacked toward the top.

When removing ladders from an apparatus side on a narrow street with parked cars, sometimes it is necessary to carry the ladder to the front or rear of the apparatus to gain access to the fire building. Lifting the ladder over parked cars might be an option, but one that must be done slowly to allow both firefighters room.

In a one-firefighter evolution, lifting the ladder off the side of the apparatus is difficult when the ladder's balance point is not marked. Many times firefighters guess the balance point, and when they lift or slide the ladder off the side of the apparatus, it tilts toward the heavier end. Sometimes in this situation, firefighters quickly compensate for the tilting with shear muscle, which can cause a pulled or strained muscle. The firefighter should transport the ladder to the front or rear of the apparatus, then try to lift it over a car and maneuver it when working alone.

Roof ladders mounted on the side of the bed section of an aerial ladder.
Many of today's newer aerial apparatus are equipped with a roof ladder mounted to the side of the bed section or on the inside of the fly section of the aerial ladder. The roof ladder is usually a 14- or 16-ft (4.3- or 4.9-m) ladder mounted in a holding bracket assembly. Prior to lifting the ladder out, a firefighter must release the hold-down mechanisms. If any of these ladders are needed on the ground for

portable ladder operations, they must be handed down off the side of the apparatus prior to raising the aerial. If a ladder is transported up a ladder for use as a roof ladder, there are a few options.

If only one firefighter is available to lift the ladder out of the brackets, he or she should find the balance point and lift the ladder out of the brackets once the aerial ladder is positioned on the roof. Depending on the incline of the ladder, he or she has a few choices on transporting the ladder up the aerial ladder. If the ladder is on a slight incline and no obstacles are present to either side of the aerial ladder, the roof ladder may be laid flat across both rails of the aerial ladder and slid up the ladder as the firefighter slides his or her hands up the rails. The firefighter will be in good control of the ladder and the ladder will be well-balanced. Another way to transport the ladder up a slight incline is to place the ladder on one of its beams and slide it up the rungs of the ladder as the firefighter climbs. Some firefighters prefer to open the hooks of the roof ladder prior to sliding it up the ladder because it enables them to quickly secure it to the ridgepole of the structure once they reach the top of the aerial ladder. Remember that the open hooks can strike an obstacle or part of the ladder and cause a firefighter to slip. No matter how slight of an incline, firefighters must remain in constant contact with a ladder at all times.

On a steeper incline, the firefighter must secure the ladder in a shoulder-carry position. Then the firefighter should climb the ladder using a hand-over-hand motion on the rungs. Climbing at steep angles is dangerous, and with a roof ladder, it becomes more dangerous. At steeper angles, it is often better to perform this tactic with more than one firefighter or it might take more than one trip to transport the ladder and tools.

Roof ladders mounted inside the fly section of an aerial ladder.
Some apparatus have roof ladders mounted in holding brackets on the inside of the aerial ladder's fly section. When the aerial ladder rises to its desired location, the roof ladder also rises mechanically and is easily accessible. Mounting the ladder in the fly section eliminates having to carry the roof ladder up the aerial ladder. The ladder securing brackets should be released, and now the ladder may be lifted out of its brackets for use on the roof (fig. 13–36).

Figs. 13–36. Roof ladder mounted on aerial

Use caution when climbing an aerial ladder with a roof ladder mounted in the fly section. The roof ladder takes up space inside the fly section, decreases the space between the rails, and makes climbing more difficult. This is especially true if other tools are mounted on the opposite side of the fly section, the ladder is at a steep incline, or a firefighter is carrying up tools or a saw. Roof ladders mounted inside the fly section can make it difficult to slide a Stokes basket up or down the aerial when performing a technical rescue operation. Removing the roof ladder from the fly section before the rescue might be necessary.

Folding ladder mounted inside the tip of an aerial ladder. For buildings with high, front parapet walls (the front section of a building's wall that extends above the roofline), folding ladders mounted inside and near the tips of aerial ladders are common. To use these ladders for roof access over a high or steep parapet, a firefighter must first release the ladder from its holding brackets. At a high elevation or steep incline, a firefighter must lock into the ladder with an approved safety belt prior to releasing the folding ladder.

After releasing the ladder, the firefighter opens it and slides it down onto the roof. As the ladder comes in contact

with the roof, the firefighter should **sound the roof** with the ladder to make sure the roof is stable. Making the transition from the aerial ladder to the folding ladder can be dangerous at high elevations. Always use caution and keep one hand on the aerial ladder prior to transferring yourself to the folding ladder (fig. 13–37).

Fig. 13–37. Folding ladder mounted inside aerial

Collapsible ladders mounted inside a tower ladder bucket. To address high parapet walls, many tower ladder companies carry some type of collapsible or folding ladder mounted inside their buckets or the fly section of the main ladder assembly. Some tower ladder apparatus have a short folding or extension ladder attached to the inside or outside of their bucket doors. Once the apparatus is in position, these roof-access ladders can be deployed (fig. 13–38).

FIREGROUND NOTE
Marking the ladder's balance point can make removal off any apparatus easier.

Fig. 13–38. Collapsible ladder mounted inside tower bucket

PLACEMENT, CLIMBING, AND OPERATIONAL GUIDELINES

Transport

Ladders may be carried numerous ways. A firefighter performing the carry must take command of the operation. Normally, fire academies teach that the firefighter assigned to the butt of a ladder controls the evolution. The butt is normally transported first because it must be properly positioned in line with a window or the objective. Therefore, the firefighter leading the transport should control the overall operation of the ladder.

The firefighter at the ladder's butt must consider ladder length in negotiating turns around corners and obstacles. In some situations, the firefighter at the tip of the ladder must swing out or turn wide. Both firefighters must communicate with one another. "Obstacle to the right," "Swing out," and "Okay, clear," are simple statements that communicate much during transport.

When rescuing a civilian hanging onto a window ledge, firefighters may transport a ladder tip-first. In cases such as this, the firefighter at the ladder's tip takes command. If a firefighter lacks the confidence or skill to control a ladder operation, it might be necessary for the other firefighter to take command

Uneven ground surfaces. FFI 5.3.6 Uneven ground surfaces are obstacles on numerous firegrounds. Many times, the spot in which the ladder must be placed is not

level, and one of the ladder's feet dangles far from the ground. Because the ladder is not supported evenly at the base, it tends to lean toward the unsupported side. One of the easiest ways to overcome this is to find a better location for the ladder. Often this is not feasible and the ladder must remain at this location.

When the ladder is on soft surfaces such as grass, dirt, or even hot asphalt, use the sharp point of an axe or the adze end of a Halligan to dig a trench wide and deep enough for the ladder's foot that touches the ground.

Insert the ladder's foot into the cutout. Both of the ladder's feet should touch the ground, and the ladder should be evenly supported at the base. It might be necessary to lift the base out of the trench and dig deeper or along the area in which the bottom rung sets for the ladder's base to rest evenly on the ground. Remember, climbing a ladder with an unsupported base is dangerous and can cause injuries.

When firefighters face an uneven ground terrain with a hard surface such as a poured concrete walkway or street curb, breaking up the area and digging a trench is not feasible. Many fire departments carry a set of wooden step chocks, angular wood cribbing, and 2×4 or 4×4 in. (51×102 or 102×102 mm) cribbing on their apparatus. Using a combination of chocks on hard surfaces levels the ladder base, assists a firefighter in footing, and maintains the ladder's balance. Many fire departments drill a hole at one end of each piece of a 2×4, 4×4 in. (51×102, 102×102 mm), and piece of angular cribbing. Next, they place a short section of rope through each hole to make a loop. Now a firefighter can grab the chocks, which come in various heights and shapes, and take them with the ladder (fig. 13–39).[1]

Fig. 13–39. Various chocks. (Courtesy of Nicole Ciampo)

Some cribbing is available in a plastic resin design, but it can be slippery. Ensure a firefighter properly butts a ladder when another firefighter climbs on these hard, uneven, cribbed-up surfaces. It is dangerous, but when life is at stake, it might be necessary.

Another technique passed through numerous fire academies is that a firefighter should survey his or her work area. Sometimes nearby objects such as landscape bricks, blocks, wooden railroad ties, pallets, and lumber can level a ladder's base. Placing a large piece of wood such as plywood on a wet, muddy surface prevents a ladder's base from sinking. When ladders sink into mud, suction develops and it is often difficult to lift them out of the mud. This can cause havoc if a ladder is needed for another fireground task.

Some firefighters place a Halligan bar or other tool beneath the foot of the ladder not touching the ground for support. The Halligan bar, when placed with the adze and point facing down, creates a slope and acts like a wedge with variable height adjustments under the ladder's foot. This creates a few problems: First, on terrain with a slight slope, the metal base of the ladder may slide on the metal tool and cause the ladder to move. Second, why would a firefighter want to leave a valuable tool on the ground when he or she might need it at the top of the ladder or inside a building (fig. 13–40)?

Today's technology assists firefighters combat uneven ground surfaces. Some ladder manufacturers make adjustable legs that bolt onto the bed section of ladders near the base. When needed, these legs may be adjusted to level the base.

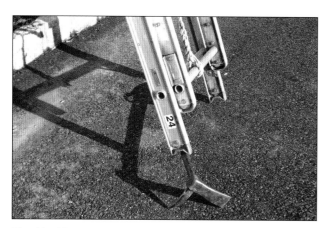

Fig. 13–40. Halligan used as ladder support

Proper climbing angle. **FFI 5.3.6** Once a ladder has been removed from the apparatus and transported to its objective, it must be raised and set in a proper climbing angle. Portable ladders must be set in 65–75 degree angles against buildings to ensure the ladders can carry their maximum load capacities. This angle range increases the overall safety for firefighters climbing, descending, and operating ladders. A portable ladder angled lower than 65 degrees increases the probability of the ladder sliding down the building or having its base kicked out; it also

reduces the ladder's maximum load capacity. A portable ladder positioned in an angle greater than 75 degrees creates a steep climb and increases the probability that a firefighter will fall.

To attain the proper climbing angle, place the base of the ladder one-fourth the **total working length of the ladder** away from the building. The total working length of a ladder is the distance from its base to the spot of its upper support. For example, the base of a portable ladder raised 24 ft (7.3 m) should be 6 ft (2 m) from the building for a proper climbing angle.

Another quick method of checking proper climbing angle exists. Position yourself in front of a ladder with both feet on the ground. Now, reach outward at about chest level. The ladder's rung should be in a comfortable location for climbing. Although this is not a foolproof way to check a ladder's climbing angle, it is often relied upon during firefighting operations (fig. 13–41).

Also, some ladder manufacturers place stickers on the bed section of portable ladder beams to assist firefighters in placing ladders properly. These stickers resemble a small carpenter's square on a distinctive background. When the bottom line of the sticker is parallel to the ground, the ladder is in the proper climbing position.

Physical ladder position. As a result of fire department ladder construction, most manufacturers insist that when a ladder is raised, the fly section must be in the fly-out position. Another way to describe this is that when the ladder is raised, the fly section must be positioned away from the fire building and on top of the bed section. A sticker affixed to the side of the bed section serves as a reference guide and safety reminder. Note that some ladders can be raised opposite, with the fly toward the building. Firefighters must follow manufacturers' recommendations when using portable ladders.

Fig. 13–41. Quick method to check ladder angle

Raising to the objective

When a ladder becomes vertical, the fly section may be raised to its objective. Some fire departments pre-tie their ladders' halyards or ready them in a continuous-loop design. Either way, a ladder's halyards needn't be untied to raise the ladder. Other departments tie ladders closed with the extra halyard tied or looped around the rungs. In these cases, the halyard must be untied and unwrapped from the rungs to permit raising of the fly section.

Because the halyard is behind the ladder or closest to the structure, the firefighter assigned to the butt is in the best spot to be in control. He or she may easily untie and operate the halyard. Once he or she unties the halyard, the firefighter should place the right or left boot against the ladder's butt to brace it as the ladder rises. Before raising the halyard, the firefighter verifies it is safe to begin operations by rechecking overhead and with the other firefighter. When clear, he or she pulls the halyard down in a hand-over-hand motion. The motion should be fluid and deliberate as the firefighter listens to the dogs clicking over the rungs. If the firefighter were to slip, he or she might be able to lock the dogs on the next available rung or last rung passed. Firefighters should not wrap their arms or hands around the halyard because it is dangerous. Some departments require

firefighters to tie off the halyard to a rung after the ladder raise has been completed to keep it from getting in the way of firefighters moving on and around the ladder; other departments just push it to the side, keeping the firefighter who raised the ladder from having to take the time to tie a knot, and as well to allow for the ladder to be quickly raised if needed without having to untie a knot. Determine your department's policy on this issue.

The firefighter in front of the ladder should be well-balanced with each hand on either of the beams. He or she balances the ladder as the halyard pulls downward and the fly section extends. This firefighter also watches the extending fly section and lets the firefighter operating the halyard know when the ladder could hit something such as a gutter or roof overhang and when the ladder reaches the objective. Most ladder operations progress this way. In other situations, firefighters must use a person to act as a guide, watching the tip of the ladder meet its objective. Keep in mind that buildings often have different floor heights—commercial buildings often have higher ceilings than residential buildings.

If a raised ladder lowering into its objective is about to come up short, the firefighters operating it have a few options. A ladder being laid slowly into a structure will hint if it will come up short. Firefighters must bring the ladder back to vertical and raise it to the proper height, then lay it back into the structure. If the ladder is laid into the structure and there is not time for this evolution, the firefighter operating the halyard might be able to pull it, raising it a rung, as the bracing firefighter pulls the ladder off the structure to extend the fly section. In some instances, the ladder is a little long, but bringing it down a rung makes it too short. In such cases, the butt of the ladder might need to be pulled out. Pulling the base too far, in some instances, decreases safety margin and proper climbing angle.

Footing or "butting" a portable ladder

Once a ladder is in a proper climbing angle, it must be secured before a firefighter climbs it. This prevents the ladder's butt end from sliding out while a firefighter climbs or descends. It also prevents the tip of the ladder from sliding or moving along the building, and it stabilizes the ladder as the firefighter climbs. The most common way to secure a ladder is for one firefighter to foot, butt, or heel the base while another firefighter climbs.

The preferred method of footing, butting, or heeling the base of a ladder is for one firefighter to face the front of the ladder in the direction of the climb or the building. This firefighter applies pressure with one boot against one of the bottom rails of the ladder near the base or on the first rung, preventing it from kicking backward. Then, he or she places the other foot behind in a well-balanced position and places both arms on the beams. As one firefighter climbs, the firefighter footing the ladder can apply slight pressure on the rails. This takes any bounce out of the ladder and steadies it.

As the firefighter climbs, the one footing the ladder must watch the climbing motion. If the firefighter were to lose his or her balance, the footing firefighter could quickly climb the ladder while holding the underside of the ladder rails and pin the climber back onto the ladder. The footing firefighter could also climb the ladder quickly and reach up with one arm to support the climber. In addition, if the climber were glancing at his or her tools and didn't notice another issue, the footing firefighter could relay that information.

If a climber were operating off one side of the ladder while in a leg-lock position, the firefighter footing the ladder should place his or her foot on the opposite side of the ladder's base. This prevents the base and tip from shifting and equalizes pressure on both rails, keeping the ladder secure. It might be necessary to place additional hand pressure on the opposite side rail to equalize pressure and secure the ladder.

Some fire academies and departments prefer to foot ladders from the rear. A firefighter positions himself or herself under a ladder with arms mounted on the rails and feet positioned for good balance. Then he or she leans back into the building to keep the ladder in place and remove any bounce during the climb. Problems can occur, however, when this firefighter is behind the ladder. First, if the climber drops a tool, it might hit an unprepared firefighter who was trained not to look up in order to avoid falling dirt from the climber's boot or a shingle. Second, the footing firefighter has no vision of the fire. He or she is oblivious to all conditions behind him or her. Last, if the climber were to lose his or her balance, the firefighter footing from the rear could quickly come around the ladder to offer support, but this traveling momentum could knock the climber off balance (figs. 13–42 and 13–43).

Fig. 13–42. Footing a ladder from the front. (Courtesy of Nicole Ciampo)

If the base of the ladder cannot be footed properly, substantial objects near the ladder such as cars, dumpsters, curbs, other buildings, or even parking lot bumper poles may be used. Normally, this will prevent the base from sliding or kicking out. Also, a firefighter with a piece of tubular webbing pre-tied in a loop may tie the ladder's base to a substantial object with a chocker hitch around the ladder's rung (fig. 13–44).

Fig. 13–43. Footing a ladder from the rear. (Courtesy of Nicole Ciampo)

Fig. 13–44. Using the environment to foot a ladder. (Courtesy of Brian Doyle)

Securing the tip

In the past it was recommended that the first firefighter to reach the objective should secure the tip of the ladder to a substantial object. In theory, this is a good safety tactic. In practical fireground operations, however, it is not always acceptable. If a portable ladder will be in position for a long time for access and egress or at a technical rescue situation, secure the tip. Normally, a hose strap, short piece of utility rope, or piece of webbing on a rung, beam, or both beams can be tied off to a substantial object. Emergencies occur on the fireground and a portable ladder placed at one location might be needed at another. If the ladder were secured at its tip, it could delay its relocation to another urgent matter.

Moving a portable ladder once it is in position

Often, portable ladders raised to a window or roof must be moved for another task or because they are exposed to fire. These ladders can be in either the nested or extended position. In many situations, bringing the ladder vertical

and retracting the fly section into the bed section takes too long. Getting the ladder off the building and into a vertical position, then attempting to move it while it is extended is often difficult, especially in inclement weather or on uneven terrain.

> ### FIREGROUND NOTE
> Portable ladders with extended fly sections are heavier at the tip than they are when nested. Use care in moving top-heavy, extended ladders.

Some firefighters think sliding the ladder along the building is the answer, but a few things could happen. The ladder's tip could move too fast along the aluminum gutter of the building and slide away, causing a firefighter to lose control. This often causes the ladder to fall, and it could injure a firefighter and damage itself. Also, depending on weather and terrain, the firefighter sliding the ladder could slip and the ladder could slide away. Portable ladders slide quickly across buildings with aluminum or vinyl siding, especially if the siding is wet, icy, or snowy.

Many fire academies teach that two firefighters may position themselves on opposite sides of the ladder, lift the ladder once it is nested in the vertical position, then carry it to the new location. Carrying an extended ladder is difficult because firefighters must maintain an awkward physical position. This becomes even harder in inclement weather and on uneven terrain. In addition, firefighters might have to move the vertical ladder around overhead obstacles.

Rolling a portable ladder, whether it is extended or nested, solves that problem. One firefighter may position himself or herself at the base. If the ladder is on soft terrain and the butt is partially buried in the earth, first a firefighter must pick up the ladder or slide it upward to release it from the earth. This tactic is not necessary, but it does assist in the initial roll of the ladder. Next, the firefighter takes a well-balanced position in front of the ladder with his or her back leaning slightly into the ladder and his or her feet behind it. Now, the firefighter does a push-and-pull motion with his or her arms to roll the ladder to its desired location. When the ladder is being moved to the right, the firefighter's left arm pulls the left beam forward, and the right arm pushes the right beam backward. The motion is opposite when the ladder is moving to the left.

Keep your feet and legs away from the rotating ladder. If a firefighter loses control of the ladder during the evolution, both hands may press it into the building to regain control. It might occur if a firefighter were to roll the ladder quickly along the building. Sometimes it is necessary to take up any slack in the halyard lying behind the ladder and attach it to the bed section before rolling the ladder. If the halyard has too much slack, it might get spun around the ladder during the rotation. When performing this maneuver over a long distance, a firefighter might notice the ladder slide down or lose its proper climbing angle. All a firefighter must do is stop, pick up the base, and slide the tip farther up the building. Then, continue the roll (fig. 13–45).

When operating on a moderate-grade terrain, rolling or lifting the ladder might be difficult. It might be better to take the ladder down, carry it to the new location, and re-raise the ladder.

Fig. 13–45. Rolling a ladder. (Courtesy of Megan Ciamp).

FIREGROUND NOTE

Before moving any portable ladder, talk with the firefighters who used the ladder to determine their positions. If they give permission to move the ladder for another task, you must return the ladder to its original position upon completing the new task. In addition, verbally communicate to the firefighters that the ladder is back in its original position.

Climbing a ladder

Climbing a portable ladder. Once the portable ladder is raised in position, it is almost ready to be climbed. Prior to climbing, the first firefighter should glance up the ladder and make sure all the dogs are locked onto rungs. In three-section extension ladders, it is possible that only the lower set of dogs will lock and the top section's dogs will not engage. Once the firefighter has checked that all the dogs are locked and the ladder is heeled properly, he or she may climb.

The firefighter should climb on the balls of the feet with hands positioned on the underside of the beams and maintain a fluid, deliberate motion while ascending. Climbing this way is safest because it affords the firefighter three points of contact: both hands and a foot. While climbing, the firefighter should keep his or her eyes focused on the destination. An occasional glance at the ladder and surrounding area is okay to check for dangers. The firefighter should not race up the ladder because it could cause a slip or fall. In instances such as rescues, it might be necessary to progress quicker than normal, but firefighters should strive to maintain balance and a fluid climbing motion.

In rain, snow, or ice, the ladder-climbing technique might need to change. The firefighter should place the arch of the boot near the heel next to the rung to permit a better grip onto the ladder. The climbing motion should be slow, deliberate, and consistent with weather conditions. Ladder falls and slips increase during situations such as these.

Many firefighters climb with their hands on the rungs, but this can have bad consequences. First, as a firefighter proceeds up or down the ladder, there is only one point of contact made with the hands. Second, if he or she were to slip, only one hand would be in contact with the ladder and the firefighter could fall. Third, a firefighter climbing with a tool in one hand does not keep contact with the ladder with that hand. While he or she climbs, the other hand would release a rung to reach for the next, leaving a short time of no hand contact with the ladder. Climbing with no hand contact, even for a short period, can lead to disaster.

When more than one firefighter climbs a portable ladder, they should space themselves evenly to avoid interfering with one another. Limit one firefighter to each section of the ladder. When climbing an aerial ladder, firefighters should space themselves at 10-ft (3-m) intervals to evenly displace their weight. During many fireground operations such as a rescue, additional firefighters may be on a ladder. Fire department ladders are made to strict standards. If proper maintenance and inspections are followed, these ladders can withstand grueling circumstances.

Climbing a portable ladder with a tool. Firefighters must be proficient in carrying tools on ladders. It is a common fireground experience. Hoisting tools by ropes may be safer, but it is also more time-consuming. Improperly carrying tools up a ladder reduces a firefighter's grip on the ladder and can lead to a slip or fall. Firefighters must maintain a grip on ladders while carrying tools to prevent any slip, fall, or injury to themselves or firefighters below them.

A firefighter should find a comfortable hand position to climb with a hand tool. Sometimes firefighters prefer to carry tools by their balance points and slide them up the outside of a ladder's beam. If a tool is thin enough, it might be possible for a firefighter to grip the underside of this beam and climb the ladder, allowing both hands contact with the ladder. At all times while climbing, the free hand must maintain a position under the opposite beam and slide up the beam. If a firefighter were to climb the ladder using the rungs with the free hand, he or she would have no hand contact with the ladder for each step (figs. 13–46, 13–47, and 13–48).

When a firefighter climbs a ladder with a hook or pike pole, the tool's head can hook onto a rung, and the firefighter can climb the ladder while maintaining their hand on the underside of the beam. Using this method, the firefighter can climb with two tools: one hook and a

hand tool in the opposite hand. Initially, the firefighter reaches up with the hook and places it onto the highest rung within reach. Remember, it is not necessary to reach for the highest rung possible.

Next, two methods can move the hook up as the firefighter climbs. The first occurs as the firefighter passes the top of the hook. Once the hook is about thigh-level, the firefighter can straighten his arm and reach down to grab the hook. Now he or she lifts the hook off the rung and slides it up until he or she can hook it on a higher rung. Again, the firefighter does not need to stretch to place the hook on a higher rung. It should be a fluid motion that does not change foot position.

For the second method, the firefighter stops at the balance point of the hook while climbing. Now, he or she removes the hook from the rung and lifts it to a higher rung. This involves additional times the hook must be moved because the total length of the hook is not used when climbing. This method, however, does not cause the firefighter to bend or lean to one side of the ladder in reaching back for the hook as in the first method.

Fig. 13–46. Slide the tool up the outside of the beam. (Courtesy of Megan Ciampo)

Figs. 13–47 and 13–48. Firefighters should always maintain a grip on the ladder when carrying tools to avoid any slip, fall, or injury. (Courtesy of Megan Ciampo)

Climbing a portable ladder with a saw. Climbing a portable ladder with a saw is difficult, especially if the saw is not equipped with a saw-carrying sling or harness. If a firefighter carries a saw without a sling or harness, he or she should carry only the saw—no other tools. While climbing or descending, the firefighter must maintain constant contact with the ladder by sliding the free hand up the outside or under the beam. The firefighter can place the arm carrying the saw either alongside the opposite beam of the ladder using the ladder as a guide, or he or she can carry the saw alongside himself or herself. The firefighter must use caution. The saw, in this position, has a tendency to hit the firefighter in the leg (fig. 13–49).

Fig. 13–49. Carrying a saw

While climbing an aerial ladder at a low angle, the firefighter might be able to slide the saw on top of the ladder's sections. Use caution when the sections become narrower because the saw changes positions.

When climbing with a saw in a sling or harness, there are a few options. The firefighter may place the sling over the head and let the saw rest underneath the arm and back as he or she climbs. Another variation is to push the saw farther back and up on top of the SCBA's bottle. Doing this can assist firefighters when climbing steep angles and keeps the saw from hitting the side of the ladder.

Some firefighters prefer to climb with the saw sling over a shoulder. The sling can ride down the shoulder as the firefighter's arm position changes. The firefighter must use caution when climbing with a dangling saw because the saw can throw off the firefighter's balance and cause a slip or fall. Firefighters must maintain hand contact with the ladder at all times to prevent this (fig. 13–50).

Fig. 13–50. Using a sling to carry a saw is recommended

Climbing a portable ladder with an uncharged hoseline. When an uncharged hoseline must be carried up the ladder, have sufficient hose at or near the base of the ladder to ensure it is deployed smoothly as the firefighter climbs. Insufficient hose anytime during the climb could cause the climbing firefighter to be pulled backward off the ladder.

The firefighter climbing with the nozzle should place the hose under one shoulder and over the opposite shoulder with about 2–3 ft (0.6–0.9 m) of hose extending over the back. A firefighter at the base of the ladder should feed the hose up as the firefighter climbs. If the climb is high, a second firefighter might need to be in the middle of the climb and another firefighter at the base of the ladder to assist in hose deployment (figs. 13–51 and 13–52).

Fig. 13–51. Place the hose under one shoulder and over the opposite one.

The second firefighter should position the hose over the shoulder on the side the hose is being raised. The hose should have some slack and form a small loop to the side of the ladder. This loop prevents the second firefighter from being pulled off the ladder should the hose become taut or be pulled up during the climb.

The hose must be fed at a steady pace and kept outside the climber's body to avoid tripping and entangling the climber.

Advancing a hoseline up a ladder is easier when the hoseline has not been charged with water. If the hoseline has been charged with water, climbing might be easier if you shut the line down and partially drain it. It might be necessary to place firefighters along the line of the ladder to advance the hoseline. These firefighters should be secured to the ladder by either an approved safety belt or leg-lock maneuver. If that is not practical, send a few firefighters up to where the hoseline is needed. Drop a utility rope down and pull the hose up and over a hose roller to this location.

Ladders

FIREFIGHTER I

Chapter 13

Fig. 13–52. The firefighter at the base feeds the hose.

Fig. 13–53. Be careful when performing steep angle climbs. (Courtesy of Andy Moloney)

Climbing and working on an aerial ladder. An aerial ladder's angle often determines how a firefighter climbs it. If the ladder is at a low angle, the firefighter climbs in a hunched position and must maintain at least one hand sliding along the top of the ladder's rails. If the ladder is not extended far, the rails are wide and the firefighter is more comfortable sliding the rail toward the edge. In this manner, he or she can grip the outside of the rail to maintain grip and balance. Sliding the hand flat on the wide surface of the rails should be avoided.

When the ladder is at a steep angle, it might be difficult to reach the top of the rails and climb, especially at the first few sections. Some aerial apparatus are constructed with wide base sections that make it difficult for firefighters to reach. In these situations, they can use the rungs. Climbing should be done in a fluid, hand-over-hand motion while transferring boots from rung to rung. Steep-angle climbs should be done slowly and safely. A slip or fall could result in a severe injury or fatality (fig. 13–53).

FIREGROUND NOTE

Remember, if a charged hoseline is tied onto a portable ladder with a hose strap, the opening and closing of the nozzle will cause back pressure in the hoseline and possible shifting. An unattended ladder could shift and fall if it is not properly secured.

As with climbing portable ladders, a firefighter climbing an aerial ladder with a tool such as a hook can place it on the aerial's rung and move it as he or she climbs and descends. At some angles, it might be more comfortable to slide the tool along the upper portion of the aerial ladder's rail. When a firefighter climbs an aerial ladder at any angle, he or she must maintain a grip on the ladder. Aerial ladders slide between greased tracks, and small drops of grease on the rungs often create slipping hazards. A firefighter walking down an aerial ladder like it is a tight rope or balance beam with no hand contact is an accident waiting to happen.

When working from aerial ladders, firefighters should never perform any leg-lock maneuver through the rungs or beams. If a ladder were to move or mechanically fail, a firefighter could be injured severely. When performing any type of work from an aerial ladder, a firefighter should lock himself or herself into the ladder by wearing an approved safety belt.

Climbing a vertical ladder on a fire escape. In some areas with exterior fire escapes, firefighters commonly ascend and descend these appliances. Most fire escapes are constantly exposed to the weather, so they might not be in the best structural condition. Climbing them can be hazardous and difficult. Firefighters must use caution on these secondary means of egress.

The small vertical ladder, or **drop ladder**, that connects the first floor landing to the ground when released and the top vertical ladder, or **gooseneck ladder**, that connects the top floor landing to the roof, are difficult to climb. Prior to climbing any vertical ladder, shake the ladder to check its stability and if it is attached to the building and the fire escape's main structure.

Once a firefighter verifies stability, he or she may climb the ladder. A hook in a firefighter's hand can hook either onto the highest reachable rung or the fire escape landing itself. Then the firefighter can maintain hand position on the rails or rungs of the ladder. With these narrow, straight ladders, it is often difficult to maintain a hand position on the rails. Climbing with hands on the rungs is permissible. A firefighter should climb slowly, placing feet toward the rail on each rung and ensuring with each step that the ladder can maintain his or her weight.

Fig. 13–54. Position yourself under the landing to avoid a falling ladder.

Operating and working from a ladder

Throughout their careers, firefighters work with hand tools on portable ladders. Usually, firefighters place ladders to the side (overhauling window trim) or possibly under the work area (removing window bars). In both cases, a firefighter's hands are on his or her tools and he or she won't be able to hold the ladder properly. The first solution is for firefighters to wear and use certified ladder belts or personal safety belts and hook into the ladder. Hooking a safety belt into the middle of a rung, however, can allow a firefighter to slide. If you hook onto a ladder's rung, position the safety hook near the beam to reduce the risk of sliding. There are a few alternatives for a firefighter not wearing an approved safety belt while working from the ladder. He or she can perform a leg-lock maneuver to secure onto the ladder.

Leg-lock maneuver. The **leg-lock maneuver** (fig. 13–55) was developed years ago when firefighters still used **hip boots**, three-fourths rubber boots, and had more flexibility. Today's firefighters wear bunker pants with large side pockets that can hold numerous items. Performing the standard leg lock is difficult and often

FIREGROUND NOTE

A firefighter should always position him or herself under the fire escape landing when releasing the vertical drop ladder. These ladders have fallen out of their tracks when released. A falling ladder could injure a firefighter in the wrong position (fig. 13–54).

firefighters opt for alternatives. Whatever type of lock firefighters choose, they must secure themselves onto ladders.

Figs. 13–55. Leg lock

Firefighters perform the standard leg-lock maneuver on the ladder side opposite the work side. For example, if a firefighter were to ventilate a window on the right side of the ladder, the firefighter's left leg would perform the leg lock. The standard leg-lock maneuver is done in the following manner:

- First, a firefighter reaches the proper working height on the ladder.

- Then, he or she climbs to the next higher rung.

- Next, he or she places the leg opposite the work side through the rung spacing. As the firefighter's knee approaches the rung, he or she can begin to bend the leg back toward the next lower rung. The leg is now inserted into this spacing. Depending on the firefighter's physical makeup, the foot may lock onto the outside of the ladder's beam or onto the next lower rung. Some firefighters even place their boot behind their knee to lock themselves into the ladder.

- Now, the firefighter steps down a rung and places a boot nearest the work side, next to the beam of

the ladder. Now he or she is in the original work position on the ladder.

Normally when a firefighter completes the maneuver, he or she is two rungs below the rung through which he or she inserted a leg. Many firefighters can stand on the rung at a desired work location, lift a leg up the two rungs, and perform the maneuver. Others with shorter legs find it uncomfortable. It is fine to position themselves one rung below the bent knee.

Hook-in leg-lock (hill) maneuver. Because now firefighters carry bail-out ropes, pliers, cutters, screwdrivers, chocks, etc., in their bunker gear pockets, performing the standard leg-lock maneuver is a nuisance, takes too long to get into, and is uncomfortable. In addition, many firefighters feel trapped in the ladder because releasing the leg lock takes a while.

To prevent ladder falls by firefighters performing no leg lock, a few leg locks have been modified. The **hook-in leg-lock maneuver** is relatively quick and simple, and it reduces the bending and twisting of a firefighter's leg. Plus, firefighters of varying shapes and sizes can perform the maneuver.

Firefighters can perform the hook-in leg-lock maneuver with the leg opposite the work side of a ladder or the leg on the same side of a ladder. A firefighter's physical makeup decides which position is suitable. Follow these steps to perform the maneuver:

- Reach the proper working height on the ladder with both feet on the same rung.

- Then, place a boot in the center of the rung with the heel slid into the rung.

- Next, lift the other boot over the rung and through the rung spacing.

Variations can be performed depending on a firefighter's body:

- The standard tactic is to place the heel of the boot that has come over the rung on top of the boot's toe that is positioned on the center of the rung. By maintaining downward pressure on the boot while the thigh and knee are wedged under the rung, you are locked into the ladder. Position the thigh and knee next to the beam of the ladder to prevent sliding. Firefighters with shorter legs might have to turn the bottom boot's tip toward the beam for the thigh and knee to lock securely. Firefighters should not perform this maneuver with the thigh and knee positioned in the center of the rung. Movement in either direction could cause a firefighter to slide across a rung and the ladder or firefighter to fall.

- Some firefighters might be able to place the heel of the lifted boot over the rung onto the rung they are stepping on as the locking device.

- Some firefighters feel more comfortable placing the tip of the boot lifted over the rung onto the rung they are stepping on or over the beam of the ladder as the locking device.

Practicing the hook-in leg-lock maneuver determines which option suits a firefighter's body style (figs. 13–56 and 13–57).

Figs. 13–56 and 13–57. Hook-in leg-lock (Hill)

Hyperextend leg-lock (hell) maneuver. Many times firefighters execute unique, dramatic ladder rescues with no time for safety maneuvers. There are also times when victims hand a child to a firefighter who must release his or her hand grip on a ladder to accept the child. Positioning into any of the leg locks can be difficult and dangerous for the firefighter and victim during such a transition.

Lt. Ciampo has also developed the **hyperextend leg lock** to assist firefighters who might momentarily lose their grip on a ladder, slip, or who perform rescues. Its primary purpose is to help firefighters maintain balance, control, and prevent ladder falls. Although nothing is safer than being belted in or performing a leg-lock maneuver, sometimes those are unachievable. To perform the hyperextend leg-lock maneuver:

- Reach the proper working height on the ladder with both feet on the same rung.

- Then, raise one leg, similar to standing on the tip of the toe or flexing a calf muscle. You may use either leg to perform this tactic and should be well-balanced, not attempting to balance on the toe itself.

- As the leg extends upward, wedge the lower thigh or knee under the ladder's rung. Firefighters with short legs might not reach the rung with a knee. If you can't reach, do not attempt to rise all the way up on a toe, but rather follow the next direction.

- As this is performed, you may press outward with both legs and wedge yourself between the ladder's beams for additional locking support. This tactic might be the only one to follow for firefighters with short legs.

This maneuver should be done with the raised leg near the ladder's beam to prevent sliding and movement, especially if a firefighter must reach off the side of the ladder for a victim. Firefighters should never come up on both legs to wedge themselves under the rungs. This gives them little foot contact with the ladder, and any sudden movement could cause them to slide back or lose their balance on the rung and possibly fall (figs. 13–58 and 13–59).

Fig. 13–58. Raise one leg up on tip-toe.

Fig. 13–59. Press outward with both legs.

Arm-lock maneuver: venting windows from a portable ladder. The **arm-lock maneuver** can be performed by a firefighter venting windows from a portable ladder.[2] It is relatively easy and requires minimal time to get into position on the ladder, thus saving time for other tasks. It may be used in conjunction with the leg-lock maneuvers previously described or by itself.

To perform the arm-lock maneuver, follow these steps for ventilating a window to the right side of a ladder:

- Reach the proper working height on the ladder with both feet on the same rung. When venting the window off the side of the ladder, place a leg and foot up against the ladder's beam. This offers more support and balance as you swing the hand tool. It also braces you onto the ladder.

- Then, hold the hook in the right arm and place the left arm between the two rungs directly in front of you.

- Then, place the butt end of the hook behind the ladder and grab it with the left hand.

- Next, position the hook to the window and check that no part of the ladder or structure will interfere with the swinging. Now the window can be ventilated (figs. 13–60 and 13–61).

Fig. 13–60. Arm-lock

Fig. 13–61. Place your left arm between the rungs.

The hook used for ventilation acts as the safety brace for you. If the hook were to bounce off the window and the recoil were too much, you must only pull yourself back into the ladder to prevent falling. When performing the arm-lock maneuver:

- Don't choke up on the hook. The entire length of the hook must be used to clear the opposite beam of the ladder while swinging the tool. If the tool is not used properly, it could cause the swing to come to an abrupt halt, shake the ladder, and cause the hook not to vent the window.

- You must split the rungs with your arms. Hugging the ladder can cause you to pinch a hand between the hook and the ladder's beam.

- Resist pulling material out of the window. The butt end of the hook could come back and strike you or the ladder.

- You can create a small working space between your body and the ladder that allows for easier swinging of the hook.

Another method to vent a window involves the hook's butt end being placed behind the firefighter's back with his or her arm holding the hook. The firefighter's opposite hand holds the rung of the ladder and secures him or her to the ladder. Next, the firefighter can twist or quarter turn with the upper body. The momentum assists in letting the hook strike and break the window. If the firefighter chooses this method of venting a window, he or she must remain below or toward the side of the window and out of the path of the escaping heat, smoke, and gases (fig. 13–62).

Fig. 13–62. This allows the firefighter's free hand to secure him or her to the ladder.

FIREGROUND NOTE

When you first make physical contact with a victim, ask if anyone is trapped in the building.

PORTABLE LADDER RESCUES

FFI 5.3.6 One of the most harrowing experiences for a firefighter is a portable ladder rescue. A victim waiting for a ladder under smoke, fire, and heat conditions normally is panicked and irrational. A firefighter must be trained in rescue procedures for the ladder rescue to be successful.

Often victims reach for and grab onto ladders being raised in their vicinity. Some have even jumped for ladders being raised toward them. Firefighters must constantly watch victims. Once a victim is on a ladder, he or she might become aggressive and panicked. Firefighters must be prepared for and in control of victims once they reach the safety of ladders.

When first faced with victims at windows, make verbal contact with them. Firefighters must take command and judge victims' conditions and states of mind. A severely panicked victim might lead a firefighter to throw a ladder out of the victim's reach, then roll the ladder to him or her after it contacts the structure. In other instances, a victim might remain calm and self exit with no coaxing when a ladder arrives.

When a firefighter reaches a victim able to self exit onto a ladder at a window, the firefighter should make sure the victim faces the ladder. The firefighter should place both arms around the victim and onto the back of the ladder's beams. If the victim becomes panicked during descent, the firefighter can press him or her into the ladder to gain control or stop the descent.

Firefighters must not place their hands on ladder rungs while descending with a victim. If a victim were to suddenly move, turn, or become panicked while the firefighter changes hand position, both victim and firefighter could slip and fall. During the descent, it might be necessary to reinforce verbal commands or encouragement to keep the victim focused and not panicked.

If there are enough firefighters, another firefighter may climb up behind the firefighter and victim, extend an arm up to the firefighter's back, and offer physical and verbal support as they descend.

If two firefighters are available at the start of the rescue, one firefighter might enter the building prior to the victim's removal. If conditions aren't immediately dangerous, the victim might be able to be sheltered in place. If conditions are intolerable or if the victim is panicked, however, this firefighter can assist in lifting or placing the victim into the window and onto the ladder for the other firefighter to remove.

Semiconscious removals

Victims might become disoriented, semiconscious, dazed, or confused. In a **semiconscious removal**, a firefighter can continue their descent down a ladder much like a conscious removal, with one exception: the firefighter may place a knee into the buttocks of the victim as they descend. As the firefighter goes from rung to rung, he or she may transfer the victim's weight from knee to knee. Some firefighters prefer to use just one knee during the whole operation, but on longer climbs, this leg could become more fatigued. The firefighter must place only the ball of the boot onto the next rung. If he or she places the boot too deeply into the rung, lifting the victim's weight and completing the removal is harder (fig. 13–63).

Fig. 13–63. The semiconscious removal

FIREGROUND NOTE

When faced with aluminum gutters on a structure, a firefighter may gently drop the ladder into the gutter or apply pressure into the ladder with the beam to dent the gutter. A good spot is between the attachment spikes. This prevents the ladder from bouncing or sliding as the firefighter climbs. It also allows more room on the rungs for a firefighter's boot when he or she nears the top.

Unconscious removals

In an **unconscious removal**, a firefighter may place both arms out and onto the beams of the ladder, accepting a victim across both arms. The firefighter can control the descent by pressing the victim into the ladder with his or her chest. Sometimes, the victim's legs can be split to assist in the carry down. Cradling an adult victim can be dangerous because the victim might slip through the arms during the descent.

If additional personnel are on scene, a second ladder may be placed next to the first to assist in the rescue. The ladder may slide up behind the victim on the leg side so two firefighters support the victim.

Children are always carried down ladders. In addition, a rescue is not complete until victims are out of harm on the ground. These techniques may also be used to rescue downed firefighters.

In the case of multiple victims, firefighters must decide who is in the most danger and needs to be rescued first. Normally, the most critical places to address first are adjacent areas, then the floor above. Victims two floors above a fire and a few rooms away might also need to be removed, but they might not be the first priority (fig. 13–64).

Fig. 13–64. An unconscious removal

PORTABLE LADDER PLACEMENT

Access and egress

FFI 5.3.6 Safely placing a portable ladder's base is important, but equally important is resting the ladder's top against a reliable structure. Normally the top of a ladder rests on a roofline, eave line, parapet, or wall. Both beams of the ladder near the top must make contact with the structural support. As a firefighter climbs a ladder in this position, the ladder rests firmly on the support. If one of the beams did not touch the support, the ladder being climbed could twist, bounce, or slide off the structural support. Beware of awnings on the front of a row of stores—they have no structural stability. Placing a ladder against the awning and walking on it may cause the awning to collapse, dropping firefighters to the ground.

As the ladder reaches the reliable structure near its tip, the firefighter should check the support's sturdiness. If the support is questionable, weak, or unreliable, the firefighter should gently press in on the ladder about chest level. This added pressure shows whether the structure can support the firefighter. If doubt still exists, the ladder must move to a reliable support area. If a firefighter were climbing the ladder and the support were to fail suddenly, he or she must attempt to quickly climb down the ladder. Remember, before a firefighter climbs a ladder, he or she must ensure that the base and tip are positioned properly, securely, and safely.

Roof level

Portable ladders providing roof access (fig. 13–65) should extend at least five rungs above the roofline because:

- This increases the ladders' visibility when smoke obscures rooflines and means of egress.

- Extra rungs above the roofline assist firefighters dismounting and mounting ladders when they get onto or off roofs. Firefighters have better hand grips on ladders and don't overreach as they get on or off ladders. In addition, they are in more comfortable, upright body positions to transfer onto roofs or ladders. Ladders that aren't raised high enough make firefighters bend over rooflines to grab the ladders. When firefighters lean forward to grab ladders, they lean off the edges of buildings, which is dangerous. A fall could be fatal.

- If ladders have a light beacon attached to the end of one of their rails, they might be more visible in smoke.

- If a firefighter were to accidentally slide down a pitched roof, more rungs above the roofline could stop his or her descent.

- When placing a roof ladder to a pitch roof, a firefighter at the top of the ladder can lean into the ladder for support as he slides the roof ladder up onto the roof.

In situations such as short porch roofs with varying grades of slope, extending the ladder five rungs above the roofline might interfere with firefighting operations. It might be necessary to decrease the number of rungs extended over the roofline.

A firefighter may perform a simple procedure prior to transferring completely off the ladder. If he or she steps onto a pitched or flat roof, a boot or hand tool may **sound the roof**. This means banging a boot or tool to test a roof for structural soundness. In many instances, this tactic informs firefighters that a roof's underside is weak or burned away.

Firefighters should avoid jumping off ladders onto roofs. The impacts could be a problem, especially on a roof weakened by fire. Firefighters should slowly transition from ladders to roofs. Doing it too quickly sometimes causes ladder tips to slide along rooflines.

Fig. 13–65. The ladder should extend five rungs above roof level.

Windows

A portable ladder should be placed to a window with its tip slightly below or level with the windowsill. A tip extending into a window decreases the window's size, which hampers entering, exiting, and performing victim removals and rescues. In addition, during a headfirst, ladder-slide maneuver, the ladder could be knocked

from its position or a firefighter could get caught on the ladder's tip. A ladder at this location provides the safest, most effective window-entry method.

Until recently, firefighters relied on an older window-entry technique. They placed ladders next to windows with the tips even or level with the tops of the window-sills. Once a window had been entirely removed to create an access point, a firefighter stepped from the ladder onto the sill and into the building. This is dangerous for a few reasons. First, the firefighter enters high in the window and exposes himself or herself to exiting smoke, gases, and heat. Second, a slip could mean a high fall. And last, it is common for a ladder's tip to slide once the transition from ladder to window occurs.

There is another danger in placing the ladder in this position. If a firefighter must exit a structure rapidly, it can be a long reach for the ladder under difficult circumstances. During this reach, ladders often slide when firefighters transfer their weight from windows to ladders. Fire debris on firefighters' boots can also increase slips and falls during this evolution.

After the tip of the ladder is in position at the window and the ladder is footed by another firefighter, it is ready to climb. The climbing firefighter approaches the window and prepares to ventilate the window for climbing access. Prior to venting, the firefighter positions himself or herself into a leg-lock maneuver. Now the entire window and sash should be removed for easier entry. After completing window removal, the firefighter checks the floor conditions with the **sweep-and-sound maneuver** before entering the window. The firefighter keeps his or her head outside the building toward the window's side and uses the structure's wall for protection. Next, he or she sweeps the floor with a hand tool to look for a victim. If the tool meets no resistance, the firefighter sounds the floor with a tool. Sounding the floor ensures that there is a stable floor in the immediate area and moment. Then the firefighter may drop the tool forward and listen for that distinct sound, reinforcing that the floor exists.

Now the firefighter may enter the window, driving the right shoulder into the bottom of the left side of the window frame with his or her face facing outward while climbing toward the top rung. While climbing over the top rung, the right leg enters the window while the left hand maintains a grip on the ladder's rung or beam. Next, he or she slides the buttocks back toward the right side of the window frame. This way the firefighter is low in the window frame—away from escaping heat, gases, and smoke. As the firefighter's right leg enters the room, it again sweeps and sounds the floor. The firefighter's physique and the window's size determine which of two options to select. If the window's opening is small, a typical firefighter lifts his or her head into the room and over the sill, riding down the wall to the floor. The left leg naturally follows as the firefighter enters the room. If the window's opening is larger, a firefighter can bring the left foot up behind and into the window while keeping the head outside. Numerous safety items protect the firefighter performing this maneuver:

- He or she maintains contact with the ladder at all times. If the room were to suddenly ignite, the firefighter could reverse direction and exit quickly.

- A large portion of the firefighter's body is outside the window and limits exposure to superheated gases and smoke that could ignite.

- The firefighter can quickly exit a building in the same fashion as entering. He or she does not have to reach or look for a ladder placed to the side of the window. This also reduces the chances of slipping and falling.

- If a firefighter is trained in self-exiting techniques such as the headfirst ladder slide, the ladder is in position from the start.

In another window entry, the firefighter goes over the sill headfirst after sweeping and sounding the floor. Some instructors teach this tactic because it allows the firefighter to slip under the escaping gases and heat. Many fire academies shy away from teaching this method because of its disadvantages:

- With today's newer **lightweight construction**, a firefighter going in headfirst could travel through the fire-weakened floor itself.

- A firefighter could land on furniture near the window, causing it to tumble over and land him abruptly or farther from the window.

- If a quick escape were needed, the window that the firefighter came through might not be visible. He or she might dive into the wall looking for it on an escape.

- Broken glass on the floor could cut a firefighter as he or she extends the hands during the headfirst descent.

- Firefighters entering head first often do this much faster than when entering leg first. Controlling the complete entry is more practical.

FIREGROUND NOTE

As firefighters leave ladders and proceed along roofs, occasionally they should sound the roofs for weakness with hand tools or their feet.

Balcony, deck, or fire escape

Firefighters face numerous victims trapped or congregating on balconies, decks, and fire escapes. Or, this avenue might be the only access point to a fire building, so firefighters must ladder it. All are exposed to weather and constantly deteriorate. Introducing a fire department ladder with a firefighter's weight could break them. It is common to see bent, rusty, or even missing handrails, railings, and balusters on these structures.

It is best to ladder the side of the balcony, deck, or fire escape and use the building as the ladder's main support. When a ladder is placed to the side of a structure, it should be placed with the tip several rungs above the side of the railing with the ladder's beam next to the railing. After climbing, a firefighter can swing a leg over the railing and maintain a hand on the ladder while checking the structure's stability with his or her leg. It is also easier to remove victims because the ladder is more stable. In addition, the ladder is out of the way and does not interfere with operations on the platform. Plus, it is less likely to slide along the handrail and fall.

If a ladder's beams were placed on and just over the front of the railing when a victim transfers his or her weight over the railing, the ladder might slide along the handrail, which could cause panic. This can also happen when a firefighter transfers his or her weight off the ladder and onto the platform. A firefighter must butt the ladder when any firefighter transfers from ladder to platform. If it is necessary to place a ladder in this position, a firefighter must remember before climbing to forcefully tap the handrail with the tip of the ladder to ensure it is structurally sound and can carry the weight of the ladder and firefighter.

Another option for decks that are lightweight, have minor structural defects, or that can't be laddered on the side is to place the ladder at the front of the deck. Both beams of the ladder should rest on the structure's platform frame or flooring. Now, a firefighter with a hand tool may climb the ladder and remove some balusters, permitting an egress point. Using the deck's structural frame is often better than placing the ladder's beams on the top handrail.

Fire escapes often become overcrowded in an instant because the vertical drop ladder is hard for civilians to descend. To relieve overcrowding and make descent easier, place a portable ladder to the first landing opposite the fire escape from the drop ladder. If the fire escape is severely overcrowded, another portable ladder may be positioned on the second landing on the same side of the drop ladder.

CARRIES AND RAISES

There are many ways to carry, transport, and raise a ladder. Many carries and raises depend on the number of firefighters available. Normally, ladders are taken butt-first toward their objectives. Sometimes it is necessary to carry the ladder with the tip forward. As we often find in firefighting tactics and techniques, each has advantages and disadvantages. It is up to the operating firefighters to choose the best technique for each situation.

Single-firefighter evolutions

Although not the preferred method to transport or raise a ladder, one firefighter sometimes finds himself or herself performing the tasks of two. It is essential to learn single-firefighter evolutions when dealing with portable ladders.

Single-firefighter shoulder carry. A firefighter on one side of a vertically stowed ladder may lift the ladder at its balance point with the butt end facing the front or direction of travel. Then, he or she inserts a shoulder between the rungs and rests the ladder on the shoulder. He or she may place this arm's hand on the bottom of the beam, at the base, middle, or top of the rung, or on the next forward rung. If the other hand is free, this hand can grasp the next forward rung to balance the ladder. As the ladder sits on the firefighter's shoulder, it may be tilted slightly down toward the base to help control the ladder, provide good visibility, and prevent striking another firefighter with the butt (fig. 13–66).

Single-firefighter suitcase carry. A firefighter on one side of a vertically stowed ladder may locate the balance point of the ladder and hoist the ladder with one arm. He or she may then carry the ladder like a suitcase with

his or her arm dangling to one side. Ladders carried in this position often strike firefighters in the leg if they move quickly or walk over rugged terrain. If a ladder is to be picked up off the ground, a firefighter should bend his or her legs to prevent a back injury. This carry is practical for short distances and small, straight ladders. It also allows a firefighter to carry tools in the other hand (fig. 13–67).

Fig. 13–66. Single-firefighter shoulder carry

Fig. 13–67. Single-firefighter suitcase carry

Single-firefighter ladder drags. During fire operations, firefighters might find themselves shorthanded or alone when tactics must be performed simultaneously. To assist a single firefighter in transporting ladders, firefighters have created ladder drags. These drags may be used on all surfaces during any weather. Both drags incorporate dragging tools and two ladders to a destination in one trip, which benefits short-staffed firegrounds.

The **Swick method** was created by Robert Swick of the Fairborn (Ohio) Fire Department who was assigned to a one-man truck company for 17 years. To perform this drag, a firefighter lays an extension ladder fly-section-up on the ground. Then, he or she places a roof ladder with open roof hooks on top of the extension ladder. The hooks bite into the top rung of the extension ladder, connecting the ladders. Next, the firefighter lays his tools on top of the ladders. Now, he or she goes to either side of the ladder nearest the tip, crouches, and places his or her arm downward to pick up the extension ladder's bottom rung. The firefighter stands up to lift the ladder with the leg and back muscles. It is more comfortable for some firefighters to place the bottom rung inside the elbow and place the hand under the ladder's rail. The ladder sits higher and into the firefighter's chest area. Now the ladders may be dragged to their destination (fig. 13–68).

Fig. 13–68. The Swick method

There are pros and cons. When a firefighter turns a corner with a long roof ladder on top, the longer ladder can catch on uneven terrain and spin slightly off the top of the extension ladder. In this case, the firefighter must only slide the roof ladder back on the extension ladder and continue dragging to the destination. Another drawback is that the ladder's tips or spurs can scratch during dragging over pavement or concrete. If this happens, small damages may be filed or sanded.

One other thing that bothers firefighters is the uncomfortable drag. The ladder has a tendency to rub the turnout coat under the armpit, and firefighters with shorter arms don't have the reach to carry the ladder in this position. When firefighters come across a problem or situation, they quickly find a cure.

The **Creed method** of dragging a ladder evolved after Creed McClelland of the Orlando Fire Department performed the Swick method at a fire conference. After pondering a few minutes about the drag, he came up with a variation. A firefighter may place a roof ladder flat on the ground with its open hooks pointing up. Now, he or she slides an extension ladder bed-section-down on top of the roof ladder and into the hooks. The hooks act like a stop and permit the extension ladder to ride on top of it. Now, the firefighter may come to the foot section of the ladder, lift the first rung, and drag the ladders to their destination. When using a longer roof ladder on the bottom of the drag, a firefighter has more rungs accessible near the base of the ladders, making it easier to drag. This method also removes the possibility of the ladders separating during the maneuver (fig. 13–69).

Fig. 13–69. The Creed method

FIREGROUND NOTE

The Stokes basket may be placed into the rungs of the roof ladder, filled with tools and equipment, and dragged to the fire scene for rapid intervention team operations or during inclement weather (Fig. 13–70).

Both drags take little time to set up and are easy. They allow a firefighter two ladders and tools in one trip, conserving energy for other tasks.

Fig. 13–70. Using a roof ladder to transport a Stokes basket

Single-firefighter flat raise. Although it is preferable to raise a ladder with another firefighter, it is not always possible on the fireground. All firefighters must know how to raise a ladder with one person and practice the skill. After a single-carry transport technique, a firefighter must check for overhead obstructions such as tree branches and electrical service lines, then place the ladder's butt end against a structure for bracing. Now, the firefighter kneels or bends at the tip of the ladder and lifts the tip off the ground using the leg muscles. He or she then walks the ladder up with hands sliding up the rails of the beam and eyes focused on the ladder rising overhead. As the firefighter slides hands up the rails, the fluid motion should not include a bouncing rhythm, which puts undue strain and stress on the firefighter's body (fig. 13–71).

If the firefighter uses a hand-over-hand motion on the rungs to raise the ladder to vertical, a few things may occur. First, the ladder balances on only one arm as it rises. If a loss of balance occurs, the ladder could drop. Second, ground conditions determine the possibility of slipping, and balancing a ladder with one arm might be difficult for the strongest of firefighters. Those who use this method often proceed quickly, which has caused

lost grips on the rungs and ladder drops. When using the hands-on-the-rail method to raise the ladder, a firefighter slipping or losing balance could push the whole ladder away to avoid injury.

Fig. 13–71. Single-firefighter flat raise

Single-firefighter high-shoulder carry and raise. Before becoming firefighters, many of us worked on job sites with lightweight, easy-to-maneuver ladders not built to fire department standards. Some fire academies instruct firefighters on a high-shoulder carry and raise that evolved from other occupations. The cons outweigh the pros. There are better, safer ways to perform a single-firefighter carry and raise evolution.

As a firefighter removes a ladder from an apparatus, he or she carries the balance point of the lower beam on top of the shoulder or places the shoulder inside the beams and rungs near the balance point. Then, the firefighter raises the other hand to grab the upper beam or a forward rung to balance it. He or she then transports the ladder, tilting the base toward the ground to avoid striking another firefighter (fig. 13–72).

Fig. 13–72. High-shoulder carry and raise

As the firefighter approaches the proper distance from the fire building, he or she plants the base of the lower beam in the ground to act as the foot. Now, the firefighter uses upper-body strength to push the ladder up and walk it up in a hand-over-hand motion and beam-raise position. In other situations, a firefighter may place the base against the base of the fire building and then raise it upward. This carry and raise puts a lot of stress on the firefighter's upper body. Time and conditions permitting, it is better to transport the ladder to its location in the high-shoulder carry than to perform the single-firefighter flat raise.

Two-firefighter evolutions

When two firefighters begin ladder work, they must perform safely, communicate effectively, and use teamwork. One firefighter must lead the operation. The firefighter at the ladder's butt normally leads and gives commands. This firefighter leads the operation because the butt of the ladder arrives to the structure first with this firefighter in the lead. Once the ladder rises, he or she controls the halyard and raising the ladder.

Two-firefighter shoulder carry. Two firefighters face the same direction on the same side of the ladder, one at the butt, and the other at the tip. Then, both squat, grab a rung, and with their leg muscles lift the ladder onto their shoulders. As they place the ladder onto their shoulders, each firefighter's same arm can enter between rungs and grab the next forward rung. The butt firefighter should be inside the first or second rung spacing to protect the butt and use the other arm to warn approaching firefighters, move obstacles, and open doors and gates. The firefighter at the tip following the butt firefighter steers the ladder around obstructions and corners (figs. 13–73 and 13–74).

Figs. 13–73 and 13–74. Two-firefighter shoulder carry

The two-firefighter shoulder carry is for removing a ladder from an engine or ladder truck and for farther distances than the suitcase carry. If a third firefighter is available, he or she goes in the middle. A very tall third firefighter will throw off the ladder's balance. He or she might have to keep the shoulder free from the ladder and use only arm strength.

> **FIREGROUND NOTE**
>
> Firefighters must attempt to stay at least 10 feet from electrical power lines when raising portable ladders. In some instances, electrical power has jumped from power lines to ladders.

Two-firefighter suitcase carry. Two firefighters position themselves on the same side of the ladder and face the same direction. One firefighter is at the butt of the ladder and the other is at the tip. Both firefighters squat, grab the beam of the ladder, and prepare to lift it. Using their leg muscles, both firefighters begin to stand.

Their arms and bodies raise the ladder to a vertical carry position that resembles a suitcase. The butt firefighter must maintain a position to protect the butt of the ladder from striking another firefighter or an object. If a third firefighter is available, he or she may go to the center of the same side (fig. 13–75).

Fig. 13–75. Two-firefighter suitcase carry

Remember, the suitcase carry is designed for carrying ladders a short distance. Note a few disadvantages:

- The ladder often strikes firefighters in the lower leg, making it a nuisance or injuring firefighters.

- The ladder can strike uneven terrain. In addition, if a firefighter were to lose balance or stumble, the ladder increases the risk that the firefighter would fall if the ladder were to strike his or her leg.

- Carrying large ladders is difficult and can injure and tire a firefighter.

Two-firefighter beam raise. After the ladder reaches the desired location, the butt-end firefighter places the ladder the proper distance from the building with the fly section out and, if possible, out of the way of overhead obstructions. Remember, this should be about one-fourth the working distance of the ladder so the ladder won't need to be repositioned once it is vertical. The firefighter places the ladder with one beam planted on the ground so it is in the vertical position on one beam.

The firefighter at the ladder's butt or foot is commonly called the footer. His or her main objective is to apply body pressure to the ladder as a counterweight to help the other firefighter raise the ladder. The footer places one foot forward and onto the ladder's butt end on the ground. The other foot goes comfortably behind the firefighter. This leg must not be directly in line with the

other leg and the ladder because it could get struck as the ladder rises. The footer's hands go onto the beam. The arm that's on the same side of the body as the leg on the ladder's butt extends forward. The back arm now goes on the beam near the ladder's butt. Do not place this hand under or on the foot or spurs of the ladder's base. If the raise were performed rapidly, this hand could be pinched between the ladder and the ground. As the firefighter at the tip raises the ladder, the footer slowly leans backward and pulls slightly with his or her arms, reducing the weight of the ladder and assisting in the raise.

The firefighter at the tip rechecks the overhead clearance before raising the ladder. Next, the firefighters position themselves inside the ladder or nearest the building, with the ladder sitting on the opposite shoulder. By doing this, they are out from under the ladder and have a constant view to the objective. They raise the ladder by walking hand over hand, glancing up at the objective, and watching for overhead obstructions or changing conditions. If an obstruction such as a tree limb were problematic during the raise, the firefighter could pivot the ladder on its butt as it raises to avoid the limb.

Now that the ladder is vertical, both firefighters assume positions on opposite sides of the ladder with one foot against the butt to steady it and the other leg behind them to balance. Now they can untie the halyard and extend the ladder. The firefighter pulls the halyard down in a hand-over-hand motion and resists wrapping his or her hand or arm in the rope as it is pulled. If the rope were to snap, break, or slip without warning, it could injure the firefighter. As the halyard is pulled down, the other firefighter positions both hands outside the ladder's beam to steady it as it rises. Placing hands on the outside of the beams reduces the chance of an injury should the fly section suddenly retract. This firefighter has the best view of the raise and can give verbal commands to stop the raise. When the ladder reaches the desired height, firefighters slowly lean it into the building. They place one foot against an opposite foot on the ladder and use their arms to control the ladder's lowering into the building.

The two-firefighter beam raise is preferred over the two-firefighter flat raise because:

- The ladder is in a reduced-profile position because it is more narrow than when raised flat. In this position, the ladder is less likely to hit overhead obstructions. In addition, it is easier to pivot around overhead obstructions because only one foot is secured to the ground.

- Both firefighters can maintain good, balanced positions throughout the raise. The footer does not have to bend over and get onto the base or bottom rung of the ladder, which is a difficult position to assume and maintain. It also removes the possibility that the footer could slip off the ladder's base or rung as it is raised.

- The beam raise is the preferred portable ladder raise in a narrow alley or between overhead obstructions. The ladder's narrow profile allows for use in small, narrow areas (figs. 13–76, 13–77, 13–78, and 13–79).

Fig. 13–78. The firefighter at the tip positions himself between the ladder and the building.

Figs. 13–76 and 13–77. Two-firefighter beam raise

Fig. 13–79. The firefighter at the foot acts as the counterweight.

Two-firefighter flat raise. Once the ladder reaches the desired location by the footer, it can be raised flat. The ladder is positioned flat with both feet lying on the ground. The footer positions his or her feet onto the bottom rung or onto both rails of the ladder. Then he or she crouches with arms extended to grab a forward rung of the ladder. A firefighter's physical makeup determines which rung is feasible and comfortable to grab. As the ladder is lifted and raised, the footer maintains the position and leans slightly back to counterweight and assist in lifting the ladder. As the ladder approaches the vertical position, the footer removes one foot from the ladder and places it behind him or her for balance.

The firefighter raising the ladder checks again for overhead obstructions, then raises the ladder. He or she walks at a steady pace sliding hands up the ladder's rails to raise it to the vertical position. When walking the beams of the ladder up, the firefighter slides his or her arms up the ladder and uses leg muscles to drive the ladder upward. Firefighters should not bounce the ladder up while sliding the rails because a slip could mean an injury.

Many firefighters prefer to walk the rungs up to raise a ladder. This has a few problems:

- As the firefighter proceeds up the rungs, for a moment only one hand balances the ladder, which introduces a tendency to twist. If the firefighter were operating on uneven terrain, a slip could cause a loss of grip and injury.

- A firefighter walking up the rungs normally watches his or her hand position on the rungs and takes his or her eyes off the objective and tip of the ladder.

- When the ladder rises rapidly, it often bounces and twists as a firefighter proceeds up the rungs (figs. 13–80, and 13–81).

Now that the ladder is vertical, both firefighters assume positions on opposite sides of the ladder with one foot against the ladder's butt to steady it and the other placed behind them for balance. They can untie the halyard now and extend the ladder to its objective.

Fig. 13–80. The footer reaches the bottom rungs.

Fig. 13–81. Slide your hands up the rails of the ladder.

Two-firefighter flat-arm carry and raise. Some U.S. fire departments must adapt daily to peculiar hazards such as catenary wires strung across roadways and intersections for light rail train cars. These overhead obstructions make raising ladders difficult because they carry a lot of voltage. Fortunately there is a method for dealing with these situations.

Because ladders can be stored horizontally on some ladder company apparatus, the firefighters can position the ladder between them for removal. As the balance point approaches the firefighters, they grab the ladder and begin walking to the rear of the apparatus. Once they remove the ladder from the apparatus, the firefighters bend their arms and carry the ladder flat to its objective. If the ladder were not stored flat, the firefighters could pick it up, rotate it into the flat position, lift it at the balance point.

As the firefighters approach the objective, they raise the tip with the forward hand or the one nearest the structure. The back hand grips the ladder firmly and drives the ladder forward and up to assist in the lift. Some firefighters perform a short dip with the tip as they begin the raise, which gains momentum. As the ladder reaches the building, the firefighters bring it to the vertical position, brace it, and prepare to extend the fly if needed (figs. 13–82 and 13–83).

The flat-arm raise is difficult with large ladders and must be practiced before fireground use. It can cause back injuries and its use should be limited. The flat-arm raise is extremely valuable for rescuing a victim hanging to a windowsill by his or her arms when firefighters arrive. Getting the ladder underneath the victim provides support and allows the victim to assist in the rescue.

Fig. 13–82. Both firefighters are positioned at the ladder's balance point.

Fig. 13–83. Raise the tip toward the objective.

Three-firefighter evolutions

When three firefighters begin ladder work, they must perform safely and with proper communication and teamwork. One firefighter must lead the operation. The firefighter at the ladder's butt normally leads and gives commands when performing ladder evolutions. He or she leads because the ladder's butt reaches the structure first. Once the ladder is raised, he or she controls the halyard and raising the ladder.

Three-firefighter suitcase/shoulder carry. The methods to transport a ladder described in the two-firefighter carries also apply to the three-firefighter carry, with one exception. The additional firefighter goes on the same side of the ladder at the center. To perform the shoulder carry when firefighters differ in height, the tallest goes at an end, not in the center. This way the ladder's weight distributes equally among all three firefighters (figs. 13–84 and 13–85).

Fig. 13–84. Three-firefighter suitcase carry

Fig. 13–85. Three-firefighter shoulder carry

Three-firefighter flat-arm carry. Three firefighters can also carry a ladder in flat position with their arms. Two of them go on the same side of the ladder at the tip and the butt. The third goes on the opposite side in the center. All three firefighters crouch onto one knee. On command, they lift the ladder off the ground using their leg muscles. They can place their hands on either the rung or beam, whichever is more comfortable and helps maintain their grip while they lift and transport the ladder (fig. 13–86).

Fig. 13–86. Three-firefighter flat-arm carry. (Courtesy of Joseph Alvarez)

If the ladder were removed from a ladder apparatus with rear horizontal storage, the two firefighters would position themselves on one side of the ladder with the third on the opposite side. Remember, a ladder should be carried butt first to the fireground and tip first upon return to the apparatus. This allows it to slide back into the apparatus storage compartment easier.

Three-firefighter flat-shoulder carry. The three-firefighter shoulder carry's steps resemble that of the flat carry, except the ladder rides on top of the firefighters' shoulders during transport. The positioning is the same as the flat-arm carry, with two firefighters on one side and the other at the center of the ladder. All three lift the ladder from the ground to waist level, then continue lifting upward. Now, they can use both arms in lifting and placing it onto their shoulders (fig. 13–87).

Fig. 13–87. Three-firefighter flat-shoulder carry. (Courtesy of Joseph Alvarez)

Some firefighters learned to face the direction opposite where the ladder is needed (face the tip because the butt goes to the fire building). When the ladder reaches about chest level, the firefighters pivot and rotate by turning into the ladder and placing a shoulder under it. Now they face the butt ready to transport. Each method is acceptable, so firefighters should learn and practice both.

Three-firefighter beam raise. The same method of raising the ladder described in the two-firefighter raise applies to the three-firefighter raise, with one exception. The additional firefighter, depending on physical size, either walks the ladder up in front of or behind the firefighter raising the ladder to the vertical position. The tallest firefighter goes behind the other firefighter or toward the tip. This way, both firefighters can reach the ladder and raise it in unison. If the taller firefighter were in front during the raise, the smaller firefighter could be unable to reach and assist in the lift.

Another option is for the additional firefighter to go in the middle of the ladder and face the tip. When the ladder rises, this firefighter pulls the ladder toward them, self-assisting in the lift. As the ladder passes his or her position, this firefighter turns toward the base and either maintains a position on the outside of the ladder assisting in balancing the ladder or follows the raising firefighter assisting in the raise (fig. 13–88).

Fig. 13–88. Three-firefighter beam raise. (Courtesy of Joseph Alvarez)

Three-firefighter flat raise. The same method of raising the ladder described in the two-firefighter raise applies to the three-firefighter raise, with one exception. The additional firefighter goes at the ladder's tip alongside the other firefighter. They raise the ladder using either a hand-over-hand motion with their inside hands on the rungs or they slide the rail of the ladder on their shoulders, using their leg muscles to assist them. Both firefighters must use caution while raising the ladder. They could strike the other's arm or bump one another. Either action could cause a slip or mishap. Many fire departments rely on this raise for the three-section, 35-ft (10.7-m) ladder becoming more prevalent on fire apparatus (figs. 13–89 and 13–90).

Four-firefighter evolutions

When four firefighters begin ladder work, they must perform safely as a team and communicate properly. One firefighter must lead the operation. A firefighter at the ladder's butt usually leads and gives commands because the ladder's butt reaches structures first. He or she controls the halyard and raising the ladder. Firefighters should "step off left"—start on the left foot when commanded to move to the building by the ladder.

Figs. 13–89 and 13–90. Three-firefighter flat raise. (Courtesy of Joseph Alvarez)

Four-firefighter flat-arm carry. Four firefighters can also carry a ladder in the flat position with their arms. Two firefighters go on each side of the ladder, two at the tip and two at the butt. All four crouch onto one knee. On command, they lift the ladder off the ground with their leg muscles. They may place their hands either on the rung or beam, whichever is more comfortable and helps maintain a grip on the ladder during lifting and transport (fig. 13–91).

Fig. 13–91. Four-firefighter flat-arm carry. (Courtesy of Joseph Alvarez)

If the ladder were removed from a ladder apparatus with rear horizontal storage, two firefighters would go at the ladder's tip, and the other two would go at the butt. Remember, the butt should lead to the fireground,

and the tip should lead on return to the apparatus. This makes sliding back into the apparatus storage compartment easier.

Four-firefighter shoulder carry. The four-firefighter shoulder carry's steps resemble those of the flat carry, except the ladder goes on top of the firefighters' shoulders during transport. The positioning is the same as the flat-arm carry with two firefighters at the tip and two at the butt. All four lift the ladder from the ground to waist level, then continue lifting the ladder upward. Now, they can use both their arms in the lift and placing the ladder on their shoulders.

FIREGROUND NOTE

It might be necessary to push down and dent ornamental or sheet metal ridge vents for a roof ladder to sit properly on a roof. If this doesn't work, use a Halligan tool to make two holes on the opposite side of the roof's ridge so the roof ladder's hooks can secure onto the roof.

Some firefighters learned to face away from where the ladder is needed (face the tip because the butt arrives first at the fire building). When the ladder reaches about chest level, the firefighters pivot and rotate by turning into the ladder and placing their shoulders under the ladder. Now they face the butt ready to transport the ladder. Each method is acceptable and should be learned and practiced (fig. 13–92).

Fig. 13–92. Four-firefighter shoulder carry. (Courtesy of Joseph Alvarez)

ROOF LADDER OPERATIONS

Firefighters often ventilate structures with steep roof angles and ones covered with ice or snow. Working on these structures without a roof ladder can be dangerous and should be avoided. If there is no way to work from a roof ladder, position an aerial or tower ladder to the roof for a work platform.

A **roof ladder** is a straight ladder with solid aluminum or steel hooks attached to the tip. The hooks are mounted in a small bracket with a tension spring wrapped around the base of the hook and a square stop. To release the hooks, a firefighter must apply moderate downward pressure then turn the hook 90 degrees either away or toward himself or herself. This motion resembles pushing the hook down toward the base of the ladder and spinning it a quarter turn. Firefighters usually hold the ladder about waist level to release the hooks, but a firefighter can also perform this tactic while the ladder is flat on the ground. Applying pressure to the hooks with the inside portion of a boot might release them. Once the hooks are turned, pressure is released and the hooks spring up into a locking position inside their holding brackets. Roof ladder hooks secure the ladder to a structure's roof by allowing the hooks' tips to bite into the roof on the opposite side of the roof's ridge (fig. 13–93).

Fig. 13–93. Roof ladder hooks

There are a few methods to raise a roof ladder to a fire building's roof. The method depends on the size of the roof ladder and the type, angle, and length of the roof.

Single-firefighter evolution

It might be possible to raise an 18- or 20-ft (5.5- or 6-m) roof ladder from the ground to the roof of a one-story structure with a steep pitch. A firefighter transports the ladder to the structure, lays it down, and extends the roof hooks to the open position. Next, the firefighter

performs a single raise. When the ladder leans onto the roofline in the proper climbing angle, the firefighter lifts up the ladder's base and slides the ladder onto the roof and over the ridge. He or she must pull down on the ladder to ensure the roof hooks have bitten into the roof and will support the firefighter's weight.

Another ladder is brought to the base of the building and raised next to the roof ladder. Now the firefighter climbs the ladder and transfers to the roof ladder at roof level. With this method of sliding the roof ladder upward, firefighters often prefer to slide it flat so both rails ride up the roof. They can use both arms and push as the ladder slides upward.

When tall structure must have an extension ladder to reach the roof, another method must be used. After the extension ladder reaches proper climbing position, the firefighter opens the roof ladder's hooks and the ladder rises next to the extension ladder. Next, the firefighter may place the roof ladder on one beam and next to the extension ladder with the roof hooks facing away from the extension ladder. Now the firefighter climbs up the extension ladder. When he or she reaches the roof ladder's balance point, he or she places a shoulder between the rungs. The ladder now balances on the firefighter's shoulder as he or she begins to climb.

As the firefighter reaches the roofline, the roof ladder begins to pivot over the roof's edge. The firefighter pushes the roof ladder up the roof either on the beam or laid flat. Once it goes over the roof's ridge, the firefighter pulls back on the ladder, sinking the roof hooks into the ridge. Care must be taken while pulling back because the ridge could have a **ridge vent** made of fibers and shingles that tear. Firefighters must ensure the hooks bite into the roof and will be secure so the roof ladder can carry the weight of firefighters on the roof.

Two-firefighter evolution

The roof ladder must be raised after an extension ladder is in position. One firefighter climbs to a position near the top of the extension ladder that allows him or her to transfer the ladder from the extension ladder to its locked position on the roof. This firefighter locks into the ladder with a leg-lock maneuver or safety belt. Now the firefighter on the ground raises the roof ladder to the firefighter on the ladder.

There are two common methods: Have the roof hooks open or have them closed. There are pros and cons to both, but both are acceptable. Raising the ladder from the ground to the firefighter on the extension ladder may be done a few ways. The firefighter on the ground can remain on the ground and transfer the ladder up using his or her arms. Or, the firefighter on the ground may first hand the roof ladder up to the firefighter on the ladder. Then, the firefighter on the ground may climb up the extension ladder and assist with the roof ladder's raise and balance.

Roof ladders are removed in the reverse fashion. Now and then roof hooks set deeply into a roof and are difficult to release. Use caution when trying to release them. Apply steady pressure to the ladder. Striking the ladder with a hand tool to release it could damage to the ladder.

VENTING A WINDOW WITH A LADDER

It is not the preferred method to vent windows, but venting a window with a portable ladder is often necessary because of manpower shortages, a lack of time, or numerous windows needing to be ventilated. There are a few methods, all of which start with raising or positioning the ladder's tip in contact with the top third of the window. Striking a window high has two advantages. First, the window might break easier as a result of being weakened or distorted by heat. Second, heat, smoke, and gases rise and collect at the ceiling and mushroom downward. Breaking the window high can help release these elements quickly (fig. 13–94).

Fig. 13–94. Venting a window using a ladder

Extension ladder throw

The extension ladder can be used in the beam or flat position to break a window. Some firefighters think the weight and structural makeup of throwing the beam into the window works better. Others think the flat position covers more surface area and breaks more glass. Both techniques work.

To begin, a firefighter raises the ladder vertically to the proper level near the top third of the window. Then the firefighter at the ladder's base forcefully drops or pushes the ladder into the window. As the ladder strikes the window, the firefighter removes his or her hands from the ladder to avoid glass that could slide down the beams. His or her hands remain in the vicinity of the ladder in case the ladder bounces off the window. This way, he or she can grab the ladder's rungs or beams to maintain its stability. Done properly, this often breaks the window's center sash and bottom windowpane as well. Sometimes it takes one or two attempts to break a window sufficiently for ventilation.

After ventilating windows with a ladder and completing fireground duties, the firefighter inspects the ladder for embedded glass shards, structural damage, and thermal damage from vented heat or fire.

Roof ladder throw

A firefighter may also use a roof ladder to ventilate a window. The roof ladder's two large roof hooks attached to its tips resemble firefighting hooks and pike poles. To perform this tactic, a firefighter first opens the roof hooks and places the ladder at the proper height. Then, the firefighter at the ladder's base throws or pushes the ladder into the window.

After the ladder breaks the top pane, the firefighter has a few options. If the window frame is wood, the firefighter places the ladder's hooks onto the center sash. Next, he or she picks up the base of the ladder and gives it a slight tug or pull backwards or out of the window. Usually this additional pressure lets the hooks break the bottom pane of glass and removes the center sash of the window. If the ground's terrain is bad, the firefighter avoids this method and instead drops the ladder into the window again to complete ventilation of the lower panes of glass.

Remember, firefighters must use all eye protection and personal protective equipment when performing these tactics.

Ladders

FIREFIGHTER I

Chapter 13

FIREGROUND NOTE

If there are not enough firefighters to perform the flat raise with the Bangor ladder, consider using the building to physically butt the ladder as it is raised.

ADDITIONAL LADDER TYPES

Three-section extension ladder

Increasing numbers of fire departments are placing three-section extension ladders onto first-line apparatus for many reasons. Most departments put them on apparatus to meet standards and guidelines for ratings, while others encounter manpower shortages. Those departments think having a large ladder on the apparatus on scene immediately lets them handle any situation. Plus, many bedroom communities are experiencing growth in new and higher townhouses and condominiums.

Firefighters must be aware of three-section ladder characteristics before using it on the fireground. Most noticeable about the short-looking, three-section ladder is how heavy and bulky it is with the added fly section. Also, pulling down the halyard raises both fly sections and raises the ladder 28 in. (71 cm) compared with the 14 in. (36 cm) of regular extension ladders. Before climbing the ladder, a firefighter must ensure both fly sections are locked in place. Sometimes these ladders lock only one fly and require halyard adjustments to lock the other fly. Firefighters have suffered severe injuries using this ladder when it was not properly locked.

Firefighters may raise the three-section ladder in a beam- or flat-raise evolution. Three firefighters should be used if they are available. Once the ladder is vertical, two firefighters position themselves on the ladder's sides or beams. They place both hands out of danger on the back beam. Remember, this ladder has two moving fly sections that shouldn't be held during the raise. The firefighters place their feet behind them, not near the front base of the ladder, because the fly sections might strike the ground if something were to go wrong during the raise. The third firefighter goes behind the ladder

at the base to control the halyard. He or she ensures both sets of dogs are locked once the ladder rises to the proper position.

Bangor or pole ladder

The **Bangor** or **pole ladder** is a large extension ladder that has a permanently attached support pole hinged and mounted to each side of the bed section. Firefighters use these poles to assist in raising, lowering, and stabilizing the ladder. These ladders are normally raised only in a flat-raise evolution because of the position of the support poles. In emergencies, the ladder may be raised with the beam-raise evolution, but only one support pole can be used. The ladder should be raised flat and then pivoted to its desired location once the ladder is raised.

The support poles on the ladder's sides are usually attached to the beams with a pivoting bracket near the top of the bed section and either a clevis or cotter pin and mounting rod at the base of the bed section. A firefighter must remove the pin and lift the pole from the rod to release it. Next, he or she reattaches the pin to the rod to reduce the chance of slipping on it. These pins are often attached to a short chain or cable so they remain attached to the ladder and won't become lost.

Once the support poles are released, the firefighters at the base of these poles remove them. Next, they bring them to the vertical position if room allows or bring them up and around in a semihorizontal position to two firefighters near the center of the ladder. Once these firefighters have the support poles, they walk back past the ladder's tip to the ends of the poles. These two firefighters at the base of the poles are ready to assist in the lift by walking forward and pushing upward with the poles. They must keep the spur attached to the base of the poles between their fingers and palm up as they raise the ladder to avoid injuries (figs. 13–95 and 13–96).

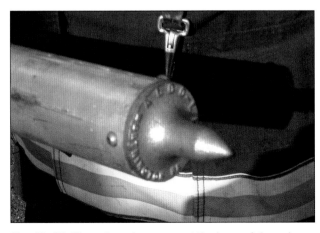

Fig. 13–95. There is a sharp spur at the base of the poles.

Fig. 13–96. Keep the spur between your fingers as you raise the ladder.

With two firefighters at the ladder's tip, one at the base, and two on the support poles, the ladder is ready to be raised. The firefighter at the base foots the ladder and gives the command to raise it. In most instances with the flat Bangor raise, this firefighter positions himself or herself on the ladder as a counterweight. The two firefighters at the tip begin to walk forward, use their arms in a hand-over-hand motion, and raise the ladder. Most of the time, these firefighters position one hand on the rung and the other on the beam.

The two firefighters on the support poles are positioned to the outside of the poles with one hand holding the butt end as described above and the other arm extended up onto the pole at a comfortable position (fig. 13–97).

Fig. 13–97. Two firefighters at the tip, one at the base, and two on the poles.

As the ladder rises, the firefighters push the support poles forward and walk with the poles. They must advance at the same rate as the firefighters raising the tip of the ladder, not running or gaining too much momentum. If they go too fast, the ladder can get away from the firefighters at the tip and cause the ladder to become unstable. If the ladder is being raised properly, all the firefighters should feel about the same pressure or weight throughout most of the lift. Initially, the firefighters on the support poles don't feel a lot of pressure or weight, but this changes once the ladder begins to gain height and the angle increases.

When the ladder is vertical, one firefighter on the support poles proceeds to the side of the ladder with the pole. The other firefighter moves more toward the center of the ladder in line with the beam with the support pole. Now both firefighters are stabilizing the ladder at a 90-degree angle. The firefighter on the side of the ladder controls the ladder's side-to-side movement while the firefighter in front of the ladder controls the front-to-back movement (fig. 13–98).

As the ladder is being raised vertically with the halyard, the pressure on the support poles increases and the firefighters holding the poles maintain their positions and balance the ladder. Next, as the ladder lowers into the building, the firefighter on the front support pole leans back into the pole and assists in the ladder's speed and descent. Now that the ladder is positioned and needs no further adjustments, the two firefighters with the support poles walk toward the building. They place the poles toward the back of the ladder and rest them on the ground.

Fig. 13–98. One support pole to the side and another toward the center stabilize the ladder.

The support poles are not designed to act as an outrigger and carry the ladder's weight. Use caution when positioning the poles because poles angled far from the ladder can cause problems. An unsuspecting firefighter could walk into the pole or an advancing hoseline could knock it out of position.

Ladders

FIREFIGHTER I

Chapter 13

Folding ladder

The **folding ladder**, commonly called the **closet**, **attic**, or **scissor ladder**, can do more than provide access. If a firefighter were trapped or injured in a basement, the ladder could be lowered through a small cellar window and function as a stretcher. The firefighter would roll onto it and be attached with tubular webbing or hose straps. Then the ladder could slide out of the basement. Sometimes it is necessary to remove an injured firefighter's self-contained breathing apparatus from his or her back and put it between his or her legs. Remember, the face piece must remain attached to the firefighter to deliver fresh air. Repositioning the SCBA should allow enough clearance to slide the firefighter through the small window (figs. 13–99 and 13–100).

For a firefighter facing burned-out floors or a firefighter trapped in the floor, a closet ladder might be able to span the joists to reach the firefighter or distribute the weight of the rescuing firefighters. In addition, if a firefighter were to fall through the floor and into the floor below, firefighters could bring a closet ladder through the building and lower into the hole to reach the firefighter. Once the closet ladder is open, it does not matter which end enters the hole. The ladder usually has adjustable feet at one end and a square end design at the tip. This enables the ladder to sit evenly on either end when placed on a level surface. Plus, once weight is put on the rungs, the ladder can support it in either position, upright or upside down.

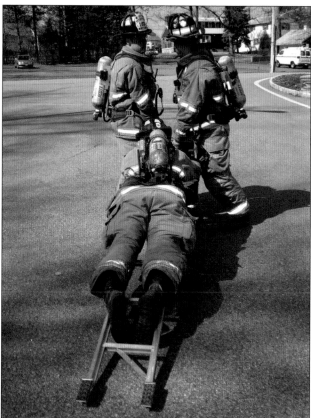

Figs. 13–99 and 13–100. Using a folding ladder as a rescue device

MISCELLANEOUS LADDER USES

There are numerous other uses for ladders on the fireground, and often firefighters develop ways to use them while operating at a fire or emergency scene. The following is a short list of ways ladders can be used:

- An exhaust fan can attach to a ladder outside a window to assist in ventilation efforts.

- A ladder covered with salvage tarps, runners, or plastic can function as a chute to divert water during salvage operations.

- Ladders placed on stanchions can serve as barriers.

- Two short ladders placed on opposite sides of a fence provide access to both areas.

- A ladder can prop open or act as a safety bracket for large roll-up and garage doors.

- A ladder can be a bridge from roof to roof. These ladders should remain closed or in bedded position to offer the most structural stability and load-carrying capacities.

- A ladder can be used as a hoisting point or high anchor point for technical rescue situations and firefighter removals.

- Lights attached to ladders add additional overhead lighting.

- Ladders can latch together to form a square frame for salvage covers to become a collection area for hazmat operations or a water-holding tank.

- Two ladders on opposite walls with a plank supported by each ladder's rungs can span the distance to create a work platform.

For firefighters to operate safely on the fireground, they must comprehend and understand the evolutions and tactics described in this chapter. Firefighting is a hazardous, unavoidably dangerous activity, and operating unsafely with ladders increases the risk of a serious injury or death. It is each firefighter's responsibility to operate within safety limits during any ladder activity.

NOTES

1. Mathew Rush, "Ground Ladder Chocks," *Fire Engineering*, March 2007.

2. Michael Ciampo, "The Arm Lock Maneuver," *Fire Engineering*, March 2006.

Ladders

FIREFIGHTER I

Chapter 13

LESSON FROM THE FIREGROUND

Over the course of the years, having worked in two "big city" fire departments in some very active units, I've seen that learning from actual rescues and firefighting experiences is a large part of the educational process of becoming a seasoned firefighter. During some of these experiences some minor mishaps or "close calls" were averted, mostly due to luck and training. After experiencing some of these ladder rescues and close calls as well as reading and hearing about others who experienced similar mishaps during ladder evolutions, I felt there was a need for additional training and tactics on ladder operations.

Not long after presenting a "Street-Smart Ladders" hands-on training seminar which reviewed some of the procedures in this ladder chapter, I received one of the most rewarding gifts of my career, a manila envelope in the mailbox. I opened it and sat in awe as I read about the heroic act the letter described and the photos that accompanied it. Briefly, it read:

"As the first due units arrived, they were greeted with heavy fire on the 1st and 2nd floors that was rapidly extending to the 3rd floor of a wood frame dwelling. In addition, seven occupants had already jumped from the 2nd floor and were lying on the ground with a multitude of injuries. As firefighter Kevin Galligan proceeded down the narrow alleyway, a distraught woman was dangling an infant out the window on the 3rd floor. After verbally communicating with the woman, he began to raise a 35-ft (10.7-m) ladder with the assistance of Lieutenant Daniel Santry. Firefighter Galligan proceeded up the ladder and removed the infant, handing her down to the Lieutenant, and then entered the dwelling and removed her mother, helping her safely to the ground.

Once they got to the ground the woman informed the pair that two of her teenage children were still trapped inside. Without hesitation, the two then ascended the ladder in search of the children. The first child was quickly located and removed and placed into the bucket of Tower 2. As the two searched, they located the second child and dragged her back to the window, just as their air tanks were depleted. Now the duo had to exit and allow Firefighter Eonas to enter the window in order to remove the last child."

After reading the unit citation report, a personal letter followed. The letter briefly stated:

"As a fellow instructor and newly promoted Lieutenant, I would like to inform you that the information you were instructing was accurate and very useful to me at this fire. The methods I found particularly helpful were the modified leg lock (HELL), the arm lock maneuver, Body to the Building while raising the ladder, and victim removal operations. These methods made a lot of sense to me and utilizing them assisted me in completing the successful rescues and may very well have saved some lives. From one firefighter and instructor to another, thank you. The methods and tactics you are teaching are right-on and street smart knowledge that firefighters need. I appreciate all that you're doing for the fire service."

This letter is one that any fire instructor would hope to receive and one that encourages me to keep on teaching ladder techniques to the fire service. Hopefully, some of the information in this ladder chapter will also be able to help you in your firefighting career.

QUESTIONS

1. Identify the primary functions of portable ground ladders.

2. What is the minimum distance that firefighters should maintain from overhead electrical wires when raising a portable ground ladder?

3. What is the main function of a heat-sensor label?

4. A firefighter should hold onto what part of a portable ground ladder while climbing and descending to maintain three points of contact?

5. Generally, there are four classifications of portable ground ladders. A roof ladder is classified as what type of ladder?

6. When working from the side of a ladder to remove burned siding, a firefighter should perform a leg-lock maneuver. Which leg does the firefighter use to perform this tactic if he is working from the right side of the ladder?

7. Prior to climbing an extension ladder, the first firefighter to climb the ladder should ensure that what are in the locked position?

8. What should a firefighter do while cleaning an aluminum ground ladder to ensure that soot, ash, and debris are removed from the inside of each rung?

9. What are the horizontal cross members of a portable ground ladder called?

10. How frequently should portable ground ladders be inspected?

11. Why is it important to regularly check the rails and rungs of wooden ground ladders?

12. Identify and explain a critical safety factor when placing an aluminum ground ladder against a building with aluminum siding.

13. What main function is served by a firefighter footing or butting a ground ladder?

14. Prior to placing a ground ladder in position, what should a firefighter do?

15. What quick reference can a firefighter use to identify the proper length of ground ladder to reach a desired floor level?

16. What part of a ground ladder should be carried first to the positioning point and why?

17. What steps should a firefighter follow to release the hooks of a roof ladder for use?

18. Which firefighter gives the commands when carrying or raising a portable ground ladder?

19. Identify the normal range of a ladder's angle when the butt is positioned one-fourth the distance from a building.

20. When a portable ground ladder is raised to a flat roof, how many rungs should there be above the roof surface?

21. When two firefighters are performing a suitcase carry, where should the portable ground ladder be positioned?

22. When raising a portable ground ladder equipped with tormentor poles, where should the spike on the end of the tormentor pole be placed?

Ventilation

by John Mittendorf   with Michael N. Ciampo
and Kurt Zingheim

This chapter provides required knowledge items for the following
NFPA Standard 1001 Job Performance Requirements:

FFI 5.3.11

FFI 5.3.12

FFI 5.3.20

This chapter contains Skill Drills. When you see this icon, refer to your Skill Drill book for step-by-step instructions.

OBJECTIVES

Upon completion of this chapter, you should be able to do the following:

- Define the term ventilation in regard to fire service operations
- Describe principles of venting for fire and venting for life
- Describe the importance of smoke and fire gases in relation to ventilation
- Identify those items needed to perform an effective ventilation size-up
- Identify and describe seven types of ventilation
- Identify common construction features in a building that aid in ventilation operations
- Describe the proper methods for venting a window
- Identify the equipment used to perform ventilation
- Identify the firefighting tools used to vent windows and roofs
- Describe the proper procedures for venting flat and pitched roofs
- Identify safety procedures to use when performing a roof ventilation
- Identify the type of roof cuts used in ventilation
- Describe the procedures for performing a "trench/strip cut of a roof"
- Identify the hazards associated with venting truss constructed roofs
- Identify tactical considerations for venting five types of occupancies

INTRODUCTION

Similar to the term firefighting, the word ventilation has several definitions and may be successfully performed using a variety of operations and techniques. In spite of its potential complexity, the word **ventilation** is easily defined and applied to firefighting operations as follows: "Procedures necessary to effect the planned and systematic redirection and removal of fire, smoke, heat, and fire gases from a structure." However, this definition may be too simplistic when we consider that safe, timely, and effective ventilation operations are often performed in hazardous atmospheres and under dangerous conditions.

FFI 5.3.11 Ventilation does not put out fires. However, safe, timely, and effective ventilation is integral to control and extinguish structure fires. According to the International Society of Fire Service Instructors (ISFSI) 2013 *Position Statement on Fire Dynamics Research,* "Fire departments should manage and control openings to the structure to limit fire growth and spread, and to control the flow path of inlet air and fire gases during tactical operations." Controlling ventilation reduces fire development as well as firefighter risk from increased heat release rates.

To understand how fireground conditions dictate the need for ventilation, consider a simple example: An unconfined fire will draw cold air into the bottom of a fire as heated smoke, gases, and air rise vertically. Because the fire is unconfined, it can draw as much cold air (as compared to the heated air from the fire) as necessary to sustain combustion. Any fire must have heat, fuel, and oxygen in the appropriate ratio for combustion.

As our fire utilizes the correct amount of oxygen, heat, and fuel, the result is a free-burning fire. Now, transfer our free-burning fire to a confined room in a building. Initially, the fire has the proper ratio of fuel, heat, and oxygen, which is about 21% in air. As this process continues, the quantity of hot gases and smoke in the room increases, and available oxygen necessary for combustion is reduced. As the oxygen content is reduced below 21%, the burning rate will decrease and the production of smoke and fire gases will increase. The increased smoke will fill the interior of the room and try to exhaust through any available openings.

As the fire continues to burn, the oxygen content will be reduced to about 17%, levels of carbon monoxide and other products of combustion will increase, and temperatures can exceed 1,300°F (704°C). At this point however, another condition will rapidly become significant. As the fire continues to burn, the ratio of heat, fuel, and oxygen becomes unbalanced, with levels of oxygen approaching 13%–15%, which is not adequate to support a free burning fire. When the percentage of oxygen reaches 13%–15%, the fire will begin to smolder due to insufficient oxygen.

Several interesting events will have taken place simultaneously with the fire smoldering and the subsequent reduction of oxygen in the room. First, fire gases will rise vertically until they reach the highest level in the room and then spread horizontally across the underside of the ceiling. Secondly, if this process continues, the structure will become filled with heated smoke and fire gases, offer poor visibility, and develop a level of heat within the structure that can be intolerable for occupants and suppression personnel. At this point, if fireground personnel must enter this environment to conduct a search and/or extinguish this fire, then they are faced with a choice:

- Enter the structure without ventilation and encounter a hot, flammable environment that is dangerous to suppression personnel.

- Use horizontal, pressurized, and/or vertical ventilation to improve visibility, reduce the dangerous concentrations of heat, smoke, and fire gases, and allow suppression personnel to effect a timely and safe extinguishment.

This simple ventilation example points to a common problem. Whether a fire is small or large, smoke, fire gases, and other products of combustion are by-products of any fire and can be expected to be encountered by building occupants and/or suppression personnel.

VENTILATION PRINCIPLES

Some fire departments classify ventilation operations into two basic principles: venting for fire and venting for life.

Venting for fire

Venting for fire assists the engine company's advance and extinguishment of the fire (fig. 14–1). Normally, this type of ventilation is performed and coordinated in unison with the engine company's advance on the fire. Proper communication must be coordinated between the outside and inside firefighting teams when performing this type of ventilation. Venting prematurely or venting prior to the engine company having water and preparing to attack the fire can increase a fire's size and intensity.

Venting for life

Venting for life is accomplished to assist a firefighter's movement into an area where there is a known or suspected life in danger. There is a calculated risk of pulling the fire, smoke, heat, and gases toward this opening; but it is performed to help firefighters reach trapped victims as soon as possible. Again, proper communication must be coordinated between the outside and inside firefighting teams when performing this type of ventilation.

Fig. 14–1. A firefighter using a 6-ft. (1.8-m) hook to vent a window from the outside. Stay upwind and lower than the window using the reach of the tool to avoid fire, smoke, and gases.

SMOKE

FFI 5.3.11 From a simplistic perspective, **smoke** is nothing more than by-products from a fire. Therefore, as the burning substance changes, so does the composition of smoke. This is best illustrated by considering the basic elements of smoke. Smoke is a mixture of three basic elements: solid particulates, liquid particulates (aerosols), and fire gases. Unburned particulates are primarily comprised of the materials that are burning and carbon. These particulates can burn if their ignition temperature is sufficient.

Fire gases are a combination of various gases released by burning materials, and are also capable of burning if their ignition temperature is sufficient. However, fire gases are much more complicated than particulates, as burning materials can yield a wide range of fire gases. Here are common examples of fire gases that are released during the combustion process:

- Carbon monoxide
- Sulfur dioxide
- Hydrogen fluoride
- Hydrogen chloride
- Hydrogen cyanide
- Aldehydes
- Benzene
- Acrolein
- And the list goes on . . .

Firefighters should be aware that all of the aforementioned fire gases can be harmful or fatal to any human. However, if asked to choose the most common and deadly fire gas, an average firefighter would most often choose carbon monoxide. Carbon monoxide is well known for its ability to be present in smoke and cause death by asphyxiation if inhaled in sufficient quantities. However, hydrogen cyanide may be the most dangerous fire gas encountered by fireground personnel. It is estimated that hydrogen cyanide is more than 30 times more toxic than carbon monoxide!

This fact was underscored in 2006 when a firefighter at a "routine" fast-food restaurant fire was hospitalized and diagnosed with toxic levels of cyanide. Interestingly, over the next 14 hours, two additional fires in the same area were responsible for four more firefighters being hospitalized. They were also diagnosed with toxic levels of cyanide, and one of the firefighters suffered a heart attack. These incidents have generated a new look at this common combustion product that may be present in high quantities at structure fires. Let's take a brief look at hydrogen cyanide and its inherent risk to fireground personnel.

Hydrogen cyanide can be found in either a liquid or gas form and is a powerful poison that reduces the capacity of blood to carry oxygen. Bodily organs that are vulnerable to cyanide poisoning are the brain, heart, and central nervous system. The toxicity of hydrogen cyanide is emphasized by its use in gas chambers and as a chemical warfare agent. Unfortunately, hydrogen cyanide is found in common materials such as wool, paper, wood, and cotton. However, it is also found in elevated levels in synthetic materials such as foam, pesticides, plastics, synthetic fibers, polyurethane, fiberglass insulation, and other similar modern materials.

These materials are common in the typical residential structure fire as well as other types of structure fires, resulting in hydrogen cyanide likely being present in readily detectable amounts in smoke from smoldering fires, free-burning fires, and overhaul operations. Stated from another perspective, hydrogen cyanide is an extremely toxic gas that is released during the combustion process from any material that contains nitrogen, which is commonly found in structural occupancies. Although there are numerous other toxic gases released during the combustion process, carbon monoxide and hydrogen cyanide are prime examples of why ventilation should be an initial consideration at structure fires, and a primary reason why fireground personnel should not breathe smoke. That statement applies to structure fires, automobile fires, dumpster fires, and other similar incidents. Toxic gases that are inhaled by fireground personnel give credibility to the phrase "when firefighters breathe smoke, they can die."

Ventilation, therefore, is critical for the survival of both building occupants and firefighters.

GENERAL VENTILATION PROCEDURES

Ventilation operations should be governed by a set of standard operating procedures (SOPs), the values of which determine the course of a ventilation operation. Personnel must know how to accomplish the various types of ventilation operations, tactics, and techniques for a specific fire scenario. Other than actual fireground conditions, there is no substitute for training to help determine how to accomplish these types of operations. Discuss and practice ventilation on a frequent basis. If you do so, basic operations will be automatic at a fire, giving personnel a greater opportunity to focus on the specifics. The fireground provides the opportunity to hone operational skills.

Initial ventilation size-up

When sizing up for ventilation operations, firefighter must ask the following questions:

- What is the type of building and the time of day?

- Is there a fire and, if so, what is its severity?

- Is it a small food-on-the-stove fire that may only require opening a few windows to vent the area or a room-and-contents fire that will need immediate ventilation to assist in firefighting operations?

- What are its extension or auto-exposure possibilities before venting?

- Are any occupants endangered?

- Is immediate ventilation needed?

- Is horizontal or vertical ventilation feasible?

It is crucial to take a few seconds and determine the size and location of the fire and the building type before haphazardly venting.

Building type, age, and characteristics

What type of building is on fire? Suppose it is a multi-story hotel. Depending on conditions, personnel may consider venting the stairs and hallways to aid in evacuation. In some larger multiple dwellings, it may be important to ventilate the roof's **bulkhead**, an extension of the stairwell shaft above the roof, or **scuttle**, a hatch in the roof of a building, to alleviate the mushrooming affects of the smoke and permit residents a means of egress down the interior stairs. It is also wise to consider the age of the building. Does it appear to be an older style of construction? If so, it could be balloon frame construction, and introducing forced air into the building could rapidly extend the fire. In newer contemporary homes, firefighters often see numerous skylights on the roof, which aid in vertical ventilation. Often, factory windows are covered with security mesh or grating, which may delay ventilation operations. It is important for firefighters to be familiar with the basic types of construction and buildings in their response district to help them determine appropriate ventilation operations when a fire occurs.

Location, size, and extension of fire

First, what are the fire's location, size, and extension possibilities? If there is a small rubbish fire on the first floor of a five-story apartment house, going to the roof to cut ventilation openings into the roof may not be vital. It may only be necessary to open the bulkhead or scuttle, relieving the stairwell of smoke and gases, and vent the windows in the immediate fire area. However, if the fire is on the top floor of a five-story apartment house, venting the top floor windows first and then cutting the roof open over the fire is an appropriate tactic (fig. 14–2).

Fig. 14–2. Fire and smoke pushing from the top floor of a five-story building

Fig. 14–3. a) Clay tile roof b) Slate roof c) Wood shingle roof

Type of roof

It is important for firefighters to be familiar with the different types and styles of roofs and construction in their response district (fig. 14–3). In some situations it is vital to know the types of construction on which personnel are working.

Inverted roofs (flat roof construction with a relatively slight pitch that allows water to flow to a roof drain) are normally *spongy*. Firefighters must know how to use the roof construction to their advantage when cutting ventilation openings, and also the approximate time available for ventilation operations. Firefighters must also be familiar with types of roof coverings such as clay tile, slate, wood shingle, and asphalt shingle on a peaked roof of a single-family home or a "built up" roof consisting of successive layers of asphalt and felt paper on the flat roof of a multiple dwelling.

Ventilation

FIREFIGHTER I

Chapter 14

Fig.14–3 (continued). d) Asphalt shingle roof e) Built-up roof

A relatively new type of roof surface is the "rubber roof," a membrane made of synthetic rubber or certain types of plastic. This material is used on flat roofs to provide a more leakage-resistant barrier. They are often laid down using a torch; sometimes the rubber roof itself is ignited, causing a rapidly moving fire with heavy black smoke.

When ventilating a rubber roof, it is beneficial to remove the rubber first before cutting the roof deck below, if possible. This will make the saw more efficient and speed up the ventilation process if using a rotary saw, as the rubber membrane can become entangled in the guard. However, membranes can be easily cut without entanglement if using a chain saw with a sharp chain run at full rpm.

Ladders

Determining the type of building and the roof's pitch helps firefighters determine the type and length of ladders needed for roof access or horizontal ventilation. In some instances, an aerial ladder, a tower ladder, or portable ladders (extension and roof) are needed in ventilation efforts.

Hazards

Often, hazards stand in the way of ventilation operations. For example, consider the problems and solutions necessary if electrical wires or razor wire security measures block ladder placement to a roof (fig. 14–4). Also once on the roof, firefighters must use caution and be aware of any air and light shafts or slipping off of a high pitched roof. In one recent incident, a firefighter removing a scuttle cover received numerous electrical shocks. The occupant of the building was tired of break-ins from the roof, so he or she created a homemade security device. Another hazardous condition may be a chain-link fence or steel fences blocking emergency egress to the adjoining roof.

Fig. 14–4. Caution should always be used when working around electrical lines. They are just one of many hazards on rooftops that can have fatal consequences.

TYPES OF VENTILATION

Firefighters should begin ventilation operations by identifying the direction that smoke, heat, and fire gases will travel to exit the structure. Once the direction of travel has been determined, the appropriate method of ventilation should be used. Ventilation can occur both horizontally and vertically. The two methods most commonly used are natural and mechanical (or forced) ventilation. Normally, both methods are used for vertical or horizontal ventilation of a structure.

Natural ventilation

Natural ventilation at most fire scenes consists of opening up doors, windows, scuttles, and skylights to let the by-products of combustion (smoke, heat, and gases) rise naturally and escape to the outside atmosphere (fig. 14–5). Unfortunately, natural ventilation can be enhanced or limited by prevailing wind currents or atmospheric conditions. This method of ventilation works well when there is a light smoke condition and time to vent the structure out. Small fires such as food on the stove, light ballast odors, or a small rubbish fire may be areas to use natural ventilation procedures.

Fig. 14–5. Natural ventilation

Another process for providing natural ventilation is to cut a hole in a roof to relieve the building of smoke, gases, and heat (fig. 14–6). These elements naturally rise up and out of the ventilation hole. Although the means to cut the hole might be mechanical (power saw), the natural tendency is for smoke, gases, and heat to follow the path of least resistance to the outside atmosphere.

Fig. 14–6. A firefighter venting a roof with a saw.

Mechanical ventilation

SKILL DRILL

FFI 5.3.11 Firefighters often rely on mechanical means to ventilate a structure. The items or systems to provide mechanical ventilation can include an electric, gas, or hydraulic powered exhaust fan or blower; a hoseline to provide hydraulic ventilation; a building's heating, ventilation, and air conditioning (HVAC) system; or a build-

ing's smoke management system (covered in more detail in chapter 30, Fire Protection Systems).

These types of ventilation practices are also referred to as pressurized ventilation. This type of ventilation can be used to assist or replace natural ventilation operations at a fire (fig. 14–7). Mechanical ventilation can enhance horizontal and vertical ventilation operations, but must be used when fireground operations favor its implementation.

Fig. 14–7. Mechanical ventilation

Pressurized ventilation is normally classified into two different types: **negative pressure ventilation (NPV)** and **positive pressure ventilation (PPV)** (fig. 14–8). The following material describes the difference between the two types of ventilation.

Fig. 14–8. A firefighter has set up a PPV fan and checks to ensure that the entire doorway is covered by the flow of air into the building.

Negative pressure ventilation. **FFI 5.3.12** To better examine both negative and positive pressure ventilation, assume that the room in fig. 14–9 will be ventilated. In this example, the room is filled with the various by-products of combustion. The warmer gases rise toward the ceiling, and the cooler gases settle toward the floor (thermal layering), assuming that the door and window are closed. In fig. 14–10 the room is now being ventilated by means of negative pressure. The door has been opened and a blower has been placed inside the window frame, or attached to a ladder on the outside of the building. The blower will be turned on to exhaust the contaminants in the room, coaxing them to the exterior by creating suction within the room.

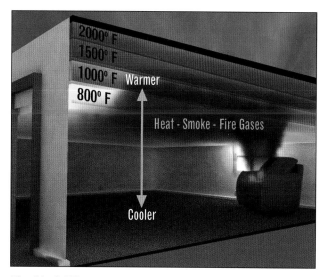

Fig. 14–9. When contaminants fill a room, thermal layering causes the lighter, hotter gases to rise to the top, and the cooler, heavier gases settle to the bottom.

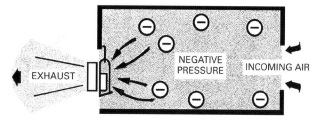

Fig. 14–10. Negative pressure involves placing a blower inside a room to exhaust the contaminants to the exterior.

Although NPV can prove satisfactory, it has several disadvantages, not the least of which is that personnel may be exposed to hazardous contaminants when positioning the blower. Also, when the blower is placed in the window, the suction pulls in air from the room and recirculates some of the exhausted air and gases if the opening around the blower hasn't been sealed with a salvage tarp or plastic. Another problem is that the contaminants from the fire are drawn through the blower, creating a need for additional equipment cleanup and maintenance. Smoke from a wood fire always contains some unburned gases and a fog of unburned tar-like liquids. When plastics burn in a fire, they release hydrocarbon

particulates and heavy dense black smoke particulates. When these materials and particulates come in contact with the blower's mechanisms, they stick and form a film that is often difficult to remove. A buildup of materials or a dirty blower passageway can restrict air flow and prevent the unit from functioning up to its capabilities.

Remember, blowers placed in doorways, windows, or hallways can block pathways in and out of the building and firefighters must use caution to avoid striking them with their heads while operating on the fireground. To position blowers effectively, you must often suspend them in doors or windows using straps, ladders, or other accessories. Blowers placed inside buildings can add to the overall noise and confusion, hindering communications. Gasoline-powered blowers should not be put inside a structure because of the addition of more carbon monoxide into the area. Finally, interior blowers aren't totally efficient at removing all the contaminants from the tops of rooms. Air follows the path of least resistance, normally a straight line, from the fresh air inlet to the blower, which can limit the flow of air in the areas near the ceiling.

Positive pressure ventilation. Over the course of the years, with the continual improvement of firefighting equipment such as portable fans and blowers, positive pressure ventilation (PPV) has been an increasingly used tactic on many firegrounds. In fig. 14–11, the same room is pressurized by a blower placed on the outside of the structure to create PPV. Firefighters using this method of ventilation are forcing fresh, pressurized air into the room, creating a positive pressure within the entire room. As in a balloon, the pressure is equal at the top, bottom, and corners of the room. When the window is opened, it becomes an exhausted opening and the contaminants from all parts of the pressurized room ventilate to the exterior. Remember, implementing PPV effectively depends on controlling the flow of pressurized air between an entrance point and exhaust opening.

Compared with negative pressure ventilation, PPV has some distinct advantages in certain fire situations. First, personnel aren't normally exposed to hazardous interior contaminants while positioning exterior blowers. Second, the contaminants aren't drawn through blowers, thereby reducing the need for cleanup and maintenance. Also, doorways, windows, and halls don't need to be blocked by blowers, reducing the chance of a firefighter striking their head on suspended blowers. Some exterior blowers aren't dependent on additional equipment or accessories for setup, because they are self-propelled and self-sufficient for ventilation operations. Placing these types of blowers into service on the fireground requires fewer personnel to deploy them. Exterior blowers may have a minimal effect on the interior noise levels, but many add to the noise level on the outside of the structure. In addition, if gas blowers are not equipped with the proper exhaust flow extensions, the blowers may add to the carbon monoxide level in the structure.

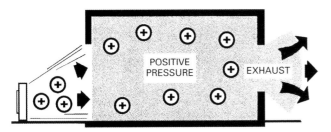

Fig. 14–11. Positive pressure ventilation involves placing a blower outside of a room to force pressurized air inward, thereby driving contaminants to the exterior.

Compared with negative pressure ventilation, PPV is approximately twice as efficient at removing contaminants from a building as long as specific requirements are met. First, exhaust openings should be selected to provide either horizontal or vertical channels for escape of the by-products of combustion. *The exhaust openings should always be created prior to pressurizing the structure or area to be ventilated.* If this is not followed, the pressurized airflow and by-products of combustion have no means of escape from the structure.

Second, it is imperative that the flow and path of pressurized air between an entrance and exhaust opening is controlled to achieve maximum ventilation. If pressurized air is directed from an entrance to an appropriate exhaust opening without being diverted to other openings, contaminants are removed in a minimal amount of time. Simultaneously opening unwanted windows and doors won't facilitate successful PPV operations.

As with many tactics and techniques used on the fireground, a proper size-up must be made to choose the right tactic for the right situation. There are times when PPV may not be a viable option to use on the fireground:

- **Positive pressure ventilation** is used by many departments both just prior to fire attack and for smoke conditions after the fire has been knocked down. Some fire departments, however, use PPV *during* fire attack; this tactic can have deadly results if not conducted properly. If used during fire attack, PPV should only be conducted if the location, extent, and spread of the fire has been established. Additionally, PPV should only be conducted during fire attack if hoselines are in place and operating. The use of PPV during fire attack—which does not meet this criteria—can drive fire at trapped victims and firefighters operating in the building.

- **Balloon construction:** Fire traveling up the walls of these structures could rapidly spread if PPV is initiated before a sufficient exhaust opening is opened. Fire in such structures is difficult to chase if it is in the walls, so use caution in feeding the fire with forced air if fire is in more than one location. In balloon-frame construction, only use PPV if the exhaust opening is opened first.

- **Vent, enter, and search (VES):** Creating an opening to perform VES can become an exhaust opening for PPV and possibly make the area to search untenable for the firefighter.

- **Location of the fire:** If the location of the fire is unknown, carefully analyze the consequences before putting PPV into service. A large structure with a complex layout may make PPV operations unsuccessful if it has multiple exhaust openings.

- **Search and rescue:** While these tactics are deployed, the incident commander must evaluate and size up the fire prior to performing any PPV operations.

For more tactical considerations and PPV operations, refer to the end of this chapter.

EQUIPMENT FOR VENTILATION OPERATIONS

Portable fans, blowers, and smoke ejectors

Although natural ventilation is a viable method, it can be assisted or replaced with portable exhaust fans, blowers, or **smoke ejectors** (figs. 14–12a and 14–12b). These fans and blowers can rapidly force the by-products of combustion out of a contaminated area. They also allow you to use openings remote from heat, smoke, and fire, directing such contaminants through preselected, controlled openings or openings not normally viable by natural means. Portable fans, blowers, and ejectors can overcome interior and exterior temperature differentials, as well as the effects of humidity. Overall, they reduce the time necessary to ventilate a building as compared with natural ventilation.

Fig. 14–12a. Various tools may be used to perform both positive and negative ventilation, such as fans, blowers, smoke ejectors, and fog streams.

Fig. 14–12b. A smoke ejector placed in a doorway to remove smoke via negative pressure ventilation

Hydraulic ventilation

Fog streams from hoseline can also be used for ventilation purposes; this is called **hydraulic ventilation**. Simply direct a fog pattern out of a window so that the resultant venturi action expels the contaminants to the outside atmosphere. You can obtain maximum effectiveness by holding the nozzle a few feet back from the door

or window. Direct the fog pattern toward the window so that it almost fills the entire opening, leaving some room around the edges. Fog stream effectiveness depends on the size of the opening, the area to be ventilated, the size of the nozzle and hose, the quantity of smoke present, and the discharge pressure. Although some textbooks advocate that hydraulic ventilation must be performed within a few feet of a window (after having first placed the nozzle outside the window, opening it to the correct pattern, then moving it inside the building), it can be applied from a further distance away from the window. If the room in front of the nozzle has burned out floor boards or is possibly compromised, the nozzle can be directed from the door opening to the window frame. The resulting pressure from the stream will pull smoke and contaminants from the structure but may take more time to ventilate the structure. It is also important to note that when firefighters are fog venting, they must remain aware of the fire reigniting or **lighting up** behind them, because more air is introduced into the area.

If a smooth bore nozzle is used for initial fire attack, it can still be used to fog vent out the window. The firefighter can crack the nozzle open slightly to make a coarse pattern that fits inside the window frame. This stream will also ventilate the structure but possibly not as good as a fog nozzle.

Hydraulic ventilation is normally accomplished by a firefighter standing in a contaminated environment and using a spray/fog nozzle to direct contaminants from interior to exterior through available openings such as windows. Although this method can be beneficial, a drawback is that it requires a firefighter to stand in the contaminants while they are being exhausted to the exterior.

For more information on fog venting, see chapter 16, Fire Streams.

HVAC systems

Many multistory buildings use **heating, ventilation, air conditioning (HVAC) systems** to control the environment inside the structure. Such systems draw in outside air, change it to the desired temperature, circulate it, and exhaust it to the exterior. It is possible to use an HVAC system to rid a building of contaminants; however, doing so depends on the capabilities of the system and the expertise of the personnel operating it. It is imperative that the capabilities and operational techniques of a particular system be thoroughly understood, because an HVAC system is also capable of spreading contaminants and fire to uninvolved portions. Initially, during a fire, firefighters must determine if the system was automatically shut down by its safety overrides. All other operations should be handled by the appropriate building engineer or other similar responsible person in conjunction with firefighters.

VENTILATION PRIORITIES

FFI 5.3.11 Integral to any ventilation operation is determining appropriate priorities. The top priorities in any ventilation operation are improving the interior environment to aid in evacuation and increase a victim's chance of living and enhancing the working environment for suppression personnel. Ventilation operations also reduce fire loss and damages to the structure and its contents. The priority of specific ventilation operations is predicated on fireground conditions. Normal ventilation operations are usually performed using a horizontal or vertical ventilation method.

Horizontal ventilation

FFI 5.3.11 For reasons of ease and safety, horizontal ventilation is the most popular method. It is often accomplished simply by opening doors and windows. Using horizontal ventilation to remove heat, smoke, and fire gases can be effective; however, its effectiveness depends on the size of the opening and its proximity to the contaminants. Horizontal ventilation does not take advantage of the natural vertical path of heated gases and smoke. It also has a minimal effect on the hottest portion of a room (ceiling), where most flashovers originate. Therefore, horizontal ventilation will ventilate that portion around the opening (open door or window) but could have a minimal effect on a flashover.

Before using horizontal avenues, consider these factors regarding wind and fire location:

1. Determine whether the direction of wind could carry contaminants to uninvolved areas of the fire building or exposures. If the building has multiple stories and windows that will be opened on the lower floors, will the direction of smoke then contaminate the upper floors?

2. Consider the speed or force of the wind. When windows are opened on the windward side, will the wind accelerate the fire and enhance extension?

3. Open the windows on the leeward side of the building first. Windows on the windward side can then be opened to allow the wind to force contaminants from the structure (fig. 14–13).

Fig. 14–13. When the wind can be used for horizontal ventilation, open the leeward windows before the windward windows.

4. Opening windows close to the seat of the fire is a top priority. This provides ventilation to the fire area and allows the expanding gases and steam from fire-suppression operations to escape. It also reduces the chances of the fire, heat, and gases from lighting up overhead or wrapping around the nozzle team, because they are escaping through controlled openings.

5. Remember, prematurely opening windows in a fire area can increase the supply of oxygen and cause the fire to accelerate. Therefore, coordinate communication between the hoseline's advance and ventilation operations to maintain a safe working environment.

Once windows in the fire area have been opened, open others away from the fire area if doing so ventilates other contaminated areas without enhancing extension. Firefighters should remove blinds, curtains, and shades when opening windows to ensure that they won't restrict the removal of contaminants. In addition, it is vital to ensure that screens are removed, because they can restrict the movement of air by at least 50%.

When firefighters open **double-hung** or **casement windows**, there are normally two rules to follow. If there is a light wind blowing toward the ventilation opening, the window can be opened in the following manner: two-thirds down from the top and one-third up from the bottom (fig. 14–14). Doing this allows some fresh cool air to enter the bottom of the window while the hot contaminated air exits at the top. When there is no prevalent wind, the windows may only need to be pulled down from the top to allow the room to ventilate. Pivoting windows must be opened according to their design. If a window can't be opened, you may need to break or force it open.

Fig. 14–14. A double-hung window opened two-thirds down from the top and one-third up from the bottom

Horizontal ventilation can be enhanced by mechanical means. If multiple areas need ventilation, ventilate each area by using doors as partitions to reduce the size of each. This maximizes the flow of fresh air through each area to be ventilated. When opening these doors, remember to wedge or chock them open so that they don't inadvertently close.

Vertical ventilation

FFI 5.3.12 Depending on conditions and building construction features, vertical ventilation can be the preferred method when the heated products of combustion rise and collect at the highest levels of the structure (fig. 14–15). Vertical ventilation takes advantage of the natural travel path of heated contaminants and ventilates the area that needs it most—the ceiling area, which prevents mushrooming. This is the common term for when contaminants collect at the highest level of a structure and deflect downward, or bank down, onto lower floors.

Firefighters should try to open a vertical artery to displace these contaminants. This decreases both the amount of explosive gases, heat, and smoke collecting at the structure's upper levels and the chances of fire extension. In addition, the release of these by-products also pulls in and introduces cooler fresh air at the lowest levels. This can improve conditions at the floor level and assist firefighters in their fire attack operation.

Vertical ventilation permits firefighters to proceed and perform a more thorough search for victims and fire extension on the floors above the fire. It also relieves the interior hallways and stairwell of smoke, which can assist in the evacuation process.

Note that not all fires require vertical ventilation; a small rubbish fire in a structure doesn't require immediately cutting the roof open to provide vertical ventilation. Firefighters must use an appropriate size-up to decide which ventilation tactic to perform. Vertical ventilation takes additional time, staffing, and equipment for completion, and can also place ventilation personnel in a dangerous location (over a fire).

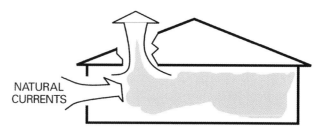

Fig. 14–15. Vertical ventilation takes advantage of natural convection currents.

VENTILATION USING NATURAL CONSTRUCTION FEATURES

It will always be easier for firefighters to use the natural construction features of a structure for initial ventilation operations. Building features such as windows, scuttle covers, bulkhead or penthouse doors, and skylights can be a fast and efficient means of ventilating a structure. There are a variety of tactics to follow when opening the following construction features for ventilation operations:

Air shafts. Air shafts, also know as **light shafts** or **light wells**, may be found in many different types of structures, such as row frames, multiple dwellings, tenements, and hotels. They are intended to provide air and light to inner rooms of a structure. In a situation where there is a small fire and no concerns of a direct flame exiting the structure, an air and light shaft can be used for ventilation purposes by opening windows within the shaft to rooms that need ventilation (fig. 14–16). However, firefighters must close windows within the shaft as appropriate to prevent fire extension into the shaft or autoexposure to the floors above or an adjoining building. In some instances, a skylight is at the top of the shaft to prevent inclement weather from entering it. If the shaft is covered, the skylight may have to be removed to provide ventilation.

Fig. 14–16. An exterior light well may be used to aid in ventilation provided upper story windows are closed prior to venting.

Skylights. Skylights in dwellings are normally located over a stairwell or hallway. In commercial occupancies, larger skylights are often placed over manufacturing areas. Depending on the type of structure, individual skylights may also be placed over stairways, light shafts, and air shafts. If a building has an attic or cockloft, the area below the skylight is normally boxed off from the attic/cockloft space. Therefore, when the skylight is opened, the interior of the building is ventilated but the attic space is not. These small walls that extend down from the inside of the skylight are commonly referred to as the returns. When checking for fire extension inside the attic or cockloft, firefighters can open up the returns to size up the conditions. In some instances, firefighters should not open up returns that are remote from the original fire because it could possibly pull the fire in that direction and assist in horizontal spread.

Skylights may be opened for ventilation purposes by removing the entire assembly, removing the glass panels, or breaking the glass panels (fig. 14–17). If the glass panels are removed individually, additional time may be required and broken glass may fall into the building.

When a firefighter isn't equipped with a portable radio and is going to break a skylight, a good procedure to follow is to break a small section of it first. This should give warning to the members operating below that ventilation operations are going to take place overhead.

Once any skylight has been vented, the firefighter should take a hook and reach down into the hole to ensure a **draft-stop** (a piece of glass, Lexan®, plastic, or drywall installed at the ceiling level, preventing the loss of heat up into the skylight—not to be confused with a draft stop in an attic) isn't secured below and interfering with ventilation operations. If conditions below reveal a fire is evident under the draft-stop, a hand tool tied to a utility rope can be dropped down to vent the area. This safety measure keeps the firefighter a safe distance away from the escaping flames exiting the skylight.

Fig. 14–17. A skylight

Glass skylights. The most effective method to remove the skylight assembly is by completely prying it up from its attachment points or tipping it onto the roof. This takes minimal time and reveals the entire opening. It also allows you to replace the skylight later.

Skylights can also be opened as follows: If it appears that tar hasn't been used around the edges of the glass and the panels can be quickly and easily removed, then remove the metal tabs or metal stripping along the bottom edge of the panels. This will allow them to slide out. If tar has been used as a sealant and the glass panels can't be removed easily, then attempt to remove the entire skylight's frame attached to the roof if possible. If these attempts do not work, break the glass panels (fig. 14–18). Remember, if you break the glass panels, the resulting shards of glass within the building will be a hazard to interior operations.

It is important to note that on many bulkheads or penthouses, roofs are slanted and dangerous to climb up on and operate on these spaces. Breaking the glass may be the only safe option for firefighters to perform.

Fig. 14–18. Older skylights are often sealed with tar, making them difficult to remove.

Plastic skylights. Newer buildings have plastic skylights, usually a plastic bubble in a metal frame attached to a metal riser. First, try to pry the skylight away from the roof (fig. 14–19). If this can't be done easily, you may have to cut the plastic around the junction of the metal and plastic. Use an axe or power saw to make the cut. If conditions on the roof necessitate operations must be done quickly, attempt to break the plastic bubble with a hand tool for rapid ventilation.

Fig. 14–19. Plastic skylights can often be removed by prying upward.

Often, because of water leakage or to beef up security, roof skylights have been replaced with plywood/oriented strand board (OSB) and lightweight support beams or just tarred over. Thus, firefighters should avoid walking on any skylight or alteration. In situations such as these, firefighters may have to use a power saw to open up the roof or skylight area. Remember, once a skylight is removed, it should be placed near the ventilation opening to warn firefighters of an open shaft on the roof.

Bulkheads and penthouses. Opening the door to a **bulkhead** or **penthouse** can provide significant ventilation to the interior stair shaft and any hallways open to it. Because of the importance and simplicity, opening it up should be a primary consideration. If it has a lower door at the bottom of the stairs, verify the conditions on the other side before opening it. Firefighters proceeding down the interior stairs to open this door could be subjected to severe smoke and fire conditions behind it, so they must use caution.

Depending on the type of door (wood or metal) located on these structures, firefighters can use normal forcible entry tactics to open them up. Usually, these doors are outward opening because they are an exit door. In some cases they may have added security such as a slide bolt or eye bolt and hook, and if they are difficult to force, firefighters should size up the hinge size of the door. As always, remember our cardinal rule of forcible entry: **try before you pry**.

Another typical feature of these structures is that they often have a skylight mounted on top. This skylight provides additional vertical ventilation. In some instances, the skylight has a draft stop mounted on the ceiling of the bulkhead. If the skylight is vented and no smoke issues from it, check for the presence of the draft stop. It may be possible for the firefighter to strike the draft stop from the door of the bulkhead with a hook to ventilate it.

Often, firefighters encounter a bulkhead or penthouse with high walls, making it difficult to climb in bunker gear and reach the skylight mounted above. If an aerial ladder is placed to the roof and it has a folding, attic, or scissor ladder mounted at its tip, it can be removed and used to access this skylight. If not, there are a few other options.

A firefighter can remove the bulkhead's door and lay it on an angle on the wall of the structure. If the firefighter has two tools, one tool punctures the roof at the base of the door to act like a brace, preventing the door from sliding outward as they climb. Once on top of the bulkhead, vent the skylight (fig. 14–20).

If the firefighter has a hook and Halligan tool, he or she can place the Halligan alongside the bulkhead's wall with the fork pressed into the roof and the adze resting on the wall. This tool creates a step or small platform. The hook's head is placed on the top edge of the bulkhead's wall and the handle of the tool hangs downward. Now the firefighter can step on the Halligan and use the hook to pull him- or herself upward while climbing.

Fig. 14–20. Sometimes we need to be creative when gaining access to vent.

Fig. 14–21. Bulkhead and penthouse

It is *extremely* important that firefighters enter and exit the roof of the bulkhead in the same location. Many bulkheads are aligned next to a shaftway; and exiting in the wrong place can cause a firefighter to fall many stories, possibly suffering a severe injury.

Remember, any time a firefighter opens one of these doors and is met with a heavy smoke condition, he or she should still probe inside the landing with a tool to check for victims. Also, opening the door to reveal little or no smoke may indicate that the fire apartment door hasn't been opened yet. Also, don't forget to chock the door open to prevent it from relocking if it accidentally closes.

There are a few variations in the type of bulkheads prevalent on buildings across the country (fig. 14–21). Many have two doors and are a larger sized bulkhead that provides access to the roof in two separate locations. Also, it isn't uncommon to find the elevator motor room located inside the larger sized bulkhead. Firefighters must be careful when working around the **walk-through bulkhead**. This bulkhead normally cuts the roof section of a building into two sections and has doors at both ends. Firefighters must resist the urge to transverse through the interior of the bulkhead under heavy smoke or fire conditions, as this places them in peril. Access to the other side of the roof should be done by aerial ladder, tower ladder, or the top of the bulkhead if sufficient room exists.

Roof scuttle. As shown in fig. 14–22, a **roof scuttle** is a small, covered opening providing access to the roof. Some scuttles consist of a wood cover over wooden risers on the roof. The cover is normally protected by a composition covering. Unless the cover has been attached to the risers, it can be removed by prying it up with an axe, Halligan, or similar tool. Newer scuttles consist of metal risers with a spring-loaded metal door that is fastened and locked from the inside. These are difficult to open and may take more time and effort to open. Sometimes it may be easier to cut the scuttle with a saw in these situations. If a scuttle is found tarred over, it also may be easier to cut the scuttle cover open with a power saw to provide vertical ventilation.

In many buildings with scuttles, an interior vertical ladder is mounted inside the scuttle's opening, providing access to the roof (fig. 14–22). These are normally located in the top floor hallway or in a closet in the hallway. Once the scuttle cover has been removed and no smoke is present, position yourself so that only your arm is placed over the open scuttle; and reach down with a hook to probe the walls, looking for a door. Use caution and do not subject yourself to climbing down the narrow scuttle opening and on the steep vertical ladder to open this door. That is a dangerous practice and could seriously injure you if there is fire behind the closed door.

In many of the commercial occupancies, for increased security, these scuttle covers are made of heavy steel plating with heavy security locks. A rotary saw and metal cutting blade may be the best tool to provide rapid ventilation.

Ventilation

FIREFIGHTER I

Chapter 14

Fig. 14–22. A roof scuttle with a fixed access ladder

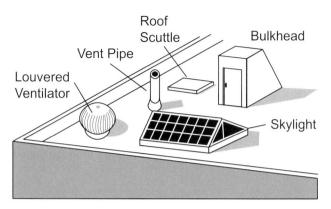

Fig. 14–23. Roof ventilation personnel should be able to recognize and use various types of natural construction features to assist ventilation.

Elevator house or bulkhead. Structures with elevators may have an equipment or motor room located on the roof. **Elevator houses** vary in size according to the number of elevators they service. They are above the elevator shafts and open, by varying degrees, to the shafts. Opening the door and skylight can provide ventilation to the elevator shafts, reducing concentrations of heat and smoke within the structure.

Additionally, the equipment in an elevator house supports the full weight of the attached elevators. Therefore, any fire that has extended to this area may weaken the structural integrity of the elevator equipment supports, possibly causing collapse of the equipment and elevator cars. The resultant hazards and damage that this might cause cannot be overemphasized. Firefighters must use caution if they enter into these rooms; there are holes in the floor that are normally covered with steel grating to allow air currents in the shaft to flow while the cars move up and down. It is common to find these gratings in poor shape or missing.

Ducts. Heating, air conditioning, and other **ducts** of various sizes are often found on roofs (fig. 14–23). Because these passageways may lead to the interior of a building, they must be checked for heat and smoke. If heat and smoke are present, open the duct to provide some ventilation to the interior of the building, as well as to check for extension (fig. 14–24). Also, when firefighters are faced with a grease fire in ductwork, it may be necessary to do the following:

- Tear open the top of the ductwork to allow proper ventilation

- Open the roof near the ductwork to ensure that no fire has left the duct at its seams and extended into the cockloft or roofing materials

Fig. 14–24. A rooftop duct

Dumbwaiter bulkheads. Some older multiple-dwelling structures may still have their **dumbwaiter shaft's** bulkheads on the rooftops. Although the shafts are now illegal to use in most parts of the country, they haven't been removed from the structure. Most shafts served more than one apartment and were located in the kitchen area so tenants could send down their trash to the basement for the maintenance people to remove. Often fires in the kitchens or apartments can extend into the unused shaft and upward (fig. 14–25).

Venting these shafts allows the fire to vent vertically and possibly prevent it from extending to other apartments. Often, fires in these types of buildings have smoke showing from the dumbwaiter bulkheads on the roof (fig. 14–26). Venting these bulkheads is important and must be a quickly accomplished task. The bulkhead may or may not have a skylight on the top and can easily be ventilated by prying up on its sides and hinging it open. Also, the dumbwaiter bulkhead normally has an access door on it, providing access to the pulley and gears located at the top of the shaft. These doors are now normally sealed up and covered with roof tar.

Fig. 14–25. A dumbwaiter shaft door inside an apartment.

Fig. 14–26. There are many avenues for fire to travel horizontally, as well as places to perform ventilation, such as this dumbwaiter bulkhead.

The doors open outward and can be forced open using outward-opening-door techniques. One of the best methods is the baseball swing with the Halligan tool. The point of the tool can be embedded in the door, opposite the side of the hinges. Now the tool can be pulled or pushed toward the door's hinge side to force it open. In some instances it may take a few attempts to force the door open in this manner because of the magnitude of tar that has sealed the shaftway.

Vent pipes and soil pipes. Plumbing **vent pipes** extend through a given roof at various locations and sometimes can indicate the locations of bathrooms and kitchens. Although they aren't considered ventilation avenues, they do travel vertically within a building. Therefore, they are capable of spreading heat and fire. Smoke issuing from acrylonitrile butadiene styrene (ABS) plastic vent pipes is an excellent indicator that the pipe is burning somewhere within the building. ABS plastic pipes can burn readily and serve as extension avenues wherever the pipe travels. After a firefighter feels the base of a metal or plastic vent pipe and notices signs of heat or smoke, the roof must be opened and checked. Additionally, a vent pipe that appears to be growing upward is an excellent indication that the roof is sagging and possibly about to fail.

Ventilators. Many types, sizes, and shapes of **ventilators** may be found on roofs. Ventilators can be classified as either venting a particular area within a building or providing some type of ventilation for a device or appliance, such as kitchen appliances. The size and shape usually reveal the type; or if it is covered with grease or oil residue, it can inform the firefighter that it is connected to a cooking device. Ventilators for heat-producing appliances generally have a serrated top suspended over the pipe, whereas those that vent the attic or top floor usually have a capped top or the familiar turbine.

Smoke or heat coming from a ventilator indicates that the area it serves is affected by smoke or a fire, or a fire exists in the ductwork itself. If a ventilator is equipped with a screen or cover, it should be removed, because it restricts the efficiency of escaping smoke. Don't remove the top of a rotating ventilator, because the ventilator stack can easily be damaged and restricted. Rotating ventilators are 30% more efficient when the turbine is operational, compared with when the turbine has been taken off. Be aware that these ventilators can detach and fly off the pipes with fire venting from it. If these items are the only ventilation objects on the roof and a firefighter has to check the cockloft for smoke and fire conditions, remove them. It is easier to remove them for a quick size-up of the conditions in the cockloft and the construction features.

WINDOWS

Firefighters encounter numerous different types, sizes, and shapes of windows on the fireground. It is important to learn and identify the basic concepts of windows and how they operate for ventilation tactics to be performed rapidly. Most windows in residential structures have **double hung** (upper and lower sash), **casement** (hinged window, pivots to one side), and **solid frame** (non-opening).

These windows are also constructed in a wood, metal, or vinyl frame with single, double, or triple pane glass. In addition, in areas near the ocean, a new laminated or hurricane-resistant glass is becoming a regular feature. It is also common to find Lexan™ and other heavier gauge plastic laminates used for windows, because of their high security features.

Again, it is important for firefighters to size up the fire conditions and then decide or be told to open a window or vent a window with a hand tool. Remember, it is important to communicate with the interior teams and coordinate ventilation efforts with extinguishment operations. When venting windows, a common theme exists in the fire service: Remove everything and make the window turn into a door. Remove the screen, shades, blinds, cross members, sash, glass, and any other obstacle. This allows unimpeded access for firefighters to enter or exit the structure without becoming hung up on anything.

Venting the windows

Prior to venting windows, firefighters should size up the window for any cracks from the heat or if the glass is discolored. These conditions could be a good indication that fire exists directly behind the window, so firefighters must use caution when venting begins. When firefighters ventilate a window with a hand tool on a level surface, they often maintain a safe distance away from the window and position on the windward side of the window (wind at their backs) at a level lower than the window. Firefighters often crouch when ventilating windows at this level. Crouching ensures that the firefighter remains low and out of the flow of hot air, gases, smoke, and possibly fire venting from the new ventilation opening .

Using a tool to its maximum length or choosing a tool with a long handle helps firefighters maintain a safe distance away from the window. It is important to maintain a safe distance away from a window because the escaping by-products of combustion could ignite or explode when escaping to the fresh air. Now that a safe distance has been attained, the firefighter uses the tool to strike the upper sash or pane of glass to vent the window. The upper pane is struck first because it may already be compromised by the heat generated by the fire and break easily. It also doesn't really mater what part of the tool strikes the window with single pane glass; a metal tool is often no match for glass. When firefighters are faced with double or thermo-pane glass, it may be more advantageous to strike the window with the sharp end or point of the tool to break the glass.

As the firefighter strikes the upper pane of glass, it is usually in a downward motion; and the center sash and bottom pane of glass may also break with the downward swing. If so, once both panes are broken, the center sash can be pulled out and then the window can be trimmed.

Trimming a window means that the firefighter goes around the outside of the frame with a hand tool and removes the leftover shards of glass from the window (fig. 14–27). This allows a safer means of egress and access if the window must be used by the firefighter. Once the large glass shards are removed by striking or trimming, the firefighter must ensure the blinds, curtain, shades, and screens are removed.

Figure 14–27. Trimming the window by removing remaining glass shards with a tool.

When operating on a level surface, it is okay for a firefighter to pull out any remaining glass, curtains, and blinds from the inside of the structure to assist ventilation efforts. Dropping them inside the structure could cover a victim. Once ventilation efforts are concluded on a window, the firefighter should always sweep the floor just inside the window to check for a victim who may have attempted to reach a point of safety.

Ventilating windows with a portable ladder

The extension ladder can be used either in the beam or flat position to break a window. Some firefighters believe that the weight and structural makeup of throwing the beam into the window works better than flat, whereas others believe that the flat position covers more surface area and breaks more glass than the beam throw. Either technique can be used to vent the window.

The ladder is raised vertically to the proper level, near the top third of the window. Then the ladder is dropped or pushed into the window with some force by the firefighter positioned at the base of the ladder (fig. 14–28). As the ladder strikes the window, the firefighter should remove his or her hands from the ladder, in case glass slides down the beams of the ladder. Hands should be in the vicinity of the ladder in case it bounces off the window; this way they can grab the ladder's rungs or beams to maintain its stability. It is very important to note that firefighters performing this tactic must have the proper eye protection and wear all personal protective equipment. Also, sometimes it may take one or two attempts to sufficiently break out the window for ventilation. If this ladder evolution is properly executed, often it also breaks the window's center sash and bottom window pane.

Fig. 14–28. A ground ladder venting a window on the second floor

Roof ladder's hooks used to ventilate a window

Another method of performing window ventilation is to use the roof ladder. The roof ladder has two large roof hooks attached to its tips that resemble the firefighting hooks or pike poles firefighters use daily. To perform this tactic, the roof hooks are placed into the open position.

Then the ladder is placed at the proper height and thrown or pushed into the window by the firefighter positioned at the base of the ladder.

After the ladder has broken the top pane, the firefighter has a few options. If the window has a wood frame, the ladder's hooks can be placed on the center sash. Next, the firefighter can pick up the base of the ladder and give it a slight tug or pull backward or out of the window. Normally, this additional pressure lets the hooks break the bottom pane of glass and remove the center sash of the window. If the ground's terrain is in bad condition, avoid this method and drop the ladder into the window again to complete ventilation efforts of the lower panes of glass.

Remember, all eye protection and personal protective equipment must be used when performing these tactics.

The arm-lock maneuver—venting windows from a portable ladder. The arm-lock maneuver is a tactic that can be performed for venting windows while working off a portable ladder. It is relatively easy to perform and requires minimal time to get into position on the ladder, thus saving critical time for other important tasks. It can be used in conjunction with the leg-lock maneuvers previously described, or it can be used by itself (fig. 14–29).

To perform the arm-lock maneuver, the firefighter should use the following steps for ventilating a window to the right side of the ladder:

- A firefighter reaches the proper working height on the ladder with both feet placed on the same rung. Note that when venting the window off the side of the ladder, place the leg and foot up against the ladder's beam. This offers more support and balance when swinging the hand tool. It also can help brace the firefighter onto the ladder.

- The hook is then held in the right arm, and the left arm is placed between the two rungs directly in front of the firefighter.

- The butt end of the hook is now placed behind the ladder and grabbed with the left hand.

- Next, position the hook to the window, checking that no part of the ladder or structure will interfere with the swinging motion. Now the window can be ventilated.

For more in-depth information on the ladder tactics mentioned, see chapter 13, Ladders.

Fig. 14–29. A firefighter demonstrates hand position for the arm-lock maneuver.

Ventilating top floor windows. Ventilating windows at top floor fires is a vital tactic to follow because it allows fresh air to enter the structure and helps the superheated gases and smoke escape through the roof ventilation hole. If the top floor windows can be reached using a hook, position above and slightly to the windward side of the window. Swing the hook inward toward the window to ventilate it (fig. 14–30). Once the glass breaks, pull the body backward and away from the rising smoke, heat, and gases. Remember to coordinate communication with the inside teams prior to ventilating any windows.

Fig. 14–30. Breaking a window with a hook

In some instances, a hook might not reach the window; however, with a piece of utility chord and a hand tool such as a Halligan bar, a different tactic can be used. The first step is to secure the tool with a knot and a safety to one of its ends. Next, the tool is lowered to the window to be ventilated. Secure the rope by using the foot to step on it at the roof level; maintain this position for the method to work effectively. The rope and tool are then pulled up to the roof. Finally, toss the tool out and away from the building, causing it to arch into the window with sufficient force to break it (fig. 14–31).

Whenever this tactic is used, firefighters operating in the vicinity must use caution. Flying glass drops from the window, and occasionally utility ropes, are severed by the glass and the tool flies into the structure or down to the ground. Unfortunately, this tactic does not clear all the glass, screens, or curtains from the windows; but it can afford some ventilation efforts when there are limited means to do so.

This technique works well in many fireground situations, and some fire departments have made adjustments to their tools and tool inventory to accomplish the task. In addition, some tool manufacturers have made tool modifications for the utility rope to *clip* to the Halligan bar. Also, the hook and Halligan can be secured together by a short chain and safety clips that allow this tactic to be performed.

Fig. 14–31. A Halligan bar secured with a rope can be an effective ventilation tool.

Ventilating windows covered with security grating or steel mesh. Many factories place metal grating or mesh over their windows to prevent vandalism and illegal entry into the building. These security devices are normally comprised of a steel frame with the grating or mesh welded inside the frame, which is then attached to the building by lag bolts or through bolts. The following are a few options to choose from when encountering these windows that need to be ventilated:

- A forcible-entry saw can be used to cut a section of the grating or mesh out so that a hand tool can be used to ventilate the window.

- A forcible-entry saw can cut the brackets where the security frame attaches to the building (fig. 14–32). This releases the frame from the building, exposing the windows for ventilation operations. Use this method on small frames, but use caution if the frame is large. A large falling frame could injure unsuspecting firefighters operating around the building.

- Some fire departments have created a homemade hand tool to combat these windows. The tool is a piece of ½-in. (13-mm) metal rod or rebar about 4 ft (1.2 m) long, with one end bent downward to form a handle and the other end left blunt. The tool is inserted between the grating, and the glass is punched out. The method works well but requires additional time because it must be inserted and removed numerous times to ventilate the windows.

- In some instances, the distance between the grating is large enough to insert the butt end of a hook to ventilate the windows.

Fig. 14–32. Firefighters use a power saw to cut attachment points of mesh grate to ventilate windows at a one-story commercial building. The tower ladder bucket facilitates the operation.

Note that operating a power saw on a portable ladder is a difficult tactic to perform; use caution when doing so. If possible, working out of a tower ladder's basket can make this operation easier and safer.

Ventilating windows protected by security bars.

Many structures around the country have steel security bars placed over their windows for security and protection. Normally, these bars are either attached to a frame or individually embedded into the bricks of the building. There is usually sufficient space between the bars to insert a hand tool to ventilate the windows. Once the windows have been ventilated, remove the bars to permit a secondary means of egress for firefighters operating inside the structure.

After a complete size-up of the installation and types of the security bars, firefighters can chose a particular method of removing them. There are a few ways to attack the bars, and each situation may require a different method (fig. 14–33). One method is to attack the ends of the bars, where they are embedded into the brick walls. Breaking the bricks may release the bars. This may also work when the lag bolts are set into brick or blocks. Another method is to use the forcible-entry saw and cut the bars for removal. A hydraulic forcible-entry tool may also help: Place the jaw behind the bar frame and push the lag bolts out of the building's walls, releasing the bars or their frame. In other instances, cutting the bars with a rebar cutter or torch may also work. Many of these installations can be defeated with a set of forcible-entry tools; they may be pried off the building, forced off, or even sheared off.

For more information on removing security bars, see chapter 12, Forcible Entry.

Fig. 14–33. Window bars vary. Some are flush mounted, some are recessed. Look at your district and consider which tools and techniques can negate these security devices.

Ventilating hurricane resistant glass windows.

Hurricane resistant glass windows are a common construction feature in areas where hurricanes are prevalent. Because they are difficult to penetrate and offer increased security, they are becoming more widespread and found in all types of communities. These windows are designed to take an impact load from the outside and can hamper ventilation efforts severely.

The windows are constructed with either two or three layers of glass that are laminated together with a polyvinyl-butyrate and argon gas. They are attached to either a metal or vinyl frame, which is securely mounted into the building. Their locking devices are heavy-duty mechanisms and help prevent intrusion from the outside.

Attacking these windows for ventilation operations can be difficult. They normally cannot be broken by a firefighter swinging a hand tool. When faced with these windows, firefighters must revert to using power tools in order for rapid ventilation operations to be successful. The chainsaw with a carbide-tip blade is perhaps the quickest tool to deploy against these windows. A rotary power saw with a carbide-tip blade also works well. Tests have shown that a reciprocal saw can cut these windows, but the blade can quickly dull. Some firefighters have had success using an auto extrication hand saw or pruning saw when faced with these windows. These saws can cut the material but it may take considerable time to do so.

It is of utmost importance that all personal protective clothing and eye protection be used when cutting these windows. Small glass shards and fragments can cause serious injury to firefighters that aren't properly protected.

Because these windows are designed to take the brunt of a load from the outside, they are weaker and sometimes easier to remove from the inside. Any time firefighters come across these windows on the fireground, the incident commander should be notified immediately.

For more information on these windows, see chapter 12, Forcible Entry.

Ventilating Lexan™ windows.

Firefighters often encounter Lexan™ windows on commercial occupancies. Lexan™ is a high-grade plastic material that is resistant to impact loads. It is often chosen for windows in these occupancies for increased security measures. When Lexan™ is exposed to high heat conditions it melts, creating its own ventilation process. Unfortunately, it is no easier to strike and remove the Lexan™ once it has melted and cooled; it still retains its impact resistance.

Firefighters can ventilate these windows with either a rotary or chainsaw. Full protective equipment and eye protection must be used to prevent an injury. Cutting Lexan™ is dangerous because fragments can become projectiles, so use caution when performing these tasks. If firefighters don't have the necessary power tools available, they can attack the frame and molding and attempt to remove the Lexan™ in this manner. If Lexan™ windows are present in a structure, communicate to the incident commander by way of a radio.

Ventilating blocked-up windows.

Frequently, firefighters face fires in vacant structures that have had their windows blocked up with either cinder or concrete blocks or bricks for security measures. In other instances, factories block up large windows to reduce energy costs. Ventilating these structures often requires more time than normal ventilation operations. Firefighters must use hand tools to remove the brick or blocks to ventilate the structure.

If firefighters are operating on ground level, they should attempt to break the brick or block slightly higher than waist high. Here they have a good baseball swing and can use the momentum of their body to help break out the brick. It is important to attempt to swing in the same area and penetrate a brick or block with a few blows to make an entry point. Once the entry point is made, begin to work either next to it, above it, or below it, knocking out the next brick.

Also, when the brick or block is broken just above waist level, it leaves much of the upper portion unsupported. Many times the weight of the brick or block allows it to collapse when it is no longer supported from below, or a few simple strikes with a hand tool cause the remainder of the brick or block to tumble down. Firefighters often leave this unsupported piece in place as they complete knocking out the bottom portion of the brick. Leaving in the top section at this point sometimes keeps the area free from smoke and allows the firefighter to see the work area in front of him or her. Firefighters must keep the upper portion under constant watch; knocking out the lower section can create movement and vibrations, and the unsupported top section could come crashing down without notice. Clearing the entire window allows a better means of egress and escape if it is needed later in the operations. This tactic of opening up brick or blocked windows reduces the time and energy the firefighter must use to ventilate these windows.

When faced with these windows at upper levels, the easiest way to ventilate them is from the safety of a tower ladder's bucket. The bucket is placed slightly below the intended work area and the firefighter swings a hand tool to knock out the brick. The area below must be safeguarded by a firefighter to prevent anyone from possibly being struck by a falling brick or mortar. When working out of the tower ladder's bucket, the firefighter must remain cognizant of the fact they could strike their arm or hand on the bucket's safety rails while swinging.

Ventilating wired glass windows. Many windows in walls that require a level of fire resistance—exterior walls near a property line or near other buildings—have glass with wire safety mesh embedded in its layers. These windows are also found in high-traffic areas of structures such as hallways and stairwells. Ventilating these windows often takes a little longer than regular windows because of the wire mesh holding the glass together.

The glass can be struck with a hand tool and broken, but it may only shatter. Firefighters may need to strike it again to break a section out or create an entry point. Once an entry point has been made, a firefighter has a few options:

- A hand tool can be inserted into the entry point and can cut the glass and wire mesh with its sharp end. Once a substantial section has been cut into the glass, it can be pulled in one direction to ventilate the window.

- A firefighter can punch out a *U*-shape around the edge of the glass and then pull it in the direction of the bottom of the *U* to release the glass.

- In some instances it may be easier to attack the mullions around the window's frame and release the entire piece of glass to ventilate the window.

- Punching out the center and pulling the glass often takes numerous attempts to ventilate the window. It often leaves exposed wire and glass dangling from the window that could cause an injury.

- Some firefighters smash the perimeter section of glass out around three sides of the window. Next they cut the wire mesh with cutting pliers and pull the glass toward the attached side, ventilating the window.

Ventilating windows covered with plywood/OSB. Many vacant structures have their windows protected by plywood/OSB that has been nailed or screwed into their window frames to prevent intruders and protect the vacant structures from vandalism. Most of the time, these sheets of plywood/OSB are easily removed by a firefighter prying it off with a hand tool (fig. 14–34). Some firefighters prefer to start at the top and release those fasteners and then pull the entire sheet down and out of the window. Others prefer to work around the base of the window, pry outward to release it on both sides, and then lift the plywood/OSB sheet up to gain access to the window. In both situations, firefighters must use caution, because a sheet of plywood/OSB can be heavy and cause an injury when it is dropped or released.

Fig. 14–34. Use a prying action with the Halligan to remove plywood/OSB that has been nailed or screwed into window frames.

Firefighters can also use a baseball swing technique with a Halligan tool, pick-head axe, or hook's head to pry these sheets off. Simply position the tool about 6 in. (150 mm) from the edge of the plywood/OSB and drive the point through the sheet. Next, pry back on the tool's handle and push it toward the sheet of plywood/OSB, pulling the screws or nails out of the window frame. This technique may only release one side of the plywood/OSB, and the firefighter must perform this same technique on the opposite side of the window.

These types of security measures are also being modified to make it even more difficult to enter the structure. Often the plywood/OSB is now covered with a thin metal mesh and then a **skim-coat** of concrete mastic is layered over the plywood/OSB. This step reinforces the plywood/OSB and makes removal more difficult. The same method used previously can be attempted, but it may be more advantageous to take a rotary power saw with a carbide-tip blade and cut along the outside edges of the plywood/OSB sheet to release it. If the plywood/OSB sheet is recessed into the window frame, the operator may have to cut a few inches in for the saw blade's assembly to access the plywood/OSB. Firefighters *must* use caution and not plunge the saw's blade entirely into the plywood/OSB sheet. This could cause the saw to hit the glass, window sash, or another obstacle such as security bars behind the plywood/OSB, which could cause damage to the saw and injure the operator. Plunging a chainsaw through the plywood/OSB sheet can also be dangerous for the same reasons, so firefighters should avoid doing this. In addition, if another firefighter or victim comes to that window from the inside, a serious injury could occur.

Ventilating windows covered with HUD window coverings. Firefighters may encounter vacant buildings that have been covered with a HUD-style window covering, a means of sealing up vacant buildings accepted and approved by the U.S. Department of Housing and Urban Development (HUD). Although they are less prevalent than in years past, they are still present in numerous areas.

The **HUD window,** as it is called by firefighters, is made up of a sheet of plywood/OSB that is attached to a window frame by four cross members: 2 × 4–in. (50 × 100–mm) pieces of wood (fig. 14–35). Two smaller pieces of this material can be seen from outside the structure, whereas the other two longer pieces cannot. These two pieces are supported on the inside of the building, spanning the window frame on each side, adding strength and rigidity to the device. All the pieces of wood are connected

by through bolts or a piece of threaded metal rod and become secure when they are tightened up. Normally, there are two bolts on each of the upper and lower cross member supports for a total of four. These devices can be installed with the windows opened and left in place, or the entire window and frames may have been removed prior to their installation.

Fig. 14–35. Notice the 2 x 4 cross members that tip off the firefighter that these are H.U.D. window security devices.

To ventilate these windows, there are a few options to consider after sizing up the material. If the wood shows signs of being compromised or rot, it may advisable to attack it. A hand tool such as an axe or Halligan tool can be used to split the outside 2 × 4–in. (50 × 100–mm) cross members, exposing the four metal through bolts. The bolts can then be pushed or struck into the structure to release the inside cross members. Firefighters must use caution because the sheet of plywood/OSB can now become loose and swing down and out from the window, and the cross members are now unsupported. Firefighters must maintain some type of grip on the plywood/OSB to prevent it from falling away from the building and causing an injury. One way to tackle this is to drive a hand tool into the plywood/OSB and maintain a hold of the tool. This controls the sheet of plywood/OSB once its cross members are released.

Another method to remove these devices if they are present on the upper levels of a building is to operate from the safety of a tower ladder basket and use a forcible-entry saw or rotary saw blade capable of cutting the metal through bolts. Once the tower ladder's bucket is placed slightly below the window, place the point of a hand tool through the plywood/OSB as a safety hold; this *must* be maintained the entire time to prevent the plywood/OSB sheet from falling from the building. Another firefighter then uses the saw to cut the upper and lower head of the bolts on one side of the window. The saw's blade cuts through the 2 × 4 at an angle and cuts the bolt head and rod at one time. Next, they cut the top and bottom bolt on the opposite side of the window. Firefighters can now either strike the bolts back into the building, releasing the device, or they can pry up the outside 2 × 4s. These actions normally release the inside cross members and the sheet of plywood/OSB. If no window is present, the sheet of plywood/OSB can be put back into the fire building rather than dropping it down onto the fire scene and possibly causing an injury. If it can't and there is room inside the tower ladder, it may be placed inside the bucket rather than dropping it to the ground.

Some firefighters prefer another method of removing these devices. They use a chainsaw and cut a small triangle in the middle of the plywood/OSB sheet. If fire conditions behind the sheet are severe, they can move onto another window. If they aren't, the chainsaw can be inserted into the hole (once it is safe) to cut the upper and lower inside cross members, releasing the tension of the device. In some instances, when performing this tactic, the plywood/OSB may have to be pried toward either side to remove the inside cross members from the window frame after the cuts are made. When performing this tactic, firefighters must remember to maintain a grip onto the plywood/OSB to prevent it from falling to the ground and causing an injury to an unsuspecting firefighter operating below.

It is also important to assert that plunging a live chainsaw through a HUD window can be a dangerous evolution. This could cause the chainsaw to hit the glass, window sash, or other obstacle such as security bars behind the plywood/OSB, which could damage the saw and injure the operator. In addition, if another firefighter or victim comes to that window from the inside, a serious injury could occur.

Metal casement windows. Many older structures have single-pane glass set in metal casement window frames (fig. 14–36). The glass panels are usually 8 × 8 in. (200 × 200 mm) or 12 × 12 in. (305 × 305 mm) and are easy to ventilate with a hand tool. The windows may or may not have a hinge section(s) that pivots and opens outward with the turn of a handle. If these windows need to be removed for the rescue of a trapped civilian or firefighter, it can be time consuming using hand tools. It often requires numerous strikes of the cross members and uprights to remove them if that's even achievable. Sometimes all they do is bend and warp from the hand tool's impact. A much faster way is to use a rotary saw equipped with a metal cutting blade to remove the uprights and cross members. This reduces the firefighter's exertion level and requires less time to make an opening in the window frame for the rescue.

Post fire control window ventilation. After the fire has been extinguished and the structure is still full of toxic smoke, gases, and heat, the building still must be ventilated. Firefighters should resist the urge to break windows after the fire has been extinguished; this looks unprofessional and increases the workload of those performing salvage operations. Firefighters should size up the windows and see if they can be opened or removed to assist in ventilation efforts.

Fig. 14–36. These casement windows on this Tudor-style multiple dwelling will be difficult to force.

Many newer types of double-hung windows have release clips mounted on the sash that allow the windows to be removed to help clean. Firefighters can release these tabs, then lift one side of the window up and the other side slid downward and the window comes out of the tracks. In some instances, the tracks are spring loaded and slight tension or compression on one side prevents the window from releasing from the track. By performing this technique, we're reducing fire damage and looking more professional (fig. 14–37).

Fig. 14–37. Taking the time to open a window instead of breaking it during post control ventilation helps to reduce fire damage and makes us look more professional.

VENT, ENTER, AND SEARCH

The **vent, enter, search (VES)** technique of search and rescue is used by some fire departments in certain fire situations. Most commonly, it occurs when access to a trapped victim is unattainable through the main entrance of a structure. This technique allows a firefighter to access the alleged location of the victim by another avenue. In some fire departments around the country, the VES technique is used daily in their firefighting operations, while in others it is only used for specific rescue operations. Firefighters must understand and learn this concept prior to operating on the fireground.

Prior to discussing the VES technique, it is important to note that firefighters must understand and grasp the meaning of two ventilation concepts: venting for life and venting for fire. Venting for life is performed to permit firefighters access into an area where there is known or suspected life hazard exists. There is a calculated risk of eventually pulling the fire toward the area to be searched with this tactic, because a ventilation opening has been created to release the by-products of combustion. However, these calculated risks are performed to reach potential victims as soon as possible.

Venting for fire is performed to assist the engine company's advance into the fire area to extinguish the fire. The venting is usually performed once the engine has water in the hoseline and prepares to move in and attack the fire. This venting assists the by-products of combustion and steam from the hoseline's water to escape from

the building, lessening the burden on the firefighters operating inside. These two concepts *must* be understood, because premature ventilation can increase the fire's intensity, speed, and location as well as decrease the chances of a trapped victim's survival. Remember, all types of ventilation efforts must be coordinated between firefighters operating inside and outside the structure.

Normally, the VES tactic is performed by one or more firefighters going through a remote opening, such as a window to access a suspected or known life hazard area. Prior to window entry from a ladder, porch roof, fire escape, deck, or platform, the firefighter should size up the entry point (fig. 14–38). They should recognize the amount of smoke, heat level of the smoke, and its condition (puffing, rolling under pressure, or a haze) prior to opening the entry point. Once the window is opened, firefighters should position themselves away from the escaping heat, gases, and smoke and probe inside with a tool to see if an unconscious victim is on the floor and tap the floor to check its structural stability.

Fig. 14–38. A firefighter venting from an extended roof, preparing for entry

Once the floor has been checked and found to be clear, the firefighter should vent the window with a hand tool and remove any sash in between the clearing. They should also remove any screen, drapes, blinds, or curtains to promote ventilation efforts and prevent these items from entangling the firefighter entering the area. Next, the firefighter enters the structure with one leg first and then the other, rather than going in headfirst. The weight of a firefighter diving into a room can cause an impact load to the floor and a possible collapse if the floor is of questionable stability. Also, if a firefighter *dives* into the window and hits a piece of furniture, he or she could go flying across the room and lose all sense of direction and whereabouts.

Once the firefighter has entered the window, the search begins. There are two basic concepts firefighters may use:

1. Firefighters can probe the area with a hand tool looking for a victim while keeping one hand on the wall to maintain his or her bearings while searching the room.

2. Firefighters can use a hand to search for a victim while using the tool to maintain contact with the wall to keep their bearings.

Following the wall, proceed across the room to shut the room's door. With a 6-ft (2-m) hook in one hand, you may be able to close the door to the room from your initial entry point. The hook can be run along the midsection of the walls feeling for the door, so use all your senses and listen for the sound of the door closing if it is struck with the hook. If you hear the distinct sound of glass, do not immediately break it because you feel it will vent the room more quickly. Remember where you are operating. Premature venting could allow autoexposure of the fire right into the search area. Remember that the sound of glass in the room could also be a mirror, television set, or even a fish tank. Your hands and senses can tell you what you're feeling in a severe smoke condition.

Closing the door to the room can help in a few ways. It decreases the chances of pulling the fire into the room entered. Closing the door may increase visibility in the room and make finding a victim easier. Finally, it creates a safety factor with the door holding back the fire while searching the room.

If a victim is found in the room prior to finding the door, you must decide if conditions allow for the door to be closed or if you'll have to immediately retrace your way back to the entry point with the victim in hand. Remember, if the victim is large and you need time to remove him or her, closing the door to the room increases the overall safety margin of the rescue operation. If the fire has been controlled below, the victim may also be removed through the interior of the structure.

If no victim has been found, searching firefighters can leave the room's door closed and exit the room to safety. Or they can size up conditions out in the hallway to see if an interior search of other rooms may be feasible; if not, a portable ladder can be used to gain entrance to a window in another section of the structure to perform the VES tactic. VES can be a dangerous tactic to perform, so firefighters must operate in pairs and in conjunction with the tasks of the interior teams to make

this a safe evolution. If done properly, this tactic can save numerous lives.

WINDOW GATES AND CHILD BARS

In some situations firefighters find window gates or scissor gates behind a window to protect the occupants from intrusions (fig. 14–39). These gates are normally a hinge-style gate or in a slide track and both locked from the inside. In newer installations, a release button is mounted on the wall to unlock these gates; the button can be located at the base of the wall or somewhere on the wall next to the gate. Unfortunately, these devices can delay VES operations and can be difficult to force open from the outside.

Fig. 14–39. Although typical in residential multiple dwellings, scissor gates can be found in commercial occupancies as well, and will delay egress through these windows.

If firefighters encounter these devices while trying to make entry, they should first attempt to see if they are unlocked and can be pushed or slid open. If they are not, they must begin forcible-entry procedures on them. For scissor window gates in a slide track, it may be easiest to work on the stationary side and insert a hand tool behind the frame to pry it out and away from the wall. These installations are normally screwed into the framing and pull out with the use of leverage. If smoke is issuing from the window, pull down the top sash first and pry the top of the gate off first. Then push the window back upward to cut down on the smoke exiting and use it for a protection measure. Next, lift up on the lower sash and attack the gate at the bottom. Once the gate is released from the stationary wall, slide it in the track toward the lock side or hinge it and push it inward. Remember, if this window is going to be used for VES, it should be cleared entirely out.

In heavier installations with steel bars, the same method of attacking the gate may be feasible. In some situations it may call for additional tools such as a forcible-entry saw or hydraulic forcible-entry tool to gain entry. In some installations it may also be possible to pry on a set of bars to make an opening to insert a gloved hand into the building. Next, attempt to lift the lock guard and then turn the locking mechanism to open the gate.

Some cities require that windows have child bars on them to prevent a child from falling out of a window. These bars are different from regular security bars; they are a two-piece system that includes interconnected bars and uprights that normally run horizontally across the bottom of the window (fig. 14–40). They are screwed into each side of the window frame and, if struck with a hand tool on one of the center uprights, can be pulled out from the side of the frame. The frame then can be pushed inward or struck in the other direction to remove the opposite side, permitting entry into the building.

For more information on these devices, see chapter 12, Forcible Entry.

Fig. 14–40. Child bars are installed with good intentions

ROOF VENTILATION

Tools used for roof operation

When firefighters are performing horizontal or vertical ventilation operations, the following tools or compli-

ment of tools (some of which are shown in fig. 14–41) can be used to perform the ventilation tactics:

- Full personal protective clothing with eye protection
- Breathing apparatus
- Axe (pick-head or flat-head)
- Pike pole, rubbish hook, or other suitable tool
- Power saw (chain or rotary saw)
- Communications (portable radio)
- Halligan tool
- Utility rope
- Flashlight

Fig. 14–41. These are various tools that can be very useful for roof ventilation operations. It is important to understand the strengths and weaknesses of various ventilation techniques.

Pick-head or flat-head axe. The axe is an indispensable and dependable tool for ventilation operations. The pick-head axe is versatile, because the pick can be used for a variety of tasks:

- Driving the pick-head into the roof and using the axe as a foot brace if cutting with a saw
- Prying off scuttle covers or lifting up skylight frames
- Making quick inspection holes in the roof and tearing off roof coverings

Also, when traversing a pitched roof, firefighters should keep the pick-head axe ready. The pick can be used to pierce the roof and act as an anchor in case you slip or fall.

Most training material regarding axes suggests cutting at a 60° angle to the roofing material. Although this can provide acceptable results, it has several drawbacks:

- Not all of the energy expended for cutting is effectively used.

- It is an inefficient way of cutting plywood/OSB and difficult to cut through shingles and sheathing.

- The axe head may plunge beneath the surface being cut and become trapped.

These problems can be overcome by bringing the axe downward in a smooth arc motion so that the cutting edge is 90° to the work surface at contact. This results in more cutting power due to the velocity and natural swing of the axe requiring less effort. Remember it's very important to position your feet properly apart so that the axe doesn't accidentally strike your leg or foot. If the head of an axe becomes trapped in or below the work surface, simply use the toe end of a boot as a fulcrum at the junction of the axe head and the handle to lever the axe out again (fig. 14–42).

Fig. 14–42. An axe head that is trapped below roof decking can be levered out by placing the toe of your boot between the roof and the junction of the head and handle.

When firefighters are cutting a roof with an axe, they should try and determine the location of the rafters by sounding the roof with the head of the axe. To sound the roof, the firefighter bangs down on the roof with the top of the axe and listens to the sound it makes. A solid thump can alert the firefighter to the position of the joist. A hollow sound means an area between the joist. Cuts should be made as close to the rafter as possible, providing a firmer foundation for the cut.

Although less versatile than the pick-head axe on the roof, a flat-head axe can also be used to cut open roofs. The axe is swung and used the same way as mentioned above. In addition, if the roof sheathing is made up of plywood/OSB or pine boards covered with shingles,

another method of using the axe is available. Firefighters can first sound the roof and attempt to cut alongside a joist. Next they'll use the flat end of the axe and swing downward and strike the roof. Each strike makes a cut into the roof; and when these cuts abut each other, they make a cut line. Using this method it is easy to make a louver in a roof. Some firefighters use the maul or a splitting maul to perform the same tactic of opening the roof.

Pike pole or hook. Firefighters must bring a pike pole or hook with them when reporting to the roof for roof ventilation operations. Once the roof has been cut open, the roof sheathing must be pulled up or louvered to create the roof opening. To pull up the sheathing, the hook's head is placed into the knockout and then the sheathing is pulled upward away from the roof (fig. 14–43). If a knockout was made on both sides of a cut, two firefighters can pull up the roof sheathing. If the sheathing or roof planks are difficult to remove by pulling upward, the hook can be used as a giant pry bar. Simply place the hook's head on the joist and pull it so that it bites under the roof planks or sheathing. Now simply push up and away from your body to pry the sheathing upward and off the joist.

Fig. 14–43. Pulling roof boards with a Halligan hook

Once the roof planks or sheathing is removed, the ceiling must be pushed down to ventilate the room and area below. If it is not, the cockloft or attic is the only space ventilated. Using a hook rather than a shorter hand tool allows the firefighters to position themselves away from the ventilation opening. This helps them keep out of rapidly escaping smoke and gases that could ignite without warning. In some buildings with deep cocklofts, hooks longer than 6 ft (1.8 m) are needed on the roof to reach the ceiling below. The hook can also be used to sound the roof as a firefighter proceeds across the roof to check its stability. Also, the hook can used as a safety brace when operating on a peaked roof.

Rubbish hook. The rubbish hook was originally designed as a companion to the pike pole to move debris during rubbish fires, during overhauling operations, and to strip shingles from roofs. Although the pike pole is versatile, the rubbish hook also benefits firefighters performing roof operations. The hook can be used as a sounding tool as firefighters transverse the roof. Firefighters can use the wide heel of the hook's head to strike and sound the roof as they proceed. The width of a rubbish hook's head also simplifies pulling up cut portions of a roof. Firefighters can place the head of the hook over the joist, with both hook tines on either side of the joist; this creates equal pressure on both sides of the sheathing when it is pulled open by the firefighter. The head's large size also assists firefighters in pushing down the ceilings once the roof is open. Remember, it is possible for a hook to catch onto wiring, cable, or ductwork when pushing down the ceilings.

Power saws: rotary and chainsaw. Power saws are versatile tools that can simplify ventilation operations by reducing the time it takes to open a roof with a hand tool. Using power saws also reduces the physical exertion level on a firefighter, increasing his or her effectiveness to perform other tasks once the roof is open. Although power tools are beneficial, they do have some drawbacks (bulky, cumbersome to operate at some angles) and can break at a moment's notice (the saw's starter chord can snap or tear out of the saw), requiring firefighters to use hand tools to provide ventilation.

Rotary power saws are excellent tools to use for cutting the thick or heavy roof composition usually found on older roofs. The saw's rotating blade is very good for cutting through thick tar and expelling the material through the blade guard and out of the saw. For these reasons, the rotary saw is better equipped to handle these types of roof operations on these structures.

As with a rotary saw, a chainsaw can simplify numerous ventilation operations to a significant degree. The chainsaw can be effective on roofs with asphalt shingles and wood plank decking or plywood/OSB sheathing. Depending on the type of chain used, the saw should be able to cut directly through the shingles and sheathing in one operation, enabling the roof to be opened in less time.

FIREGROUND NOTE

When faced with thick tar roofs, firefighters often attempt to pull the whole cut section of tar off the roof first. Then they attack the roof planks or sheathing to complete the roof opening.

Using a rotary saw or chainsaw to perform roof ventilation tactics presents a variety of hazards to firefighters. All safety measures must be followed and all firefighters must be aware of the dangers when a live saw is operating.

For more information on operating saws, see the saw sections of chapter 11, Tools.

Radio

Firefighters performing either vertical or horizontal ventilation efforts must carry and use a radio to communicate with interior teams on ventilation tactics. This is extremely important when performing horizontal ventilation, because it must be coordinated with the hoseline's advance on the fire. Firefighters *must* keep this in mind when ventilating top floor windows from the roof. It is also vital for firefighters to communicate when performing roof ventilation operations.

A firefighter opening up a roof's bulkhead door when a fire is in a large multiple dwelling can simply relay to their officer that the **roof is open**, meaning that initial vertical ventilation over the stairwell is complete. This informs the officer that the firefighter has gotten to the assignment and the mushrooming effects of the smoke and hazardous gases may have been eliminated.

Another simple communication statement should be made to units operating on the fire floor once the roof has been cut open. Prior to the ceilings being pushed down, the roof firefighter should quickly announce over the radio that it is going to be performed. By stating this message, firefighters operating on the floor below can prepare for a falling ceiling to crash down. A simple safety measure is for a firefighter to be positioned in a doorway, thus protected by the door frame when a ceiling is pushed down from above.

It is of the utmost importance for all firefighters to relay any pertinent information (heavy loads on the roof such as HVAC units, etc.) or delays that may affect ventilation operations to the incident commander.

Halligan tool. Firefighters often carry a Halligan tool to the roof for roof operations. The tool has a number of uses and is an excellent tool to force open doors on bulkheads, elevators, and penthouses. It also helps firefighters open up scuttle covers and make a safety step for peaked roof operations.

For more information on the Halligan tool, see chapter 11, Basic Firefighting Tools.

Rope: utility rope and life-saving rope. FFI 5.3.20
Firefighters should carry some type of utility rope; it is another tool on which they often rely. During roof operations the rope can be used to tie a hand tool to ventilate top floor windows. It is also good for hoisting additional tools and equipment to the roof. Firefighters can also use this rope to section off a dangerous section of the roof, preventing a fireground mishap.

In some areas it is necessary to carry a lifesaving rope to the roof. This rope is not to be used for ventilation efforts; its intended use is to save any life that may be trapped by the fire and to provide an emergency escape device for firefighters operating on the roof if no other avenue of escape is accessible.

Access to the roof

Firefighters must have a pre-formulated plan on how to reach the roof of the fire building. For many private dwellings, access to the roof is by portable, aerial, or tower ladder. In many instances, because of the roof's high pitch, a roof ladder is needed as well. For larger multiple dwellings, firefighters should communicate with the inside teams to see if there is an alternate enclosed stairwell other than the attack stair that has access to the roof. If another stairwell is not available, firefighters should use the following:

- The adjoining building. Cross over at the front of the roof if the buildings align. Remember, if they are on a slope or hill, it is always better to choose the higher building and drop down to the fire building than it is to try and climb up to the fire building from the building below.

- An aerial or tower ladder to gain roof access to the fire building. If necessary, use one of these devices to reach the exposure, and use a portable ladder for access to the fire building.

- A fire escape that provides roof access (fig. 14–44). The fire escape should be the last resort because of their age and maintenance issues. Also, they can be narrow and be difficult to maneuver on, often requiring firefighters to perform the reduce profile maneuver.

On row-frame dwellings, using an adjoining building is not always wise, because of the **common cockloft**. A firefighter could get injured climbing up an interior scuttle ladder if the fire breaks out while he or she is climbing. A safer means of travel is to use a portable, aerial, or tower ladder to gain access to these structures' roofs.

Fig. 14–44. At times, the quickest way up is via an exterior fire escape.

Encountering obstacles during roof access and operations. Access to the roof to perform ventilation tactics can often be hampered by a variety of obstacles, such as trees, overhead electrical wires, and street lights, to name a few. These obstacles can often delay placement of ladders to the roof and overall roof operations, because a firefighter may have to find an alternate way to the roof. Many times, using the adjoining building for roof access can be the quickest and simplest method available. Firefighters should notify the incident commander whenever they encounter obstacles that severely delay their work assignment.

Security fences. On many structures that have adjoining roofs, security fences have been placed on the adjoining parapet walls to prevent rooftop intrusions. These fences may be chain link, steel bars, or ornamental aluminum fences. In some instances, the top of these fences have razor wire or barbed wire strung across them for increased security. Also, many of these fences jut out over the front and rear cornice or parapet walls. This prevents access around the ends of the fence.

For access through a chain-link fence, a firefighter should locate the small wire tie bands that wrap around the piping of the fence. These ties secure the chain-link fence to the pipe structure. A firefighter should attack these ties starting at the bottom of the fence. Inserting the point of a hand tool into the chain link next to the wire band and prying in one direction normally pops the tie or pulls it off the fence. Some firefighters carry small wire cutters, which can also cut the wire ties off the fence.

As the bottom ties are removed, the firefighter cuts or releases a few vertical ties on the vertical pipes of the fence. Once a small area has been released, the firefighter can lift up the bottom of the fence and place a hook under it to keep it suspended. Now he or she can transverse to the other rooftop for roof ventilation operations.

When steel bar fences are in between rooftops, access to the adjoining roof can be more difficult. Attacking the welds or trying to bend the individual metal bars is often time consuming and still does not permit access to the adjoining roof. If these fences are visible from the street level, a firefighter should take a forcible-entry saw to the roof. Cutting the steel bars of the fence provides a quick means of egress to the adjoining roof for ventilation operations.

Cell phone sites. Many buildings are now leasing their rooftop space and **air rights** to cell phone service providers. The roofs of such buildings are now loaded with new structures that increase the weight load on their structural components and presents other problems for roof operations (fig. 14–45). In numerous installations, wire conduit and pipe chases provide power and signal service for equipment, and antennas run along the rooftop surface. These conditions can restrict the area available for cutting the roof for vertical ventilation.

It is also important to note that these antennas emit microwaves and are harmful to the health of human beings. If firefighters are within 10 ft of an operational cellular antenna when it is transmitting, serious or fatal damage can occur from radiofrequency (RF) radiation. When operating on the roof, firefighters must restrict the time they must operate in front of these antennas, and stay as far outside a 10 ft radius from a cell tower as possible (fig. 14–46). This reduces exposure levels to the microwaves and increases overall safety while working on the roof. In some installations, natural gas lines are run along the roof from an auxiliary generator in case of an electrical malfunction. These gas lines can become severe exposures and a hazard if the roof is engulfed or compromised due to fire.

Fig. 14–45. Cell site equipment introduces new hazards to roof operations.

Fig. 14–46. Cell site antennae add more risk from RF wave radiation, which can be dangerous or fatal if standing within 10 ft while transmitting. Look for cell site installations on tall buildings or buildings built on high ground in your district.

Remember, inform the incident commander whenever a **cell phone site** is found on the roof or tied into the roof's parapet walls.

Multiple roofs. **Multiple roofs** are common on many renovated buildings. When the building was retrofitted instead of removing the original roof, a new roof was just placed on top of it (fig. 14–47). If firefighters perform roof ventilation operations and find a second roof below the original roof, they should immediately inform the incident commander. Judging from the fire conditions below, the incident commander may have firefighting operations on the roof cease or attempt to cut the roof below the original roofline. Remember, the addition of the new roof also adds a significant weight load to the structure.

Fig. 14–47. During some building renovations, peaked "rain roofs" are sometimes added over existing flat roofs, which makes ventilation operations difficult.

Determining feasibility. FFI 5.3.12 Beyond reading the status of the roof, personnel must determine whether or not ventilation operations on it are feasible. This entails knowing such factors as the location, size, and extension of fire and the type of roof construction present. The roof may be constructed of 2 × 12 in. (50 × 305 mm) joists/rafters and 1 × 6 in. (25 × 150 mm) sheathing, 2 × 3 in. (50 × 75 mm) wooden I-beams and ⅜-in. (10-mm) plywood or OSB, heavy wood timber beams, lightweight wood truss systems, or open-web steel bar joist construction covered by corrugated metal.

All these roofs may look similar from the top, yet each reacts differently when exposed to fire. Before committing personnel onto an unknown roof, determine whether it is structurally sound and whether it provides adequate time to perform the intended operations. The roof must also be sized up for items on the roof such as air conditioning units, HVAC units, billboard frames, cell phone sites and antennas, and any unusual conditions. These items can increase the weight load on the structural joist and supports and could cause an early collapse in adverse fire conditions. Remember to communicate the location of these things to the incident commander.

The type of construction can determine the location of a ventilation opening. For example, conventional construction obtains its strength from the size of its structural members. This often allows ventilation openings to be made over or near the fire if the roof is deemed safe. The key ingredient is the time available between impingement by flame and structural collapse. Conversely, lightweight construction is subject to fast failure rates and may not allow adequate time for these operations. Therefore, any ventilation operations on lightweight roofs should focus on uninvolved portions. While working on a roof, consider the potential of fire

underneath. Start ventilation cuts in the weakest portion of the roof (near the fire) and work away toward the strongest portion. Spend as little time as possible on the weak portion. Also, work away from the fire and toward the means of egress.

To underscore an important point, consider the following about roof construction: Roofing material is usually made up of an under-laminate or sheathing, corrugated steel decking covered by composition-type materials (insulation board, polystyrene [Styrofoam]), or shingles (asphalt or cedar). It is important for firefighting personnel to be familiar with a particular building and roof and the structural members because sheathing or plywood/OSB decking can weaken or burn away without burning through the composition covering. Therefore, although a roof may look normal from the top, it may not support any weight.

Once firefighters have vented the natural roof openings and the top floor fire or attic area needs additional ventilation, the longer task of cutting the roof open begins. When the first firefighter assigned to roof ventilation accesses the roof, he or she should have a tool to sound the roof as they proceed. The firefighter is also trying to determine if the roof is strong enough to support the weight of personnel or if the decking has been burned away under the roofing material. The strength of a roof can easily be determined by sounding it with an axe, pike pole, rubbish hook, or other such tool. Always evaluate the integrity of a roof before stepping onto it (fig. 14–48).

Fig. 14–48. Always sound the roof ahead of you to evaluate its integrity.

The firefighter on the roof should also use his or her feet in conjunction with the sounding tool. Being sensitive with the feet can reveal a roof's bounce, flex, or sponginess. Sounding a roof also provides an additional benefit; firefighters can often determine the location of its supported and unsupported sections, particularly on lightweight roofs. In addition, firefighters can always cut inspection cuts into the roof to determine roof construction and roof joist layout.

When the first ventilation member sounds a roof to determine its safety, that member also determines the path of travel for other firefighters. Inexperienced members shouldn't determine the path of travel across a roof. A good rule to follow on flat roof structures is to walk along the building's perimeter to access the area of the fire. The roof beams are normally supported at the ends of the building; and in many cases if a firefighter must seek an alternate means off the roof, he or she may be able to cross over to safety on the next building. When operating on peak roofs, the firefighter should work on a portable ladder, on an aerial ladder, or from the safety of a tower ladder basket.

Before venturing off the ladder, personnel must take the appropriate time to read the roof. What is the location of the fire? Is it burning in a specific location, or is it extending from its original location? How long has the fire been burning? Is fire showing through the roof? Is a portion of the roof sagging? Does the roof have ventilators, and are they issuing smoke or fire? Consider evaluating the building as a building under demolition. What type of roof is it? Is it of conventional construction? Is the roof covered with slate or tile, making it difficult to traverse? Such materials can be deceptive, changing the way the roof feels underneath you. Do you know where your means of egress is located? Know where and how to exit the roof and whether or not you have an alternate means of escape (fig. 14–49). If roof ventilation personnel discover that skylights are available and appropriately located, they may be able to accomplish ventilation without cutting the decking.

Fig. 14–49. A good practice is to set up an additional ladder as a second means of egress from the roof in case access to the primary ladder is compromised.

Determining where to cut. Normally, firefighters are directed to cut the roof directly over the fire when performing roof operations (fig. 14–50). Sometimes it may be difficult to determine where to cut the roof. Firefighters can look for certain clues to assist them in choosing a cutting location. The following items should be surveyed for clues:

- Melting or bubbling tar
- Asphalt shingles curling upward
- Wood shingles smoldering or smoking
- A wet roof with a dry area
- A snow- or ice-covered roof with a melting area
- Location of the fire area gathered from a perimeter search
- Checking the base of soil or vent pipes for heat
- Radio communication from the interior firefighting teams

Although cutting directly over the fire is a good theory for firefighters to follow, sometimes it needs adjustment. If a roof is not structurally sound, firefighters should not position themselves over the fire to cut it; moving back to a safer location may be more beneficial. *Firefighters should never attempt to ventilate a roof of lightweight wood construction involved in a fire.* Also, if a fire is already ventilating out of the windows, firefighters should position the cut a little further back, not directly over the fire. Because the fire is already venting to the outside from this specific location, it may be advisable to cut a little further back to assist vertical ventilation. This channels and ventilates the heat, gases, and smoke upwards and also relieves the punishing conditions in the immediate area of the fire. This can assist the engine company's advance into the fire area with their hoseline.

Fig. 14–50. Use visual clues and communication to determine where to cut.

Making the cut. When possible, firefighters should plan ventilation cuts so that the wind is at their backs, with smoke and heat moving away from the cut. They should also attempt to make the long side of the ventilation cuts parallel to the roof joist. Following this method allows more joist channels to be ventilated. When cutting the roof decking open, don't make the cuts deeper than the thickness of the decking, this can cause the saw's blade to hit a joist and possibly damage a structural member.

Remember, to adequately ventilate any building, make the opening commensurate with the amount of heat and smoke inside. Observe the pressure of the venting smoke. If the contaminants are coming out lazily, the opening probably doesn't have to be enlarged. However, if the contaminants are venting under significant pressure, the opening is too small. Keep increasing its size it or create additional openings as necessary.

Openings made in roof decking involve specific considerations to make them quickly and efficiently. This doesn't imply that the openings should be small and made in haste. They should be easy to open and of a size appropriate to the needs of the incident. Therefore, when cutting and removing roof decking, don't cut a ventilation opening that cannot be easily and completely opened. A common recommendation for roof ventilation openings is 4×4 ft (1.2×1.2 m) or 3×6 ft (1×2 m) for dwellings and 8×8 ft (2.4×2.4 m) for commercial properties. Remember these are only guidelines and some fire departments have changed SOPs in roof cut's sizes because of the fire load of today's fire environment.

Often firefighters face stone or gravel placed over the roof membrane on the structure's roof. Placing a rotating saw blade into these materials can create flying projectiles and injure a firefighter. It is important for firefighters to use their boot and sweep or drag the material away from the cutting line. Another option is to use a shovel or brush broom to remove the material from the cut line.

After the cut: pushing down the ceiling. Once the cut in the roof has been made and the roof sheathing is pulled and detached from the roof joist, ventilation operations are not completed. Just cutting and pulling up the roof sheathing only affords ventilation of the cockloft or attic space. To properly ventilate the fire room or rooms below, the ceilings must be pushed down from the roof (fig. 14–51). A good firefighting tactic to perform is to verbally announce this over the radio to inform the interior firefighting crews of the impending ceiling situation.

When firefighters are going to push down the ceiling from the roof, they should position their bodies to the windward side of the ventilation hole. They should be in line or parallel with one of the sides of the hole and only expose very few body parts over the hole to push the ceiling down. In this situation, if they were to slip on the roof surface or loose their balance and fall forward, they could keep from falling directly into the ventilation hole. Using this technique also keeps them out of the direction of escaping heat, smoke, and gases that could ignite once they escape to fresh air. Firefighters should not bend over and square themselves up to the hole and push downward with a hook. If they slip, they might fall directly into the ventilation opening and be injured.

Fig. 14–51. After cutting the roof and removing the sheathing, the task is completed when the ceiling is pushed down.

If another firefighter is assisting with roof operations, he or she should hold onto the bottom of the firefighter's coat or hold onto the safety harness for support while the firefighter pushes down the ceiling. If operating on a roof ladder, the firefighter pushing down the ceiling can also hook into the roof ladder with his or her safety belt to ensure he or she stays on the roof.

When using a hook to push down the top floor ceiling, some fire departments encourage their members to push the ceiling down with the butt end of the hook's handle. By using this technique, the hook's head is less likely to hit and snag on any wire, cable, or ductwork in the attic or cockloft space as it is pulled upward. Some fire departments use larger hooks such as rubbish hooks; this increases the area of the ceiling the hook's head can penetrate. Another method to use for pushing down the ceiling is to use some of the roof planking that was pulled up off the joist. The roof planks are wider than standard roof hooks and can also push down a greater area of ceiling. In addition, if the plank slipped out of the firefighter's hand, he or she would not lose the tool.

Safety considerations for roof operations

FFI 5.3.12 In most cases, these safety considerations apply to both flat and peaked/pitched roofs, except where peaked/pitch roofs are specifically identified.

- When faced with severe smoke conditions, firefighters should crawl on the roof with a tool out in front of them, probing the area for any open shaftways or hazards. Many firefighters have accidentally walked off roofs in smoke.

- Initially, when firefighters arrive on the roof, they should size up an alternate means of escape in case of an emergency retreat. Placing at least two ladders to a roof can provide a secondary avenue of escape. Ladders placed to each side of a building can ensure an avenue of escape to all sides.

- Cutting an inspection hole in a roof can reveal the type of construction of the roof's framing system.

- When firefighters proceed with a live rotary saw, they can push the saw across the roof like a wheelbarrow, eliminating the chances of the blade striking another firefighter.

- As firefighters proceed across a roof, they should sound the roof with a tool to ensure its stability. Skylights may have been removed and covered up with skimpy materials, which could collapse under a firefighter's weight. It is also recommended that firefighters proceeding across a roof with a large area make inspection holes/cuts if the roof is of questionable stability.

- If time and conditions permit, firefighters can cut a rubber membrane covering off a roof prior to cutting it (fig. 14–52). This inhibits the membrane from gumming up the blade and interior of the blade guard of a rotary saw, but more importantly it prevents the membrane from catching on fire. This can create a flash fire condition and fire extending across the roof's surface rapidly, making a firefighters retreat a priority. *Note:* Membranes can be easily cut without entanglement if using a chainsaw with a sharp chain run at full RPM, rather than a rotary saw.

- When a roof cut is pulled open or skylight removed, the section or skylight should be laid on the roof in the vicinity of the cut or opening. This piece of material should serve as a warning to firefighters that a hole or opening exists in the roof.

- Firefighters operating on peaked or pitched roofs should work from the safety of a roof ladder, tower ladder, or aerial ladder. Wearing an approved safety belt or harness is recommended.

- If footing on a pitched roof is questionable, the firefighter can place the point of the Halligan bar or the blade of an axe into the roof to make a safety step (fig. 14–53).

- For additional safety considerations, see the "Size-up" section in chapter 31, Advanced Fire Attack.

Fig. 14–52. A firefighter using a knife to remove roof membrane to avoid having rubberized material bind the rotary power saw

Fig. 14–53. A tool such as a pick-head axe can be driven into the roof as a safety step while working on a peaked roof.

FIREGROUND NOTE

Many of today's roofs are insulated with thick materials that also create a pitch in the roof for drainage. These thick materials can prevent the rotary saw's blade from reaching the roof sheathing in the initial cut. If an inspection cut reveals thick insulation, firefighters can use a knife to cut off the roof covering, expose it, and cut the insulation away from the sheathing. This helps overall roof operations.

- In some instances it may be necessary to make a hole in the peaked roof on the opposite side of the ridgepole for the roof ladder's hook to sit in. This ensures the roof ladder's hook bites into the roof, securing the ladder over a high ridge vent.

- Prior to transferring from a ladder to a roof ladder, a firefighter should pull down on the roof ladder to ensure it is secured to the roof.

- If when cutting a roof a white/gray powdery residue is found, firefighters should relay this information to the fireground commander and evacuate the roof. This indicates a lightweight gypsum roof, which is prone to collapse.

- When operating at attached row frames, brownstones, or multiple dwellings, firefighters should cross over at the front of the buildings. Open-ended shaftways between buildings can exist toward the rear, and a firefighter could fall.

- If climbing up onto a bulkhead to vent its skylight, always get on and off the bulkhead in the same location. One side of the bulkhead could face an open shaft between buildings.

- Prior to removing slate or tile from a roof, advise the fireground over the radio that this tactic is being deployed to reduce the risk of injury from flying debris.

- Wearing an approved safety belt or harness when operating on the roof ladder can allow the firefighter to work with both hands while properly attached to the ladder.

- Prior to getting to the roof, firefighters should have a preplan regarding what they will be performing and a back-up plan in case the first plan of action cannot be achieved or fails.

- Once on the roof, the presence of any heavy equipment such as air conditioning units, billboard frames, and cell phone sites should be relayed to the incident commander. These things can lead to an early collapse of the roof under fire conditions.

- If a fire wall is separating a common cockloft or adjoining buildings and there is fire inside the cockloft space, consider cutting an inspection hole into the building not on fire. The adjoining building's joist pockets may have deteriorated over the years and fire could spread horizontally, despite the fire wall.

- If a life-saving rope is part of a firefighter's standard equipment, it should be placed near a substantial object on the roof, where it would be tied off to perform an **emergency escape slide** or a **rescue pickup evolution**.

- Because of the complexity of roof operations and their danger levels, firefighters should always operate in teams of two. Whenever a saw is removed from the roof cut, the saw operator should engage the chain brake, if using a chain saw, or place the blade of a rotary saw onto the roof to stop it from spinning. Engaging the chain brake or stopping a blade from rotating reduces the chances of striking and injuring another firefighter.

- Whenever noise levels on the roof make it difficult to monitor radio communications, one firefighter should move to a quieter location to monitor the radio. This firefighter should be in line of sight of the cutting operations, in case they must relay information to the saw team.

- Firefighters should not use satellite dishes mounted on the roof for foot support; they may be insufficiently attached to the roof.

- If a firefighter must use a fire escape for roof access, he or she should always shake the gooseneck ladder before climbing to ensure it is attached to the building's wall and roof.

- Firefighters operating on the roof should always perform a perimeter search, looking for trapped or fallen victims who may be in shrubbery or shafts. They should also check for the fire's location, extension, and autoexposure possibilities.

Inspection holes

When firefighters operate on roofs of burning structures, it is vital that they operate safely. An important safety tactic to follow is to cut **inspection hole(s)**. Inspection holes provide a firefighter with a lot of information pertaining to the conditions below a roof covering if the firefighter is uncertain about the extent of fire in the roof structure. These conditions may include the following:

- The nature of the smoke (i.e., color, volume, temperature, pushing under pressure)

- The volume of fire, direction of fire travel, and the fire's extension

- The type, size, and run of the structural elements supporting the roof

The three most common types of inspection holes firefighters' use on a variety of roof types are a **punched hole**, a **kerf cut**, and a **triangular cut**.

When making an inspection hole, make it small enough that a firefighter cannot accidently step in it and break an ankle when visibility is low.

Punched hole. It is normally relatively easy to punch a hole in most roofs. Firefighters can forcibly drive the following tools through the roof to create an inspection hole:

- Pick end of a pick-head axe

- Sharp point of a hook

- Pry bar end of a hook

- Pick end of the Halligan bar

Once the tool has been driven into the roof surface, the firefighter can pry the tool back and forth to expand the hole; this also helps release the tool from the roof. Once the tool is released, the firefighter can judge the smoke and fire conditions below (fig 14–54).

The punched hole inspection method has a drawback: The hole that the tool creates is not that large (fig. 14–55). This can cause a firefighter to miscalculate; the actual fire or smoke conditions under the roof covering and construction components. The punched hole inspec-

tion hole does offer the firefighter an additional safety benefit at fires. As a firefighter proceeds across a roof, he or she should sound the roof with the sharp end of a tool or its butt end. In this manner, if the roof's stability is questionable or the roof's tar is melting, the tool may perforate the roof covering, which can alert firefighters to the dangerous condition below or help them find a good area for roof cutting operations.

Fig. 14–54. A firefighter punching a hole in a roof to make a quick inspection hole using a hook.

Fig. 14–55. An inspection hole punched in an asphalt shingle roof.

Kerf cut. The kerf cut is a quick and easy inspection hole to use during roof operations; it is also commonly referred to as a plunge cut. Firefighters can use an axe, power saw, or chain saw to cut one blade's width into the roofing material. If a power saw is used to make the cut, the firefighter should bring the saw up to full rpm prior to contacting the roofing material. This will prevent the blade from binding into the roof or the saw from stalling. As the blade is pulled out of the roof, it creates an opening the width of a single blade (known as the kerf). This kerf allows the firefighter to judge the conditions below. The kerf cut is often used when a firefighter is quickly trying to determine the boundaries of the fire's extension. The downside of the kerf cut is that it is also small, and often on membrane roofs or rubberized roofs the kerf can close up if the roof is subjected to heat from the fire (fig. 14–56).

Fig. 14–56. The Kerf cut is a quick way to make an inspection hole during roof operations.

Triangular inspection hole. The **triangular inspection hole** is also commonly referred to as a tepee cut or an A cut because of its resemblance to them. The cut is far superior to the other types of inspection cuts and holes because it is larger and gives the firefighter better visibility into the attic or cockloft space. This helps firefighters quickly identify today's modern lightweight construction features. The only setback in making this cut is that it takes a little longer time to cut the three legs of the triangle.

To complete the triangular inspection hole, stand in a well-balanced position, with feet spread open and aligned. Next, flex and bend at the knees, so the saw touches the roof surface. Hold the saw out in front at all times, performing the cuts in the leg space area (fig. 14–57).

Fig. 14–57. An inspection hole can be used to indicate the type of roof, size of structural members, thickness of the roofing material, and the presence of any fire or smoke. Limit the size of the inspection hole to avoid stepping in it.

The sequence of cuts should be preplanned and become second nature to all firefighters. The first cut should be diagonal. The firefighter starts at the center, and cuts down toward the right boot. The second cut is vertical, starting at the top of the first cut and cutting down toward the center of the firefighter's stance. It is extremely important that all cut lines overlap, so the roofing material is cut all the way through. The last cut is the easiest cut to make. It is performed from left to right, overlapping both cut line and forming the bottom leg of the triangle.

Once the cuts are completed, the roofing material can be removed by striking it downward, pulling it out of the cut; or it may fall into the hole once the cut has been completed. In some instances, the roof material may hinge on a joist once the cut has been made.

Roof ventilation cuts

Pullback method. The **pullback** method of roof ventilation uses three cuts in the roof deck for removal and is designed to work on a roof sheathed with roof boards or planking of 1 × 6, 1 × 8, or 1 × 12 in. (25 × 152, 25 × 200, or 25 × 305 mm). It cannot be used successfully on roofs with plywood or OSB decks, as it is too difficult to pull. Once the cut is made it resembles an upside down U.

To perform this cut, first make a head or top cut across three joists/rafters. If on a pitched roof, make the head cut approximately 1 ft below the ridge. Avoid cutting into the rafters by rolling the saw up and over when it makes contact with a rafter. Use chain saws in the vertical position (at a 90-degree angle) for the head cut.

- Then make two downward cuts (the sides of the U), starting at the head cut and moving toward the bottom of the roof, parallel with the rafters between the center and outside or between both outside joists/rafters. Remember to overlap the cut lines with the saw to permit the roofing to be pulled. These joists/rafters are on 24-in. (610-mm) centers.

- To make pulling up the roof boards easier, make a simple crossover or knockout cut in the top corner of the cut. This allows a tool to be inserted under the sheathing to assist in removal. Remove the top board using a hook to pull upward, which separates the board from the joist. When performing this on a roof with joist spacing on 16-in. (406-mm) centers, two firefighters may find it easier to release the roof boards with hooks at each end.

- Continue to remove the decking material with a steady hooking motion adjacent to the center rafter. If necessary, roof covering can be scored (a light cut in the surface material only) at the bottom portion of the opening to ensure a clean and easy break.

Some benefits of using this method are as follows:

- The head cut reveals the location and spacing of the roof joist.

- A ventilation opening can be initiated near the ridge and opened toward the point of egress.

- A section of decking to be removed is only nailed to a single rafter, or possibly two.

- The decking material doesn't drop into the structure, possibly injuring operating members or trapped civilians.

- The cutting process is a quick method, reducing time for other important tasks to be accomplished.

- Firefighters can use this method with or without a roof ladder on pitched roofs, depending on the pitch.

Some fire departments have another version in their arsenal of cuts and one referred to as the *tepee cut*. Normally, this cut is used in forcible entry on roll-down gates but can be used in roof ventilation. It is much like the pullback method of roof ventilation; instead of cutting an upside down U, the firefighter cuts a tepee design with one crosscut. This cut also reduces the time it takes to cut open a planked roof and only employs three cuts to be performed. The tepee cut can be performed on plywood/OSB-sheathed roofs, but it may be difficult to remove the sheathing once the cuts are made. It is also easy to perform the teepee cut out of the tower ladder's bucket or off of an aerial ladder.

To perform this cut, make one diagonal downward cut from the ridge about 3 to 5 ft (1 to 1.5 m) long. Next put a small crosscut about 8 in. (200 mm) down from the peak; this is a knockout for tool insertion to pull the roof. Ensure that the crosscut overlaps and goes across both downward cuts. The last cut is the second diagonal downward cut. Now that the cuts are complete, a hook can be inserted into the knockout and the roof planking pulled off the roof (fig. 14–58). Remember, once the roof planks have been removed, the top floor ceiling must be pushed down to ventilate the top floor (fig. 14–59).

Fig. 14–58. Roof sheathing is removed after a teepee cut has been made.

Fig. 14–59. Knowing how to use your tools can get the job done faster and easier.

Dicing. The **dicing** method of roof ventilation consists of making multiple downward cuts between and with the direction of the roof joist. This method can be used on roof planking systems and sheathed roofs. A head cut may not be required if there is a ridge vent, but it is required when there isn't one present. Dicing the roof is performed by following these three steps:

1. Make a head cut perpendicular to and across the joist, measuring the desired length of the ventilation opening. This cut should be located near the ridge if on a pitched roof. It is also good practice to make a knockout or crossover cut to allow the roofing to be opened up.

Note: After the head or top cut is made, the firefighter can look into the space and see where the joists/rafters are physically located. Also, visible rafter tails present under the eaves of the structure can indicate where to make the next series of cuts.

2. Make two downward cuts on either side of a single rafter. The length of these cuts should be less than the length of the tool used to remove the severed section. This ensures that personnel stand on uncut portions of the roof while they remove the decking.

3. Step 2 is continued as necessary to achieve the desired length of the ventilation opening. Firefighters must remember to overlap all cut lines to permit the roofing to be pulled.

The cut sections of decking are then removed by beginning near the start of the head cut. Loosen the first section of sheathing to be removed by hitting the end of the first-cut board with an appropriate tool if no knockout cut was made. Then with the same tool, use an upward pulling motion to remove the decking. Firefighters should work down and across the slope of the roof until the entire cut portions of the roof have been removed.

Some benefits to using this method are as follows:

- The head cut can reveal the location of the joist and their spacing.

- Firefighters can remove the decking away from the fire and toward their means of egress.

- Removing decking that is nailed only to a single rafter can be quick and easy.

- A large section of roof is opened with minimal cutting operations.

- The decking material doesn't drop into the attic or into the structure.

If the need to increase this opening is necessary, firefighters should have the foresight to remove the pulled up roof decking a sufficient distance away from the bottom legs of the cut. Doing so allows the cut to be quickly expanded downward.

Louvering. The **louvering** method (also known as the butterfly or hinging method) can be effectively performed on most types of roofs and roof decks, often more quickly than the coffin cut described below. A power saw and the principle of leverage do most of the work. The following five steps are followed to louver a roof:

1. Make a head cut perpendicular to and across the joist, the desired length of the ventilation opening. This cut should be made near the ridge if performing this tactic on a pitched roof. Remember, when making contact with a joist, roll the saw up and

over it to prevent doing structural damage. Chain saws must be used in the vertical position (at a 90-degree angle, perpendicular to the roof). Typically, chain saws are more effective than rotary saws for this operation.

2. Next look into the kerf of the head cut and spot the joist's location. Then make downward cuts between the centers of the joists/rafters. The length of these cuts is determined by the size of the ventilation opening; however, 4 to 6 ft is an approximate rule of thumb.

3. The last cut is a parallel cut made along the entire bottom of the cut, similar to the cut in Step 1.

4. Remember where all the cuts intersect; they must continue to cut several inches past the intersections to ensure that the decking has been completely severed. Remember to avoid compromising structural members.

5. The cut section of decking can now be louvered on the rafter to complete the opening. Use an appropriate tool to push down or pull up on one side of the panel to open it. It may be possible to use one tool to push down and another tool to pull up on the opposite side. The object is to open the roof and not push the material into the hole. The material remains attached to the center of the joist and will be in a *hinged* position.

The benefits of using this method are as follows:

- The head cut can reveal the location and spacing of the rafters.

- Louvered decking that is nailed only to a single rafter can be opened easily, because personnel can use the weight and leverage of the panel against itself.

- Firefighters can louver the decking away from the fire and toward their point of egress.

- The decking material isn't usually dropped into the structure. This point depends on how the covering is secured to the base material. Composition material shouldn't slide into an attic. It must be removed from the decking and placed on the roof.

Note: A cut section of decking must be removed if it cannot be louvered because of contact with sprinkler pipes, bracing, conduit, or other obstacles. Remember, this method is faster and requires less effort than the pullback or dicing method of roof ventilation.

Ventilation

FIREFIGHTER I

Chapter 14

Coffin cut or expandable cut

SKILL DRILL

When a serious fire occurs on the top floor of a structure or in the attic or cockloft space, it is important to provide ventilation. Initially, windows, scuttle covers, bulkhead doors, and skylights should be ventilated first, prior to the slower task of opening up a roof with a saw. When the roof is going to be **opened up**, firefighters should have a preformulated plan or sequence of cuts to follow. A good plan of action to follow is to make an expandable opening or coffin cut in the roof.

The **coffin cut** is a relatively easy cut to make and for firefighters to remember the formula: the 7, 9, 8 cut sequence. Normally, the hole's size runs somewhere between 3 × 6 ft (1 × 2 m) or 4 × 8 ft (1.2 × 2.4 m). Prior to cutting, a firefighter should attempt to determine the run of the joists/rafters. Sometimes this requires making an inspection cut, whereas at other times it may be figured out by looking at the size of the building. For example, a row frame dwelling or narrow building may have the joist run side to side; the distance is short and the joist will rest on the outside bearing walls.

Once the run of the joists/rafters has been determined, the long leg of the coffin cut runs perpendicular to the joist; this enables ventilation of more area of the attic or cockloft space. As with all cutting sequences, firefighters try to have the wind blowing at their backs. In this manner, once the cut is made, the wind drives the smoke and gases away from the firefighters. This increases visibility and also puts the firefighters in a clean

atmosphere. Unfortunately, many times this may not feasible because of a blowing or swirling wind condition, so firefighters must use the best approach they can.

Firefighters should perform the following sequence of cuts when cutting the coffin cut (fig. 14–60):

1. Cut line #1 is the top of the seven, approximately 3 to 4 ft long.

2. Cut line #2 is a knockout cut, which allows for tool insertion to pull the roof boards.

3. Cut line #3 is approximately 6 to 8 ft.

4. Cut line #4 and #5 is approximately 3 to 4 ft, making the number 9.

5. Cut line #6 and #7 is approximately 3 to 4 ft, making the number 8.

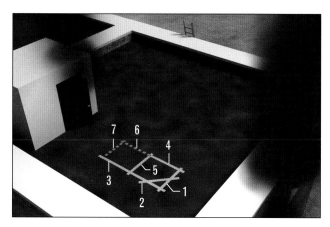

Fig. 14–60. The sequence of cuts needed to make an expandable coffin cut.

If there is time, a second knockout cut can be made just before making cut #4. This enables both sides of the cut to be pulled open by two different firefighters using hand tools.

It is extremely important that the roof cut is not pulled open until all cuts are complete. If conditions on the roof begin to deteriorate before the whole cut is complete, the first box section of the coffin can be pulled open for ventilation efforts prior to firefighters retreating from the roof. If the opening needs to be enlarged, the coffin can be continued in either direction of the rectangle. In addition, it is extremely important that, once the roof has been cut and pulled, the top floor ceilings are pushed down to permit ventilation of the top floor. Also, the top floor windows must be ventilated for a draft of air to flow into the floor and out through the roof opening. By following this procedure, firefighters decrease the chances of horizontal fire spread in the attic or cockloft space.

Trench cut/strip cut. Often in the fire service, firefighters face a large fire in control of an attic or cockloft space. Many fires occur in large buildings that may be shaped in a wing-type design, such as *H, U, E, L*, or even a double *H* type. It is common in such structures to lose or give up a wing to protect the rest of the building. A **trench cut** (also known as a **strip cut**) is a defensive operation that helps firefighters prevent the extension of fire in the attic or cockloft space and reduces the chances of loosing a large portion of the building to fire (fig. 14–61).

Fig. 14–61. A trench cut must extend from one side of the building to the other side and be wide enough to stop the spread of fire.

Firefighters must remember that before any trench cuts are made or opened, a sufficient ventilation hole should be made over the fire. A trench can be cut while a vent hole is being cut, but it should not be opened (if possible) until there is an adequate opening over the fire. One of the main ideas of the trench is that it introduces air into the cockloft space from this remote opening and allows the initial vent hole to pull a draft toward its opening. This reduces the chances of horizontal fire spread in the cockloft and ventilates the area of fire, gases, heat, and smoke.

The trench cut should be made about 20 to 25 ft (6 to 7.6 m) from the initial vent hole or in an advantageous position on the roof. This may be achieved by using the narrowest available roof section or taking advantage of other building characteristics such as the throat section between wings, bulkhead, elevator bulkhead, skylights, or outside walls of the building. The cut must run from wall to wall or another suitable fire stop and be approxi-

mately 3 ft (1 m) wide or wide enough for a firefighter to safely transverse it (fig. 14–61). While cutting across the building, a firefighter can make crosscuts and knockout cuts, similar to those used when making a coffin cut, to assist in opening up the roof. The initial position of the trench should also be chosen in an area that isolates the fire to a certain section of the building and allows the firefighter sufficient time to make the cut, before the fire overruns his or her position.

Inspection cuts can be made on the fire side of the trench, and these holes should be monitored for smoke and fire conditions below. Normally, these holes are located about 5 to 8 ft (1.5 to 2.4 m) in front of the trench. Once the fire has reached these holes, pull open the precut trench. In some cases, inspection holes can be made on both sides of the trench. These additional holes inform the firefighter if the fire has overrun the trench while pulling it open or if there is other fire extension.

If firefighters are overrun by fire while pulling open the trench, they must retreat and possibly begin a second trench in a safe area, if conditions warrant. A charged hoseline positioned on the roof allows firefighters to protect themselves and the trench opening. An additional hoseline positioned at the top floor and the ceiling, removed where the trench is located, can also help prevent the fire from extending across the trench.

Performing a trench cut is a time-consuming tactic, so the need for additional saws and personnel on the roof is of paramount importance. If at any time during the cutting operations firefighters feel that this cut may not stop fire extension, they can pull back to a safe position and begin a second trench.

The ridge vent: ridging the roof. On many new homes, condos, and townhouses, the construction can and normally has a ridge vent incorporated into the peaked or pitched roof. The ridge vent is an area at the peak of the roof, where a space is made between the sheathing and covered with a ridge vent (decorative aluminum vent) or roofing material that allows the roof to vent the hot air from the attic space. Many times the ridge vent is just a mesh fiber covered with shingles; firefighters can easily pull this up with hooks to ventilate the attic space. Unfortunately, the ridge vent space is narrow and permits inadequate ventilation for fire conditions.

However, buildings with ridge vents can aid firefighters in roof ventilation. A common technique used by firefighters is known as **ridging the roof**. Prior to describing the technique, it is important for firefighters to understand a common construction practice. When a building is constructed and the roof is being sheathed with 4 × 8 ft (1.2 × 2.4 m) material, roofers start at the bottom of the roof and work upward, with each course of sheathing staggered. When the last course of sheathing is laid in place, it is normally a smaller section of sheathing and can measure anywhere from 8 to 24 in. × 8 ft (203 to 610 mm × 2.4 m) (in some instances it may be wider).

When firefighters reach the roof, they can pull off the ridge vent and attempt to pry up the last sheet of sheathing from the roof. In many instances it can be pried up and allow a larger ventilation hole. In some instances it may be difficult for it to be pried up in 8-ft (2.4-m) lengths. In these cases a saw or axe can be used to cut the sheet in half and then pry it upward to vent the roof. Firefighters can work right along the peak of the roof and continue opening it up in this manner to allow vertical ventilation.

Another method of ridging the roof is to use a saw and cut downward on both sides of the ridge vent. The length only needs to be as much as the last piece of sheathing applied to the roof. This distance can easily be figured out by a firefighter removing the shingles from the roof in a small area to size up the distance needed to cut. Then relief cuts are made about every 4 ft (1.2 m) to make it easier to remove the sheathing on both sides of the roof. Now a sufficient roof ventilation hole has been made for a fire that involves the attic space or cockloft. Note that if a top floor must be ventilated in this fashion, it may take a long hook to push down the top floor ceilings from this higher position on the roof. Also, when performing this tactic, it is very wise to have a ladder or means of egress off the roof on both sides of the building. A firefighter doesn't want to be cut off from his or her access if the fire lights up out of the ridge vent.

Ridge venting is a newer technique used in firefighting and also performs well when working out of a tower ladder or off an aerial ladder when working on buildings with lightweight truss construction.

Cutting peaked or pitched roofs. When firefighters conduct ventilation operations on roofs that are slightly sloped, walking, operating, and maintaining a solid footing on them are normally minor concerns. However, as the pitch of a roof increases, the firefighter's balance, footing, and stability decreases. The importance placed on maintaining stability during ventilation can't be stressed enough. When faced with a high pitched roof, firefighters must properly use a roof ladder or cut from the safety of a tower ladder or aerial ladder to conduct a safe and efficient roof ventilation operation.

Unfortunately, because of overhead obstructions such as wires and trees, aerial or tower ladders may be unable to reach the roof on some structures. If this is the case, use an extension ladder and a roof ladder. Place the roof ladder next to the section of roof to be ventilated on the windward side, allowing the escaping smoke to blow away from the operator. The roof ladder's base should be near the top of the extension ladder in case the firefighter must retreat from the roof. When the roof ladder is attached to the ridge, the firefighter must ensure that it *bites* into the ridge of the roof. Normally, this is done by the firefighter pulling back down on the roof ladder to ensure it is attached.

Once the roof ladder is secured into the roof, a firefighter can proceed up the ladder with a power saw or hand tools. Most firefighters will bring either an axe or Halligan tool up the ladder with them; the tool will be used to make a safety brace into the roof so the firefighter can place one foot on it for balance while making the cut. Remember, a safety brace can assist in maintaining a safer work environment but if the attic is well involved with fire, it can release smoke and pressurized gases around the tool.

If a second firefighter is available, he or she should proceed up the ladder behind the first firefighter, be equipped with a hook to help remove the roofing material, and push down the interior ceiling once the cut has been completed. While the first firefighter cuts, place the hook on a ladder rung, keeping it out of the way, or its head can be driven into the roof across from the work location. The hook can act like a safety brace in case the upper firefighter slips and loses balance.

The following method is presented as a simple and effective method of working off a roof ladder with two firefighters when cutting on a pitched roof:

- To facilitate working away from the roof ladder, insert the pick end of the axe or the point of the Halligan tool into the roof about 2 ft (0.6 m) from the ladder and below the work area.

- The firefighter operating the saw can now use the embedded tool as a foot brace.

- The second firefighter can now act as a safety person, enabling the saw operator to cut away from the ladder.

- The saw operator can now cut either one or two louver panels, depending on his or her reach and position from the ladder. The firefighter may also cut by using the pullback method of roof ventilation if faced with roof planking.

- Once the cuts have been made, the saw operator should shut down the saw or engage the safety brake and then reposition onto the roof ladder.

- Once on the roof ladder, the firefighter can open up the roof section by louvering or pulling it. Remember, the top floor ceilings should be pushed down once the cut is made.

Using this method results in the following:

- The firefighters maintain stability and efficiency while operating on the roof ladder.

- Decking that is nailed only to a single rafter is easily louvered.

- Decking material should not drop into the building.

- A ventilation opening is easily enlarged as necessary.

Another technique to use for a foot brace and for the saw operator to maintain balance is for the backup firefighter to position the head of a rubbish hook into the roof as a foot brace. The head is placed into the roof out from one side of the ladder, and the butt end of the hook is supported on the roof ladder and braced by the backup firefighter who stands on it. The handle of the hook is now a few inches above the roof and can be used as a support for the saw operator's feet as he or she cuts.

Personnel can also use two roof ladders on either side of an area of roof to be ventilated. Although this is a safe and proven method, its effectiveness is minimized by the number of personnel required and the time necessary to raise two roof ladders, which may be long enough to negate the effects of timely ventilation. Additionally, one of the roof ladders may be in the the path of escaping heat and smoke, depending on the direction of the wind.

When using this method on tile or slate roofs, remember that you may have to remove ridge tile to increase the stability of the roof ladder and ensure positive engagement of ladder hooks into the ridge. You must remove tile to embed an axe and before using power saws or axes to cut the decking. Tile and similar materials can be heavy and may reduce the structural integrity of a roof under fire conditions. In addition, they can cause injuries to members below if they are being removed and slide off the roof.

Operating on a severely pitched roof is a dangerous activity; add some rain, sleet, or snow and it becomes even more dangerous. Firefighters should attempt to work on these roofs from the safety of a tower ladder's

bucket or from an aerial ladder. If using the tower ladder, place the bucket below the intended cutting area at roof level. The saw operator can now open one door of the bucket, place one foot on the roof, and keep one in the bucket. Remember, whenever operating in the tower ladder bucket, wear the installed safety belts or an approved belt tied into the bucket. The saw operator can perform either the louver or pullback cut from the safety of the bucket.

The aerial ladder can be used in place of the roof ladder if it can be placed onto the roof for ventilation operations. These same procedures mentioned earlier can be used on the aerial ladder. In some instances, the aerial ladder accesses the roof, and the roof ladder must be used off the aerial ladder.

FIREGROUND NOTE

In some communities, homes with high peaks are spaced closely together. Firefighters may be able to place a 35-ft extension ladder in line with the pitch of the roof and footed by the adjoining home. Performing this task reduces the time it may take to ventilate the roof, because the roof ladder evolution did not need to be performed. The extension ladder acts as the roof ladder in this scenario.

Another tactic to use is to place the tip of the aerial ladder about 4 ft (1.2 m) back from the intended site to be cut open. The saw operator can kneel on the rungs and lean forward and cut the roof with the saw. The firefighter should be wearing a safety belt and can hook onto the rail behind him or her for added support while cutting. The Charlotte Fire Department developed a method of sending a second firefighter up behind the saw operator. This firefighter ties the safety belt into the belt of the saw operator. The saw operator's belt should be placed with the safety ring on the back side. This way, while they are tied together, the saw operator has more reach with the saw. This method of roof cutting works well with practice and is achievable when cutting open truss roof construction.

Gable end venting. On many homes with attic spaces, **gable end vents** are placed into the exterior walls to permit air flow. Usually, these vents are placed in between the wall studs and near the top peak of the side of the home. The vent is usually either an aluminum louver vent or plastic decorative louver vent and can be easily removed by a firefighter with hand tools for ventilation efforts.

When firefighters are faced with severe weather conditions such as ice, snow, or rain and it may be difficult to perform roof operations for an attic fire, they can attack the gable vent (fig. 14–62). Working from the safety of a tower ladder's bucket or off an aerial ladder is the preferred method of performing this tactic. Once the device is placed to the side of the home, just below the vent a firefighter can quickly remove the louver with a hand tool. The firefighter performing the operation must position himself to the side of the louver so as not to be directly exposed to the venting smoke and fire. Once the louver is removed, the firefighter can use a power saw and cut downward along both sides of the vent, removing the exterior sheathing of the home. If the interior wall is finished, the hand tool can be used to knock in the wall and complete the ventilation tactic.

Fig. 14–62. A gable vent being opened for a concealed space helps the ventilation process.

Although most walls in homes are constructed with the wall studs being on 16- or 24-in. (406- or 610-mm) centers, this type of ventilation doesn't provide an excellent means of smoke and gas removal; but it works well and doesn't chance a firefighter from falling off the roof. In some instances, once firefighters have opened up one bay using this technique, they'll open up the adjoining bays to provide more ventilation to the attic space.

Miscellaneous types of roofs

Open-web steel bar joist. Open-web steel bar joist construction usually supports a metal deck roof or a metal built-up roof that may be covered with multiple layers of insulation material, tar, and composition (fig. 14–63). The building industry considers the metal built-up roof to be an efficient form of construction because the materials are widely available, the cost is less than that of a comparable wood roof, and it is an easy roof to install. Unfortunately, the steel bar joist and metal deck roof can be dangerous when exposed to fire. Steel loses a large portion of its strength at 1,000°F (538°C), and such roofs have a quick failure rate with minimal warning, resulting in an unannounced collapse. In addition, the joists can be spaced from 2 to 8 ft (0.6 to 2.4 m) apart, leaving a large section of roof unsupported between the joists. These roofs demand specific ventilation techniques after a comprehensive size-up of the fire conditions below. It is imperative that safety be the number one priority when deciding to vent a metal deck roof. Moderate or heavy fire conditions in the building below will dictate that firefighters will not be positioned on the roof because of the substantial collapse potential.

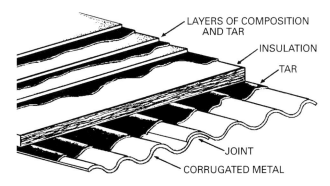

Fig. 14–63. The decking of an open-web bar joist roof normally consists of corrugated metal covered with multiple layers of insulation, tar, and composition.

In many instances these roofs are equipped with glass or plastic skylights, permitting easy initial ventilation tactics to be performed after a detailed size-up. When faced with severe fire conditions in this type of operation, roof operations may be considered too dangerous to perform. In many instances firefighters must rely on horizontal ventilation operations: opening up windows and garage doors when faced with steel bar joist construction.

When dealing with steel bar joist construction, firefighters may face a specific type of fire that does not involve the interior of the building. Many times, vents extending through the roof from grease duct equipment can ignite a fire in the roofing materials. These fires can often spread between the metal deck and the composition covering. Cutting these roofs with a roof saw can be achieved to limit the extension of fire and extinguish the fire. When faced with a fire that only involves the roofing material, firefighters can cut the roof tar, membrane roof, and composite coverings while avoiding the metal decking. Once the cuts have been made, the material can be pulled away from the steel decking.

Remember, when corrugated metal is heated, it expands and the tar liquefies and then gasifies. The gases cannot escape upward, so they travel between the corrugations in the steel decking and burn (fig. 14–64). As the gases burn, they generate more fuel. Thus, the fire can be self-sustaining and independent of the original fire in the room below. This type of fire can exhibit several hazards. For one, the insulation becomes a source of fuel. The fire is difficult to access, and it can cause or contribute to roof collapse if the fire should extend rapidly. Such a fire also creates large volumes of dense smoke, which may hamper suppression efforts.

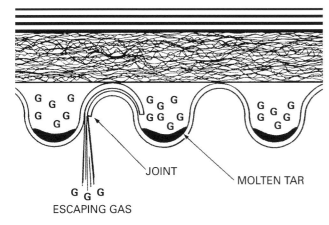

Fig. 14–64. When corrugated metal is heated, the tar liquefies and then gasifies. These gases can easily travel between the corrugations in the steel decking and burn, creating a self-sustaining fire that is difficult to reach.

Lightweight wood truss roofs. Unfortunately, because of costs, many of today's homes are constructed with **lightweight wood truss** and even lightweight wooden I-beams (fig. 14–65). The truss components are normally connected by thin galvanized metal gusset plates that only penetrate into the wood about ¼ to ⅜ in. (6 to 10 mm). Under moderate to severe fire conditions, these metal plates can start to expand and pull out of the wooden truss, which could cause a collapse of the roof. Firefighters must make an initial inspection hole into a roof to size up the roof's construction features. In truss construction, there is no **ridgepole** and normally a ridge

vent exists. Firefighters can simply remove the ridge vent to size up the type of roof construction.

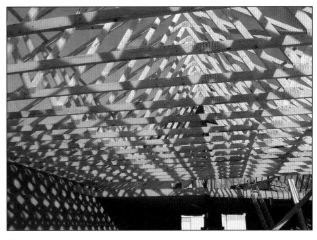

Fig. 14–65. Lightweight wood truss roofs make up most of the new construction today. (Courtesy of Emergency Training Solutions)

Working on or under roofs with a severe fire can be a dangerous and deadly practice (fig. 14–66). Firefighters should strive to make a ventilation hole in these roofs by operating out of a tower ladder's bucket or off of an aerial ladder. Working off of a roof ladder should not be an option because there is no ridgepole to support the roof ladder, and the ladder cannot bite into the roof.

Fig. 14–66. There is considerable danger involved in working on or under roofs with severe fire.

In many cases it is preferred to move to a safer location—surrounding areas not involved in fire—and make a trench cut to stop the horizontal spread of the fire. Draftstopping (vertical non-fire-rated barriers such as gypsum board or plywood/OSB installed to compartmentalize an attic space; draftstopping is often compromised when holes are made in them for cable TV, electrical wires, etc.), if properly installed, will help slow the spread of fire in the attic. Remember, firefighters must be deployed to the interior of the structure below the trench to open the ceiling with the protection of a charged hoseline. After notifying the incident commander, the hoseline may be used into the attic or cockloft space to stop the horizontal spread of the fire. Safety is again the number-one priority—if the fire is quickly "running" the attic and is spreading faster than firefighting forces can be deployed, firefighters should not be committed to the building.

All operations in lightweight wood truss roofs must be evaluated prior to employing interior operations. *Never trust a truss.*

Bowstring truss roofs. Perhaps one of the most dangerous roofs for firefighters to face is the **bowstring truss roof** (fig. 14–67). This roof is commonly used on large structures where a wide open floor space is required. The most telltale sign of spotting a truss roof is its two large humplike ends. A comprehensive size-up must be performed before committing any firefighters to roof operations. These trusses have failed without warning and killed numerous firefighters over the years.

Equally dangerous are other truss roof types such as gable truss, bridge truss, or the tied truss (which is the most dangerous of all). The differences are in the roof shapes, but the construction is the same.

It is recommended that if any fire involves the truss area or fire is impinging on the truss, no firefighters should be committed to roof operations. The failure of one truss can result in a very large collapse area since they are spaced far apart.

Fig. 14–67. Bowstring truss roofs can be dangerous for firefighting operations. (Courtesy of ETS)

If ventilation must be performed, a tower ladder can be used to access the humplike ends of the roof. Here, firefighters can cut a ventilation hole into the roof from the safety of the tower ladder basket. Some of these roofs also have skylights in them. Again, after firefighters perform a comprehensive size-up, the decision must be

made on whether or not it is safe to let a firefighter operate on the roof to vent these skylights. Many firefighters have been killed in buildings in which bowstring roofs have collapsed. Six firefighters were killed in a Brooklyn, N.Y., supermarket in 1978, and five were killed in a Hackensack, N.J., auto dealership in 1988.

Gypsum roof decking. Gypsum concrete is a prefabricated material made up of calcined concrete and wood chips or shavings milled together. The material is then molded and laminated into planks, which are normally 2 in. (52 mm) thick, 2 ft (0.6 m) wide, and 8 ft (2.4 m) long. These planks are supported by bar joists and subpurlins and then grouted together at all of their ends. Unfortunately, the ends of these planks are often unsupported and end in an area between joists. Once the grout material dries, a roofing material such as a rubber membrane covers the planks. **Gypsum roofs** are vulnerable to moisture and conducive to an early collapse under fire conditions.

As with any type of roof installed over steel metal bar joists, firefighters must use caution and perform a comprehensive size-up before attempting roof operations. When a roof is cut with a power saw and a white or gray powdery residue emits from the saw, a gypsum roof is present. Many fire departments inform their members that if a gypsum roof is found while ventilating the roof with the saw, they should notify the incident commander and exit the roof.

Slate roofs and terra-cotta slate roofs. Many dwellings have roofs covered with slate. The slate is nailed to the roof and laid in rows over each other. The slate is slippery and dangerous to work on without the use of a roof ladder, aerial ladder, or tower ladder. Firefighters operating around the outside of the fire building must be aware of the **slate roof**. These slates can detach easily from each other, slide down the roof, and severely injure or cut a firefighter operating below.

One of the easier tactics to follow for venting these roofs is to use a maul or the pick of a pick head axe to strike the slates. This causes the slates to crack, break, and slide down the roof, exposing the roof decking. Normally, this decking is either plywood/OSB sheathing or wood planking and can be cut with a roof saw with one of the tactics mentioned above.

New materials are always created, and it is common to find slate or terra-cotta made of a plastic material and attached to the roof. From the street level it resembles slate, but closer inspection reveals that it is a type of man-made plastic. The same procedure for venting these fake slate roofs can be performed. Firefighters may also cut right through the plastic slates with a roof saw to perform roof ventilation.

C-joist roof construction. Pre-engineered metal **C-joists** are another product used to support roofs. Like steel bar joists, they are directly affected by fire and heat and prone to a quick collapse under severe fire conditions (fig. 14–68). After an inspection hole is made in the roof and C-joist are determined to be supporting the roof, the incident commander must be notified. A comprehensive size-up determines if roof operations should be performed or firefighting forces pulled off the roof. If the roof needs ventilation, performing this tactic from the safety of a tower ladder's bucket or aerial ladder is recommended.

Fig. 14–68. A "C" joist

Lightweight steel-tile roofs or tin roofs. **Lightweight steel tile** or **sheet tin roofs** have become popular, because they can be installed over tar and gravel, wood shakes, shingles or composition, fiberglass shingles, plywood/OSB- type materials, or open rafters. Installation often involves placing the panels on wood battens that have been nailed to an existing or new roof (fig. 14–69). Although these panels result in an attractive roof, they can be difficult to remove by hand and cause severe cuts to the hands, even through gloves. In addition, when pulling on the light-gauge steel with firefighting hand tools, it often tears and makes ventilation efforts more difficult.

When you encounter this type of roof and ventilation operations are necessary, an opening is best created by using a carbide-tipped power saw. Simply simultaneously cut the steel panels, the batten substructure, and the original roof decking. One roof cutting technique mentioned earlier can be used. Remember, it is important to cut deep enough to sever the various layers of materials to permit roof ventilation.

Fig. 14–69. Lightweight steel-tile roofs are often comprised of stone coated interlocking panels of 26-gauge steel that are nailed to 1 x 4 in. (24 x 102 mm) wood battens nailed to an existing or new roof. (Courtesy of Jim Plaster)

VENTILATION OPERATIONS FOR VARIOUS TYPES OF STRUCTURES AND FIRES

The preceding material presented in this chapter is the foundation of ventilation theory, tactics, and techniques. The following section of this chapter reviews the ventilation concepts and principles in relationship to structure fires as they pertain to certain types of fires in residential, commercial, and high-rise type occupancies.

Basement fires

Because of their subterranean location and lack of openings such as windows and doors, providing either vertical or horizontal ventilation to a basement can be a difficult process (fig. 14–70). In addition, because of the pressure of the smoke and gases created by the fire, they travel into as many cracks, crevices, and voids as they can. Fire, smoke, and gases can fill up an entire building and expose its occupants to these dangers.

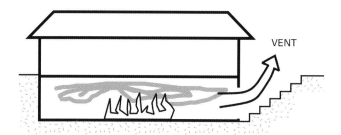

Fig. 14–70. In a basement fire, often the only available ventilation opening is the route that will be used by personnel.

Also, many basements may have limited access and are partitioned off into many rooms with a high fire load because they are used for storage. Partitioned rooms present a problem for searching for the seat of the fire and can make ventilation operations difficult. Another hazardous condition inherent during basement fires is exposed beams, which can lead to a collapse situation when exposed to fire.

Tactics

Timing. Initiate timely ventilation of a basement fire to permit the stretching of attack lines, to reduce vertical extension to other portions of the building, and to minimize rapid development of the fire. Normally, venting operations should be performed in conjunction with the attack lines' initial advance and progress whenever possible.

Openings. FFI 5.3.2 To ventilate the basement, use any of the available openings to the area: doors (outside entrance doors to the basement, garage doors, **Bilco-type fold-up doors**, old coal chute hatches or doors), windows, and dead lights. In some instances in the larger structures, it may be important to open the elevator bulkhead or dumbwaiter shafts at the roof level that begin at the basement level to provide additional ventilation.

If the initial attack line is entering the outside entrance of the basement to attack the fire, opening and controlling the interior basement door at the top of the stairs for additional ventilation is necessary. Remember, this door should only be opened if it does not expose firefighters to punishing conditions, and first-floor windows must be ventilated for the smoke and gases to escape. A hoseline positioned at the interior door can protect the first floor and the firefighters operating there.

If there is only one route into the basement and no openings to ventilate, the hoseline uses this avenue for fire attack, and ventilation is still necessary, consider opening the floor over the fire, adjacent to exterior

windows or doors. (For more information on basement fires, see chapter 20, Basic Fire Attack.) This may be a time-consuming operation, but relief of the heat and gases in the basement is needed to assist the firefighters operating in there. Always ensure that the first floor is well ventilated, vertical passageways are controlled, and a charged protective hoseline is in place. Remember, vertical passageways begin in the basement and can travel to the top floor of a multistory building, requiring search and ventilation of the upper floors and attic area. These conditions appear in balloon-framing structures and many larger multiple-dwelling buildings.

Always keep in mind that, from a simplistic viewpoint, the floor over a basement (normally the grade floor) is also the roof of the fire. So, until the fire in a basement is extinguished and/or the integrity of the floor is verified, remember where you are standing.

Pressurized ventilation. Pressurized ventilation can be used effectively for basement fires if there are openings in the basement and/or first floor to channel the heat, gases, and smoke out of the building. Remember, unlike platform construction, balloon construction can allow fire to travel unrestricted from the basement into the attic. PPV can rapidly enhance the fire if an exhaust isn't opened prior to the pressurization. If an exhaust opening is created prior to PPV, most of the pressurized air flows toward the opening and has little affect on the spread of fire in open walls. Therefore, when you encounter fire extension in balloon construction, the key is to create an exhaust opening before initiating positive pressure. For more information of basement fires, see chapter 20: Basic Fire Attack.

Single-family dwellings (single story)

Single-family dwellings (sometimes referred to as ranch or shotgun homes, bungalows, or single-frame dwellings) may be ventilated by using either vertical or horizontal ventilation tactics. Because most homes are usually accessible from the exterior, horizontal ventilation operations should be the firefighter's first consideration. Remember, just because a window is in reach of a hand tool, indiscriminate ventilation should not be performed; proper and initial ventilation should be initiated as close to the fire as possible (fig. 14–71).

Fig. 14–71. Single story, single-family dwellings are usually accessible; however, indiscriminate horizontal ventilation should be avoided. Always size up and follow your plan.

Tactics

Horizontal ventilation. Ventilating the appropriate windows can improve the interior environment of a structure, aid in search and rescue, and speed the advancement of attack lines (fig. 14–72). Normally, the venting and removal of windows close to the fire or fire area should be sufficient. Ventilating these windows provides an exit for the expanding gases when water from the hoseline is applied. However, just opening windows generally only ventilates the bottom (moderate heat) and central (high heat) portions of a structure and has little effect on the upper (extreme heat) regions. Remember that the upper portions are where the highest concentrations of heat accumulate, supporting flashover. These areas must be cooled down by the attack hoseline and can be ventilated to the outside once fire-suppression is completed.

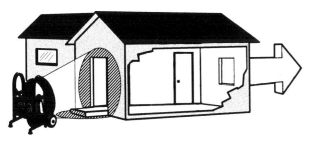

Fig. 14–72. Air blowing in one side and out the other is a form of horizontal ventilation.

It is important to note that opening the wrong windows or premature ventilation can supply additional oxygen to a fire, causing it to accelerate. Numerous broken windows in unfortunate areas can also reduce the effectiveness of pressurized ventilation. Windows away from the fire area should only be broken if they cannot be opened easily or are being used for VES operations. Remember, breaking windows may put broken glass inside the structure, hindering interior operations and causing an injury to a firefighter. If security bars are evident on the windows, inform the incident commander, and attempt to remove the bars if firefighters will be operating inside the structure.

Vertical ventilation. If a fire in these structures is extensive and backdraft conditions are present or a fire is present in the attic space, firefighters should consider vertical ventilation of the roof after a proper size-up (fig. 14–73). Although horizontal ventilation operations should be performed first, the need for vertical ventilation may be necessary. Ventilation of the attic can improve the interior environment of the structure, particularly at the ceiling and upper levels of the structure. The roof openings should be located over the fire and at the peak of the roof. Attic windows or louvered vents can also be removed as appropriate to accelerate venting or if weather conditions don't allow roof operations. Firefighters must use caution when opening an attic vent or a ventilation hole at the far end of the structure; it may draw fire throughout any uninvolved portions of the attic.

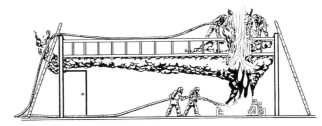

Fig. 14–73. An opening above the fire that allows fire, smoke, and gases to rise and exit the building is vertical ventilation.

Pressurized ventilation. Pressurized ventilation can be used effectively for fires in these types of structures (fig. 14–74). Remember that the exhaust openings should always be created prior to pressurizing the structure or area to be ventilated. If this is not followed, the pressurized airflow and by-products of combustion have no means of escape from the structure. In addition, it is also imperative to control the flow and path of pressurized air between an entrance and exhaust opening to achieve maximum ventilation. If pressurized air is directed from an entrance to an appropriate exhaust opening without being diverted to other openings, contaminants are removed in a minimal amount of time. Simultaneously opening unwanted windows and doors does not facilitate successful PPV operations.

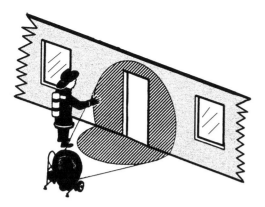

Fig. 14–74. The cone of air pushed towards a building opening during PPV operations should cover the entire opening.

Single-family dwellings (multistory)

These structures are commonly two-, two-and-a-half–, and three-story dwellings, each of which is normally inhabited by a single family. Firefighters should not be surprised to find single-family dwellings turned into multiple-family residences or containing a separate apartment. The age of these dwellings is an indicator of potential vertical extension avenues. Old construction may conceal balloon construction, which provides open passageways within the exterior walls from the lowest floor to the highest. Newer construction uses open space floor plans, which can have features such as fascia, zero-clearance fireplaces, ductwork, balconies, and cathedral ceilings, which can allow fire to spread rapidly. These structures come in a variety of shapes, sizes, and designs and firefighters must become familiar to those structures prevalent in their response areas.

The location of the fire determines where the firefighter must perform ventilation operations. A fire on the first floor of a multistory dwelling calls for coordinated horizontal ventilation, whereas fire on the top floor may place initial emphasis on horizontal ventilation followed by vertical ventilation operations (fig. 14–75) Firefighters must remember that depending on the height of the building, access above the ground floor requires ladders before ventilation operations can be initiated. Firefighters can ventilate upper windows by using the portable ladder throw, roof ladder throw, or the arm-lock maneuver with a hand tool (described earlier in this chapter).

Tactics

Ventilation. If a fire is only on the first floor, the first priority should be to ventilate this floor horizontally. The immediate fire room and area should be the first priority, in coordination with the attack line's advance.

Firefighters searching on the floor above the fire must use caution and not indiscriminately ventilate any windows they come across. Doing so could cause an autoexposure problem by pulling the venting fire into the floor they are searching. Firefighters operating on the outside of the structure must use caution and not ventilate windows on the upper floors if they are in jeopardy of fire entering them from the floor below. Remember, in most instances performing vertical ventilation for a first floor fire could draw the fire and contaminants to the upper floors.

If extension above the first floor has occurred, horizontally and vertically ventilate the second floor. This reduces the heat and smoke in the building and minimizes mushrooming on the top floor. If the fire is on the top floor, perform horizontal ventilation and then begin vertical ventilation operations. For fires involving the attic space, perform vertical roof ventilation or remove the attic vents at the gable end of the structure.

In newer or contemporary homes, removing skylights can benefit ventilation operations of the upper floors. Many such homes have high pitch and irregularly angled roofs, on which it can be dangerous to operate; firefighters should use roof ladders or work from the safety of an aerial or tower ladder. Accurate roof ladder placement depends on determining the location of the fire and the appropriate location for the opening. Firefighters should place these ladders on the windward side when possible, directly adjacent to the likely roof opening. This allows firefighters to ventilate with the wind at their backs, and the by-products of combustion escape in the opposite direction.

Fig. 14–75. Single-family multi-story dwelling. A fire on the first floor of a multistory dwelling calls for coordinated horizontal ventilation, whereas fire on the top floor may place initial emphasis on horizontal ventilation followed by vertical ventilation operations. (Courtesy of Mike Blatchly)

Pressurized ventilation. If a multiple-story dwelling needs ventilation, always start at the lowest level with PPV and ventilate toward the top. To ventilate the first floor, ensure that all the exterior windows on the upper floor are closed or that a stairwell door to the upper floor is closed. Position a blower at an appropriate entrance opening, and then ventilate the contaminated areas on the first floor to provide maximum pressurized air for ventilation on the first floor and no flow of air on the second floor (caused by a lack of an exhaust opening). To ventilate the second floor, leave the blower in the same position and ensure that all the exterior windows and doors have been closed on the first floor. If a stairwell door has been closed, open the door and sequentially ventilate the contaminated areas on the second floor.

Multiple dwellings and center-hallway buildings

Multiple dwellings, multiunit apartments, and some condominiums are normally designed with a hallway in the center of the structure and units on either side, which allows for the maximum number of rooms in a building. Normally present in these structures is an open interior stair running from the first floor to the roof. Buildings with a **center hallway layout** may also have one or more skylights, bulkheads, scuttle ladders and covers, penthouses, and fire escapes. Fire doors may or may not exist in the interior hallways of these buildings. A prior knowledge of these types of buildings in a specific district is essential for firefighters (fig. 14–76).

Fig. 14–76. Multiple dwelling and center-hallway buildings. A prior knowledge of these types of buildings in a specific district is essential for firefighters to learn. (Courtesy of Ed Evers)

Determining the location of the fire in these structures often indicates the ventilation priorities. The main concept to understand is that vertical ventilation in these buildings is a priority. It relieves the upper floors of smoke, prevents mushrooming, and allows occupants to survive or escape from the building. Opening up the bulkhead or skylight is considered vertical ventilation and allows the gas and smoke build up in the hallway and the stairway leading to it to be relieved. This allows the truck companies to access the upper floors while searching and allows the engine company to advance to the fire floor in moderate smoke conditions.

The stairs and public hallways must be checked for fire, heat, and smoke, as well as any victims overcome by smoke. The presence of smoke and its quantity in the public hallways is an excellent indicator of the fire's extension and location. The presence and status of fire doors can dramatically affect this; closed fire doors limit an area and the smoke, whereas open doors allow the smoke to enter the entire public hallway. Opening a bulkhead door ventilates the stairway and public hallways while indicating the smoke level in the stairway. Firefighters must remember that if there is a light smoke condition or no smoke condition in the hallway, the fire apartment's door may still be closed and preventing any smoke from entering the stairs or hallway. It is imperative that vertical ventilation still be completed. Although smoke conditions could be light, the buildup of carbon monoxide could be high and overcome individuals or firefighters.

Tactics

Horizontal ventilation. If the fire is on a floor below the top floor, use an appropriate combination of horizontal, vertical, and pressurized ventilation. Firefighters must ensure they do not create an autoexposure situation when performing horizontal ventilation.

If horizontal ventilation is to be performed off of the fire escape, the firefighter should size up the situation first. If any occupants use the fire escape as a means of escape, no windows should be vented; occupants could be overcome by smoke or burned if fire vents from the windows. If the windows are to be ventilated, the windows farthest from the fire escape should be broken first and then those nearest the fire escape.

In some fireground situations, the aerial ladder may be used for ventilating windows and firefighters must adhere to their fire department's SOPs in these matters.

Vertical ventilation. Vertical ventilation operations should focus on three basic priorities: stairwells, skylights, and, for a top floor fire, cutting a hole in the roof over the fire. Opening a bulkhead door or skylight provides initial ventilation of the stairwell and public hallway. In some cases the skylight may have been removed and covered up with a new roof. When faced with these conditions, firefighters can use a power saw to cut an opening where the skylight was, which enables stairwell ventilation. If there are operable sprinklers in the skylight openings, they can form a water curtain and hamper ventilation. If ventilation is necessary under these conditions, consider eliminating the flow of water in the appropriate skylight opening by wedging the sprinkler head. Remember, only stop the flow of water from the sprinkler if it has controlled the visible fire below. If fire reappears and takes control of that area below, remove the chock with a hand tool to avoid a burn injury.

If there are doubts of fire in the attic or cockloft space, the **returns** in the skylight should be opened for a fast and easy way to check for extension. Firefighters should avoid opening up returns in skylights remote from the fire, as they could draw the fire toward the open returns.

For fires on the top floor, it is still important to ventilate the bulkhead or skylight and then provide initial horizontal ventilation to the top floor windows. Ventilating these windows in conjunction with cutting a hole in the roof provides vertical ventilation and extension into the cockloft. Venting the top floor windows creates an influx of fresh air and allows that air to be drawn into the room and up and out of the ventilation hole in the roof. The process of cutting some of these roofs may take some time if they have been built up over the years.

Firefighters should cut a hole in the roof over the fire. They must also size up the building's features and what the fire is doing. If a fire is venting out of two windows of one room, they should not cut directly over the room, because it is already self-venting. The cut can be pulled back a few feet to attempt to cut over two rooms and assist the engine company's advance into the fire area.

Condominiums and townhouses

Condominiums and townhouses are a common type of structure scattered across the country. Condominiums can have an interior or exterior stairway that serves the individual units. **Townhouses** are normally one, two, three, or even four stories, constructed side by side in a row with an open interior hallway within the unit. Both occupancies normally consist of a common attic that may have draftstopping or fire walls constructed within them and are supported by dimensional lumber or prefabricated truss roof systems (fig. 14–77).

Fig. 14–77. Condominiums and townhouses. Both of these occupancies normally consist of a common attic that may have draftstopping or fire walls constructed within them and are supported by dimensional lumber or pre-fabricated truss roof systems.

Ventilation operations in condominiums should focus on improving the interior atmosphere in the public hallway and stairwell to facilitate the evacuation of occupants and entry by firefighting personnel. Many such structures have a skylight or scuttle over the stair enclosure, which permits rapid vertical ventilation. Horizontal ventilation should be performed and used for fire in a unit. If the unit is two stories, they can be ventilated by both horizontal and vertical means. It is extremely important to check the attic space for fire and extension throughout the operation.

Ventilation in townhouses may be of a different strategy than condominiums. Although horizontal ventilation is performed for most fires, the townhouse unit should be checked for a skylight. Ventilating the skylight can relieve the open interior stairs of smoke and gases, making the interior tenable for firefighting operations. Townhouses may also have offset windows on the end units; these windows normally provide light into the stairwell area. They are good windows to ventilate to assist in vertical ventilation efforts.

The attic or cockloft space is a main concern with fires on the top floor of these units. Firefighters must check this area for fire extension and involvement during the course of the fire. A visible inspection of the roof may reveal that a fire wall extends through the roof, separating the individual units. Unfortunately, because of builders running wires, ductwork, or plumbing through this space, the fire walls can be compromised. Firefighters must not rely on fire walls alone. A simple procedure for checking the cockloft is to find a hatchway in the unit providing access to the space. It is normally located at the top of the stairs, on the top floor hallway, or in a closet on the top floor. If it takes too long to find, inspection holes can be made in the top floor ceiling with a hook to check on conditions above.

Garden apartments

Garden apartments lack several features that are typical of the center-hallway dwellings. They lack an interior stairwell and enclosed hallway. Many have an unenclosed exterior stairwell serving a few units and exterior balconies on the upper floors. The layouts of the units are less complex in design and have units that open directly to the exterior (fig. 14–78). These apartments also have common attics that run the length of the entire building. Typically, the roofs have a low or zero pitch and rafters that support the roof decking, making roof operations feasible.

Fig. 14–78. Garden apartments. Garden-type structures, whether residential or commercial, have units that open directly to the exterior.

Tactics

Ventilation operations. The floors below the top floor must be horizontally ventilated. This is easily done by natural or pressurized ventilation of an individual unit. A fire on the top floor can be ventilated by horizontal or vertical ventilation operations. A size-up of the fire and its extension possibilities can help decide whether or not to open the roof. Sometimes it is more feasible to open the top floor ceiling to check the cockloft area for extension and then cut the roof open. If a fire has extended into the attic or cockloft space and a ventilation hole has been made, it may be necessary to cut a defensive trench or strip cut in the roof to suppress the travel of the fire.

Commercial occupancies

Strip stores, taxpayers, shopping centers, and mini-malls include multiple occupancies attached to each other that may share a common attic or cockloft space. The cockloft area can be as small as a few inches high to as large as a few feet high. It also provides an open channel above the ceilings where fire can rapidly spread undetected. Many older buildings may have old gas lines that once provided lighting to the store, running through the cockloft. The risk of escaping gas can also lead to increasing fire conditions in this space.

When entering the structure, immediately check the cockloft for conditions above the firefighters. It may also be feasible for firefighters to determine whether the space is common to the entire structure or only a portion. Firefighters operating on the roof should check for division walls, fire walls, smoke from vents, and other such indicators.

Such a structure may have a fascia attached to the front, which may hide the actual age of the building (fig. 14–48). Consider a fascia to be an additional common attic built onto the exterior wall of the building. In some older buildings, ventilating the front fascia exposes the joists and the cockloft and allows access into the cockloft for the penetration of a master stream device for fire attack. Newer buildings are most commonly built of lightweight construction (steel bar joist, lightweight trusses, C-joist construction), and firefighters should make inspection holes into the roof to check for construction features. On these newer buildings, consider a fascia to be an ornamental feature and an additional common attic running only on the exterior of the building (fig. 14–79).

Tactics

Horizontal ventilation. Horizontal ventilation is generally limited to ventilating the front store windows once the engine company has water in the attack line and is ready to proceed into the fire. Firefighters must use caution in ventilating these heavy plate-glass windows, as they can break in large sections, fall outward, strike the firefighter, and cause a severe injury. Firefighters should attempt to use a long hook to ventilate the window from the side so that they don't place their bodies in front of the opening. Rapidly expanding smoke, gases, and heat exit the space and could ignite, causing a serious injury to a firefighter.

Fig. 14–79. Many commercial occupancies have fascias attached to the front of the building and it may hide the actual age of the building. Consider a fascia to be an additional common attic built onto the exterior wall of the building.

It may also be feasible to use PPV, pressurize each contaminated unit, and use the rear door as the exhaust port for minor fires inside the store. Many such structures have rear doors but no windows for security purposes and are perfect for PPV. A fire involving the cockloft area should not be fed by the forced air from a PPV operation.

Remember, fires in these types of occupancies are prone to backdraft conditions. Vertical ventilation can be accomplished before horizontal ventilation is performed.

Vertical ventilation. If possible, vertical ventilation operations should begin over the seat of the fire, reducing the chances of horizontal extension into the common cockloft. Initial operations should be to ventilate any skylights, scuttles, or other openings present on the roof. Cutting the roof open is a longer, more involved process; and these openings take less time to open up, thus possibly preventing flashover conditions inside the building.

When roof cutting operations are to begin, firefighters should cut over the store involved in fire. Unfortunately, this operation may not be possible because of the fire's progress; it may be difficult to conclude where the point of origin is, what store is on fire, or where is the largest body of fire located. Communications with the inside crews can relay the fire's location to the outside crews to ventilate the roof in the proper location.

If horizontal extension within a common attic is verified, it may be possible to cut a trench or strip ventilation ahead of the fire as long as the roof area isn't too large and the fire isn't rapidly spreading. Although strip ventilation is extremely effective, it is time consuming. When selecting a location for strip ventilation, cut the initial strip between the fire and the longest portion of the uninvolved attic to protect the greatest portion of the uninvolved building. Also, leave enough room between the strip and the fire to allow enough time to complete the strip. Two strips may be necessary to cut off an attic fire emanating from a single source but extending in opposite directions. In this case, protect the greatest portion of the building first and the smaller portion second. Strip ventilation should not be used in lieu of a primary ventilation hole over the fire, if possible.

Vertical ventilation for basement fires may have to be accomplished by cutting opening the first story's floor beneath a skylight, cutting open the floor near the front showroom windows, and in some cases removing the stepped up displays or platforms in the front of the store to help ventilate the basement. Remember that a charged hoseline should be near these openings for protection.

Fascias. Fascias in these structures can readily promote fire extension under their sheathing. If the fascias are a separate decorative structure added to the building at a later date, any fire involved in the space may not be as important as if it had access to the cockloft. If opening a fascia to check for extension or to ventilate, consider these three methods. Openings underneath or on top of the fascia can be dangerous to personnel, because they could pull material on top of themselves and be injured. It also puts the firefighter in a dangerous area, operating under a portion of a structure that could collapse if it was fire ravaged. Openings can easily be made by cutting the vertical projection above the roof if the sheathing extends above the roofline. In some instances, this fascia ties into the brick parapet wall, and access with this method will not work. Using this method, a fascia would collapse away from personnel on the roof. Opening this fascia up from the safety of a tower ladder's bucket is another proven method.

Note that commercial structures often have heavy equipment such as air conditioning units, HVAC, billboards, and cell phone sites directly on their roofs or supported by steel I-beams above the roof. These features can add a tremendous weight load to the roof; and if fire involves the cockloft, the weight of these items can lead to an early collapse of the roof. In some instances, these frames may be tied into the parapet walls and can cause the failure and collapse of these walls under fire conditions. Firefighters should relay all pertinent information on the whereabouts of these items to the incident commander (fig. 14–80).

Fig. 14—80. Heavy equipment on the roof—this information should be relayed to the I.C.

Factories and warehouses

Many different construction methods are used to build industrial structures and complexes. Often, multiple manufacturing processes or tenants are housed in the same building with different hazards. Older buildings tend to have been modified and retrofitted throughout the years. In these cases it is common to find older construction in one section of the building and newer construction features in others. Most of the newer buildings are constructed of lightweight materials and are not conducive to firefighting operations like the older buildings.

Industrial occupancies may have large, open floor plans with a large amount of stock. These conditions can rapidly enhance the spread of fire. Although division walls may be present, the fire doors may be inoperative or blocked open, rendering a division wall ineffective and exposing additional areas of the building to fire and smoke. Larger buildings and roofs may require extensive operations to adequately ventilate. Firefighters must always consider the type of roof on a structure before ventilating it. Many industrial buildings may have flat or truss roofs. They may be of lightweight wood, concrete, steel bar joists with built-up metal decking, mill construction, or conventional wooden construction.

Windows of many such industrial structures may have been removed and covered with bricks for security purposes, whereas others be covered with wire mesh security screens. These obstacles may mandate the use of vertical ventilation and increase the time it takes to provide horizontal ventilation. If horizontal operations aren't feasible in some situations, it may have to be limited to the building's entrances, exits, and loading docks.

FIREGROUND NOTE

During a size-up of factories or warehouses, firefighters should also check for items such as the name and type of business on the front of the building. They should look for the National Fire Protection Association 704 hazardous materials placard ("diamond") on the exterior, the size of the electrical service, the type of equipment or machinery on the roof, stock type and supplies stored out in the yard, and whether hazardous materials are present.

Tactics

Horizontal ventilation. Horizontal ventilation operations can often be done by ventilating windows, doors, or larger openings, such as loading dock doors and display windows. Pressurized ventilation can enhance or replace the natural ventilation process.

Vertical ventilation. Initial roof operations should take advantage of natural features such as skylights, scuttle covers, and any bulkheads that may be present on the roof. Roof operations are predicated on the size and progress of the fire and the type of roof. Initial operations should be offensive and an opening made over the fire. If necessary, they should be followed by defensive tactics if personnel and conditions allow. Larger buildings require additional or larger ventilation openings than the standard hole made in dwellings. Because additional equipment and personnel are required, emphasize safety.

Institutions

The location of a fire in institutional buildings must be determined to evaluate its potential effect. Prime locations for fires in these types of buildings are in the kitchens, lounges, and storage areas. Hospitals, sanitariums, and rest homes are characterized by non-ambulatory residents who may need assistance or need to be removed. Jails and other detention facilities have occupants who may need to be released by security personnel. If a detention facility is in your district, plan your responsibilities ahead of time for incidents that might involve your services.

Firefighters must consider the height and number of floors in relationship to the location of the fire. A fire on the lower levels of a multistory institution can expose the floors above. Rescuing occupants on the upper floors may prove difficult. A fire on the upper levels may not expose the lower floors and may easily be ventilated with roof or stair shaft techniques.

Tactics

Single story. Ventilation efforts should initially focus on creating a ventilation opening as close to the fire as possible to reduce the extension of fire elements to other portions of the building. Openings should be large enough to ensure rapid and effective ventilation so as to facilitate the removal of occupants and the deployment of suppression personnel. Additional operations should provide ventilation for hallways and other passageways to minimize horizontal extension within. Pressurized ventilation in conjunction with horizontal ventilation can be effective.

Multistory. Begin initial ventilation operations with the vertical passageways such as stairwells and hallways if they are contaminated by fire or smoke. If a fire is on the top floor, always consider ventilating over the fire to reduce horizontal extension. Likewise, always consider the effect of using an uninvolved stair shaft to ventilate the floors below. Remember, it is crucial for all firefighters to be aware of the attack and evacuation stairwells in buildings with multiple levels. Lower floors can be ventilated by using a combination of pressurized ventilation, horizontal openings, or stairwells. When ventilating the lower floors, particularly through a stairwell, always consider its effect on the upper floors. Regardless of the size or height of the structure involved, always try to compartmentalize and restrict the extension of fire and its by-products.

Note that access into the stairwells of many institutions is restricted to prevent people from leaving or entering a floor. Many times it is more advantageous for a firefighter to get a key than to force the doors.

High-rise office buildings

Of the various types of structures encountered by the fire service, high-rises can be the most challenging in

which to perform ventilation operations (fig. 14–81). In the older high-rises, there may be windows that open, but in the newer structures there are none. The newer high-rises are built with curtain wall construction and tempered glass windows, which are designed to be broken by firefighters to remove smoke from the floor. These windows are typically identified by a glass etching or reflecting sticker of the firefighter's Maltese cross (tempered windows break into small pieces as opposed to large, dangerous shards of glass from a plate glass window). The air in these buildings is pressurized and moved by HVAC systems located on various floors throughout the structure. Firefighters must realize that although a high-rise building may have windows, it may not be wise to indiscriminately ventilate them. Fires on upper floors can be affected by the wind currents present at upper levels of the atmosphere. In addition, falling glass from these high levels could injure anyone in its path.

The migration of smoke and toxic by-products throughout a high-rise building can often present a greater hazard to life than the spread of fire itself. During fires, the migration of air throughout a high-rise, frequently by its HVAC system or natural channels, results in the spread of smoke and toxic gases to areas far removed from the actual fire. This can render vertical and horizontal escape routes impassable and hamper fire-suppression efforts. Because smoke normally travels upward, the floors above become prime exposures for stratification, mushrooming, and possible fire extension. Thus it is important to have some type of guidelines for ventilation operations.

Smoke movement is also affected by a phenomenon known as "stack effect." In essence, smoke will be aided in its movement up through a building when temperatures inside the building are warm and the temperature outside the building is cool. Conversely, reverse stack effect will tend to drive smoke down through a high-rise building when temperatures are warm outside and cool inside the building (fig. 14–82).

Consider that some buildings will be equipped with smoke management systems. These may protect parts of a building (such as pressurization of an elevator shaft to keep smoke out) or may be installed throughout a high-rise building to exhaust the floor that is involved in the fire and pressurize the floor above and below to keep smoke from migrating to those areas. Most modern high-rise buildings have stairwell pressurization systems that inject air into a stair shaft during a fire to keep smoke out. It is important to identify all smoke management systems and how they work during preplanning operations.

Fig. 14–81. A high-rise office building. Of the various types of structures encountered by the fire service, high-rises can be the most challenging for firefighters to perform ventilation operations.

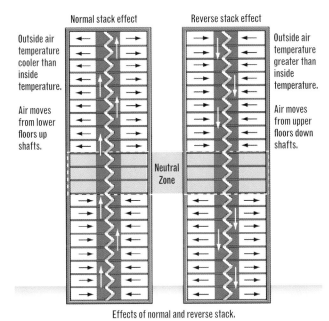

Effects of normal and reverse stack.

Fig. 14–82. The effect of normal and reverse stack effect in a building

HVAC operating guidelines. The following measures should be taken in regard to the HVAC system when units arrive at a fire in a high-rise:

- Determine the location of a building representative (fire safety director or maintenance worker).

- Determine the status of *all* HVAC systems. Manually shut down any system that has not automatically shut down (including supply and return fans).

- Determine the fire floor or floors.

Once the fire floor(s) have been determined, activate the supply fan in *all* HVAC zones that do not include the fire area. Activating these fans provides fresh air and pressurizes the zones, limiting the spread of smoke and gases. All units operating in the building should report any adverse conditions to the incident commander.

PPV used in high-rise operations. Opening the bottom and top doors of a stair shaft quickly develops a natural upward flow of air. Placing blowers at the bottom of the shaft can augment this flow, regardless of the height of the building. Such currents can be used to keep contaminants from accumulating in a stair shaft (if the roof opening is kept closed) or to remove accumulated contaminants and keep the shaft clear (roof opening kept open). Emphasis is placed on stair shafts that may be used by attack personnel. This creates better visibility in the stairwell, allowing the engine company to hook up to the standpipe system and the truck company to search the floors above and the stairwell. Note that such operations can be affected by the presence of a stairwell pressurization system.

High-rise fires present unique and varied ventilation problems. Firefighters should never attempt a haphazard approach to ventilation without specific plans for the effective use of personnel and equipment. Additionally, when ventilation operations are necessary, it is essential to have a clear understanding of the parameters imposed by high-rise buildings.

High-rise multiple dwellings

In many cities across the country, large high-rises have numerous apartments per floor. These buildings may have windows that open or not and outdoor balconies in some instances. Another common type of these buildings is referred to as *projects* and are prevalent in lower-income areas. These buildings come in various shapes, heights, and sizes and also have ventilation issues to handle. Recently, many major cities and outside agencies have been studying on the effects of wind-driven fires at these occupancies. Unfortunately, numerous firefighters have been killed in fires in such dwellings over the course of the years.

When fires occur in these buildings, firefighters begin with their normal ventilation efforts: ventilating the fire apartment windows from the floor above in coordination with the hoseline's fire attack. The first firefighter who reaches the apartment on the floor above should relay the wind conditions to the incident commander and follow their directions. Ventilation of an upper-floor fire in these dwellings is usually performed by a firefighter reaching downward with a 6-ft (2-m) hook, a Halligan tool attached to the hook, or a Halligan attached to a utility rope to break the fire apartment's windows. The roof's bulkhead is normally opened to clear the stair shaft of contaminants. Opening the door at the base of the shaft also allows a draft to be pulled up the stairs to help clear the stairwell of contaminants.

Unfortunately, the pressure of the wind causes significant problems for firefighters. As they commence their initial fire attack into the fire apartment or public hallway leading to the fire apartment, windows fail and wind currents blow fire and heat back on top of the operating crews. The heat levels become unbearable, because the apartment's fire load burns at a furious pace from the wind, and chase firefighters out of the apartment or hallway. Firefighters have reported that the conditions changed so rapidly that they did not know what happened.

Recent studies have shown that by pressurizing the attack stairwell with large PPV fans, firefighters can lower the hallway temperatures and diminish the effects of the wind-driven fire back onto the fire attack teams. Also, by pressurizing the stairwell at wind-driven fires, the fire attack team can attempt to proceed into the public hallway or fire apartment to extinguish the fire. Another method of controlling the wind at these fires is to prevent the influx of wind into the fire apartment by dropping a **fire blanket** out the window from the floor above (fig. 14–83). The fire-resistive blanket blocks the window channel from the wind, allowing interior crews to attempt an aggressive fire attack on the fire. This tactic will require additional personnel and time for implementation, and the height and location of the fire will be a major consideration.

Fig. 14–83. A fire blanket or wind control device being placed over the window of an apartment to block wind from entering. (Courtesy of NIST)

QUESTIONS

1. What are the differences in the two basic principles of ventilation?

2. Smoke contains many different gases that are toxic to civilians as well as firefighters. Among those listed in the text, which are the two most common gases firefighters should be concerned about?

3. When performing ventilation size-up of a structure, what are some of the considerations firefighters must ask?

4. Both negative pressure and positive pressure ventilation may use mechanical methods to ventilate a structure. What is the theory behind how each displaces the smoke and by-products?

5. The improper use of PPV during fire attack can have deadly results for firefighters as well as the civilian occupants of a structure. List three conditions that would prevent PPV from being utilized during fire attack.

6. Regardless of type of ventilation used on a fire scene, what is the goal of effective ventilation principles?

7. In relation to ease and safety of firefighters, what is the most popular method of quickly ventilating a compartment of a structure?

8. After removal of skylights to provide ventilation, what must the ventilation crew check to ensure full access of the opening?

9. How do roof scuttles and bulkhead doors differ in the overall effect of ventilation?

10. If presented with multiple panes when ventilating a window, what are the correct steps to open the window?

11. When ventilating windows that are covered with security grating or steel mesh, what are the different methods that may be employed?

12. Lexan windows can present a unique problem to firefighters attempting horizontal ventilation. What steps can be taken when forced to ventilate these types of windows?

13. VES techniques are generally used when accessing the alleged location of victims when not accessible by other means. This is known as venting for _____?

14. What are the proper steps of performing VES?

15. Why is closing the door early in the VES technique so critical?

16. List some of the typical tools needed for roof ventilation.

17. The Kerf or plunge cut is commonly used to accomplish what task?

18. When using the "pullback" method of roof ventilation, what are some of the advantages?

19. An effective ventilation technique that can be accomplished more quickly than the coffin cut is?

20. When ventilating pitched roofs, what is the primary purpose of the setting a roof ladder?

21. Caution must be used when ventilating open web steel bar joist supported roofs. What are some of the hazards associated with these types of roofs?

22. Identify the most dangerous type of roof and list the reasons why.

Water Supply and Hose

by Dennis LeGear

This chapter provides required knowledge items for the following NFPA Standard 1001 Job Performance Requirements:

FFI 5.3.10   FFII 6.5.5

FFI 5.3.15

FFI 5.5.2

This chapter contains Skill Drills. When you see this icon, refer to your Skill Drill book for step-by-step instructions.

OBJECTIVES

Upon completion of this chapter, you should be able to do the following:

- Identify the basic properties of water
- Differentiate between flow and pressure as they relate to water supply
- Define the term friction loss as it relates to water supply
- Define static and residual pressure
- Identify the common elements of a municipal water system
- Describe the differences between wet barrel and dry barrel fire hydrants
- Describe the proper procedures for opening and closing a fire hydrant
- Identify and describe the proper procedures for inspecting, maintaining, and testing of fire hydrants
- Identify types of rural and auxiliary water supply systems
- Describe the classifications of fire hose
- Identify types of fire hose construction
- Identify the common types of hose and their typical flows that are used by the fire service
- Identify the types of couplings used to connect fire hose together and to various appliances
- Identify the types of hose fitting used by the fire service
- Identify the types of hose appliances used by the fire service
- Identify the types of hose tools used by the fire service
- Describe the proper procedures for testing, maintaining, and cleaning fire hose
- Identify and describe the different methods of storing hose used by the fire service
- Identify and describe the different types of hose rolls used by the fire service
- Describe the different types of hose loads for supply and attack hose
- Describe the different types of hose lays
- Describe the proper procedures for deploying hose at a fire emergency incident

INTRODUCTION TO WATER SUPPLY

Establishing an adequate water supply is the one of the first critical elements of all successful fire attacks. An adequate water supply has to be in place quickly and last for the duration of the incident. Many failed fire attacks can be squarely blamed on a lack of an adequate water supply. Establishing a good water supply is often accomplished under extreme stress, as the firefighter in fig. 15–1 can attest to. From the firefighter to the incident commander, one critical item must be addressed early on at all fires: water supply. Water is the most common extinguishing agent used by fire departments around the world because is relatively plentiful, absorbs large quantities of heat, is easily transported, and follows a fixed set of physical rules and characteristics.

Fig. 15–1. A firefighter struggles at a hydrant to charge a large diameter supply line. (Courtesy of Danny Barlogio)

Basic water characteristics and terms

FFI 5.3.10 Two of the most important physical rules governing water supply are that water is **noncompressible** (as far as the fire service is concerned) and is capable of being pumped. This means that one cubic foot of water will occupy one cubic foot (1 ft^3) regardless of the pressure.[1] It also means that it can be moved from one location to another. These two basic physical properties allow water to be easily stored, transported, and moved in pipes and hoses by both gravity and pumps.

Two specific terms are used to describe the movement and use of water on the fireground: **flow** and **pressure**. Flow is the volume of water being moved or used and is expressed in **gallons per minute (gpm)** or **liters per minute (L/min)**. Pressure is a force applied over a given area, commonly expressed as **pounds of force per square inch (psi)** or **kilopascals (kPa)**. Pressure (psi or kPa) is the force used to move the volume (gpm or L/min) of water through a hose and out of a nozzle.

As a member of the fire service, you should know a few other basic properties about water. A gallon of water (3.8 L) weighs about 8.33 lb (3.78 kg), and 1 ft³ of water (12 in. × 12 in. × 12 in.) is approximately 7.48 gallons (gal) (28.31 L). This means 1 ft³ of water weighs about 62.4 lb (28.3 kg). Water pressure is commonly measured in psi. If we took a 1-in.² column of water (1 × 1 in.) that is 1 ft tall, the weight exerted at the bottom of that column would be measured as 0.434 psi. A column of water 2 ft high would have a pressure at the base of the column of 2 times 0.434, which equals 0.868 psi, and so on. Take a look at fig. 15–2 to help you understand the concept of water pressure. Expressed a different way, "water pressure increases 1 psi for every 2.3 ft (0.7 m) of depth." The actual pressure at the bottom of a 10-ft (3-m) column of water would be 4.34 psi (30 kPa). One can see the advantage of an elevated water tank. For example, if the water level in the tank in fig. 15–2 (a and b) was 200 ft (60 m) above the ground, the water pressure would be roughly 87 psi (600 kPa) at the bottom. This force (pressure) is due to one thing: gravity, which acts continuously on all objects on earth. The pressure created by a column of water is called **elevation head**.

Alternatively, the fire service commonly uses a rough estimate of 5 psi (34 kPa) for the amount of pressure that is needed to move (force) water up every 10 ft (3 m) of building height, the approximate height of a building story. While we *gain water pressure* (force) at the bottom of an elevated tank (column of water), we must *apply pressure* (force) to move the water up to the top of that tank (water column). Fire department pumpers (engines) are used to provide the pressure to move the water through hoses and up into the upper stories of a building that is on fire.

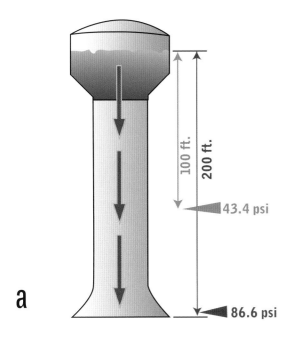

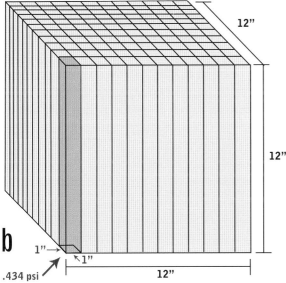

Fig. 15–2 a, b. Understanding water pressure is important to effectively use your water supply on the fireground.

In addition to gravity, we must consider the force of **atmospheric pressure**. That force is literally the weight of the air that makes up the earth's atmosphere that is exerted on objects on the earth. At sea level, a common place to measure atmospheric pressure, the atmosphere produces a pressure of 14.7 psi (100 kPa). Let's take a look at a bottle of liquid (fig. 15–3). The surface of the liquid in the bottle is under the pressure of the atmosphere above it. At sea level that pressure is 14.7 psi (100 kPa). If a straw were placed in the bottle of liquid, the level of liquid inside the straw would be the same as the liquid level surrounding the straw in the bottle. This is because the air in the straw has the same atmospheric

pressure, 14.7 psi (100 kPa). However, when you drink from the straw, you lower the pressure inside the straw to below 14.7 psi (100 kPa). The liquid is then forced up the straw because the liquid surrounding the straw is still under the greater atmospheric pressure. If you lowered the pressure in the straw by 1 psi to 13.7 psi (94.5 kPa), the straw could be as long as 2.3 ft (0.7 m) and still force the liquid to the top of the straw. If you were to remove the entire atmosphere (14.7 psi) from inside the straw at sea level—creating a perfect vacuum of 0 psi (0 kPa) inside the straw—it would function to a height of 2.3 ft (0.7 m) × 14.7 psi (100 kPa), or about 33.9 ft (10 m)!

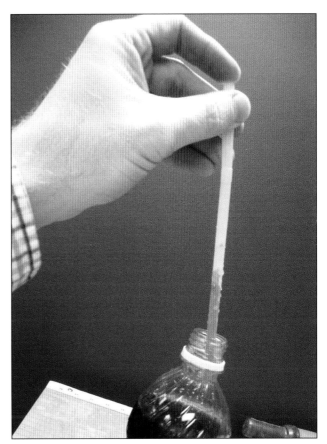

Fig. 15–3. A simple way to demonstrate atmospheric pressure is with liquid and a straw.

To measure pressure, fire department pumpers use pressure gauges. They are mounted on the pumper's **pump panel**, the location where the pumper's operator (chauffeur, motor pump operator, or driver) controls the pumps. All water pressure gauges in the fire service read in **psig**; the "g" stands for gauge, which means that the reading has been corrected to zero psi after taking into the account the weight of earth's atmosphere.

Now that we understand the physical properties of water better, let's move on to how this knowledge is applied in the fire service. For any water supply system to work, one has to be able to move water from one point to another. As we have seen, pressure can be created by gravity, pumping, or the combination of gravity and pumping together. Pressure is used to move the water from short to very long distances. Because pressure is a form of energy, some of this energy will be dissipated (lost) when water is flowing. This loss of pressure (energy) is called **friction loss**. Friction loss is created as water flows through a hose and literally rubs against the inside of the hose, losing pressure all along the way. Friction loss increases as more water is flowed though a given size hose (gpm or L/min); friction loss can be decreased if the size of the hose is increased with the flow kept the same. For example, a 1¾-in. (45-mm) hose flowing 175 gpm (662 L/min) loses more pressure due to friction than a 2½-in. (65-mm) hose of the same length and flow. Since nozzles and other appliances need certain minimum pressures to operate properly (covered in chapter 16, Fire Streams), friction loss is a very important factor to consider.

There are two other terms used to describe types of pressure: **static pressure** and **residual pressure**. Static pressure is the amount of pressure in a hoseline or water main in a street while *no* water is flowing. Residual pressure, on the other hand, is the pressure remaining in a hose or water main while water *is* flowing.

Let's take a look at how a common garden hose is used to define some of these concepts (fig. 15–4).

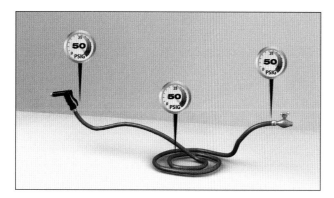

Fig. 15—4. When the garden hose is not flowing, but is charged, it is a closed system, and the water pressure will be equal at all parts along the hose.

Most of us take the common garden hose with an attached spray nozzle for granted. We use the it to wash our cars and to water our plants without wondering how it works. Let's take a closer look at what makes this possible. Once you open up the hose bib, water travels down the hose and stops at the closed nozzle. If you bled the trapped air off by cracking open the nozzle momentarily and then took a pressure reading at the closed

nozzle with no water flowing, you would get the static pressure. Imagine that the static pressure reading was 50 psig (350 kPa). If you then went back to the hose bib and took another pressure reading, again with no water flowing, it would read the same 50 psig (350 kPa). The same would be true if you took a third reading halfway between the nozzle and the hose bib. The fact is that if you took a pressure reading anywhere along this charged garden hose with no water flowing, you would get 50 psig (350 kPa). This 50 psig (350 kPa) reading is an example of static pressure; in this example, it represents the **potential energy** of the water in the garden hose waiting to be released.

Now let's take a look at the garden hose and the effect on pressure once we open the nozzle (fig. 15–5). Notice that with water flowing, the pressure is highest at the hose bib and lowest at the nozzle. The 45-psig (315 kPa) reading on the gauge at the house near the hose bib is called the residual pressure. The 45-psig (315 kPa) residual pressure represents the extra capacity left over in the house's water supply system when the garden hose is flowing water. This extra capacity allows other people in the house to still wash the dishes, take a shower, and so on. The 35 psig (245 kPa) on the middle gauge represents the fact that as the water travels down the garden hose, energy is lost to friction. This drop in pressure represents a loss in the kinetic energy available in the hose. In this case the friction loss is 10 lb (4.5 kg) in the first half of this hose. Now take a look at the gauge located at the nozzle; it reads 25 psig (175 kPa), which means the water leaving the nozzle is at 25 psig (175 kPa). This 25 psig (175 kPa) is the energy used to force the water out of the nozzle and throw the stream a distance away from the nozzle.

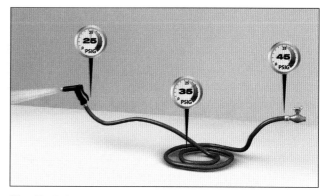

Fig. 15—5. When water is flowing, the residual pressure represents the extra capacity available in the system. The 25 psig (274 kPa) represents the pressure of the water leaving the system. The 20 psi (239 kPa) difference is the friction loss in the system.

Another important concept is water hammer. A typical garden hose will flow about 10 gpm (38 L/min). At 8.3 lb/gal (1 kg/L), a typical garden hose would produce a flow of 83 lb/min (10 kg/min). A typical garden hose squeeze sprayer nozzle stops the water rapidly as soon as you stop squeezing the handle. You may have noticed how garden hoses sometimes jump when you stop flowing water. This is because all that water in motion was abruptly stopped by that closed nozzle. Since we know water does not compress, that energy must be dissipated in one way or another. This violent dissipation of kinetic energy that occurs when flowing water is stopped rapidly in a closed system is called **water hammer**. In this example, the garden hose stretches and moves, and the pipes in the house shake. This small 10-gpm (38 L/min) flow is not enough to cause damage; however, in the fire service where typical flows are 150 to 1,000 gpm (568 to 3,785 L/min), rapidly stopping water by slamming shut intakes, discharges, or nozzles can result in major damage. This includes damage to nozzles, fire hose, pumps, and water mains. The best practice to prevent water hammer is by always operating valves and nozzles in a slow, deliberate, and cautious manner.

MUNICIPAL WATER SYSTEMS

Now that you have a basic understanding of some of the physical concepts and characteristics regarding water, we will discuss larger water supply systems. Most communities have a water supply system that serves both its drinking water needs and fire-suppression flows. This type of **municipal water system** is designed to provide sufficiently clean water for consumption while providing adequate residual capacity of that same water for fire suppression. The modern water supply system is usually run by a public or private water department. The water company bills consumers for their consumption and in return administrates the system under heavy local, state, and federal regulations to ensure that both drinking water standards and minimum fire-suppression capacities are met. Municipal water systems are typically made up of the following critical elements:

- Sources of raw water
- Treatment and storage facilities
- Distribution system
- Valves
- Hydrants
- Hydrant inspection, maintenance, and testing

Sources of raw water

Typical sources of water are broken into two distinct groups: **groundwater** and **surface water**. Groundwater is stored beneath the ground in naturally occurring aquifers. These groundwater aquifers are exploited by drilling wells. Communities are often supplied by groundwater wells alone, and substantial sustainable amounts of water can be acquired by drilling wells and pumping the water out. Groundwater has accumulated in these aquifers for thousands of years through rainfall in their watersheds, which then percolates down into the aquifer. We can think of large aquifers as lakes underground.

Most of us are also familiar with surface water sources, of which the most typical types are freshwater sources. Some examples of surface freshwater sources are lakes, creeks, rivers, deltas, and engineered freshwater storage such as large reservoirs (fig. 15–6 a and b). Some water departments have now started to use saltwater sources like bays, oceans, and brackish areas of estuaries to augment their fresh surface water sources. Most water districts or departments usually use only one source of raw water; however, as water becomes more valuable and water resources more scarce, many water systems are now taking advantage of multiple sources.

Treatment and storage facilitates

After possible sources of water have been identified, the water has to be transformed from raw water to treated, **potable water**. This process is done at a water treatment plant. The raw water is transported by gravity, pumping, or both to the treatment plant. Sometimes the direct source for a treatment plant is a small-terminal, raw-water-storage reservoir. This type of terminal reservoir acts as a buffer to the main source of water, so that in case of an earthquake, drought, or other natural disaster, the water district or department would still have a limited supply of water for treatment and distribution (fig. 15–7).

Water treatment can be very complex and can have many steps. The amount of water treatment that is required is directly related to how clean the raw water entering the system is. Treatment can include any of the following processes: desalinization, aeration, coagulation, flocculation, sedimentation, filtration, fluoridation, ozone disinfection, and ultraviolet light disinfection. Some of these processes are mechanical, and others are chemical. Some of these treatment processes remove substances and contaminates from the water, while others add things.

However, the main goal of water treatment remains the same no matter what processes are employed. That goal is to ensure that the water is safe for human consumption before it enters into the distribution system. Ideally, these water treatment facilities should be designed to handle emergencies like power failures and other situations, to ensure that both adequate drinking water and fire capacity can be maintained through most foreseeable emergencies.

Fig. 15–6 a, b. A man-made reservoir and a nearby creek

Distribution system

The **distribution system** is the most important part of a municipal water system for fire departments. It is the system of treated water storage reservoirs, tanks, pumps, and water mains or pipes that supply the fire hydrants with water. The system should be designed to provide the best flow of treated water throughout the municipality, maintain safe water quality, and meet the service area's minimum standard fire flow. Figure 15–8 shows a basic water system, where a treatment plant receives raw water

from a lake, treats it, then pumps the water into a distribution system of several treated water storage tanks in the community. Using the force of gravity, these storage tanks then provide pressurized treated water to the community's water main system. This pressure is created by the elevation head, discussed earlier in this chapter.

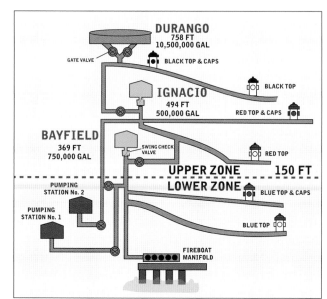

Fig. 15–7. An example of a high pressure system that is fed with non-potable water and is only for firefighting

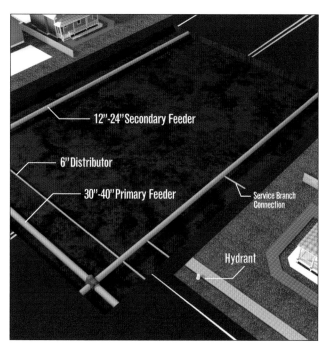

Fig. 15–8. A small water main system

These larger treated water storage tanks ensure sufficient stored treated water capacity for the water main system. This extra capacity could be used to maintain the flow at a large fire. Figure 15–9 (a and b) represents two different examples of treated water tanks that supply the water main systems for the neighborhoods below and around them. Both of them are using gravity to supply their water main systems. Most likely, they are pumped full at night to replace the water used during the day. They are usually refilled at night because demand for water in most communities is lowest at night.

Fig. 15–9 a, b. These treated water tanks use gravity to supply the municipal water supply.

The water main system is very important to the fire department. It is ideally designed to have low friction loss and good residual pressure during normal use. This is done in several ways. First, by laying out the water distribution system in a grid, water is received at most locations from multiple directions and from different sized mains. This efficient design lowers friction loss because no one pipe has to flow all the required water being supplied to a hydrant. Remember, as flow increases in a given size pipe, so does the friction loss. Friction loss can be reduced by increasing the size of the pipe or reducing the flow, which is what happens when flows are split in a grid pipe network (fig. 15–10). Another way water departments and districts lower friction loss in the water main system is to have a series of large-diameter pipes reduced to medium-diameter pipes, and then reduced even further to smaller-diameter pipes that are laid out in a gridlike fashion.

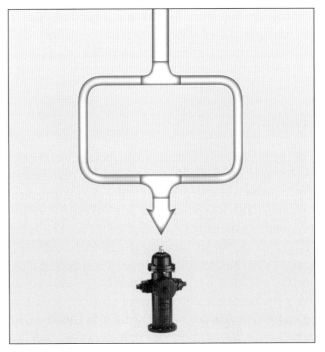

Fig. 15–10. Split flow in a pipe grid is a great way to combat friction loss in a water supply system.

Throughout the water main system, **water main valves** are located at frequent intervals. Water main valves are used by the water district to shut down certain areas of the system or grid for issues like repair and maintenance. Most water main valves are always left in the open position. Water main valves can also be kept in a closed position to separate grids or pressure zones. They are commonly spaced at 500 ft (152 m) and 800 ft (244 m), so only a small section of water main would need to be turned off for repairs, leaving other areas still supplied.

- Large-sized water mains are sometimes called **treated water aqueducts** or **primary feeders**. They can be very large: some are 20 ft (6 m) in diameter in cities with heavy water demand like New York. However, in most cases they are between 30 in. and 48 in. (76 and 122 cm) in diameter. Typically, no hydrants are connected to these primary feeders.

- Medium-sized water mains are commonly referred to as **secondary feeders** and are generally sized from 12 to 24 in. (31 to 61 cm) in diameter. These secondary feeders are common throughout most municipal water main systems. Many fire hydrants are connected to these secondary feeders.

- Smaller-sized water mains are usually referred to as **distributors**. These pipes make up the bulk of most water main systems and generally range in size from the outdated 4-in. (10-cm) main to 12-in. (30-cm) mains. Because of their small size and high friction loss, 4-in. (100-mm) mains are not commonly used anymore; 6-in. (150-mm) pipe is the current minimum size pipe used to supply hydrants. Hydrants are primarily installed on these small distributors.

Hydrants

Fire hydrants are the main access points for the fire department water supply in municipal water systems. Hydrants are connected directly to the water main system by a pipe. This is typically at 6 in. (150 mm) diameter pipe with a gate **valve** (also called a roadway box valve) located in the street between the hydrant and water main. This valve allows the hydrant to be shut off using a special long wrench called a **hydrant key or tee wrench**. It is sometimes necessary to shut off a hydrant at the gate valve for maintenance or if a hydrant is knocked over during a vehicle accident. Ideally, hydrants are supplied by a water main from two directions. Sometimes it is not possible to easily supply a hydrant from two directions; for example, when a water main goes down a dead end court or cul-de-sac street. This is called a dead end water main, and the hydrants on it are called dead end hydrants. Dead end hydrants have less capacity, as they do not have the same redundant supply as those located within the grid. Some water districts mark these with symbols like an arrow showing the direction of water flow in the main and a vertical line denoting that it is a dead end hydrant.

Typically, you will encounter two types of fire hydrants: wet barrel and dry barrel. **Wet barrel hydrants** have water inside right at street level and are usually used in nonfreezing climates. In fact, wet barrel hydrants were first developed around 1900 in the San Francisco Bay area and are sometimes called California hydrants. A typical modern wet barrel hydrant will have more than one outlet. Each outlet has its own operating stem and valve. Figure 15–11 (a and b) shows a picture and a diagram of a typical wet barrel hydrant installation. Notice some of the terms used in the diagram:

(1) stem guide seal, (2) body, (3) stem, (4) stem O-ring, (5) valve rubber, (6) retainer, (7) O-ring seat, (8) retaining nut, (9) cotter pin, (10) stem guide O-ring, (11) stem guide, (12) carrier, (13) valve seat, (14) cap, (15) cap washer, and (16) chain ring.

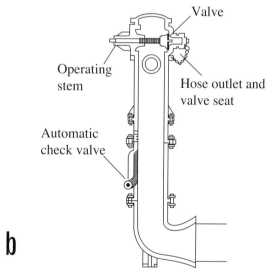

Fig. 15–11 a, b. Wet barrel hydrants are common around the world. Water resides inside the hydrant at street level.

The **dry barrel hydrant** is typically found in freezing climates. However, dry barrel hydrants can be installed in nonfreezing climates as well. This means that you may find dry barrel hydrants, which are specially designed to work in freezing climates, in warmer climates. The main difference between the two designs is that the dry barrel hydrant is just that: dry. In a dry barrel hydrant, the water is held in the pipe serving the hydrant safely below the frost line by a valve that is controlled by an operating nut at the top of the dry barrel hydrant. Figure 15–12 (a and b) contains a picture and a diagram of a typical dry barrel hydrant installation.

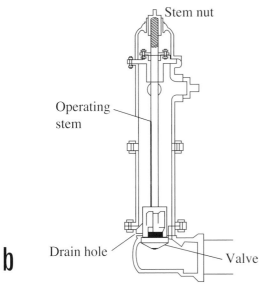

Fig. 15–12 a, b. Dry barrel hydrants are common in freezing climates. The water resides safely below the frost line.

Outlets on both wet and dry barrel hydrants are threaded. The current national standard is **National Standard Hose Thread (NST)**, sometimes known as National Hose Thread (NHT). Most fire hose in the United States uses this standard, although there are a number of cities with their own hose threads. The number and size of hydrant outlets vary, but generally include one or two

2½ in. (65-mm) outlets and a single **steamer** connection (also known as a **pumper** connection) of 4 or 4½ in. (100 or 115 mm) Some cities have incorporated a 5-in. (125 mm) Storz connection on their newer hydrants. (Storz connections are described later in this chapter.)

Basic hydrant operation. FFI 5.3.15 Before we go any further, it is appropriate to briefly discuss basic hydrant operations. These methods apply to both wet and dry barrel hydrants (fig. 15–13). Hydrant operations begin with sizing up the area around the hydrant and the hydrant itself. It is important to make sure that it is accessible and that there is no exterior damage to the hydrant that would impact its operability. Before charging the hydrant it is important to check the interior of the hydrant for any damage as well. Once it is determined that the hydrant is operational, it is time to charge the hydrant. Prior to charging the hydrant, it is recommended that the hydrant be flushed by removing the steamer cap and opening the hydrant a few turns so that a fair amount of water is discharged from the hydrant. The hydrant is opened by using the hydrant wrench to turn the operating nut. This will vary between wet and dry barrel hydrants. Look on the hydrant for a directional arrow that will indicate the direction to turn the operating nut (clockwise or counter-clockwise). Once it is flushed, close the hydrant and attach the supply hose to the appropriate hydrant discharge opening or nozzle. When you are ordered to "charge" or "open" the hydrant, slowly and smoothly open the hydrant fully, usually 10–14 turns in order to avoid a "water hammer," and then turn back the hydrant wrench a quarter turn.

Fig. 15–13. Understanding basic hydrant operation is crucial to maintaining a proper water supply on the fireground.

Once the operation is completed and the order is given, the hydrant can be shut down. Shutting down the hydrant is the reverse of the procedure to open it. Place the hydrant wrench on the operating nut and turn in the reverse direction you did when you opened it, or look for the indicator arrow on the hydrant and turn in the reverse direction. As before, close it slowly and smoothly, to avoid a "water hammer." Once fully closed, turn the operating nut a quarter turn in the opposite direction to prevent over tightening it. Once the hose has been drained, disconnect it from the hydrant and replace to hydrant discharge caps by hand tightening.

Hydrant inspection, maintenance, and testing.

A large percentage of all firefighting around the world is made possible by water supplied from fire hydrants. In the United States, hydrant spacing is typically every 300 ft (90 m) in high-fire-load areas (high value), and 500 ft (150 m) in lower-fire-load areas (low value) such as single-family-dwelling neighborhoods. For example, the City of Oakland, California, with a population of 400,000, has roughly 6,500 hydrants located within 56 square miles (145 sq km).[2] The fact is that an incredible number of hydrants in the world, once installed, will probably never be used unless there is a fire. Based on this fact, inspection, maintenance, and testing of hydrants are critical to ensure that fire hydrants remain functional and perform to their fullest capability during an emergency.

In the United States, it should be the goal to inspect and maintain fire hydrants annually. **Flow testing**, a more detailed test, can be done on a rotating time schedule. Flow testing is covered in chapter 29, Pre-Incident Planning. Many jurisdictions mandate that all of their hydrants must be inspected annually, with a certain percentage to be flow tested. For example, if 20% of hydrants were flow-tested during their annual inspection, it would take 5 years to flow-test every hydrant in the jurisdiction.

Annual company district **hydrant inspections** should address the following items: location, clearance, caps/chains/threads, barrel empty (dry), valves, paint, color code, blue reflector, hydrant gate pot, and curb paint. Minor problems can be corrected immediately, and major problems reported for repair. It is more critical that dry barrel hydrants are inspected annually because they are more susceptible to failures than wet barrel hydrants. Examples of serious failures in dry barrel hydrants are debris in the barrel and failure to drain properly. Both of these issues could easily lead to an unusable dry barrel hydrant. The following list describes what you should look for when performing an inspection of a wet or dry barrel hydrant:

- Location: Make sure the hydrant is on your map, and, if working from a list, confirm the hydrant number or address.

- Clearance: Ensure that the hydrant is readily visible. Typical fire code provisions require that "a 3-ft clear space shall be maintained around the circumference of fire hydrants except as otherwise required or approved." The hydrant shown in fig. 15–14 needs to be dug out and have vegetation trimmed back. If a retaining wall is required to keep it uncovered, it should be reported.

- Caps, chains, and threads: Caps should be free of damage, attach to the hydrant by chains, and turn freely. Remove caps and check for gaskets, because the rubber seals are used to maintain a leakfree condition in unused outlets in dry barrel hydrants when in operation. The other primary purpose of gaskets when hydrants are not in operation is to prevent electrolysis and severe rusting of caps. Ensure that threads are in good condition. The 2½ in. (65 mm) cap nut in fig. 15–15 has broken off, and its chain is missing.

Fig. 15–14. This hydrant needs to be dug out and have the vegetation trimmed to ensure access when needed.

- Barrel empty (dry): With the caps off the hydrant, ensure that dry barrel hydrants are empty and free of visible debris.

- Valves: Check for leaks around the operating stem on wet hydrants and for water in the barrel of dry hydrants. Open the hydrant slowly and operate all valves, making sure that they work easily. It is not important to achieve full flow; just make sure the hydrant works. Turn the hydrant off slowly. Ensure dry barrel hydrants drain completely by verifying that the water is draining down the hydrant barrel. If the water only drains down to the level of the open hydrant outlet, it is not draining properly. This can be pumped out with a dry barrel hydrant pump (fig. 15–16). If the hydrant is not draining properly, it must be repaired. Dry barrel hydrants with frozen water in them will not flow correctly, if at all. When operated, dry barrel hydrants should be fully opened. When fully opened, water is stopped from flowing out of the drain hole. Partially opened dry barrel hydrants can undermine themselves if pressurized water flows out of their drain holes.

Fig. 15–15. This hydrant is missing a cap nut and chain.

Fig. 15–16. Dry barrel hydrant pump

- Paint: Check the condition of the paint. It should be in good condition, but can have minor cracks and light rust. If the hydrant is severely rusted and needs a complete repainting, report it. The hydrant shown in fig. 15–15 should be repainted.

- Color code: Many jurisdictions use **color codes** from NFPA 291, *Recommended Practice for Fire Flow Testing and Marking of Hydrants*, located on the bonnet indicating the hydrant's available flow at 20 psi residual pressure. If so marked, have the proper paint in aerosol cans for touch-ups (table 15–1).

- Reflector: A roadway reflector is a method for identifying a hydrant's location. If your jurisdiction uses them, check them during the annual inspection and replace damaged ones or install new ones when necessary.

Table 15–1. Properly color coding the hydrants in your jurisdiction helps to rapidly identify expected flow rates.

Class C	Less than 500 gpm (1,892 L/min)	Red
Class B	500–999 gpm (1,892–3,782 L/min)	Orange
Class A	1,000–1,499 gpm (3,782–5,674 L/min)	Green
Class AA	1,500 gpm and above (5,678 L/min and above)	Light blue

- Hydrant valve cover (roadway box): Ensure that the hydrant gate valve cover is not paved over. Some jurisdictions also paint them white to help locate them during emergencies such as sheared hydrants.

- Curb paint: Make sure the curb is painted red. If the red curb paint is missing or needs repainting, report it.

The annual test just described is a good basic inspection for determining serviceability of the hydrant. What it does not determine is the maximum flow of the hydrant, nor does it assess the available capacity of the water distribution system in the area. To attain this important information, one must subject the hydrant to a flow test. Flow tests need to be coordinated with water district. All information collected should be done under a mutual program with shared data. This is because the information will be used by the water district to determine how their distribution system is performing. Has there been a drop in flow in an area? Is it because the pipes have become clogged? Is there a regulator valve not opening properly? Has a change in the system had a negative impact in an area of the distribution system? Is the

Water Supply and Hose

FIREFIGHTER I

Chapter 15

hydrant street valve partially closed? The data gathered from annual flow testing of hydrants can be an invaluable tool for both fire departments and water districts.

Usually, large municipal water districts will have a telephone number to call at least 24 hours before flow tests are performed. Proper notification of the water department during flow testing is imperative, so the system operators will understand the sudden spike in usage. It is also good for the fire department to foster a solid relationship with the agency that oversees the water distribution system. Large water districts sometimes have an employee or department that is assigned to manage all the flow testing data and hydrant testing programs. Sometimes they will even provide the training and necessary equipment for flow testing.

RURAL AND AUXILIARY WATER SUPPLY

Many firefighters work in rural areas of the country where large portions of their response area are not served by water main systems with fire hydrants, or the systems in place have inadequate capacity and pressures to supply enough water to mount an effective fire attack. In other cases, some older highly urbanized areas have outdated or obsolete water supply systems that are no longer capable of providing an effective fire flow. Municipal water supply systems become obsolete when the size and age of the water mains become inadequate or when regular demand on the system has grown to a point where it no longer has enough reserve capacity to provide large fire flows. Poor maintenance of a water supply system can also lead to dramatically less water capacity from fire hydrants. Furthermore, many cities in earthquake zones have water main systems that may completely fail during a large earthquake.

In all of these cases, it is still necessary to provide an adequate supply of water for fire control. Fortunately, effective fire control may be accomplished if an adequate water supply is established in a timely manner. In the rural firefighting world, many well-prepared fire departments have identified reliable auxiliary sources of water and have made plans to access them during emergencies. To these rural agencies, alternate water supply operations are considered bread and butter. In the urban world of firefighting, many municipal fire departments are now developing these same types of auxiliary systems to ensure adequate water service in times of disaster. Some fire departments, like San Francisco, have good auxiliary water supply systems already in place. Others cities, for example, Seattle, have recently completed a plan that addresses auxiliary water supply.

The following are examples of auxiliary water supply:

- Water tenders and portable tanks
- (Static sources) Drafting hydrants, cisterns, ponds, lakes, swimming pools, and jet siphons
- Relay pumping
- Fireboats and dry main systems
- Reclaimed water main systems and hydrants

Water tenders and portable tanks

FFI 5.3.15 The modern fire engine is a **triple-combination pumper**, which consists of three key critical items: a pump, fire hose, and a water tank. The water in the engine's tank usually does not exceed a storage capacity of 1,000 gal (3,758 L). This water carried on the engine is only good for mounting initial attacks on small fires. However, a purpose-built **water tender** apparatus can have a water tank that holds up to 4,500 gal (17,034 L) of water. These specialized units make large-scale **water shuttle operations** possible. Typically, these water tenders have an easily deployable, folding, portable water tank that has a slightly larger capacity than their water tender tank (fig. 15–17).

Fig. 15–17. Most water tenders have an easily deployable, folding, portable water tank.

An efficient water shuttle operation can supply large fire flows (fig. 15–18). A basic water shuttle operation consists of three elements, a **dump site**, a **fill site**, and the necessary fire apparatus. The dump site is located at the fire. It is usually made up of portable tanks taken off water tenders and then filled by those water tenders. The attack engine then drafts from these portable tanks. As the attack engine uses the water in the portable tanks, the water tenders travel to the fill site and fill their tanks. The water tenders must then return to the dump site and refill the portable water tanks supplying the attack pumper. This must all be accomplished in a safe manner.

The fill site should be located as close as possible to the fire. The fill site should have a capacity of at least 1,000 gpm (3,785 L/min), have good access, and be located on the best available roads that preferably provide a circular traffic pattern between the fill site and the dump site. The fill site does not need to be the nearest good hydrant; a static source of water, such as a lake, river, swimming pool, or bay can also be a good fill site. If your water supply is a static source of water, you must have a means of moving the water. This is usually accomplished by a drafting fire engine, which in turn fills the water tenders.

Fig. 15–18. A simple water shuttle operation can effectively supply water for fireground operations.

The most basic of water shuttle operations from a static water source need the following apparatus, equipment, and actions: (1) A dump site by the fire with a portable tank is initially filled by the water tender. (2) A route is established to a nearby water source with the capacity to fill a water tender in a rapid fashion, preferably at least 1,000 gpm (3,785 L/min). (3) Upon arrival at the fill site, the water tender is filled by an engine drafting from the static water source. (4) Once filled, the water tender returns to the dump site and fills the portable tank again. This completes one shuttle cycle, which provides a limited capacity of water at the fire scene. Ideally, repeating this cycle will supply a continuous water supply to the attack pumper during the fire until the fire is extinguished.

Fire department personnel involved in water shuttle operations should never try to increase the amount of water that can be delivered by speeding up the shuttle cycle. Rushing these types of operations can lead to serious and sometimes fatal injuries. Firefighters have been hit and run over at fill and dump sites. Water tenders are heavy vehicles that demand respect when operated and must be driven cautiously and in a defensive manner at all times. Many firefighters have lost their lives in vehicle-related accidents involving water tenders. The simple fact is that if more water is required, the water shuttle operation must be scaled up. This means using more portable tanks, possibly multiple dump sites, more water tenders, more routes, possibly multiple fill sites, more attack engines, more fill engines, better routes, road closures to all traffic but emergency equipment, and so forth. During this whole process, positions must be assigned at critical areas: dump site officer, fill site officer, traffic control officer, water supply group supervisor, and the like. Many safe options are possible to increase capacity and efficiency in water shuttle operations. Speeding up can be fatal and is not an option in water shuttle operations. In the end, fire departments that rely on this difficult operation must train actively and often.

Obtaining water from static sources

FFI 5.3.15 Many fire departments are surrounded by raw water supplies such as lakes, rivers, bays, and even the ocean. Note that saltwater from the ocean or brackish water from a river that empties into the ocean must be flushed from fire department pumpers, hoses, and nozzles because the saltwater can damage them. Cities across the United States are often located by vast sources of water; these bodies of water are used for commerce and transportation. If a bay-front warehouse is on fire, and the old water mains servicing that district of the city are inadequate for the volume of fire encountered, the fire department can draft water right out of the bay. This is a good, solid tactic, and some fire departments have addressed their outdated water systems further in waterfront areas by installing drafting hydrants and providing some engines with jet siphons to assist with waterfront supply issues.

A drafting hydrant, properly designed on a reliable static water source, will easily provide the full-rated capacity of the engine's pump (fig. 15–19 a and b). A typical **drafting hydrant** is a specialty hydrant that consists of the following components: a strainer basket submerged at least 2 ft (0.6 m) at the end of a 6-in. (15 cm) diameter pipe, and a pumper connection with a female swivel pumper connection in easy reach of an engine's drafting hose. These drafting hydrants are just that: ideally, pipes into a static water source, with less than 10 ft (3 m) of lift. Drafting hydrants function is an easy way to draft water from an untreated static water source. If a drafting hydrant is not provided, you can still draft using the **hard suction hose** on the engine (described in detail later). However, this is usually less efficient and can have many disadvantages when compared to using a drafting hydrant. Some of these disadvantages include access issues, lack of access to water, poor bank conditions, leaves and debris clogging the strainer, and frozen surface water during the winter.

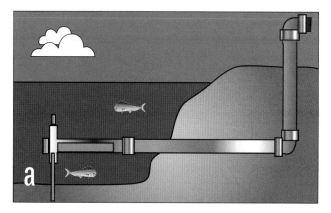

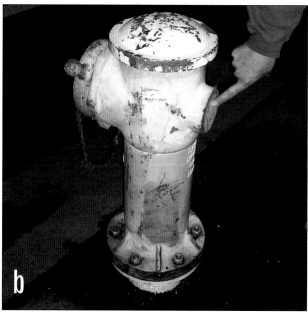

Fig. 15–19 a, b. A drafting hydrant allows the fire service to easily access an untreated water source. Notice that there is no operating spindle on the hydrant.

Cisterns are large, watertight underground tanks used for storing liquids, especially water. In the fire service, jurisdictions that would like to add emergency stored water capacity for firefighting sometimes build cisterns.

In cities, cisterns are typically located below ground at major intersections. These cisterns can hold hundreds of thousands of gallons of water. Cisterns in large cities are usually filled by the nearest hydrant via an access plate in the street. This plate also serves as the drafting port. Cisterns are also commonly found in rural areas. Building codes in rural areas are starting to require property owners to provide water for firefighting, and cisterns fill this role. It is now possible to buy precast concrete or plastic cistern kits that have fill ports, vents, and drafting hydrants as part of the overall design. Chemicals are added to prevent the growth of algae and other aquatic organisms. Cisterns, once filled, are basically tanks of nonpotable water for drafting during emergencies.

Jet siphons are typically used to move water from one portable tank to another in water shuttle operations. A **jet siphon** (fig. 15–20) is a device in which water is pumped into a small, 1½-in. (38-mm) intake and then under high pressure, rapidly discharged into a large hard-suction hose. New strainer-equipped jet siphons now can generate up to 700 gpm (2,650 L/min) utilizing regular, soft-suction hose. However, it is always better to try to achieve a true drafting operation using properly sized, traditional hard-suction hose with a total distance of less than 30 ft (9 m) and with no more than 10 ft (3 m) of lift. Drafting in this manner should provide the full rated capacity of an engine's pump.

Relay pumping

Relay pumping in its simplest form refers to one pump supplying water through fire hose to another pump (fig. 15–21). Fire departments relay pumps to overcome water supply problems where the fire is at a distance from the nearest water source, but typically not more that a mile away. Pumping water through hose takes energy, and fire hose has friction loss. For example, a 4½-in. hose at 1,000 gpm (3,785 L/min) has 10 psi (69 kPa) friction loss per 100 ft (30.5 m). A mile (roughly 5,300 ft or 1,609 m) of 4½-in. (115-mm) hose would require 530 psi (3,654 kPa) of pump pressure to overcome the friction loss to continuously supply 1,000 gpm (3,785 L/min) through the mile of hose. 530 psi (3,654 kPa) of friction loss a mile in 4½-in. (115-mm) hose at 1,000 gpm (3,785 L/min) is not possible to achieve with the standard fire department hose and equipment. However, to pump a mile of 4½ in. (115 mm) hose at 1,000 gpm (3,785 L/min), a fire department could place a pumper every 1,000 ft (304.8 m), which would bring the required pressure per pumper down to 100 psi (700 kPa) for each 1,000 ft (304.8 m) section of 4½-in. (115-mm) hose it is assigned to pump for friction loss. Friction loss in hose is the main reason fire departments establish relay operations.

Fig. 15–20. Jet siphons are typically used to move water from one portable tank to another.

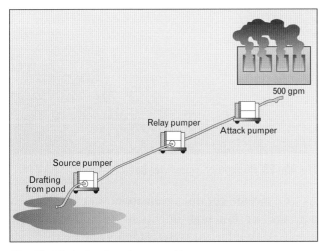

Fig. 15–21. A simple relay operation

For terminology purposes, let's take a look at a three-pumper relay operation. The pumper located at the water source that pumps water to a second pumper is called the **source pumper**. The second pumper, or **inline pumper**, receiving water from the source pumper then pumps the water to a third pumper. The third and last pumper in this example is called the **attack pumper**. It supplies the

fire attack lines and is located at the fire. The number of required pumpers, size of hose, length of lay, type of lay, required gpm, and elevation change are just some of the factors that have to be accounted for a successful relay-pumping operations.

Fire departments that routinely use relay operations should be well practiced and drilled; they should also be aware of the limitations of their relay operations in their training. These fire departments sometimes have special hose wagons and relay valves to help speed the deployment of large amounts of hose. This makes engaging in relay-pumping operations in rapid fashion more possible. Long relay-pumping operations can be established in a rapid manner by departments that routinely train in this tactic. In some jurisdictions, fire departments have set up preformed relay-pumping task forces that can be special-called by the incident commander. These task forces then establish any entire secondary water supply upon arrival, with a goal of attaining a certain water supply capacity, usually no less then 1,000 gpm.

Fireboats and dry main systems

Many fire departments located near large bodies of water have **fireboats** with pumping capabilities. These fireboats vary in size and use, but we will discuss them based on solely on pumping capacity. The NFPA classifies fireboats as Class A, B, or C. Class A is the largest class of fireboat.[3] It must be 65 ft (20 m) in length or larger, with at least a 5,000-gpm (18,927 L/min) pumping capacity. This is followed by the Class B fireboat, which is between 40 ft (12 m) and 65 ft (20 m) in length with a minimum of 2,500-gpm (9,463-L/min) pumping capacity. Class C is the smallest class of fireboat, is 20–40 ft (6–12 m) in length, and has a minimum pumping capacity of 500 gpm (1,893 L/min). Many fireboats greatly exceed their suggested minimum pumping capacities. One such example, operated by the Los Angles City Fire Department, is a 105-ft (123-m) fireboat with a pumping capacity of 38,000 gpm (143,846 L/min).

Fireboats are amazing pieces of equipment. Typically, they are designed to continuously pump water at their rated capacity for at least 8 hours. Following the terrorist attack of September 11, 2001, on the World Trade Center in New York City, fireboats were used to fight the ensuing fires and supplied a peak flow of 60,000 gpm (227,125 L/min) to the World Trade Center site through fire hose.[4] Fireboat pumping operations continued for days at Ground Zero.

The 1989 Loma Pretia earthquake caused several major fires in San Francisco's Marina District. San Francisco Fire Department's (SFFD) fireboat *Phoenix* (fig. 15–22) pumped roughly 5.5 million gal (20.8 million L) of water over a 15-hour period through a portable water supply system built out of 5-in. (125-mm) hose because water mains in the area had been severely damaged by the earthquake.[5] No hydrants were working reliably in the area of the main fires near the waterfront. During this conflagration, the pumping capacity of the *Phoenix* was largely credited with saving a whole district of the city. Soon after the 1989 earthquake and fire, SFFD purchased a second fireboat to augment their waterfront fire protection.

Fig. 15–22. SFFD fireboat Phoenix and waterfront-mounted dry hydrant. (Courtesy of Danny Barlogio)

Some cities with fireboats have wet or dry **manifold systems** connected to special water main systems. This type of water main system carries nonpotable or raw water, which can be pumped into fireboats or pumping stations that draw water from a static source, fed by large reservoirs under the force gravity, or a combination of all of these methods. San Francisco's Auxiliary Water Supply System is the best example of this in the United States.

Other cities have a separate high-pressure water supply systems—in some cases using water supplied directly from an adjacent river—in their downtown congested commercial districts. These systems are activated during large fires.

Reclaimed water main systems and hydrants

As drinking water becomes an increasingly scarce natural resource, a new trend has begun on the West Coast: the use of **reclaimed water**. Sometimes called **gray water**, reclaimed water is becoming so regularly used that waste-

water treatment plants (sewage treatment plants) are now providing it back to consumers through reclaimed water distribution systems. Gray water is used to water golf courses and flush toilets in high-rises, and it is used in other situations where potable water is not needed. Some fire departments are now requesting hydrants to be installed on these newly installed gray-water main systems and are using these hydrants as auxiliary water supply sources. These gray-water hydrants are painted purple, which is the same color as reclaimed water pipes. See fig. 15–23, which shows just such a gray-water hydrant. This gray-water fire hydrant is located on a reclaimed water main system that waters a very large city park and school grounds.

Fig. 15–23. Reclaimed water wet barrel hydrant

As we conclude our discussion about water supply, you now can see just how important an adequate water supply is. A sufficient water supply is necessary at all fires once an attack has begun, and it needs to last the whole incident without interruption. There are billions of dollars of water supply infrastructure throughout the United States. In addition to the municipal water supply infrastructure, billions of dollars have been spent on fire department equipment to use that available water. In the end, it is up to us, the fire service professionals, to get the most out our available water supply system. As you move forward in your career, it will become necessary to expand your knowledge regarding water supply. This chapter is just a basic introduction to effective and efficient water supply. Remember, poor water supply equals poor service.

INTRODUCTION TO HOSE

Now that we have discussed water supply systems, we need a way of moving the water from place to place. The moving of water in the fire service is accomplished with the use of hose specifically designed and constructed for the fire service. The ideal fire hose must be low in friction lost, durable, lightweight, and easy to couple. Fire hose must also be made in a cost-effective manner. Weighing these needs and characteristics, the major manufacturers of fire hose provide a wide array of choices to the modern fire service. In this discussion about fire hose we will be covering the following topics:

- Classification of hose
- Hose anatomy and construction
- Size and type of hose and common flows
- Couplings
- Fittings, appliances, and hose tools
- Basic hose testing and maintenance
- Hose storage
- Water supply evolutions

Classification of hose

The breakdown in classification of fire service hoses is based on its tactical uses. Typically, hose is discussed in terms of drafting, supply, attack, and wildland. **Drafting hose** is a rigid hose that is used by a pump to acquire water from static water sources. **Supply hose** is designed to move larger volumes of water; naturally these supply hoses have a larger diameter than attack hoses. **Attack hose**, sometimes referred to as hand line hose, must have a diameter large enough to move the required flow, which can be up to 325 gpm (1,230 L/min), but must be small and lightweight enough to be easily moved around the fireground by firefighters. **Wildland hose** is a type of specialty attack hose designed to work well for combating vegetation fires. Wildland hose is not produced in diameters greater than 1½ in. Two main criteria for wildland hose are reduced weight and toler-

ance for higher pressures. One other type of specialty hose used extensively in the fire service is booster line or reel line. It is basically a big rubber garden hose made in either a ¾- or 1-in. (20- or 25-mm) diameter. The booster line typically is only used for nuisance fires, but has its place in fighting both small urban nuisance fires and in the control of small vegetation fires. Booster line has a limited role in fighting fire due to its low flow and fixed length. The full length of booster line is mounted on a hose reel and is usually no longer than 200 ft (60 m) in length. A typical maximum flow from a booster line is 60 gpm (227 L/min). *A booster line is never to be used for fire attack in a building or for a vehicle fire.*

Hose anatomy and construction

Hose anatomy and construction is another area of the fire service that has seen dramatic changes with the help of technology. Advances in materials science have led to fire hoses that far exceed the performance characteristics of hose manufactured as recently as two decades ago. It is common now to have fire hose capable of withstanding continuous pressure of up to 400 psi (2,800 kPa), even though regular fire service pumps are not designed to operate efficiently at pressures above 250 psi (1,750 kPa). This increased capability is a demonstration of just how tough currently manufactured modern fire hose really is.

When fire hose is constructed, the manufacturers try to build it for the task it will be performing. For example, is the hose going to be used for attack, supply, or wildland? What types of pressures will the hose encounter? Will it be exposed to unduly harsh environments inside fire buildings, or will it mainly be used outside? Is it going to be continually exposed to sunlight in open hosebeds or routinely be exposed to moisture for prolonged periods? Is the overall weight of the hose likely to be a big issue? With these things in mind, manufacturers set out to construct hose based on consultations with fire departments and industry experts while meeting written industry standards and laws. The goal is to make fire hose that performs its function well with low overall weight, low friction loss, and reasonable cost, while maintaining adequate durability and service life.

Hose must be resistant to all types of mechanical damage, such as that caused by sharp objects or being regularly dragged over rough surfaces. It must be able to handle long-term storage without deteriorating in a variety of conditions in apparatus hosebeds, compartments, bundles, packs, rolls, and hose racks. Fire hose needs to absorb heat without failing or easily catching fire. Furthermore, it must be resistant to damage from long-term exposure to sunlight. On top of that, modern fire hose will routinely be put away wet, which promotes mildew and mold. Although constructed to overcome these performance demands, fire hose must maintain its ability to flow water while holding its shape and not easily kinking. Fire hose must also fold easily and store in a space-efficient manner, lying nearly completely flat when not in use. Facing all of these challenges, the fire service hose manufacturers have stepped into a world of synthetic materials and exotic rubbers to meet these demands.

Typical fire hose can be broken down into **lined hose** with either one or two outer reinforcing **jackets**. The linings of the hose can be made out of rubber compounds, thermoplastics, or blends of both, as well as polyurethane or natural rubber latex.[6] This liner must be smooth, watertight, and durable while maintaining a surface that provides a low friction loss based on the amount of water that the hose is designed to flow. A common liner material is an ethylene propylene diene monomer (EPDM) rubber and polyurethane. The inner liner, which is the waterway, is always protected by one or two outer jackets.

The first hose jacket serves many purposes, so it must be tough. The main purpose of the first jacket is to resist the expansion of the waterway, which enables the fire hose to retain its shape and not deform under pressure. Hose jackets or reinforcements are commonly made out of synthetic fiber, natural fiber, or a combination of both.[7] The first, critical jacket allows the liner to operate at high pressures, though usually not more than 250 psig (1,825 kPa) during normal fire service application. In the case of **single jacketed (SJ) hose**, a fire hose designed with only one jacket, the outer sheath must also provide a layer of protection from mechanical, thermal, and chemical damage. The first hose jacket is usually made from nylon, or in some cases, cotton. For example, wildland hose is still sometimes single-jacketed hose lined with cotton and rubber. Wildland hose also comes in SJ nylon rubber–lined hose construction. The cotton jacket performs its functions well, especially under heat, but it is susceptible to mold and mildew damage more than the SJ nylon version of wildland hose. A fire service agency must spec the type of hose they wish to purchase, because there is a wide variety of construction available for similar uses.

Double-jacketed (DJ) hose is used throughout the United States and is commonly referred to as structure fire hose. DJ structure fire hose is a very widespread specification for urban fire departments for operations at building

fires. DJ structure fire hose is commonly purchased in sizes ranging from 1½ to 5 in. (38 to 125 mm). The extra outer jacket is usually made of similar material as the first. It is designed to shed water and resist mechanical abrasive forces, heat, and flame. One added benefit of having this extra outer jacket, which encloses the first or single jacket and liner, is that it provides an extra layer of protection against forces on the fireground that can cause hoses to fail. Both jackets are treated to minimize mold and mildew even when put away wet. In addition, modern hose jackets are usually designed to be resistant to petrochemicals. Figure 15–24 (a and b) shows the difference between SJ and DJ fire hose.

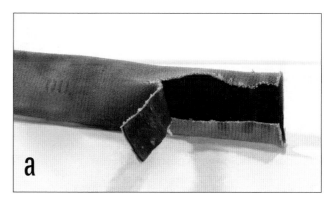

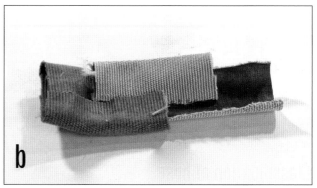

Fig. 15–24 a, b. Top: 1½-in. (38-mm) SJ cotton rubber hose; Bottom: 1¾,-in. (45-mm) DJ nylon structure hose. Both have rubber liners. (Courtesy of Adam Weidenbach)

Two other types of hose the fire service uses are drafting hose and booster hose. *Drafting hose*, also called *hard suction hose*, needs to maintain a waterway under a vacuum (i.e., negative pressure, at or below 0 psi). Suction hose was traditionally made out of a wired frame wrapped with rubber belting and coated in rubber. This made a hard semiflexible black hose that was very heavy and rigid. Drafting hose is now frequently either made out of an EPDM rubber liner with outer nylon and wire reinforcement or a durable, flexible, lightweight polyvinyl chloride (PVC) plastic. Drafting hose allows pumps to acquire water from static water sources by providing a waterway in which a vacuum can be created and maintained. Once a good vacuum is attained, water from the static source simply flows up the hose under atmospheric pressure into the pump. This is the same principle that is at work when you use a straw to drink a glass of soda. The straw is basically a drafting hose made of plastic tubing. Typically, drafting hose is made in 10-ft (3-m) lengths, and engines carry two lengths of it. Fire engines carry only 20 ft (6 m) of drafting hose because the laws of physics dictate that the practical limit in the fire service for drafting vertically is around 20 ft (6 m). Drafting hose is manufactured in a variety of diameters; large pumps need large drafting hose. A 1,500-gpm (5,678 L/min) pump requires 6-in. (15 cm) diameter hard suction hose to reach capacity at a 10-ft (3-m) draft.

Even though the lion's share of all attack and supply hose is either single jacketed or double jacketed, there are other options. One type of uniquely constructed hose being offered by hose manufactures is an **extruded hose** made out of nitrile rubber or polyurethane with a weaved matrix providing the backbone of the hose (fig. 15–25). In essence, it is a jacketless hose designed with a nitrile rubber or polyurethane material composing both the waterway and jacket, and the embedded, woven fabric matrix providing the required strength. Extruded hose is offered both in supply and attack hose diameters. Its main advantage is that it is lightweight while still providing the majority of all required aspects of fire service hose. However, extruded hose is notorious for its tendency to kink.

Fig. 15–25. Extruded 1½-in. structure fire hose. (Courtesy of Adam Weidenbach)

The main use of extruded hose is for large water supply operations and is usually ordered in 4-in. (100-mm) diameters and larger, although it is also found in smaller-diameter hand lines. It is now even purchased in diameters of 6, 8, 10, and 12 in. (152, 203, 254, and 305 mm). These diameters are referred to as **ultra-large-diameter hose (ULDH)**. This is an exciting new type of hose, which is providing solutions in governmental and big industrial applications. ULDH hose is uniquely suited for large-scale disasters where flows of up to 10,000 gpm (37,854 L/min) through a single hose are required. The Department of Homeland Security funded a ULDH system in New Jersey, and even cities as small as Berkeley, California (population ca. 100,000) are investing in this technology. Berkeley is purchasing a ULDH system to combat large-scale water main failures that are predicted by the water district serving their community following a major earthquake on the Hayward Fault. ULDH systems with portable pumping capabilities are becoming more and more common and can act as a buffer to overcome the inevitable large-scale water problems during catastrophic events.

Size and type of hose and common flows

FFI 5.3.10 In this section, we will look at different diameters, flows, and standard lengths of various fire hose. The nice thing about fire service hydraulics is that it is based in math and physics. There is always one manufacturer or another trying to say that their hose flows the best or claiming that their 2-in. (51-mm) hose is as hydraulically efficient as a competitor's 2½-in. (65-mm) hose. Do not fall into this trap. Technological advances are usually applied to all similar types of hose at the same time, no matter who the manufacturer is. The simple fact is that the larger the diameter of the hose, the more water it will flow.

Take, for example, a flow of 200 gpm (757 L/min) in a 1¾-in. (45-mm) DJ attack hand line hose. A 200-gpm (757 L/min) flow in 1¾-in. (45-mm) attack hose will require 62 psig (434 kPa) per 100 ft (30 m) of hose just to overcome the friction loss. On the other hand, that same 200-gpm (757-L/min) flow in 3½-in (90-mm) DJ medium-diameter supply hose (MDH) only loses 4 psi (28 kPa) per 100 ft (30 m) due to friction loss. This example clearly demonstrates the need for different hose sizes for different jobs in the fire service. Note that in table 15–2 the largest attack hand line hose is 2½ in. (64 mm). This is because a 2½-in. (65-mm) diameter fire hose can reasonably move the maximum recognized hand line flow of 325 gpm (1,230 L/min). There is no need for a larger-diameter hand line hose in most circumstances. This is discussed in more detail in chapter 16, Fire Streams. The other type of hose used in supply situations is commonly referred to as **large-diameter hose (LDH)**. Look at table 15–2 to get an idea of the size and type and common flows of these types of hose, attack/hand line, MDH, and LDH. The table includes the dry weight of 100 ft of hose as well as the same

Table 15–2. Size and type of hose and common flows, based on nylon double-jacketed structure fire hose construction

Size	Typical flows, gpm (L/min)	Type	Weight per 100 ft (30 m) empty, lb (kg)	Weight per 100 ft (30 m) full, lb (kg)	Typical length, ft (m)
1½ in. (38 mm)	60–150 (227–567)	Attack/hand line	30 (13.6)	107 (48.5)	50 (15)
1¾ in. (45 mm)	95–200 (960–757)	Attack/hand line	32 (14.5)	152 (68.9)	50 (15)
2 in. (51 mm)	150–250 (568–946)	Attack/hand line	40 (18.1)	176 (79.8)	50 (15)
2½ in. (65 mm)	200–325 (757–1,230)	Attack/hand line	52 (23.6)	264 (119.7)	50 (15)
3 in. (75 mm)	0–500 (0–1,893)	MDH/supply	68 (30.8)	375 (170.1)	50 (15)
3½ in. (90 mm)	0–800 (0–3,028)	MDH/supply	78 (35.4)	493 (223.6)	50 (15)
4 in. (100 mm)	0–1,200 (0–4,542)	LDH/supply	88 (39.9)	631 (286.2)	50 or 100 (15 or 30)
4½ in. (115 mm)	0–1,500 (0–5,678)	LDH/supply	100 (45.4)	787 (357)	50 or 100 (15 or 30)
5 in. (125 mm)	0–2,000 (0–7,571)	LDH/supply	110 (19.9)	958 (434.5)	50 or 100 (15 or 30)

100 ft (30 m) of hose when charged with water. Notice again in the attack hose section the dramatic difference in weight between 2½-in. (65-mm) attack hose and 3-in. (75-mm) MDH.

The fire service fights more than just structure fires. So far, the hose we have discussed is mainly used to supply and attack fires related to buildings, and thus is commonly referred to in the broadest sense as structure fire hose. Most common structure fire hose is double jacketed in design. If you look again at table 15–2, you will notice that it states that all information is based on nylon double-jacketed structure fire hose construction.

Beyond structure fires, the fire service is responsible for extinguishing all types of fires. One specialized facet of the fire service, wildland firefighting, has its own type of hose, called single-jacketed (SJ) wildland hose. Wildland SJ hose was developed strictly for wildland firefighting and is usually either 1 in. or 1½ in. (25 or 38 mm) in diameter. It is designed to be lightweight and to withstand higher pressures than DJ structure fire hose. In contrast to a standard DJ structure fire hose with couplings every 50 ft (15 m), wildland hose generally comes in standard 100-ft (30-m) lengths, thus eliminating a full coupling every 100 ft (30 m), which reduces its overall weight. This same goal of weight reduction was applied when

the outer jacket was removed from the specification of wildland hose. The main reason for this reduced weight is that wildland SJ hose is usually carried long distances, commonly on foot while hiking. Wildland SJ hose can also commonly be used to form very long continuous progressive hose lays where pressures can become high, based both on distance and terrain. There is even a special lightweight ¾-in. (20-mm) wildland hose. Flows during suppression of wildland fires from a single line rarely are more than 70 gpm (265 L/min) in 1½-in. (38-mm) SJ wildland hose and 30 gpm (114 L/min) in 1-in. (25-mm) SJ wildland hose. These low flows can be complicated by high pressures due to hilly terrain and portable, low-volume capacity high-pressure pumps. These are some of the reasons why there is a special hose developed specifically to combat wildland fires.

As far as booster hose and reel lines are concerned, they typically flow between 30 and 60 gpm (114 and 227 L/min). They are used in both urban and wildland environments. The booster hose is stored on motorized reel line. When the booster hose is in use, you pull out only the required amount. When finished, you can take it up quickly onto the reel. Booster hose should only be used in situations where required and expected flows will not exceed their limited capability, and *never for building or vehicle fires*. Booster line hose is made in

100-ft (30-m) lengths in both ¾-in. (20-mm) and 1-in. (25-mm) diameters. Booster hose is stored on reel lines in coupled lengths of up to 300 ft (91 m). In an urban environment, booster hose is commonly used at small outside trash fires or during overhaul. In the wildland environment, booster hose is commonly used on small grass fires: the vehicle it is attached to slowly moves while firefighters extinguish the burning grass. This type of wildland fire attack is called a mobile attack. These reel lines with booster hose are severely limited to low flows of 60 gpm (227 L/min) and less and have a fixed length usually not exceeding 200 ft (60 m). Some highly urbanized departments do not even use them; the Los Angeles Fire Department (LAFD) is good example of this. Other departments have stopped using booster lines because they are frequently misused due to their ease of deployment. One must recognize that speed is no excuse for bringing the wrong tool for the job. Hoses are tools used to move water. It is imperative that the right size of hose and flow is selected for the job at hand. There will be further instruction on selecting hose in the fire stream and fire attack chapters.

Couplings

Couplings are a key component in making fire hose versatile. The coupling makes it possible to join two pieces of hose together or break apart two joined pieces of hose in a rapid manner. The two most common types of couplings in use today in the U.S. fire service are the threaded coupling (made up of individual male and a female couplings) with NST or a type of sexless coupling called **Storz**. Both types of couplings allow good, strong, watertight connections to be made in a rapid manner. Modern couplings can handle great pressures and stresses developed inside the hose during pumping operations.

Today, couplings are typically made out of hardened aluminum. In the past, brass was a very commonly used material. Some fire hose may still be in service with brass couplings today. However, the vast majority of all fire hose now has hardened aluminum couplings. Hardened aluminum couplings resist all of the following areas of concern regarding fire hose: corrosion, abrasive forces, compressive forces, and expansive forces. This durability makes hardened aluminum ideal for the fire service.

Hose lengths are individually marked for identification purposes. A unique number is stenciled on the hose jacket. Alternatively, a special steel numbering die is used to number a hose coupling on a length of hose when it is received new; for example, the first 2½-in. (65-mm) hose length purchased in the year 2009 is marked 2009-1, the

next is designated 2009-2, and so on. Records are kept of each hose length so that the age of a hose can be tracked when it is tested (described later). In addition, in large departments the engine company that receives the new hose may have the couplings painted with a specific combination of colors or provided with another numerical designation in order to return the hose to the proper company after a large fire.

The common features of male and female coupling design are shown in fig. 15–26.

Fig. 15–26. Male and female set of hardened aluminum coupling with brass expansion rings. (Courtesy of Adam Weidenbach)

Male and female couplings are one of the most commonly used hose couplings in the fire service. They are attached usually at the factory to lengths of fire hose typically in 50- or 100-ft (15.2- or 30-m) lengths. Hose commonly comes from the factory standard, with a female coupling on one end and a male coupling on the opposite end. The couplings in fig. 15–26 are a male/female set designed for use on DJ 3-in. (75-mm) hose. One way to attach a coupling to a piece of hose is by using what is called a brass expansion ring system. On the right in fig. 15–26, the male coupling has a brass expansion ring sitting in its bowl or shank. Notice that this male coupling has **rocker lugs** extending the full length of the bowl. A lug is a raised part of a coupling that allows a **spanner wrench** to grab onto it. On the left in fig. 15–26, the female coupling has rocker lugs only on the swiveling part of the female coupling and its bowl is smooth in nature. Also notice the female coupling has a gasket inside the female threaded area to allow for watertight connections. Both of these couplings are threaded with, 2½-in. (65 mm)

NHT. These couplings are designed to attach to one another with or without the use of spanner wrenches.

Shown in fig. 15–27a is a 2½-in. (65-mm) NH female coupling designed with a bowl for 3-in. (75-mm) DJ hose sitting on top of a machine called a hose expander. This removed bowl gasket sits on top of the machine, and the expansion ring is visible on the draw bar. The draw bar is the part of the machine that will eventually expand the brass expansion ring inside the hose. To get a watertight seal, the brass expansion ring is inserted into a cut piece of 3-in. (75-mm) DJ hose, and then the hose with the expander ring in it is pushed into the bowl of the proper sized coupling. In the bowl, the expansion ring makes contact with a rubber bowl gasket located inside at the end or bottom of the bowl. The assembled hose, expansion ring, and coupling are then pushed as a unit onto the expander (fig. 15–27b). The expansion ring is then hydraulically expanded under tremendous force by the expanding machine. This particular application for 3-in. (75-mm) DJ hose with 2½-in. (65-mm) couplings requires about 1,300 psi (9,100 kPa) of expansive force. The brass expansion ring ends up sandwiching the hose and the tail gasket against the inside of the coupling's bowl, which is ribbed to help the hose remain in place when pumped under high pressures. In this case, you end up with a 2½-in. (65-mm) female coupling joined to a length of 3-in. (75-mm) DJ hose. This is a very strong, mechanically pressed attachment.

In fig. 15–28, you can see four different hose sizes, all with male and female couplings. The top example (4½-in. [115-mm] red supply hose) has extended lugs on the female swivel. The next hose down is a 3-in. (75-mm) tan DJ MDH, which has a coupling design to allow for a 2½-in. (65-mm) threaded connection. The blue hose is 2½-in. (65-mm) DJ hand line hose, with 2½-in. (65-mm) threaded couplings. The last example is 1¾-in. (45-mm) DJ hand line hose with 1½-in. (38-mm) couplings. All the hose in fig. 15–21 is of DJ construction with hardened aluminum couplings that were attached to the hose using brass expansion rings.

Fig. 15–27a. Coupling expander

Fig. 15–27b. Hose mounted with coupling expander

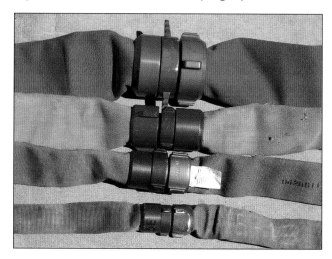

Fig. 15–28. Different hose sizes with male and female couplings

Coupling fire hose. We will now discuss techniques of joining two hoses together using male and female couplings. Anyone who has screwed together a nut and bolt or joined two garden hoses together can understand the basic principles of coupling and uncoupling threaded fire hose. Firefighting is a team endeavor, but there are times when one must do a certain operation alone. This applies to coupling and uncoupling lengths of fire hose. There are various methods that can be used if you are by yourself. Some of the methods are the "foot-tilt method" and the "knee press method." If there is an additional firefighter, both of them can assist in coupling or uncoupling the hose (fig. 15–29). One common method is called a "stiff-arm method." For each of these methods it is important for the firefighter to make use of a thread design incorporated in the male thread of a fire hose coupling, called a "higbee cut." This allows for an easier connection of male and female connections. The "higbee cut" can be located by finding the "**higbee indicator,**" usually located on the coupling lugs. Most times, fire hose can be coupled and uncoupled by hand-tightening the coupling. If they are too tight to be uncoupled in this manner, a spanner-wrench can be used, but only to uncouple, not to couple, as this can damage the gaskets in the female couplings.

The other common coupling that has gained widespread use in the United States is the Storz sexless coupling. It is manufactured for use on all sizes of hose. However, the most common sizes are 4-in. and 5-in. (100 and 125 mm) Storz couplings. These unisex couplings have some advantages over a male/female design. The most obvious is the fact that one does not need any **double male** or **female adaptor fittings,** which are needed when you find yourself in a situation where you are trying to join two hoses together with the same sex threaded coupling. No matter which side of the hose you grab, it will automatically be able to attach to another Storz fitting of the same size. Storz couplings are also fast to connect, needing just a quarter turn to lock together. This can lead to problems if the hose has twisted during operation, because they have been known to uncouple themselves in older hoses without a locking mechanism. (See fig. 15–30 for nonlocking 5-in. [125-mm] Storz coupling.) Modern Storz fittings have a locking mechanism that has solved the uncoupling issue.

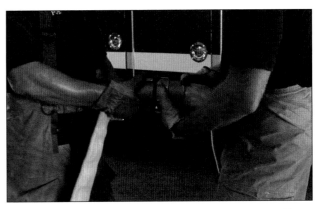

Fig. 15–29. Firefighters utilize various techniques to aid in coupling and uncoupling hose.

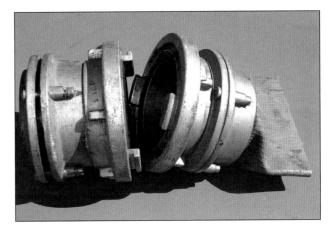

Fig. 15–30. Nonlocking 5-in. (125-mm) Storz coupling

Coupling and uncoupling a Storz fitting is basically the same as working with threaded hose. They also tighten to the right or clockwise and loosen to the left or counterclockwise. The same coupling techniques discussed previously—both the single-firefighter and two-firefighter coupling methods—can be applied to Storz couplings. The notable difference is that it only takes a little more than half a turn to completely couple and uncouple a Storz fitting. It is therefore necessary to ensure that when completing a coupling, both locks are secure and the lugs are lined up. This will ensure that the Storz coupling will stay together under pressure. If you work in a fire department still using nonlocking Storz, it is critical to make sure the Storz lugs are lined up and excessive twists are not in the uncharged hose. Not doing so can lead to catastrophic self-uncoupling of nonlocking Storz hose when charged.

The 5-in. (125-mm) Storz coupling in fig. 15–31 does not use an expansion ring attachment to join it to the hose. Instead of a bowl, there is a tail piece and an attached external collar or retaining ring. The hose is simply cut and pushed over the tail piece, usually with a **hose gasket** of some sort (fig. 15–32). Then the retaining ring goes over the hose and the tail piece. The retaining ring is then mechanically fastened to the hose with (in this case) four heavy-duty bolts. The retaining ring design also makes a strong watertight connection between the hose and the coupling.

Fig. 15–31. Locking Storz coupling

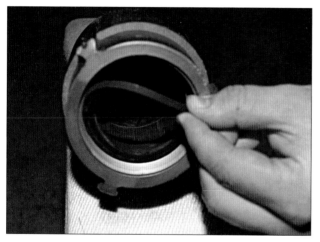

Fig. 15–32. It is important to check hose gaskets for wear and tear, on a regular basis.

Per NFPA 1962, *Standard for the Inspection, Care, and Use of Fire Hose, Couplings, and Nozzles and the Service Testing of Fire Hose,* couplings should be visually inspected after each use for the following problems: damaged threads, corrosion, slippage on the hose, out of round, swivel not rotating freely, missing lugs, loose external collar or internal gasket, and other defects that could impair operation.

When inspecting couplings for damage, the best tools you have are your eyes and hands. First, look for abrasion damage to the shanks and excessive wear from use. If they are excessively worn from dragging, they should be put out of service. Corrosion is not common because the hardened aluminum is very resistant to corrosive forces. Hold the coupling and pull on the hose, and there should be no movement. Any sign or feeling of movement of the hose from the shank is a failure, and the hose and

coupling should be put out of service. Any collar-type coupling should have all of its collar bolts, and there should be no signs of collar slippage or looseness. Any collar problems should cause the coupling and hose to be put out of service. Any female swivel should be checked by freely spinning it. If stiff in motion, the female swivel can be washed in hot soapy water and lubricated with silicone lubricant.

One specific item that is often overlooked, but is easy to address, is the female swivel gasket in the common threaded coupling. If it looks old, worn out, cracked, nonpliable, or smashed, just pull it out and check it. The gasket simply sits in a groove, and it is easily removed by pinching the gasket with a thumb and index finger and pulling it out of the groove (fig. 15–32). If it fails inspection because it is cracked or no longer elastic, just replace it. Once again, pinch it, place it back in its groove in the female coupling, and make sure it is seated all the way. It is good practice to join the hose to another male couple after replacing a gasket to ensure proper working condition. This also guarantees that proper installation has been achieved.

It is obvious that great care must be taken to ensure that couplings work in a flawless manner. This takes discipline in inspection and care of fire hose. Without a properly coupled hose, you do not have a means of moving water efficiently, and without that, you cannot successfully use water to mount an effective fire attack. Couplings are a keystone item found on all fire hose, and they are vital to fire hose function.

Earlier in this chapter, it was mentioned that there was specialty hose called ultra-large-diameter hose, or ULDH. This type of hose can be coupled in many ways, and fig. 15–33a shows an example of a two **Victaulic couplings** joined together with a retaining ring and gasket. Victaulic couplings (mechanical couplings) are designed to be field repairable and are used on very large hose (up to 18 in. [457 mm] in diameter). Figure 15–33b shows a 12-in. (305-mm) coupling with no hose on it. This ULDH special hose is simply cut and pushed onto the tail piece. Then, a series of metal bands are tightened over the hose in the grooves located on the coupling's tail piece to make a watertight connection. This is not a fast method of coupling hose, but when using ULDH in a major emergency, the ULDH hose may be in place for months. Having couplings every 100 ft (30 m) is just not an option, given that the hose lay may be miles long. There are, of course, many other ways to couple hose used in all types of industry. In the United Kingdom, the fire service uses British Instantaneous Hose couplings.

Japan has a new sexless coupling system as well. The point is that as a professional firefighter, you must know what your agency uses and also understand that there are other types of coupling systems that may be used in your mutual aid response areas.

Fig. 15–33 a, b. There are various specialty couplings that are utilized in the field, such as those used in ULDH.

Fittings, appliances, and hose tools

Now that we have a general understanding of what fire hose is—a conduit for flowing water—a question comes to mind: How do we get all these different types of hose to work together? How do we join two different sizes of hose together or two different couplings designs together? How do we get a hose to divide into two hoses or combine into one hose? This is where hose fittings, appliances, and hose tools come into play.

First, let's take a look at **hose fitting**s. They used to be made out of brass, but today they are made from the same hardened aluminum that couplings are made out of. When looking at a fitting, it is always good to take a systematic approach. One must have a common way of identifying a fitting, so that when you need a fitting,

it is easy to describe. It is always proper to start with the female side when describing a fitting. However, if the fitting has a Storz side, start naming with it. Other items that need to be identified are the sizes of both sides of the fitting. After you have addressed those two main steps in naming a fitting, do not forget to identify anything else that is special about it. For example, it could have different types of thread, swivels, or extended lugs. If you do not name a thread type, it is assumed that the fitting is NHT. Take a look at the fittings and naming examples in fig. 15–35. All the fittings are named from left to right. Notice that some of these fittings are still made of brass. In the past, all fittings were generically called *brass*.

All the reducing fittings in fig. 15–34 do exactly what their names imply: They go from larger to smaller. Most of the time, reducing fittings are just called **reducers**.

Fig. 15–34. Reducers. (Courtesy of Adam Weidenbach)

1. 4½-in. (115-mm) female to 2½-in. (65-mm) male reducer

2. 3-in. (75-mm) female to 2½-in. (65-mm) male reducer

3. 2½-in. (65-mm) female to 1½-in. (38-mm) male reducer

4. 2½-in. (65-mm) female to 1½-in. (38-mm) male bell reducer. (Bell component keeps it from hanging up on corners or objects.)

The couplings in fig. 15–35 are all increasing fittings; they simply make it possible to go from small to larger. Most of the time increasing fittings are just called **increasers**.

Fig. 15–35. Increasers. (Courtesy of Adam Weidenbach)

1. 3-in. (75-mm) female swivel to 4½-in. (115-mm) male pin lug increaser. (Notice that the swivel end and also the pin lugs were mentioned.)

2. 2½-in. (65-mm) female to 3-in. (75-mm) male increaser

3. 1½-in. (38-mm) female to 2½-in. (65-mm) female increaser

Figure 15–36 shows all double female fittings. They make it possible to join two males together. These are the most common type, as they join males of the same diameter together. Most double female fittings swivel on both sides. It is assumed they do, so if you have a specialty double female that is ridged on one side, you must state it.

Fig. 15–36. Double female. (Courtesy of Adam Weidenbach)

1. 4½-in. (115-mm) double female (DF)

2. 2½-in. (65-mm) DF

3. 1½-in. (38-mm) DF

Fig. 15–37 shows all double male fittings. They make it possible to join two females couplings together. These are the most common type, as they join females of the same diameter together.

Fig. 15–37. Double males. (Courtesy of Adam Weidenbach)

1. 4½-in. (115-mm) double male (DM)

2. 2½-in. (65-mm) DM

3. 1½-in. (38-mm) DM

Figure 15–38 shows a common type of adaptor fitting used in the fire service. This is the first adapter we have looked at that changes thread type. These types of adapters are often needed because many departments use Storz fittings on their large-diameter supply hose. The two Storz adapters in fig. 15–38 are identical and have a locking feature on the Storz side. This safety feature is now required with Storz fittings. Since Storz fittings only require about a half turn to couple, they also only take about a half turn to uncouple. This half turn feature does make coupling Storz fittings easy, but also makes them susceptible to self-uncoupling if the hose twists too violently during operation. This is why modern Storz fittings have locking mechanisms. Storz fittings with locking mechanisms should be able to be coupled and uncoupled by hand without wrenches. Figures 15–38 and 15–39 both show 5-in. (125-mm) Storz adapters, but another common Storz size is 4 in. (115 mm). Remember the naming rules: If there is a Storz side, you start by naming it first.

Fig. 15–38. Storz adapter: 5-in. (125-mm) Storz locking to 4½-in. (115-mm) female swivel, extended lug. (Courtesy of Adam Weidenbach)

Fig. 15–39. Storz adapter: 5-in. (125-mm) Storz nonlocking to 4½-in. (115-mm) male. (Courtesy of Adam Weidenbach)

The fittings in fig. 15–40 are examples of fittings that change thread types. In older cities, some existing buildings predate the standardization of thread **pitch** and

count of the standard NST. Other times, you many need a thread adapter to be able to connect to other types of common thread design used in construction. For example, you may need an adapter such as a 3-in. (75-mm) pipe thread (a common thread used to join pipes) female to a 2½-in. (65-mm) NH male. This adapter would be very useful if you needed to connect fire hose to an industrial pump that had a 3-in. (75-mm) male pipe threaded outlet. Figure 15–40 shows some examples.

Fig. 15–40. Thread adapters. (Courtesy of Adam Weidenbach)

1. 2½-in. (65-mm) Female National hose thread to ¾-in. (20-mm) male garden hose thread (GHT)

2. 1½-in. (38-mm) Female Pacific Coast thread (PAC) to 1½-in. (38-mm) male National hose

3. 1½-in. (38-mm) Female National hose thread to 1½-in. (38-mm) male Pacific Coast thread (PAC)

Notice that the fittings are clearly stamped with their thread designators. The two Pacific Coast (PAC) thread adapters are reverse of each other. Look at their male end and you can see that PAC has a finer thread than the NHT.

The fittings in fig. 15–41 are elbow fittings. Elbows are sometimes called drop fittings. Their main purpose is to allow a hard bend from a ridged outlet, so that hose connected to it will not flex or kink. You commonly see them on pump panel discharges, and some departments carry them in standpipe kits to overcome poorly designed standpipe outlets. They can be very useful.

Fig. 15–41. Elbow fittings. (Courtesy of Adam Weidenbach)

1. 5-in. Storz locking to 4½-in. (115-mm) female swivel, 30° elbow

2. 2½-in. (65-mm) female swivel to 2½-in. (65-mm) male, 60° elbow

Figure 15–42 shows a simple cap and plug. A cap covers a male outlet, and a plug fills a female inlet. Most caps and plugs have some sort of chain attached to them. This is so that when the plugs are removed from their male outlet or female inlet, they will be hanging nearby, so they can be reinstalled after use and are not easily lost.

Fig. 15–42. Cap and plug. (Courtesy of Adam Weidenbach)

1. 2½-in. (65-mm) cap

2. 2½-in. (65-mm) plug

Appliances. Now that we have looked at some common fittings, there is another set of equipment that is used when working with water and fire hose. This general category is called **appliances**. Simply put, an appliance in a piece of equipment that water flows through that is portable in nature. Appliances include gate valves, wyes, siameses, water thieves, water distributors, portable hydrants, and hydrant valves. Water appliances allow water flow to be manipulated in different ways. As you have probably noticed, the fire service names many of its tools based on function and appearance, and appliances follow this same basic principle. Again, we call it as we see it. When talking about an appliance, generally they are described based on the direction of water flow through the appliance. Figures 15–43 to 15–46 demonstrate this commonsense naming practice.

Fig. 15–43 a, b. Wyes. (Courtesy of Adam Weidenbach)

Figure 15–43 (a and b) shows examples of **wye** appliances, commonly just called wyes. A wye is a device in which water enters through a single female inlet and then leaves through two male outlets. For this reason, when naming them, it is just a given regarding the sexes of the one female inlet and the two male outlets. When asking for a wye, it is critical to include the sizes of inlets and outlets, and whether you need a gated wye (a wye with individual control valves for each outlet) or not.

1. 2½-in. (50-mm) straight wye. You need only to name the size since all inlets and outlets are the same; **straight** refers to the fact that there are no valves to control the flow of water.

2. 2½-in. to 1½-in. (65-mm to 38-mm) gated wye. This wye changes size as water flows through it, and it also has quarter turn ball valves. The valves allow the water to each outlet to be controlled individually. The inline handle on the left is an open outlet, and the perpendicular handle on the right is closed outlet.

Figure 15–44 (a and b) shows two appliances called **Siamese**. A Siamese is the opposite of a wye. A Siamese takes two female inlets and turns them into one male outlet. For this reason, when naming a Siamese, it is a given regarding the sexes of the two inlets and one outlets. When requesting a Siamese, it is necessary to include whether or not it is straight or **clappered**.

1. 2 ½-in. (65-mm) straight Siamese.

2. 2 ½-in. (65-mm) clappered Siamese. The clappers, or sometimes a single, swinging clapper, prevents water from flowing out the other female inlet if only one of inlet is being supplied water under pressure.

Appliances are made for all sorts of special purposes. There are pressure reducers, hydrant valves, portable hydrants, ladder pipe assemblies, and ground monitors. Technically, nozzles are considered appliances, but we will not discuss them here because they are covered in great detail in the chapter 16, Fire Streams. Appliances are much like fittings. There are just too many variations to cover them all. Fire departments stock the fittings they use and need, and the same holds true for appliances. Figure 15–45 has one such example: a 5-in. (125-mm) Storz to three 3-in. (75-mm) gated wye with a built-in pressure relief valve. Many appliances that are used with LDH have a built-in pressure relief device to help reduce the chance of water hammer damage. These pressure relief devices have become mandatory in many applications regarding LDH and large flows of water. Before we move on to hose tools, look at some of the Web sties maintained by fitting and appliances manufactures. You will see that the options out there are amazingly diverse, and many special appliances and fittings exist for firefighting.

Fig. 15–44 a, b. Siamese. (Courtesy of Adam Weidenbach)

Fig. 15–45. 5-in. (125-mm) Storz to three 3-in. (75-mm) gated wye. (Courtesy of Adam Weidenbach)

Hose tools. Hose tools aid firefighters in the use of fire hose. Some examples of **hose tools** are spanner wrenches, hose rollers, hose edge rollers, hose jackets, hose clamps, chafing blocks, and hose bridges. Figure 15–46 shows a variety of spanners. Starting at the top of fig. 15–46 is a large spanner with one end for use on couplings between 2½ and 3½ in. (65 and 90 mm) and the other end for 3½ and 5 in. (90 and 125 mm). This large, stamped, aluminum spanner is good to use with Storz fittings as well. Remember that when using a spanner it is always good to grab a set of spanners. If you have two identical spanners, then it is easy to hold both the male and female sides of the hose when you are trying to couple or uncouple the hose. Typically, you can couple hose by hand, but many times when uncoupling hose after use, you many need to use two spanners because the connection has become very tight. The second spanner down in fig. 15–46 is a smaller pocket spanner. It is an old design, made to be used on pinhead coupling lugs and fittings. The third spanner down in fig. 15–46 is another pocket spanner. Firefighters should have a small pocket spanner on hand at all times. This particular pocket spanner is the Oakland (California) Fire Department's (OFD's) version. If you look at the end, you will see that it can be used with either pin lugs or the more modern rocker lug. It also has a hydrant pentagon and a smaller striking surface. The bottom spanner is the smallest of the four. You can see a small protruding pin at the end of it. This small pin is for recessed designed couplings, which are found on booster lines. This is because booster hose is stored on a reel, and smooth couplings without raised lugs prevent the booster hose from damaging itself when reeled in on top of itself.

Fig. 15–46. Spanners. (Courtesy of Adam Weidenbach)

FIREFIGHTER I

Water Supply and Hose

Chapter 15

Hydrant spanners are included in the hose tools section. Hydrant spanners are also sometimes called hydrant wrenches. A hydrant spanner is just a wrench designed to open and close hydrant, as well as take off hydrant caps. The most standard type of hydrant spanner is the one on the top in fig. 15–47. This standard type hydrant spanner, as you can see upon closer examination, is fully adjustable by screwing the handle in and out to make the pentagon opening larger or smaller, and it can also be used to couple and uncouple hose. The standard hydrant spanner is shown with a 2½-in. (65-mm) regular hydrant outlet cap. Notice the pentagon protrusion, which is usually the same size as the operating nut on the hydrant it is attached to. On the bottom in fig. 15–47 is one type of specialty locking cap hydrant spanner, which is becoming more common because the illegal use and vandalism of hydrants has become common in some areas of the country. Drinking water is very valuable and open hydrants waste a lot of water. For example, a flow of 1,000 gpm (3,785 L/min) in just 1 hour equals 60,000 gallons (227,125 L) of water, enough to fill about three average residual swimming pools. Locking caps, like the one shown with the locking cap hydrant spanner, make it more difficult to illegally turn on a hydrant or gain access to the water. Notice that the hydrant operating nut pentagon is not adjustable, and also the locking cap spanner has no built-in lug grabber for use with hose; this one is truly a specialty tool. The locking hydrant outlet cap is designed to be tamper-proof and requires a special hydrant spanner to remove it. As a firefighter, you should become familiar with all types of hydrants and locking mechanisms used in your jurisdiction, including the types of failures and troubles these systems have. Access to water in a rapid fashion by using the proper tools, such as hydrant spanners, is one of the most basic tasks assigned to a firefighter at a fire.

Hose clamps are not used today as much as they were years ago. This is mainly attributable to the more common use of LDH for supply operation. Basically, a hose clamp is just a clamp that can be screwed down in design, has lever action, or is even hydraulic. They were commonly used on fire hose before charging. This allowed water to flow into the hose until it arrived at the clamped section. Firefighters working beyond the clamped section then had time to make the necessary connections and hose lays. They would then return to the closed clamp that had stopping water from continuing down the fire hose and carefully open it to allow water to continue to its destination. Hose clamps were primarily used on 2½-in. (65-mm) (when it was still considered a supply line), 3-in. (75-mm), and 3½-in. (90-mm) supply line.

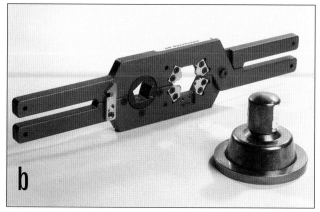

Fig. 15–47. (a) Standard hydrant wrench/spanner (b) Locking cap hydrant spanner. (Courtesy of Adam Weidenbach)

Figure 15–48 shows a common screw-down hose clamp on a length of 3-in. (75-mm) MDH. Notice that it has stopped the water from the hydrant just before the rear hosebed. This is because it was placed by an engineer who called for water before he or she broke the supply line. This maneuver allowed the hydrant firefighter to charge the hydrant and come up to do other tasks. This technique of using a hose clamp to free the hydrant firefighter from the hydrant was once common practice in fire departments that used MDH as supply line. Releasing clamps or applying hose clamps to charged hoseline must be done in full personal protective equipment (PPE) including gloves and helmets. Hose clamps are under a tremendous amount of force and have been known to break spontaneously and/or rapidly come undone. One should never partly unscrew a screw-down hose clamp that is holding back water and then just kick the latch open. This is a dangerous practice.

Fig. 15–48. Screw-down hose clamp

Fig. 15–50. Wildland hose clamp

Figure 15–49 shows a press-down type hose clamp, which achieves its mechanical advantage from a level type action instead of a screw. Press-down hose clamps are used the same way as screw-down types; however, they are more effective at stopping flowing water because they can be more smoothly and quickly applied. The screwing action of a screw type hose clamp is a cumbersome endeavor when used against an already charged line.

Using a hose clamp to stop the flow of water to replace a burst section of hose is a difficult and dangerous task, and this task is much easier to accomplish by simply closing the proper valve at the pump panel.

One other technique that should be mentioned is the simple field hose clamp. This action does not require any special tools, just good technique and strength. Also, it is not effective in hose size above 2½ in. (65 mm). Basically, a simple field hose clamp is just a simple double bend in the hose that is then just pressed down on itself. This creates two kinks in the hose in close proximity to each other. The goal is not to stop the flow of water completely, but merely to slow it enough to allow a burst length to be replaced or (usually) to add an extra length of hose. The firefighters in fig. 15–51 are performing the field hose clamp maneuver.

Fig. 15–49. Press-down hose clamp

Fig. 15–51. Field hose clamp maneuver

Some departments still use hose clamp, especially departments that use 3-in. (75-mm) supply line; however, it is usually not part of their standard operating procedures (SOPs). Many times these clamps are carried on the apparatus but not regularly used. One place hose clamps are still used regularly is for a wildland hand line evolution call or a progressive hose lay. Figure 15–50 shows a wildland hose clamp designed to be used on 1-in. or 1½-in. (25 or 38 mm) SJ wildland. It has a simple clamping design and is handheld.

Hose jackets are another hose tool that are not in regular use anymore. A hose jacket is a hose tool that is put around a hose that has sprung a leak. They were mainly designed for use on fire hose sizes between 1½ and 3½. in. (38 and 90 mm). While no longer commonly used, they can serve an important function if a department still has one. Some hose jackets were made of a metal clam-type clamp design with a hose orifice in the middle and a rubber seal at each end. This clam-type clamp hose jacket was simply placed over the leak and then clamped into position. Another type of hose jacket was simply made out of leather, straps, and buckles. The use of a leather-type hose jacket is self-explanatory in nature. All hose jackets mainly just slowed a flowing leak and did not function well above 150 psi (1,050 kPa). You can still order them or make them; however, they are not used frequently anywhere. Figure 15–52 shows a metal clam-type clamp hose jacket on a 3-in. (75-mm) MDH. This type of design works on 2½-in. (65-mm) to 3-in. (75-mm) fire hose, partly because of modern hose construction, in which the outer jacket of fire hose is designed in a ripstop fashion so that small leaks usually do not become bigger ones rapidly. Hose jackets also have proven to be ineffective on LDH, mainly due to the difficulty of maneuvering LDH because of its heavy charged weight.

Fig. 15–52. Metal clam-type clamp hose jacket. (Courtesy of Tim Olk)

Hose rope tools serve a very useful purpose. They help firefighters move and secure hose. Some hose rope tools are designed with a cast hook that also serves as a handle with an attached piece of webbing or rope that forms a loop. These types of hose rope tools are used by the fire department to secure fire hose to aerial ladders during ladder pipe operations and to secure hose to ground ladders, fire escapes, and window ledges. Figure 15–53 shows a traditional cast metal hook and rope hose tool, known as a **hose strap**. Notice that the metal hook also has a opening for your hand. One could just loop the rope around the hose and pass the hook through. This creates a **lark's foot** around the hose, which acts like a hand of rope. The cast hook part could then be hung on a ladder fire escape or grand ladder or just used as a handle to help manipulate the charge hoseline. This was particularly useful for large hoseline like 3-in. MDH.

Fig. 15–53. Hose strap

Hose rope tools do not have to be custom-designed, as discussed previously. Some fire departments require firefighters to carry a length of 1-in. (25-mm) tubular webbing tied into a loop with two overhand bend knots. This inexpensive hose tool usually forms at least a 4-ft (1.2-m) loop that can be used not only on fire hose but also on victims and injured firefighters as a rescue aid. This loop of webbing is very strong and can easily be wrapped around the hose and passed through itself, forming a lark's foot knot around a charged hoseline. In this fashion, it can be used as a handle to pull on a large hose or help move it around. Figure 15–54 shows just such a piece of looped webbing lark's foot around an uncharged hose. This 1-in. (25-mm) tubular webbing hose rope tool can also be lark's footed around a charged vertical hoseline below a coupling and then clove-hitched to a banister or railing to prevent the charged hoseline from slipping backward under the force of gravity. The lark's foot and clove hitch (a simple knot covered in chapter 8) are easily tied with gloves on.

The final hose tools that will be covered are **hose bridges** and **chafing blocks**. These two items are not used enough in today's fire service. Many departments have stopped their use all together. Both of these tools are used to prevent hose damage. As has been mentioned previously, fire hose has come a long way since the time of simple, single-cotton-jacketed, rubber-lined construction. This has led to some complacency because of the durability of current specification of fire hose. The item in fig. 15–55a is a chafing block. This chafing block has an obvious channel for fire hose and straps to attach it to the hose. Chafing blocks should be used especially on supply hose that bends up from street level to a pump inlet connection. This is a point where supply hose is exposed to a lot of vibrations, which cause the hose jacket to wear as it rubs back and forth against the pavement. One of the reasons supply hose is mentioned is that much of it is still of SJ design.

Fire hose should never be driven over, whether the hose is charged or uncharged. If it is necessary to drive where there is fire hose, the hose should be protected using a hose bridge.[8] This commonsense rule is often broken. Although fire hose is very durable, it is not intended to be driven over. In fig. 15–55b, the hose tool is a hose bridge used for 3-in. (75-mm) fire hose. The hose bridge in this case is two pieces of triangular shaped wood jointed by two nylon straps. To use it, you simply lift up the 3-in. (75-mm) fire hose and place the hose in the valley formed between the two pieces of wood. This hose bridge is only around 20 in. (508 mm) in length, so you need two hose bridges to make a spot where vehicles can safely drive over. All types of hose bridges are available for fire hose up to sizes of 12 in. (305 mm) in diameter. However, as fire departments have begun using more and more LDH, it has become difficult to find space for efficient storage and easy deployment of hose bridges stored on fire apparatus. The lack of hose bridges on apparatus has led to some poor practices, like running over hose that is not properly bridged.

Fig. 15–54. Rope hose tool with lark's foot. (Courtesy of Adam Weidenbach)

Fig. 15–55. (a) Chafing block and (b) hose bridge. (Courtesy of Adam Weidenbach)

Basic hose maintenance and testing

Cleaning. FFI 5.5.2 Fire hose must be properly cared for. The vast majority of fire departments load hose back onto the apparatus at the scene. Before loading hose back onto a fire apparatus after use, one should wash the dirty used lengths with clean water. This can be accomplished by spraying water from a reel line or another type of charged hoseline and a stiff, long-handled broom kept on the engine. Once sufficiently clean, the hose can be loaded back onto the apparatus. Remember that if the fire hose is cotton jacketed, it should be thoroughly dried before being loading onto the apparatus, using a **hose dryer** or **hose tower**. This is done to prevent the growth of mold and mildew. In the case of cotton jacketed hose, just roll it up and thoroughly clean and dry it back at the station.

When loading hose onto a fire apparatus, make an attempt to reload the hose in a different order than the way it deployed. To avoid permanent folds, try to pack the hose in such a manner that the folds are in different locations than before. Fire hose that has been used must be checked for serviceability, because it could have incurred serious damage during use. One should check for obvious damage to couplings and the outer jacket. It is good practice to check for leaks in attack and supply lines after use by simply inspecting them while they are still charged. Many leaks and other damage to fire hose are found this way; take those particular lengths of hose out of service. This practice prevents damaged or leaking hose from making its way back onto the engine in service at fire scenes. Simple actions such as these can really help prolong the life of hose and also prevent premature failure of fire hose. They also help prevent unexpected fire hose failure at emergencies.

Some fire departments have to deal with extremely cold temperatures. In these cases, fire departments that have this type of severe weather problem usually take wet, used hose back to the station where they can then clean the hose properly and dry it. Sometimes hose used in freezing temperatures has to be thawed. It is best to never let hose freeze completely, especially with water in it. Hose that has frozen completely with water in it needs to be thawed and then be subjected to an in-service hose test before being placed back into service. Dealing with freezing temperatures is one of the toughest weather conditions for firefighters. Some agencies that have to contend with cold weather on regular basis have specialized equipment like mechanical hose washers and dryers. Many of these departments store many extra lengths of hose, sometimes up to entire second hose complement, back at the station.

When cleaning fire hose, it is also necessary to check the couplings for damage to the male threads or to the female swivel. Ensure that there is a pliable rubber gasket in each female coupling. Female couplings that are sticking and not swiveling freely can be dunked in warm water with a mild detergent. Once dry, apply some silicone lubricant to the swivel. Mild detergent can also be used on the fire hose if necessary, for example, if the hose was exposed to some oil. It is not necessary for fire hose to be scrubbed completely clean or beaten into a germ-free state suitable for eating off of it. It is only necessary to keep the hose free of large pieces of dirt and debris that can be easily scrubbed or washed away.

Fire hose is susceptible to gaining a **memory** at the folds. In other words, if fire hose is left for a long enough time, a heavy crease will develop where it is folded. This memory at the folded areas can lead to hose failure caused by damage to the liner. To prevent this failure, "hose shall be removed from the apparatus and reloaded so that the folds occur at different positions with sufficient frequency to prevent damage and the setting of permanent folds in the rubber lining."[9] This is called exercising the hose. All hose should be removed from the apparatus at least four times a year. One of these times will be for the annual in-service hose test. At each of these times, hose should be inspected and then loaded back on the apparatus, using care to make sure the hose is loaded in such a way that the folds end up in different locations.

Fire hose testing

FFII 6.5.5 NFPA 1962, the *Standard for the Inspection, Care, and Use of Fire Hose, Couplings and Nozzles and Service Testing of Fire Hose*, is really the definitive resource for fire hose testing and maintenance. This standard has become more complex over the years as fire hose has become increasingly diverse. Standards like recommended pressures for service testing hose have changed a lot over the years as new hose has become more resistant to high pressure. It has gotten to the point where testing companies exist strictly to test fire hose to the NFPA in-service test standard. Some fire agencies now hire testing companies to complete the annual in-service hose test and help meet some of or all of the requirements of NFPA 1962. These testing companies have specially built hose-testing rigs that test thousands of feet of fire hose at a time. Test procedures will be discussed in the following paragraphs.

In addition to the previously mentioned general hose care, fire hose has to be hydrostatically tested once a year. The annual in-service hydrostatic test is defined in NFPA 1962, chapter 7, Service Testing. Before we discuss the details of the annual service test, it is important to understand that when testing hose, all fire hose is described based on its ability to withstand pressure. For example, a 5-in. (125-mm) LDH marked as "supply hose" by the manufacturer has a maximum operating pressure of 185 psi. However, similarly sized 5-in. (125-mm) LDH marked "attack hose" by the manufacturer has a 270 psi maximum operating pressure. Obviously the 5-in. (125-mm) LDH "attack hose" cannot be used as a hand line. The stenciled "attack line" on this particular 5-in. (125-mm) LDH is referring to its ability to withstand high pressures that are used to supply hand lines, standpipe, and sprinkler systems.

Figure 15–56 shows a 3-in. (75-mm) DJ 50-ft (15-m) length of fire hose. Earlier in this chapter, 3-in. (75-mm) fire hose was described with respect to its use as medium diameter hose (MDH), mainly for supply operations and sometimes as a hand line. We discussed how 3-in. (75-mm) hose is too large to function properly as a hand line and slightly too small to act efficiently as supply line based on modern fire flows. However, pump-supplied 3-in. (75-mm) hose can still move a lot of water. The 3-in. (75-mm) DJ hose shown in fig. 15–56 is stenciled by the manufacturer as "Attack Hose" and also "Service Test to 400 psi PER NFPA 1962."

Fig. 15–56. 3-in. DJ Hose

Using the 3-in. (75-mm) DJ hose in fig. 15–56, we will define the following terms: **service test pressure**, **proof/acceptance test pressure**, **burst pressure**, and **operating/working pressure**. All of these pressures are defined using the service test pressure as a guide. The service test pressure is required to be stenciled on all new fire hose. It is the pressure used to determine if fire hose is still suitable for use, and it is the pressure the hose is tested to during the annual service test by the user. In fig. 15–57, the service test pressure is 400 psi (2,800 kPa). The proof/acceptance test pressure is the pressure the hose is subjected to by the manufacturer at the factory prior to shipment. The proof/acceptance test pressure is to be no less than twice the service pressure, and in this case that would mean a minimum of 800 psi (5,600 kPa). Burst pressure is tested by the manufacturer when the hose is new, and it is at least three times the specified service test pressure, which in this case is 1,200 psi (8,400 kPa). Operating/working pressure should not exceed 90% of the service test pressure, so if the service test pressure is 400 psi (2,800 kPa), then the operating/working pressure should not exceed 360 psi (2,520 kPa). This 10% safety factor over the service test is designed to ensure that hose that passes its annual hose test will not fail during use. Most fire department pumping operations will rarely exceed operating pressures of 250 psi (1,750 kPa); however, water hammer can expose hose in use to higher pressures.

All fire hose should be kept track of using a written record. This record can be kept at the firehouse or in a central location. It is beneficial to have this information in a computerized database. If this is done, things like common failures or the need to order hose can be identified easily. Hose records should include the following for each length of hose: identification number (usually stamped or inscribed on the male coupling), size, length, type of hose, in-service date, repairs, annual service tests, and service test pressure. Some organizations record more or less information about their fire hose. The

details listed here are considered the minimum acceptable practice. This hose record should be updated any time a length of hose is put into or out of service.

Testing process. Annual service testing of fire hose is a requirement of NFPA 1962. This testing should always be reflected properly in the hose records. The following will just cover the basics of the service test. NFPA 1962 should be consulted for definitive step-by-step procedures and requirements. If your department does not follow the NFPA standard, they should follow the manufacturer's recommendations.

Fire hose testing involves two parts, visual inspection of the hose and couplings and the pressure testing of the hose. Both are critical parts of hose testing. Visual inspection of the hose involves inspecting the couplings, gaskets, and the interior rubber lining of the hose. Some damaged parts, such as a gasket, may require replacement. Others, such as damaged inner lining or couplings, will require that the hose be condemned.

If the hose passes the visual inspection, it needs to be identified. Hose will have stenciling on it indicating the manufacturer, type, and size of the hose, as well as service test pressures. Testing of the hose should be in an open area where the hose can be laid out. It is recommended that all personnel wear a minimum of a helmet and gloves during the testing process. The hose can be tested by using a **hose testing machine** (fig. 15–57). If a pumper is being used, the operator should be fully qualified and certified on that particular pumper.

Fig. 15–57. Proper hose testing is important to ensure proper working equipment on the fireground.

To conduct the test, lay the hose out straight, with no bends, and coupled together up to 300 feet (90 m). Place a mark with a pencil behind each coupling to determine if slippage occurs during the test. Cap the last male coupling with a cap and bleeder or a fire service nozzle, and secure the hose to prevent it from whipping during the test. Bleed the air out of the hose while slowly filling it with water. When all the air is out of the hose, close the nozzle or bleeder and begin the test. First check for leaks, and then bring the pressure up to the recommended service test pressure and hold for 5 minutes while observing the hose visually from a distance of 15 ft (5 m). If no problems are observed, reduce the pressure in the hose and open the nozzle or bleeder valve to release the pressure, and record the results. If a problem occurs such as slippage, burst length, etc., remove the length from service, mark it as condemned, and record the results.

Proper service testing is the only way we can determine the suitability of hose for fire-suppression use. As of now, there is no recommendation for the maximum life span of hose. Committees of industry leaders and manufacturers have come up with a guideline of 10 years. It is probably more reasonable to state that hose can become unserviceable at any time based on use. Heavily used fire hose can fail an in-service hose test after just a few years. Rarely used hose may pass a service hose test 30 years after its date of manufacture. Generally, hose that passes its service-pressure hose test is suitable for use and should be retested every year to confirm this. The maximum life span issue will be more definitively addressed in the near future, but most likely it will be closer to 15–20 years. Hose has a definite cost factor associated with it, and it is very durable. It should not be discarded strictly based on age if in good serviceable condition.

Hose storage

FFI 5.5.2 Fire hose is typically stored in one of two places, either on the apparatus or in the firehouse. We are first going to address hose stored in the firehouse. Typically, hose stored in a firehouse should be in-service hose. Hose that is out of service or marked for repair should never be stored anywhere near or next to in service hose. Hoses stored in a firehouse are typically rolled in a straight roll. Figure 15–58 is a 2½-in. (65-mm) DJ attack hose in a 50-ft (15 m) length. It is rolled in-service with male coupling at the center of the roll, which protects the NH threads.

Hose that is out of service should be clearly tagged "out of service" and then rolled into a straight roll with the male coupling out. If the firefighter placing the hose out of service knows that the hose is not repairable, both couplings should be cut off the fire hose before discarding it. This ensures that bad hose will not be used

in error. In some circumstances, the removed couplings can be reused. Figure 15–59 is an out-of-service straight roll with the male coupling exposed, that is, missing a clear and complete repair tag. You will notice that just by looking at this 3-in. (75-mm) DJ hose you cannot tell what is wrong with it. The repair tag is very important!

Fig. 15–58. In-service straight roll, with male-threaded coupling protected. (Courtesy of Adam Weidenbach)

Fig. 15–59. Out-of-service straight roll, with male coupling exposed, but with no repair tag. (Courtesy of Adam Weidenbach)

Figure 15–60 shows a 3-in. (75-mm) DJ hose rolled out of service with the male coupling removed and clearly labeled with an attached repair tag. Originally, it was a 50-ft (15-m) length of 3-in. (75-mm) hose. The damaged section has been removed, and it is awaiting a new male coupling. The repaired 3-in. (75-mm) DJ will be a 25-ft (8-m) jumper and will need to be service tested after the coupling is installed. This will ensure that it is ready to go back into service as a 25-ft (8-m) jumper, sometimes called a **pony length** (often used to hook up to a hydrant close to the pumper to fill the water tank).

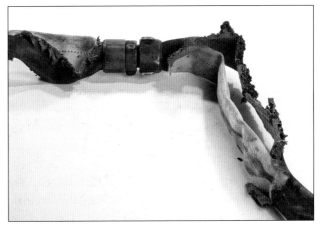

Fig. 15–60. Out-of-service hose, male coupling removed, with properly filled-out and attached repair tag. (Courtesy of Adam Weidenbach)

Finally, fig. 15–61 shows a returned out-of-service hose. This set of couplings is from the same length of 50-ft (15 m) DJ 1¾-in. (45-mm) attack line. The outer jacket of this hose was severely damaged at a structure fire; however, the hose did not fail. The first jacket and liner remained intact, and the engine company was able to successfully complete its fire attack. You can now see how valuable an extra outer jacket can be. This is an example where both couplings should be cut from the hose, and the hose discarded. The couplings should be inspected thoroughly and may be reused if in serviceable condition.

Figure 15–62 shows an example of clean, serviceable hose stored on a hose rack. Notice that all lengths are in-service, straight-rolled with the male coupling protected. In-service hose should be clean and dry, and it should have passed an annual in-service hose test. Hose stored in this manner should be good for a year. It is important not to hang hose in hose towers for longer than it takes to dry the hose. Excessive hanging of fire hose can lead to extreme drying of the hose liner, which can cause liner failure. Hose is best stored as shown in fig. 15–62, where it is kept in a climate-controlled area of a building. Remember, hose that sits can be damaged by passing equipment or environmental degradation, and even attacked by rodents. When a year of proper storage has passed, stored fire hose should again be subjected to an annual in-service hose test.

Fig. 15–61. Severely damaged 1¾-in. (45-mm) DJ hose. Cut the couplings off and discard hose. Do not roll. (Courtesy of Adam Weidenbach)

Fig. 15–62. In-service hose properly stored on a hose rack. (Courtesy of Adam Weidenbach)

Hose loads

FFI 5.2.2 Hose is stored on apparatus in many ways. The most common ways are in rear hosebeds, crosslays (also known as a "Mattydale load," which was invented by the Mattydale, New York, Fire Department), reels, and compartments. Hose can be stored in different types of tactical manners, depending on how it is going to be deployed. This is one area of the fire service where there are many differing opinions. Depending on the type of district a company responds to, it may alter the design and layout of how hose is carried on apparatus. These factors include available water supply, types of buildings, types of hose used, and common overall lengths of hose stretches, to name a few. It is good for fire departments to have a standard hose complement and hose load developed for their particular district or city. This standard

load should be the right mix of hose sizes and loads for their particular needs.

Fire hose is mainly carried in one of two ways on a fire apparatus: either preconnected to a discharge or suction inlet or not attached to any discharge or pump inlet. First, we will take a look at attack lines. **Preconnected** attack lines, sometimes called live lines, are generally attack hand lines not usually exceeding 300 ft (90 m) in length. They are usually made with either 1½-, 1¾-, 2-, or 2½-in. (38, 45, 50, or 65 mm) hose with the last female coupling attached to a pump discharge, and in turn, the last male coupling having a nozzle attached to it. The preconnected attack lines in fig. 15–63 are called preconnected crosslays (hose stored in a "trough" that runs from one side of the apparatus to the other). They are both made with 1¾-in. (45-mm) DJ hose. The front (left) preconnect crosslay is 150 ft (45 m), or three lengths of hose, and the rear crosslay (right) is 200 ft (6 m), or four lengths of hose. Preconnected hose does not have to be mounted in a crosslay bin. Many fire departments have preconnected attacks lines that lay off the back of the rig as opposed to a crosslay. Once deployed, a preconnected attack line must be pulled off and completely flaked out. After the deployment of all the preconnected hose, the pump operator can then open the discharge outlet that the preconnected deployed hose is already attached to. This is only done after the call for water is made by the members manning the pulled preconnected attack line.

The preconnected attack lines in fig. 15–63 are loaded in the simplest manner. Both are loaded in a simple flat-load style. The flat load is the gold standard of loading hose in today's fire service. It is simple, reliable, reasonably deployable, predictable, and easily duplicated and reloaded, even when handled by extremely fatigued members. It requires no special setup or folds; simply connect the female couplings to the proper discharge in the crosslay and then load the correct number of lengths of hose one after another. The final step is to attach a nozzle. The company in fig. 15–63 also included some **pull loops** when loading their 1¾-in. (45-mm) flat-loaded preconnects. The loops, in this case, are on both sides and appear to be roughly at every length of hose. The loops are made to help facilitate the deployment of hose as additional members join in the stretching of the selected preconnected line. Remember that, with preconnected or live lines, all of the hose must clear its bed before charging, because premature charging of a preconnected line without complete clearing of its bed leads to catastrophic tangling and delays in proper deployment.

Fig. 15–63. Preconnected attack crosslays. (Courtesy of Daryl Liggins)

There are other ways of loading preconnected lines. Two very popular methods of loading preconnected lines go by the names **minuteman load** and the **triple fold**. Both of these techniques of loading preconnects come with pros and cons. The first alternative load we will discuss is the minuteman load. Basically, this is a hose load designed for preconnected operation no longer than 200 ft (60 m) and using attack hose with a maximum diameter of 1¾-in. (45-mm). The main reason for these limitations is that all of the hose, when initially deployed, is pulled onto a single firefighter's shoulder. Overall lengths exceeding 200 ft (60 m) and hose sizes larger than 1¾ in. (45 mm) invite common failures related to tangles and loss of stability and control during deployment. It is difficult to properly deploy this much hose from a single bundle on a shoulder without practice.

The minuteman load can be a time and labor saver; however, it is best served with 1½-in. (38-mm) attack hose, preferably in a maximum length of 150 ft (45 m). The minuteman load, because of its design, is best suited for rear-facing preconnects in the hosebed. This is because the nozzle sits at the bottom of the load in the direction it must be pulled. Some departments that load their crosslays with minuteman loads have one load facing toward the officer side of the engine and the other facing toward the engineer side.

Neatness counts for this load. A messy minuteman load is almost a guaranteed tangle because you must neatly carry all of the hose for the load to properly work.

Minuteman load. A minutemen load is a method of deploying fire hose and a nozzle with minimal effort using minimum manpower. To load the minuteman on a fire apparatus for a 150-ft (45-m) stretch of hose you connect a 50-ft (15-m) length to a pump discharge and make one pass and let the rest sit to the side for later. Connect the other 50-ft (15-m) lengths together and place in the bed with a nozzle on the open male end at the bottom and the rest of the 100 ft (30 m) of hose on top. Then connect the first 50-ft (15-m) length to the 100 ft (30 m) already in the bed and you have a finished minuteman load.

To deploy the minuteman load, grab the entire bundle of hose onto your shoulder with the nozzle on the bottom. Walk away from the pumper and allow the hose to deploy off the load from the top. When you get to your destination you will have all the hose smoothly deployed and the nozzle in your hand ready to be used (fig. 15–64 a and b).

Triple fold. Another method of storing and deploying hose for fire attack is the triple fold method. The triple fold method has the hose folded in three layers and then laid in the hose bed in an S-shaped fashion with one layer on top of the other so the nozzle is placed on top. It is designed so one person can easily remove the hose pack. For this hose lay to be used, all of the hose must be removed from the hose bed before deploying the nozzle. It is typically used for 150- and 200-ft (45- and 60-m) hose stretches (fig. 15–65).

Static attack loads, sometimes called **dead loads**, are beds of attack hose usually 1½, 1¾, 2, or 2½ in. (38, 45, 50, or 65 mm), with nozzles attached to last male coupling. These static attack loads are not attached to pump discharges when loaded onto the apparatus. To use a static attack load, a firefighting team simply removes the desired amount of hose and then calls for water once properly in place. The pump operator then goes to the static attack load that has been used, breaks the hose at the next female coupling, attaches that female coupling to a pump discharge, and then supplies the deployed hose with water. Figure 15–66 shows the crosslay bin area of a Los Angeles Fire Department (LAFD) pumper. Notice the large amount of attack hose, which is all loaded in a static flat-load fashion. None of LAFD's attacks lines is preconnected to discharges.

Fig. 15–64. (a) The minuteman load and (b) deploying the minuteman load

Fig. 15–65. The triple fold load

Fig. 15–66. Static attack crosslays. (Courtesy of Daryl Liggins)

Fig. 15–67 a, b. Static attack lines loaded in the hosebed. (Photos courtesy of Daryl Liggins)

Attack hose can also be carried at the rear of the apparatus in the hosebed area, along with the supply hose. In the hosebed, attack hose can either be preconnected to a rear discharge and loaded or be loaded in a static fashion. Figure 15–67 shows two pumpers with two different static attack loads. Figure 15–67a shows a single 2½-in. (65-mm) horseshoe finish, and fig. 15–67b shows both a 2½-in. (65-mm) and a 1¾-in. (45-mm) attack line. Notice that the 1¾-in. (45-mm) attack hose line is filled out with 2½-in. (65-mm) hose on the bottom. This horseshoe finish is sometimes called a reverse horseshoe finish. It is usually just the last length of hose with the nozzle attach fed back upon itself in a U-shaped (thus horseshoe) fashion. This makes a nice 50-ft (15-m) pack of hose to grab when deploying the hose from a static bed. In that case, make sure the nozzle team has at least a 50-ft (15-m) length of working line. Notice also that the hosebed in 15–67b has vertical divider separating the beds; these are called hosebed dividers, and they are adjustable. There are other options regarding finishing static hosebeds to aid in the deployment of hose depending on fire department preferences (fig. 15-68).

Fig. 15–68. Reverse horseshoe finish

Hose bundles

FFI 5.5.2 We have discussed attack hose loaded on the apparatus in crosslay and at the rear of the apparatus in the hosebed. In both places you can find the attack hose loaded in both a static or preconnected fashion. One other way attack hose is often carried on apparatus is in **bundles** or specialized rolls. Bundles and specialized rolls of hose are commonly kept in compartments or seat-belted onto running boards and fenders. Once again, there are many types of bundles and specialized rolls used by the fire service. Many departments choose the one they feel best suits their operations. Let's take a look at the **horseshoe bundle**. A horseshoe bundle is easy to fold, does not get tangled, and deploys in an efficient fashion. Figure 15–69 (a, b, and c) shows a series of pictures:: a completed 2½-in. (65-mm), 50-ft (15-m) horseshoe pack with a nozzle on it; a firefighter rebuilding a 2½-in. (65-mm), 50 ft (15-m) horseshoe pack using a self-contained breathing apparatus (SCBA) bottle as a guide; and two 50-ft (15-m) horseshoe packs of 1¾-in. (45-mm) joined together at the coupling and then strapped together.

Bundles of hose are necessary for many reasons. For example, if you enter a building to use a standpipe (bundles in this case are called **standpipe packs**), or walk up a hill during a wildland fire, you have an easy way to carry the hose. The bundle should be folded in such a way that it is easy to deploy and couple the hose. Figure 15–70 clearly shows the value of a hose bundle. All of these firefighters are able to climb the stairs of a building while having both hands free. Also note their front and side profiles do not increase much. This will allow them to pass by civilians or others who are attempting to exit the building easily.

In addition, the hose bundle, some specialized hose rolls need to be discussed, including the donut roll, twin donut roll, and self-locking twin donut roll. Hose rolls are used as a means of storing hose on the apparatus or in a hose rack in the fire station. There are several variations of hose rolls: the straight roll, the simple donut, and the twin or double donut. The straight roll is designed for storing hose at the fire station on a hose rack. It is made by laying the length of hose straight out and, starting with the male coupling, rolling the hose so that the male coupling is in the center and female coupling is on the outside.

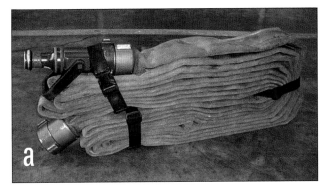

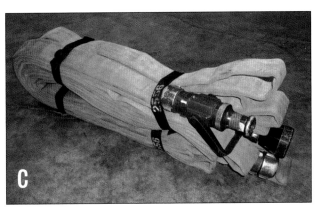

Fig. 15–69 a, b, c. Horseshoe hose bundles of 50 ft (15 m) and 100 ft (30 m). (Courtesy of Daryl Liggins)

Fig. 15–70. Firefighters ready to enter a building with 2½-in. (65-mm) hose in bundles. (Courtesy of Daryl Liggins)

Water Supply and Hose

FIREFIGHTER I

Chapter 15

Donut roll. The simple **donut** is made by folding the hose length onto itself so that the male end of the hose is about 3 feet (1 m) in from the female end. The hose is then rolled on to itself so, when completed, the male coupling is inside the roll and protected from damage (fig. 15–71).

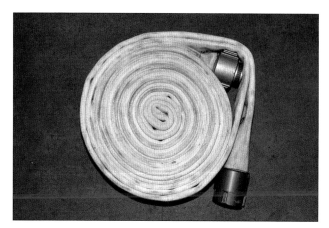

Fig. 15–71. The donut roll

To deploy this roll, you simply grasp the two couplings and roll the hose out from where you are standing or in congested areas hold on to the two couplings and drag the hose with you while the roll deploys behind you.

The donut roll is a staple in the wildland firefighting environment. During progressive hose lays, wildland hose is easily deployed from the donut roll.

Twin donut roll. Another popular donut roll is the **twin donut roll** (fig. 15–72). The twin or double donut roll allows for a compact roll that can be stored in a smaller compartment on an apparatus or can be used for applications such as stand-pipe packs or high-rise packs. It is made by laying the length of hose out so that the two couplings are side-by-side. The hose is then rolled so that, when it is complete, both coupling are on the outside and easily accessible. This roll can be held together by using a hose strap or by a variation known as a self-locking twin donut roll. To deploy it, simply remove the hose strap that is locking it, and, by grasping the couplings, roll the hose away from you so that, when deployed, you have both couplings in you hands

The self-locking twin donut roll. This roll is particularly useful because it forms a carrying handle without the aid of hose strap or other securing devices such as hose packs (fig. 15–73).

There are additional hose bundles and hose rolls that will not be discussed here. There are several types, and they all have their pros and cons. Your department will only use a few of them. Please pay close attention when your instructors go over the bundles and hose rolls because you will be responsible for how to use them properly.

Fig. 15–72. Twin or double donut roll

Fig. 15–73. Self-locking twin donut roll

Reel line. The last type of attack hose carried on an apparatus is a form of preconnected attack hose called **booster/reel line.** Earlier in this chapter, we detailed the many downfalls of using a reel line as an attack line. It has a very limited flow and should only be used in situations such as very small outside fires. Most reel lines, even if 1 in. (25 mm) in diameter, do not flow more than 60 gpm (227 L/min). This is a very small flow and is completely inadequate for any interior building operations. As stated previously, some departments no longer spec hose reels for their apparatus. Reel lines can provide a good utility function. A reel line, like all tools, is useful only if used properly. Using a 60-gpm (227 L/min) reel line on an inappropriate fire is not the fault of the reel line, but of the person who selected it.

Water supply evolutions

Supply line is fire hose used to supply water for fireground operations. Supply line is typically deployed in hose-laying operations where the engine is in motion, and the supply hose pays out of the hosebed as the engine is driven. These supply hose-laying operations are typically made either from a hydrant toward the fire, called a **forward lay**, or from the fire to a hydrant, called a **reverse lay**. In this section we will cover forward lays, reverse lays, and also **split lays**, as well as the basic use of hydrants. These are the most common water supply evolutions using supply hose.

Supply line is almost always loaded statically in the hosebed. An exception to this rule is short, preconnected intake jumpers, usually no longer than 35 ft (10.7 m) in length. These short lengths of supply hose are commonly preconnected to the pump's intakes to assist firefighters in making rapid connection to hydrants or already laid or deployed supply lines. LDH supply jumpers are made in various lengths: 15, 20, 25, 35, and 50 ft (4.5, 6, 7.6, 10.7, and 15 m). Supply line in the hosebed may be loaded with the female coupling out, male coupling out, or Storz couplings. Depending on which sex coupling or type of adapter with Storz is the first out of the hosebed, one can determine what tactic a department usually uses during its water supply evolutions. You have probably noticed by now that most of the figures in this book show hose loaded in a flat style. In fig. 15–74 (a, b, and c) an engine company loads 4-in. (100-mm) DJ LDH in a flat load, taking care to place the large 4½-in. (115-mm) couplings at the front of the hosebed. Placing the large couplings in carefully is a must, because they should not be allowed to flip during a hose lay operation. When loading supply hose, it is sometimes necessary to take a short fold of hose, not only to ensure that the coupling does not flip over while paying out, but also to allow placement of the coupling in a desirable location in the hosebed. This short fold of hose is commonly called a **Dutchman**. The flat load has become the standard practice for loading hose. In fact, "excessive edge wear can occur when 100% synthetic yarn-reinforced hose is loaded on the apparatus in the conventional manner (horseshoe U-load, accordion, or skid loads). To prevent this edge wear, hose manufactures recommend that if 100% synthetic yarn-reinforced hose is used, it should be loaded on the apparatus in the flat load manner."[11]

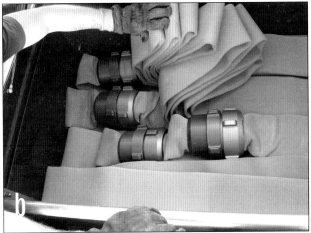

Fig. 15–74 a, b, c. Firefighters load 800 ft (244 m) of 4-in. (100-mm) hose in a flat load. This 4-in. (100-mm) NST LDH is set up for a forward lay with the female coupling out.

Fig. 15—75. The horseshoe load

Fig. 15—76. The accordion load

Some departments may still use a **horseshoe (U-load)** or **accordion load**, both of which require the fire hose to be loaded on its edge. Let's take a brief look at a horseshoe load, as shown in fig. 15–75. You can see that the hose is loaded in a U-shaped horseshoe fashion. The original main advantages of this horseshoe load are that it promotes good air flow for cotton jacket hose, minimizes severe bends in the hose, and is very difficult to hang up on laying line. The negatives of the horseshoe load are that all the lengths, if hand-jacked or pulled, are of unequal sections due to the nature of its outside in loading technique, and it also promotes excessive edge wear of the supply hose.

The accordion load promotes good air flow for cotton jacket hose, although it can be easily packed too tightly and might hang up upon deployment. The accordion load provides easy shoulder-carrying capabilities with each layer being of the same back-and-forth distance. Firefighters can merely walk up to an accordion load, grab a few folds, and know exactly how much hose they are pulling and then easily place it on their shoulders. Figure 15–76 shows an example of a accordion load. Horseshoe and accordion loads are usually made up of 3-in. (75-mm) MDH, which can be set up in forward or reverse fashion and also in dual beds. Another reason that both the horseshoe and accordion loads have been generally phased out is that they do not work well with any type of LDH supply hose. In addition, both the accordion or horseshoe load's bottommost layer of hose is in direct contact with the metal hosebed bottom on edge. This lower layer of hose on edge is exposed to excessive wear and is not recommended, because with modern synthetic hose, it has been know to cause premature failure.

However, finishing the last length or two of supply hose in a horseshoe or other edge-laid finish to aid in hose evolutions is an acceptable practice, because there is no added weight of hose above the finish, and the finished, on-edge hose is on top of the other hose and not the metal hosebed bottom. Many departments practice this tactic to aid their lead-off or hydrant person in gathering enough hose to complete a water supply evolution.

Supply line is usually no smaller than 3 in. (75 mm) MDH because of the friction loss encountered when moving large volumes of water. The NFPA states that the minimum size supply line is 3½ in. (90 mm) However, many departments still use 3-in. (75-mm) hose. With the trend toward increased hand line flows due to harsher fire conditions caused by modern fire loads, 3-in. (75-mm) MDH is beginning to be too small to appropriately act as supply hose. Some departments use dual beds of 3-in. (75-mm) MDH, which does overcome single 3-in. (75-mm) MDH supply line high-friction loss when moving a large amount of water. This is made possible by laying two supply lines from a single engine; hence the name **dual bed**. For example, the friction loss for a 1,000 gpm (3,785 L/min) in a single 3-in. (75-mm) hose lay per 100 ft (30 m) is 80 psi (560 kPa). However, if two 3-in. (75-mm) MDH supply lines are laid side by side and share the 1,000 gpm (3,785 L/min) flow by each flowing just 500 gpm (1,892 L/min), the friction loss is only 20 psi (140 kPa) per 100 ft (30 m). Laying dual 3-in. (75-mm) supply lines is the hydraulic equivalent to a single 4-in. (100-mm) LDH supply line.

Modern fire departments that continue to use a 3-in. (75-mm) MDH supply line are usually heavily urbanized cities with dual 3-in. (75-mm) MDH supply beds that also have a strong water supply infrastructure that supports its use. This infrastructure includes close hydrant spacing of no more than 300 or 500 ft (91 or 152 m) and good water pressure, as well as using the tactic of placing their pumps at hydrants to provided pumped 3-in. (75-mm) MDH supply. These characteristics and tactics allow for continued use of 3-in. (75-mm) supply line in some cities. Supply line is like any other tool in the fire service: there is a vast array of choices and selection is based on many variables, including available water supply infrastructure and tactics.

Forward lay. A forward lay is just what it sounds like. An engine spots a hydrant near the fire and then lays a supply line towards the fire building. Most fire departments that use a forward lay water supply tactic use a single bed of supply hose, usually in any of the following sizes of LDH: 3½, 4, 4½, and 5 in. (90, 100, 115, and 125 mm). Figure 15–77a shows an engine performing a forward lay evolution by laying a single supply line from a hydrant to a residential building fire. Fire departments that utilize a forward lay should load their LDH supply line with the female coupling out to provide easy connection to the male hydrant outlets/nozzles.

Forward lay tactic departments that have Storz fittings on their LDH supply line usually pre-attached a Storz to threaded swivel female adapter to speed hydrant connections; the attached adapter is usually sized to the largest common outlet on their jurisdiction hydrants. If forward laid supply hose is attached directly to the hydrant outlet, the fire department utilizing this tactic is relying on the residual pressure in the water mains to overcome the friction loss in the supply hose. This limits the practical water capacity of the hydrant. This downside to a forward lay can be overcome using a four-way hydrant valve.

Figure 15–77b, is a Akron four-way hydrant valve being used to augment pressure in an existing 3-in. (75-mm) forward lay supply line. A four-way hydrant valve appliance offers an immense advantage to departments using a forward lay tactic, because if it becomes apparent that due to water supply issues (a extremely long forward lay, for example) placing a pump at the hydrant will significantly increase water supply, one has the option of accomplishing this without interruption of water flow in existing forward laid water supply hose.

Placing a pump at the hydrant is the best way to use all the existing flow capacity in water main system. The engine in Fig. 15–77b could be called upon to supply more water; it could easily gain access to more water by stretching an LDH to the other non-used outlet on the hydrant and then supply additional water through more hose. An engine assigned to a hydrant that uses all of the hydrant's outlets and then pumps it down to only a 10-psi (70-kPa) hydrant residual pressure has effectively

used all of the available water from that hydrant; this is called welling the hydrant.

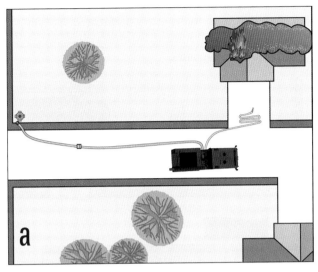

Fig. 15–77. a) Diagram of a typical forward lay. b) Engine pumps through a four-way hydrant valve.

Reverse lay. The reverse lay is simply a water supply evolution where an engine company lays supply line or attack line back to a hydrant (fig. 15–78). This means an engine performing a reverse lay stops at the fire building and then lays hose to the nearest hydrant. The reverse lay is typically used in two different ways: for water supply or fire attack. In the supply scenario there is usually an engine already on the fire scene with attack lines deployed. The attack engine either has no water supply or has an inadequate existing supply. One such example would be an engine operating off its tank. The supply engine that is performing the reverse lay to establish a water supply would pull near the attack engine either by passing it on a wide street or by backing down the street when access is an issue. Once the reverse laying supply engine is in position, the crew would pull the proper supply hose for attack pumper and then release the supply engine, whose crew would proceed to lay out to a nearby hydrant. Once at a hydrant, the engineer would then connect the pumper to the hydrant and the reverse laid supply hose to the engine's discharges. The supply engine at the hydrant must strive not to block access for arriving ladder companies.

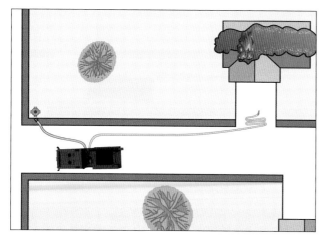

Fig. 15–78. Reverse lay

The other type of reverse lay is an attack line operation. In this case the engine pulls up to the fire building and the crew gets out. The engine crew then proceeds to make a line selection (typically either a single attack line or both an attack line and a backup line are pulled). These lines are located in the hosebed and must be static loads. The company must select the proper size of attack line and estimate how much hose is needed at the fire building to make an effective attack. At the same time, they must strip any equipment they need. Some examples of this would be SCBAs, lights, and hand tools. Sometimes a gated wye or manifold is attached to the engine's supply hose; later, the attack lines, usually removed from engines in bundle configuration, will be connected. Once all of that is accomplished, the engine is then released by the company officer, laying supply hose as it travels. The engineer then drives to the nearest hydrant, leaving the company behind at the fire scene. As the engineer makes the necessary connections to the hydrant and engine, the rest of the company at the fire building starts to flake their attack line and get into position. Once a call for water is made by the attack crew, the engineer charges the proper attack line. Reverse lays for attack hand line operations are typically done in large urbanized areas where hydrants are closely spaced. This leaves the front of the building open for extensive use of aerial devices.

Many fire departments use reverse lays as a water supply evolutions for apparatus located near the fire building. Figure 15–79 depicts the Milwaukee (Wisconsin) Fire Department's (MFD's) rear hosebed and a diagram of a supply reverse lay. Notice that they still use 3-in. (75-mm) MDH as a supply line in the two center hose bins. Both 3-in. (75-mm) MDH supply beds have the male coupling facing out to facilitate reverse lays. Each hose bin has 750 ft (230 m) of 3-in. (75-mm) hose, in 50-ft (15-m) lengths. One 3-in. (75-mm) MDH supply bed has a red hose strap, and the other 3-in. (75-mm) hosebed has a tan hose strap. The MFD can either reverse lay a single or dual 3-in. (75-mm) lay. Pumped supply of 3-in. (75-mm) MDH in this configuration can easily supply 1,000 gpm (3,785 L/min) even if the full 750 ft (230 m) is used, as long as a dual 3-in. (75-mm) hose lead is taken. This leaves a 500-gpm flow in each 3-in. (75-mm) lead at 20 psi (140 kPa) per 100 ft (30 m) of friction loss. The MFD also benefits from optimal hydrant spacing of 300 ft (90 m). Such short lays are a good match for 3-in. (75-mm) hose, especially when it is pump-supplied.

Fig. 15–79 MFD hosebed setup for reverse lays

Another example of a city that uses 3-in. (75-mm) hose is San Francisco. The SFFD benefits from both an excellent water supply system and close hydrant spacing. The SFFD also deals with a densely constructed city, predominately of multiple-story wooden structures. They use dual beds of 3-in. (75-mm) MDH, one with the male coupling out and the other with the female out. This allows them to accomplish a single 3-in. (75-mm) forward lay or a single 3-in. (75-mm) reverse lay with ease. They can also take dual reverse lays or dual forward lays by using either a double female or double male adapter. In fig. 15–80, the engine at the hydrant is pumping two 3-in. (75-mm) leads. Notice one of the leads is attached to a pump discharge by a brass 3-in. (75-mm) double female adapter. The engineer operating the engine has welled the hydrant with two suction jumpers. This engine is properly positioned, out of the way, and connected in a manner such that it will supply all the available water from the hydrant. This SFFD engine could easily be called upon to supply more lines until the hydrant flow reached the available capacity. Notice that in the background extensive aerial operations and ground ladder operations are taking place directly in front of the fire building. Although the SFFD uses 3-in. (75-mm) MDH as supply line on their engines, they also maintain a small fleet of 5-in. (125-mm) LDH hose tenders. This is a common practice for departments that use 3-in. (75-mm) MDH, given that there is truly no substitute for size of hose when called to move very large amount of water—2,000 gpm (7,571 L/min) and up. These hose tenders are usually for special calls or assigned to certain alarms.

Fig. 15–80. SFFD pumps dual 3-in. (75-mm) MDH lay at hydrant

Split lays

Now that we have discussed the water supply evolutions of both forward and reverse lays, we will describe another useful operation called a split lay. The split lay is basically where two engines are used to complete one water supply line evolution from the hydrant to the building fire. The split lay is not commonly done; however, split lays can be extremely effective in the right circumstances. For example, the first due engine arrives at an extremely long alley way or private drive with a building fire located at the end of it. This engine in fig. 15–81 came across just this circumstance. The company officer in this case decided to use a split lay by dropping a supply line at the beginning of the private drive and continued into the fire building. The first due company officer then radioed the second due engine company to pick up their dry lay. This second due company now was then tasked with finishing the water supply line. The second due company stopped

and attached their supply line to the dry supply line laid by the first due company.

The second due company's engineer then drove back to the nearest hydrant. Once at the hydrant, all necessary connections were made. Then engineer ensured that the middle connection or **split connection** had been completed and the attack pumper was ready for water. Once all of this was confirmed, water was pumped from the hydrant through the now completed split laid supply line to the attack pumper.

Let's say in this case the total length of the split lay worked out to 1,000 ft (305 m) of 5-in. (125-mm) hose, and each engine in the example only carried 800 ft (245 m) of 5-in. (125-mm) LDH. This would mean that due to the long driveway and distance to the nearest hydrant, it would have been impossible for either company to have made this supply operation on their own. It is not necessary to only consider split lays if the amount of hose required is more than one company's complement. Split lays are sometimes performed for access issues alone.

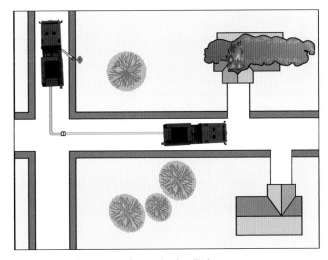

Fig. 15–81. Diagram of a typical split lay

Drafting operations

In rural settings, drafting operations are commonplace. This may involve the use of a dry hydrant connected to a lake, a cistern, or a swimming pool, as described earlier. Perhaps the most common operation is simply the use of a rigid (hard suction) hose placed in a body of water.

Once the engine has been placed at the edge of the source of water (lake, pond, river, etc.), the two hard suction hoses are removed and connected. The strainer is then attached.

A **floating strainer** is typically a square-shaped device attached to the hard suction hose that floats on the surface of the water, maximizing its ability to avoid underwater debris and to draft from shallow water depths. It can simply be placed on the water, and the pump operator can begin to pump after establishing a vacuum (fig. 15–82).

A traditional, round strainer (a circular tube with many holes cast into it) is deployed into the water using a rope to keep it off the bottom of the lake, pond, or other body of water. The rope is then tied to the engine, and the pump operator can initiate creating a vacuum and then begin pumping operations (fig. 15–83).

Fig. 15–82. Floating strainer in operation

Fig. 15–83. Traditional barrel strainer

HYDRANT APPLIANCES

Departments across the country use different **hydrant appliances** to accomplish a variety of tasks. Figure 15–84a depicts an LDH four-way valve attached to a hydrant, which provides the option to pump at the hydrant after water flow is established through the initial

supply line. Many departments use four-way hydrant valves. In fig. 15–84b, the dry barrel hydrant with two 2½-in. (65-mm) outlets has a hydrant gate valve attached to it and a single 3-in. (75-mm) MDH supply line. The gate valve allows the use of the other hydrant outlet without turning the hydrant off.

The yellow hydrant in fig. 15–84c has a 5-in. (125-mm) lead attached to it, which is using a Carlin automatic hydrant valve.

The last picture on the right in fig. 15–84d shows a large high-pressure hydrant. The water available from this hydrant is under such tremendous pressure that it is necessary to put a pressure-reducing valve on it. This type is called a Gleason valve, and it is used by SFFD on their high-pressure auxiliary water supply hydrant system. Boston is another city that has a unique hydrant system; one part is a hydrant stem system located under manholes that require a Lowry hydrant. The Boston Lowry hydrant is carried on the engine and is attached directly to a connection in the street. The City of Boston has three hydrant systems; the Lowry system is located mostly in downtown. Today, five engine companies still carry Lowry hydrants.

In summary, many fire departments use different hydrant appliances. Some of these appliances are very simple (like gate valves), and others are rarely used and complex (like the Carlin automatic hydrant valve). You must be familiar with your own fire department's operations as well as the water supply operations and capabilities of your surrounding jurisdictions. The Carlin automatic hydrant valve is used by a jurisdiction near the fire department of one of the chapter authors. Therefore we should know how it works, even though we think it is very impractical.

Basic hydrant use

The ability to use a hydrant correctly is a critical skill that all members of the fire service should not only master but also routinely practice. Engine companies should routinely drill with fire hydrants. It is a bread-and-butter operation that needs to be second nature to all firefighters. All common problems related to hydrants in your particular jurisdiction should be preidentified, and solutions should already be in place. Very few fire departments have the luxury of hydrants that are perfectly maintained and work properly very time. Many departments face significant hydrant problems from vandalism and poor maintenance. I strongly recommend that fire departments outfit all of their engine companies with

Fig. 15–84 a, b, c, d. From left to right: a four-way hydrant valve, a gate valve, a Carlin automatic hydrant valve, and a Gleason pressure-reducing valve.

hydrant bags. A hydrant bag should have all of the necessary equipment to make a good connection to a hydrant, even when problems are encountered.

Take a look at the hydrant bag in fig. 15–85. Fire departments can encounter significant problems with their hydrants based on a variety of factors. This hydrant bag was design by a department that use wet barrel hydrants. It includes a pipe wrench for stripped spindles, a **cheater bar** to apply extra force (avoid breaking the hydrant stem connected to the operating nut by applying too much force), a 3-lb (1.4-kg) maul to knock loose rusted or stuck caps; a Hydra-Shield® locking cap spanner to deal with locking caps; a 2½-in. (65-mm) female to 4½-in. (115-mm) male increaser, in case the steamer outlet is nonfunctional; and a regular screw-type hydrant wrench. Fire departments that access water with dry barrel hydrants should consider these additional items to aid in hydrant connections: extra hydrant caps (in case one or more are missing), outlet plugs or blocks (in case of damaged outlet threads), and different hydrant gate valves.

Hydrant bags are especially useful for departments that rely on forward lay water supply evolutions. During a forward lay, the engine company leaves a firefighter at the hydrant. This firefighter has only the equipment that has been removed from the engine, to obtain a good water supply by rapid connection of the supply line to the hydrant. By placing all of the necessary equipment in a hydrant bag, the lead-off firefighter should have all of the tools required to "catch the hydrant." After checking the PPE and SCBA, one of the first things the lead-off firefighter at shift change should check is the hydrant bag. Hydrant bags are also useful for departments that use reverse lays. In case of a reverse lay, the engineer is able to grab one bag to locate all the tools necessary to make a good hydrant connection.

Let's walk through hitting a hydrant while performing a forward lay.

The forward lay is used when the water source, static or municipal, is located before the structure on fire. In a forward lay, the pumper approaches the water source— in this case a hydrant—and stops. A firefighter, sometimes known a "hydrant firefighter," gets off the pumper with the needed equipment: hydrant wrench, spanner, gates, hose traps, etc., and removes a sufficient amount of supply hose to "wrap" the hydrant. As mentioned previously, the hydrant firefighter checks the hydrant for damage and access, and then proceeds to secure the hose (wrap) around the barrel of the hydrant to anchor it safely in place. The pumper then proceeds to the fire

scene. The hydrant firefighter then checks the hydrant, removes the caps and flushes the hydrant. The hose and gates are then connected to the hydrant, and the hydrant firefighter awaits a signal from the pump operator or fire officer to open or charge the hydrant.

Fig. 15–85. An example of tools in a hydrant bag

Once water is received at the pumper, then those necessary functions (fire attack, exposure control, hydraulic ventilation, etc.) can be accomplished at the fire scene to control and extinguish the fire.

Once the fire is extinguished and all overhaul functions have been accomplished, the process of shutting down the operation can begin. At this point the incident commander notifies the pump operator to begin shutting down attack lines and the hydrant firefighter is notified that they can begin closing the hydrant, as discussed in a previous section. Once the hydrant has been shut down and the pressure bleeds off the hose, the gates can be disconnected. The hydrant caps are replaced and the supply hose is drained of excess water and prepared to be repacked on the pumper.

LESSON FROM THE FIREGROUND

The fire department arrived at a well-involved two-story garden apartment fire. The fire was burning throughout a second floor dwelling unit and the fire coming from the windows had spread the fire into the combustible attic space. The buildings were situated between 1,000 and 1,200 ft (305 and 366 m) off the main road. There was a hydrant in the complex but the fire department knew this hydrant was fed by a dead end 6-in. (150-mm) water main. The first arriving pumper (1,500 gpm [5,678 L/min] with 500 gal [1,892 L] tank) stopped at the hydrant at the entrance to the complex and dropped a 5-in. (125-mm) supply line.

The volume of fire dictated the use of heavy caliber streams. A deck gun was ordered to hit the main body of fire. The pre-piped 1¾-in. (45-mm) smooth bore tip master stream was charged. A 2½-in. (65-mm) hoseline with a one and ⅛-in. (3-mm) smooth bore tip was ordered to the adjoining second floor apartment where the fire was now spreading. A second two and ½-in. (13-mm) hose line with the same nozzle was stretched to combat the fire in the attic, which was now rapidly involving the attic space over the entire building.

As the hand lines were charged, the pump operator realized the supply line was collapsing. A second supply line was called for and an additional 5-in. (125-mm) supply line was stretched from the dead end hydrant using two 100-ft (30-m) lengths of hose. Although this improved the situation slightly, there was still a problem supplying adequate water to the single deck gun and two large hand lines.

The immediate assumption was there had to be a problem with the hydrant and the public water supply. The initial static pressure was 70 psi (490 kPa) but quickly bottomed out. An examination after the fire showed that there was plenty of water. The problem was a basic pump operations flaw. There was too much friction loss created when flowing the large volume of water through the five-inch supply hose from the hydrant. The simple answer would have been to have another pumper at the hydrant to overcome the friction loss problem.

NOTES

1. Bachtler, J. R., & Brennan T. F. (Eds.). (1995) *The Fire Chief's Handbook* (5th ed.). Tulsa, OK: PennWell.

2. Oakland Fire Department. (1997). *Water Supply Reference Course.* Oakland, CA: Oakland Fire Department (OFD).

3. FEMA U.S. Fire Administration (2003). *Fireboats Then and Now, Special Report*, Retrieved November 2007 from http://www.fireboat.org/FEMAfire-boatsthennowMay2003.pdf.

4. FEMA U.S. Fire Administration (2003).

5. FEMA U.S. Fire Administration (2003).

6. NFPA 1961. (2007). *Standard on Fire Hose.* Quincy, MA: National Fire Protection Association.

7. NFPA 1961.

8. NFPA 1962. (2008). *Standard for the Inspection, Care, and Use of Fire Hose, Couplings, and Nozzles and the Service Testing of Fire Hose.* Quincy, MA: National Fire Protection Association.

9. NFPA 1962.

10. NFPA 1962.

11. NFPA 1961.

QUESTIONS

1.   What is normal atmospheric pressure and how does it register on a standard fire service gauge?

2.   Explain the effect friction loss has on flow pressure in a fire hose.

3.   In the water distribution system, on what type of water main are hydrants normally found?

4.   Why are dry barrel hydrants typically found in climates where the temperature can be expected to drop below freezing?

5.   What items should be included in a hydrant inspection?

6.   What color should the bonnet of a hydrant capable of flowing more than 1,500 gpm (5,678 L/min) be painted?

7.   When setting up a water shuttle, what conditions make for a good fill site?

8.   When is relay pumping typically needed?

9.   How would a 2½-in. (65-mm) hoseline be classified? Why?

10.   What is the advantage of double-jacketed hose when compared to single-jacketed hose?

11.   Can large-diameter hose (LDH) be used to draft water from a static source? Why or why not?

12.   Why are Storz connections commonly used on large-diameter supply hoses?

13.   Prior to reconnecting sections of hose together, what should the couplings be inspected for?

14.   What is the definition of a hose appliance?

15.   Explain the difference between a gated wye when compared to a clappered Siamese.

16.   Why should a fire hose not be folded or reloaded in the same order it was prior to being used?

17.   What does it mean if a fire hose is stamped "400 psi service test"?

18.   What advantage do attack lines stored preconnected on the pumper have over attack lines stored in a dead load?

19.   Laying a supply line from the hydrant to the fire is referred to as what?

20.   In what circumstances might a split lay be utilized?

Fire Streams

by Jay Comella with Jeff Shupe

This chapter provides required knowledge items for the following
NFPA Standard 1001 Job Performance Requirements:

FFI 5.3.10   FFII 6.3.2

FFI 5.3.11

FFI 5.3.13

OBJECTIVES

Upon completion of this chapter, you should be able to do the following:

- Identify the advantages of water as an extinguishing agent
- Identify the factors that affect the firefighter's ability to handle fire hose
- Describe the characteristics of the four nozzle types
- Identify the mnemonic device "ADULTS" as it applies to using a fire hose and nozzle
- Describe the three methods of fire attack
- Identify the three types of fire streams
- Describe the proper procedures for advancing a charged hose line
- Describe the proper procedures for advancing an uncharged hose line
- Describe the responsibilities of the three positions on a charged hoseline
- Describe the proper procedures for using a hoseline to perform hydraulic ventilation
- Describe the proper procedures for using hoselines during exposure and overhaul operations
- Identify the different types of master stream devices used by the fire service
- Identify the types of specialty nozzles used by the fire service
- Describe the basic care and maintenance of fire service nozzles

INTRODUCTION

Over the years the leading instructors of the fire service have repeatedly made statements such as "The greatest lifesaving action on the fireground is the proper placement of the proper size initial attack hoseline," and "As the first line goes, so goes the fire."

FFI 5.3.10 Such statements denote the critically important actions involved in the proper selection, deployment, and use of **hoselines**, **nozzles**, and **fire streams**. When applied properly, they diminish or extinguish the fire completely, reduce the temperature of burning materials, and stop the spread of fire. They directly affect lifesaving by extinguishing fire and inhibiting the products of combustion. They also allow all other fireground lifesaving functions to proceed more quickly, efficiently, and safely. The entire job revolves around the acts of stretching and advancing hose and operating the nozzle to extinguish fire. The members who perform this work are the tip of the spear of the fire service.

WATER AS AN EXTINGUISHING AGENT

Today's fireground is a much more volatile environment than that of the past. The flow rates of 95–125 gpm were deemed adequate at a time when fuel loads were lighter and comprised of so-called ordinary combustibles, such as wood, paper, and cloth (**cellulosic materials**). Quantities of combustibles have dramatically increased. Fuels are heavier and largely **hydrocarbon**-based (plastics); plastics are petrochemical products that behave like **solid gasoline** and generate large quantities of thermal energy. Higher heat release rates associated with plastics (discussed in chapter 5, Fire Behavior) bring a room to flashover more quickly. Couple these factors with better insulated buildings that inhibit fire from self-venting (tight building syndrome), and today's engine company most definitely faces a much more dangerous enemy than in the past.

FFI 5.3.10 Because the enemy has become much more dangerous, the weapon used to combat the enemy must be upgraded accordingly. Akin to the police evolving from the 38-caliber revolver to the 9 mm semiautomatic, the fire department also must make a more intelligent weapon selection. The hose and nozzle system is the engine company's weapon for attacking the fire. Most of the American fire service now considers 150 gpm (568 L/min) to be the minimum acceptable flow rate for interior structural fire attack. Many fire departments use a target flow rate of 180 gpm (681 L/min) to ensure an added margin of safety.

In his brilliant treatise on the art and science of applying water on fire,[1] the late Andrew Fredericks (a New York City Fire Department [FDNY] firefighter who was killed at the World Trade Center on 9/11), the foremost expert on engine company operations in modern times, further states that in addition to 150 gpm (568 L/min)

being the minimum acceptable flow for residential fires, 250 gpm (946 L/min) is the minimum acceptable hand line flow for operations in commercial occupancies.

The establishment of robust, occupancy specific, minimum flow rates is in effect an extension of the Powell Doctrine to the fire service. The Powell Doctrine is the culmination of General Colin Powell's many years of battle experience, training, and study of the military arts. The doctrine is a set of guidelines meant to ensure the highest probability of success in the conduct of military operations. The essence is that once combat is joined, one must bring overwhelming force to bear upon the enemy in an extremely rapid manner (shock and awe) to ensure the highest likelihood of victory in the shortest duration. This in turn reduces the overall depletion of one's resources, both material and human.

The outcome of fireground operations depends on the outcome of the battle between the water the engine company delivers (gpm) and the fire's heat release rate. The flow at which the engine company can win the battle and kill the fire is defined as the critical flow rate. If the critical flow rate is not met, the battle will be lost. This dictates that the single most important characteristic of a hose and nozzle system is water flow capability. The water the engine company delivers must not merely meet theoretical flow rates; it must be sufficient to expediently overwhelm and kill the fire. Maneuverability of the hose and nozzle are important factors, but sacrificing flow for ease of use has proved to be suicidal in too many instances.

Water is an ideal fire-extinguishing agent. Besides the fact that it is readily available and inexpensive in most locales, it is efficient in terms of its fire-extinguishing capabilities. Water extinguishes a fire primarily through cooling, reducing the temperature of the burning fuel and the fire gases. In addition, water applied to unburned fuel surrounding the burning materials wets them, making it difficult, if not impossible, for the fire to spread.

Water has a high **specific heat** compared to other materials (pound for pound, it absorbs more heat than many other substances). Thus it takes more heat energy to raise the temperature of water compared to other materials. It takes one **British thermal unit (Btu)** of heat energy to raise 1 lb water 1°F. (You may be familiar with Btu in the context of air conditioners and the amount of heat energy they are capable of handling, it is a measurement of their **cooling power**.)

For every 1°F, 1 lb water is raised by a fire, it absorbs 1 Btu of heat energy. When the water turns to steam at 212°F, it absorbs an additional 970 Btu, called the **latent**

heat of vaporization. In fig. 16–1 for example, 1 lb water at 55°F heated until it turns to steam absorbs

$$157 \text{ Btu } (212 - 55) + 970 \text{ Btu} = 1,127 \text{ Btu}$$

Taken a step further, because 1 gal water weighs 8.3 lb, 1 gal water at 55°F turned into steam absorbs

$$8.3 \times 1,127 \text{ Btu} = 9,354 \text{ Btu}$$

When liquid water turns to steam, it expands approximately 1,700 times its original volume (see fig. 16–2). Although smothering by steam is a useful firefighting tactic in unoccupied buildings and equipment, it is neither safe nor desirable to generate large quantities of steam because of the danger to occupants and firefighters. In typical compartment (room) fires, firefighters must avoid creating steam by applying water properly and in the right quantities. Creating larger quantities of steam is dangerous and can lead to **steam burns**. This issue is discussed in the following text in terms of nozzle selection and fire streams.

Although an adequate flow rate cannot be sacrificed for ease of use, handling characteristics cannot be completely overlooked, either. The **nozzle operator** must exert enough force to resist the nozzle reaction. Nozzle reaction is measured in pounds of force and is a function of two factors: flow rate and **nozzle pressure (NP)**. An increase in one or both factors results in increased nozzle **reaction force (RF)**. The higher the nozzle RF, the more difficult the nozzle is to control. Because adequate flow rate is the ultimate goal of a well-conceived hose and nozzle system, the logical way to keep nozzle RF within the manageable range is to keep nozzle pressures low and avoid sacrificing flow. More than 75 lb (34 kg) RF is considered to be too much reaction force for a hand line. However, RF less than 45 lb (20.4 kg) is considered a sign of an ineffective stream.

Hoseline handling characteristics are a function of the following factors:

1. Flow rate

2. Hose size

3. Friction loss

4. Pump discharge pressure

Hand line maneuverability is determined by the pressure at which a given size line must be pumped to attain a desired flow rate. If hose size remains constant and flow is increased, pump discharge pressure must be increased to account for greater friction loss. This reduces maneuverability as the line approaches the stiffness of a pipe.

Conversely, if hose size increases while flow remains constant, pump discharge pressure may be reduced because of lower friction loss requirements. This results in improved maneuverability because the line becomes more bendable.

The aforementioned parameters lead to certain conclusions about what constitutes a well-planned hose and nozzle system for residential fires. The hose should be capable of flowing between 150 and 180 gpm (568 and 861 L/min) with relatively low friction loss. The nozzle should have similar flow capability at a nozzle pressure that will maintain reaction force in the range of between 45 and 75 lb (20 and 34 kg).

Because of the pressures required to account for friction loss, the practical flow limit for 1½-in. (38-mm) hose is 125 gpm, whereas the practical flow limit for 1¾-in. (45-mm) hose is 200 gpm (757 L/min) (fig. 16–1).

Fig. 16–1. The 1¾-in. (45-mm) hose allows significantly higher flow than the 1½-in. (38-mm) line, yet size and weight differences are nominal.

NOZZLES

FFI 5.3.10 **FFII 6.3.2** The tool at the very heart of the entire fireground operation is the nozzle. It is the weapon with which members enter into close-quarter combat with the enemy. If the nozzle malfunctions or is improperly used, all other tools and tactics on the fireground are likely to become quite limited in their effectiveness in saving life and protecting property. All kinds of nozzles perform their all-important mission by providing some rather simple, uncomplicated, albeit incredibly necessary functions. They control flow, create shape, and provide reach. Because the functional requirements for a nozzle are relatively simple and yet immensely important, it intuitively makes sense to select the nozzle with the least complicated design and the fewest moving parts. The most low-tech choice in nozzle selection ensures the greatest degree of durability and reliability. Simple, durable, and low tech are all qualities that contribute to low initial and long-term costs. More importantly, these qualities lead to reliability, which leads to increased safety. The use and care of nozzles is covered under National Fire Protection Association (NFPA) 1962: *Standard for the Inspection, Care, and Use of Fire Hose, Couplings, and Nozzles and the Service Testing of Fire Hose.*

In the early days of fire service, hoses were leather and the first nozzle was nothing more than a piece of pipe on the end of the hose. The addition of a controlling device, or shut-off, between the male hose butt and the piece of pipe was the genesis of today's fire nozzle. The bore of the pipe, or **smooth bore nozzle (tip)**, was eventually tapered to improve hydraulic efficiency. The controlling device consists of a shut-off valve and a handle by which to control it. Over the years various valve and handle sizes and types have seen use. Most configurations fell by the wayside as the shut-off evolved into the modern incarnation: a quarter turn ball valve with a 1⅜-in. (35-mm) waterway activated by a bale-type handle.

The rule of thumb for smooth bore tip orifice size is that it should be one-half of the inside diameter of the hose. This equates to a ⅞-in. (22-mm) tip for 1¾-in. (45-mm) hose and a 1¼-in. (32-mm) tip for 2½-in. (65-mm) hose. However, many fire departments have had great success with slight variances from this rule. The ¹⁵⁄₁₆-in. (24-mm) tips for 1¾-in. (45-mm) hose and 1⅛-in. (30-mm) tips for 2½-in. (65-mm) hose are the most common sizes, and practical experience proves they deliver efficient and effective fire streams.

The first **fog nozzle** was developed in 1863 by Charles Oyston of Little Falls, New York. Fog streams are fog nozzles, and fog streams went relatively unnoticed and had little effect on the fire service for quite some time. It was not until the post–World War II period that fog nozzles gained widespread use. This increased favor within the fire service was a result of wartime experiences gained by the naval services who successfully used fog streams to control shipboard fuel oil fires in confined spaces. The intervening years have seen combination nozzles, variable flow nozzles, constant gallonage nozzles, adjustable gallonage nozzles, and constant pressure nozzles (also known as automatic nozzles) all come into being.

After a relatively short-lived duration, the variable flow nozzle fell into disfavor. As its name indicates, it deliv-ered varied flows by design. As the pattern selection changed, so would the flow. It soon became obvious that tying one's ability to achieve critical flow rate to stream selection was a distinct disadvantage in the design of the variable flow nozzle. This characteristic caused its use to decline and then cease.

The three other types of combination nozzles mentioned, constant gallonage, adjustable gallonage, and constant pressure, all remain in present day use.

Nozzle characteristics

Fog streams are characterized by small droplets of water in a dispersed pattern compared with the tight, compact stream of a smooth bore nozzle; the distinct droplets of water in a fog stream evaporate more readily, generating steam (figs. 16–2a and 16–2b). The kinds of nozzles available today, in descending order of simplicity and durability, are smooth bore, constant gallonage (single-gallonage) fog, adjustable gallonage fog, and constant pressure (automatic) fog (fig. 16–3). Fog nozzles are sometimes called **spray nozzles**, nozzles which can be adjusted to discharge a straight stream or fog pattern.

Fig. 16–2a. A firefighter using a spray nozzle discharging a fog pattern

Fig. 16–2b. A firefighter using a spray nozzle discharging a straight stream

Fig. 16–3. Left to right: ¹⁵⁄₁₆-in. (24-mm) smooth bore nozzle (180 gpm at 50 psi [681 L/min at 45 kPa]), constant gallonage nozzle (150 gpm at 50 psi [568 L/min at 345 kPa]), and an automatic nozzle (50–300 gpm [189–1,136 L/min]). (Courtesy of Jerry Knapp)

Smooth bore nozzle

The smooth bore is the most low-tech of all nozzle designs. It consists of a ball valve shut-off device onto which is threaded the smooth bore tip, which is basically a piece of tapered pipe. Together, the shut-off and tip present a compact (7¾ in. [20 cm]) and lightweight (2½ lb [1.1 kg]) package. Genius lies in the simplicity of its design. It has only one moving part: the ball valve (fig. 16–4).

It is difficult to clog a smooth bore nozzle. It requires the least maintenance of any nozzle type and has the longest service life.

Smooth bore nozzles are by far the least expensive kind to purchase and maintain. Of all nozzles, the smooth bore requires the least amount of training for pump and nozzle operators to become proficient (fig. 16–5). The incredible reliability of the smooth bore nozzle is a significant safety feature. Because you can produce only a solid stream with the smooth bore nozzle, its use ensures that members and victims are not being exposed to the potentially debilitating or lethal effects associated with introducing a fog stream into the fire area.

The smooth bore nozzle is a safe and efficient weapon for combating interior structural fires. Therefore, it is the nozzle that is often taken into the most hostile work environment on the face of the earth—the interior of a burning building. Fog nozzles are appropriate for other uses, such as flammable-liquid fires, outdoor rubbish fires, vehicle fires, and the like. However, some departments use fog nozzles as their primary nozzle for **interior fire attack**. Fog nozzles used during interior fire

attack must use the straight stream pattern to avoid the possibility of creating large quantities of steam from the vaporization of the fog droplets, scalding firefighters, and trapped occupants.

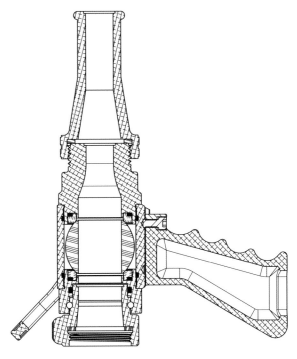

Fig. 16–4. Cut away of a smooth bore nozzle. (Courtesy of Elkhart Brass Mfg. Co.)

Fig. 16–5. California's Oakland Fire Department (OFD) members operate a 2½-in. (65-mm) hoseline with a 1⅛-in. (30-mm) smooth bore nozzle (266 gpm at 50 psi [1,007 L/min at 345 kPa]) during testing and evaluation. (Courtesy of Daryl Liggins)

Constant gallonage fog nozzle

The **constant gallonage fog nozzle** is the simplest, most reliable, least maintenance-intensive and, hence, safest member of the fog nozzle family. Of all fog nozzles, this type requires the least training. It does, however, require somewhat more training than the smooth bore nozzle. Constant or single gallonage indicates that this nozzle is designed to flow a specific gallonage when operated at the specific pressure for which it is designed, such as 150 gpm at 100 psi NP (568 L/min at 700 kPa). In addition to the 100-psi (700-kPa) model, constant gallonage nozzles also come in 75-psi (525-kPa) and 50-psi (345-kPa) models. The nozzle is 12¼ in. (311 mm) long and weighs 6.1 lb (2.8 kg). As the name suggests, there is the distinct possibility of introducing fog stream into the fire area. This has the potential to turn a still-tenable environment into one that is untenable in short order. As with all fog nozzles, when the water flows from the hose—through the shutoff, into the tip, to be broken into a spray stream—a clog point exists.

Adjustable gallonage fog nozzle

The **adjustable gallonage fog nozzle** takes fog nozzle technology to the next level of complexity. It has more moving parts and is more maintenance-intensive than the constant gallonage nozzle and, hence, has an increased potential for nozzle failure or malfunction. Using a flow-selection ring, the nozzle operator can choose a desired flow. This operation requires an increased level of training for both nozzle and pump operators. If the nozzle operator changes the flow setting, the pump operator must be informed so he or she can adjust pump discharge pressure to the appropriate level for the selected flow. It is possible to put the flow-selection ring on the wrong setting, so the nozzle's flow is less than the desired amount of water. So, in addition to possibly introducing a dangerous fog stream into the fire environment, there is a great potential for producing a flow that is less than the acceptable minimum. The adjustable gallonage nozzle is 12¼ in. (311 mm) long and weighs 5.6 lb (2.5 kg).

Automatic fog nozzle

Automatic nozzles originally were designed in the late 1960s by Chief Clyde McMillan of the Gary Fire Task Force, an auxiliary unit of the Gary Fire Department in Indiana. One role of the task force was to respond to large fires and put master streams into operation. Often, initial water supply was inadequate when transitioning to defensive operations. McMillan set about designing a master stream appliance nozzle that would produce a stream with good reach, even at the low flows available during the transitional phases of operations. He also wanted that same nozzle to be appropriate for the high flows achievable after augmentation of the water supply.

The automatic nozzle is also called the **constant pressure nozzle**. Constant pressure refers to the fact that the nozzle produces a stream of reach and appearance consistent with 100-psi (700-kPa) tip pressure regardless of the pressure actually coming into the base of the nozzle. This is accomplished by a baffle and spring arrangement. As a given amount of water enters the nozzle base, it puts the spring under a given amount of compression. This, in turn, moves a baffle that changes the nozzle's orifice size. As the amount of water flow fluctuates, so does the orifice size. The orifice is thus maintained at a size that, for the given amount of water, provides approximately 100 psi (700 kPa) nozzle pressure (NP). This allows the nozzle to create a visually attractive stream with good reach over an extremely wide range of flows. Often, the stream produced by the automatic nozzle looks good but doesn't contain much water. Remember, volume of water is critical to fire extinguishment.

The automatic fog nozzle is bulky (length: 13¾ in. [350 mm], weight: 6.5 lb [2.9 kg]). It is at the high-tech end of the spectrum of fire service nozzles (fig. 16–9). To be used properly, it requires more training for both nozzle operators and pump operators than any other nozzle type. It has the most complicated design of any nozzle and the most moving parts. Many automatic nozzles come with a shut-off that has a slide valve as opposed to a ball valve. A ball valve (on a smooth bore nozzle) has a completely unobstructed waterway, while the slide valve can become a significant clog point. Given the potential for clogging, the nozzle is equipped with a protective screen at its base to keep debris from entering the slide valve. Clearing the clog necessitates shutting down the hoseline, resulting in problems during a fire attack. The automatic nozzle is the most maintenance-intensive nozzle type.

Fig. 16–6. Cutaway illustration of automatic nozzle.

Operating characteristics of smooth bore and fog (spray) nozzles

Smooth bore nozzles are simple to operate. To flow water, firefighters need only pull back on the bale and water discharges from the nozzle. The bale can be adjusted between the fully closed (the **bale** is in the forward position, farthest away from the firefighter) and the fully open positions (the bale is in the rear position, closest to the firefighter). Positioning the bale between these two extremes allows the firefighter discharge smaller amounts of water. To open or close the bale, move in a slow, deliberate manner (figs. 16–7a and 16–7b).

The bale of fog nozzles operates in the same way as a smooth bore nozzle. Typically, the nozzle has a rotational control to adjust the pattern from straight stream to the wide-angle spray also known as a **wide fog** (characteristically, a 100-degree angle). Turning the adjustable rotational control from left to right changes the pattern from a wide-angle fog to a narrow fog, and then finally to a straight stream (and shutoff in some cases) (figs. 16–7c, 16–7d, 16–7e, and 16–7f). Some fog nozzles use a lever-type control to adjust the pattern and open or close the nozzle. Some fog nozzles have a **flush feature** that allows small pieces of debris to be discharged.

Fig. 16–7a. Smooth bore nozzle in open position

Fig. 16–7b. Smooth bore nozzle in close position

Fig. 16–7c. Fog nozzle in open position

Fig. 16–7d. Fog nozzle in closed position

Fig. 16–7e. Fog nozzle adjusted to straight stream

Fig. 16–7f. Fog nozzle adjusted to wide fog

SELECTING THE PROPER HAND LINE SIZE

FFI 5.3.10 FFII 6.3.2 The first step in planning a hose and nozzle system is to establish the needed flow for the occupancy type in question. The flow requirement is derived by determining the flow at which the engine company most often will overwhelm the heat generated by the encountered fuel load. To deliver the desired volume of water, parameters for hose selection are based on flow and friction loss characteristics. Parameters for selecting a nozzle to couple to the business end of that hose are based on flow and reaction force characteristics. This holds true for residential occupancies and for fires in commercial buildings.

Under most circumstances, a 1½-, 1¾-, or 2-in. (38-, 45-, or 50-mm) hand line suffices for a typical room and contents fire in a low-rise residential buildings and the **bread and butter** structures of the fire service: single- and two-family homes. This rule of thumb does not apply to high-rise residential structures or heavily involved residential structures. The company officer (following the particular fire department's standard operating procedures) decides what size hand line to use in a particular building.

As mentioned earlier, the minimum acceptable hand line flow for operations in commercial occupancies (including industrial and institutional occupancies) is 250 gpm (946 L/min). For this type of flow, 2½-in. (65-mm) hose is the line of choice. Friction loss at 250 gpm (946 L/min) is 10 psi per 100 ft (70 kPa per 30.5 m) of 2½-in. (65-mm) line. For the same flow in 2-in. (51-mm) hose, the friction loss is 50 psi per 100 ft (345 kPa per 30.5 M). Although a 2½-in. (65-mm) line is a substantial piece of equipment, it is not too heavy to aggressively advance as a hand line, as would be the case with 3-in. (76-mm) hose.

The key to efficiently using a 2½-in. (65-mm) line is proper nozzle selection. The 100-psi (700 kPa) combination nozzle effectively removes the 2½-in. (65-mm) line from many a fire department's arsenal of offensive weaponry because of the very high nozzle reaction force of 126 lbs (57 kg) while flowing 250 gpm at 100 psi (946 L/min at 700 kPa) nozzle pressure. Low-pressure nozzles (50-psi [350-kPa] tip pressure) impart significantly less reaction force."

Many departments successfully employ a 1¼-in. (32-mm) tip. Its 324-gpm (1,226-L/min) flow technically classes it as a large-caliber stream, making this size tip possibly better suited for use with master stream devices. A far greater number of departments use the 1⅛-in. (30-mm) tip. With a flow of 266 gpm at 50 psi (1,007 L/min at 350 kPa) nozzle pressure, it has a reaction force of 95 lb (43 kg). Although it is still crucial to keep nozzle reaction force low, it would be impractical to try to apply

the previously cited 75-lb (34 kg) cap to flows from large-caliber hand lines.

Paired together, the 2½-in. (65-mm) line and the 1⅛-in. (30-mm) tip create a user-friendly, offensive, large-caliber weapon. Fredericks states the following:

> *No combination of smaller hand-lines can duplicate the volume, reach, and pure knockdown power of a single, well-placed 2½-in. line. In addition to its high-volume flows (between 250 and 320 gpm) and long stream reach, 2½-in. hose provides the following benefits when used with a 1⅛-in. solid stream tip:*

> . *Low friction loss per 50-ft length (only about 5 psi at 266 gpm).*

> . *Exceptional penetrating power due to hydraulic force of the stream.*

> . *Little premature water vaporization in highly heated fire areas.*

> . *Easy reduction to smaller hand-line(s) after knockdown, and much better maneuverability than 3-in. hose (sometimes used as a hand-line) or portable master-stream devices.[2]*

Using a 2½-in. (65-mm) line is indicated in situations in which fire conditions are likely to overwhelm smaller hand lines. Fredericks cites the oft-used mnemonic device ADULTS, which refers to scenarios requiring the use of 2½-in. (65-mm) line:

- **A**dvanced fire on arrival
- **D**efensive operations
- **U**nable to determine extent (size) of fire area
- **L**arge, uncompartmented areas
- **T**ons of water
- **S**tandpipe system operations

The ADULTS acronym is reminiscent of an anecdote related by retired Chicago Fire Department Battalion Chief Ray Hoff regarding proper hand line selection. On seeing an engine company stretching a 1¾-in. (45-mm) line toward a commercial occupancy exhibiting a heavy fire condition, Chief Hoff requested, "Would you please put that down and bring me an adult-size line?"

Advanced fire on arrival. When the engine company encounters advanced fire on arrival, the high flow available from 2½-in. (65-mm) hose is needed for rapid control. Even a private dwelling may exhibit a fire condition heavy enough to warrant the quick knockdown power of the 2½-in. (65-mm) line. This is especially true of extensive involvement of the first floor or front porch.

Although using master stream appliances is not recommended for occupied residential buildings, the same cannot be said of 2½-in. (65-mm) hose. The 2½-in. (65-mm) line coupled with the 1⅛-in. (30-mm) smooth bore nozzle is a large-caliber weapon that is aggressive, mobile, and offensive. It can rapidly darken down a heavy fire condition to allow an interior attack. This permits three tactical options:

1. The 2½-in. (65-mm) hand line can be advanced into and through the structure.

2. The attack can transition to the use of a smaller line with the big line left where it is.

3. The 2½-in. (65-mm) line can be reduced down to a smaller line to press the interior attack for final extinguishment.

Defensive operations.
Whether operations are initially defensive or transition from offensive to defensive, smaller-caliber hand lines should not be used. The 2½-in. (65-mm) line is a much safer and more efficient alternative. The reach afforded by the larger line allows it to be operated from outside the collapse zone. Once its high-volume stream penetrates the fire area, it has a much greater effect on conditions than does a stream from a smaller line. The 2½-in. (65-mm) hand lines are much more mobile and easier to deploy than master stream devices. This allows streams to be brought to bear from a greater variety of locations.

Unable to determine extent (size) of fire area.
If the engine company officer is unable to determine the extent (size) of the fire area, use a 2½-in. (65-mm) line. The high-flow stream allows for unforeseen contingencies. During the course of operations, it may be determined that the amount of fire encountered can be handled with smaller hose. As with the above-mentioned private dwelling scenario, the 2½-in. (65-mm) hose can be reduced to, or replaced by, a smaller line.

Large, uncompartmented areas.
Fires in large, uncompartmented areas require levels of reach, penetration, and volume that are beyond the capabilities of smaller hand lines. In addition to wide-open floor plans, occupancies such as supermarkets, bowling alleys, warehouses, theaters, houses of worship, and the like often have high ceilings. High ceilings allow massive

amounts of heated fire gases to accumulate. Once these flammable vapors ignite, they may prove to be too formidable for streams from smaller lines. The reach and tremendous cooling power of the 2½-in. (65-mm) line with 1⅛-in. (30-mm) tip allows operation from an entranceway into the rolling flame front of combustible gases beneath the ceiling. Once the hazard in the fuel-laden overhead area has been contained, the attack can be pressed deeper into the structure's interior.

Tons of water.
At some fires, extinguishment simply requires tons of water. This is often the case for fires in piles of tires, junkyards, garbage dumps, and lumberyards, to name a few. A 2½-in. (65-mm) line with 1⅛-in. (30-mm) tip operating at 50 psi (350 kPa) NP discharges more than a ton of water a minute. The use of smaller lines in this kind of situation would be an exercise in futility.

Standpipe System Operations.
Proper consideration for members' safety demands the use of 2½-in. (65-mm) hose and smooth bore nozzles for standpipe operations. For many years, NFPA 14, the *Standard for Standpipe Systems*, was based on the use of 150 ft (45 m) of 2½-in. (65-mm) hose equipped with a 1⅛-in. (30-mm) smooth bore nozzle at a 65 psi (455 kPa) standpipe hose valve outlet pressure. Depending on which version of the standard a given standpipe system was designed under, outlet pressures can be either 65 psi (455 kPa) (pre-1993) or 100 psi (700 kPa) (post-1993). Outlet pressures such as these simply do not meet the friction loss requirements for smaller-diameter hose, especially in conjunction with 75-psi (525 kPa) or 100-psi (700 kPa) nozzles.

Many standpipe systems have pressure-reducing valves that are not field adjustable. This means that no matter what pressure fire department pumpers pump into the system, outlet pressure does not rise above a given outlet's rated pressure. Retired New York City Fire Department Deputy Chief John Norman[3] admonishes that to use anything other than 2½-in. (65-mm) hose and smooth-bore nozzles for standpipe operations is to misuse the standpipe system. Prior to becoming a member of the career fire service, Norman was a fire protection engineer and made his living designing sprinkler and standpipe systems.

Because of design configurations and conditions of standpipe systems, flow and pressure problems chronically plague operations. As stated by Fredericks, "A standpipe system is like a big black box which fire department Members did not design or install, do not maintain, and in most cases do not inspect or test yet Members expect to put water in one end and have it come out at the other end at the proper pressure and flow." Although certainly not an ideal situation, even at a low outlet pressure, the combination of 2½-in. (65-mm) hose and a 1⅛-in. (30-mm) smooth bore tip still can develop a usable fire stream.

In February 1991, the Philadelphia Fire Department had a disastrous experience dealing with a fire in the One Meridian Plaza building. At the time, the Philadelphia Fire Department used 1¾-in. (45-mm) hose and 100 psi (700 kPa) automatic fog nozzles for standpipe operations. Misadjusted standpipe hose valve pressures combined with the smaller hoseline size and pressure intensive automatic fog nozzles resulted in a weak stream with which to fight the large fire. Three firefighters were trapped in the building and killed. Firefighting forces were pulled from the building in anticipation of possible collapse; the fire consumed several floors until its upward progression was stopped by nine sprinkler heads in the partially sprinklered building.

METHODS OF FIRE ATTACK

FFII 6.3.2 For quite some time, firefighters have debated the various methods of applying a fire stream to attack a fire. Only one method existed by which to extinguish fire and that was to apply a solid stream of water directly to the burning solid fuels, commonly known as the "direct attack." This is one of several types of fire attack; it is described below along with three other types: the indirect, combination, and modified direct attack.

Indirect method of attack

Prior to World War II, direct attack was the long-established mainstay of the fire service. During the war Lloyd Layman, Chief of the Parkersburg Fire Department in West Virginia, became the commandant of the United States Coast Guard firefighting school. His duties included determining the best way of combating fuel oil fires in the confined below-deck spaces of ships. Toward this end he conducted extensive research and testing. A major part of his efforts consisted of a series live-fire tests aboard a decommissioned liberty ship.

Results of Layman's research and testing led to new theories about fire attack and eventually to the formulation of the **indirect method** of fire attack. He found that it was efficient to remotely inject a fog stream into an unoccupied compartment. To use this method, the space must be unoccupied, because it would rapidly become untenable upon the introduction of a fog stream. After the fog nozzle operates for a sufficient amount of time, it shuts down. The hatch through which the nozzle operated is then shut to preclude ventilation and confine the expanding steam. The steam is the major factor in extinguishment, through cooling as well as smothering. When water turns to steam, it expands by a ratio of 1700:1 (fig. 16–8). Water turns to steam at 212°F (100°C). Few fires only reach a maximum 212°F (100°C). What many people fail to realize is that at 1,000°F (538°C), a ceiling temperature easily reached at structure fires, the expansion ratio of water is 4,000:1.

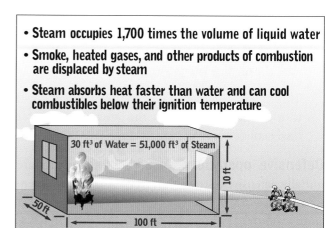

- Steam occupies 1,700 times the volume of liquid water
- Smoke, heated gases, and other products of combustion are displaced by steam
- Steam absorbs heat faster than water and can cool combustibles below their ignition temperature

30 ft³ of Water = 51,000 ft³ of Steam

Fig. 16–8. When water turns to steam it expands by a ration of 1700: 1.

At the war's end Layman resumed his peacetime career as the Parkersburg, West Virginia, fire chief. This is when he began to transfer what he had learned about the efficient extinguishment of shipboard fuel oil fires in unoccupied confined spaces to the suppression of interior structural fires (fig. 16–9). He did, however, maintain the following tenets for the use of the indirect attack for fires in buildings.

- First and foremost, there must be no life hazard within the fire compartment. The term **life hazard** includes both building occupants and fire department members. The application of the indirect method of attack rapidly destroys the thermal balance of the fire compartment, making it an environment both untenable and unsurvivable.

- The ceiling temperature must have reached at least 1,000°F to have an environment conducive to the efficient conversion of the water fog into steam to cool and smother the fire.

- The water fog must be remotely injected into the fire compartment from the exterior, preferably from a window. The fog stream is held in a fixed position, because it is directed into the overhead area of the fire compartment. The injection of water fog into the overhead area results in the fine water droplets, rapidly vaporizing and expanding, which destroys the thermal balance and pushes a high level of wet heat down to the floor. Avoid ventilation to keep the voluminous amounts of expanding steam necessary for efficient extinguishment within the fire compartment.

Layman emphasized that if any of the above-listed tenets could not be fulfilled, a direct attack on the fire is then the proper course of action.

Fig. 16–9. The indirect attack as described by Lloyd Layman

Combination method of attack

The **combination method** of attack was developed by Keith Royer and Floyd W. Nelson during numerous Iowa State University test fires in acquired structures. They expanded on Layman's work and deemed it more efficient to rotate the fog stream in a clockwise direction hitting the ceiling, walls, and floor. They also deemed it appropriate to inject the fog stream through either a window or a doorway. The reason that they stated that the nozzle be rotated in a clockwise manner is that during their many test fires they were able to observe that clockwise nozzle rotation pushed products of combustion and extinguishment away from the nozzle operator. Counterclockwise nozzle rotation, they observed, would draw products of combustion and extinguishment toward the nozzle operator (fig. 16–10).

Like Layman, Royer and Nelson maintained that there must be no life hazard within the fire compartment

(again referring to building occupants as well as department members). They also stated that ventilation should be as limited as possible to confine the massive amounts of steam generated by the combination attack to the fire compartment. As with the indirect attack, the combination method of attack required a ceiling temperature of a minimum of 1,000°F (538°C) to take advantage of water's expansion ratio of 4,000:1 at that temperature. Also, like Layman, they maintained that if the aforementioned parameters did not exist, a direct attack on the fire would be the best course of action.

Fig. 16–10. The combination method of attack requires a fog stream injected through a door or window and rotated clockwise to push products of combustion away from the nozzle operator.

Direct method of attack

The **direct method** of attack is simply the application of a solid stream or a straight stream directly on the burning solid fuels (fig. 16–11). This type of attack is used when the fire is relatively small: a single object or a small number of objects are burning and can be easily extinguished by applying the water directly on the burning materials. When several objects or an entire compartment is on fire, then the modified direct attack (described below) is called for.

Larger metropolitan fire departments have a long tradition of aggressive interior direct attack of structural fires. This is because they are most often tasked with the protection of a high life hazard in the form of dense concentrations of people in large buildings. Experience has proved time and again that the best way to protect life is to put out the fire in the most expeditious manner. Once the fire is extinguished, every other fireground activity (entry, laddering, search, rescue, removal, ventilation, etc.) can be performed more safely and efficiently. This results in greatly enhanced probabilities of safe outcomes for both building occupants and operating members.

Prior to the widespread use of breathing apparatus, evidence of the use of such aggressive tactics at more arduous fires was the presence of numerous members prostrate on the sidewalk and incapacitated because of smoke inhalation. It was realized that this risk was worth taking because of the likely reward of saving many lives and thus fulfilling the fire service's custodianship of the populace.

During and after the development of the indirect and combination methods of attack, most large fire departments never varied from their tried and true tactics of aggressive interior direct fire attack coupled with aggressive natural ventilation and aggressive primary search. With the advent and consequent widespread use of more efficient, user-friendly breathing apparatus, many smaller fire departments began to emulate the aggressive interior tactics of larger urban departments.

Along with this seemingly positive development came efforts by many to press into service for interior operations the indirect and combination methods of fire attack. The indirect and combination methods of attack are basically exterior or defensive operations. Combining defensive tactics with offensive interior operations is normally dangerous and counterproductive. Always keep in mind that Layman, Royer, and Nelson—the creators of the indirect and combination methods of attack—strongly stated that the indirect and combination methods should not be employed if a life hazard exists within the fire compartment. Even if the building is unoccupied prior to the arrival of the fire department, once members enter the building to operate, a life hazard exists in the building.

The foremost mission of the fire service is to protect life, which is why operating members enter burning buildings, plain and simple. Because the paramount mission of the fire service is to save life, members must make extreme efforts to access the area of the building near the seat of the fire. That is the area where victims are in the most extreme peril. All efforts must be made by engine company members to aggressively push the initial attack line in to extinguish the seat of the fire. All efforts must also be made by ladder company members to aggressively vent, enter, and search the building as near to the seat of the fire as possible. The parameters set forth earlier indicate a method of fire attack appropriate to deal with

the life hazards of occupied buildings. A major facet is that it allows members to enter fire compartments for extinguishment, ventilation, and search. In conjunction, the chosen method of fire attack should be that which does the most to preserve the thermal balance of the fire compartment as well as to first preserve and the expediently improve the tenability of the fire occupancy.

Aggressive interior direct attack coupled with aggressive natural ventilation is best tactic for expediently improving the tenability of a fire compartment without compromising thermal balance. Combined with aggressive primary search, this is the operational doctrine that most greatly enhances the probabilities of survival for both victims and operating members. The synergistic effect of simultaneous operations, a combined arms approach if you will, allows the fire service to most completely fulfill its custodianship of the public's safety.

Fig. 16–11. A direct attack procedure

Modified direct method of attack

The **modified direct method** is a two step attack: the application of a solid stream or a straight stream is directed into the overhead area (the first step), out front ahead of the nozzle team. The nozzle must be moved vigorously in a clockwise or side-to-side motion, splattering the stream against the ceiling and upper walls. Breaking the stream up in this way causes large chunks of water to rain down all over the fire area, finding the seat of the fire in the burning solid fuels. The stream is then directed on to the burning solid objects in the room (the second step) to achieve knockdown and extinguishment. (If the stream was to be applied first directly onto the large group of burning solid fuels it would very likely forcefully push fire ahead of itself, into and then up a wall, then sending it rolling back across the ceiling above the heads of the nozzle team.)

It should be noted that some texts refer to the modified direct attack as a "combination attack." This is historically incorrect; the combination attack involves the use of a circling fog stream in an uninhabited compartment, as described above.

Applying the stream first into the overhead area simultaneously does two things. It cools the superheated area near the ceiling where flashover and other rapid fire progress phenomena are born while also dropping water down onto the burning solid fuels. The application of water onto the burning solid fuels quenches the fire at its source, the fuel-flame interface, and quells the production of flammable vapors.

All four methods of interior structural fire attack will accomplish extinguishment. However, only two of the four methods of attack are in keeping with the life-saving operational doctrine which places operating members in the fire compartment to perform extinguishment and primary search often in close proximity to the seat of the fire. The methods of attack that are most conducive to supporting this doctrine of operation is the direct attack and the modified direct attack.

FIRE STREAM TYPES

FFI 5.3.10 All three stream types (solid, straight, and fog) accomplish extinguishment when applied for sufficient duration and in sufficient volume that meet or surpasses the critical flow rate. In the case of fog streams, however, prior to extinguishment, conditions in the fire area—especially in the fire compartment itself—first worsen before finally improving. Upon initial application of the fog stream, scalding steam is produced because of a large degree of premature vaporization of the water fog. This excessive steam generation destroys the thermal balance of the fire compartment. As a result floor level temperatures increase and visibility is reduced. In addition to the quantitative increase of the heat at floor level, there is also a qualitative change in the heat. Because of excessive steam generation, conditions at floor level change from dry to wet heat, further multiplying the debilitating effects to firefighters and fire victims. All these factors lead to the existence of a period of decreased tenability between the time of first water application and the time of extinguishment and ventilation of the products of combustion and extinguishment (flame, heat, smoke, gases, steam, and air movement). This decreased tenability can be inadvertently caused when using a straight stream on a fog nozzle and changing the pattern to a fog while firefighters are in the fire area.

Much discussion revolves around the tenability of conditions within the fire compartment at floor level.

This is because the floor level is where members operate and more importantly where victims wait to be rescued, unprotected and vulnerable. The potential to save human life is the major motivating factor that compels members to go into burning buildings in the first place. Hence, the fire service must focus attention on how its operations either increase or decrease the window of survivability in the area where human life is expected to exist.

This text also touches on the concept of products of combustion and extinguishment. Products of combustion, as well as the various methods by which to combat combustion, have differing consequences. Each method of fire attack and each type of fire stream affects the tenability of the environment in the fire compartment differently. Products of extinguishment include steam generation, air movement, visibility reduction, and temperature change. Hence, members of the fire service must be aware that the choices of method of fire attack and type of fire stream significantly affect the probabilities of survival for the civilians they vowed to protect from fire.

The amount of air, fire gases, and smoke pushed ahead of a fog stream is so voluminous that it quickly overwhelms the likely ventilation openings ahead of the nozzle in a residential setting (e.g., windows). Only so much product of combustion and extinguishment can be forced through the window(s) at any given moment. The significant portion of products that cannot be vented when forcefully pushed forward by the fog stream then impact the wall surface and roll back over and around the nozzle team. This phenomenon has been observed in innumerable building fires and tested at the Rockland County, NY Fire Training Center. The phenomenon known as **fog nozzle ricochet** is a major contributor to the destruction of thermal balance, excessive steam generation and accumulation, and loss of tenability. This phenomenon is not caused by a fog nozzle, but by the untrained use of a **fog stream**.

Another attribute of a hose stream that greatly affects both speed of extinguishment and member safety is the reach of the stream. A stream with greater reach allows members to apply water to the seat of the fire sooner and from a greater distance than does a stream of lesser reach. Ability to engage the fire sooner leads to quicker extinguishment and hence greater overall safety for everyone on the fireground. The greater distance also enhances safety; members need not be in as close a proximity to the seat of the fire to initiate extinguishment. The closer the nozzle team must approach the fire to initiate and accomplish extinguishment, the greater the compromise to their safety (fig. 16–12). A close approach to the fire in order to achieve extinguishment is dictated by the limited reach of a fog stream (the wider the fog, the closer that you have to get to the fire to extinguish it).

Fig. 16–12. A rather graphic illustration of the limited reach of a fog stream.

The superior efficiency and efficacy of solid streams versus fog streams is further evidenced in tests performed by William Clark, former FDNY battalion chief and director of Wisconsin's fire training programs. Clark's test results showed that at equal flow rates and with equal fuel loads:

- Solid stream extinguished the fire faster than did the fog stream.

- Solid stream required less total water to achieve extinguishment than did the fog stream.

- Solid stream led to less measurable runoff water than the fog stream.

Thus, it is not a great leap in logic to conclude that a solid stream applied at a high rate of flow causes flame, heat, smoke, and gas production to cease in the shortest amount of time, accomplished by using the least amount of water. Thus, the solid stream is the most efficient and effective in the limiting of property damage caused by fire, smoke, and water. Far more important, however, is the fact that it is the most effective, efficient, and expedient method for the fire department to attack and kill a dynamic, out of control, untenable physical phenomenon that is threatening the lives of victims. In this manner fire department operations return the environment to nonthreatening equilibrium in the shortest possible amount of time and preserve to the greatest degree any savable human life.

ADVANCING THE CHARGED LINE

FF1 5.3.10 The efficiency and effectiveness of the advancement of the charged line is in no small way determined by the efficiency with which the dry hoseline is stretched and flaked prior to charging. A major factor in the efficiency of stretching is determined much prior to arrival at the fire building. Engine company apparatus design directly effects the proficiency with which engine company members can stretch and use fire hose. An apparatus design that highlights user-friendly attack hosebeds greatly facilitates the performance of the engine company's primary function, its reason for existence, the stretching, advancing, and use of fire hose to kill fire. User-friendly attack hosebeds are low enough so that even the shortest member of the fire department can reach the top layer of hose in the attack hose load while standing on the ground. They also provide ample room for sufficient lengths of hose to make up static attack hose loads capable of covering the distances of any foreseeable stretch in the response area. Static loads also allow the supply line and the attack line to, in effect, simultaneously stretch via the backstretch as opposed to supply and attack lines stretched sequentially with preconnected attack lines. This also has the advantage of placing the apparatus where the pump is most efficient: at the hydrant. This type of hose load is best situated in a section of the main, or rear, hosebed (fig. 16–13).

Fig. 16–13. A bed of supply hose on the left and three beds of static attack hose loads. Static loads are not preconnected and are also known as dead loads. (Photo by Jay Comella)

In addition to apparatus design, policy makers determine the degrees of efficiency, effectiveness, and safety with which engine company members are able to perform their lifesaving function is through the levels of company staffing deemed adequate to protect the public from fire. The quantity and quality of well trained members in a company has an extremely significant effect on the outcome of the company's operation and by extension the outcome of the entire fireground operation. A successful outcome of a fire department operation equates to lives and property saved. Unsuccessful outcomes of fire department operations result in the loss of life and property that was salvageable upon arrival. Fire departments able to stop the shrinking of staffing at six members per company should be emulated in this respect. Company staffing directly relates to the efficiency of the work performed as well as death and injury rates in the fire service. Personnel is a fire department's most valuable commodity regarding mission capability.

Over the years staffing levels have shrunk in many departments as the budget axe has fallen time and time again. Governmental entities that have repeatedly tasked fire departments to do more with less have effectively increased the risks of injury and death to both department members and the citizens they are sworn to protect. In light of this negative external influence, the fire service's traditional organizational mind-set must change. Long accepted practice in many departments has been for engine companies to compete to get first water on the fire. The approach to a company's role within the entire fireground operation must change so that engine companies work in concert with one another, rather than in competition. Sufficient personnel must be committed to getting the first line to the seat of the fire before addressing the deployment of additional lines. Attack lines are best stretched in series, not in parallel. Even the better staffed, forward thinking departments take the approach that all but the simplest hose stretches or advances are, at a minimum, two-company evolutions.

POSITIONS ON THE LINE

Engine company officer

FFI 5.3.10 Ideally, if staffing levels allow, the engine company officer should not physically take part in handling the line. The officer bears overall responsibility for the operations of the company and member safety. Staffing levels that allow the engine company officer to be a true supervisor positively affect the highest order on the efficiency, effectiveness, and safety of engine company operations. By remaining physically uninvolved in the operation, the officer is better able to

direct it. The officer must be able to avoid the potential tunnel vision when tied into the line and assisting with its movement. The officer's proper position is to the side of the line and opposite the nozzle operator. It is important that the officer is at the point of attack to observe and experience conditions as they are encountered by company members.

When unencumbered by the need to perform the physical labor of moving the hoseline, the officer is at liberty to move out ahead of engine company members to perform reconnaissance regarding the fire's location and nature. This in turn provides the information needed to perform the following:

- Properly direct members to the correct route to the fire, the size of line needed, the number of lengths sufficient to cover the entire fire area.

- Ascertain forcible-entry problems and life hazard.

- Perform search prior to arrival of line to the extent allowed by fire conditions.

- Confine fire by closing door if possible.

Confirming, to the extent possible, the location of the fire is necessary prior to initiating the hoseline stretch. Failure to do so can lead to many unwarranted mistakes:

- Stretching short

- Stretching long

- Stretching to the wrong location on the fire floor

- Stretching to the wrong floor

- Stretching via the wrong stair well

- Even stretching into the wrong building

The consequences of stretching short are obvious: failing to reach the seat of the fire. It is often wise to include one or two extra lengths in one's hose stretch estimate to err on the side of caution. However, realize that as the amount of excess hose increases, the difficulty in managing the hoseline and the potential for kinks also increases. Kinks in the hoseline lead to significantly reduced water flow. Stretching long can also lead to unduly high pump pressures.

Ensure that all doors through which the line is stretched and advanced are positively cocked open. A door closing on the line can severely hamper the stretch and/or advance, sometimes with dire consequences. This is especially true if the door closes over a dry line that is then charged while it is under the door. The door becomes, in effect, a hose clamp and little or no water gets to the nozzle. The charged line becomes an effective door chock that secures the door in the closed position. Those caught on the wrong side of the door in this situation are definitely in dire straits. As is so often the case, in fire department operations, the devil is in the details. The use of an inexpensive wooden wedge properly positioned to securely chock the door in the open position can quite literally mean the difference between life and death. Shakespeare addressed the importance of paying attention to detail thusly, "For want of a nail the shoe was lost. For want of a shoe the horse was lost. For want of a horse the battle was lost."

Hose should be stretched dry as far as is safely possible to avoid expending time and energy on undue labor. The hoseline must be charged before entering the fire area or that which may rapidly become the fire area. Prior to the line being charged, sufficient dry hose must be properly **flaked out** at the entrance to the fire area. Properly flaked hose is laid out so that the bights in the line are open enough to have the least propensity for **kinking** (fig. 16–14). The fire is often referred to as the enemy and the fire building as the battleground. The logical extension of this line of logic is that kinks are collaborators. Kinks rob valuable amounts of water flow from the attack hose stream. It is the duty of all personnel to remove kinks whenever they are found. Removing kinks is such an important consideration that it is responsibility of all personnel on the fireground, whether engine company or ladder company members, the newest probie or the chief of the department (fig. 16–15).

Fig. 16–14. Properly flaked hose greatly lessens the propensity for kinking.

The pump operator must be notified to charge the line only after it has been properly stretched and flaked out. To do so any earlier invariably increases the time necessary to get water on the fire. Whenever a hoseline is prematurely charged, the labor and time involved in advancing the line and removing the kinks increases dramatically.

Fig. 16–15. Kinked lines prevent maximum flow of water to the fire.

Prior to entering the fire area, bleed entrapped air from the charged line (fig. 16–16). The nozzle must be opened fully to ensure the attack line is supplied with sufficient water flow and pressure before commencing the attack. This is known as **bleeding the line**. At this juncture more than any other, the engine company truly reaps the benefits of having an officer in a purely supervisory role, free to coach, guide, and direct the members through prompt extinguishment and also be a custodian for their safety throughout the process.

Fig. 16–16. Nozzle operators should bleed the charged line prior to entering the fire area.

The officer must strive for the utmost possible awareness of conditions as the company prepares to enter the fire area and throughout the advancement of the line and extinguishment of the fire. Although senses are severely muted, the officer must make use of what little sensory input he or she is afforded. After advancement into the fire area begins, smell is negated with the donning of the self-contained breathing apparatus (SCBA) facepiece. Hearing can be affected by a cacophony of competing fireground noises. Sense of sight is severely diminished in most cases because of voluminous, thick, black smoke. Perhaps most damning is the fact that the total embunkerment of today's fire service severely dulls one's sense of feel and the ability to gauge temperature or increases in temperature.

Important audible stimuli that compete with other fireground noises include victims' muffled coughs, moans, and cries for help; crackling fire; falling or collapsing construction material; breaking glass; forcible-entry procedures; and operating saws. All these things give clues about the conditions that exist, how conditions may change, and how operations should be conducted. All this aural input must be constantly received and analyzed while the officer concurrently maintains the ability to continually monitor the handheld radio for vital communications. The remote microphone/speaker is an invaluable tool for tactical fireground communications.

Smoke impairs an officer's sight while advancing through the fire area. The most significant visual input to consider may, in fact, be that there is no visual input. Prior to entering the fire area, while observing the smoke issuing from it, may be the last opportunity to visually analyze conditions.

The personal protective equipment of today's operating forces has significantly curtailed the ability to feel the level of heat and discern rapid increases in heat in the operating environment. Prior to this development, the ability to receive this physical stimulus on one's skin from the environment was the gauge by which many veteran members of the fire service determined how and how long they could operate in a given environment. The time between feeling a painful heat stimulus and being able to remove oneself from the environment or take action to improve it is called **alarm time**. As the insulation from the environmental heat stimulus increases, the environmental temperature at which one feels heat inside the protective envelope also increases. This delay in becoming aware of high heat decreases alarm time, the window of opportunity one has to improve the chance to avert a catastrophic outcome.

Significant reconnaissance can be gained if the door to the fire area is open and conditions allow approach to the doorway without water application. At floor level one may be able to look under the smoke layer to ascertain the layout of the occupancy, location of victims, location of fire, and presence of potential obstacles in the path of the advancing line. Sweeping the beam of one's hands-free, forward-facing hand light under the smoke layer will aid immensely in this task (this is covered in greater detail in chapter 19, Search and Rescue). Of course, severe conditions warrant immediate stream application. Once the stream is operating, however, visibility is likely nil, even at floor level.

If the door to the fire area is closed, ensure the nozzle team is low and to the side of the doorway. The side of the doorway that is chosen will depend on a number of factors including the expected layout of the fire compartment, the layout of the area outside the entrance to the fire compartment, which way the door swings, and so forth. The nozzle team should be at an angle relative to the doorway that allows stream application, if necessary, when the door is opened.

The door can be opened once the nozzle team is ready with ample charged and bled line and forcible-entry issues have been addressed (fig. 16–17). The nozzle operator must be ready to flow water if conditions dictate. If a fog nozzle is being used it must be adjusted to the straight stream pattern. If possible take a few seconds to **stay low and let it blow**. It is beneficial to pause the operation briefly while the energy behind the pressurized, venting products of combustion diminishes somewhat. This is a wiser choice than occupying the doorway as soon as it is opened and being in the path of whatever may vent through it. The doorway used for access of the initial attack hand line may be the first ventilation opening to which the fire has access. The initial amount and pressure of the products of combustion that vent through this opening can be significant, and it is unwise to be directly in their path of travel. Of course, if fire venting through the doorway threatens members' position, immediately meet it with copious water from the hand line. If conditions allow a brief delay in water application, a quick look under the smoke layer reaps information beneficial to the operation.

Fig. 16–17. The nozzle team's position at a doorway prior to entering the fire area is critical for a successful operation.

In the past most members of the fire service were drilled with the mantra, "Don't open the nozzle until you see fire, never put water on smoke." This was fine back when dictum came into being. It was consistent with the type of fire and smoke conditions normally encountered during that time period. With the advent and proliferation of plastics, the amount and type of smoke has drastically changed. At many fires one cannot depend on seeing the fire at all, in which case it is common to use heat to indicate when to open the nozzle. The advent of full personal protective equipment negated that tactic. Now when a member feels heat it may be too late to open the nozzle in time to avoid burn injury. In the modern fire environment, the prudent method of determining when to open the line is to do so based on observation of the smoke condition before becoming immersed in its blinding cloak.

Prior to entering the fire area, the smoke condition must be rapidly observed and analyzed. Thick black smoke is heavily laden with unburned fuel. A compartment whose volume is full or nearly filled with thick black smoke contains a lot of ignitable fuel. Rapidly moving smoke is under pressure, a result of heat in the fire compartment; the higher the heat, the higher the pressure. Thick, black, rapidly moving smoke is a mixture of heat and fuel that only needs oxygen to complete the fire triangle. A fire compartment disgorging a heavy volume of thick, black, pressurized, **angry smoke** may contain black fire, which may also light up (cause rapid fire growth). If smoke conditions at the entrance to the fire occupancy are light enough to not indicate a potential rapid fire progress event, the line can be advanced, without flowing water, until either the fire is found or conditions indicate the need for stream application. Once fire is visually located, or angry smoke conditions are encountered, the nozzle must be opened to begin gaining control of the environment and improving conditions (fig. 16–18).

Fig. 16–18. Angry, black smoke usually indicates unburned fuel which could ignite within the fire compartment.

Let the water do the work. Long before members are ever close to the enemy, decide on proper weapons configuration and selection to ensure they are armed with a powerful, long-reaching, high-volume, hard-hitting attack stream. Open the nozzle as soon as the stream can affect conditions. Members need not be in the close proximity to the seat of the fire required by the short reach of a fog stream. The long reach of a solid or straight stream allows extinguishment to begin sooner and from a farther distance than does the short reach of fog streams. The time and distance aspects associated with solid streams are both factors in increasing the safety of operating members. Even when stream application is at an obtuse angle to the doorway of a room involved in fire, as when approaching the doorway from down a hallway, getting water into that room begins to improve conditions. It is unnecessary to wait until the members of the nozzle team are in the doorway to start getting water into the fire area (fig. 16–19).

If, on opening the doorway to the fire compartment or approaching the open doorway, a voluminous and angry smoke condition is indicative of a rapidly deteriorating environment, copious amounts of water from the nozzle must be swept back and forth across the ceiling out front and ahead of the nozzle team. A fire exhibiting such characteristics is an ominously volatile environment. The smoke is a large quantity of superheated fuel seeking enough oxygen to become ignitable. Members cannot afford to give any concern in this situation to the outdated cliché, "Don't put water on smoke." In these circumstances the characteristics of modern fuel loading (plastics) and the effects of tight building syndrome are likely combining to create a **black fire** scenario. Without any visual indicators, black fire has the potential to instantaneously transition into flashover. Water kills flashover. The tool to improve the environment is literally at the nozzle operator's fingertips. For members who have had both visual and heat sensing capabilities taken away, it is highly imprudent to push into this environment without preparing it to have a higher degree of human survivability. Sweeping the ceiling with copious amounts of water out front and overhead through the superheated fuel–laden smoke serves to sever the chain reaction of rapid fire development through the cooling effect of the stream.

The phrase concerning stream application, "sweep the ceiling with copious amounts of water," is purposefully used to convey the need for adequate water to kill the potential for flashover. Another phrase, "pencil the ceiling with the stream," has widespread exposure in the fire service. **Penciling** has numerous interpretations, one of which is to use limited amounts of water for short durations to delay flashover. When restoring control to an out-of-control environment at a building fire, the goal should not be to delay flashover or to cool fire gases just enough to hold conditions back from crossing the threshold of rapid fire progress phenomena. The greatest contributions an engine company can make to protecting the most savable human life in the shortest amount of time are bringing the highest practicable flow rate to the fire at the earliest opportunity and continuing stream application until extinguishment.

Fig. 16–19. A long stream applied to a fire area allows extinguishment to begin sooner and from a farther distance.

Once water has been applied to the overhead area of the fire compartment, the stream should be swept across the floor prior to advancing any farther (fig. 16–20). This is necessary to cool the scalding runoff created by applying water into the superheated upper areas of the fire compartment where temperatures can exceed 2,000°F (1,093°C). In a further attempt to reduce the potential for knee burns, members must advance so the knees are not in contact with the floor. If this is unfeasible, members must limit the time that knees are in contact with the floor by frequently raising them from the floor to interrupt heating. Knee injuries occur, even through bunker pants, because the insulating layer of the pants becomes thinner as it stretches and compresses when kneeling. Sweeping the deck with the stream can also blow debris out of the path of advance. This can include a wide range of things from hypodermic needles to all manner of feces. It is important to pay attention to the sound of the stream sweeping the floor. If it becomes quieter, there may not be any floor ahead of the nozzle team. There may be hole or an open stairway.

Fig. 16–20. Sweeping the floor with the water stream prior to applying it to the burning objects in the room (for final knockdown and extinguishment) removes debris from the path of the advancing nozzle team.

While engaged in active fire-suppression, the bale of the nozzle should be in one of two positions: either fully open or fully closed. Many fires can be extinguished with the hit and move technique, where the line is operated from a static position and then briefly shut down to ease advancement. However, fires of greater magnitude and/or intensity require the cooling power of a continuously operating stream throughout the advance. Small incipient fires can be extinguished with the bale cracked partially open.

Nozzle operator

FF1 5.3.10 During the stretch the nozzle operator ensures sufficient lengths of dry hose cover the entire fire area are near the entrance to the fire area (fig. 16–21). This is always a minimum of 50 ft (15 m), or one length of line. The nozzle operator is responsible for carrying one folded length, often called the **working length** to the **drop point**. The drop point is the point near the entrance to the fire area where the working length is flaked out so that slack line can be advanced into the fire area. If more than one length of line is required to cover the fire area, it may or may not be carried by the nozzle operator. However, the nozzle operator must ensure that all necessary slack hose is flaked out as near as possible to the fire area entrance. Having sufficient slack line to cover the entire fire area prior to the advance pays off in the proficiency with which nozzle team advances through and extinguish the fire.

Fig. 16–21. The nozzle operator must ensure that sufficient lengths of dry hose reaches the entrance to the fire area.

The nozzle bale should be a slightly bent arm's reach out in front of the nozzle operator. The line should be on the side of the nozzle operator's dominant arm; however, there is a school of thought that the line should always be on one's right side because of the direction a burst length tends to rotate. Being on the dominant side puts the dominant arm to the rear, and this arm does the bulk of the labor in holding the line. For ease of explanation, further description refers to a right-handed nozzle operator.

The forward, or left, hand controls flow and directs the stream. The forward hand operates the bale (fig. 16–22a). Once the bale has been operated, the hand moves to the hose behind the last male hose butt. The hand must be in an underhand position on the hose (fig. 16–22b). This is the position from which the stream is directed by the forward hand. If the hand were to be left on the bale, nozzle, or hose butt, a hard-to-control kink would likely develop behind the hose butt. A further negative aspect of leaving one's hand on the bale is the likelihood of partially closing the bale and reducing flow. If the hand is placed on the hose in an overhand manner, there is great likelihood of forcing an unwieldy kink into the line behind the forward hand.

The rear arm creates the nozzle operator's stable base of control for the line. The line must be placed well up into the armpit of the rear arm and clamped against the body. Although still using one's hands to grip the hose, this method also brings into play the larger muscles of the chest, shoulder, and back. This staves off muscle fatigue longer than only depending on the smaller weaker muscles of the hands. Although not appropriate for all body types, some nozzle operators attain and maintain a position in which the rear knee is up off the ground all or most of the time. If the knee is kept up high enough, the inner thigh can be used to help clamp the hoseline against the body. Using the leg for this brings yet larger

muscles and increased leverage into play to achieve rock solid control of the nozzle.

Fig. 16–22a. The nozzle operator's forward hand operates the bale.

Fig. 16–22b. Once the bale is operated, the forward hand should be placed under the hose behind the last hose butt.

Prior to operating the nozzle, the nozzle operator must expect that when the nozzle is opened up, reaction force must be overcome. The body must be in an attitude that reflects this. He should be leaning forward into the direction from which the nozzle reaction force will come, with the upper body positioned so the spine's angle roughly mimics that of the hoseline. In this manner the body is ready to receive, absorb, and overcome the nozzle reaction force once the line begins to operate.

In any fire that is past the incipient stage, advancing the hoseline takes members into a volatile high-heat environment. Members must be able to advance the line while operating in the lowest portion of the fire compartment (i.e., floor level). Using a solid stream maintains the thermal balance and preserves the floor area as the coolest portion of the fire compartment. Down on the deck is the safest place to be in the fire compartment should any rapid fire progress event occur.

The classic duck walking method keeps one low and keeps one's knees off the floor (fig. 16–23). However, this can be an awkward position to maintain and may not be the most efficient for achieving forward momentum. Some variation of the duck walk where one or both knees touch the floor at intervals may be more efficient. It is important to avoid having both knees on the floor all, or even a significant amount, of the time. Not only does it place one at a higher risk for knee burn injuries, but it is also harder to achieve both forward momentum and traction. It is also an unstable body position. To be on one's knees is to place oneself in a subservient position.

It is also important to ensure that the part of the foot in contact with the floor is the bottom of the foot, chiefly the toes and the ball of the foot. Some people end up on their knees with the tops of their feet in contact with the floor. This is a weak and unstable position and should be avoided. It is amazing how much more muscle mass can be brought into play when the bottom of the foot is used. It provides far greater traction, power, and stability.

Fig. 16–23. The classic duck walk keeps firefighters low and their knees off the floor.

While engaged in active fire-suppression, the nozzle bale should be in one of two positions: fully open or fully closed. Many fires can be extinguished with the hit and move technique where the line is operated from a static position and briefly shut down to ease advancement. However, fires of greater magnitude and/or intensity require the cooling power of a continuously operating stream throughout the advance. Small incipient fires can be extinguished with the bale cracked partially open.

During most of the advance, the stream should be directed outward and upward at an angle such that water is applied to the overhead area well ahead of the nozzle team. Sweeping side to side or rotating in a clockwise direction are the best patterns of nozzle movement (figs. 16–24a, 16–24b, 16–24c, and 16–24d). The nozzle must be moved in a rapid vigorous manner to physically distribute the water in the form of large drops by splattering the stream off the ceiling and upper walls (figs. 16–25a, 16–25b, 16–25c, and 16–25d). Using the nozzle in this manner is the most efficient for extinguishment, and it also has the tertiary benefit of lessening the reaction force burden that the nozzle operator must bear. If the stream were horizontal, the nozzle operator would receive the full reaction force burden. As the stream is angled upward from the horizontal, a greater and greater portion of the reaction force is directed into the deck. When the nozzle is moved vigorously to break up the stream, it significantly diffuses the energy of the reaction force.

Once the overhead has been cooled, the stream is applied directly onto the burning objects in the room to achieve final extinguishment . This is the modified direct attack.

Fig. 16–24a, b, c, d. The clockwise pattern of stream application is the most efficient method for extinguishment, and lessens the burden on the nozzle operator.

Fig. 16–25a, b, c, d. Rapidly moving the stream pattern side to side off the ceiling helps distribute water droplets to the fire area.

Backup position

FFI 5.3.10 In comparing the nozzle team to a vessel, the nozzle operator is the pilot and the backup is the engine room. The **backup position** does the lion's share of the physical labor and provides the bulk of the momentum to the nozzle team.

The backup person must be on the same side of the line as the nozzle operator (fig. 16–26). Backup should be like a tractor motor: always in low gear and always providing momentum to the nozzle operator without pushing him or her faster than he or she wants to go. The nozzle operator is an effective heat shield for the backup position and may become aware of extreme temperatures before the backup does. The nozzle operator may also become aware of holes in the floor or other obstructions before the backup position.

Fig. 16–26. The backup position does most of the physical labor in the nozzle team, and provides the bulk of the momentum.

The goal of the backup position should be to make the nozzle operator's job as easy as possible. Ideally, the nozzle operator should only have to think about operating the bale and directing the stream. To relieve the nozzle operator of the bulk of the reaction force burden, the backup must physically back up the nozzle operator. The backup must attempt to maintain physical contact with the nozzle operator throughout the advance and extinguishment. Through physical contact between the nozzle operator and the backup position, the bulk of the reaction force burden is transferred through the nozzle operator's body to the backup.

Another goal of a good backup is to keep the line straight behind the nozzle operator. Keeping the line straight helps make dealing with the reaction force manageable. The backup achieves this by treating the line as the first 5–8 ft (1.5–2.4 m) of hoseline behind the nozzle is a straight piece of pipe. Working together to move this section of line as if it were a straight piece of pipe, the nozzle operator and the backup person should be able to prevent any kinks directly behind the nozzle operator. Any bends in the line should occur behind the backup position. If the line bends between the nozzle operator and the backup, the nozzle operator's job gets much tougher (fig. 16–27).

Fig. 16–27. The backup position should keep a straight line behind the nozzle operator, moving the section like a straight piece of pipe.

The fact that the stream is predominantly directed outward and upward dictates that the hose usually trails from the nozzle at a downward angle. The hose trailing from behind the nozzle operator's armpit also naturally falls at a downward angle. While providing forward momentum, the backup position must also maintain the line's natural downward inclination. Many inexperienced backup people lift up the line behind the nozzle operator (fig. 16–28). This may make it easier for the backup, but it definitely makes things tougher on the nozzle operator. Lifting the line up behind the nozzle operator tends to force the nozzle tip down, making it harder to direct the stream into the overhead where it is needed for efficient extinguishment. Lifting the line while the nozzle is pointed upward also forces a bend into the line directly behind the nozzle operator, making it more difficult to deal with the nozzle reaction force.

Fig. 16–28. The backup firefighter should not lift the hose behind the nozzle operator.

The backup position takes a grip on the line so that the forward hand is underhand and the rear hand is overhand (fig. 16–29). The backup grabs the line where it naturally falls, at downward angle from the rear of the nozzle operator. After the forward hand is wrapped around the line, it is slid up the line fast and hard to make positive contact with the nozzle operator. This brings the forward forearm into contact with the nozzle operator. Leaning forward then brings the shoulder into contact with the back or trailing side of the nozzle operator, further solidifying physical contact. As forward movement occurs, space between the two bodies slightly fluctuates. Simultaneously, at a minimum the backup's forearm must stay in contact with the nozzle operator to physically provide momentum. Depending on the backup's body position, the rear hand can pull the line in against the leg. This applies friction to the line to assist with gripping the line.

Fig. 16–29. The correct position for the backup firefighter behind the nozzle operator.

The backup must be in a low compact position. The downward angle of the line behind the nozzle operator dictates that if the backup can attain and maintain a body position lower than that of the nozzle operator, it benefits the biomechanical efficiency of the operation.

The backup position needs to apply force outward and upward along an angle approximating that of the hoseline and through the body of the nozzle operator, as if trying to push forward a piece of pipe that is screwed into the base of the nozzle. He or she should face forward with eyes scanning to monitor whatever visual clues exist regarding conditions ahead of and around the nozzle team. The backup should lean into the direction needed to apply force, with the spine approximating the angle of the hoseline. The nozzle operator and the backup drive forward with the hoseline, focusing their energy outward along an upward angle similar to the way that football players drive a blocking sled or the way in which rugby players provide motive power to a scrummage.

The backup position is the engine room of the nozzle team. The power plant truly resides in the muscles of his lower body. To make efficient use of the calves, thighs, and gluteus he or she must push off of the floor with the bottoms of his feet. Having the tops of the feet in contact with the floor effectively negates a significant amount of the potential to harness the power of the muscles of the lower body.

If the nozzle operator needs to direct the stream horizontally or downward, the backup can facilitate this by raising the line accordingly so that the first section of hose, from behind the nozzle to behind the backup, is maintained in a straight line (fig. 16–30). If the nozzle operator turns to the left the backup's movement must swing through a wider faster arc. This is so that as the nozzle is turning to the left the hose behind it will move correspondingly to the right to avoid the occurrence of any bends directly behind the nozzle operator (fig. 16–31). If the nozzle operator turns to the right the backup's movement must swing through a wider faster arc. This is so that as the nozzle is turning to the right the hose behind it will move correspondingly to the left to avoid the occurrence of any bends directly behind the nozzle operator (fig. 16–32). If the two members are working in concert as if to move a straight piece of pipe, there will be no bends between them.

Fig. 16–30. As the backup firefighter lifts the hose, the nozzle operator can direct the stream downward.

Fig. 16–31. As the nozzle moves to the left, the back-up firefighter moves the hose to the right.

Fig. 16–32. As the nozzle moves to the right, the backup firefighter moves the hose to the left.

Door position

FFI 5.3.10 Although perhaps not apparent, one of the most important positions on the attack hoseline is that of the door position. The **door position** has two primary responsibilities: to ensure the smooth and sustained movement of hose to the set of the fire and to eliminate any kinks in the hoseline. This is a critical firefighting position that ensures the hoseline is not be starved of water because of a kink and is not hung up under a door or caught on some obstruction. Although this may not be a glamorous position, it is nonetheless an essential job that must be performed.

The term "door position" refers to the physical location of this firefighter as the hose moves through the structure to the fire. The door position is *not* with the nozzle operator and the backup; this firefighter is at least a length or two behind them. If assigned to this position, it is important to avoid the tendency to *move up* on the hose to the nozzle operator and the backup position. They depend on the door position to stay back.

Once the hoseline has been initially stretched and charged, the door position must **chase kinks** and take them out of the hoseline. While doing this, the door firefighter positions the hose for advance. The excess hose on the outside of the structure is arranged in large loops on the front lawn or sidewalk to avoid kinks and ease movement into the building (fig. 16–33). The loops help the advance by allowing the hose team to only pull on the last few lengths of the hose as they move in on the fire, not the entire hoseline starting at the engine. The portion of the hose from the engine to the front of the building does not move; only the last few working lengths of the hose move with the final advance on the fire.

Fig. 16–33. Arranging hose in loops in front of the building entrance reduces kinks and allows easier access of the hose into the building.

If the fire is on the first floor of a building, the door firefighter should position the hose in front of the building so that it can move easily through the doorway (fig. 16–34). This entails keeping the hose in a straight path as it enters the building (as it comes out of the loops) and doesn't get caught under the door (that is why this title position has been termed the *door position*). It may be necessary to also move objects out of the way to avoid the same problem.

Fig. 16–34. Door position moving hose through a door.

As the working lengths of the hoseline move inside, the door firefighter must assist in its movement. This position takes finesse; it is important for the door position to give the nozzle operator and backup position just enough hose to keep it moving and help them advance at the proper speed to the seat of the fire. Too much **push** on the hoseline creates kinks in the hose because the nozzle team is moving slower into the fire area than the hose is pushed. Too little push on the hose and the backup position has difficulty moving the hoseline forward, forcing the nozzle operator to pull on the hose instead of controlling the nozzle.

Once the hoseline has been properly positioned and is advancing into the building, the door position may advance forward along the hoseline to help move it through the structure. The door firefighter must remain mobile, moving back and forth between the front door and a length behind the nozzle, looking for kinks or possible hang-up points.

When advancing a hoseline up a stairwell and down a hallway in larger structures, the door position may help the nozzle operator and the backup position by creating loops in the hose to ease the advance inside the building (fig. 16–35). These loops are usually located a length behind the nozzle so as to not affect the operation of the nozzle.

Advancing hoselines up stairwells inside multiple dwellings and commercial buildings or through large area buildings is covered in detail in chapter 20, Basic Fire Attack. Such hose stretches require precise estimates of how much hose is required to get to the seat of the fire (fig. 16–36). Occasionally, firefighters and fire officers underestimate the number of lengths needed to get to the fire. In such cases, a hoseline may need to be extended.

Fig. 16–35. A firefighter can create loops in the hose to ease advance inside the building.

Fig. 16–36. Stretching hoselines into multi-story buildings requires precise estimates of length needed to reach the fire.

Many smooth bore nozzles are actually a series of **stacked tips**, essentially a set of decreasing nozzle tips threaded into each other. Some fog nozzles can also be **broken down** in similar fashion. To extend the hoseline, additional hose and *another* nozzle are brought to the nozzle attached to the end of the hose. With the attached nozzle shut down, the tip or tips are removed until the 1½-in. (38-mm) outlet of the nozzle is exposed (depending on the size of the original hose). New hose and the new nozzle are attached. When completed and the hose has been flaked out, the original nozzle can be opened, charging the line. The original nozzle now becomes a control valve. Some departments use 2½-in. (65-mm) attack lines to knock down the fire and later bring in 1¾- or 1½-in. (45- or 38-mm) hose as a **mop-up line** for overhaul purposes. In such cases, the same procedure is used to attach the mop-up hoseline to the original attack line (fig. 16–37).

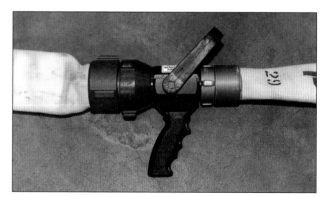

Fig. 16–37. The stack tips on a 2 1/2-in. smooth bore nozzle can be removed allowing a smaller hoseline to be attached. The 2 1/2-in. then functions as a gate valve.

HYDRAULIC VENTILATION

FFI 5.3.11 Some fire departments use fog nozzles exclusively for fire attack as well as ventilation. This type of ventilation process is known as **hydraulic ventilation.** It is where firefighters use the power of a fog fire stream to exhaust heat, smoke, and gases from a room or an enclosure after a fire has been controlled and/or extinguished.

Fog streams are effective for helping to ventilate fire buildings and have been used effectively throughout the fire service for many years. In fact, in some cases a fog stream used for ventilation is more effective than fans because of its ability to move greater amounts of air. This may be because of the location of the fire in the fire building, or wind conditions, or other circumstantial items. It is quick and easy to employ because the attack hose and nozzle is all that is needed and is right there in the fire room or area as soon as the flames are being controlled. After the fire is darkened or extinguished, and the area is checked and ready for ventilation and overhaul, then firefighters need only to find an opening for venting the environment to the outside—usually through a window or door. While ventilation is taking place, overhaul can also begin.

Mechanical ventilation is most effective with fog streams from fog nozzles. This is because of the ability to change the shape of the stream from a straight stream to a wide-angle pattern that resembles a hollow cone. Smooth bore nozzles can also be used to ventilate fire rooms, but the speed of the water leaving the nozzle is not as fast as that from fog nozzles, and the ability to adjust the stream pattern is less accurate than a fog nozzle. The fog stream is able to function as a ventilation tool because of some laws of nature. Because we live in a positive pressure atmosphere (14.7 psi [100 kPa] at sea level), as a fog stream takes on a wider angle, a low pressure point exists where the stream comes out of the nozzle. It is at this point where the room air, smoke and heat, and the whole environment are drawn to that low pressure point and then carried along the jets of water that form the steam's umbrella pattern and are exhausted from the building.

To perform a nozzle vent using a fog nozzle, the nozzle operator must ensure that the nozzle is in the straight stream position and aimed at the open window or door. Once the nozzle has been opened, the stream is adjusted so that the fog pattern fills the window or door without hitting the wall and running onto the floor, causing water damage (fig. 16–38). Similarly, a smooth bore nozzle is aimed at the opening and is opened, making sure that the water is leaving the building and not ending up on the floor. Additionally, smooth bore nozzle streams should be rotated *within the inside perimeter of the window or door*, which increases the volume of smoke moved by the stream (fig. 16–39).

In the past, some fire training programs have taught that nozzles must first be placed outside the opening, opened, and then brought back into the building. It should be positioned to ensure that water damage is held to a minimum because there is a possibility of water hitting the interior surfaces of the room. However, such procedures take time to accomplish; if properly done, the procedures described in the previous paragraph ensure minimal water damage.

Fig. 16–38. Venting out a window with a fog pattern

Fig. 16–39. Venting through a window with a broken spray stream from a smooth bore nozzle

When a wide-angle fog stream is directed out a window or door, it can ventilate an average size room or two in a matter of a few minutes depending on the volume of smoke inside the building. For the stream to be most effective, the window or discharge opening should be completely free of any glass, debris, curtains or screens so the water can flow freely without any thing to stop it.

As a safety precaution when ventilating by fog stream, it is important to watch for changes in smoke and heat conditions in the fire area. In some cases firefighters have knocked down flames and moved quickly to begin hydraulic ventilation before the fire has been controlled.

In these situations, the room clears of smoke and heat after a minute or so; but soon after, a rush of fresh smoke and/or heat is drawn to the nozzle, because the fire reignites and grows intensely from being fanned by air currents created by the fog streams. Any undetected fire in walls and ceilings grow in volume and intensity and may burst through and fill the room with flame. This testifies to the adverse nature of a fog stream's ability to push or pull (depending on the nozzle's location and what it is doing at the time—either attacking a fire or ventilating), which firefighters must know.

Mechanical ventilation is not limited to just fire operations. The power of a wide fog stream makes it able to direct vapors away from serious exposures where there may be a life and/or property concern. An example of this could be illustrated where there is a gas leak near an occupied building. The stream may be used to push or force vapors away to make a temporarily safer condition. It can also be used to divert liquids such as in hazardous materials incidents.

Note: It should be emphasized that this type of ventilation is absolutely no substitute for actual ventilation—where there is a need to force entry and open windows, roofs, doors, shafts, or use other means necessary to rid a building of fire products and to create a safer atmosphere inside.

EXPOSURE PROTECTION

FFI 5.3.10 Exterior exposures need to be considered for protection from fire extension. Many exterior exposures become involved where the fire building is heavily involved and there is a tremendous amount of convective heat or radiant heat being given off. Remember, convective heat is the air and atmosphere around a fire. If an exposure building is located within a few feet of a raging fire, the superheated air and gases may be all that is necessary to ignite an exposed building. However, where there is plenty of fire coming out of a fire building, there is plenty of radiant heat; it travels equally in all directions from the heat source, in this case the fire. In the past, many people in the fire service believed that to stop convected heat from traveling to an exposure, you would direct a fog stream between the buildings for protection. In many of those cases, the exposure buildings burned to the ground! The cause of this was the radiant heat's ability to penetrate a curtain of water fog. Most fire departments that have experienced this have realized that an exposure stream must be played *onto*

an exposure surface to keep it cooled below its ignition temperature. Otherwise, there is good possibility that the exposure will reach its point of ignition.

Another point to consider about exposure streams is their size. Smaller hand lines like those used for interior firefighting do not provide the amount of water needed to cool the side of an exposure in most cases. Remember, if there is a large amount of flames, there must be a large amount of water used for cooling. Exterior exposure lines of 2½ in. (65 mm) should be considered for maximum cooling efficiency. After the fire has been contained or knocked down, this exposure line can be reduced to more mobile hand lines that handle the lesser amount of fire.

As a matter of safety when protecting exterior exposures, hoselines should be positioned so that in the case of any possible collapse, firefighters are not in any collapse zones. Larger streams have greater reach and allow firefighters to operate at safe distances under heavy fire conditions.

When selecting an exposure hoseline, choose a stream big enough to do the job. If the fire is severe, use an effective volume of water and stop the fire. Don't gamble or believe that a small amount of water from a lighter hand line controls a large amount of fire—it won't work!

HOSELINE USE DURING OVERHAUL

FFI 5.3.3 One of the basic steps of firefighting is overhaul. It generally takes place after the main body of fire has been controlled or extinguished. In this process firefighters use tools to open walls, ceilings, and floors and to examine furniture and anything that looks like it may contain any hidden fire. A hoseline should be present in an area where there has been fire damage and should be in the possession of an assigned firefighter. In many cases overhaul begins quickly with the knockdown of flames. As firefighters are afforded better personal protection from turnout gear, they sometimes approach or move into a fire area quickly without realizing the amount of fire yet to be extinguished. This example and others make overhaul one of the more dangerous times of a working fire, even though the bulk of flames has been knocked down.

FFI 5.3.13 Overhaul operations generally require less water volume and pressure than fire attack operations, therefore 1¾- or 1½-in. (44- or 38-mm) hoselines are usually adequate. Follow your department's guidelines for hose selection with overhaul.

Depending on the amount of damage from a fire, the use of water during overhaul should not be excessive. Realistically, there are fires where a little amount of water is used for actual extinguishment compared to the amount used for overhaul, predominantly because of unusual conditions within the structure. In so many cases, firefighters risk their personal safety to get as close to the fire as possible to extinguish it with a good, quick hit from the hose stream, then shut the line down quickly and move in for the final kill, only to flood the room out 10 minutes later with a deluge after overhaul! The result is little fire damage but great water damage. Water use should be used carefully.

One of the first things firefighters should look for during overhaul is any structural damage from the fire. A deadly combination is a fire-damaged structural framing system, the added weight of several firefighters working with their tools, and the added live load of water that may have not drained away or has collected in clothing and furniture. This new live load has resulted in structural collapse and firefighter fatalities in the past.

It is important that an attack hoseline is never left unattended while firefighters are actively opening walls, ceilings and floors to search for hidden fire. Many ceilings have been opened or "pulled" and flames have come rushing out and down to the floor, catching unsuspecting firefighters. When this happens there should be someone ready with the hoseline to extinguish the fire. Firefighters have also fallen through fire–weakened floors and have needed protection from any debris burning around them.

During extended overhaul operations where there is plenty of debris, such as plaster and lath, dry wall, or other wall and ceiling materials, the hoseline can become buried; and if there is a need for the line, it may be difficult to locate. Even if the hoseline is found, the nozzle may still be buried and inaccessible in time of need. Again, it is important to keep a firefighter with the hoseline just for any unexpected situations.

MASTER STREAM DEVICES AND SPECIALIZED NOZZLES

Master stream devices

FFII 6.3.2 When an incident commander has ordered firefighting forces to assume defensive operations because the fire has taken possession of the building, **master stream devices** are employed to contain the fire (when there are no living people, including firefighters, inside the building). Master stream devices, by definition, flow in excess of 300 gpm (1,136 L/min). There are a variety of master stream devices used. Although care must be exercised with all nozzles, flowing such large quantities of water makes them dangerous when misused. Master stream devices must never be pointed at people. They must be operated within manufacturer's recommendations; for example, master stream nozzles must not be operated outside their specified range of elevation angle and lateral (side to side) movement. Nozzle reaction is substantial for such devices; and operating them outside the specified ranges can make them unstable, allowing them to move and injure people. They should never be overpressurized.

Elevated master stream devices include **ladder pipes** used on aerial ladders and monitor nozzles used on tower ladders. Each of these devices is capable of flowing in excess of 500 gpm (1,893 L/min). Their advantage is that they can apply water from above (e.g., through a collapsed roof) or through an upper-floor window.

The ladder pipe is a nozzle attached to the rungs of an aerial ladder. Some ladder pipes are detachable, others are permanently attached, or prepiped. The detachable models use supply hose from engine companies on the ground to provide water. These models also typically use a camlock system for attachment. Always follow manufacturer recommendations for attachment and use (fig. 16–40a, 16–40b, and 16–40c).

Once an aerial ladder has been raised, it is controlled (raised up and down, moved side to side) using halyard ropes or, in the case of newer models, using electronic remote controls. A firefighter should never be positioned on a ladder to operate a ladder pipe, it is simply too dangerous.

Tower ladders typically use mounted **water monitors** (also known as a **water cannon** or **water turret**) controlled from the platform (bucket). These master stream devices have individual control valves that allow them to be opened and closed slowly (fig. 16–41). Before operating these nozzles, make sure that there are no obstructions or dangers in the path of the stream (such as power lines). Powerful streams such as these, flowing at more than 1,000 gpm (3,785 L/min), can knock down walls.

Deck guns are mounted on the top of engine companies. They are used to apply water from the ground onto burning piles of debris, over walls, and sometimes into unoccupied buildings to get a quick knockdown. Some devices are permanently mounted to the engine; others can be detached and moved to a location on the ground and supplied with water at that location (figs. 16–42a, 16–42b, 16–42c, and 16–42d).

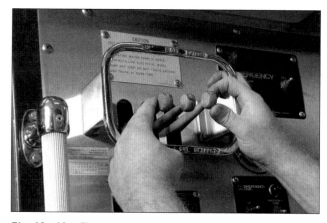

Fig. 16–40c. Electronic controls for ladder pipe

Fig. 16–40a. A permanently mounted ladder pipe

Fig. 16–41. A tower ladder water monitor and control valve

Fig. 16–40b. A detachable ladder pipe

Fig. 16–42a. A deck gun on apparatus

Fig. 16–42b. Locking device

Fig. 16–42c. Handle to raise and lower nozzle

Fig. 16–42d. Attaching nozzle to base

Deck guns have a rotating wheel so that they can be adjusted up and down, angle, and swivel so the nozzle

can be adjusted side to side. Locking devices secure the nozzle in position. A key safety issue is making sure that the deck gun is securely attached to the engine, particularly if it is a detachable model and has not been reattached properly after use. These nozzles also often have a base, which can be taken off the engine and used on the ground. The base often has spiked feet (to dig into the ground) and a securing chain/strap to attach it to a fixed object. **Deluge guns** are portable monitors that are similar to detachable deck guns except that they are always used on the ground (fig. 16–43). The same safety issues apply here as well.

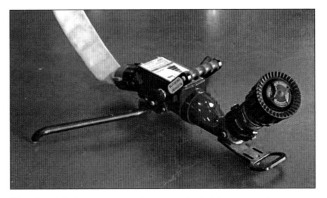

Fig. 16–43. A non-apparatus mounted deluge gun is a portable monitor that is always used on the ground.

Specialized nozzles

Over the years, specialized nozzles have been developed to deal with specific fireground problems. One such problem is that of hidden fire in void spaces and inaccessible areas. **Piercing nozzles** apply water to hidden spaces such as in wall and floor cavities (fig. 16–44). These tapered nozzles have a pointed end that can be driven through a wall or floor surface to penetrate the void space. The nozzle is charged and discharges a fog spray into the burning void space, creating large quantities of steam. This nozzle has been used to fight fires inside attics, walls, and floors.

Fig. 16–44. A piercing nozzle applies water to hidden spaces such as in wall and floor cavities.

The **distributor**, more commonly known as the **Bresnan distributor** after inventor FDNY Battalion Chief John J. Bresnan, is a spinning 1½- or 2½-in. (38- or 65-mm) nozzle with multiple orifices pointed in different directions, spraying water in all directions. (Bresnan also invented the hose roller for passing hose over a roof's edge and improved the **swinging harness** for fire horses who pulled fire apparatus in the 19th century. He was killed at a fire in 1894.) These nozzles are used primarily for basement fires where normal fire attack is not possible, and they have been used on attic fires as well (fig. 16–45). A hole is cut in the floor and the nozzle is lowered into the basement, just low enough to clear any overhead obstructions to get the widest possible distribution. The hose is secured to an object at the point of entry to the floor. In addition, a gate valve should be located between the last two sections of hose before the nozzle (50 ft [15.2 m] before the nozzle) to control flow to the nozzle.

Fig. 16–46. Cellar pipes have a directed stream that can be pointed in any direction underneath a floor.

Fig. 16–45. A Bresnan distributor is used primarily for basement fires where normal fire attack is not possible.

The 2½-in. (65-mm) **cellar pipe** (a common model is named after its inventor, Baker) are used in similar situations as the distributor nozzle (fig. 16–46). These nozzles, however, have a directed stream that can be pointed in any direction through the use of a lever at floor level. Some of these pipes have control valves attached to them; if no gate valve is attached, one must be inserted between the last two sections of hose before the cellar pipe. Similar nozzles are used to fight fires under shipping piers as well.

CARE AND MAINTENANCE OF NOZZLES

Although nozzles are designed to be used in a rough environment, take care to keep them fully operational at all times (fig. 16–47a, b, and c). Nozzles must not be dropped or thrown. After each use they must be cleaned and inspected. Inspection procedures include checking that the waterway is clear of obstructions, the bale works properly, there are no dents or nicks in the tip of the nozzle, and there are no missing parts. Worn out gaskets must be replaced.

A fire stream is the heart of all fire attacks. Knowledge of the correct volume of water, the proper attack method, and the best nozzle to use are essential to become an effective firefighter. Practice what you have learned in this chapter to ensure that you are prepared for meeting the fire head on as the "point of the firefighting sword."

Fig. 16–47a. Nicks and dents on a nozzle

Fig. 16–47b. A blocked waterway inside a nozzle

Fig. 16–47c. Replacing a worn out gasket in a nozzle

NOTES

1. Fredericks, Andrew. "Little Drops of Water: 50 Years Later," Parts 1 and 2. *Fire Engineering*, February and March 2000.

2. Fredericks, Andrew. "The 2½-Inch Hand-line." *Fire Engineering*, December 1996.

3. Norman, John. *Fire Officer's Handbook of Tactics.* Fire Engineering, 1998.

4. Clark, William. *Firefighting Principles and Practices.* Fire Engineering, 1991.

5. Fornell, David. *Fire Stream Management Handbook.* Fire Engineering, 1991.

QUESTIONS

1. Describe why the needed flow rates of handlines have increased over the years.

2. How does the Powell Doctrine apply to firefighting tactics?

3. When presented with various nozzle selections, list some of the advantages and disadvantages of each.

4. List advantages of the 2½-in. (65-mm) attack line.

5. When a life hazard exists in a structure, identify which method(s) of attack are appropriate and why.

6. How does the direct attack method differ from the modified direct attack method?

7. Explain how the indirect and combination attack methods extinguish a fire.

8. According to William Clark's test, which stream was found to be most effective in extinguishing an internal structure fire?

9. How does company staffing relate to advancing hose lines?

10. When positioning the hoseline into operation, what are some of the mistakes that should be avoided?

11. Which position on the hoseline is responsible for ensuring that enough hose is stretched to cover the entire fire area?

12. Describe proper positioning of the nozzle operator while flowing an attack hoseline.

13. What is the goal of the backup position on an attack line?

14. The door position is one of the most important positions on the attack hoseline. What are the door positions responsibilities?

15 How would you perform hydraulic ventilation with either a smoothbore or fog nozzle?

16. When would master stream devices be employed?

17. Bresnan and Baker nozzles are most often used for what type of fires?

Firefighter Safety and Survival

by Anthony Avillo, Frank Ricci, and John Woron

This chapter provides required knowledge items for the following
NFPA Standard 1001 Job Performance Requirements:

FFI 5.2.4	FFI 5.3.9	FFII 6.1.1
FFI 5.3.2	FFI 5.3.10	
FFI 5.3.3	FFI 5.3.17	
FFI 5.3.5	FF1 5.3.18	

This chapter contains Skill Drills. When you see this icon, refer to your Skill Drill book for step-by-step instructions.

OBJECTIVES

Upon completion of this chapter, you should be able to do the following:

- Identify the reasons for and preventative measures for firefighter injuries and fatalities

- Describe the importance of injury reporting

- Describe the importance of Fire/EMS Safety, Health, and Survival Week

- List the 10 rules of engagement for structural firefighting

- List the four basic components of a fire department PER plan

- Describe the need for a fire department safety committee

- List the responsibilities of a incident safety officer

- Define the terms *accountability officer*, *fireground rehabilitation*, and *on-deck air management*

- Describe the purpose of a fire department wellness program

- Describe methods of limiting injuries to firefighters during response and return form emergency incidents

- Describe the role that the Occupational Safety and Health Administration (OSHA) plays in firefighter safety

- Describe the role staffing plays in firefighter safety

- Describe the role the National Fire Protection Agency (NFPA) Standards 1710 and 1720 plays in fire department staffing

- List at least five tactical mistakes made at an emergency incident that impact firefighter safety

- Differentiate between "top-down" emergency transmission and "bottom-up" emergency transmission

- List the required tools for a rapid intervention team (RIT)

- List the on-scene actions of a RIT

- Describe the proper procedures for packaging and removing a downed firefighter for a hazardous environment

- List 10 factors relating to poor air management at an emergency incident

- List five types of drags and carries for removing a firefighter from a hazardous situation

INTRODUCTION

The day will start like any other, with thoughts of the weekend or an upcoming vacation with the family. You are dispatched to a working fire, and everything seems routine: light smoke is showing, and *all hands* are working. Then, in a tenth of a second, everything goes wrong and your life is ended or the course of it is changed forever.

Due to the inherent dangers of this job, most firefighters will be injured over the course of their career. Each year more than 100 firefighters are killed in the line of duty, with an additional 81,000 injured. We work in a hostile and dynamic environment that can change rapidly (fig. 17–1).

We must control what we know by using safe practices and preparing ourselves for the unknown. On a routine basis, life-and-death decisions will be made based on imperfect information adapted to fit the circumstances at hand. Simple, almost meaningless actions or habits that we should strive to achieve will serve to minimize the risks we all face. Although some failures at fires will be catastrophic, most will happen incrementally until the sum is greater than the parts, resulting in an injury or death. This is commonly known as **drifting into failure**. It is your responsibility to keep yourself safe and to look out for your fellow firefighters. You are no longer an individual. You are a member of a team, and your attitude toward safety will have an impact on that team. By following your department's standard operating procedures (SOPs), training regularly, and developing proper

habits, you will strive to become proficient. Almost all the skills that you learn will incorporate safety into the lessons. It is critical to realize that these skills are perishable and must be practiced, always keeping the safety aspect of the task in the forefront. The goal is to operate safely, effectively, and efficiently.

There is no greater priority on the fireground than that of firefighter safety and survival. In fact, firefighter safety must be the common thread that runs through three general priorities of fireground operations: life safety, incident stabilization, and property conservation. If we cannot make an operation safe, we must seriously consider whether that operation should be conducted at all. This is called **risk versus gain**. If the risk to be taken is not worth the gain to be accomplished, then alternative courses of action may need to be considered. For example, a building that is fully involved in fire does not typically receive a primary search. This is because the likelihood of finding any live victims in this fiery environment is extremely remote, if not impossible (fig. 17–2).

FIREGROUND NOTE

Safety is the overriding concern of *all* fireground operations, firefighter training, and station activities.

Fig. 17–1. Fire conditions and fire buildings must be constantly monitored for clues to changing conditions. Ignition of heavy smoke may cause firefighters to become trapped and buildings to become unstable. Failure to recognize changes in conditions can be fatal. (Courtesy of Ron Jeffers)

Fig. 17–2. Buildings that are fully involved or in danger of collapse present a risk to all responders. The risk \taken by entering such buildings far outweighs what could be gained. No one survives this. (Courtesy of John D'Atilio Jr.)

These decisions should not be made by the probationary firefighter or even a 3-year firefighter (a rookie by most accounts), but must be carefully considered by more seasoned veterans of the fireground. There is an old adage in the fire service: "If you cannot make things better, at least make them safe." According to Phoenix Fire Chief Alan Brunacini (ret.), there is another saying that addresses the same concept and deals with the same risk versus gain issues: "Risk a lot to save a lot, risk a little to save a little, risk nothing to save nothing."

Firefighter safety is rooted in training and awareness. It is the responsibility of all department members, and the department as a whole. Safety is an attitude. It starts with the chief of department and must permeate all ranks right down to the probationary firefighter. Unsafe conditions or actions are absolutely unacceptable and must not be tolerated at any level. To this end, the chief and company officers, as well as senior firefighters, have the responsibility to set the example with regard to safe operations and actions on the fireground and beyond. No one is tougher than a fire.

This chapter will cover the four critical principles:

- Safety
- Prevention
- Self-rescue
- Intervention

Survival is predicated on training, knowledge, and experience coupled with safe staffing, **situational awareness**, and tactics that occur in unison to and with each other. This chapter will address common tactical mistakes, driver safety, scene safety, and actions to take to avoid getting jammed up in the first place, while recognizing that even when operations are conducted right, things can still go wrong. It will take the student through tactics to effect self-rescue and provide an understanding of the roles and responsibilities of the rapid intervention team (RIT). Ideally, the RIT should be made up of experienced, well-trained firefighters, but in reality a recruit may be assigned to intervention on his or her first fire. By no means are these the only methods or evolutions for firefighter removal. It is important to establish a "foundation of safety" during Firefighter I and II training. That foundation must be built upon for the rest of a firefighter's career. By incorporating a safety mind-set and reinforcing it continuously, we can reduce the number of firefighter deaths and injuries.

Statistics

Firefighter fatality and injury statistics. To properly take the steps toward firefighter fatality and injury prevention, we must first analyze the causes of death and injury. On average, there are approximately 105 firefighter **line-of-duty deaths (LODD)** per year in the United States. This is more than two per week! None is acceptable. All are preventable. There is no such thing as an acceptable loss in the fire service (fig. 17–3).

Fire doesn't care whether we are firefighters or civilians. Fires do not discriminate between career and volunteer firefighters, old or young firefighters, or superior officers or subordinate firefighters. Fire kills and injures at every opportunity. With that in mind, all fire department personnel need to understand the ways in which our brothers and sisters are becoming casualties so we can begin to take the steps of injury and fatality prevention.

Firefighter fatalities and prevention. According to provisional statistics from the National Fire Protection Association (NFPA), there were 64 on-duty firefighter fatalities in the United States in the year 2012. That is an approximate 5% increase from the previous year when 61 firefighters made the supreme sacrifice during the execution of their duties. There were four multiple fatality incidents. Of the total number, 24 fatalities were career firefighters while 30 were volunteer firefighters. The ages of those who died ranged from 21 to over 70.

Fig. 17–3. This sight is all too common in the fire service. Prevention of casualties must be the number one priority of all fire departments. (Courtesy of Ron Jeffers)

Of these fatalities, the three most prevalent duty types were during fireground operations, while responding to or returning from alarms, and training. Fireground operations accounted for 21 deaths, with 12 occurring at structure fires. This was reported as the lowest number of structure fire deaths ever. In one study done by the

United States Fire Administration (USFA), interior firefighting operations (advancing hoselines) accounted for 13 firefighter fatalities in 2012.

The NFPA further reports that there were 19 fatalities that occurred while responding to or returning from alarms. These fatalities included 8 from crashes, 7 attributed to sudden cardiac deaths or stroke, and 2 separate incidents of firefighters struck by falling trees en route to or returning from a response. Of these, 16 of the 19 were volunteer firefighters. Incredibly, 8 deaths occurred during training activities, an environment that is supposed to be strictly controlled and supervised.

Causes of the fatalities were as follows:

1. Exertion and stress: 32 fatalities—27 were due to sudden cardiac death.

2. Struck by an object or contact with an object: 24 fatalities—19 were motor vehicle-related.

3. Caught or trapped: 6 fatalities—1 was a result of rapid fire development.

Included in these figures are 4 fatalities that were collapse-related or a result of firefighters getting lost and running out of air in a structure.

Exertion and stress: Sudden cardiac death. Sudden cardiac death, most often as a result of heart attacks, is a leading cause of death for firefighters, accounting for close to half of the LODD per year. Many of the victims have had some type of prior condition.

FFI 5.1.1 Firefighters who follow a proper diet and exercise **regimen** and are part of a department **wellness program** are less likely to fall victim to exertion and stress fatalities. In addition, regular physical fitness checkups, including stress tests, will assist in proactively identifying potential cardiac concerns. No-smoking policies and **smoke cessation programs** for department members are also part of a healthy wellness programs. Departments who practice regular relief and rotation of the fireground, including limiting firefighter work time in immediately dangerous to life and health (IDLH) atmospheres will put less work-related stress and exertion on its members. Fatigued firefighters rapidly become injured and possibly dead firefighters.

Struck by an object or contact with an object. Motor vehicle–related injuries are the second leading killer of firefighters. This category also includes firefighters that have been killed by falling objects such as collapsed walls and roofs. It also includes contact with live electrical

equipment. A portion of vehicle fatalities occurs in the wildland environment where terrain is less than conducive to safe driving. In addition, of 25 fatal crashes that were reported, 11 of the victims were not wearing seat belts, and 7 of the deaths were in crashes where excessive speed was a factor.

Caught or trapped. This is usually the result of either 1) a rapid fire development such as a flashover or backdraft or 2) firefighters losing their orientation with their surroundings, losing contact with their partner or team, or both, and running out of air. Building collapse is also included in this category, as firefighters fall through collapsed floors or are trapped under collapsing ceilings or roofs. Another overlooked issue when firefighters are categorized as being "caught" is when their personal protective equipment (PPE) is not worn properly and becomes a liability, causing them to get caught up on an object, become trapped, and subsequently run out of air. One item that is often ignored as an important piece of gear is the self-contained breathing apparatus (SCBA) waist strap. Failure to properly fasten the waist strap has cost firefighter lives when the straps become hung up on something inside a building.

Prevention

Driver safety. Departments should actively engage members in driver safety courses and driver evaluations on at least a yearly basis. Training should be in accordance with NFPA 1002, *Fire Apparatus Driver/Operator Professional Qualifications*, and NFPA 1421, *Standard for a Fire Service Vehicle Operations Training Program*. Departments must have driver safety SOPs in place and enforced at all times, for both apparatus response and volunteer response from home in privately owned vehicles (POVs). In addition, seat belt regulations should be equally enforced with a zero-tolerance policy, and all accidents must be both investigated and documented. Departments should also see that apparatus maintenance is proactively pursued and there is a mechanism in place to address issues regarding same.

Collapse safety. A comprehensive training program regarding building construction and collapse, as well as a hazardous building marking system and building familiarization program, should be in place. Buildings that are dangerous should be brought to the attention of all department members via department safety bulletins and computer-aided dispatch (CAD) print-outs. On the fireground, emergency transmission protocols should be in place to warn firefighters of dangerous building conditions. Proactive reconnaissance, ongoing awareness, and

FIREGROUND NOTE

On the average, there are approximately 105 firefighter line-of-duty deaths (LODDs) per year in the United States.

None is acceptable.

timely communications should be the cornerstone of the fireground safety plan.

Electrical safety. Departments should conduct joint training sessions with local utility companies. In addition, electrical safety SOPs should be in place, and members should be trained to give all electrical equipment a wide berth. Operations such as overhaul should not be initiated without power shutdown in affected areas (fig. 17–4).

Fig. 17–4. All equipment should be kept at least 10 feet from power lines. Operations here show a reprehensible disregard for safety. (Courtesy of Ron Jeffers)

Fire behavior safety. The need to train firefighters in fire behavior and to further train them to recognize and properly react to deteriorating fire conditions cannot be underestimated. Enforcing the proper wearing of turnout gear may save a firefighter from laziness and apathy. Strictly enforced **mandatory mask rules** for SCBA use,

as well as training firefighters in proper air management and awareness, is a must for safe interior firefighting. Many times, firefighters become lost and disoriented because they are operating outside of the established attack plan; in essence, **freelancing** (described later in this chapter). Structured command and control along with disciplined officers and firefighters operating under the parameters of effective scene assignment SOPs are the best accountability system and the backbone of firefighter freelance prevention. Ongoing training in Mayday policies and rapid intervention procedures also helps prevent casualties.

Firefighter injury statistics and prevention.
FFI 5.3.10 Firefighter injuries often occur for some of the same reasons that fatalities occur; sometimes we are just lucky that we only got hurt instead of killed. Overexertion, lack of awareness (not paying attention), failure to properly wear protective clothing, freelancing and lack of discipline, and just plain lack of common sense all contribute to firefighter injury.

Injury statistics from the NFPA show that there were over 83,000 firefighter injuries in the year 2006. Over half (53%) occurred on the fireground, that is, more than 44,000 injuries. The leading types of injuries during fireground operations are strains, sprains, and muscular pain (46.7%), followed by wounds, cuts, bleeding, and bruising (17.3%). Next are burns (5.9%) and smoke or gas inhalation (5.6%). Of all nonfireground injuries, strains, sprains, and muscular pain account for more than half the reported injuries (56.7%). Overexertion and strain were the leading causes for injury (25.5%), and falls, slips, and jumps (23.9%) were the second highest cause (fig. 17–5).

Other estimates for injuries include almost 12,000 exposures to **infectious disease** (HIV, hepatitis, meningitis, methicillin-resistant *Staphylococcus aureus* [MRSA], etc.) and over 23,500 exposures to hazardous materials and conditions such as asbestos, radioactive materials, chemicals, and fumes.

The study also shows that although both fires and injuries have been on the rise in the past 5 years, the number of injuries has decreased steadily over the previous 20 years, and so, in an almost parallel decrease, has the incidence of fire. The Northeast has the highest fireground injury rate, over twice that of the rest of the country.

Fig. 17–5. Fireground injuries account for more than half of all reported injuries. Injury prevention must be a main priority of all fire departments. This injury occurred when an aerial device was accidentally retracted on a captain's leg. (Courtesy of Ron Jeffers)

Summary of firefighter fatalities and injury statistics. Even a statistic that represents 1% of the fatality totals is significant. Remember that 1% represents someone who left behind a family and friends and whose department and community are no longer recipients of that individual's service, dedication, and talent. Statistics exist for one reason—so that you don't become one.

Types of injuries and exposures

In all cases, the best ways to prevent injuries are proper training and supervision, adopting a proper safety attitude, having a philosophy of continuous vigilance and awareness (paying attention to your surroundings), promoting and enforcing anti-freelance policies, maintaining the proper relief and rotation of companies, and wearing PPE properly. A safety-conscious department will experience fewer injuries than one that allows safety violations on a routine basis; thus, as was mentioned earlier in this chapter, safety of personnel begins at the top and must permeate the entire departmental structure. Unsafe actions must be subject to a zero-tolerance policy at all times.

Strains, sprains, and muscular pain prevention.
A progressive program in muscular and cardiovascular fitness can minimize strains, sprains, and muscular

pain. There are many parallels between firefighting and athletic competition; however, unlike athletic competition, our opponent is not human. Instead, it is fire, smoke, buildings, blood, and other nonhuman hazards. Although we cannot warm up as an athlete does for a game, we can ensure that we use common sense in physical endeavors, such as not overextending ourselves or attempting something alone that we should get help with. Proper relief and rotation is the key to injury prevention, especially in extremes of weather.

Falls, slips, and jumps. Falls, slips, and jumps are also often the result of fatigue. Therefore, proper relief is a key to prevention of not only these but all injuries. In addition, providing proper lighting at night and in reduced visibility conditions will help prevent falls. To prevent slips on ice, all apparatus should carry ice-melting compounds such as rock salt during the winter months. These compounds should be spread around the fireground, on the steps of the fire building, and around the pump panel. There are also traction devices available that fit on firefighting boots to help prevent slips and falls.

Falls from heights have severely injured and killed many firefighters. The severity of a fall is often a function of the height of the fall and how properly the firefighter wore the turnouts. Chinstrap policies are ignored in many departments. Firefighters have fallen from heights as low as 10 ft and have been killed when their helmets fell off on the way down. On the other hand, firefighters have been spared from death because their helmets stayed in place during the fall by virtue of a properly fastened chinstrap.

Conditions that cause firefighters to jump out of a window can come about as a result of a failed size-up, a failure to secure a secondary means of egress, or some type of uncoordinated fire operation. An equally unacceptable failure in recognition of rapid fire development signs has also led to many jumps from buildings. Jumps occur when all other methods of self-preservation have failed. A firefighter jumping out of a building or leaving a building by way of an emergency bailout represents a failure at every level of the fireground organization, from the firefighter who jumps or bails out to the incident commander (IC) and other commanding officers to the department as a whole. Mechanisms such as effective and enforced scene assignment SOPs, a proper accountability system, disciplined communications, and ongoing departmental training in bailout prevention are all remedies to the jump (and fall) dilemma. Gravity never takes a day off.

LESSON FROM THE TRAINING GROUND

In one case, a fire instructor fell approximately 30 ft during a training evolution at a fire academy after the wind blew the ladder over that he was working on. His helmet cracked in half on impact, but stayed on his head on the way down as his chinstrap was properly fastened. The severity of his other injuries, a broken jaw, a cracked cheekbone and orbital, as well as shoulder and hip injuries suggests a more severe head injury would have been suffered had the helmet fallen off on the way down.

LESSONS LEARNED

1. Always wear your gear properly, especially during training evolutions.

2. Just because you are an instructor doesn't entitle you to forego safe PPE practices.

3. Ladders should be properly tied off or footed at all times. This ladder was tied off. The fall occurred as the instructor disconnected the chain that was securing the ladder to the building.

Responding and returning injuries. Responding to calls and returning to the firehouse together are the second leading cause of firefighter deaths and are also a major cause of injuries, accounting for nearly 5,000 injuries. There were over 16,000 fire apparatus accidents in 2006. This number does not include accidents involving firefighters' personal vehicles, which accounted for over 1,000 additional collisions and more than 200 injuries (figs. 17–6 and 17–7).

As mentioned earlier in response to motor vehicle-related fatalities, training, awareness, and enforced driver safety SOPs will help prevent these occurrences. Firefighters must understand that they do not have the right to circumvent motor vehicle laws such as speed limits and right-of-way just because they have a big truck and make a lot of noise (or they have a personal vehicle with a flashing light on it). Firefighters have been judged to be liable for violations of motor vehicle laws and in some cases have been prosecuted, convicted, and jailed for the same.

Injuries during nonfire emergency calls. Nonfire emergency calls include responses to nonfireground rescue situations, hazardous calls such as spills, and disaster responses. Often the cause of the injury is directly related to incident awareness (or lack thereof) when conducting operations that personnel are not adequately trained for or equipped to handle. When responding to these incidents, firefighters must choose caution over aggression and not get involved in an issue they were not trained to handle. Statistics have shown that in many of these types of incidents, over half of victims are would-be rescuers—many times firefighters who got too close to

Figs. 17–6 and 17–7. Seven firefighters were injured in this squad company versus rescue company versus building collision en route to a reported fire. Seat belts saved their lives. (Courtesy of Ron Jeffers)

the problem before they realized the magnitude of the consequences. This issue boils down to discipline. Disciplined firefighters are safe firefighters.

Weather-related injuries. Injuries such as frostbite and heat exhaustion that occur in weather extremes are best minimized by proper relief of personnel, medical monitoring, and providing shelter and other comfort measures based on the weather. For example, getting firefighters out of turnouts, ensuring proper hydration (in all seasons!), and providing cooling equipment like misters and tents will help reduce the effects of heat and humidity on personnel. Speaking of hydration, once you are feeling parched, it is probably too late to sufficiently rehydrate quickly enough to avoid the consequences. When the weather is hot and humid, firefighters should prehydrate all day long and stay away from caffeine and heavy foods.

On the opposite extreme, in cold weather, providing shelter, urging firefighters to carry additional dry clothing, and providing early and regular rotation and relief all help minimize the effects of cold on firefighting personnel. In all cases, the answer to proper rotation is to summon additional personnel. In weather extremes, a one-alarm fire may require a three-alarm response to ensure proper relief and rest for weather-fatigued firefighters (fig. 17–8).

Fire departments can be proactive in injury prevention by conducting training on recognition and prevention of heat-related injuries in the spring and cold-related injuries in the fall before the onset of the extreme weather. Training for recognition of symptoms is extremely important because the victim of these injuries is usually unaware that he or she is being affected until it is too late. Thus, early recognition by observant colleagues can be a lifesaver in many cases.

Fig. 17–8. This rehabilitation and care (RAC) unit is a converted passenger bus. It was modified and reequipped to serve as a rehab unit.

Exposures to infectious disease. The department must conduct annual training on the dangers and prevention of bloodborne contamination occurrences. Training must be documented. In addition, there must be in place a comprehensive and enforced SOP regarding operations where bloodborne pathogens may be encountered. Recognition of the potential for exposure and contamination is the first step in safeguarding personnel. Once the potential is recognized, proper body substance isolation (BSI) protection should be available and worn. Policies should be in place for decontamination of personnel and equipment. Departments must have **disinfection** equipment available dedicated to simple decontamination operations of tools and other equipment, as well as procedures for the proper isolation and disposition of contaminated clothing and turnout gear. In addition, as will be mentioned in the next section, all exposures to bloodborne pathogens must begin with a process that includes a trip to the hospital for medical evaluation as well as documentation.

FIREGROUND NOTE

Red lights, sirens, or blue lights should not be a signal to the public that says, "Watch out for me. I am about to do something stupid."

Exposure to hazardous conditions. Annual refresher training, along with solid and enforced SOPs outlining the parameters of personnel involvement when hazardous materials and conditions are encountered, must be in place. Documentation is also mandatory, especially the completion of department exposure forms whenever any member is exposed to a harmful chemical or agent, including chemicals used by firefighters in the fire station and from equipment at an emergency scene.

Preventing injuries

Preventing training injuries. A good majority of injuries occur during training sessions. Recall that training is often the third highest category of fatalities and injuries. In 2006, there were over 7,600 documented training injuries. As such, training sessions should be well planned with safety as the overriding concern. The area where the training will occur should be safe and checked out in advance, especially if a dedicated building is being used. Many states prohibit burning except in a dedicated burn building at a fire academy. For those states that do allow live burning of structures, strict compliance with NFPA 1403, *Standard on Live Fire Training Evolutions,*

LESSON FROM THE FIREGROUND

At a structure fire in a residential occupancy, a captain and his crew were trapped above a fire. This occurred because the attack teams two floors below in the basement did not know they were up there. When the order to evacuate the building was given by command, the lines were withdrawn, allowing the fire to roar out of the basement and block the stairwell, their main egress point. They realized they were trapped, and they began making their way to the rear and a secondary means of egress. Visibility was extremely poor, and as a result the captain tripped over a footstool and crashed headfirst out a second floor window and into a *light shaft*. He landed on his head. His chinstrap was in place. Like the fire instructor in the previous lessons learned, his helmet cracked in half on impact, but had it come off on the way down, he would have been killed. His injuries were enough for him to leave the fire service on a disability pension.

LESSONS LEARNED

1. You cannot trip when you are crawling. If you can't see your feet, you need to crawl.

2. Our turnout gear is our first line of defense and is meant to be used as a system. Don't ever compromise that system by cutting corners.

3. Always let someone know when you are going above the fire without a hoseline.

4. Inadequate firefighter management systems and accountability controls often lead to loss of coordination on the fireground.

must be followed. Even when not burning a structure, the parameters of the drill should be explained and an area familiarization should be conducted for the participants. This should include any considerations regarding the dangers associated with the particular operation being trained. A safety officer (SO) should always be assigned, and the span of control of instructor(s) to trainees should be maintained.

Preventing nonfireground injuries. These injuries are classified by the NFPA as "other on-duty" activities. Nonfireground injuries are those injuries that occur at the station, during fire prevention and maintenance duties, while exercising, and during everyday routine activities. All of these injuries are preventable and many times directly attributed to lack of communication, not cleaning up after oneself, and basically not doing the right thing. The following is an excerpt from North Hudson, New Jersey, Regional Fire and Rescue's *Safety Matters* bulletin. It was put together as a result of a plethora of nonfire duty injuries and is titled, "There's No Fire, But We're Still Getting Injured."

Don't be a slip-and-fall guy. Preventive maintenance prevents injuries.

- Report broken steps, cracked sidewalks, leaks, etc.

- If you spill it, clean it.

- If you notice it, see above rule.

- "I" = ownership.

- "I saw it" = "I will take care of it."

- Don't touch things twice: When you are done with something, put it away. (Your mother does not work here!)

- If it's wet, icy, oily, you will slip—unless you dry it, clean it, de-ice it.

Details should not equal disaster.

- Be aware of your surroundings at all times.

- Don't just check out the rig, check out the house.

- Use the same caution, care, and common sense in a different firehouse as you would on a fireground.

Firefighter Safety and Survival

FIREFIGHTER I

Chapter 17

- House duties, routine maintenance, meal preparation areas, and work-out equipment and areas differ from house to house—familiarize yourself before using.

- House and apparatus familiarization should be ongoing.

- Check with the "normal" crew about idiosyncrasies before you discover them by "accident."

All rigs are not created equal.

- Doors and compartments open and are secured in different manners—be aware that some also don't secure well at all—and some are as insecure as a first-day probie!

- Warning devices may not be the same as your "home" rig.

- Watch your step: Heights, footholds, and hand grips for mounting and dismounting apparatus can vary.

- Check what's above your head before you step up; ditto for stepping down.

- Overlooking small details can cause big injuries.

Don't be a tool—Let your equipment work for you.

- Some items may have shifted during travel, so use caution when opening overhead compartments.

- Nothing ever falls up, and gravity never takes a day off.

- If it falls out once, straighten it out; if it falls out twice, you need straightening out.

- It's a scientific fact that what you don't secure today will hit you or someone else on the foot or head tomorrow.

- Securing devices need attention too: If you don't check to see that they are doing their job, you are not doing yours.

Respect your back, or you'll wind up on it.

- If it looks heavy, it probably is, so get help.

- We are in a team sport all the time, not just on the fireground.

- When lifting, remember that your knees bend for a reason—bend your knees, not your back.

- Giving someone a hand doesn't mean clapping for him or her—everyone pitches in.

- Try to keep the object you are lifting close to your body.

- The extent of the injury is often in direct proportion to the haphazardly hasty manner in which it is performed. If you are looking to get done quickly, take your time, think it out, do it safely.

Summary

- Pass information on—chances are someone knew about an unsafe condition before it hit you in the head.

- Set the example—don't be the example.

- Your personal safety is your own responsibility.

- Accident prevention is rooted in awareness and begins with you. Although in some circumstances ignorance may be bliss, in the fire service it can be deadly—be aware!

- If you can't make it better, at least make it safe.

Injury management and reporting

Injury reporting is a vital part of the injury prevention cycle. An injury properly analyzed and accurately reported may be an injury prevented in the future. Departments must have a protocol in place for the reporting and management of injuries. It is generally the responsibility of the immediate supervisor to report and document injuries. Other individuals may also be involved, such as the department safety officer (SO) or the department health officer. Regardless of who is responsible for documentation of an injury, one thing must be made clear to all department personnel: All injuries must be reported and properly documented no matter how minor they may seem.

As an example of improper injury reporting that has played out many times in fire departments, suppose Firefighter Jones twists his ankle as he is getting off the apparatus after a run. After the initial pain, he feels it is OK, and he will walk it off. He declines a request from his officer to seek medical attention, and the incident goes undocumented. Two days later, Firefighter Jones's ankle has swollen considerably, and he decides to go to his own doctor to have it checked. It turns out that there is a fracture. Firefighter Jones calls on injury leave. The department has no record of the injury and places Firefighter Jones on sick leave instead. Firefighter Jones now has to expend six weeks of sick time, which comes out of his sick bank and affects his payout at separation

FIREGROUND NOTE

Statistics exist for one reason—so that you don't become one.

of service. Because the department has no record of the injury being documented, it is treated as if it did not happen while on duty. In addition, in order for a firefighter to receive workers' compensation for an on-duty injury, he or she has to go to the department's doctors, usually at the time of the injury. Firefighter Jones went to his own doctor, which, if he wants to make an issue of this being an on-duty injury, probably violates department policy in regard to medical treatment for on-duty injuries. This may also result in disciplinary charges for Firefighter Jones and his officer for not following the departmental injury policy. Most departments' insurance policies do not recognize any diagnosis other than that of their own doctors for on-duty injuries. All this hassle, disciplinary charges, and lost benefit potential for Firefighter Jones occurred because of improper documentation of an injury. Document everything!

Injury management and documentation create a paper trail that will follow an individual through the treatment and recovery process, and beyond. Documentation should begin as soon as the injury occurs. Even jotting some notes down on a notepad is better than trying to remember the details of what happened later on: The palest ink is better than the sharpest memory. Fire departments are required by law to retain personnel documentation for many years after an individual terminates service with the department. Litigation might surface years later from an injury that occurred today, and the department has the responsibility not only to protect the individual but also to protect itself.

Injury management begins as soon as the injury is reported. If the injury requires care at a medical facility, prompt notification of emergency medical services (EMS) should be made. A department representative should accompany the injured member to the medical facility and act as a liaison between the medical authorities and the department. This includes updates, further documentation, and arrangements made for travel back to the department once the individual is released. We cannot just send our injured firefighters to a medical facility and then forget about them! Decisions and

notifications may have to be made on the injured person's behalf while at the medical facility. It is a departmental responsibility to provide a representative to accompany and support that member from the beginning of treatment to release from the medical facility. Once the individual is released, the department must follow up on recovery orders and monitor the recovery (fig. 17–9).

Causes of all injuries must also be investigated. Departments should have forms to document this information, and supervisory personnel should be thoroughly trained in proper completion of these forms. The injured member, his or her superior, and anyone who witnessed the injury should be directed by department protocol to submit reports documenting the incident. Information regarding the illness and injury should also be entered into the company's house journal or logbook. Failure to properly document an injury can have severe consequences at a later time, which could result in monetary loss for the department and the individual, caused by either litigation in the case of the department and its officers and proper compensation in the case of the individual.

Fig. 17–9. Injured firefighters must be cared for properly. Assigning a department representative to accompany the injured firefighter to the hospital is part of that care. (Courtesy of Ron Jeffers)

Another critical area for documentation that is often overlooked is when department members are exposed to hazards during or after an incident. Such exposures may be to bloodborne pathogens, hazardous materials, or other potentially contaminating substances. The department must also document these exposures on the proper reports and ensure that medical attention is made available as required. In the case of bloodborne pathogen exposure, department members exposed to blood or bodily fluids must be transported to a medical facility, and their contaminated gear or clothing must be bagged, properly tagged (documented), and dealt with according to department policies for bloodborne exposure. Follow-up treatment and testing must be performed in accordance with the department's bloodborne policy, which is mandated by OSHA (fig. 17–10).

In regard to exposure to an atmospheric contaminant, or a hazardous material or substance, many times it is not clear what the individual was exposed to, such as in the case of a fire where toxic smoke (all smoke is toxic!) has blanketed the area. In these cases, it is prudent to have the air monitored, but even more important to document an actual or possible exposure. There have been cases where firefighters have been exposed to toxins such as carcinogens at some time during their career and later developed cancer, emphysema, or other diseases, but because the exposure was never documented, no compensation was awarded.

Fig. 17–10. Hazardous exposures are not just limited to blood. At this fire in a live produce store, firefighters were exposed to runoff that contained animal waste. A decontamination station was established and exposure forms completed to document this exposure. (Courtesy of Ron Jeffers)

Fire/EMS Safety, Health, and Survival Week.
Formerly called the National Firefighter Safety Stand Down, Fire/EMS Safety, Health, and Survival Week was initiated by the International Association of Fire Chiefs (IAFC) in 2005. That year, an estimated 10,000-plus fire departments participated in the event. Safety, Health, and Survival Week usually takes place during the third week of June and is announced on the IAFC Web site (www.iafc.org). Safety, Health, and Survival Week raises awareness and calls national attention to the unacceptable number of firefighter LODD. Information specific to the year's theme and suggested activities can also be downloaded from the site. Each year, a different focus is highlighted. In 2007, the theme was *Ready to Respond* and focused on proper training, preparation, and equipage before a call. The theme promoted the idea that all members can respond to, work at, and return home

safely from the emergency. In 2008, the focus reflected on the need for organizational action that supports and encourages a safety culture. Three key areas were incorporated into this theme: to fully implement NFPA 1500, *Standard on Fire Department Occupational Safety and Health Program*, especially sections addressing PPE, fully implementing the Wellness-Fitness Initiative, and implementing an emergency vehicle policy. The IAFC recognizes that safety initiatives and policies must be instituted at the organizational and administrative levels and filtered down and enforced through the chain of command. If the uppermost levels of the department do not think safety is important and do not create and enforce policy that addresses these issues, it will never be important to the department's members or become a reality on the fireground, on the training ground, or in the firehouse.

The rules of engagement for structural firefighting.
The IAFC created and adopted the 10 Rules of Engagement for Structural Firefighting. They are relatively simple and straightforward, but failure to abide by them has led to both injury and LODD on the fireground. The rules are split into two categories: the acceptability of risk and risk assessment.

The acceptability of risk

1. *No building or property is worth the life of a firefighter.* Often, our ability to keep out of harm's way is directly proportional to how well we abide by this all-important rule. Although this does not mean we will operate in a defensive manner and let all buildings burn down once everyone is evacuated, it means that the risk to personnel must be properly managed if we are going to continue to operate inside a structure. It also means, if in doubt, see rule number one.

2. *All interior firefighting involves an inherent risk.* These risks can be minimized by the use of SOPs, accountability systems, and the recognition of hazards that comes about through training and reinforcement of areas such as fire behavior and building construction. Further, a structured command system and disciplined operations assist in minimizing the risks inherent in interior firefighting (fig. 17–11).

3. *Some risk is acceptable in a measured and controlled manner.* Whatever the risk that is taken, it must be tempered by the consideration of the unintended consequences of that risk. For example, using a hoseline in the area of a propane tank fire may extinguish the flames issuing from the tank. This increases the potential for an explosion because of

Fig. 17–11. Accountability systems assist in minimizing risk on the fireground by allowing command to keep track of assignments. (Courtesy of Ron Jeffers)

the resultant accumulation of unburned propane, which could be reignited. This measured and controlled risk must be supported by a continuous evaluation and monitoring of that risk to determine the operational tenability of the action. In other words, keep your eye on the operation to determine if it is still worth the risk.

4. *No level of risk is acceptable where there is no potential to save lives or property.* Fully involved buildings are not the place where live victims will be found. Direct intervention, including attempted entry and/or operating inside the collapse zone, is an unacceptable display of recklessness.

5. *Firefighters shall not be committed to interior offensive firefighting operations in abandoned or derelict buildings.* According to the NFPA, during the years 1996–2000, over 18 firefighters per 100,000 incidents were killed in vacant building fires. That was four times more than were killed fighting fires in residential dwellings. Thankfully, from 2001 to 2005, that figure dropped to nine firefighter fatalities per 100,000 vacant building fires. It is still way too many.

Although we must always consider the presence of squatters in vacant buildings, this must be decided on a case-by-case basis. Safety support systems such as CADS information and hazardous vacant building marking (HVB) systems will assist responding personnel in minimizing the amount of unknown hazards in the building. Fire personnel must think twice, choosing caution over aggression when confronted with incidents in these dangerous buildings.

Risk assessment

6. *All feasible measures shall be taken to limit or avoid risks through risk assessment by a qualified officer.* All officers and firefighters must make safety their business. This philosophy must permeate the entire department at every level. Unsafe actions and unsafe conditions are absolutely unacceptable.

7. *It is the responsibility of the IC to evaluate the level of risk in every situation.* The IC's decision-making process is only as good as the information being received from operational areas around the fireground by virtue of delegation and decentralization. Informed decisions are safer decisions. To this end, the IC must depend on eyes and ears of chief and company officers.

8. *Risk assessment is a continuous process for the entire duration of the incident.* Risk assessment is basically a size-up followed up by an analysis of the perceived threats to safety, a continuous evaluation of all fireground concerns and activities. It is best for all personnel to consider the fireground extremely hazardous from dispatch to return. Practicing this philosophy will prevent anyone's guard from being down at any time, especially once the fire is under control, one of the most injury- and freelance-prone times on the fireground.

9. *If conditions change and risk increases, change strategy and tactics.* Fire personnel must always be on the alert for changing conditions and be prepared to react to those conditions without hesitation. As stated in the previous rules, reports to command regarding changing conditions should be issued without delay. Command cannot wait to change the strategy. It can always be changed back, but being out of the danger area 5 minutes early, whether it is a building or other area, is better than 5 seconds too late.

10. *No building or property is worth the life of a firefighter.* This is reiterated here just in case you missed it

the first time. It is interesting that the first rule is repeated as the 10th. This is because complacency kills. Experience on the fireground is a great teacher, but it can also be a contributor to tragedy as personnel who have "seen it all" let their guard down and wind up paying for it (or someone else pays for it). No one in this business is tougher than a fire. The best thing to pay on the fireground is attention.

> ## FIREGROUND NOTE
>
> Get 'em in safe
> Work 'em safe
> Get 'em out safe

Risk management personnel

Risk management and casualty prevention begins well before any fire department personnel even set foot near the incident or on the fireground. One of the best ways for a department to prevent an injury or LODD is to be proactive in its approach to the conditions and actions that lead to these events. Dealing with identified hazards by minimizing the chance of injury is called risk management. Fire departments must have an official, written risk management plan in place according to NFPA 1500. This program must cover all fire department policies and procedures including the following areas:

- Administration
- Facilities
- Training
- Vehicle operations
- Personal protective equipment (PPE)
- Operations at emergency incidents
- Operations at nonemergency incidents

Addressing risk management should be thought of as a cycle that repeats itself over and over as new information is discovered, analyzed, and resolved. It will follow four basic components of the risk management plan:

1. Risk identification
2. Risk evaluation
3. Risk control techniques
4. Risk management monitoring and follow-up (fig. 17–12)

Fig. 17–12. This collapse occurred several hours after fire operations ended. Fire watch was still on scene. The risk was evaluated, and control measures were taken by cordoning off the area, which kept personnel away from the danger. No one was injured.

Department safety committees. A valuable tool the department has in its quest to reduce injuries and fatalities consists of its own members. Who better than the major stakeholders to address and correct safety concerns? To this end, many departments have developed departmental safety committees to address risks and identify methods and controls to inform department members of safety concerns and give members an active voice and participation in addressing these concerns. A departmental safety committee should be represented by department members of all ranks and provide an alternate avenue outside of the chain of command to advocate for safety. The committee should be a mechanism by which concerns can be addressed and fixed, thereby preventing unsafe actions and unsafe conditions. The department chief and the administrative staff must also be active members of this committee. In a career department, members of the collective bargaining unit may also be represented on the committee. The members of the safety committee usually meet once a month and discuss issues, both old and new, that have been brought to their attention. Some areas that may be addressed include PPE, station concerns such as diesel exhaust and maintenance issues, and apparatus concerns. Through cooperative efforts, many problems can be addressed and solved when they are small rather than serious problems, causing injury or worse. This committee can also be effective in bringing about change in a progressive manner and potentially saving the department millions of dollars in legal fees by prevention of, rather than reaction to, unsafe conditions or actions. The committee works to ensure compliance with a myriad of OSHA and safety regulations and fosters a positive relationship between labor and management. We all benefit when labor and management work together to increase safety.

The committee can also keep department members informed with newsletters and bulletins, reminding members of safety issues and giving important information about current safety concerns, both at the department and at state and federal levels.

One effective information tool used by the North Hudson (NJ) Regional Fire and Rescue is a newsletter focusing on a specific safety topic, either a current trend in the fire service or one that has affected the department recently. The bimonthly newsletter is called *Safety Matters*. It is written by the platoon SOs on a rotating basis. Anyone, however, can submit information for a topic or for inclusion into a specific portion of the newsletter (fig. 17–13).

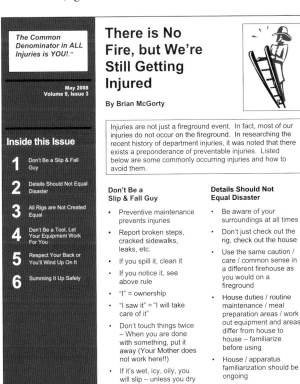

Fig. 17–13. Safety always matters.

The fireground scene safety officer. SOs monitor and assess safety hazards and unsafe situations, and develop measures for ensuring personnel safety. SOs

have the emergency authority to alter, suspend, or terminate any operation they deem hazardous to the operating personnel. On the fireground, the authority of the SO is on par with the IC. Because the IC has the responsibility for everyone and everything that happens on the fireground, it is critical that the department or the IC assign someone who is reliable, safety conscious, and rich in fireground knowledge. The IC can delegate the authority for the SO to operate, but the IC must retain the responsibility for any actions of the SO.

The department should adopt SOPs that address the duties, responsibilities, and the authority of SOs so that no ambiguity exists regarding the scope of their duties. The scope of these roles is addressed in NFPA 1521, *Standard for Fire Department Safety Officer*. These are outlined in a course called Incident Safety Officer, developed by the National Fire Academy.

Proper deployment of the SO can assist the IC in running a controlled, safe, and informed fireground. The SO should not be shackled to the command post, but rather assigned as the eyes and ears of the IC. Orders and directives that come from the SO carry the weight of the IC, and personnel should be directed to follow them as such. The SO should be mobile, going where the areas of concern are and furnishing reports back to command, either face-to-face or via radio. This concept, sort of a "roving recon," puts an arm of the IC where it is needed most at all times. Basically, the SO becomes another division supervisor, one with the flexibility to check on all areas of the fireground as the need arises (fig. 17–14).

Fig. 17–14. The safety officer should be in full protective clothing and operate as an arm of command, alternating between areas of concern and the command post. (Courtesy of Ron Jeffers)

Many departments have the luxury of a dedicated SO on duty at all times. Others must assign this at the scene. The position may be assigned to a company or a chief officer.

Regardless of who or how the SO is assigned, upon arrival to the scene, the SO reports to the command post to check in with the command. Once checked in, the SO should immediately do a 360° tour of the fireground. After giving a face-to-face report to the command post—or via radio, if something critical arises—the SO begins to move to the areas of most concern to liaison with personnel assigned to that area. This officer provides support from the operational safety point of view and advises as required. Safety reports back to the command post are issued by the SO at regular intervals and are a vital part of command operational evaluation.

All personnel must understand that the role of the SO is not that of a safety cop. The SO should not have to micromanage a fire scene. This means that obvious safety actions, such as wearing PPE properly and operating within the parameters set forth by department SOPs, should not have to be addressed on the fireground. Disciplined officers supervising disciplined firefighters will make the SO's job easier, which in turn enables the SO to focus on greater safety issues, making the fireground an overall safer place. In contrast, how could an SO, who had to spend most of the time telling personnel to get dressed properly, watch for signs of building failure or other dangerous conditions? It would be a crime if the SO was telling a company to put their masks on while the building was collapsing on personnel in another area of the fireground.

In technical rescue situations such as confined space, trench rescue, and high-angle incidents—as well as at hazardous materials incidents—the resources designed to handle these exotic incidents usually entail an SO being on hand who has an equal level of expertise in the area of concern as those who are being requested to handle mitigation. In this instance, there would be assigned a hazardous materials safety officer (HMSO) or a technical rescue safety officer (TRSO), depending on the incident. This specialized SO oversees the safety of the immediate incident hot zone, while the department SO usually addresses the perimeter and overall scene safety. Just as it is unsafe for personnel, it is not a good idea to assign SOs to an operation that they have not been trained for. Often in these cases, the mark of the true professional is the ability to recognize that the incident is best handled by someone else.

The accountability officer. The accountability officer serves to coordinate the flow of personnel into and out of the fire area with the IC. The accountability officer should use a command board to track the location and assignments of resources. This officer should also carry a riding list of all personnel on duty for a career department, or of all personnel on scene in a volunteer department. To best do the job, the accountability officer should be at the command post. Mobile human command boards do not work on the fireground (fig. 17–15).

Further responsibilities of the accountability officer are to continually monitor the radio and to liaison with command about deployment and tactical reserve. A headset is helpful to use in these duties. Some departments also give the duty of the personnel accountability report (PAR) to the accountability officer. Others give that duty to dispatch and require that the accountability officer use the roll call to update the command board and ensure that companies are where they should be.

To support the accountability officer, the department should have a strong personnel accountability SOP in place and enforce it at all incidents. Operational safety starts with accountability, and it is everyone's responsibility.

Fig. 17–15. The accountability officer should use a command board to track movement and assignment of companies. A headset will assist in the distraction-free monitoring of communications. (Courtesy of Ron Jeffers)

Risk management programs

Fireground rehabilitation. **FFI 5.1.1** Firefighter rehabilitation is vital to the well-being of personnel as well as the continuity of the operation. Policies need to be established and enforced to rotate crews from IDLH areas. Firefighters need to be properly rehydrated and replenish their caloric intake, have their turnout gear removed, have their vital signs monitored, and either be returned to service or removed from service. Improper rehabilitation not only affects air management but also leads to cardiac events, which are one of the top killers of the members of the American fire service. Fire departments must ensure that when members are removed from the IDLH environment, they report to fireground rehab and are properly cared for, as just described.

A rehab division with supplies appropriate for the season should be present at every major fire, and should be at all fires when the weather is extreme. All apparatus should carry water coolers so that personnel can constantly rehydrate themselves during an incident, no matter what season it is or how minor the incident. The water should be changed every day. In addition, ICs must see to it that shelter is provided in the extremes of weather. A warm shelter in the winter where firefighters can change into dry clothes is a necessity. Firefighters should be urged during all seasons to carry extra clothes and especially gloves on the apparatus. In cold weather, while the firefight is continuing, one tends not to feel the cold. But after the fire is knocked down and it is time to pick up equipment, or when faced with a long, drawn-out defensive battle, cold-related injury can occur, especially if the firefighter is wet. In the summer months, provide shade and fans for relief. Large fan-driven misters are excellent for cooling down firefighters during the battle. Cooling towels worn around the neck also provide welcome relief from the heat. ICs who do not provide for their firefighters are not meeting the most important fireground priority, that of providing for firefighter safety (figs. 17–16, 17–17, and 17–18).

Fig. 17–16. Rehabilitation is a critical element of the fireground safety profile of the incident. Rehab equipment appropriate for the season should be available. (Courtesy of Ron Jeffers)

Fig. 17–17. Firefighters should be evaluated for exposure to carbon monoxide as part of the rehabilitation process. (Courtesy of Nancy Ricci)

Fig. 17–18. Cooling towels used at a fire scene during a hot day. (Courtesy of Tim Olk)

On-deck air management. On-deck air management refers to having on hand properly staffed companies ready to relieve crews that are nearing their one-fourth reserve air and meeting them inside the structure to give the exiting crews ample time to remove themselves. Many fire departments are utilizing the on-deck system developed by the Phoenix, AZ, Fire Department. This allows the operations section to monitor air consumption levels of the crews electronically. As the crew nears their one-fourth reserve air level, an on-deck crew is sent in to relieve them. This system allows them to exit the IDLH before they begin to consume their reserve air. Once outside the structure, they get a bottle change and are put back on deck. Based on factors such as available personnel, weather conditions, and fireground operational status, when a crew has used two bottles of air, they are sent to rehab for medical evaluation, hydration, caloric intake, and cooling or heating as needed. If conditions just stated limit working time, one bottle may be the limit before being assigned to rehab. Through personnel management, the initial attack crews once released from the rehabilitation division are returned to quarters to clean up, change clothes, and be put back into service. Refer to chapter 10 for more information on air management.

Fire department wellness programs. Wellness programs improve the overall health and well-being of our firefighters. The better we take care of ourselves, the better we can take care of each other and the public we are sworn to serve. To this end, firefighters should take advantage of every opportunity to incorporate and bolster their own health and fitness, both physically and mentally. Wellness programs include annual physicals; fitness programs including dietary, flexibility, and exercise programs; rehabilitation of injuries; critical incident stress management (CISM) programs; and employee assistance programs (EAPs). The most important part of any department-sponsored program is willing participation by its members and the support of the department administration.

Fire department physicals. A firefighter first entering the service should have a physical used as a baseline. Physicals should follow on an annual basis after that. Annual physicals are of the utmost importance to firefighters. When one considers the frequency with which cardiac sudden death takes the lives of firefighters, it is vital that this be a part of a comprehensive fitness and wellness program. We can relate fire prevention and fire suppression to illness and injury prevention. Our main job is to prevent fires. Only when that prevention fails do we need to suppress fires. In regard to health, we should focus on illness and injury prevention as an alternative to medical intervention once our poor habits have caused a bodily malfunction. To this end, many departments offer incentives for firefighters who pass their annual physicals, and still more offer comprehensive physical checkups to firefighters free of charge. Stress tests, blood testing for cholesterol levels and prostate screening, lung capacity testing, calcium screening to determine the extent of arterial plaque buildup, and electrocardiograms (EKGs) are all ways that firefighters can determine disease potential in a proactive manner and thus begin to take steps to prevent serious illness or injury.

In New Jersey, there is a program called "A Gift from Captain Buscio," which has been endorsed by the unions and the departments alike. It was started by the wife of a captain from Jersey City who died at a very young age of a cardiac sudden death. The program, which is offered to firefighters across the state, consists of a strictly confidential, comprehensive medical evaluation with no out-of-pocket expense to firefighters. The program is also offered to immediate family members as well. All firefighters must take advantage of opportunities regarding fitness and medical evaluations, not just for themselves, but for the loved ones they might leave behind (fig. 17–19).

FIREGROUND NOTE

Firefighters should focus on illness and injury prevention as an alternative to medical intervention.

Fig. 17–20. Firefighters must be prepared both mentally and physically for the many challenges of the profession. This bus versus light rail train created additional hazards such as electricity, unstable vehicles, jagged metal, multiple injuries, and bloodborne pathogens. (Courtesy of Ron Jeffers)

Fig. 17–19. Medical evaluations provide a baseline in case of a future work-related illness or injury. (Courtesy of Christine Ricci)

Firefighter fitness. Firefighting is one of the most demanding occupations in the world, both physically and mentally. Firefighters in top physical condition can perform their jobs with more efficiency and less risk of injury than those firefighters who do not regularly practice cardiovascular and strength/endurance/flexibility conditioning. At a moment's notice, firefighters can be thrust into a veritable pressure cooker of stress, strength-depleting manual labor, and split-second, life-or-death situations. These demands on the body and mind require that firefighters be in top physical shape. This includes not only cardiovascular and strength/endurance conditioning but also a major emphasis on flexibility conditioning. Since sprains and strains are the most predominant injury in the fire service, stretching should be part of the pre-and postexercise routine. In addition, a healthy diet must also be part of the regimen for all firefighters (fig. 17–20).

Departments should have exercise rooms and encourage personnel to use them during the course of the day. In fact, many departments are mandating exercise and setting aside time so that firefighters can engage in some sort of aerobic exercise, as well as strength/endurance conditioning as part of the daily duties. A note of caution: When in the station's exercise room, never work out alone. Be sure to use a spotter when lifting weights, and consult a certified trainer before starting a workout program. Remember to inspect all equipment beforehand, and after use, put all equipment where it belongs to prevent a trip hazard. Clean the equipment with an approved disinfectant. Fire personnel should also be encouraged to prepare healthy meals at the station. In addition, many departments consult with or employ nutritionists, health specialists, and physical trainers to assist their members in developing and maintaining physical fitness and dietary regimens. This is one way for a department to protect and support its greatest resource: its members.

Injury rehabilitation. For years, many firefighters have felt forgotten when they received an injury. Today, many departments have comprehensive programs to aid the firefighters in their return to work. Firefighters who are not ready but return to duty anyway not only endanger themselves but also place their team and the citizens at risk. The Injury Rehabilitation Initiative of New Haven, CT, focuses on three components:

- Clinical pathway training: This training takes doctors and physical therapists through a fire department orientation period that includes riding with the fire department and participating in a full day of hands-on training.

- Physical therapy that is geared to our essential job functions.

- Practical evolutions that allow the firefighter to build strength and confidence.

Departments have found that these programs reduce secondary injury and reduce the number of lost days from work (fig. 17–21).

Fig. 17–21. An occupational therapist guides a firefighter through a practical evolution so that he can aid the doctor in making better return-to-duty decisions. (Courtesy of Mike Cianciulli)

Critical incident stress management (CISM).

Behavioral health is just as important as mental and physical health. All fire department personnel, at some point in their career, will be exposed to the more gruesome aspects of the profession, and most, if not all, will experience some effects of critical incident stress. As firefighters, you must be prepared to witness and participate in emotionally disturbing events. Although

you may be affected by these events, you must keep your composure and conduct yourself professionally on scene. The severity of such effects will vary from person to person and from event to event. Some people will not be affected by a certain event, while others will be. Sometimes a later incident may trigger a reaction that was buried after a traumatic event months earlier. There is no abnormal reaction (fig. 17–22).

Fig. 17–22. The events of September 11, 2001, exposed not only firefighters to critical incident stress but also the entire nation, who were witnesses to the tragic events that day. Countless emergency responders and their families have sought counseling as a result of this incident. (Courtesy of Ron Jeffers)

Critical incident stress evolves from normal reactions to abnormal situations and events. When the effects of these reactions begin to affect the individual's life to the point where lifestyle, family and peer relationships, and job performance are affected, intervention in the form of peer-focused counseling and possibly further professional counseling may be necessary. Symptoms of critical incident stress can vary in not only severity and scope but also in time. Sometimes, symptoms may not surface until weeks or months after the traumatic event occurred.

Although the effects of critical incident stress cannot be prevented completely, they can be reduced by the establishment and maintenance of a department support mechanism. Written policies should be in place, and mental health care facilities should be partnered with to provide the best stress management program for department members. Department members, especially supervisory personnel, must be trained in the recognition of symptoms of critical incident stress.

Some of the signs members should be on the alert for include, but are not limited to: head and body ache and tremors, difficulty making decisions and concentrating, memory loss (especially of the incident), anxiety, guilt, fear, feelings of abandonment and isolation, emotional outbursts, withdrawal from others, and any significant change in behavior.

Some departments have their own CISM team, and others rely on hospital-sponsored teams or regional teams. In several states, there are teams that respond based on which geographical region the incident occurred in. To best use their services, CISM teams should be requested as soon as the potential for exposure to a critical incident is suspected.

CISM teams usually consist of health care professionals, fire personnel from different departments (peer support), and other support personnel trained in addressing the concerns of those in need. On the fire end of it, many times the members of the team are fire personnel who have been through traumatic events and are now taking an active role assisting others in need. Working with peers who have "been through it" and can empathize with those who are experiencing critical incident stress offers great benefits in the way of support and reduction of the effects brought on by the incident. Contact information for these teams should be kept available and current. Dispatch may be required, at the request of the IC or designee, to request the CISM team while personnel are still at the scene of an incident.

CISM, in the initial stages, usually takes the form of a defusing or debriefing. Especially at incidents where an emotionally charged environment exists, it is best, if personnel permit, to relieve all on-scene companies and send them to a designated CISM area away from the scene. Medical personnel should also be available in this area. Debriefings are aimed at getting people to talk, although speaking is not mandatory. Some people feel better just listening and identifying with other members' feelings. Intervention by the team is focused on both listening and offering helpful ways in which members can relieve the stress they are experiencing and get on with their lives. There may also be a further and more comprehensive debriefing a few days later, sometimes on the next shift, where all members are invited to participate and continue the process of discussion and healing. It is a very effective process. If further counseling is required, it is usually channeled through the CISM team and network.

Employee assistance programs. Employee assistance programs (EAPs) exist for both the physical and mental welfare of firefighters. They exist to help a department member and/or family to get through troubling times and returning their lives to normalcy. Departments should have written policies outlining the parameters of this assistance as well as the steps involved in accessing and utilizing the available programs. Departments need not have an exclusive program available, but must provide access to a program. Some larger departments have a fully staffed employee assistance division, while most other departments offer this service through their health care provider. The programs offered by EAPs encompass a wide variety of help, including smoking cessation programs, weight control programs, family and marital counseling, substance abuse programs, and stress counseling programs, to name a few. Some also offer financial counseling and legal counseling, such as living will documentation. There may also be affiliations with larger, well-known national counseling groups such as Narcotics and Alcoholics Anonymous, which have vast resources in confronting and conquering both mental and physical problems. These programs are confidential and are usually offered to not only the employee, but also the members of the immediate family.

There may be times, especially in the case of substance abuse, where completion of a program through the EAP is the criterion to retain the job of firefighter. Absent that condition, neither the department nor its supervisors can intervene in the private lives of their members unless job performance has been affected. They can, however, if the members allow, offer counseling as a way to assist the members in addressing a troublesome concern in their lives.

Personal risk management

Personal responsibility. The key to the safety mind-set starts with everyday actions and attitude toward work, self, and others. You should embark on this path with the goal of always doing a little more than required. This goes for housework, equipment maintenance, and fireground operations. Laziness and complacency contribute to injuries in the firehouse and on the fireground.

Firehouse and personal safety. Many preventable injures can occur at the stations. The remedy for most unsafe conditions is proper and diligent house work. Make sure that paths to apparatus are clear and wet floors are clearly marked. When cooking, ensure the stove is turned off before responding to an alarm. Fire poles should be safeguarded, and sliding a pole when wet is not recommended. Cleaning supplies should be properly marked and stored in a designated area. Material safety data sheets (MSDS) should be kept in a highly visible place and updated whenever a potential hazardous product is brought into the station or taken out (figs. 17–23 and 17–24).

Fig. 17–23. This right-to-know station on the apparatus floor is clearly marked MSDS.

Fig. 17–24. Safety postings throughout the station serve as constant reminders to be vigilant. (Courtesy of Jim Duffy)

FFI 5.3.2 Horseplay can also lead to injuries. Although jokes are part of the fire service, there are several lines that must never be crossed. Any practical joke that contains references to race, sex, or religion, or that involves any safety equipment, has no place in the fire service. These inappropriate actions can lead to a breakdown in the team and have a direct impact on safety as well as invite litigation. Treat others as you would like to be treated. You are now part of a family that must work together (fig. 17–25).

Fig. 17–25. The kitchen table is a great place to learn, and it brings the company closer together. (Courtesy of Nick Ricci)

Responding and returning safety. Responding to and returning from an alarm is the second leading cause of firefighter LODD in the United States. It is also a leading cause of firefighter injury. Driver safety SOPs, seat belt policies, and annual driver evaluations are some of the tools that can lower this figure. Probably the biggest reason the casualty rate is so high is that the rules are not enforced. Also, if a company that arrives before us transmits a report of a working fire, we tend to want to speed the response up. This is counterproductive and contrary to safe response actions. In almost all cases, the first thing that must be changed is our attitude. Once that is on track, we can begin to address these totally preventable tragedies. The issue to be aware of is that if we don't get there safely, we can't help anyone (fig. 17–26).

Fig. 17–26. Response to an obvious working fire is not justification to jeopardize the safety of personnel and civilians alike by driving in an unsafe manner. Arrive safely first, then address the situation. (Courtesy of Ron Jeffers)

Maintenance. Most day-to-day operations will work toward the goal of ensuring operational readiness. When the alarm comes in, there is no time to find out that something doesn't work. Preventive maintenance programs should be incorporated into every firefighter's day. They can be broken down into three sections:

- Apparatus
- Hand tools
- Power tools

Firefighters are often charged with assisting the driver in completing the morning apparatus checks. In volunteer departments, apparatus checks are generally done on a weekly basis. This will include the Department of Motor Vehicles pre-trip. A pre-trip is a systematical check of the vehicle inside and out. Too many firefighters have paid with the lives so we could learn this lesson. Brakes, fluids, gauges, and tires are just a few of the critical items that must be inspected. The pre-trip inspection should be logged in the company log book (fig. 17–27).

Fig. 17–27. A firefighter conducts a pre-trip inspection at the start of his shift to ensure the safety of his crew.

These added responsibilities will be in addition to your position checks. Often, riding assignments will direct what equipment a firefighter is responsible to check. This firefighter must go over the inventory and conduct an in-depth inspection of the tools assigned to that position. If you are assigned on an engine company to the nozzle, your responsibility may be to take the nozzles off, check for debris and any other abnormality that may affect proper operation, and make sure there is water in the booster tank. On author Frank Ricci's first-time assignment to the nozzle ("pipe"), he took off the nozzle to find parts of a plastic bag lodged in the ball valve. Know where all the equipment is located on each apparatus and verify that all is in working order. External equipment must be securely mounted.

When checking hand tools, make sure they are clear of rust, properly marked, and free of damage. Power tools

should be started regularly and run till the motor heats up. For a saw, this is usually 3–5 minutes. This will run the fuel through the system. Make sure that blades, chains, and disks are free of damage. If a chain is missing three teeth in a row or a total of five teeth, notify the officer and take the chain out of service. The chain should be sharp and be under enough tension so that if you lifted it out of the track with two fingers it should snap right back into place.

Having a piece of equipment fail on the fireground often leads to unnecessary delays. Because time is a constant factor, safety precautions may tend to be overlooked. If a problem is suspected with your tools or apparatus, it is your responsibility to report it to the driver and officer. There are no time-outs or do-overs on the fireground. The only way we can be sure that our apparatus and equipment will perform properly is by developing good habits and conducting proper maintenance.

Seat belts. Fire departments must have SOPs in place for the use of seat belts for each occupant of any department vehicle. Seat belts must be fastened at all times. It is the responsibility of both the apparatus operator and officer, or senior firefighter if no officer is assigned, to ensure that all personnel are safely on board and belted before the apparatus begins to move. It is also a responsibility of each and every individual on the apparatus.

Firefighters should don the proper level of PPE for the response prior to the vehicle responding. Drivers should be permitted to wear PPE that does not restrict their driving. At no time should personnel be allowed to remove their seat belts to don PPE or SCBA. If they cannot properly sit in their seats with their SCBA on and use their seat belts, they must wait until they arrive and remove their seat belts to don the SCBA.

Firefighters not riding in enclosed cabs should wear head, eye, and hearing protection. In addition, a ManSaver™ safety bar should be used in conjunction with a seat belt. Tail board riding must be prohibited at all times. In this day and age, it should not even have to be mentioned.

Mounting and dismounting apparatus. FFI 5.3.2
Firefighters should always use the handrails and steps while mounting and dismounting the apparatus. Use of handrails reduces the chances of falling or slipping. Firefighters should always try to maintain three points of contact with the apparatus. They should face the apparatus when mounting or dismounting. This allows a safe check of traffic or hazards in each direction. It is recommended that if the apparatus comes into contact with live electrical lines, the firefighter should stay on the

apparatus until the power company removes the power. In an extreme case where you would have to dismount from the apparatus, you must make sure to jump clear of the apparatus and not touch it and the ground at the same time to avoid electrocution.

Firefighters should also not stand or attempt to dismount the apparatus while the vehicle is still in motion, including when the vehicle arrives at the emergency scene. Trying to save a few seconds by dismounting as the vehicle pulls up is extremely dangerous. One slip can result in a fall that lands you in the path of the rear tires. The best way to ensure that this does not happen is to wait until the apparatus has stopped before unbuckling your seat belt.

Safety and the Emergency Scene

Traffic and scene control

FFI 5.3.3 One of the biggest dangers firefighters will be exposed to occurs in the streets in which they respond and operate. Firefighters have been killed or severely injured when stepping off apparatus at scenes where traffic has not been controlled. Firefighters have been struck by civilian vehicles, police and EMS vehicles, and even other fire apparatus. Night is a particularly dangerous time. Hit-and-run accidents, civilian vehicles crashing into stopped fire apparatus, and (even more prevalent, though almost never reported) near-misses all take their toll on firefighter well-being, the ability of apparatus to respond, and the general feeling of security when operating. Firefighters must be vigilant at all times and take early preventive actions to safeguard themselves and other firefighters on the scene from becoming victims. Traffic scene control can be accomplished in many ways by utilizing any and all of the following:

- **Local or state police** should block roads and secure the fireground perimeter.

- **Volunteer fire department fire police** (typically older, retired members who direct traffic at a fire scene) can take proactive steps to assist in establishing a perimeter.

- **Fire department personnel** can perform traffic control duties if no police or fire police are on the scene, until police agencies arrive.

- **Traffic cones** should be carried by all apparatus to identify perimeters.

- **Road flares** can be used at night to alert motorists, but should be used judiciously, because they present an ignition source that might not be desirable at some incidents.

- **Fire apparatus** should be positioned to block traffic, especially for highway incidents.

- **Traffic-diverting warning lights** on apparatus should be turned on at all times when companies are operating where traffic is still moving past.

- **Reflective trim on apparatus** assists in making apparatus more visible at night or in visibility-obscured areas.

- **Reflective trim on turnout gear** helps denote presence of emergency responders, but reflective trim will only work if it is kept clean and serviceable, not worn out.

- **Reflective Department of Transportation (DOT) Class II vests** can be worn in addition to or in lieu of (if not in danger zone) turnout gear.

The bottom line is that if motorists, including other apparatus drivers, can't see you, they can't stop in time or get out of the way. All illuminating devices and equipment should be used as a first action when arriving at incidents at night or when visibility is obscured or expected to be obscured (fig. 17–28).

Fig. 17–28. Safety vests provide optimal visibility for oncoming traffic when working on the road. (Courtesy of firegroundimages.com)

Roadway emergencies and traffic hazards. Roadway emergencies include car fires, motor vehicle accidents, and hazardous materials responses. These incidents pose many potential problems for responders, including stopped traffic, which can cause a delay in response. When confronted with this concern, companies should relay their predicament to dispatch. They can suggest alternative routes for other responding companies and advise dispatch to alert other responding companies to avoid congested area. Additional concerns involve access problems and long distances between exits and turnarounds or jug-handles. In these cases, if communications are timely, companies can be directed into an emergency scene in the most efficient manner, avoiding traffic tie-ups and response delays. Failure to communicate properly can cause a delay in scene arrival and loss of operational coordination.

There may be times, especially on a highway, where companies may need to respond against normal traffic flow. This is not recommended unless communications are properly transmitted and the police are on the scene to prevent accidents. This operation must be strictly controlled.

When arriving, fire apparatus must slow down to walking speed and turn off audible warning devices. If backing in, always use personnel as guides. Never back up without personnel in the street guiding you. This rule goes for return to quarters as well. Apparatus illumination and warning lights should stay on to warn others that an emergency operation is in progress.

When on scene, especially an accident scene on a highway, it is critical that at least one lane be closed in addition to the lane the accident is in. This will provide a buffer for personnel operating. This practice is also recommended at other incidents such as structure fires, provided it does not block the movement of apparatus into and out of the scene. For the purposes of safety, additional lanes can be closed. If this is the case, it would be wise to coordinate with local or state police agencies or highway personnel.

For personnel safety, it is a good idea, especially if police are not yet on scene, to use apparatus as a shield from oncoming traffic. Place the apparatus between the scene and the normal flow of traffic. Do not get between apparatus and traffic; firefighters have had their turnout gear snagged by vehicles that passed too close and then dragged them. It is best to place apparatus at a 45° angle with the hosebed in the area furthest from the traffic. This is especially important when packing hose. This is usually the time when the police agencies want to reopen as many traffic lanes as possible. It is critical to maintain this one-lane buffer during this time until you are ready to leave the scene.

When leaving the scene, turn off warning lights so as not to confuse civilian motorists who may think you are on a response. This can cause panic on their part, irrational actions, and further accidents (fig. 17–29).

Fig. 17–29. Apparatus blocking an accident scene with its wheels turned away from personnel working on scene. (Courtesy of firegroundimages.com)

Traffic control devices. Section 61 of the 2003 edition of the Federal Highway Administration's *Manual On Uniform Traffic Control Devices* (MUTCD) addresses the control of traffic through incident management areas. The guidelines in MUTCD are federal laws, not standards, and thus are required to be followed. They apply to all areas on or near roadways that firefighters will encounter. These laws were established to improve responder safety at incident scenes, keep traffic moving as smoothly as possible, and prevent the occurrence of secondary crashes. There are five main points of section 61 in MUTCD.

Section 1 contains general clauses outlining requirements for interagency coordination, training, visibility, estimating incident scope and length, ETC sign colors, and use of initial devices such as road flares and cones.

Section 2 addresses major traffic incidents. These are incidents whose duration will exceed 2 hours. If the incident will exceed 24 hours, full MUTCD work zone requirements will need to be implemented.

Section 3 covers intermediate traffic incidents. These incidents range from 30 minutes to 2 hours in duration. They typically require lane closures. Typical vehicle collisions with injuries fall into this category.

Section 4 covers minor traffic incidents. These incidents are those whose duration is less than 30 minutes. Simple actions such as the use of initial control devices will be sufficient to handle the incident. Minor non-injury collisions and stalled vehicles are examples of minor traffic incidents.

Section 5 covers use of emergency vehicle lighting and provides direction on appropriate types of lighting for use at nighttime roadway incidents.

Size-up at a roadway incident scene. Fire responders must size up the scope and severity of the incident within 15 minutes of scene arrival. First responders should determine:

- The magnitude of the incident (number of vehicles, injuries, etc.)

- Proper apparatus placement

- The estimated duration that roadway will be blocked or affected

- The expected length of the vehicle **queue** (a backup line of vehicles) that will occur as a result of the incident

FIREGROUND NOTE

Regarding traffic tie-ups at the incident scene, as far as the fire department is concerned, the overriding concern is safety, not congestion.

For every 1 minute a lane of traffic is blocked, 4 minutes of backup can occur. Regarding traffic tie-ups at the incident scene, as far as the fire department is concerned, the overriding issue is safety, not congestion.

Traffic incident management area (TIMA).
According to MUTCD, the traffic incident management area (TIMA) includes four main parts:

1. The advance warning area that tells motorists of the situation ahead

2. The transition area where lane changes or closures are made

3. The activity area where responders are operating

4. The incident termination area where normal flow of traffic resumes

The distances for the advance warning and transition areas will differ depending on the speed limit in the area of the incident. Higher speed limit areas will require longer advance warning and transition areas. The MUTCD contains charts that detail the appropriate length based on the speed limit in the area.

Emergency vehicle lighting at roadway incident scenes.
The use of emergency lighting at roadway incidents is essential. This lighting is intended for the safety of both responders and civilian motorists. Emergency lighting provides warning but no traffic control, and it may be confusing or blinding to motorists, especially at night.

According to MUTCD, emergency lighting may be reduced if proper emergency traffic control procedures are being used. It is safer to divert traffic with advance placement of signs and cones rather than relying on warning lights and vehicles alone. Reduce lighting at the scene as much as possible, without compromising the safety of responders.

Responders should turn off all forward lighting, such as headlights that might blind on-coming drivers. Many departments turn off all warning lights, except for selected amber lights, especially at night. Some apparatus are designed so that all lights except amber turn off when the apparatus is parked. An override switch will allow all lights to be turned off when the apparatus is parked. The override switch also allows all lights to be turned on if necessary.

Apparatus operators are urged to use caution in the deployment of floodlights at nighttime roadway scenes. Floodlights must be raised and deployed in a manner so as not to blind motorists driving past the incident scene. When floodlights are used, they must be raised to a height that allows the light to be diverted down onto the scene.

Protective clothing for roadway incidents.
The reflective trim that is found on most firefighter turnout clothing is insufficient for providing adequate safety on the roadway. MUTCD states that reflective trim must be supplemented with additional garments that make the firefighter more visible. SOPs must clearly dictate that all personnel wear appropriate reflective vests when operating on the roadway. All personnel must police themselves and their fellow firefighters to ensure that all are following this policy.

Reflective vests must be used to increase worker visibility regardless of the use of turnout gear. The vests must have both retroreflective and florescent properties. **Retroreflective** material returns most of the light from the light source back to the observer. Florescent material absorbs ultraviolet light of a certain wavelength and regenerates it into visual energy. ANSI/ISEA Standard 107–19999, *American National Standard for High Visibility Safety Apparel*, specifies the minimum amount of fabric and reflective materials to be placed onto safety garments that are worn by workers near vehicular traffic.

Lighting the incident scene

Many emergency incidents require emergency power or lighting. If the incident location has poor lighting or the incident happens in the dark, firefighters must be aware of and have the knowledge to properly set up and use the required equipment to light the emergency scene. Lighting is often brought into a building after the fire has been knocked down. The key to lighting is to make sure all areas are covered, including lighting specific hazards both inside and outside the building.

Power plants. Fire apparatus and other emergency service vehicles utilize several different methods of power generation, including inverters and generators.

Inverters. An inverter is a device that converts the vehicle's 12 or 24 volt DC (VDC) current into 110 or 220 volt AC (VAC) current. Inverters are usually used when small amounts of power are needed. These systems are advantageous for fuel consumption and initial cost, but the amount of power they can produce is very limited.

Generators. Generators are the most common type of power source used to provide emergency power. These systems can be either vehicle mounted or portable equipment.

Portable generators. Portable generators are usually powered by gasoline or diesel fuel (fig. 17–30). They typically have a power output of 110 or 220 V. Smaller systems can be carried by small groups of firefighters, whereas larger units are usually equipped with wheels and handles to transport them. A portable system is essential for areas that a fixed system on a vehicle cannot access. The disadvantage of a portable system is the limited power that can be produced by the unit.

Fig. 17–30. A gas powered portable generator. (Courtesy of Lou Tibor)

Vehicle-mounted. Vehicle-mounted generator systems usually provide greater power capacity than the portable units. Vehicle-mounted units can be used to power vehicle-mounted lighting equipment along with providing outlets for portable lighting, power cords, or electrical powered equipment. The vehicle-mounted systems can be powered by any of the following:

- Gasoline
- Diesel fuel
- Propane
- Hydraulic oil
- Power takeoff (PTO) systems

These systems have power outlets of 100 or 220 V with capabilities up to 60 kilowatts (kW). Some vehicle-mounted systems are very noisy and require the vehicle's motor to be running to power them. This can cause noise pollution near the apparatus.

Lighting equipment. Lighting equipment falls into two categories: portable and fixed.

Portable lights. Portable lights are used at night or dark emergency scenes to provide a safe working environment (fig. 17–31). Adequate interior and exterior lighting makes fireground operations safer for everyone involved. Portable lighting is important to illuminate the incident scene for investigation as well as providing visibility for salvage and overhaul. Apparatus floodlights and light towers provide visibility for exterior operations. For the interior, portable lights allow firefighters visibility to enter and exit the structure safely, as well as perform overhaul operations.

FFI 5.3.17 These lights are constructed in many different ways, and they can range from 500 to 1,500 W. These portable lights can be supplied by either a fixed-vehicle or portable power plant. They are usually attached to a power cord. Portable lighting can be set up as string lights nailed to walls or other supports. Some portable lights are mounted on tripods or telescoping poles. For centralized lighting, an A-frame ladder can set up in the center of a room as a tripod to mount portable lighting. Try not to string lights along the floor if at all possible, so that firefighters will not step on fixtures or trip over lighting cords.

When using portable lighting equipment and power generators on the scene, remember the following safety practices:

- Keep electrical equipment and power cords dry, and position off the ground or away from areas of standing water.

- Inspect electrical cords for damage or fraying before connecting to a power source. Re-inspect cords and equipment for damage after use.

- Keep power cord, string lights, and other equipment out of traffic paths inside the structure or around the fire scene.

- Make sure portable generators and other electrical equipment are properly grounded with ground fault indicators.

- Always make sure the amp requirements for lighting devices match the rated amps of the generator and power lines or junction boxes.

Generators create carbon monoxide and should only be used in well-ventilated areas.

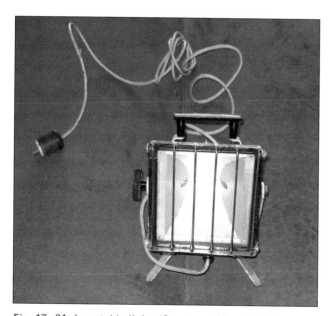

Fig. 17–31. A portable light. (Courtesy of Ken Nolan)

Fixed lights. Fixed lights are mounted permanently on the apparatus (fig. 17–32). They can provide immediate lighting around and under the vehicle. They are wired so that they may be turned on by a breaker panel or switches in the cab of the apparatus. When it is dark out, these lights should be switched on as soon as the company arrives on scene. If a generator is used to power the lights that are operated by the cab switches, they should be turned on during the response. On many apparatus, they too are usually operated from a switch inside the cab.

Another popular configuration is the fold-up or telescoping light mast. This device can contain multiple banks of lights. The system of lights can be rotated and tilted up and down to get the desired effect. A typical bank of lights ranges from 500 to 3,000 watts per light. These systems, along with other anticipated electrical loads, are matched to the vehicle's fixed generator capacity.

FIREGROUND NOTE

Overhead lighting works well for major incidents. Light mast and tower ladders will make it look like daytime.

Fig. 17–32. A fixed light on an apparatus

Auxiliary electrical equipment. Auxiliary electrical equipment constitutes many different devices that can be used in conjunction with power cords, lights, and generation systems to help provide emergency power. This equipment should meet NFPA 70E, *Standard for Electrical Safety Requirements for Employee Work Places.*

Electrical cords. Electrical cords can be rated at 15, 20, or 25 amps, and they come in different lengths. Most fire departments will carry a combination of electrical cords that terminate with twist lock and conventional plugs. This allows a department to have multiple options.

Twist locks and regular adaptors. Most fire department electrical cords have either twist-lock connectors or standard two- prong and ground plug male and female connections (figs. 17–33, 17–34, and 17–35). Twist-lock connectors require the same amperage rating for the male and female connections. You cannot mate a 15-amp connector with a 20-amp connector.

Fig. 17–33. A twist-lock connector. (Courtesy of Lou Tibor)

Fig. 17–34. A three-prong connector. (Courtesy of Lou Tibor)

Fig. 17–35. A two-prong connector. (Courtesy of Ken Nolan)

Electrical cord reels. Electrical cord reels can be either vehicle-mounted or portable units. They are designed to carry a specific amount of electrical cord. The advantage to a portable unit is it can be brought to wherever it is needed. The fixed unit is typically hard-wired to the apparatus and cannot be easily removed. Fixed units hold more cord.

Junction or gang boxes. Junction or gang boxes may be used when multiple outlets are needed (fig. 17–36).

They are supplied by one connection back to the power source. They can provide multiple connections for twist-lock or conventional plugs, or a combination of both. The advantage to this device is that multiple cords can be powered from the same location. A variety of electrical adaptors should also be carried to make sure all electrical cords and equipment can be used for maximum efficiency. All electrical equipment should also be equipped with ground fault interruption (GFI) capabilities to eliminate the possibility of electrical shock for the users.

Fig. 17–36. A gang box. (Courtesy of Ken Nolan)

Controlling utilities

SKILL DRILL

Electricity. If an emergency incident warrants that the electrical power to a structure be turned off, the local utility should be immediately requested by the IC. In the short term, it may be necessary for firefighting personnel to locate the electrical panel or fuse box and disconnect the main switch (figs. 17–37 and 17–38). Many times, these disconnect areas are in the basement on the wall directly below where the electrical service enters the building. Firefighters should make a mental note if a breaker that they turned off was tripped. This must be documented and reported to command and the fire marshal. Pulling the electrical meter from the socket on the structure is not an acceptable method. This should only be done by qualified electrical personnel. Improper removal of an electrical meter can cause serious injuries or even death.

In some commercial occupancies, it may be required to leave the power energized for certain processes or electrical-sensitive systems. The fire department officer must check with plant personnel before randomly cutting the power to a building. Buildings, whether they are commercial or residential, may also have auxiliary power supplies or be fed with electrical power from two sources. This information must be ascertained beforehand.

FFI 5.3.18 Utility disconnections should be handled in accordance with the safety procedures of your department and any guidelines or training required by the local utility companies for the specific systems.

Gas. If it becomes necessary to shut off gas utilities to a building, the local gas utility or propane company should be notified by command. Natural gas utilities usually can be shut off on the street side of the gas meter (fig. 17–39). This can be accomplished by turning the gas cock one-quarter turn into the off position (fig. 17–40). Individual gas appliances should also have an inline shutoff with a one-quarter-turn valve. In rare instances, the gas may have to be controlled by turning off a valve in the street. If the gas cannot be controlled by the fire department, firefighters must take a defensive position until the utility crew arrives. This means protection of exposures while letting the gas burn. Extinguishing the gas flame may cause a gas buildup inside a structure, which can lead to an explosion.

FFI 5.3.18 Once the gas is shut off at the meter, it should not be turned back on until the system undergoes a safety inspection by the utility company personnel or another qualified professional. Only after inspection should gas service be restored and pilot lights re-lit.

Personal protective equipment should always be worn when working with live utility systems in the event of electrical shock or gas explosion

Fig. 17–38. A fuse box

Fig. 17–39. A gas meter with a gas cock

Fig. 17–37. An electrical panel with circuit breakers

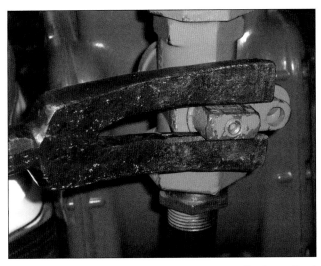

Fig. 17–40. A tool closing a gas cock (perpendicular to flow)

Most propane systems have shutoff valves on the top of the tank and also inline shutoff valves at the appliances (fig. 17–41). Once the gas supply is shut off, the area should be metered to verify the reduction of gas vapors. It is not recommended that the fire department turn the gas back on at the end of the incident.

FFI 5.3.18 Personal protective equipment should always be worn when working with live utility systems in the event of electrical shock or gas explosion.

Fig. 17–41. The valve on a propane tank. (Courtesy of Lou Tibor)

Water. Most water utilities can be controlled by closing the valve where the water enters the structure. Most water utility companies recommend shutting the valves on the building side of the meter, not the street side. If the fire department encounters difficulty finding or shutting down the water service to a facility, they should contact the local water company. At times it may be necessary to have the water shut off in the street. In multiple occupancies or large buildings, there may be multiple water services that need to be controlled.

PERSONNEL SAFETY

Personal protective equipment

NFPA 1500, *Standard on Fire Department Occupational Safety and Health Program*, under requirement 7.1.3, states, "Structural fire fighting clothing shall be cleaned at least every six months as specified in NFPA 1851." (See fig. 17–42.) Chapter 7 of the NFPA 1851, *Standard on Selection, Care, and Maintenance of Protective Ensembles for Structural Firefighting and Proximity Fire Fighting*, addresses the cleaning and drying of turnout gear ensembles. Wet and unclean turnout gear is an important health and safety issue. Wet turnout gear is thermally unstable. Section A.7.4.3(6) of NFPA 1851 states, "Ensembles and ensemble elements should be completely dry before reuse to avoid the potential for steam burns caused by moisture remaining in the layers of the ensemble." Moreover, the storage of wet or moist turnout ensembles can affect the strength of some materials and promotes the growth of mildew and bacteria, some of which can lead to serious medical conditions. Gear that is not cleaned can also contain toxic products of combustion that can result in an exposure. Volunteers should not keep gear in the passenger compartment of their personal vehicle, and they should be sure that gear is stored out of direct sunlight. Also, wet turnout gear can place further stress on the firefighter. It is recommended that a firefighter be issued two sets of gear. Further details on protective clothing is found in chapter 9, Personal Protective Equipment.

> **FIREGROUND NOTE**
>
> If your gear gets saturated during training, it will not provide the same protection as dry gear, and live fire evolutions should stop!

Firefighter Safety and Survival

FIREFIGHTER I

Chapter 17

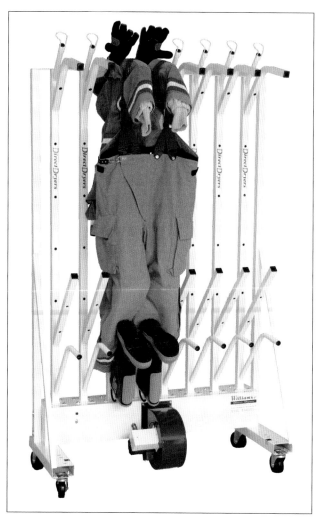

Fig. 17–42. Ideally, gear should be dried in a nontumble-style dryer with a forced-air dryer around 100°F (38°C). (Courtesy of Williams Direct Dryers)

Hearing protection. As firefighters, we can be exposed to noise levels above 115 decibels on the fireground. NFPA 1500 and OSHA *Standard on Occupational Noise Exposure* 1910.95 both require that firefighters be provided with hearing protection when charted levels exceed 90 decibels. The standards further state that fire departments shall establish hearing conservation programs. Personal responsibility plays a large role in ensuring that the provided hearing protection is used when responding to alarms and windows are kept closed to minimize the noise from the sirens. It has been well established that when responding to alarms, you will be exposed to over 90 decibels. OSHA does recognize that it is impractical to use hearing protection once on scene because it could interfere with other life-saving equipment. Many departments, however, urge firefighters operating power equipment such as saws and jackhammers to use hearing protection (fig. 17–43).

Fig. 17–43. Hearing protection is recommended, although not always practical on the fire scene. (Courtesy of Lou Tibor)

Occupational Safety and Health Administration (OSHA)

FFII 6.1.1 OSHA standards are federal regulations that mandate minimum training standards, equipment performance, administration, and operations. It is important to realize that the fire service is unique in the way we are regulated because of the type of work we must perform. For example, the fire service has no fall protection standard for the fireground. Although it may sound counterproductive, the time it would take to set up protection on a roof would place firefighters at greater risk of falling through the roof. All departments should strive to exceed all OSHA (or state) standards. That can only happen if you commit yourself to safety.

Staffing and safety

FFII 6.1.1 Lack of proper staffing is a leading contributor to firefighter injures and death. The tactics that you have learned cannot occur incrementally. They must take place in unison with each other to allow us to control the building and safely mitigate the incident. At a structure fire, tasks are time sensitive. NFPA 1710, *Standard for the Organization and Deployment of Fire Suppression, Operations, Emergency Medical Operations, and Special Operations to the Public by Career Fire Departments*, mandates that the first-arriving company shall be staffed with four personnel and arrive in less than 4 minutes (fig. 17–44).

Fig. 17–44. Company staffed with four personnel. (Courtesy of Dave Esposito)

The standard goes on to say that the entire first-alarm assignment of 15–17 should arrive in 8 minutes. These requirements are based on a 2,000-sq-ft (186-sq-m) house with no exposures. Numerous studies have found a definitive link between injures and crew size. The International Association of Fire Fighters (IAFF) report, "Analysis of Fire Fighter Injuries and Minimum Staffing per Piece of Apparatus in Cities with Populations of 150,000 or More" (December 1991), found that crews smaller than four almost doubled their percentage rate for injuries when compared with crews of four or more firefighters.

A study by the Providence (RI) Fire Department, analyzed in an applied research project submitted to the National Fire Academy as part of the Executive Fire Officer Program by Curtis Varone (1994), found that "four-person staffing led to a 23.8% reduction in injuries, a 25% reduction in time lost injuries and a 71% decrease in time lost due to injury when compared to three-person staffing." Inadequate staffing contributes to companies having to play catch-up. This increases risk to firefighters and contributes to firefighters taking shortcuts that lead to injures.

Safe staffing requires ESP:

- *Education and emotion:* Be passionate about your job. Take classes, read trade magazines, and continue your education. Take advantage of educational opportunities. At fire prevention talks, explain the role of all the different companies on scene. Participate or conduct the Fire Operations 101 program developed by the IAFF. This program takes elected officials through an orientation program and educates them on the dangers of firefighting. Fire Operations 101 gives them a firsthand view of how

difficult fire operations are with limited personnel and builds lasting relationships with officials.

- *Standards and statistics:* You should be well-versed in standards such as NFPA 1710 and the OSHA Two-in, Two-Out Rule (discussed in a later section). Read reports from the National Institute of Occupational Safety and Health (NIOSH), NFPA, and the U.S. Fire Administration to stay informed on safety and current trends.

- *Politeness and political action:* Get involved in your department and your community. Standing up for appropriate staffing is protected speech because it is a legitimate matter of public concern. Note that until you are off probation, you are not entitled to an opinion, so be quiet and learn. You have two ears, two eyes, but only one mouth for a reason.

Volunteers and staffing. The majority of fire departments are made up of volunteers. Commitments to work and family and many members working out of town have placed a strain on many volunteer departments to respond during daytime hours. NFPA 1720, *Standard for the Organization and Deployment of Fire Suppression Operations, Emergency Medical Operations and Special Operations to the Public by Volunteer Fire Departments,* applies to volunteer fire departments.

Many departments have instituted innovative approaches to increase staffing. Rockville, MD, started a college live-in program in which students receive room and board in return for service to the department. Other departments have started duty nights in which the members commit to staffing the station during a predetermined night. This builds camaraderie and provides many of the benefits of career departments. Departments have also established Fire Explorer programs or Junior Firefighter programs to increase interest in the fire service from younger members of the community. This is a valuable tool that many career and volunteer fire departments have benefited from. Volunteer departments in Long Island, NY, assign members to cover certain types of calls to limit the impact on their family and encourage greater participation. For example, five or six members may be assigned to cover single engine calls for a particular night for such responses as activated alarms and car fires.

Firefighter Safety and Survival

FIREFIGHTER I

Chapter 17

FIREGROUND NOTE

The Washington Post Theory:

Conduct yourself so that if your actions were to be published on the front page of the Washington Post, you would be proud.

—Captain Michael Abrashoff
U.S. Navy

Staffing, you, and the budget. You may be asking yourself, "I am new to the fire service. How can I have an impact on achieving or maintaining safe staffing?" As a new firefighter, you can play a key role by interacting with our "customers." Take time to ensure that you treat all citizens with respect and go out of your way to make their interaction with the fire department a positive one. Be friendly; talk to the elderly a little longer; and at the completion of a call, show the kids the fire truck. It is always a good idea, during the conversation or when the children are playing, to mention fire prevention issues (fig. 17–45).

Your department's reputation will play a direct role in the budget process. The budget, whether career or volunteer, has a direct impact on the training funds, equipment repairs, protective clothing, and staffing. Your actions in the field may determine if the community supports funding newer apparatus or if they stand with you when need to save a neighborhood firehouse from being closed.

Fig. 17–45. Firefighters taking time to interact with the community. (Courtesy of Jacqueline Bender)

Personnel accountability systems. FFI 5.1.1

Ensure that you have read and understood your department's SOP on accountability. Accountability is everyone's responsibility and must be strictly adhered to. Accountability systems make tracking personnel and crews more manageable. First and foremost, they establish who is on scene and what companies those personnel are assigned to. Departments use many different tag systems, boards, or written logs to track crews on scene (fig. 17–46).

Fig. 17–46. An example of a tag system. Firefighters clip their tag into a ring on the apparatus when they report for duty. (Courtesy of firegroundimages.com)

Whatever system is used, it must address the following:

1. Who is on scene

2. What company they are assigned to

3. Where they are operating

Tracking dynamic crews is difficult and requires the human factor to continually update the locations of companies. Manufacturers are working to establish electronic accountability using radio waves and other technology (fig. 17–47).

Fig. 17–47. Accountability officer tracks location of crews on an accountability board. (Courtesy of firegroundimages.com)

Personnel accountability report. The personnel accountability report (PAR) provides a roll call to ensure that all personnel are accounted for. A PAR can be called at anytime by the IC. An accountability officer may be designated to track crews. Some departments require the dispatcher to notify them at predetermined intervals (e.g., every 15 minutes) as a way to mark time for command and ensure that PARs are conducted. PARs can also be given after each radio transmission. PARs are usually called for after an evacuation order or a catastrophic event. They should be requested once the fire is declared under control.

Diagramming the fire. All firefighters should have a radio, but not everybody should talk on the radio. Think before you speak. Ask yourself, "**D**oes **I**t **M**atter **W**hat **I**'m **T**ransmitting?" (DIMWIT). Radio discipline leaves radio channels available for necessary transmissions.

All members must listen to the radio. Time and time again, Mayday calls are being missed. Radio transmission is one of the ways in which operating crews are tracked. Officers and firefighters should give their location with every radio transmission when inside a hazard area.

For example: "Truck 4 to command: Second floor kitchen, we have fire running the stud spaces with possible extension to the attic, Truck 4 has PAR."

This information is not only beneficial for command, but it also allows the RIT and other companies that haven't arrived to track crews. If a Mayday is given that is missing all the necessary information, it allows for a starting point to locate the member(s) in trouble. Fire department personnel who are not on the alarm should monitor the radio and try to track crews on a board. This helps develop listening skills and gives multiple ears the task of listening to the radio.

Evacuation order. This is the one order that can never be questioned. As firefighters involved at the task level, you are only seeing part of the picture. Command is basing their decision to evacuate a structure or area on the totality of the incident. They are positioned to see visual cues such as collapse and are receiving input from other officers. If ordered out, get out with your crew! Most departments will issue an order and have the closest fire apparatus blast their air horns three times in case a radio message is missed. Emergency fireground transmissions such as withdrawal orders will be discussed later in this chapter.

Crew integrity and hazard area exit. Complete fireground accountability can only be effective with 100% commitment to the team concept. Firefighters should not work alone. If you are separated from your crew, you must immediately call for help. At times, you will lose your crew or get mixed into the wrong crew. If this occurs, notify your commanding officer that you are separated and identify what company you are from. If one member must exit the hazard area, he or she should exit with another team member. When exiting the hazard area and vision is obscured, you must crawl. If you are following a guide line that is taut, grasp the line and slide your hand on the rope. If you are exiting on a slacked line, one method is to kneel on the line and grasp the line with a closed hand, then slide your hand on the rope. Next, move your knee and repeat the process (figs. 17–48 and 17–49). Hoselines may also be used to guide you to the outside by using the hose coupling lugs.

Furniture should not be moved during fire operations. When exiting, the location of furniture will help keep you oriented to your location. Even when using a **thermal imaging camera (TIC)**, move along the walls in a systematic fashion. This method has worked for rats for hundreds of years, and, as with any technology, the camera can fail. When crawling, keep a low center of gravity and always check for the floor. When we crawl, we need to move quickly, but we must also ensure that we will be able to pull back if a weak floor or shaft is found (fig. 17–50). Make an effort to look up and check conditions above you. Periodically stop and listen, as you might be able to hear the fire above you.

Fig. 17–48. This method is slower than crawling along the line, but it ensures you will not get turned in the wrong direction if the guide line crosses over itself. (Courtesy of Kris Sundwall)

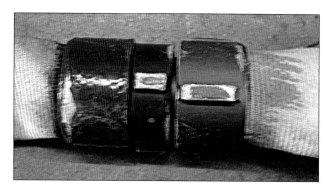

Fig. 17–49. If you are lost and you find a hoseline, remember the phrase "bumps to the pumps" as a guide. Move in the direction of the hose coupling lugs. Couplings that are painted identify particular engine companies. (Courtesy of Maureen Duffy)

Fig. 17–50. Photo of the shaft that author Frank Ricci fell into when searching for a trapped security guard. Make sure that if you encounter a shaft, you can pull yourself back up.

TACTICAL MISTAKES

This section will cover predicable and preventable events that the fire service has paid the highest price to learn. If you are on the RIT and are activated, it is a clear indication of failures on multiple levels. If you look at the NIOSH LODD reports as a random report card of our service, we are failing in many areas. This is mentioned with the disclaimer that mistakes will be made at every fire. It is not the mistake that you make, it is how you recover from it and the fact that you recognize it, share it, and learn from it. It takes a balance between experience, training, and knowledge to be safe and successful in this field. Experience is not enough. When we develop unsafe habits and they are reinforced with positive experiences, they become the norm and contribute to greater failures later that will culminate with an injury or death. Although most of these things are covered in

other chapters, the seriousness of failing to heed these warnings can cause serious injury or death. Let's take a look at some of these failures.

Command and control

Failure to properly size up the situation. Improper size-up costs lives. Taking a couple of extra seconds to analyze a situation can save you minutes and maybe your life. The New York City Fire Department came up with the acronym, COAL WAS WEALTH (construction, occupancy, apparatus and staffing, life hazard, water supply, auxiliary appliances and aids, street conditions, weather, exposures, area, location and extent, time, and height), to standardize size-up. This is an effective method, but experience has shown that new firefighters often miss the very basic points due to adrenaline. You need to first concentrate on the task at hand. If hooking up the hydrant, then focus on this task and accomplish it first. When you are performing any task that will put you inside or around the building, at least five points should come into your mind:

1. Construction
2. Occupancy
3. Layout
4. Where the fire is located
5. Where the fire is going

This will give you a foundation to build on as your experience increases. Take advantage of routine calls to size up homes and buildings in your district. You will find similarities that will aid you in size-up of other similar occupancies.

Combining offensive and defensive attacks. This action pushes heat and fire back inside, causing burns and deteriorating conditions. If you are ordered to extinguish fire that is coming out of a window, and you know that crews are operating inside, direct the line at the eaves of the house or above the window. This will allow the water to cascade down the house and stop the fire from enveloping the exterior of the structure. This action will also prevent the fire from being pushed on the members inside. Once the interior hoseline is working the fire, shut the exterior line down. It must never enter the window of fire, or heat will be pushed at members on the interior. The exterior hoseline always wins in these cases.

Uncoordinated fireground operations. Another major tactical error, one that has caused countless firefighter injuries and LODDs, is uncoordinated fireground operations. There are three crucial fireground operations that must go hand in hand to keep the operation as safe as possible. These are fire attack, search and rescue, and ventilation, represented by the fireground coordination triangle (fig. 17–51). If any one of these three principles of the fireground coordination triangle is out of sync with, missing, or unsupported by the operation, the triangle, like a truss, will collapse. A complete triangle will support the center of the triangle—fireground safety.

Fig. 17–52. Technical rescue operations such as this trench rescue require expertise beyond most first responders' capabilities. Firefighters must know their limitations in regard to operational capability. (Courtesy of Ron Jeffers)

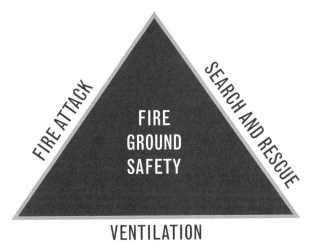

Fig. 17–51. Fire coordination triangle

Failure to recognize when your incident is beyond the scope of your training. Incidents such as technical rescues, biological and hazardous materials incidents, and major utility failure incidents like ruptured gas mains require intervention by specially trained personnel, sometimes from agencies other than the fire department. Firefighters should understand that they are limited by their training and the capability of their equipment. Fire personnel may still operate in a support posture, providing such assistance as evacuation of exposed areas, conducting decontamination operations, and operating exposure lines. They should not get directly involved in these incidents, meaning hands off the problem. The mark of the true professional is the ability to recognize that your incident may be best handled by someone else (fig. 17–52).

Failure to pay attention to your surroundings. It has been mentioned several times in this chapter that complacency is a killer. A large proportion of firefighters who become casualties are usually not brand new firefighters, but seasoned veterans who have been allowed by lack of leadership and supervision to become too comfortable in their settings. There is no firefighter tougher than the fire. When working near or above the fire, failure to pay attention to the location of the fire, as well as paths that it can spread to has cost many firefighters their lives. In addition, firefighters who become too complacent may fail to recognize such dangers as overhead power lines, dangerous vacant buildings and their hazards, signs of rapid fire development and collapse, and traffic hazards. There is also no firefighter tougher than electricity, a falling building, or a moving vehicle. The fireground should be treated as extremely hazardous from arrival to termination. Firefighters should be continuously watching out for hazards and for each other. Casualties can be prevented by identifying hazards and taking appropriate action (fig. 17–53).

FIREGROUND NOTE

Combining offensive and defensive attacks is like ordering artillery on yourself.

—Alan Brunacini

Fig. 17–53. The truss above this firefighter's head is clearly involved in fire. This is a tragedy waiting to happen. (Courtesy of BC Mike Oriente NHRFR)

Failure to request early assistance. Fires and other emergency incidents are mitigated by people. Not having enough people on scene is a major case of incident escalation and firefighter casualties. Additional personnel are required for relief purposes, for reinforcement of operational areas, and to address those little surprises that often pop up on the fireground. When there are enough personnel on scene to address them, small concerns stay small. When you are behind the eight ball in the personnel game, small concerns become big problems and may affect both the strategy and the safety of personnel. As a firefighter, based on department protocols, you may be detailed some day as an acting company officer. If this is the case, you might wind up as the initial IC. The decision to strike an additional alarm upon arrival may be your decision to make. The need for this might not be apparent when you arrive and everyone goes to work. If all personnel are working, and there is no one waiting in the street to go to work, the tactical reserve profile is at zero. The dilemma will emerge when the first-alarm companies begin to exhaust their first SCBA cylinders, when they become fatigued, when someone calls for additional help in an operational area, or when an unexpected concern surfaces. If there is no tactical reserve on the sidelines to put into the game, the game will either be lost or the fatigued firefighters will have to overextend themselves to continue the operation, risking injury. When in doubt, ensure there are enough personnel on scene or ordered to maintain the operation, especially in extreme weather. If you don't need them, you can always send them back.

Water supply and fire attack

Failure to charge hoseline before descending to a below-grade fire. **FFI 5.3.10** The water is your only protection. If a member vents early, before you are at the bottom of the stairs, you may be caught on the stairs by a rapid fire progression and will have no water to protect yourself. When ventilating horizontally (for fire), wait until the line is charged before breaking out any windows. Remember also that the basement stairs may end away from the wall. Bring an extra light to mark the bottom of the stairs as a reference.

Fig. 17–54. When descending basement stairs, go feet first with your weight to the sides, and ensure you have enough hose to clear the stairs. (Courtesy of Chris Saraceno)

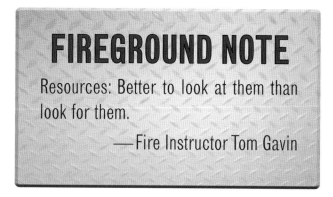

FIREGROUND NOTE

Resources: Better to look at them than look for them.

—Fire Instructor Tom Gavin

Failure to chock an entry door as the hoseline is being stretched. Chocking doors is fundamental. The cheapest and simplest piece of equipment, a block of wood, is often the most important. There is a misconception that if a line charges under an inward-opening door, you will be able to open it easily. This is not true. Having a line charged under a door will block your egress and interrupt the flow of water. Any door that a line goes through should be chocked open (fig. 17–55).

Fig. 17–55. Any door that a hoseline goes through must be chocked open.

FFI 5.3.5 When members are searching without a hoseline, just the opposite is true. Once inside, the door must be closed to provide your team an **area of refuge** (also referred to as **safe haven**) while you search. This is a place that is isolated from the main hazard, where a firefighter can retreat in event of a fireground emergency. By creating an area of refuge you can reduce the flow path and buy time for the fire to be controlled. Having a contingency plan of where to go if something goes wrong is critical.

Horizontally venting the windows, provided you are not in the fire area, will have no effect on the fire. This action will increase visibility and decrease the toxic environment. If the engine loses water or the fire extends to your location, you will have time to react. When your search has been completed and you are back at the door, be sure to check conditions before moving to the next room. If you are searching the fire room without a hoseline, do not go any farther than 5 ft (1.5 m) into the room. If the room flashes over, you will not be able to retreat fast enough. One safety tactic is to hook your foot around the door frame and sweep with a tool. Once the sweep is complete, close the door and move to an area of refuge (fig. 17–56).

Fig. 17–56. Flashover also indicates signals that the structure itself is under attack from fire.

Stretching too many hoselines through one opening. Hoseline management, as a rule, should provide that no more than two lines are deployed through any one opening. There have been numerous cases where firefighters have become disoriented because the hoseline they were following out of a building was tangled with other lines (fig. 17–57).

Fig. 17–57. Stretching more than two lines through one opening makes the lines difficult to advance and manage. (Courtesy of Tim Olk)

Firefighter Safety and Survival

FIREFIGHTER I

Chapter 17

Failure to stretch the appropriate hoseline to match the present or potential fire conditions.

Improper line size for the volume of fire encountered has resulted in numerous deaths. In some situations the firefighter will have to determine the size of the hoseline to pull. Understand that proper water volume puts out fires, and fire volume is based on potential fire load. This having been established, stretching a hoseline that is too small and therefore delivers a less than adequate supply of water will not only put all members in the fire building in jeopardy, it will not put the fire out.

Large area buildings, commercial structures, and below-grade areas are no places for anything smaller than a 2½-in. (65-mm) hoseline. Attack teams have been outflanked by fire, burned, killed, caught in collapses, and have caused casualties to other firefighters in the area because small-diameter hoselines have been stretched into buildings that are showing heavy fire or have a fire load conducive to rapid fire spread. Staffing should not be an issue here. If it takes two companies to get the first line in place, then that is what will have to done if the fire or occupancy demands it. The time to stretch the 2½-in. (64-mm) hoseline is with light smoke when it is easier to facilitate a clean stretch. In a commercial building you will need the reach and sufficient gallons per minute to overpower the fire.

Booster lines should never be used inside a building. They are meant for trash fires only. Small-diameter, 1½-in. (38-mm) lines are similar in effectiveness. They don't belong in structures and are not even particularly effective on car fires. Residential structures require at least a line of 1¾-in. (44-mm) diameter, and high-rises should have at least a line of 2 in. The mantra of "big fire, big water" always applies. If in doubt, stretch the big line. If it is not needed, a smaller line can be stretched, or the larger line can be reduced to a smaller diameter. Attack crews who stretch lines that are too small can be outgunned and overrun by a fire with staggering speed (fig. 17–58).

Fig. 17–58. Firefighters stretching the wrong size hoseline at a commercial structure increase property damage and places firefighters in jeopardy. (Courtesy of Tim Hunt)

Failure to properly flake out the hoseline. Ensuring that the hoselines are properly flaked out is everyone's job. Kinks in a hoseline can reduce water volume up to 50%. One kink can jeopardize the entire fireground. Remember that the hoseline not only extinguishes fire but also protects the primary search team and egress points for both victims and firefighters. Firefighters should never pass a kink (fig. 17–59).

Fig. 17–59. Hoseline management must be a top priority. Water equals protection for everyone. No one should ever pass a kink. (Courtesy of Ron Jeffers)

Failure to back up attack lines. Firefighters searching above the fire and operating in stairwells have been killed when initial attack lines have failed to control the fire or have burst and there was no hoseline in place to reinforce the attack. All attack lines should be backed up by additional lines of equal or larger diameter. The second hoseline should go to the same position as the first. If the first line is controlling the fire, this second line can then cover adjacent areas and/or the floor above, but only if the first line is sufficient for fire control. Hoselines that are stretched elsewhere in the building rather than as a backup line may be of little use, and their personnel will be endangered if the initial hoseline fails.

Fire attack: the right way

- Must protect the primary search

- Must protect the main areas of egress

- Must occur between the fire and any victims

- Must be properly supported by and coordinated with timely ventilation

Search and rescue

Failure to create barriers during a search operation. This is especially true when searching private dwellings where open interior stairs are present and the building is relatively small. Openings such as those used for vent, enter, and search operations are essentially vent points and create paths of least resistance for fire spread. It is critical that the first action after entering the room via a window is to close the door to the room. This also holds true for any other type of occupancy, including multiple dwellings. If the fire is nearby, it will move rapidly toward the firefighter-created vent path. It may move even faster if there is water being applied to it.

In the Lessons from the Fireground case where the captain and his crew were trapped above the fire (where the captain fell through the shaft window), the main reason the firefighters made it out alive was because they closed the door when they entered the second-floor apartment. They made their way to the door for exit when the withdrawal was sounded over the radio. When the door was opened by one of the firefighters, he stated later that there were flames in the stairwell and that the heat knocked him immediately to the ground. He struggled but was able to close the door again, most likely because it was an inward-swinging door and all he had to do was push it closed. Had the door swung the other way, he would never have been able to reclose it. Had that apartment door not been closed, they almost certainly would have been overrun by the fire (fig. 17–60).

Fig. 17–60. Fire roaring up the stairs from the cellar trapped firefighters searching above the fire. Only a closed apartment door protected them from burning to death. In private dwellings, this apartment door is not available.

Especially for cellar or basement fires in private dwellings, if you are going to search the upper floor before a hoseline is in place, ensure not only the door to the cellar is closed before you go up, but the door to the area you will be searching must be closed too. Again, it is worth mentioning that some type of notification must be made before personnel go above the fire (fig. 17–61).

Crowding the hall or stairs. These are paths of egress and should not be blocked. If an evacuation is ordered, it will be difficult to get out or down. If loss of water occurs, a door burns through, or a wind-driven fire is encountered, your escape can be blocked by a parade of firefighters. If you find this condition when entering, don't add to it—find another way. Wouldn't it be great if we had ladders and actually used them! Resist the urge to crowd the hall. Getting trapped in a center hall with no windows is one of the most dangerous positions in a structure (figs. 17–62 and 17–63).

Fig. 17–61. Basement fires have limited ventilation points and offer the greatest chance for extension through voids. (Courtesy of Chris Saraceno)

Fig. 17–62. Keep the hallway and stairs clear for a quick egress if things go bad. (Courtesy of Dan Nocera)

Fig. 17–63. Firefighters standing on stairs create an unsafe condition.

Failure to use a lifeline for search. There have been too many cases of firefighters getting lost, then dying because they ran out of air inside large buildings. They usually run out of air because they cannot find their way out of the building. Commercial buildings, below-grade areas such as cellars or basements, and any large area structures such as townhouses or estate homes should only be searched with a lifeline. In any of these areas, any firefighter not on a hoseline should be on a lifeline. A thermal imaging camera (TIC) is also a necessity, but overreliance on new technology, which can malfunction, could leave a team of searching firefighters disoriented in a large area. A **lifeline** does not malfunction nor does it need batteries.

Failure to identify and establish a secondary means of egress. Firefighters entering a building to search should take note of areas of egress before they enter. Egress-friendly areas such as porch roofs and fire escapes must be noted. The same should be practiced for roof access. If you have gotten into a building or onto a roof, you should know at least two ways out. RIT operations should include laddering all sides of the building and the roof for additional means of egress. These locations should be announced over the radio by command as soon as they are established, as personnel already inside the building will not be aware of the existence and location of these egress points. Failure to establish additional means of egress leads to an unacceptable alternative: the bailout.

Failure to identify the signs of rapid fire development. To survive rapid fire development, firefighters must be trained in the recognition of the signs leading to these developments. This recognition comes in the form of using the senses to detect these signs. This can be either from visual signs such as the reading of smoke for the signs of a flashover or backdraft, or reading the building. Reading and understanding the building and its inherent construction will give clues as to where the paths of least resistance for fire travel will be and where areas of danger from rapid fire development might exist. Rapid fire development signs can come from the sense of hearing as in the case of a fire crackling in the overhead in a smoke-obscured room or above a drop ceiling or in a cockloft. Hearing will also be the sense used when the cues of impending fire development or loss of control of the fire is transmitted over the radio. It can also come from the sense of touch as the heat conditions in a room begin to rapidly increase. This points to one basic need: Be alert at all times (fig. 17–64).

Search and rescue: the right way

- Must be protected by the attack lines

- Will be infinitely more effective with and benefit from proper and timely ventilation (fig. 17–65)

Fig. 17–64. Firefighters must be constantly aware of cues of rapid fire development. Heavy, pressurized smoke is one of those indicators. Things are not getting better when you see smoke like this. (Courtesy of Ron Jeffers)

Fig. 17–65. A hoseline is stretched through the front door to cut off fire and protect interior stairs. (Courtesy of Kurt Tiedeman)

Ventilation

Improper ventilation. Improper ventilation contributes to our failure to control the building and plays a large role in fire progression. Whether you use positive pressure or roof ventilation, it must be coordinated for firefighter safety. When venting for fire, vent as close to the fire as possible and make sure that you are venting ahead of the line. We are seeing more and more fires where the fire is venting out a window, but further size-up shows that heavy black to brown smoke is pushing down the hall and out the door. This is an indication that more ventilation is needed. The first priority is to increase ventilation close to fire and have personnel enter with a charged hoseline. If conditions dictate, cool the ceiling as you advance to push back the fire and cool the overhead. The old teaching of not placing water on smoke does not hold true anymore if the smoke is hot and pushing over you (fig. 17–66).

Fig. 17–66. With smoke pushing out the front door, crews could be caught in the hall by rapid fire progression. This is an indication of the need for more ventilation close to or over the fire. (Courtesy of Chris Saraceno)

FIREGROUND NOTE

It is not the mistake that you make, it is how you recover, recognize, share, and learn from it.

The rate of heat release experienced in today's simple house fire results in flashover much more quickly than in the past. Most furniture is made of synthetic materials. Always be aware of your surroundings. The warning signs of rollover, fire propagation down the wall, and everything going dark quickly may all be masked by thick black smoke. The only reliable sign will be rapid heat buildup or high heat. In buildings with high ceilings or drop ceilings, smoke can ignite, changing conditions rapidly.

Failure to sound the floor or roof. Not sounding the floor or roof can result in ending up at the bottom of a shaft or falling through the roof. Entering through a window onto a weakened floor will have a devastating effect. A hidden hazard consists of windows in two-story foyers that access ledges that homeowners place decorations on. When a firefighter enters, the floor or ledge will be sound, but then, about 2–3 ft (0.6–1 m) in, there is a 15-ft (4.6-m) or more drop to the first floor. When working on the roof, if you cannot see, you must crawl. Beware of light shafts and high parapets. For a commercial building, try to cross in the front where the storefronts line up (fig. 17–67). In multistory multiple dwellings, the shafts can be anywhere, and although their location may be uniform from one building to the next when built in a row, they may not be.

Fig. 17–67. Store depths will vary, making it easy to walk off the roof. Try to cross in the front where they are usually even with the street and sidewalk.

One note of caution when sounding floors: Victims who cannot get to doors often fall victim beneath windows, their next choice for egress. Before bashing your tool onto the floor to see if there is a substantial place in which to enter, sweep first to determine if a victim is below the window. In this way, you will not turn a rescue into a recovery. Blasts to the head with a Halligan tool or axe are not conducive to rescue operations.

Failure to recognize the presence of truss construction. This size-up failure has contributed and continues to contribute to firefighter deaths each year. Truss roofs should be located during preplanning. A building's occupancy will also clue you in to the potential presence of truss construction. Occupancies of suspicion include bowling alleys, auto dealerships, warehouses and "big box" stores, and fast food restaurants. When confronted with any business where a large open space is present or any new construction, especially in commercial or residential occupancies, assume that a truss is present until ruled out. In New Jersey, a system enforced by state law is in place that denotes the presence of a truss. A triangle on the building with an "R" inside it indicates that a truss roof is present. The same triangle with an "F" inside it indicates that a truss floor is present. If both a truss floor and roof are present, an "RF" will be inside the triangle (fig. 17–68). This provides safety warning at a glance. New York State and Florida have recently adopted similar guidelines for truss buildings.

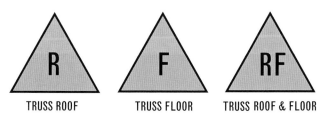

TRUSS ROOF   TRUSS FLOOR   TRUSS ROOF & FLOOR

Fig. 17–68. Triangle markings indicating the presence of trusses

A truss assembly can fail in 5–8 minutes under flame impingement. When using a TIC, confirm roof construction and report to command. You also will feel the difference when walking on a lightweight wood truss roof versus conventional construction. The truss roof will have more bounce when you walk. You should not operate above or below a truss roof with fire in the roof space (fig. 17–69).

Ventilation: the right way

- Must be conducted in a coordinated manner with the fire attack to help locate, confine, and exhaust the products of combustion in the proper direction

- Will increase visibility, enhancing the safety and expediency of the primary search (fig. 17–70)

Fig. 17–69. This truss roof in Hamden, CT, failed 6 minutes after the fire department would have arrived on scene.

Fig. 17–70. Firefighter wearing full PPE while cutting a hole in roof. (Courtesy of the Middletown, CT, Fire Department)

Accountability and safety

Failure to establish and maintain a collapse zone. Not establishing and maintaining a collapse zone can have catastrophic results. Collapse zones can be increased at an incident to fit the situation. However, collapse zones do not get smaller, and buildings that are determined to be a collapse hazard do not get safer. Firefighters must not be affected by the moth-to-the-flame syndrome, where they are inclined to move their hoseline inside of the collapse zone or out of a flanking position, thereby putting themselves in harm's way (fig. 17–71).

Fig. 17–71. Even partial building collapses can result in catastrophe, injuring or killing firefighters. (Photo by firegroundimages.com)

Failure to recognize hazardous exposure potential. Not all deaths are as dramatic as building collapses. As we get older, we are plagued by the cumulative effects of breathing toxic gases that can cause heart attacks, strokes, and even cancer. Although it is impossible to completely limit exposure to all the products of combustion, soot on your skin or a shift in the wind can result in a direct exposure. We must do everything in our power to minimize exposure. We often drop our guard at the wrong time.

Overhaul and minor fires pose many hidden hazards. Firefighters should wear breathing apparatus until the environment is metered for the presence of carbon monoxide and hydrogen cyanide. If these gases are present, they will not be found by themselves. Relying on permissible threshold limits will provide a false sense of security. Although at this time it is not practical to meter for all the products of combustion, using these two gases as a benchmark will provide a margin of safety. Masks should not be removed until the atmosphere reads zero. If, after your mask is off, you start to experience watery eyes, it is likely that you are being exposed to acrolein or hydrogen chloride. Place your mask back on or exit the area. Other strategies for limiting exposure include washing gear and taking a shower after a fire (fig. 17–72).

Fig. 17–72. Firefighters should meter the atmosphere before removing SCBA. Remember that the consequences of exposure may, in the long term, result in stroke, heart attack, and cancer.

Freelancing. The most critical tactical mistake is **freelancing**, which means wandering off to perform tasks on your own without an assignment. Maintaining company integrity and keeping personnel accounted for is the most important duty of the company officer, and maintaining self-discipline is the most important duty of each and every firefighter. Freelancing is always a mistake, and departments must have a zero-tolerance policy in regard to this dangerous issue. A simple company accountability model explains this very nicely. According to this model, there are only four places a company should be assigned on the fireground:

- At the command post awaiting an assignment

- In staging

- Operating in an assigned area

- In the rehabilitation division

The keyword here is *assigned*. The only time a company deploys without direct orders is when they are one of the first-arriving companies and their actions are being guided by scene assignment SOPs. For example, according to a department's initial scene assignment SOP, suppose the first-arriving engine company is responsible for attack and water supply (and command if they arrive before a chief), the second engine is responsible for a backup line and a second water supply and the first-arriving ladder company is assigned forcible entry, primary search, reconnaissance, and ventilation duties. Unless something out of the ordinary is going on, that is where they should be and what they should be doing. If a later-arriving company self-deploys without orders from command, they are freelancing. This is usually more prevalent with later-arriving companies and additional alarm companies. The moral: *Do not go to work without orders!*

Emergency bailouts. FFI 5.2.4 An emergency bailout is an absolute failure of the fireground at every level of the game. Firefighting personnel who exit a building any way other than where they entered it have more than likely become disoriented and are often exiting by sheer luck. Emergency bailouts are usually a result of a combination of factors that may include, but are not limited to, the following:

- Failed size-up

- Freelancing

- Failure to properly wear PPE and SCBA

- Communications failure

- Failed command and control

- Failure to follow SOPs and the action plan

- Failure to coordinate fire operations

- Improper and uncoordinated ventilation

- Failure by firefighters to confine the fire

- Failure by firefighters without hoselines to create barriers between themselves and the fire, and/or passing fire with no known exit

- Undisciplined hoseline operations

- Fire streams applied from the wrong place

- Opposing hose streams

- Complacency

Training on the proper procedures to execute an emergency bailout is absolutely necessary, but training in the prevention of the points of failure mentioned in the last sentence are more important and will serve as bailout prevention measures.

Company accountability model: the right way

Step 1. Companies report to the command post as a unit.

Step 2. Companies are assigned to an operational area, reporting to a division supervisor.

Step 3. Companies operate *only* in assigned division.

Step 4. When relieved, companies report as a unit back to the command post.

Step 5. If reassigned, go back to Step 2.

Step 6. If sent to rehab when complete, go back to Step 1.

Note that with each assignment and reassignment, including the order to take-up, the company officer must ensure that the accountability officer is aware of that assignment and where that company will be operating. Note also that they always report back to the command post once an assignment is complete, whether it is in a fire building or in the rehab division. The command post should be like an organizational manifold. All activities must pass through it. Anything or anyone who goes around it is freelancing (fig. 17–73).

Fig. 17–73. Companies must report as a unit, receive orders as a unit, and operate as a unit. Freelancing is unacceptable. (Courtesy of Ron Jeffers)

FIREGROUND NOTE

Many firefighters fail to focus on size-up but allow adrenaline to take over.

Prevention, not intervention

Tactics are the building blocks that make up our overall strategic objectives of life safety, incident stabilization, and property conservation. It is commitment to the basics—safe staffing and company excellence—that will prevent most tragedies. If we increased physical fitness, healthier lifestyles, and quality training for all ranks, there would be little need for intervention. However, we must acknowledge that we can do everything right and still find ourselves in dangerous situations on this job. Prevention of fatalities and injuries is difficult at best given the places we must conduct operations. We must do our best, and then some, to prepare for working in dangerous buildings through activities such as **prefire planning** and building inspections. Departments must also actively engage in and encourage information exchange between personnel and between shifts. To take this a step further, information exchange is also a concept that mutual aid groups should embrace. How many departments fight large fires alone, especially in large and dangerous buildings? Information exchange as well as interagency drills with neighboring departments lay the groundwork for a safer, more cooperative fireground. To this end, the following sections outline some ways to share the information, both locally and regionally.

VACANT BUILDING MARKING SYSTEM

The purpose of vacant building marking systems is to alert responders at a glance to HVBs and their inherent dangers. Marking buildings with orange spray paint (the international color of hazard) is SOP-driven. Buildings are usually marked by the SO on orders of the IC at a fire scene or by the SO when notified by company members that they have come across a HVB, either on a response or on a building survey. The markings are placed in a conspicuous position so they are easily recognized by arriving personnel. This system should be adopted by entire mutual aid groups.

Level 1 vacant building: entry permitted

Vacant buildings that may be entered should be signified by a box painted on the exterior of the building's walls. The department's initials or other adopted distinguishing mark should be written below the box, as should be done with any building hazard notification symbol. This will alert members that the symbol is department-approved.

NHRFR

Level 2 vacant building: enter with extreme caution

Other buildings may be entered, but only with extreme caution. This condition is denoted by a box with one line cutting diagonally across it (like a spare in bowling). This building may have suffered damage from previous fires, vandalism, and rot due to neglect. Firefighters should not take unnecessary risks in this building. Any attack should be carried out with extreme caution and with a pessimistic prediction of success. This and the no-entry symbol may be accompanied by another symbol, such as the ones that follow.

NHRFR

Level 3 vacant building: no entry

Vacant buildings that have undergone previous fire damage or other destructive forces or circumstances should be considered off-limits to all members at all times. A building that has hazards so severe that firefighters should not enter it under any circumstance should be denoted by a box with an X covering the whole box (like a strike in bowling).

NHRFR

Identifying unsafe building features

Some buildings may be safe to enter, but because of some safety concerns, firefighters should use extreme caution in the particular area denoted by the box. The boxes below show an example of a building with a dangerous fire escape on the left and dangerous stairs and/or landings on the right. Departments are not limited to these and may create their own symbols to address a particular hazard. If building owners object to the department putting spray paint on their building, tell them that the fire department objects to their unsafe building. The choice is with the owners: Fix the hazard or have their building marked up.

NHRFR   **NHRFR**

Structural damage (postfire)

Both primary (the damage done by the fire) and secondary damage (the damage done by firefighting) may leave the building in a dangerous condition. Firefighters from other shifts who may have another fire in the same building should be made aware of the hazards. Holes in the roof and/or the floors must be noted. The building should be marked to warn firefighters of these hazards. **Roof open** is denoted by the RO symbol, and **floor open** is denoted by the FO symbol. Floor hole notations should include the floor that is in question. A building with holes in both the floors and the roof may use two separate symbols or they may be placed in the same box. If there are multiple floors with holes, the FO-M symbol may be used. These symbols may be used in conjunction with limited or no-entry symbols.

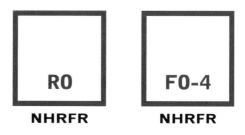

NHRFR   **NHRFR**

If both the roof and the floor(s) are opened, the symbol may look like the following. In this case, there are multiple floors with holes as well as an open roof.

NHRFR

Establishing a building hazard awareness program is an effective way of informing responding personnel about unsafe building conditions. Any discovery of this type by any company should prompt the response of the SO or battalion commander. Other notifications may include the building department, fire prevention, or the health department.

Hazardous vacant building notification system

This system works hand in hand with and is the follow-up system to the vacant building marking system. It is an SOP-driven system, and once a building is identified as a HVB and marked (fig. 17–74), a paper trail and notification system is set into motion to ensure that all personnel are made aware of the building and its hazards. It begins with the completion of a form (fig. 17–75) that is then submitted through the chain of command where the information is duplicated and disseminated to the companies. The information also goes to dispatch to be included in the CAD system and to the building official of the city. At times, a memo is also distributed with photographs taken by the SO in order for personnel to see the hazards instead of just reading about them (fig. 17–76).

Fig. 17–74. Hazardous vacant building (HVB) markings on this building prohibit entry as well as bring attention to hazards created by an open roof and floor. This is a Level 3 hazardous vacant building. Marking systems such as this allow a fire department to alert its firefighters to the dangers before they enter a building.

FIREGROUND NOTE

Before you put paint on a house, make sure it is vacant!

NORTH HUDSON REGIONAL FIRE & RESCUE STANDARD OPERATING PROCEDURES

HVB NOTIFICATION FORM

Date:_____   Day of Week:_____

Platoon:_____   Safety Officer:_____

Address:_____

Municipality:_____

Owner:_____

Fire Building ☐   Vacant (Non-Fire) ☐

Permanent ☐   Temporary ☐

HVB LEVEL: Check One

☐   Level 1 Entry permitted   _____

▨   Level 2 Caution Required   _____

Additional Symbols Added: _____   _____   _____

⊠   Level 3 Entry Prohibited   _____

Is this an HVB Level / Occupancy Status Update?   Yes_____   No_____

Comments:_____
_____
_____
_____

Signature:_____

Fax to: Deputy Chief
          Battalion Chiefs
          Headquarters (Chief of Safety)
          Fire Control
          Building Official of applicable jurisdiction

Hazardous Vacant Building Marking System

Fig. 17–75. Hazardous vacant building form

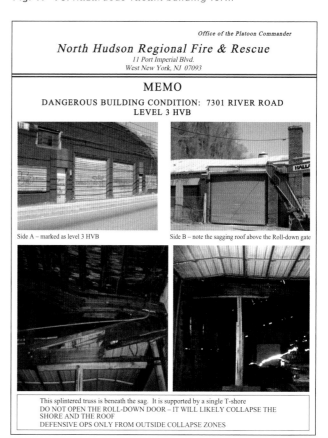

Fig. 17–76. Hazardous vacant building memo

RADIO OPERATIONS

Urgent call

When an **urgent call** is given on the radio, it is mandatory that all other nonemergency radio traffic stop until the urgent call is cleared by command. This transmission is given over the radio and repeated three times. Examples of situations where an urgent transmission may be required are an open shaft, localized collapse, and loss of water. The urgent call is an important message that usually will have an impact on tactics. These messages normally follow an unexpected event on the fireground. A proactive urgent transmission may very well avert a Mayday transmission later.

Mayday, Mayday, Mayday

Mayday is a distress call for help and an indication that you or a firefighter you are with is in grave danger of serious injury or death. Like the urgent transmission, this call is given over the radio and repeated three times. This allows all on the fireground to distinguish between the call for help and other units communicating about the Mayday. Although you must call the Mayday as soon as you realize you are in trouble, there will be times where you or your crew will have to take protective measures first. For example, suppose you and your crew are caught in a center hallway with a loss of water. There is fire rapidly progressing down the hall. In this case, you would need to get to an area of refuge first, such as going into a room and shutting the door, before transmitting the Mayday. Although the circumstances will dictate your actions, there are basic guidelines for when to call a Mayday.

- Medical emergency
- Trapped by fire
- Fall through floor or roof
- Building collapse
- Lost and can't find crew
- Lost one of your own crew
- Trapped by debris and can't free yourself on first attempt
- Low on air and not near an exit
- SCBA malfunction

Although this list is not all-inclusive, it all comes down to a simple catch-all rule of thumb: *If you think you are jammed up, you are! Call for help!* Help can always be turned back. We must keep in mind the **zero impact factor** (the amount of time it will take for a company to make an impact on your situation). Survival is predicated on your ability to remain calm. Don't wait to sound the Mayday. Every second delayed is 2 seconds (at least) that someone is not coming to help you.

FFI 5.2.4 Activate your personal alert safety system (PASS) device intermittently, but not when you are transmitting your call for help. Even if in contact with the RIT **sector officer**, periodically activate your PASS device. This will give the RIT a target to locate you. We recommend training using a modified version of the acronym LUNAR (location, unit, name and nature of problem, air supply and assignment, resources needed).

LUNAR

Location

Unit

Name and nature of problem

Air supply and assignment

Resources needed

Location. What is your location? This is where you are now or your last known location: what floor, what sector or division, front or back of the house or building. Can you describe something that will give a clue to where you are?

Unit. What company are you on? For example, Truck 4.

Name and nature of problem. Give your name. Your saving of your own life outweighs any privacy issues. There have been several incidents where the wrong firefighter has been accounted for, resulting in minutes being lost from the rescue. Your rescue will come down to seconds, not minutes. State the nature of the problem. This information may aid the RIT in getting to you quicker, having them take a different route, or other actions. Describe if you are lost, cut off by fire, or trapped in a collapse. Also, just because one member is in distress does not mean others are not with him or her. This may be the case when a team has fallen through a floor, but only one member is capable of transmitting the Mayday. Always ask the member if he or she is alone.

Air supply and assignment. How much air do you have left? If the emergency is that you are lost, time is your biggest concern. This is the hourglass nailed to the table—don't let time be a nail in your coffin. If your normal policy is to be out of the IDLH environment before your low air alarm activates (and you have followed it), you will have more time to find your way out or be located. Assignment will give clues to your likely locations.

Resources needed. What will be needed to extract you from you predicament?

Emergency fireground communication

FFI 5.2.4 It is imperative that all fire departments have an emergency fireground communications system in place, including the procedure for transmitting a Mayday message. It is best to develop joint procedures of this nature among those departments who work together on a routine basis. When buildings are falling and/or personnel are missing or in distress, SOP-driven control of the fireground will often make the difference between chaos and order.

There are two general types of emergency transmissions on the fireground:

- *Top-down* emergency transmissions (command to operating personnel)
- *Bottom-up* emergency transmissions (operating personnel to command)

Top-down emergency transmissions

There will be times during the operation where the IC needs to transmit a message of urgency to all operating personnel. It may be a warning about a dangerous building condition, a withdrawal from the building, or any other critical message that is essential to the fireground operation. It may even be an announcement regarding the location of secondary means of egress from the building or the roof. This is called a top-down emergency transmission and will usually be transmitted as an urgent message.

All firefighters should be aware of when this type message is about to be transmitted across the air. An emergency transmission should be initiated with a special radio tone dedicated for just that purpose alone. This tone should be tested every day at a specific time so that firefighters become conditioned to immediately stop what they are doing, listen up, and maintain radio silence when they

hear it. An emergency transmission has absolute priority over all other transmissions.

In North Hudson Regional (NJ) Fire and Rescue, a system has been in place for about 10 years, and it has worked well. After the emergency transmission is initiated by someone on the fireground, usually the IC, dispatch transmits a series of distinct tones followed by a boilerplate (standardized) statement announcing the emergency transmission. After the boilerplate announcement, the emergency transmission is repeated several times. Here is an example of an emergency transmission and procedure: (starts with a series of tones) "Dispatch to all companies operating on the fireground, stand by for an emergency transmission. By order of Park Avenue command, all companies operating in the fire building evacuate the fire building immediately; companies operating in exposures B and D, hold your position. Repeat (tones again), by order of Park Avenue command, all companies operating in the fire building, evacuate the fire building immediately; companies operating in exposures B and D, hold your position. 1533 hours." This message is repeated several times.

> # FIREGROUND NOTE
>
> It is better to be harassed at the kitchen table about calling for help than having everyone say what a great firefighter you were at your funeral.
>
> —Jim Duffy,
> Wallingford Fire Department

Bottom-up emergency transmissions

Just as command has a method for transmitting a top-down emergency transmission, personnel on the fireground and in the fire building must have a way of initiating a bottom-up emergency transmission. This is basically a Mayday transmission, but it can also be used for an urgent transmission. A firefighter who is lost, trapped, or in need of some type of assistance, or who needs to get some information to command or dispatch should have a system that is recognized by all personnel as an emergency transmission, which gets the same priority as a top-down emergency transmission.

FIREGROUND NOTE

A proactive urgent transmission may very well avert a Mayday transmission later.

Many departments have portable radios that have the capability to send an emergency transmission by pushing a button. Called a Mayday or emergency identification (EID) button, it sends a signal to dispatch or command, or both, and informs them by a readout exactly who is transmitting the emergency message. It also emits a distinctive tone over the all the radios except for the member who pushed the button. The drawback here is that if the button was pushed accidentally, the member who sent the transmission usually does not know it has been sent until someone comes looking for that individual. The button may be activated accidentally when the radio is inadvertently banged around while operating on the fireground—one very good reason why operating personnel should wear their radios under their coats, with only the collar microphone exposed. There have also been cases where the EID button was activated by getting it wet. This is discussed as a Lessons from the Fireground case study later in this chapter. In any case, it is a method by which firefighters can draw attention to an emergency situation.

In the fire service, there should always be a contingency plan for when something goes wrong or equipment unexpectedly fails. In North Hudson Regional Fire and Rescue, even though the portable radios have the EID button, a backup system has been adopted should the EID button fail. In fact, it is preferred that members in distress transmit an additional bottom-up emergency transmission to better ensure they can be heard amid the normal fireground radio chatter. This procedure is also tested daily over the air. The member who needs to send the message initiates the transmission in the following manner:

Step 1. The member manually activates his or her PASS device, causing the PASS alarm to sound.

Step 2. The portable radio is keyed for transmission.

Step 3. The keyed radio mike is placed next to the PASS device for a period of 10 seconds. The PASS tone is heard all over the fireground, signaling the initiation of a bottom-up emergency transmission.

Step 4. The PASS device is turned back to the arm position.

Step 5. The emergency message is broadcast using the following format:

Mayday, Mayday, Mayday, this is Firefighter _____.

Mayday, Mayday, Mayday, this is Firefighter _____.

(Message is then broadcast).

If the emergency transmission is initiated to signal that an entire company is in distress, the company name is substituted for the individual firefighter.

The key to transmitting the bottom-up emergency transmission is to use an audible alarm such as the PASS device or the radio EID button. The aim is to get someone's attention. There have been two cases in North Hudson where Mayday messages went unheard initially because the person sounding the Mayday did not use the PASS device, and thus the Mayday transmission got lost in the fireground communication shuffle. This was before we had radios with the EID button capability. Even a muffled PASS device activation is better than a muffled Mayday transmission without the audible tones. Even though North Hudson Regional Fire and Rescue has new portable radios, each of which has an EID button that sends a tone to the command post and identifying who is giving the Mayday, we still test this procedure every day and urge firefighters to use the PASS device over the air as an additional bottom-up emergency transmission.

None of these methods is foolproof, but together they can form an established procedure to allow the IC (top-down) and an individual firefighter or officer (bottom-up) to let someone know that something extraordinary or unusual is occurring. It is hoped that these procedures are never used; however, to be of any use, they must be taken seriously, be no secret to anyone, and be practiced.

RAPID INTERVENTION TEAMS/CREWS

RIT activation—reacting to and managing the Mayday

RIT activation should not cause a crisis at the command post or on the fireground. The RIT operation must be a deliberate and procedure-driven operation that is carefully coordinated and properly carried out. The IC and the officers on scene, both chief and company, have to demonstrate leadership ability, and all firefighters must demonstrate self-discipline to avoid letting the emotional pressure of the situation drive the incident. To this end, whether one is a part of the RIT team, an aide to command, or in a company that is supporting the RIT operation by continuing to fight the fire, every firefighter should understand the process of the Mayday operation.

The first priority is to determine who is missing and their location. Any LUNAR information missing from the Mayday report must be ascertained to best determine where to start looking. If the identity of the members cannot be determined, a PAR will need to be conducted. If the identity is known, a PAR should still be conducted, but possibly on an alternate frequency so it does not tie up rescue communications. The IC needs to clear the air by using an emergency radio transmission. Dispatch may be the best tool in accomplishing this, utilizing a dedicated emergency transmission tone, as was discussed in earlier in this chapter. It is advantageous to switch the firefighting operation to another frequency to concentrate on the communication requirements of the rescue operation.

If the distressed firefighter has to contact dispatch or command on a different frequency, allow that member to continue to communicate on that frequency and direct the rescue to that frequency. It might also be wise to assign the firefighting operation to another chief officer and for the IC to step back to better manage the Mayday.

Organizationally, the rescue operation should also be delegated to a chief officer designated as the rescue group supervisor. The responsibility of this position is to directly supervise the rescue operations and keep command informed of progress and needs. The officer in charge of the rescue must also become like an air traffic controller and give direction to the officer or firefighter calling for help. An additional SO should be requested as well as additional chief officers. An officer should also

be assigned to monitor fire conditions and structural conditions in the area. At least two additional alarms should be struck: one to support the rescue operation, and one for the firefighting effort. These companies should be sent to a Level 2 staging area.

It is critical that firefighting operations continue with a focus on keeping the fire from spreading to the area of the downed firefighter. If conditions require, an additional team may have to deploy a hoseline with the RIT to protect the rescue.

Additional resources must include an immediate request for an additional RIT. If possible, in the interim, one should be used from the tactical reserve for the incident so there is minimal time elapse for positioning a backup RIT. Even if this is possible, an additional RIT must still be summoned.

The original RIT is basically a recon team and should enter the building with minimum equipment to locate the downed or lost firefighter. There is no need to lug all of the RIT equipment in at this time because it will serve to slow down the team. Many departments have put together or purchased a RIT pack with all of the required tools in one easily transported bag (mentioned in the RIT tools section). If that is not available, at a minimum, a spare SCBA cylinder and mask, a ready-made rescue sling, hand lights, a lifeline, a TIC, and a set of irons (flat-head axe and Halligan tool) may be all that is needed for the initial RIT. After the firefighter is found and assessed, the equipment needs can be relayed back to the rescue group supervisor, where the second RIT can bring it in more quickly. At this point, all they have to do is follow the lifeline to the rescue area. The requirements of the rescue operation will depend greatly on the reports of the first RIT to reach the downed firefighter (fig. 17–77).

Fig. 17–77. RIT team removes a downed firefighter in training.

The IC must ensure that EMS (both basic life support [BLS] and advanced life support [ALS]) are summoned to the command post. They should be positioned in close proximity to the rescue group supervisor where the RIT has made entry. It might be best to have two medical teams standing by because RIT operations often cause injury to the rescuers. A liaison with the police should be established so that there is a lane open for the ambulance to get in and get out without delay. Arranging for and ensuring availability of a police escort may save valuable time during rush hour. If necessary, a **landing zone (LZ)** can be designated in case a **med-evac** is necessary. Med-evac protocols are usually set up in advance and may only require a phone call to be made by dispatch. Where to land the helicopter can be a concern, and the police can be of great help with that. Command should also have dispatch contact the hospital that the firefighter(s) will be taken to so the hospital personnel can make preparations prior to EMS arrival at the hospital.

After the Mayday situation has been stabilized, command should concentrate on further stabilizing the scene. Relief should be provided where needed and the troops kept focused. RIT personnel must stay disciplined, otherwise other firefighters and the public may be put in jeopardy.

All officers, including the SO, should be on the lookout for signs of critical incident stress and address it accordingly. To proactively address firefighter emotional needs, it might be a good idea to request a CISM team respond. Firefighters who were directly involved in the firefighter-down situation should be relieved. These firefighters should be sent to a common area away from the scene, such as a firehouse where CISM counselors are available for consultation and medical personnel are there to evaluate them.

Introduction to the intervention dilemma

The RIT dilemma, as we shall call it, plagues the fire service. The RIT response across the country is wide and varied. Some departments assign RIT as an engine company, while others use a squad company, a ladder company, or a rescue company. Some departments respond the RIT with the first-alarm companies, while others dispatch the RIT as soon as a working fire is confirmed. Although this is acceptable and meets most state statutes, other departments either respond with the RIT on the second alarm (which can be a deadly mistake—what if no one strikes a second alarm?), while others respond to it only on the request of the IC (an even more potentially lethal situation—what if the IC

forgets?). Some RITs respond from neighboring jurisdictions. This may be an automatic response or it may have to be requested. Other RITs are formed by committee—that is when the IC or SO takes individual personnel as they arrive, and form them into a RIT. Still others designate the RIT on the fly, over the radio, during response.

The fact is that most firefighter rescue situations occur during the first few minutes of the incident when the situation is unfolding and the least amount of information about the building or the fire is available. This is the time when firefighters are actively seeking out the fire and searching for victims, sometimes without a hoseline available and doing it with less than adequate personnel, and usually without the immediate services of a RIT.

Personnel requirements are also wide and varied. Some RITs consist of two members, and some have three, four, or more. Some have officers assigned, and some do not. In New Jersey, the *Model Fire Department Standard Operating Guide* issued by the New Jersey Division of Fire Safety states that the **rapid intervention crew (RIC)** shall be a designated crew of at least two firefighters. This is hardly enough to raise a ground ladder, let alone pull off a firefighter search and rescue mission. It does not even mention that an officer should be assigned.

Another major mistake can occur when the incident is rapidly escalating, and the first thing the IC does when the RIT arrives on the scene is put them to work fighting the fire. This is the biggest mistake of them all. Firefighter safety is the number-one priority on the fireground. If a building or a whole block burns down, but no firefighters get hurt, lost in the building, or killed, we have met the top priority. Buildings can be rebuilt, firefighters cannot. A RIT is dedicated resource with one focus—firefighter rescue capability. That is all they do. That is all they ever do.

With all these variables, we can state with some validity that the rapid intervention issue in this country is not rapid at all, but often consists of a hodgepodge of directives and agreements between departments that do not always get followed and hopefully will never have to be used. It is a gamble.

To be effective, RITs should not have to be requested, but should be a standard part of the department's response. They should operate under an established set of guidelines as outlined in the department's RIT operation SOP. For operations in large buildings, high-rises, or when exterior defensive operations cover a large geographic area, two or more RITs can be requested and assigned. In a high-rise operations, the RIT should

LESSONS FROM THE FIREGROUND

A fully developed cellar fire burned through the floor and into a first floor apartment. Seeing the fire in the apartment, the engine company on the first floor protecting the cellar stairs applied water to stop the extension. In doing so, they unknowingly pushed the fire through an open door at the rear of the apartment where it roared up a rear stairwell. There was a ladder company in the stairwell, making their way to the top floor to search for a reported missing child. As the fire consumed the stairwell, three of the four members were able to evacuate into a rear yard. The fourth firefighter, who was ahead of them, did not realize what was happening until it was too late to get back down the stairs. The fire and heat were moving so fast up the stairwell that it chased him up to and across the third floor where he had no other choice but to bail out the window. As he was scrambling up the stairs, the force of the flames actually knocked him over and he lost his helmet (no chinstrap!). Already severely burned on his ears, face, and head, he hung onto the windowsill until his hands and wrist almost burned off and then fell three floors. He smashed through a plastic awning on the way down and landed right next to an upside down picnic table and washing machine. His burn injuries required extensive surgery and therapy. His ears were almost completely burned off and had to be replaced by surgery. He survived and is back on the job.

LESSONS LEARNED

1. Always wear your protective gear properly.

2. Create barriers between yourself and the fire, especially when going above the fire.

3. Communicate your position and assignment to the attack team when you may be opposite the attack.

respond to the operations division on the floor below the fire where, if needed, they can be rapidly deployed to the area of the distress signal. If they are staged in the lobby, the reflex time for rapid intervention will be unnecessarily increased (and not rapid at all).

Standards and regulations

OSHA 1910.134 is the *Respiratory Protection Standard* that guides fire departments in procedures regarding such areas as respirator (breathing apparatus) use, maintenance, storage, and repair; mask fit testing; record keeping related to breathing apparatus; and procedures for structural firefighting. It is in this last section that regulations regarding the OSHA **two-in, two-out standard** is outlined. This standard is federal law in most states, and all fire departments and fire service personnel should comply with it. The standard states that the employee (the department), during interior structural firefighting, shall ensure that at least two employees who enter the immediately dangerous to life and health (IDLH) atmosphere shall remain in visual or voice contact with one another at all times; that at least two employees are located outside the IDLH atmosphere; and that all employees engaged in interior structural firefighting use SCBA.

The standard also allows one of the two individuals located outside the IDLH atmosphere to be assigned to an additional role, such as the IC in charge of the emergency or the SO, so long as this individual is able to perform assistance or rescue activities without jeopardizing the safety or health of any firefighter working at the incident. The authors cannot think of a situation where using these personnel to conduct a rescue would not further jeopardize the safety and health of firefighters at the incident. Many jurisdictions will also count the two-out as including the pump operator. Basically what this means is that if there is an emergency situation and no one else is available, the IC (the one running the show) and the pump operator (the one controlling the water, which may be only thing keeping the fire away from the downed firefighters) could be used to enter the building and rescue the trapped firefighter.

The standard further states that "nothing in this section is meant to preclude firefighters from performing emergency rescue activities before an entire team has assembled"—which allows us to attempt rescue with inadequate personnel. Studies done by the Phoenix Fire Department have shown that during firefighter rescue operations, the number of personnel needed to accomplish these tasks safely is about 12, and that some of them will also get lost or injured in the process. Having

only two firefighters—never mind the fact that they may have further critical responsibilities for the incident engaged in the rescue operation—is hardly an acceptable number. It is the responsibility of the department to have a mechanism in place that addresses this in a safer and more efficient manner.

The other caveat of the standard is an actual dichotomy or contradiction of the intent. It allows for the situation when, if based on dispatch reports, scene reports, or size-up indicators, an imminent life-threatening situation exists where immediate rescue activities may prevent the loss of life or serious injury, the requirements of the two-in, two-out standard may be suspended and individual members or the team may enter to save lives. During the initial phase of the fire operation, we are always in the life safety or rescue mode. Unless the building is fully involved, we must always assume a life hazard exists. Once we determine that there are no victims or they have been removed, we enter the incident stabilization phase and the standard applies.

Although the mandate for the two-in, two-out is a step in the right direction for firefighter safety, other standards such as NFPA 1710, *Standard for the Organization and Deployment of Fire Suppression Operations, Emergency Medical Operations, and Special Operations to the Public by Career Fire Departments* and NFPA 1720, *Standard for the Organization and Deployment of Fire Suppression Operations, Emergency Medical Operations, and Special Operations to the Public by Volunteer Fire Departments*, are the mechanisms by which fire departments can properly staff companies and should also be made law. At this time, these are only suggested standards, as are all NFPA standards not adopted by a state or jurisdiction, where they would then become law. As standards, they have no teeth and do not need to be complied with. It is ironic, though, that these same standards, when a firefighter casualty occurs or other legal issue arises, are the criteria used to show negligence and collect monetary damages from municipalities. Very few departments meet these staffing standards.

Self-rescue

FFI 5.2.4 Although situational avoidance is clearly the best choice, when things do go wrong—and at some point in your career they will—past training, self-reliance, and a proactive approach will give you the best chance of survival. A variety of techniques that every firefighter should know will be described next. Whether you need to help your partner clear an entanglement or

seek an area of refuge after a loss of water, you owe it to yourself and your fellow firefighters to be prepared.

Personal tools. Regardless of your position on the fireground, you should always carry tools. One of your hand tools should provide you with a way to breach a wall or force a door. The most practical and versatile tools are the Halligan tool and the flat-head axe. Beware: Never give up your tool. If you do, you will not have it when you need it. We have all seen a firefighter without a tool take the new firefighters' tool. This is unacceptable. For example, if a firefighter or officer grabs your hook or bar, hold onto it, and say, "Where would you like me to pull?" This will ensure that you maintain control of your tool. Smaller hand tools can play a role in clearing wire that you may get tangled in. You should carry a small pair of wire cutters in a pocket that is located opposite the air line on your SCBA. This will allow you to access your cutters without taking your hand off your air supply strap, so you can clear the entanglement even if you have to manipulate your SCBA to reach the wire.

Area of refuge. Having a contingency plan of where to go if something goes wrong is critical. Continual size-up of your location in the structure will aid you in planning for failure. When in a public hall in an apartment building, first force the door to the apartment next to the fire apartment. This will not only show you the likely layout of the fire apartment, but it will also give you a place to go if there is a wind-driven fire or a loss of water.

When moving down an interior hallway, map it out. Know where all the doors are, what are they constructed of, and which way they open. When inside the structure, a door that opens toward you will either be the closet or basement, which is a change in grade if you are on an upper floor or the way outside. In older buildings, and in some newer townhouses or estate homes, it may be an elevator door. Understanding the typical layouts of structures can aid you in your size-up.

As a member of a truck company, if you find the fire, you should close the door, ensure your area is safe, and call for a hoseline. If fire is coming down the hall, retreat into a room and close the door. This action should buy enough time for you to exit safely. By closing the door to the room, you may be able to prevent making a headfirst dive onto a ladder or bailing out on a rope. When seeking an area of refuge, never retreat into a bathroom. There may be no windows or only a small window high up on the wall, making escape impossible. Knowing where abutting roofs and porches are can also provide a safe haven. If there is no ladder there, you can exit the window, hook

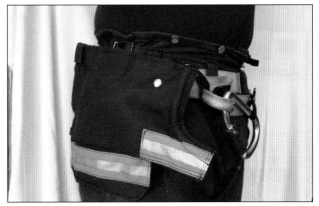

Fig. 17–78. Bailout kits provide an exit at every window for the times when you cannot close the door. (Courtesy of Coda Ricci)

Fig. 17–79. Wall breaching. (Courtesy of Local 825 president Patrick Egan)

your tool on the sill, using it as an improvised lifeline, and wait for a ladder below any venting fire and heat.

Bailout kits. Theoretically, bailout kits place a ladder at every window. They provide a way out in the most extreme conditions. Although seeking an area of refuge by closing a door may negate the need for such devices, there are circumstances where this will not be possible. You may find yourself in a living room, kitchen, or room without a door, and the bailout may be your only option. There are many different systems on the market. We recommend a device that has the ability to anchor at the window because it is unlikely that under deteriorating fire conditions that you will be able to tie off to a remote anchor. Several devices have the ability to stop you after you exit the window, so you can reposition yourself and then lower yourself to the ground (fig. 17–78).

Wall breaching. FFI 5.3.9 Breaching a wall may be necessary to exit a hazardous environment or effect the rescue of a civilian or a trapped firefighter (fig. 17–79). Wall construction differs, and your size-up will determine if this is a practical option. Brick, concrete, and block walls are not practical for a firefighter to breach for self-rescue and may require special tools. Block walls can be effectively breached for firefighter rescue by employing a sledgehammer. This option is labor intensive, requires room to swing, and is usually performed from the outside in. For self-rescue, the walls most often breached will be lath and plaster, or gypsum board. Even with this type of construction, don't be surprised to find studs that are not conventional in their spacing or a chimney inside that makes breaching impossible. Wall studs are usually 16 in. (41 cm) apart, but this may differ based on factors such as the age of the building. If a wall breach is the action you must take, the Mayday should have already been called. Breaching a wall with a Halligan tool entails the following steps:

- Check for an outlet on the wall. If one exists, move to the next bay.

- Plunge the tool completely through wall about 3½ ft off floor to ensure that the back of wall is clear.

- If you hit something solid (maybe a refrigerator, dresser, or wall unit), move down a few bays.

- Pull the bar back through the wall, drop to bottom, and pull back toward yourself.

- Breach the rest of the wall by pushing the back of the wall down with the Halligan or kicking it out with both feet.

- If wires are present, knock them down with the Halligan.

- If time permits, hit a stud sideways at the bottom. This will provide a wider opening. You may then get through without manipulating your SCBA.

Detroit dive

- Breach the wall as previously described.

- Place back to hole.

- Lean back, to allow the SCBA bottle to clear the hole.

- Rotate slightly to allow one of your arms to be placed on the opposite side of the wall.

- Lean back and rotate on your side toward the arm that went through.

- Note: In all breaches, be sure to check the stability of the floor on the other side to ensure it is actually there and you will not be entering a shaft or two-story foyer.

This method is highly effective, but works best on a gypsum board wall (fig. 17–80). If going through lath and plaster, take an extra second to make sure the bay is completely cleared. In chapter 19, Search and Rescue, the section on "Mask Confidence and Emergency Procedures" covers the reduced profile maneuver and the disentanglement maneuver. Any method that requires you to manipulate your SCBA to self-rescue shall be cause to call the Mayday. If you must use one of these methods to get by an obstruction for fire attack, you should radio a message to command apprising them of the situation and make a careful risk-versus-gain assessment of the situation.

Fig. 17–80. The Detroit dive. (Courtesy of Local 825 president Patrick Egan)

Filter technology and smoke inhalation. Since the fire department adopted high-risk technology (e.g., SCBA) to make our work more effective and efficient, many civilian lives have been saved. Note that we didn't say *safer*. The leading cause of non–heart attack deaths inside structure fires each year has been smoke inhalation. Smoke inhalation injuries reported by NFPA in 2005 were as high as 3,390 in the United States. RITs have proven not to be the answer alone. Assistant Chief Kreis of Phoenix, Arizona, conducted a study of 200 drills and timed how long it takes a properly trained and staffed RIT to locate a downed firefighter. The average time was around 8 minutes. This was with blacked out masks and no heat. This shows that if we are going to reduce these deaths and injuries, it will take a commitment to air management, proper staffing, an early call for help, survival training, and embracing filter technology.

Filter technology provides the firefighter in trouble with a last chance of being rescued or exiting the structure (fig. 17–81).

Fig. 17–81. Firefighter exits IDLH atmosphere using filter technology. (Courtesy of FirefighterSafety.net)

Filter technology is not a way to extend your working time. It is only to be deployed when the firefighter is faced with no other option than to breathe an IDLH atmosphere. These filters protect the firefighter from acrolein, hydrogen chloride, hydrogen cyanide, and the most notable firefighter killer, carbon monoxide. These filters do not provide oxygen. Although OSHA defines an oxygen-deficient atmosphere as below 19.5%, the human body can survive in an environment below that percentage.

Study data from Yale and Harvard confirm that not all fires at the floor level will experience a drop in oxygen below 19.5%. The number of smoke inhalation injuries are also an indication that in every one of those fires, there was enough oxygen to support life. The real problem is the toxic gases that do not allow the body to process the available oxygen in the blood stream, resulting in asphyxiation. Case studies show that when a firefighter runs out of air, the first inclination is to rip off his or her mask. This makes a difficult situation worse because of the difficulty and time it will take the RIT to provide air to the firefighter. With a filter, the mask remains in place, allowing the RIT to simply change out the regulator. The survival sequence is the following:

- Call the Mayday.

- Activate immediately your PASS device.

- Seek an area of refuge.

- When completely out of air, change to the filter.

- Update the Mayday and get out!

Filters are rated to last for 15 minutes and are an essential component in any survival sequence.

PASS devices and preparing to be rescued. According to the National Institute of Standards and Technology (NIST), "Personal Alert Safety System (PASS) devices are designed to signal for aid via an audible alarm." Typically, PASS devices sense movement or lack of movement and activate a 95-decibel alarm signal if the lack of motion exceeds a specific time period. The loud alarm signal alerts other personnel that a firefighter has become incapacitated. The sound also helps to guide rescue personnel to the location of the incapacitated firefighter.

Although the current NFPA 1982 *Standard on Personal Alert Safety Systems (PASS)* requires only a motion detector, some manufacturers are beginning to incorporate thermal exposure sensors into each PASS device. Some PASS devices are also being integrated into fireground personnel accountability systems. Studies have shown that when PASS devices are not integrated, they may not be armed by the firefighter.

Your PASS device is a tool that should be manually activated when you are in distress. When preparing to be rescued, you should position yourself so if you were to become incapacitated, you would not muffle the alarm. As a general guideline, in a house, if you are lost or separated, call for help and keep moving along the wall to try to find a window or area of refuge. Remember to feel up high on the wall because if you keep feeling low, you may never feel the sill but keep passing below it on your way around the wall. Coming across a register in the floor or a radiator is a good indicator that you are probably near an outside wall. This will not be the case in a bathroom. Although making noise is recommended, every now and then stop and listen to your surroundings.

In a commercial structure, most instructors recommend moving until you find an area of refuge or some feature you can describe that can aid in your rescue. If you decide it is best to stay put, calm down and conserve air.

Breathing techniques. Air consumption rates vary between individuals. Factors will include lung capacity, physical fitness, level of exertion, and emotional state.

It is critical to conduct comparative testing to evaluate emergency and normal breathing techniques for each firefighter. This is accomplished by synchronizing SCBA bottles with a digital air gauge after the bottles have cooled down. Each bottle must be labeled for the firefighter being tested. Whatever method your department uses, it is not recommended to use skip-breathing or any method that requires you to hold your breath. Holding your breath causes carbon dioxide to build in your bloodstream, resulting in an increase in respirations.

Many firefighters try to breathe in through their nose and out through their mouth until their respirations demand that they take a full breath. You must find a method that works for you. Currently the air gauge works off pressure, not volume. You must be able to judge your available air supply from your pressure gauge, and that takes practice. The following factors should be considered:

- How far did it take you to get where you are?

- What is your level of exertion?

- How much experience and training have you had?

- What is your emotional state?

Far too often, new firefighters gauge their air supply based on the smokehouse they were trained in. If your first fire is in a commercial building, the smokehouse reference will do you little good. Firefighter I an II classes should be exposed to different buildings in class, and instructors are encouraged to conduct as many evolutions on air as possible.

Reilly emergency breathing technique. As with any method, the Reilly emergency breathing technique is predicated on remaining calm. With this technique, you hum out your breath. This is a low hum and usually cannot be heard over the low air alarm. A firefighter's normal breath cycle is around to 6 to 8 seconds. By extending your exhalations to between 12 and 15 seconds, you can compound the time to escape or wait for rescue. For example, if you had 50 breaths left, and you extended your breathing cycle by just 6 seconds, the compounded time would give you an additional 5 minutes of time on air. In tests, we found this method to also have a calming effect by giving the firefighter something to focus on. If you are moving, it is difficult to use any method. If you feel like you need to take a normal breath, do it, then go back to the technique. The more you use it, the more time you will buy (see fig. 17–82).

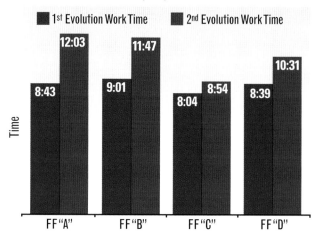

DAY 2: Breathing Technique test while firefighter in prone position 500 psi cylinder

■ 1st Evolution Work Time   ■ 2nd Evolution Work Time

FF "A": 8:43 / 12:03
FF "B": 9:01 / 11:47
FF "C": 8:04 / 8:54
FF "D": 8:39 / 10:31

Fig. 17–82. Chart of prone test for breathing technique

Intervention teams

The rapid intervention team. Response of the RIT response is crucial for firefighter safety. At the very least, the RIT, also known as a rapid intervention crew (RIC) or firefighter assist and search team (FAST), should respond upon confirmation of a working fire. Second-alarm RITs are not acceptable and, in some states, illegal. History has shown that a good majority of firefighters get themselves into assistance-required trouble in the initial stages of the operation. If the department protocol calls for the RIT to be dispatched with the striking of the second alarm, they will not be on scene when needed most.

This team should also be dispatched on any special response that is out of the normal response realm, such as hazmat (hazardous materials) incidents, technical rescue incidents, and extrications, to name a few. RIT response and operation should be part of a departmental SOP, addressed in advance. The duties, responsibilities, and assigned equipment of this team should be addressed in the SOP.

At incidents where there is an unusually large commitment of personnel on the scene, command may consider requesting two or more RITs. RIT members may also be required to don 1-hour SCBA cylinders in a large-area building. The rationale here is that if the firefighters requiring rescue are wearing 30-minute cylinders, and they can't get out, how will the second team with the same cylinders get them out in time without falling victim to the same predicament?

FIREGROUND NOTE

The quick use of a defibrillator even before firefighter removal may make the difference between a rescue and a recovery.

RIT tools. RIT operations are based on the effective use of tools. An RIT without tools is next to useless. RIT packs and RIT tools, both hand and power, should be staged at the ready in an accessible but safe area.

RIT pack. The RIT pack includes but is not limited to:

- A 1-hour bottle
- RIT connections for your department's SCBA manufacturer
- Extra facepiece
- Regulator to RIT pack
- Multiple stand-alone PASS devices
- Wire cutters with reflective handles
- Tin snips with reflective handles
- Small wonder bar
- Two lengths of 15-ft loop webbing
- Two large carabiners
- Small anchor strap
- Two filters

Make sure that there is a way to secure the RIT pack to the firefighter. Firefighters should be trained on using all of the connections to **transfill** the downed member's bottle. Note that the downed member's bottle will equalize when transfilled and will not give the downed member all of the available air. If you are rescuing a lost company, you must bring more than one pack.

Hand tools. The following is a suggested list of tools that the RIT should carry and stage:

- Portable radios (headset radio for RIT Officer)
- Spare SCBA cylinder and mask
- Supplied air respirator with spare cylinders
- Automated external defibrillator (AED)
- Ready-made rescue sling
- Hand lights
- Rope-guided search equipment with carabiners
- Thermal imaging camera (TIC)
- Set of irons (flat-head axe and Halligan tool)
- Pike pole or Halligan hook
- Knife
- Target exit device
- Sledgehammer or maul

Based on the building construction and occupancy, other tools may be required. For example, for operations in a high-rise, a hydraulic forcible-entry tool (HFT), also known as a rabbit tool, should be a standard part of the RIT equipment.

Power tools. Power saw with both wood-cutting blade

- Power saw with steel-cutting blade
- Fire service chain saw
- Concrete blade available

Where concrete may be encountered, staging a saw with a concrete blade is recommended. Do not rule out of the use of hydraulic rescue tools as required by the building construction, especially when confronted with fire-resistive buildings.

Safe power saw operation. Power saws can easily end a firefighter's career in a split second. One manufacturer stated that the limb will be gone before you feel the pain. To this end, power saw and all power tool operations should be conducted with extreme caution. The following are some safety guidelines to observe when operating power saws:

- Respect the tool.
- Wear safety glasses or SCBA.
- Ensure all saws are started in a safe area, shut down, and then taken to the area of operation. For example, before going to the roof, start the saw on the ground.
- Always be aware of ignition sources when fueling and refueling.

- Be aware of the **circle of danger**—anyone you can reach and touch with the saw (or any tool) is in the circle of danger.

- Always plan the cut and inform others of that plan.

- Never pick up the saw to start it—always start it on the ground.

- Keep good balance, with your feet in a boxer's stance 18–24 in. (46–61 cm) apart.

- When operating a saw with a wood blade (carbide tip), rev the saw to its maximum rpm before sinking it into the work.

- When operating a saw with steel blade, set the saw in the place to be cut before revving the saw. Begin to rev the saw slowly, and when the saw has a bite in the material, then progressively increase the rpm and make the cut.

- Do not store composite blades with hydrocarbons, because this can cause catastrophic failure.

- Position your legs so the plume of sparks are not directly hitting your gear. Turnouts can burn.

- Never step on anything that has been cut.

- Use the **buddy system** when cutting. Always have a guide person behind the saw operator. The guide person keeps an eye on the area, while the saw operator concentrates on the cut.

- Use the "contact-go/no-contact-stop system." As long as the guide person has a hand on the saw operator's shoulder or back, the cutting continues. If the guide person breaks contact, the saw operator stops cutting (fig. 17–83).

- Always control the saw.

- Always be prepared to stop the cut and the saw.

- Never let the saw operate more than 6 in. (150 mm) away from the cut.

- Listen to the saw—it will clue you in when to add or take away pressure.

- When the cut is stopped, bury the blade in the roof to stop the blade from spinning.

- Make sure that when the job is finished the saw is cleaned, fueled, and checked for damage.

Fig. 17–83. Nonverbal communication systems eliminate guesswork during cutting operations. This allows the firefighter operating the saw to concentrate on the cut. (Courtesy of Bob Scollan)

FIREGROUND NOTE

There is no politician on scene who is telling command that they can't call for the resources they need to protect us!

RIT on-scene actions—proactive preparation

Prior to standing by at the ready, the RIT can perform specific tasks aimed at increasing firefighter safety. In fact, the more preemptive action the RIT can take to help firefighters inside the building and on the roof help themselves out of danger areas, the safer the fireground will be. If a firefighter can get to an egress point that is already there and doesn't have to wait for one or create one by force, the job of the RIT is half done. Such actions include, but are not limited to the following:

- *Sizing up entry and exit points from the building.* The RIT should be identifying multiple ways in as well as multiple ways out for all floors or areas of the building. This includes plans for the breaching of walls.

- *Staging building construction-specific tools for firefighter rescue applications.* Without proper tools, the RIT is useless. Some departments use canvas tarps called RIT tarps on which all RIT tools are staged. The essential tools required for basic rapid intervention operations are listed on these tarps. If the building construction or some other condition requires additional equipment, the RIT officer ensures this is secured (fig. 17–84).

Fig. 17–84. RIT equipment should be gathered and staged in one place on the fireground. A dedicated RIT tarp is one way of organizing this equipment. Mandatory equipment can be listed on the tarp in permanent marker. (Courtesy of Ron Jeffers)

- *Ensuring the area is well lit.* Lighting on the fireground is a most basic safety issue. Most new fire apparatus can activate their powerful flood light systems with the flick of a switch. It should be part of the initial scene assignment duties for the ladder at the front of the building. The RIT, as required, can set up additional lighting to illuminate all sides of the fire building and possibly the roof. Illuminated operations are far safer than operations conducted in the dark. In addition, a lost firefighter may find the way to a window easier if the area outside it is lit up.

- *Raising ground ladders.* One of the main tasks of the RIT is to raise ground ladders around the building for secondary and tertiary egress from the upper floors and from the roof. In fact, they should not have to be told to do this. It should be done automatically (and directed by SOP). At one very smoky taxpayer fire, visibility was reduced to less

than a foot in the street. When an evacuation of the building and roof was ordered by command, the roof team could not find the aerial in the smoke. Fortunately, the RIT had raised ground ladders to the roof on the C and B sides of the building. The ladder company got off safely without incident. It is a command responsibility to notify personnel inside the structure and on the roof of RIT-created secondary egress points as soon as they are in place. This can be done via emergency fireground transmission. If companies know the existence and location of additional egress points there before they need it, they are halfway out (fig. 17–85).

Fig. 17–85. One of the major duties of the RIT is to provide secondary egress routes. Here a RIT is raising a ground ladder for secondary egress from the roof. (Courtesy of Ron Jeffers)

- *Removing barriers (window gates).* The RIT should not wait until someone needing help shows up behind window gates. Barred windows hamper both egress and ventilation operations. The removal of bars and properly coordinated ventilation of windows is especially critical at first-floor and below-grade fires (figs. 17–86 and 17–87).

- *Assisting in the set up and monitoring of the command board.* Keeping an up-to-date profile of where personnel are operating allows the team to have a better idea of where to begin. This will include monitoring roll calls.

Fig. 17–86. Window bars on wood frame structures are easier to get off from the exterior than from the inside. The firefighter needing to get out may not have the time to remove them from inside the building. Remove them as soon as you see them to avoid critical situations later. (Courtesy of Ron Jeffers)

Fig. 17–87. Metal casement windows pose the same hazards as window bars. (Courtesy of Jim Duffy)

- *Monitoring radio reports.* Many Mayday notifications are made during initial fireground operations when companies are most unfamiliar with the building and the fire. At this communication-heavy time, Maydays are sometimes easy to miss. For this reason, RITs must be vigilant in radio awareness at all times. This includes during the response. Rapid intervention crews must pay close attention to the initial on-scene radio report as well as the assignment of companies. When on scene, they should report to the command post for a briefing and consult and work closely with the accountability officer. It is best that both the command technician (accountability officer) and RIT officer stand by at the command post with headphones on. This

helps eliminate external noise and allows them to concentrate exclusively on fireground transmissions.

- *Forcing doors and other egress points not accessed by the initial entry team.* Providing egress helps those inside help themselves to get out faster and more easily. Egress includes rear and side doors, as well as cutting fences and releasing any fire escape drop ladders.

- *Making available a dedicated RIT hoseline and staging it in an easily accessible area.* It may be possible that fire is blocking a firefighter's egress. A quickly deployed hose stream may be all that is needed to allow a potentially trapped member get to safety.

Although these tasks are essential to ensuring the quickest ways of entry and egress are assured, the RIT must not get sidetracked and involved in firefighting. When these safety-oriented tasks are complete, the team must go back to the command post and stand by.

RIT activation considerations. When the RIT is activated, and the team members have a potential focus area to access, they should enter the building to find the firefighter and ascertain his or her medical condition. That entry area should be sufficiently illuminated. When found, one of the first things that should be relayed to command must be the status of the member and his or her predicament. They can also use the LUNAR method discussed earlier to provide the proper information. We must determine if the firefighter is conscious and assess the degree of entrapment, if any. If the victim is conscious and not trapped, a major concern will be if the victim can walk under his or her own power. If the answer is no and/or the firefighter is trapped, things will get more complicated as to how to get him or her out and transferred over to EMS. If the firefighter can walk, it may be that he just needs guidance out. If the firefighter was merely disoriented, that firefighter should still be medically evaluated and the entire company reassigned to rehab or released from the scene. Be aware that CISM may still be required and should be made available.

Height may also be an issue when a firefighter gets injured. If so, aerial devices may have to be used by the RIT for access and rescue. At one fire, a firefighter fell into an open scuttle hatch on the roof and dislocated his shoulder. The RIT was activated, and one of the aerials was dedicated to removal of the firefighter. He was helped down by his company on the roof and by the RIT working their way up from the turntable. The fact that he was able to walk helped make his predicament of being in an elevated position less complicated.

Upon finding the firefighter, the RIT should turn off any activated PASS device. This serves two purposes. It will decrease the frenzy and allow rescuers to think better. It will also help determine if there is another PASS device going off that was previously not heard by rescuers.

At the very least, RIT personnel should be trained in the basics of firefighter assessment and rescue. They should know how to check for the ABC (airway, breathing, circulation), and place the firefighter on supplied air, devise various slings for removal, and know how to perform all these skills in the dark, the smoke, and the heat.

One note about the communications in these situations: Be aware of the feedback that is often created when personnel are communicating in close proximity to one another. Often all that is heard at the command post is feedback and squelch.

Air management. **FFI 5.3.9** Poor air management has killed a number of firefighters each year, so it is important to review its implications before we discuss how to remove a downed firefighter. The following factors have contributed to these situations:

Physical limitations. All firefighters have differing amounts of air consumption. Factors include their weight, aerobic conditioning, age, respiratory capacity, condition, and weight of their PPE. Overexertion and stress are also major limitations to air consumption rates.

Environmental issues. High heat and other environmental stressors encountered will affect the firefighter's air consumption. Breathing elevated air temperatures, encountering thermal insult on the body through the facepiece, and retention of heat inside PPE will cause an increase in the core body temperature and an adverse impact on air management.

Physiological issues. Working in the certain conditions can cause physiological issues. These conditions include overexertion, issues of competence and/or trust in their equipment, and difficulty working in obscured or blacked-out conditions. These conditions lead to such physiological reactions as feelings of claustrophobia, panic, increased respirations, increased blood pressure, and critical incident stress.

Resistance to change. Change is a constant in the fire service and must not cause stress in the ranks. Resistance to change occurs through challenging of the norms set by peer pressure, traditions, and misinformation. One of the best ways to reduce the stress of change is let personnel know that change is coming and to involve those who will be affected by the change. Lack of involvement leads to resistance. Resistance leads to potential injury. Fire departments must be willing to train and enforce current practices and standards. Company officers must be willing to enforce and practice safe use of SCBAs and embrace air management techniques. It is the responsibility of Fire Department management and safety divisions, and all officers, to enforce rules and not overlook violations.

Disregarding low-air alarms. A common problem in the fire service is working under the assumption that it is acceptable to stay in an IDLH environment with your low-air alarm sounding. As mentioned in the NFPA 1404 Standard, "No firefighter will be allowed to operate with less that ¼ tank of reserve air in an IDLH environment." Fire crews must be trained to consistently monitor their remaining air and match it to the members of their crews.

Tunnel vision. Tunnel vision can cause companies to operate in an IDLH environment without being aware of the constantly changing conditions. This phenomenon, which can have (and has had) deadly repercussions, results from an individual firefighter's lack of training in situational awareness and a weak command structure that puts company-level crews in jeopardy. Some responsibility, however, must fall on the company commander. It is the company commander who, most of the time, is at the root of the issue and, coupled with the exterior size-up conducted by command, can round out critical information on conditions and potential safety concerns.

Lack of RIT. Air management emergencies are often mitigated by proper RIT actions. Problems result from fire departments not utilizing proper RIT, lack of or improper RIT training, or the RIT not being capable of performing an actual emergency deployment. Too many fire departments staff their RIT with any available firefighters. This group should have established minimum training standards. They should perform under established SOPs, and have the proper tools, equipment, and knowledge to provide adequate RIT services. In addition, the fire department command structure should have established procedures and training on how to manage a Mayday call.

Poor company-level tactics. There is a national trend of senior fire personnel and officers retiring, which has led to a new generation of younger fire officers and firefighters without the experience of operating in the ever-changing structural fire environment. This lack of experience translates to issues of improper air management that have spiked the number of close-call incidents. The answer here is more realistic and battle-ready training.

Standard operating procedures. Fire departments need to establish and enforce air management SOPs. They must ensure that all personnel are trained, practice, understand and use the procedures. The SOPs should be consistently enforced so a consistent behavior is maintained.

SCBA conversion. When a down firefighter is located, it is critical to convert his or her SCBA into a harness. This simple action will greatly assist in a rapid removal of the firefighter. Yes, it takes a few seconds to complete, but it will save you minutes when extracting the firefighter. The conversion can usually be completed while your partner is assessing the firefighter's air supply. A common mistake is for the RIT to try to convert the harness in a confined area. Although this may be necessary, size-up is the key. You will know the terrain from which you just came. If it is clear a few feet away, pull the firefighter out of the debris any way that you can, then convert the SCBA. This will help facilitate a more efficient transfer for the conversion and will ensure the firefighter has air or can be changed over to a supply of air. The following are the steps to a proper conversion:

- Extend the waist strap while it is still buckled.

- For a really large firefighter, loosen the shoulder straps and pull the SCBA bottle down.

- Lift one of the downed firefighter's legs over your shoulder.

- Grasp the straps, and never losing contact, move your hands around the firefighter's leg and buckle the straps so that they harness the firefighter's leg that is over your shoulder.

This conversion will allow the firefighter at the top to grab the shoulder straps and pull as a unit. You may choose to keep the leg over your shoulder and push while the firefighter is being pulled (fig. 17–88).

Fig. 17–88. Firefighter converting the SCBA into a harness. (Courtesy of Christopher McGuire)

Firefighter packaging and removal considerations. This section will cover likely RIT evolutions that you may have to face as a member of a RIT team or while helping one of the members out of a structure. These are not all inclusive, but will open your eyes to the necessity of safety and survival training. Pulling a firefighter out is more labor intensive than removing a victim. Case studies have shown that the team that locates the firefighter often will not be the team that completes the removal. It is important to bring in a lifeline that can be secured to an object to facilitate a quick exit and entrance path for egress, personnel, and resources. Discipline will also play a role. Too many hands can actually slow the removal. Officers will be needed to manage the rescue, not perform the tactics. This will fall to you. Make sure you are prepared!

FIREFIGHTER RESCUES AND DRAGS

2:1 Mechanical advantage system

With the 2:1 mechanical advantage system, a rope and a carabiner is used to help remove an unconscious firefighter in a restricted or cluttered area.

1. One firefighter secures the rope to a substantial object out of the danger area and deploys the rope as he or she searches for the trapped firefighter.

2. Once the firefighter is located, attach the middle of the rope to the top of the SCBA harness, where the

shoulder straps are attached, with a large carabiner or snap hook. Make sure the SCBA waist strap is secured between the unconscious firefighter's legs so that the SCBA will not be pulled off.

3. The firefighter backs up in a straight line with the remaining rope, turns toward the unconscious firefighter in a seated position, and pulls the unconscious firefighter from the danger area (figs. 17–89 and 17–90).

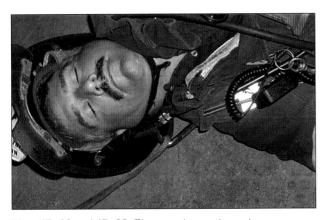

Figs. 17–89 and 17–90. The rope is run through a carabiner attached to the downed firefighter's SCBA harness. The firefighter at the anchor point pulls the rope, bringing the firefighter toward him as he pulls. (Photos courtesy of NHRFR)

Drag rescue device (DRD)

NFPA 1971, *Standard on Protective Ensembles for Structural Fire Fighting and Proximity Fire Fighting*, outlines the guidelines that all new turnout coats must meet to be compliant. The standard requires a device that enables firefighters to be manually dragged horizontally for the purpose of a quick removal from a danger area. The drag rescue device (DRD) meets this compliance.

The DRD is simple to set up and deploy. It is tucked into the collar of all new turnout coats. The harness operates by forming loops that cinch themselves beneath the armpits. The device is a continuous loop, not unlike a rescue sling. It is positioned on the wearer between the exterior portion of the turnout coat (on the inside) and the thermal barrier portion (the shell). The device basically sits wrapped under the wearer's arms between the vapor barrier and the shell of the turnout coat. When deployed, the top loop is released by pulling up on a Velcro® tab on the collar and pulling the top of the device loop upward and outward, taking the slack out of the harness and tightening it around the wearer's armpits, making it ideal for dragging (fig. 17–91).

Fig. 17–91. The drag rescue device (DRD) deployed. (Photo by Jim Ricci, courtesy of Globe)

There are some firefighter-caused limitations with deployment. Firefighters are trained to carry the weight of their SCBA on their hips. This allows easy access to the DRD. If firefighters are carrying the weight of the pack on their shoulders, it is harder to deploy. Some models of SCBA completely cover the DRD even when worn correctly (fig. 17–92).

Fig. 17–92. When SCBA is worn properly, it is easier to deploy. (Photo by Jim Ricci, courtesy of Globe)

The device comes with a user information guide, outlining the manufacturer's recommendations for the device. It is highly recommended that the wearer not only read but become familiar with the layout, setup, and deployment of the harness. After each deployment, the handle (pulling loop) must be reset on the back of the coat in accordance with the user guide instructions. It should also be periodically checked to ensure that it is properly installed and not damaged in any way.

According to the user information guide, the purpose of the firefighter DRD is to aid firefighters with the rescue of an incapacitated firefighter by dragging him or her along a horizontal plane. The DRD is intended to assist in pulling or dragging an incapacitated firefighter and is not designed nor tested for use in vertical rescue operations. The guide further states that the product is only for structural or proximity firefighting. The DRD is not an escape harness for lifting or lowering a person on a lifeline.

The handle or pull loop, once slack is pulled out of it, is big enough for two firefighters to grip it simultaneously. If the firefighter who is being rescued does not have his or her turnout coat closed all the way or the SCBA waist strap is not in place, the unsecured areas start to separate and the coat begins to ride up. In one case, it almost pulled off.

Belt or harness drag

For a horizontal drag with one firefighter we found this method to be the most effective and the least labor intensive (fig. 17–93). As the rescuer, you would convert your waist strap and send it through the loop of the

DRD. This could also be accomplished by hooking into the DRD with the Class II harness. Once hooked in, straddle the downed firefighter, ensuring that you do not dislodge the firefighter's face mask. Now you can crawl with your tool on all fours. The downed firefighter is now dragged in line between your legs.

Fig. 17–93. This photo demonstrates the belt or harness drag; note that your waist strap must go through your legs. (Photo by Jim Duffy, courtesy of Globe)

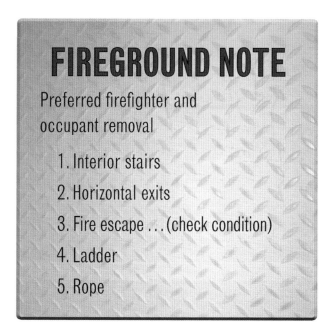

FIREGROUND NOTE

Preferred firefighter and occupant removal

1. Interior stairs
2. Horizontal exits
3. Fire escape ... (check condition)
4. Ladder
5. Rope

Stair drags

The DRD is not recommended to be used to move a firefighter up or down stairs (figs. 17–94 a and b). The problem with using it alone is that when the SCBA gets stuck, it is difficult to turn the firefighter's body with the strap. Also, the length of the strap that makes it conducive for horizontal drags is a hindrance when pulling up, and forces you, if you are the firefighter on top, to pull with your arms instead of lifting with your legs. However, when the downed firefighter's SCBA is converted into a harness and the rescuers are trained to pull the DRD

LESSON FROM THE FIREGROUND

The fire was in a two-story wood frame vacant building. It was showing heavy fire and was exposing a wood frame, 2½-story, occupied dwelling on the D side, which was 3 ft (1 m) away. Flames were licking against the soffit of the exposure. The vinyl siding on the other exposure, approximately 20 ft (6 m) away, was already melting. Having been the scene of several previous fires, it was in a state of disrepair and was marked as a Level 3 hazardous vacant building. The first engine on the scene had stretched a line to the rear via an alley where most of the fire was concentrated to try to knock it down quickly. A second line was being used to wet down the exposure on the D side. As it was early in the fire and companies were still arriving or en route, no other extinguishing actions were being carried out. Additional lines would be stretched later to protect the D exposure from inside, protect the other exposed buildings, and extinguish the main body of fire. At this time, however, only two companies were operating.

As the ranking chief arrived and assumed command, it became clear that an EID button had been activated on the fireground. Dispatch confirmed which individual had activated the button. It was the officer of the first-arriving engine company. When contact was attempted over the radio with that individual, there was no answer. Since the second alarm had been struck by the first company on scene, the IC struck a third alarm to address the Mayday. An additional RIT was also requested. The dilemma at hand was that there was no RIT yet on scene. They were still responding and were still a few minutes out. They would still have to park, finish gearing up, and bring tools and equipment to the command post. There was not enough time if someone was in trouble. A battalion chief and a ladder company who had just arrived were sent to find the company. They had none of the RIT equipment that was carried by the dedicated squad companies that responded as RITs, and this meant that some other extinguishment and support functions would not get done, but there was no other choice at the time. All this time, the Mayday transmission was sounding over the radios, but there was no answer from the officer or his company. The firefighter and his company were found in the back of the building. They were operating a hoseline at the rear and were fine. They did not even know that the Mayday was sent. The radio of the officer in had gotten wet and malfunctioned, sending out the Mayday. His collar mike had been knocked loose from the shoulder strap and was not near his face, but was dangling near his knees.

LESSONS LEARNED

1. The person who activates the Mayday button may not know it has been activated.

2. The Mayday tones come out of all radios except the person who activated it. The officer whose Mayday button was activated was never aware of it.

3. Complacency can kill. There can be no such thing as a false Mayday when the tones or a PASS device is heard. All Mayday and PASS device activations must be treated as the real thing until proven otherwise. Waiting to determine the validity of the activation will waste precious time, which is our enemy during firefighter rescue operations.

4. In the early stages of the operation, command must be prepared to take whatever steps are necessary to address a Mayday, even if it means pressing non-RIT companies into service.

5. All companies should be trained in at least simple firefighter rescue procedures, whether they are assigned to dedicated RIT companies or not.

6. RITs should be responding from as close to the incident as possible. The farther away the RIT is responding from, the more the likelihood that on-the-spot, improvised firefighter rescue tactics will need to be implemented.

in opposite directions under both shoulder straps, the DRD will provide two short loops to grab, giving you both the leverage and control to manipulate the downed firefighter up the stairs. When trying to go down the stairs, the head is not supported and will tend to hit the stairs unless the strap is used as just described.

These are just a few of the ways in which the DRD can be used more efficiently in the rescue of an incapacitated firefighter. These are by no means the only ways to accomplish this objective. Like any tool, the skills must be practiced, or they will not be successful at the time they are needed the most.

One of the most valuable attributes that firefighters have is the ability to modify and adapt to overcome and make the job more efficient. That is part of who we are. An old chief once said, "You must adapt to be effective, you must invent to overcome, and you must create to compensate." Remember the time to find out if something works should not be at 3 a.m. when the building is on fire.

One other note about the DRD: In a recent safety and survival class, the strap deployed and got caught, trapping the firefighter as he tried to breach through a wall. Make sure it is repacked according to the manufacturer's guidelines.

Removal of a firefighter down a set of stairs. Convert the SCBA harness as described earlier.

- Place the firefighter on his or her side and grasp the shoulder straps.

- Pull and guide the firefighter down the stairs.

It is easier to remove a firefighter down the interior stairs than down a ladder. If the stairs are charged with smoke, ensure that the firefighter's air supply does not become dislodged.

Removal upstairs. Convert the SCBA harness as described earlier.

- The rescuer on top will grasp the shoulder straps and pull.

- As the firefighter on bottom, you will bury your head in the crotch of the downed member and place both of the downed member's legs over your shoulders. Your hands should grasp the downed member's buttocks and push the firefighter up.

Figs. 17–94 a, b. Both straps are pulled under the shoulder straps, producing two separate short loops. Figure 17–100b shows that after the SCBA waste strap is converted, the shorter loops allow for an safe, efficient and effective pull up the stairs. (Photo by Jim Duffy, courtesy of Globe)

Removal will take some coordination between the two rescuers. This process can be enhanced if additional resources become available. Without slowing down the removal, a 2:1 mechanical advantage system can be added to assist the two rescuers (fig. 17–95).

Fig. 17–95. Firefighter being moved upstairs to safety. (Courtesy of Christopher McGuire)

Removal out a window

Upon finding a downed firefighter, the following are several methods of removing the downed firefighter out a window:

- Window cutdown

- Firefighter assist

- Aerial ladder

- Tower ladder

- Ground ladder

As the firefighter is being brought to the window, cut down the window to the floor (basically making a door out of the window) so the firefighter can be removed at floor level. This will keep you from having to lift the firefighter into the window. This requires proper size-up of the inside wall. Once the window has been cut down, the downed firefighter can be removed via ground ladder, aerial ladder, or tower ladder. As the firefighter is removed from the window, he or she should be stripped of the SCBA to ease in moving through the window (fig. 17–96).

FIREGROUND NOTE

The RIT represents a trained, fresh company with full air. The RIT should work toward proactive safety while being ready to deploy.

Fig. 17–96. The window cutdown allows the downed member to be removed with little effort, but takes resources and time.

Denver drill

The Denver drill allows an efficient method to remove a downed member from a confined area with a high window. The development of this technique was in response to a line-of-duty death. Although there are many variations to this drill, we will discuss one method that we have also found that can be used in an open area as well. The downed firefighter will be located under the window:

- Clear window of glass and drapery, blinds, and so forth.

- Rescuer 1 will sound the floor and climb over the downed firefighter.

- Rescuer 1 will roll the firefighter on their back and sit them up.

- Rescuer 2 will enter the window and manipulate their SCBA bottle so their back will be flat against the wall with Rescuer 2's knees bent.

- Rescuer 1 will lift the downed member and place on him Rescuer 2's knees.

- Rescuer 1 will place the member's legs over their shoulders and coordinate the lift with Rescuer 2 and the outside team.

- Rescuer 2 will push up on the member's bottle while Rescuer 1 pushes the member out the window (fig. 17–97).

Fig. 17–97. Firefighter removed by utilizing the Denver drill

The outside team should use the building as protection and reach in with the arm that is closest to the window. They will each use only one arm and will reach to grab the downed member. This action will allow the outside team to turn in as the member is pulled out, without switching hands, cradling the downed member, and pulling the member away from the window.

High-point removal

A downed firefighter can be removed out of a window by using a high-point removal system. This can be accomplished by rigging a pulley or carabiner to an anchor strap above the window. A ladder can be used for the **high-point** with a life safety rope run through the pulley or carabiner. A figure eight on a bight with an extra large carabiner can be attached to the two SCBA shoulder straps on the rear of the downed firefighter and a rated webbing strap that is secured to the firefighter. The downed firefighter's SCBA waist strap should be converted as outlined previously in this chapter. Once connected, the downed firefighter can be assisted out the window and lowered to the ground or into the bucket of a tower ladder utilizing the rope system. The end of the rope will be run under a rung of the ladder to add friction at the bottom of the ladder being used as the high point. This system can also be deployed using a 2:1 system. When using pulleys, keep two rules in mind:

1. If the pulley doesn't move, it only changes the direction of rope travel.

2. If the pulley moves, it will create mechanical advantage (fig. 17–98).

Fig. 17–98. High-point removal creates friction through the lower rung. Pull in the direction of the building to ensure stability of ladder. (Courtesy of Christopher McGuire)

Firefighter through the floor

Removing a downed firefighter who has fallen through the floor is a high-risk operation. You will be working at the top of a chimney. The most likely situation you will encounter is a firefighter who has fallen into a basement. This complicates removal because of mechanicals (wires, pipes, and duct work) that run along the ceiling. The hole where the firefighter falls will be jagged, may present a secondary collapse area, and may require **shoring**. When making contact with the downed member, and for any pulling operations, work from the corners and size up any obstructions that will need to be cleared. This can also be accomplished by using rope with specific knots.

Utilizing a charged hand line

1. The charged hoseline is pushed down through the opening in the floor. A team of firefighters controls one side of the hoseline, while another two rescue firefighters wrap their legs and arms around the hose and slide down it to find the downed firefighter.

2. Once located, the rescue firefighters must assess the air of downed member. Sit the firefighter up and place the charged hoseline across the victim's chest directly under the armpits. The rescue firefighter then opens the downed firefighter's waist strap and places it across the downed firefighter's upper arms (above the elbows) and tightens it.

3. The rescue firefighters pull the hose and downed firefighter up through the hole, working together as the victim comes up.

4. The hose is then pushed back down. The rescue firefighters put the hose across their chests and under their armpits and hold on. The team above then pulls them to safety. This can also be accomplished by standing in the loop and grasping the hose with your hands by crossing your arms (fig. 17–99).

Fig. 17–99. An unconscious firefighter is pulled to safety using a hoseline with no knots. It is unlikely for firefighters to use knots under hostile conditions.

POSTFIRE ANALYSIS

Something of value can be learned at every fire, and thus all fires should receive a critique or what can be better termed an incident evaluation. What is revealed and learned in the evaluation can be of value for the rest of a firefighter's career. The departments that do not hold incident evaluations because they have "seen it all" are usually the ones with the largest parking lots and casualty tolls. Each fire should be a learning experience that should go beyond the kitchen table or bar. The downside of evaluations is that by the time they are held, not everyone is there because of vacation, sick leave, or other commitments. Other members who are present may not remember exactly what happened. Sometimes the best lessons are forgotten forever.

How can the fire department effectively hold an incident evaluation where all the pertinent information is offered? Remembering that the palest ink is better than the sharpest memory, notes should be jotted down as soon as possible after the incident. This will make the evaluation more meaningful. An adapted form will work well and put everyone on the same page during the evaluation session. A form adapted by the North Hudson Regional Fire and Rescue is the After Action Report. The report is completed anytime a hoseline is charged at a structure fire. The forms are filled out as soon as the company returns to quarters and is forwarded to the battalion commander. That way, if the officer is off the next tour, his or her input will still be included in the incident evaluation. What is likely to happen in this instance is that the acting officer takes the place of the company officer and speaks on his or her behalf at the evaluation, using the form.

Incident evaluation

A specific format should be used for the incident evaluation. It should cover specific areas so that the main focus of the session is kept on track. Sometimes, incident evaluations tend to go off track and accomplish nothing. One way to head this off is to conduct a preevaluation meeting or a post-incident analysis. This is conducted by the chief officers and the SO as a way to preplan the evaluation and steer it in the proper direction. In the postfire analysis, after-action reports and dispatch tapes are reviewed. SOPs are evaluated and operational strengths and weaknesses are discussed and determined. What went right and what went wrong from the command officer's point of view must also be discussed. A strategy on how to best address those issues in the incident evaluation is the goal of the post-incident analysis. If the post-incident analysis is done properly, the incident evaluation should be productive.

The format the incident evaluation takes covers the following areas.

Communications

- Were transmissions prioritized?
- Was proper radio etiquette followed?
- Were personnel on the fireground being "stepped on?" Chief officers should never be stepped on.

Secure a copy of the dispatch tape. It is like the eye in the sky and can tell you a lot about how well things went in regard to communications. It doesn't lie. As in football, if the referee says you were holding, you were.

Apparatus positioning

- Were SOPs followed?
- Were there obstacles to response?
- Were there any unusual circumstances, and if so, how were they addressed?

One piece of apparatus out of position can affect the entire fireground. Improper positioning can never be swept under the carpet.

Company integrity

- Was freelancing an issue?
- Were accountability procedures followed?
- How well coordinated was the relief and rehab of companies?
- Were companies broken up as a result of an injury or other unforeseeable occurrence? How was that handled?

Reinforce fireground discipline at this time. Violations of the principle of company integrity are unacceptable and cannot be tolerated at any time for any reason.

Tactics and lessons learned

- Officers discuss their positions and assignments.
- What problems were encountered?
- What solutions were used? How effective were they?
- What lessons were learned from the incident?

Safety considerations—this portion is conducted by the SO

- Was everyone wearing proper protective equipment?
- Were department SOPs followed?
- Was the fire attack coordinated with proper and timely support?
- Did companies stay together, or was freelancing evident?
- Did the operation provide for emergency firefighter egress from the interior?
- Did the operation provide for emergency firefighter egress from the roof?
- Were communications conducive to safe operations?
- Were tools and equipment used safely and properly?
- Was the RIT properly equipped and ready to be deployed?

The real value of the SO's input into the evaluation is that it should be from a point of view of someone that is standing back and taking in the big picture at the fire scene. This point of view should be from a different angle than the operating companies. It should be a constructive session, aimed at improving the department's performance from a safety standpoint. A safer operation will always translate into a better, more effective operation.

Finally, anyone, regardless of rank, who has something to say should be given a chance to talk about the incident. Allowing all players to have input into the evaluation process makes them more likely to buy into the process.

In concluding the evaluation, together with the SO and the shift officers, the platoon commander should set goals that are both measurable and realistic in regard to a safer and more effective fireground operation. Unsafe practices as well as subpar scene performance should be looped back into the training process and approached in a positive manner. Remember that the further you are from the last "big one," the closer you are to the next.

Postfire analysis in many departments is conducted on scene. Montgomery County, MD, conducts company officer critiques at the end of each fire. This allows each officer to know the actions of every company. After these critiques are complete, the officer or senior firefighter will often walk through the tactics used at the fire with any new personnel. This provides valuable insight to the new firefighter. Even if your department is lacking a formal policy, ask your officer to explain the other company's actions and the fireground action plan. This will allow you to visualize and understand all the tactics that were utilized.

The goal of the incident evaluation is to improve department performance and identify training needs. The overriding concern is always the safety of the participants.

FIREGROUND NOTE
There are six sides to the box. Is there a better way to get the firefighter out while your team sets up this operation?

QUESTIONS

1. Safety is the overriding concern of _____ fireground operations, firefighter training, and station activities.

2. Explain "drifting into failure."

3. Who is responsible for firefighter safety?

4. On average, there are over _____ firefighter fatalities and _____ firefighter injuries each year.

5. Name five causes of firefighter injuries.

6. Injury _____ is a vital part of the injury prevention cycle.

7. When should injury documentation start? Why?

8. What on the job injuries should be investigated? Why?

9. List the 10 Rules of Engagement for Structural Firefighting.

10. What role does a fire ground accountability officer play?

11. What is the most important part of a fire department wellness program? Why?

12. NFPA _____ discuss the recommendations for fire department staffing for fire suppression.

13. What is freelancing and why is it dangerous on the fireground?

14. What is a fireground Mayday? When should it be initiated?

15. What does RIT stand for? When is it used?

16. A _____ should be done after every fire.

Vehicle Fires

by Doug Leihbacher

This chapter provides required knowledge items for the following
NFPA Standard 1001 Job Performance Requirements:

FFI 5.3.7

This chapter contains Skill Drills. When you see this icon, refer to your Skill Drill book for step-by-step instructions.

OBJECTIVES

Upon completion of this chapter, you should be able to do the following:

- Identify the response priorities for all vehicle fires
- Identify the five compartments where vehicle fires can occur.
- Identify the major safety concerns to emergency responders at vehicle fires
- Identify and describe proper hose selection and attack methods for vehicle fires
- Identify signs that a fire stream has been applied effectively
- Identify and describe the potential hazards of hybrid vehicles and alternative-fuel vehicles
- Describe the functions of the truck company at vehicle fires

INTRODUCTION

According to the National Fire Protection Association (NFPA), during 2007 there were 227,500 **vehicle fires** reported in the United States (fig. 18–1). These fires killed 500 people and injured more than 1,300 people. These numbers represent a downward trend in the number of fires that exceeded 350,000 annually in the 1990s. It is not surprising we experience so many vehicle fires, considering that motor vehicles are composed of complex mechanical and electrical systems involving volatile liquids, internalized combustion, many moving parts subject to friction,

Fig. 18–1. Firefighters take an upwind position and stand clear of the bumpers as they prepare to extinguish an auto fire on the side of a roadway. (Courtesy of Keith Muratori)

pressurized fuel lines, wiring, batteries, and extremely hot parts such as exhaust manifolds and catalytic converters.

Vehicle fires can occur when the vehicle is driven, when it is parked and turned off, or as a result of an accident that compromises one of the vehicle's systems. Figure 18–2 provides a breakdown of the common causes of vehicle fires based on the National Fire Incident Reporting System (NFIRS). Note that the number of incendiary fires may be undercounted because some vehicle fires are not investigated for arson.

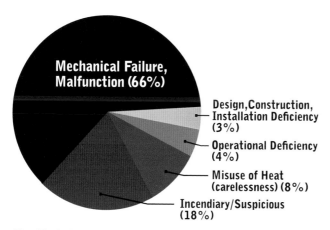

Fig. 18–2. Common causes of vehicle fires

The term **vehicle fire** can potentially refer to any fire that occurs in an automobile, truck, bus, train, plane, or boat. Unless assigned to an airport or a marine fire unit, most vehicle fires to which firefighters respond occur in automobiles. Hence, this chapter focuses on vehicles that travel on roadways.

The priorities at vehicle fires are the same as for all fires:

- Scene safety
- Life
- Exposure protection
- Extinguishment

Notice that extinguishment comes last. At an automobile fire, our first priority is to create a safe working environment for the crew to do their job in. Next is to protect and rescue any victim(s) who may be trapped in or near the vehicle. If there is a victim in the vehicle, steps must be taken to prevent the fire from entering the passenger compartment. Once the life hazard has been managed, our next priority is to protect any exposed property or vehicles by keeping the flames from spreading there. To achieve this, the hoseline should be positioned between the fire and any vehicles or buildings nearby in the direc-

tion of fire spread. After taking care of these priorities, firefighters can then extinguish and overhaul the vehicle.

To accomplish these priorities, a response assignment of fire apparatus is dispatched to the scene. Response assignments to motor vehicle fires vary from jurisdiction to jurisdiction depending on available resources, type of roadway, and local protocols. Some departments dispatch a single engine or quint; others two engines; still others, an engine, ladder, and chief. On a **divided highway**, two separate assignments may be sent, one assignment for each direction of traffic flow.

SCENE SAFETY

Regardless of the type of assignment sent, there is only one way to fight a vehicle fire: safely. Extinguishing vehicle fires safely and effectively is a process of controlling an array of hazards that can cause injuries if firefighters are not cautious and alert. Although common, vehicle fires should not be taken for granted. Crew members should expect the unexpected. Addressing these potential hazards begins with taking a look at the big picture as you approach the scene and size up the situation.

The potential hazards associated with motor vehicle fires are influenced by where they occur. There are eight probable locations where a motor vehicle fire is likely to occur. Each of the following can present a unique set of challenges and hazards for firefighters and should be considered while en route and during initial scene size-up:

1. Divided highway: high-speed traffic, limited water supply (no hydrants)

2. City Street: two-way traffic in motion, possible downed wires, onlookers

3. Garage: Gaining access to fire, exposed structure, exposed hazardous combustibles

4. Outdoor parking lot or junk yard: fire spread to nearby autos, limited water supply

5. Accident scene: potential rescue of victims from burning auto

6. Driveway: potential involvement of nearby structure, dropping house service lines

7. Overpass, bridge, or ramp: no shoulder, structural collapse, elevation, dry standpipe operation

8. Automobile repair garage: flammable liquids, structural involvement, possible victims

Responding

Safe operations commence when the crew boards the apparatus and responds to the scene. When responding to a vehicle fire, units should proceed at a safe rate of speed. Unless there are reports of a person trapped in the vehicle, it is foolhardy to put lives in danger by using excessive speed to save property (the burning auto). Instead of racing to the scene, know your district and plan the response route wisely. Consider that the quickest route may vary with the time of day and differing traffic patterns. Blocked or one way streets can cause a deviation from the most direct route. Traffic as a result of the vehicle fire may clog normal approach routes. Two heads are better than one, and discussing the best route with the officer on the apparatus may provide additional response options.

Divided highways

Divided highways can present a challenge to responding firefighters attempting to get to the fire. These high-speed roadways have a limited number of entry ramps where responding apparatus can enter the traffic lanes and, in areas where there is no shoulder, few places for traffic to pull aside.

In addition, remember that cars are traveling at high speeds and may not hear the siren. These factors call for approaching the scene with caution and patience. As mentioned previously, in some jurisdictions two assignments are dispatched to divided highways, one responding from one direction and one from the other; to allow the best opportunity to reach the fire. The preferred approach is for the apparatus to respond in from the same direction that the traffic is flowing. In some cases a safe approach to the burning vehicle is easiest from a service road running along side the highway.

On a divided highway, the fire should only be fought from the same traffic lanes in which the fire vehicle is located. If the fire is in the opposite traffic lanes, firefighters should not stop the apparatus and stretch hose across the guard rail or center barrier unless traffic has been stopped in both directions by police or fire units. Similarly, apparatus should not approach a vehicle fire against traffic unless it is confirmed that traffic has been stopped by the police or other fire department units.

Approaching the scene

As the apparatus approaches the fire scene, all crew members should begin a scene size-up. Are there hazardous materials (hazmat) involved, downed wires, a fuel spill, or icy conditions on the pavement? Is the burning vehicle situated on a blind bend? Is the vehicle a standard automobile or a hybrid? What position is the vehicle in? Is it in the roadway or off to the side? Is it stable or overturned? Is the engine running? Is the driver present? Are there any ambulance personnel, police or Good Samaritans already on the scene? Are there civilians putting themselves in danger trying to extinguish the fire? Almost half of all persons injured in vehicle fires, were injured when they attempted to extinguish the fire.[1]

All scene safety hazards must be addressed before extinguishment operations begin. Firefighters must identify the primary hazards at the scene and manage them first, before taking any other actions. Depending on local protocols and departmental standard operating procedures (SOPs), this may involve directing traffic, placing flares or traffic cones, or establishing a safety officer.

While sizing up the vehicle fire, crew members should consider what stage the fire is in: incipient, developing, or fully involved. Also note where the fire is burning. Is the fire under the hood, in the passenger compartment, beneath the vehicle or confined to the trunk? Most importantly, is there a life hazard? Is someone trapped in the vehicle?

Traffic control

A primary hazard associated with vehicular fires and extrications that occur on high-speed thoroughfares is the danger of being struck by an automobile passing the accident scene at high speed. Firefighters have been severely injured and even killed by passing motorists whose views were obstructed by smoke or terrain, or who became impatient and tried to squeeze by the incident. This danger is increased at dusk, at night, and during inclement weather conditions where visibility is impaired.

Wearing full protective gear with reflective stripes makes a firefighter more visible; but in addition, members must avoid focusing exclusively on firefighting procedures (tunnel vision) and remain mindful of oncoming traffic and other hazards at all times during the incident. This attentiveness begins when you step off the apparatus. Be sure to look before you leap off, and remain vigilant until the entire operation is complete. Often firefighters can be at greatest risk when returning to the apparatus for a tool or packing hose after the fire is out.

Traffic control and apparatus positioning are essential to protect firefighters operating at vehicle fires on highways. Notifying the police department to respond and provide traffic management is good practice. For vehicle fires on city streets, follow the guidelines for fires on divided highways even though motorists may not be traveling as fast. In both cases, vehicles in motion are the primary concern. Overhead wires are another hazard that must be taken into account, especially if the fire is the result of a collision with a pole.

Positioning the apparatus

Fire apparatus must be positioned on the roadway so that all oncoming traffic can see it. If there is a curve or steep hill, the apparatus must be visible from a safe distance. All warning lights should be left on throughout the incident and only shut off after the apparatus has merged back into traffic and is returning to quarters. When the geography makes apparatus visibility difficult, flares, traffic cones, or other appropriate visual warning devices must be set up early in the incident to prevent unsuspecting motorists from colliding with the apparatus.

In addition, police or another fire unit should be requested for traffic control upstream of the curve. Firefighters placing warning devices must be careful to face on coming traffic, stay on the shoulder, and not walk on the roadway except when placing it. The farthest warning device should be placed on the shoulder, then subsequent devices placed further onto the roadway diagonally, until the lane (or lanes) is blocked and a buffer zone is created.

When fuel has spilled at an accident scene, flares should not be chosen over other warning devices in areas where they could ignite a fire. When using flares, the firefighter placing them should carry a lit flare or flashlight to increase visibility to oncoming traffic. To be effective, flares must be placed far enough away from the incident to allow traffic to slow and stop safely.

Table 18–1 lists approximate distances visual warning devices (flares, etc.) should be placed in relation to posted speed limits. This table is based on the stopping distance in feet at a given speed plus the posted speed limit to calculate the approximate placement of **road flares** or other warning devices. It should be used only as a guideline with distances varying to match traffic and weather conditions. This task should be delegated to police personnel when they are present.

When positioning the apparatus, do not place it where it could be exposed to fire spread (fig. 18–3a). Locate the apparatus a minimum of 100 ft (30 m) from the burning vehicle, parked uphill and upwind whenever feasible. Try to position the apparatus so that it shields both the pump operator and crew from oncoming traffic. Depending on the traffic flow direction, this can mean either stopping before the fire or passing it and parking beyond.

The apparatus should be parked on a diagonal across the roadway with the pump panel facing the incident. This creates a traffic-free environment in which both the pump operator and the firefighters can work safely. Parking on a diagonal uses the full length of the vehicle so that it blocks both the lane (or shoulder) where the fire is located and the adjacent traffic lane. This positioning provides a traffic-free zone for members to flake out the hose and work (fig. 18–3 b and c).

Once the apparatus is stopped with the pump panel protected from oncoming traffic (facing the fire), the hose is stretched from the driver's side (the same side of the apparatus that the pump panel is on). This is achieved by using a cross-layed preconnect or by storing the preconnected hoseline on the driver's side fender well or front bumper. Operating on the opposite side of the apparatus from the pump panel may place either the crew or the pump operator in jeopardy if traffic has not been completely stopped (fig. 18–4a). Figure 18–4b shows an aerial view of working from the same side of the apparatus.

Incident commanders should remember to give due consideration to restoring traffic flow at the completion of the incident, while prioritizing crew safety. Coordination with police is important to achieve this. Notify a tow truck early, and pick up tools and equipment promptly after the fire has been extinguished and overhauled. If safety is not compromised, the apparatus can be moved off the roadway and onto the shoulder while hose is being repacked.

Table 18–1. Visual warning device placement

Posted speed limit, mph (kph)	Distance of the farthest warning device, ft (m)
30 (48)	150 (45.7)
40 (64)	220 (67.1)
50 (80)	310 (94.5)
60 (97)	420 (128)
70 (113)	550 (467.6)

EXTINGUISHMENT OPERATIONS

Auto fires have the potential to seriously injure firefighters. If there is no life hazard (in effect, all occupants are out of the vehicle) the fire should be attacked with consideration of the cost benefit analysis. Few motor vehicles are saved or salvageable after a fire, and none is worth the life of a firefighter. Vehicle fires should therefore be fought safely, not perilously.

Fig. 18–3. Blocking traffic

FFI 5.3.7 Firefighters should wear full protective clothing including self-contained breathing apparatus (SCBA) when operating at vehicle fires. The petrochemical-based parts of modern automobiles are particularly combustible and the smoke they produce is harmful when inhaled. Consider this: At a common auto fire, each breath of smoke a firefighter takes may contain partially combusted products of burning brake fluid, vinyl seat covers, polyurethane foam seats, polyvinyl chloride (PVC) wire insulation, rubber fan belts, and so forth. This is why crew members must use their full protective equipment including SCBA throughout the incident, from extinguishment through overhaul. Here is a list of tools commonly needed in vehicle fire operations:

Tools Required

- Traffic cones/flares
- 100–150 ft (30–45 m) of 1½- or 1¾-in. (38- or 45-mm) hose of
  with combination nozzle
- Wheel chocks

Fig. 18–4. Hose stretch

- Dry chemical extinguisher
- Class B foam and equipment
- Halligan tool or pick-headed axe
- Bolt cutters
- 6-ft (2-m) hook
- Rotary saw with metal cutting blade

Supplementary Tools

- Spring loaded punch
- Piercing nozzle
- Sledge hammer

Water supply

Water supply can be a consideration on divided highways where hydrants are unavailable. Some jurisdictions automatically send two engines to highways for this reason so that the second engine can supply additional water if needed. Most engines carry between 500 and 1,000 gal (1,893 and 3,785 L) of water on board. The pump operator supplying the attack hoseline should monitor the level of water in the tank as the operation proceeds and advise the officer when the tank is down halfway.

At most automobile fires there is sufficient water on board the engine to do the job without connecting to a hydrant. Flowing 100 gpm (378 L/min), for example, yields 5 minutes of continuous water from a 500-gal (1,896 L) tank, assuming that the tank was topped off. The pressure can be lowered after the fire is darkened down to conserve water. However, if a large truck is involved or there are multiple vehicles burning, additional units may be needed to provide extra water and should be requested early if not already assigned. The officer of the first arriving unit should size up the situation and give a radio transmission describing the initial conditions encountered and request additional resources if the incident is beyond the resources of the assigned unit(s).

Here are several circumstances where additional water supplies are likely needed:

- Multiple vehicles involved
- Vehicle fire impinging on a structure
- Fuel spill associated with vehicle fire

- Heavy involvement of a truck or bus
- Master stream foam operations in progress

Having a second source of water is a good practice at vehicle fires so that if something unexpected happens with either the burning vehicle or the pumper, the firefighters can continue operations.

Vehicle size-up and safety

When sizing up the burning vehicle take note of the make, model type, and age. This information can give clues about how the vehicle will burn. Also note what compartment(s) of the vehicle are involved in fire. There are five possibilities:

1. Engine compartment only
2. Passenger compartment only
3. Trunk only
4. Two compartments involved
5. Fully involved

Once the hoseline is charged, any extension into other compartments is unlikely, and the fire can usually be confined to the area of the vehicle involved in fire, especially if the fire is attacked from the unburned side.

Based on where the fire is located, it is possible to quickly assess the potential hazards. For example, at a fire involving the engine compartment, firefighters should be cognizant of mechanisms of injury such as hood pistons, the front bumper, and battery acid. As long as the fire is confined to that compartment, there is no need to worry about injury from an air bag inflator in the passenger compartment or an aerosol can in the trunk. Similarly, a fire confined to the passenger compartment does not affect the energy-absorbing bumpers, and so on. Fires involving two compartments are more hazardous, and fully involved vehicles present the greatest number of hazards and must therefore be approached with the most caution. A more detailed discussion of tactical considerations for each compartment of the vehicle can be found in the following text.

Securing the burning vehicle

An essential preliminary task when extinguishing a vehicle fire is securing the vehicle so that it remains stationary once knockdown has taken place. Vehicles can start up when burning ignition wires cross. If the vehicle is in gear when this occurs, it can begin to move forward or backward and even drive away. To preclude this the burning vehicle should be immobilized with wheel chocks as soon as it can be done safely (fig. 18–5). When fires result from traffic accidents, the vehicle may be on its side or roof. Such vehicles may have to be stabilized with cribbing or jacks after the fire in knocked down to allow firefighters to overhaul the vehicle safely.

Selecting the right hoseline

FFI 5.3.7 Vehicles burn vigorously. There is usually an unlimited supply of oxygen available to support combustion, and they contain a high concentration of hydrocarbon-based plastic materials throughout. These materials have a high heat-release rate and give off a lot of smoke. The faster the fire is darkened down, the safer the operation will be. That is why a booster line (a rigid hard-rubber hose of ¾- or 1-in. [20- or 25-mm] diameter) that flows only 35 gpm (132 L/min) is inadequate to the task. To provide the needed punch, an 1½- or 1¾-in. (38- or 45-mm) hand line flowing no less than 100 gpm (379 L/min) should be selected for this task.[2]

Fig. 18–5. Wheel chocks. Immobilizing the vehicle is an often overlooked but essential task at vehicle fires. Failure to chock the wheels can result in injuries.

For a 100-ft (30-m) stretch 1¾-in. (45-mm) line, this is a pump discharge pressure of approximately 140 psi (980 kPa) (to supply a 100-psi [700-kPa]–combination nozzle). The pump operator should supply higher pressure for the knockdown but lower the pressure during overhaul to conserve water. In contrast to a booster line, the 1½- and 1¾-in. (38- or 45-mm) lines have the capacity to achieve the quick knockdown you seek.

Note that some pump operators are in the habit of flowing at a rate of 150–180 gpm (568–681 L/min) whenever they charge a 1¾-in. (45-mm) hand line. This is good practice at structure fires; but unless there are unusual circumstances, it is unnecessary to charge the hoseline to 150–180 gpm (568–681 L/min) at vehicle fires. Although more water is usually better, flowing

such high volumes of water makes the nozzle harder to control; and more importantly, it drains the tank quickly, potentially leaving insufficient water to complete extinguishment when there is no hydrant available. Things can happen suddenly at vehicle fires and it is important to keep water in reserve in case it is needed.

When there is no life hazard, there is no reason to get close to the vehicle during the initial stages of extinguishment. With a **flash point** of −43°F (−42°C) and an energy-release potential of dynamite, gasoline must always be considered and respected during vehicle fire operations.[3] While flaking out hose and awaiting water, the nozzle crew should remain a safe distance away from the vehicle, out of the traffic lane, uphill, and outside the smoke plume (fig. 18–6).

Fig. 18–6. Firefighters standing at a 45-degree angle and out of the way of the rear bumper use the full length of a straight stream to darken down this jeep. Notice there is fire at road level below the gas tank. It is wise to sweep the street under the vehicle with the hose stream before widening the pattern and advancing closer. (Courtesy of Kevin Imm)

Once water reaches the nozzle and it is bled, the nozzle team should stay back and use the full reach of a straight stream pattern when initiating knock down of the fire (fig. 18–7). To exploit the stream's full reach and maintain visibility, the attack should be initiated from an upwind position if possible, especially if the wind is strong. The nozzle should be kept moving and directed at all sections of the vehicle. Periodically aiming the stream down and banking it off the street allows water to bounce up and cool the undercarriage of the vehicle and gas tank.

Whenever fire is present under the vehicle, it takes priority and should be extinguished before proceeding further. If the nozzle crew is crouching, the stream can be aimed upward and banked off the underside of the roof to create a sprinkler effect on the material burning below. This is preferable to spraying the stream through one window and out the other.

Fig. 18–7. Reach of hose stream. The nozzle team uses the full reach of the hose stream to knock down visible fire before advancing closer to the vehicle.

The right angle of approach

As a rule of thumb, the hoseline should be advanced from the corner of the vehicle at 45°, not directly from the front, back, or sides. This angle of approach keeps the crew away from energy-absorbing bumpers, hood struts, and air bag inflators that can blow during a vehicle fire. The safest direction of approach is from the unburned side at a 45° angle to the corner of the vehicle as illustrated in figure 18–8. Applying a straight stream from the corner at a safe distance allows the nozzle team to sweep two sides of the vehicle before they move in.

Fig. 18–8. Approaching vehicle from safe angle

Energy-absorbing bumpers, pressurized by hydraulic pistons, have caused serious leg injuries to firefighters during extinguishment. Though most were phased out in the 1990s and replaced by polystyrene foam, they are still found on older vehicles and some late models. If exposed to heat, firefighters should not work or stand directly in front of a vehicle bumper until it has been thoroughly cooled (fig. 18–9). Energy-absorbing bumpers can be a greater hazard when the car was in an accident preceding the fire. If the bumper was compressed, it could release without warning.

Fig. 18–9. An older vehicle with an engine compartment fire and fire beneath the front bumper presents a danger to the lower extremities. Do not approach this vehicle from the front. (Courtesy of Chief Michael Urquides, Salinas Rural Fire Protection District)

FFI 5.3.7 The nozzle crew can gauge the success of their fire attack when the flames diminish and the smoke absorbs steam and turns white. When the fire darkens down, and the crew advances, the nozzle pattern should be adjusted from a straight stream to a wider angle and eventually to a medium fog pattern to provide more coverage as well as wider protection to the crew as they advance toward the vehicle (fig. 18–10). A fog pattern also pushes noxious smoke away, redirects flammable liquids, and covers a broader area of the vehicle. The nozzle should be moved continuously so that water is directed over, under, around, and throughout the vehicle giving all involved surfaces a thorough wash.

Fig. 18–10. Wider pattern. As the nozzle crew gets closer to the vehicle, the hose stream pattern is widened.

The crew should take time to continue cooling the vehicle after visible flame has been extinguished and give the undercarriage, passenger compartment, and bumpers a final wash down, before approaching the vehicle closely. The nozzle crew should also direct the stream onto smoldering tires, which can be difficult to extinguish because of the heat retention qualities of the steel belts, which can prompt reignition.

Firefighters often hear loud bangs and pops when fighting a vehicle fire. This is caused by the expansion of liquids or gases in a confined housing. Airbags, tires, steering, air conditioner components, and the like can burst under fire conditions; or one of the numerous struts located throughout the vehicle can rupture when heated beyond its ability to expand. Struts may be found in the wheel wells as well as under hoods, hatchbacks, and trunks (fig. 18–11). These pressurized components can burst or explode when heated. If they contain a hydraulic fluid, it may spray about. If gas filled, the pneumatic strut may launch shrapnel or projectiles that can cause serious injuries. Although most ruptures are confined to the interior of the vehicle, they can penetrate the sheet metal and fly outward with great force, primarily toward the front or rear of the vehicle. Therefore, firefighters should avoid approaching the vehicle closely until it is thoroughly cooled.

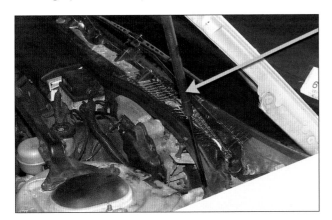

Fig. 18–11 Hood strut. This type of pneumatic hood piston, found in a wide variety of passenger cars, can rupture when heated by an engine compartment fire.

Mechanisms of injury in the passenger compartment include seatbelt pretensioners, airbags, and air bag inflators. The number of airbags found in a given vehicle varies with the manufacturer and model. Luxury models often contain more airbags, each of which is activated by a separate inflator. Still, there are other hazards inherent in vehicle fires. Tires can rupture, scattering hot rubber fragments, and should be cooled with the hose stream if on fire. When impinged on by fire, gasoline in a liquid or

vapor form can escape under the vehicle from a burst fuel line or loose connection and intensify the fire. This is especially true of fuel-injected engines. Taking the time to cool the vehicle down from a distance prevents these hazards from causing injuries.

Once thoroughly cooled inside and out, the doors can be opened to ventilate the passenger compartment if it is charged with smoke. When the doors are locked and no key is available, a hole punch or the point of a Halligan tool in the lower corner of a side window fractures the tempered glass, allows ventilation, and permits the firefighter to reach in and unlock the door (fig. 18–12).

Members working close to the vehicle should be mindful of hot surfaces and wear their gloves to avoid burn injuries. When venting a vehicle side window, stand to the upwind side and swing the tool to impact the glass in the corner of the window. Once the glass is taken, smoke and flames can push out. Ventilation is frequently unnecessary at vehicle fires, however. Vehicle side windows either self-vent when the fire grows beyond the incipient stage or shatter when the hot glass is hit with the cool water of the hose stream. Never place your head or any part of your body inside the vehicle until it has completely cooled down.

Fig. 18–12. When venting an automobile, the point of a Halligan should be directed into the lower corner of the side window. If the interior is charged with smoke, the firefighter should stay low and to the side when the glass is taken.

The gas tank

Although automobile models such as older Crown Victorias and 1970s-era Ford Pintos (whose fuel tanks were mounted aft of the rear axle) were notorious for erupting into flames following rear-impact collisions, exploding gas tanks are not common during auto fires.

This is primarily due to the position of the gas tank. It is mounted on the underside of the car. At automobile fires where the vehicle is upright, the fire is predominantly above the tank with limited heat radiating downward. Nonetheless, whenever flammable vapors are present it is necessary to consider the possibility of a failure and not take careless risks. Hose crews extinguishing vehicle fires should be mindful of the location of the gas tank and protect it from any fire in the rear of the vehicle impinging on it. Flames visible at the rear tires or under the car can heat the gas tank from below and should be doused quickly; and the hose team should keep back a safe distance until the fire under the vehicle is knocked down. **High-density polyethylene (HDPE)** plastic fuel tanks are becoming the norm on newer cars. They are lighter than metal tanks and not subject to rust. However, plastic fuel tanks can fail under conditions of direct flame impingement and release their contents. If this occurs, vapors can flash, or a stream of flaming gasoline can flow out from the vehicle and downhill, spreading the fire to other vehicles or entering a sewer.

A gas tank failure requires the quick application of a Class B extinguishing agent to control. A dry chemical or Class B foam extinguisher should be kept at the ready during vehicle fire operations incase of this eventuality. As mentioned earlier, sweeping and/or banking the hose stream under the vehicle at street level whenever fire is observed beneath the vehicle can impede direct flame impingement and prevent the gas tank or fuel line from failing.

Years ago, many firefighters believed that removing the gas cap could prevent a gas tank explosion by relieving the pressure in the fuel system. This is incorrect and should not be attempted. Although it is true that pressure increases within the tank as it is heated, especially if the fuel tank is nearly empty, the air/fuel mixture in the tank is too rich to burn. Attempting to relieve pressure by removing the fuel cap can release pressurized gasoline vapor that could burn the firefighter. The proper solution is to put the fire out at a safe distance using the full length of the hose stream, and to cool the tank and undercarriage as you do so.

Foam

In contrast to gas tank failures, fuel spills result more frequently from compromised fuel lines. Fuel lines can rupture as the result of an accident or flame impingement from below. They also frequently fail when hot catalytic converters ignite leaves and grass below the vehicle when drivers carelessly park on top of these materials. Using foam or dry chemical on the leaking fuel line is necessary until the fire is out, all sources of ignition are controlled, and the leak can be plugged. Most engine companies carry a complement of foam (in 5-gal [19-L] containers) on the apparatus along with a foam nozzle and eductor. If escaping flammable liquids are involved or there is a spill, the pump operator should get the foam equipment ready for operation.

A growing number of fire departments routinely use **Class A foam** at vehicle fires and report successful results particularly when tires are involved. They use it because they feel it is more efficient than plain water in effecting a quick knockdown. Class A foam is a surfactant that lowers the surface tension of the water molecules allowing superior penetration into dense Class A fuels. When using Class A foam at a vehicle fire, it is important to note that it does not suppress flammable liquid vapors and is ineffective in fighting fuel spill fires sometimes associated with the burning vehicle.

Class A foams do not meet national standards for use with liquid hydrocarbon fires. In contrast to the penetrating qualities of Class A foam, Class B foam floats on top of the liquid **hydrocarbon fuel**, creating a barrier between the fuel and atmospheric oxygen, thus curtailing combustion. A Class B foam blanket must suppress fuel vapors for at least 15 minutes without reapplication. If burning liquids are associated with an automobile fire, Class A foam may achieve an initial knockdown of flames. But beware: In many cases, it does not suppress flammable vapors long enough for complete extinguishment and reignition is possible until an impervious blanket of Class B foam is applied on top of the Class A foam.

When using Class B foam, some departments find that the foam blanket is breaking down at a faster rate than in the past. In most cases this is caused by the new ethanol-blended gasoline that is incorporating alcohol in varying mixtures. The solution is to use alcohol-resistant (AR) foam.

The hood and engine compartment

Opening the hood and checking the **engine compartment** are standard procedure at vehicle fires. Opening the hood is necessary at automobile fires for two reasons:

1. To complete extinguishment of the fire

2. To disconnect the battery cable to prevent a reignition

However, the engine compartment contains several potentially hazardous components and firefighters working in and around the engine must wear full protective gear including SCBA, eye protection, and gloves to prevent burn injuries. Members approaching the vehicle should avoid walking in front of a heated bumper and be cognizant of hot surfaces.

The first hazard of the engine compartment is the battery which can be found in various locations under the hood depending on the manufacturer and model. In addition to an electric charge, it contains sulfuric acid, a corrosive that can cause burns to the skin and eyes. Under fire conditions, this sulfuric acid can produce hydrogen gas as the lead-acid battery is heated. Hydrogen gas is highly flammable and can rapidly accelerate any existing fire conditions. Hydrogen flames burn clear and are easily missed. In addition to the battery, pneumatic hood pistons (or gas struts) located in the back corners of the hood can burst, separate, and become forceful projectiles. Firefighters are at risk of becoming impaled with these pistons when they explode, especially if they walk in front of the vehicle.[4] There are also several flammable/combustible liquids contained within the engine compartment. These include gasoline, engine oil, brake fluid, and transmission fluid which can add to rapid burning and reignition. Radiator and air conditioner coolant also present and may be under pressure when heated. Magnesium engine components intensify the fire when water is applied. For these reasons, members should be safety conscious when working in and around this area. Firefighters should not be in a rush to open the hood if the engine compartment was involved, and be careful where they position themselves when working in this area. Although opening the hood is required, it should be postponed until the engine compartment is thoroughly cooled.

Fires in the engine compartment are difficult to completely extinguish until the hood is opened. Bouncing the stream on the street below the engine compartment or directing it though a headlight opening may affect partial knockdown but rarely produces complete extinguishment. An alternative method of cooling the engine compartment is to use a Navy nozzle with a bent applicator to spray the engine from below. It can also be used to cool the gas tank. When using this technique to cool the engine compartment, the firefighter should stand at the side of the vehicle and position the applicator under the wheel well so that the stream contacts the engine from below. A piercing nozzle, driven through the hood or fender can also be effective.

If driven through the fender, be sure that it penetrates not only the outer but also the inner fender wall.

If a piercing nozzle is unavailable, a firefighter standing along side a fender can drive the point of the Halligan into the side of the hood 4–12 in. (100–305 mm) from the edge. Prying up raises a small section of the hood and creates an opening through which water can be directed into the engine area. This operation should be done from the side of the vehicle, not from the front as illustrated in figs. 18–13 and 8–14. Only a member in full protective gear with the nozzle alongside should attempt this procedure, because flames can issue out from under the hood as soon as the opening is pried up. Directing the stream through this hole helps cool the hood struts and generates steam while the hood remains closed. It should be left down long enough for the steam to do its job. The advantage of this method is that the line does not have to be shut down to attach a special appliance.

Fig. 18–13. This procedure begins by driving the point of the Halligan into the hood. The point should be set well before prying up the edge.

Fig. 18–14. Once the point is set, the Halligan is pried up to a vertical position. This creates a triangular opening along the edge of the hood through which the hose stream is directed to darken down fire beneath the hood.

Fig. 18–15. Skillful use of a hooked tool can snag a hood-release cable where it passes along the front of the engine compartment. Courtesy of Dave Walsh

Regardless of which method is used to effect knockdown, the hood should remain closed until the engine compartment has been cooled. It is then safe to open the hood to achieve complete extinguishment. Until this occurs, internal wiring and combustible parts such as the air filter element continue to smolder. A layer of insulation affixed to the bottom of the hood commonly drops and blankets the burning engine components, requiring removal before extinguishment can be completed. To do this, the hood must be raised.

Opening the hood. Once the engine compartment and front bumper have been thoroughly cooled, efforts can be made to find the hood release whose cable runs under the hood along the driver's side. Fires that cause heavy involvement to the passenger and/or engine compartments usually damage or destroy the hood release cable, making the job of opening the hood more complicated. An attempt to locate and pull the cable should begin where it is usually located, in front of the driver's seat. If only the plastic handle is damaged, the cable can sometimes be activated by a tug with vise grips. If this fails, an attempt to locate and snag the cable under the hood can be made (fig. 18–15). Remember that depending on the manufacturer, the hood may either open from the front or tilt forward from the back (by the windshield). Autos whose hoods tilt forward include Saabs, BMWs, Corvettes, and some imported sports cars such as the Fiat and Alpha Romeo.

On standard hoods, prying from the front is typically ineffective. Leverage is limited in this area because grills are constructed of plastic or fiberglass and collapse long before the latch gives way. Moreover, when operating in front of the vehicle, care must be taken not to inadvertently jam the tool into the radiator or battery in search of the hood latch. Firefighters have gotten hot coolant in their faces when they inadvertently punctured the radiator while attempting to gain a purchase. As an option, the plastic grill can be removed to look for the hood release cable. If the cable can be located along the front of the radiator or driver's side of the hood, the fork of the Halligan can be inserted and twisted until it releases the latch (fig. 18–16). However in many newer vehicles, the cable runs inside the radiator to prevent theft and is not very accessible.

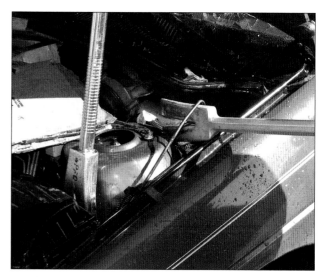

Fig. 18–16. If the fork of the Halligan can be slid under the cable, it can be twisted to release the hood latch

Fig. 18–17. Instead of prying, the Halligan's fork can be driven over the hood staple and then rotated to snap it off

Fig. 18–18. Firefighter completes a V-cut around the latch mechanism

Another option is to snap off the hood latch staple, which is attached to the bottom of the hood. The hood latch staple can be twisted off with the fork of the Halligan tool. This is done by carefully sliding the curved surface of the Halligan's fork along the bottom surface of the hood at its centerline. This is done by a firefighter from a low angle pushing the fork of the Halligan in the direction of the windshield. Once in position, the Halligan is struck with a flat-head axe or sledge by another firefighter until the fork end is set around both the front and back legs of the staple (fig. 18–17). The Halligan is then rotated either clockwise or counterclockwise to snap the staple off.

Another method that many departments have found effective is to use a rotary saw with metal cutting blade to make a V-cut in the front of the hood over the latch mechanism. This cut can be made quickly and takes the latch pin and staple out of the equation (fig. 18–18).

Whenever fire is present in the engine compartment, opening the hood introduces oxygen that could cause the fire to flare-up. Firefighters should thus stay low when lifting the hood, use eye protection, and have the hoseline ready. Once the hood has been raised, it should be propped open with a tool while the engine compartment is washed down (fig. 18–19). Do not rely on heat-damaged hinges or pistons to hold up the hood. Any smoldering material should be removed and soaked.

Finally, the battery cable should be cut at the negative terminal with a bolt cutter. Cutting the cable to the negative terminal does not produce a spark. However, cutting the positive terminal could create a spark that in turn might ignite hydrogen vapors. Similarly, crew members working with metal tools must be careful not to bridge the positive terminal to a metallic surface.

Fig. 18–19. Once the hood has been raised, it should be propped in open with a tool. A Halligan or 6-ft (1.8-m) hook serves the purpose and keeps the hood from closing while the engine compartment is overhauled and washed down.

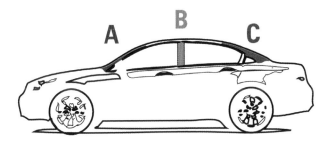

Fig. 18–20. The A, B, and C posts of a passenger vehicle

Vehicle Fires

FIREFIGHTER I

Chapter 18

This may produce a spark as well. Disabling the battery prevents rekindle, renders the air bags inoperable, and keeps the car from starting.

The passenger compartment

Separated from the engine compartment by the firewall, the **passenger compartment** burns vigorously once vented. The foam seats, padded dash, vinyl trim, and the wire harness give off a great deal of smoke and produce a substantial fuel load. There are several hazards found in the passenger compartment that can injure you, so avoid placing your head inside the passenger compartment. When heated, air bags can deploy without warning. Similarly, air bag inflators, mounted in steering wheel hubs; dashboards; seats; A, B, and C posts (fig. 18–20); and doors, may explode under fire conditions. These canisters or cylinders vary in size and contain compressed gases (usually argon or nitrogen) under high pressures. Under normal conditions they are designed to discharge and inflate the air bag during collisions. As a safeguard, many compressed gas canisters are designed to activate and release the compressed gas at temperatures ranging from 300°F to 350°F (149°C to 177°C).[5] Thus, if the passenger compartment is well involved, these canisters should discharge their contents before the fire department arrives to make firefighter injury less likely. However, there have been cases where these compressed gas cylinders have experienced a BLEVE (boiling liquid expanding vapor explosion) while the fire department is on the scene, even after the fire has been extinguished. When they fail, they can discharge fragments of shrapnel under pressure. To minimize this risk, it is important to continue thoroughly cooling all areas of the passenger compartment after the fire has been darkened down and extinguished. The cooling hose stream should be directed at the steering wheel hub, dash, side posts, and seats where the driver, passenger, and side-impact air bags are located. Close approach to the passenger compartment should be postponed until all areas have been thoroughly cooled.

An occupied vehicle on fire is another matter. Although most occupants self-evacuate at the first sign of smoke, the passenger area should be checked for victims if there is evidence that passengers are still in the vehicle. Victims are more likely to be trapped in a burning vehicle if the fire is the result of a collision. If victims are trapped, immediately direct a hose stream between the fire and the passengers to drive the fire away from them. When there is a life hazard, a second hoseline may be deployed to provide additional protection to victims in the vehicle (fig. 18–21). An immediate rescue operation must be started and coordinated with water delivery. The doors must be opened and the victims removed. The passenger compartment may also have to be vented promptly. Life takes preference over other priorities on the fireground, and a victim trapped in a burning vehicle is a true emergency.

Fig. 18–21. A second hoseline may be deployed to provide additional protection to victims in the vehicle. (Courtesy of Chris Saraceno)

The trunk

When fighting fires involving the **trunk** of an automobile, it is important to cool the gas tank and shield it from heat and flame with the hose stream. Trunk fires can be darkened down by approaching from the front at a 45° angle and directing a hose stream through the back seat if it has been burned away. Trunk fires can also be knocked down by directing the stream through a taillight opening. If fire cannot be controlled through these avenues, the point of a Halligan can be driven into the trunk a few inches from the edge of the trunk lid and pried up in a manner similar to that used with the hood; an alternative to this method is to attach a piercing nozzle to the hose. The nozzle is then driven through the trunk lid, taillight, or fender and directed into the trunk. Before the job is complete, the trunk must be opened, overhauled, and checked thoroughly. However, as with fires below the hood, this must be done carefully and only after it has been thoroughly cooled from a safe distance. The contents of the trunk can cause serious injury.

Motorists transport a wide variety of articles in the truck that can injure firefighters. A person returning home from the grocery store may be carrying a shopping bag containing aerosol cans. Aerosols can explode when heated, releasing flammable or corrosive propellants. A portable gas tank for the lawn mower can rupture and add flammable liquid to the fire. A 20-lb (9-kg) propane cylinder placed in the trunk to be refilled can cause a BLEVE. Beneath the trunk is the gas tank and fuel line. Therefore the trunk should not be approached and opened until the fire has been knocked down, the gas tank has been washed from below the vehicle, and the rear bumpers have been thoroughly cooled. Whenever the driver is present, it is a good idea to ascertain the contents of the trunk before crews get too close.

Opening the trunk can present entry difficulties similar to that of opening the hood. First, try the trunk release, which is usually located next to the driver's seat. If the driver is present, get the key. When these options are unavailable, the trunk lock cylinder can often be pulled revealing either a stem or cam. A long screwdriver or key tool can then be inserted into the locking mechanism and turned to open the trunk using the through-the-lock method. If nothing else is available, a dip stick can be used for this purpose.

Mopping up

Once the fire is extinguished, conduct a thorough search of all areas of the vehicle to confirm that the fire is completely extinguished and make sure a crime has not been committed. If flammable liquids have been spilled, containment efforts should be made to prevent them from entering sewers and waterways. The officer in charge is responsible for recording all information that can identify the vehicle and its owner. The make, model, license plate, and **vehicle identification number (VIN)** must be written down for inclusion in the incident report and given to the police for validation. They are also needed for the NFIRS report. The VIN is commonly listed on the registration sticker mounted on the windshield. If this is destroyed, look for a stamped plate affixed to the front of the dash beneath the windshield on the driver's side. Take care to avoid damaging the contents of the glove box during overhaul. If the vehicle registration, insurance card, and other documents are undamaged in the glove box, give them to the owner or police.

Firefighters should follow their local protocol relative to having a fire investigator examine the vehicle. Some jurisdictions require that all vehicle fires are investigated, whereas others do not. However, if the fire occurred in a remote area after dark with no driver present, the circumstances are suspicious. Correspondingly, if the fire originated in the passenger compartment, a gasoline can is found in or near the vehicle, or the fire otherwise appears to be incendiary in nature, notify a fire investigator to respond. Once an investigator is called, at least one fire department or law enforcement

unit must remain on the scene until the fire investigator arrives. As with any fire, the area of fire origin must remain undisturbed as much as possible, commensurate with complete extinguishment.

Magnesium vehicle components

Endeavoring to improve gas mileage and reduce carbon emissions, vehicle manufacturers are beginning to use magnesium in their engine and body components because of its reduced weight (approximately 25% of steel). Magnesium is currently used in valve, cam, and head covers as well as steering wheels, gear boxes, instrument panels, seat components, and wheels. Future uses may include engine blocks, engine cradles, transmission cases, intake manifolds, oil pans, and water pump housings.[6] Vehicles that already have magnesium engine blocks include 1970s-era Volkswagen Beetles, Porsches, and late-model BMWs and Corvettes. Cadillacs currently incorporate magnesium instrument panels, and Audi is integrating magnesium into its valve covers and power train components.[7] Future uses may include more engine blocks, engine cradles, transmission cases, intake manifolds, oil pans, and water pump housings.

When magnesium is involved in an automobile fire, firefighters see a bright white flame and the burning magnesium showers and scatters white sparks when water contacts it. The brilliant flame appears similar to a welder's arc or an arcing electrical wire and can be mistaken for a live wire on the vehicle. Firefighters should avoid staring at the luminous flashes and operate at a safe distance, away from where they may be struck by a piece of molten magnesium.

An engine compartment fire that involves magnesium can stubbornly resist extinguishment with water and flare-up, increasing in magnitude as soon as water contacts it. This is in part because magnesium burns so hot (7,000°F [3,814°C] or more); that it can chemically separate the hydrogen and oxygen in the water, negating its cooling properties and causing the fire to increase in intensity. Industrial magnesium fires are usually controlled with plentiful quantities of a Class D agent such as G-1 powder, soda ash, rock salt, or dry sand, applied in an effort to smother the fire. If a Class D extinguisher is kept on the apparatus, it can be applied to the fire. Only members trained in the application of Class D agents, wearing dry gear, and eye protection should be involved in the extinguishment process. If you do not have sufficient quantities, the best option may be to suspend water application, keep onlookers away, protect exposures, and let the fire burn itself out.

Extinguishment of other sections of the vehicle may continue, with care given not to spray the burning magnesium. Some sources have stated that magnesium fires can be extinguished with copious amounts of water. However, in many cases *copious* means far more water than a 1¾-in. (45-mm) hoseline provides. A hand line is often ineffectual unless the magnesium has been burning for some time and is nearly consumed. Apart from the manufacturers mentioned previously, magnesium auto parts are expensive and not used widely at this time. For the most part, magnesium use is still limited to small parts that are consumed quickly in the fire. Consequently, they have not presented a wide-ranging extinguishment problem to date.

Hybrid vehicles

Hybrid and alternative fueled vehicles are becoming more and more common in the United States as automotive technology seeks to increase fuel efficiency and reduce carbon emissions. Ford, Mercury, Mazda, Lexus, Toyota, Chevy, GMC, Cadillac, Saturn, and Honda have hybrids already in production; other manufacturers are to follow. In the next few years, there may be as many as 50 hybrid models in production[8] with purely electric vehicles and hydrogen fuel cell–powered vehicles to follow in the next generation. There are no reported hybrid fire hazards, and they do not appear to be more fire-prone than conventionally powered vehicles. Although the Prius and Insight have a distinctive look, other models have the same body type as standard vehicles. The only distinguishing characteristic for these hybrids may be a logo on the vehicle's trunk, hatchback, front fenders, or doors (fig. 18–22).

Fig. 18–22. Placards like this may not be visible if obscured by smoke

To date, no major problems have been reported with hybrid vehicles under fire conditions. Fires in these vehicles can be fought with water by conventional means. All hybrid manufacturers have published emergency response guides that can be accessed via the Internet. Firefighters should review these response guides to familiarize themselves with the special systems and hazards associated with these vehicles during extrication and extinguishment operations.

In addition to an internal-combustion engine and standard 12-volt electrical system, current hybrids also contain specialized electrical systems that include 144- to 300-volt **nickel metal hydride (NiMH)** direct current (DC) dry cell battery packs that supply current to 165 horsepower electric motors operating on 650 volts alternating current (AC) after the power is converted in a booster. These battery packs are usually located in the rear of the vehicle or under the back seat and enclosed in a metal housing. Power is transmitted to the electric motor(s) through high-voltage cables. You may encounter blue cables in some hybrid models, which indicate a medium (36v–42v) voltage system. There are hybrid models that operate on this lower voltage system, but the same precautions should be used as when dealing with high-voltage models. Situated on the underside of the vehicle, these orange high-voltage cables are encased in conduits, many of which are black and either partially or totally cover the cables, making identification based strictly on the orange cables difficult. Do not cut, crush, or touch these high-voltage cables during extinguishment, overhaul, or extrication; and avoid direct contact with the NiMH battery pack itself.

Although there are high voltages involved, there are no warnings advising against using water to extinguish fires in these vehicles. That is because the voltages are DC and therefore do not travel up a hose stream seeking a path to ground. Several hybrids utilize alternating current (AC) system components as well, but they are protected by ground fault interrupt circuits (GFICs). Nor is there danger of electric shock from touching the car body or chassis even if it is partially or wholly submerged. However, when overhauling or using metal tools, crew members must use caution not to create a bridge between the negative and positive sides of the circuit.

Battery pack fires

A standard fire attack can be made on hybrid vehicles with one caveat: Fires confined to battery packs should be allowed to burn. Applying water is ineffective because their shielding inhibits water penetration, even when hose streams are directed through vents.[9] However, the housing and adjacent areas can be cooled with water. Once the fire is out, make no attempt to disassemble or detach the metal cover to overhaul the high voltage NiMH battery pack. As with any vehicle fire, the use of SCBA is mandatory. Burning NiMH batteries produces hydrogen and toxic vapors containing heavy metals. A fire involving the NiMH battery may present an environmental hazard and require specialized disposal by a battery recycler. It should also be noted that hybrid vehicles are silent when stopped. Therefore it is not possible to tell if they are on or off simply by listening to the engine. This makes stabilization of the vehicle with chocks all the more essential.

Alternative fuel vehicles

SKILL DRILL

FFI 5.3.7 Alternative fuel vehicles can present a more serious hazard. In an effort to be more fuel efficient, some municipalities are purchasing fleets of vehicles powered by **compressed natural gas (CNG)**, **liquefied petroleum gas (LPG)**, **liquid natural gas (LNG)** or hydrogen (H). Such vehicles are often found at airports where taxi fleets and airport shuttles are converting to these cost-saving, clean-burning fuels. They may also be found on city streets where city owned vehicles may be powered by alternative fuels. These vehicles can be any type, ranging from small passenger vehicles, to jitneys, to full-size city busses. United Parcel Service (UPS) is powering many of its new delivery trucks with propane. Ford, Toyota, and Honda now offer some auto and truck models with alternative fuel options, the Honda Civic being the most prevalent. These vehicles have the same body type as standard gasoline fuel models, and responding firefighters may not suspect an alternatively fueled vehicle except for a small placard on the trunk lid or rear bumper (fig. 18–23). Aftermarket conversion kits are becoming more readily available to convert gasoline engines to run on alternative fuels such as ethanol, methanol, CNG, and LPG as well; and these my not display a placard at all.

Fig. 18–23. Alternative fuel vehicles display a small placard on the rear bumper or trunk lid. Under fire conditions, it may or may not be visible to responding firefighters.

Because of their chemical nature, these fuels are compressed into cylinders mounted horizontally inside the vehicle with straps in much the same way a propane cylinder is mounted to a fork lift (fig. 18–24). Although

not more fire prone than ordinary vehicles, they can explode when exposed to heat, causing catastrophic damage (fig. 18–25). When operating at a fire involving one or more of these vehicles it is important to look for the placard, get information from the driver, and determine the location and extent of the fire during initial size-up. As with all automobile fires, approach the vehicle at a 45° angle and keep a safe distance from the vehicle until the fire is controlled. Although it is impossible to predict with certainty the direction the blown cylinder will travel, it is likely to blow out from the side that is exposed to fire. Thus, for example, if the fire is coming from the front of the vehicle, the front of the cylinder will likely fail first, propelling the cylinder toward the rear, depending on how the retaining straps fail (fig. 18–26).

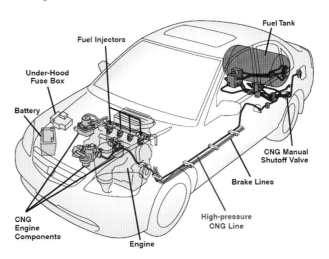

Fig. 18–24. The compressed gas cylinder is mounted in a compartment between the back seat and the trunk in most CNG vehicles. This compartment may or may not contain adequate insulation from fire. (Courtesy of the Seattle Fire Department and Honda Motor Co.)

Fig. 18–25. The aftermath of a fire in a CNG Honda Civic in which the fuel storage cylinder exploded. Note the extreme destruction to the vehicle. Fire spread to several nearby vehicles as a result of the blast. (Courtesy of the Seattle Fire Department)

Fig. 18—26. What remained of the fiberglass wrapped CNG cylinder from vehicle shown in fig. 18—25, which was propelled 100 feet to the rear of the vehicle when it exploded. (Courtesy of the Seattle Fire Department)

The fire attack varies depending on the situation found during size-up. If the fire is limited to a part of the vehicle that is separate from the fuel storage cylinder, an attempt can be made to confine the fire to the area of origin and cool the tank(s) if accessible. Preventing the fire from reaching the tanks prevents the situation from escalating. If the fire is already involving the tank area and the tank(s) is venting, a catastrophic failure may be imminent, and all personnel should withdraw from the area. If it can be done safely, cool the tank from a safe distance, protect exposures, and allow the fuel to burn off. Avoid extinguishing the flames venting from the cylinder relief valve. This could lead to vapor release and explosion. Always consider risk-benefit analysis and avoid approaching these vehicles closely unless a rescue has to be made or they have been thoroughly cooled. The Seattle Fire Department has put together an excellent PowerPoint presentation on the subject of CNG vehicle fires on their Web site.[10]

Ladder company functions at vehicle fires

Although most fire districts dispatch a ladder or rescue to fires involving school buses or larger vehicles, many assign only an engine to respond to standard vehicle fires. Although once thought to be the purview of a single-engine company exclusively, some districts and departments find that the addition of a ladder company or a second engine to perform support duties benefits safety and extinguishment. Whether an additional unit is sent or not, these support tasks must be performed by the crew members on the scene.

On arrival, the initial function of the ladder, second-engine, or other support unit is to provide for scene safety as described previously, by parking the vehicle in a position that creates a safe working area, controlling traffic, and setting cones and other warning devices

as needed. On a steep curve or grade, the additional company can be located well upstream of the curve to warn oncoming traffic that might be unable to see the engine. Scene safety also includes lighting the scene, controlling any hazardous material or flammable spills, and keeping crews and the public away from downed wires and other hazards. The ladder can be used to stretch a second hoseline for exposure protection, extinguishment, or crew safety.

When no life hazard is present, the ladder or support company vents the vehicle and provides entry into the hood, passenger compartment, and trunk for overhaul. These operations should be postponed until all areas have been extinguished and cooled thoroughly. Opening up the hood and trunk often requires particular skills, and specialized tools may be needed to gain access to some of these areas. Once the vehicle is opened up, a thorough secondary search is conducted to check for extension or victims.

Vehicle search by the ladder

Most vehicle fires are *not* associated with a collision, and if passengers are in the vehicle at the time the fire occurs, they pull over and self-evacuate. Therefore at most vehicle fires, life is not a factor, there is no rescue emergency and extinguishment is the primary assignment. However, in some instances firefighters may have to initiate a search of the vehicle on arrival at the scene. For example, a truck driver could be trapped in the cab when his 18 wheeler jackknifes. A driver who hit a tree could be unconscious behind the wheel when a spark from the battery cable ignites a fire in the engine compartment. Children could be overcome by smoke from an engine fire in a school bus. Whenever there is a serious accident that results in fire, a rescue emergency could exist. If there are reports of a victim within a smoldering vehicle, or if the scene survey indicates that not all passengers are out of the vehicle, rapid water delivery coordinated with a primary search of the vehicle is necessary.

This task is delegated to the ladder company on the scene while the hoseline is charged. Searching a vehicle is a hazardous maneuver because of the speed with which vehicles burn and the many hazards associated with the passenger compartment of a burning vehicle as described earlier. Speed and water limit the risk. Crew members involved in making a primary search/rescue must be in full protective gear, including SCBA, before initiating a search of the passenger compartment. In an auto, searches are done rapidly. Keep low (below the level of an air bag deployment), open the door, and reach across the seat. Search the front and back seats under the protection of a hose stream. If a victim is in the vehicle, rapid water delivery is vital and the stream must be placed between the occupant and the fire. If the fire has already entered the passenger compartment, a fog stream should be directed there immediately, to lessen the effects of heat and smoke while the victims are being freed. A seat-belt cutter helps free a victim.

Conducting a primary search inside the vehicle is not a routine procedure unless a victim is present. Because of the danger of a sudden air bag deployment, firefighters should keep their head and torso outside the vehicle unless they are engaged in a rescue procedure.

If the fire is associated with a crash or any vehicle occupants cannot be accounted for, initiate a secondary search of the scene on the interior and exterior of the vehicle once the fire is out. At night, a thermal imaging camera can be used to look for injured persons who may have been thrown from the vehicle.

TRUCKS AND LARGER VEHICLE FIRES

Fires in trucks and over-the-road vehicles can present distinctive challenges to responding firefighters depending on the cargo, size, and type of vehicle (fig. 18–27). Fires can occur in the engine, cab, cargo, or wheel areas. A frequent cause of truck fires is overheated brakes or wheel bearings that can ignite tires or grease deposits under the trailer. When responding to a truck fire, it is essential to determine if the truck is carrying hazardous materials before committing resources. When no hazmats are involved, the standard strategy is to rescue any passengers in the cab, confine the fire to the area or origin, and prevent extension to the rest of the vehicle. If the truck has been involved in an accident, or has jackknifed, attention must be given to the saddle tanks beneath the cab. These tanks contain diesel fuel. Although less volatile than gasoline, diesel leaking from a saddle tank should be covered with Class B foam to prevent ignition of vapors.

Fig. 18–27. A truck fire presents a heavier fire load than an automobile fire. This fire involved a pole and transformer. Downed wires are an important size-up consideration at any vehicle fire on a city street.

In general, the same guidelines about protective equipment, apparatus placement, and hose stream application described earlier apply to standard truck fires (trucks not carrying hazmats) with the consideration that more water may be needed to control the fire, requiring additional companies, tanker shuttles, or a potential relay if hydrants are unavailable. Class A foam helps penetrate layers of densely packed cargo. Overhaul can be effort-intensive, when the entire contents of a tractor trailer or garbage truck must be separated and hosed down. Ground ladders and power saws with metal cutting blades may be needed to open access holes in the side of the trailer. Members should avoid working on the interior of semi-trailers or garbage trucks, however. A truck fire is not a place for an aggressive interior attack. In some cases, the burning product may have to be pulled out onto the roadway so firefighters are able to hose it down with water or foam. This is not an ideal situation, because such an operation will tie up traffic for several hours. If it can be done safely once the fire is knocked down, the truck can be towed to a parking area, for overhaul and final extinguishment.

The hazards associated with truck fires vary with the type of cargo the truck is carrying. An immediate effort must be made to determine the contents of the truck. The best source of this information is the driver. Is the truck carrying contents that are hazardous, flammable, or water reactive? Is there a mixed cargo that could interact when exposed to heat? Over-the-road trucks are required by the U.S. Department of Transportation (DOT) to display placards on all four sides of the vehicle if they are carrying hazardous cargo. These placards reveal the general chemical properties of the cargo. Any placarding information should be cross referenced to a hazmat guide on the fire apparatus or with computer-aided management of emergency operations (CAMEO), to determine if any precautions must be taken. The shape of the truck can also tell responding firefighters a lot about what is being carried. Even from a distance, a standard trailer looks vastly different from a gasoline tanker; and a tanker, in turn, is shaped differently than a propane truck, and so forth.

Fires in large recreational vehicles (RVs), motor homes, mobile lunch wagons, and campers should be fought cautiously if there is a significant amount of fire. It is important to establish a sufficient water supply to control the fire. These vehicles may contain standard voltage AC-powered water heaters and refrigeration systems powered either by inverters or, if stationary, external hookups. LPG-powered heaters, refrigerators, and stoves are also found on these vehicles and their cylinders are subject to BLEVE under heavy fire conditions. Standards for design of recreational vehicles can be found in NFPA 1192, *Standard on Recreational Vehicles*.

Gasoline tanker fires

Each day in the United States, gasoline tanker trucks make approximately 50,000 trips delivering gasoline from distribution terminals to local gas stations.[11] Tanker fires can occur on almost any highway in any community, regardless of size (fig. 18–28). Notable gasoline tanker fires have occurred in recent years in as diverse locations as Emeryville, California; Branson, Missouri; Yonkers, New York; Chicopee, Massachusetts; and Washington, DC, to name a few. These fires present a set of challenges that can greatly challenge the capacity of any department.

Gasoline tanker fires can threaten exposures, damage infrastructure, endanger the environment, and create a severe life hazard. Any fire department that has a

gas station or interstate within its boundaries should consider developing guidelines on how to handle a tanker fire. Will a tanker fire overtax the capacity of the Class B foam supply? Are water and foam tenders available? Does your department or a neighboring department have a master stream foam capability? If not, is there a mutual aid agreement with a nearby airport or military base? Does the department have enough diking materials to contain a significant gasoline spill?

Fig. 18–28. This fire on an interstate originated in the engine compartment. Firefighters from Washington, DC, and Prince George's County, Maryland, extinguished it with hand lines before it spread to the cargo tank which contained 8,000 gallons of gasoline. (Courtesy of Mark E. Brady)

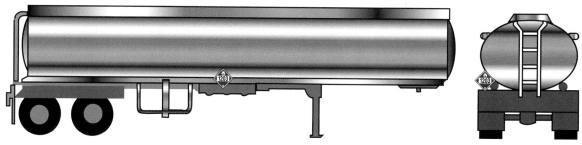

Fig. 18–29. MC 306 tanker profile

Gasoline tankers can carry up to 9,000 gal (3,407 L) of fuel when full. Their tanks are cylindrically shaped and approximately 40 ft (12 m) long. The ends are elliptical according to MC-306/DOT—406 specifications (fig. 18–29). Knowing the shape of the various DOT vehicles gives the responding firefighters an idea of the potential cargo from a distance even when the placard is not visible. Gasoline tankers have an aluminum exterior shell and are placarded with the number 1203. Because of the potential hazards, tankers are designed under DOT standards with numerous safety mechanisms designed to reduce the hazard of fire or explosion during transportation. Some of these safety devices include automatic heat-activated vents; vapor-recovery piping; pressure-relief valves; baffling to subdivide the cargo tank into separate compartments; and a reinforced aluminum exterior shell, which melts under fire conditions, thus preventing a BLEVE. Fires in gasoline tankers may occur during filling and offloading operations. However, most fires are the result of roadway accidents that may compromise these safety mechanisms.

Chemical properties. Gasoline is one of our most common fuels. It is refined to perform within the confines of the internal-combustion engine and is not hazardous when contained within properly designed vessels. However, it can become hazardous when it escapes. Gasoline is a petroleum-based flammable liquid whose vapors are 3 to 4 times heavier than air. As such, its vapors are slow to dissipate and instead gather in low areas such as drainage ditches, sewers, and basements where they can travel a great distance in search of an ignition source. Whenever operating at tanker incidents, efforts should be made to prevent spilled gasoline from entering sewers and manholes. If a source of ignition is found, these vapors instantaneously flash back to their source, igniting everything in between. For safety, crew members should remain upwind and uphill when operating at the scene of a gasoline spill, and every effort should be made to suppress vapors with foam application and eliminate potential sources of ignition.

Most people are familiar with the smell of gasoline because it is exceptionally volatile. With a flashpoint of −43°F (−42°C), gasoline generates flammable vapors at any conceivable ambient temperature. That is one reason why it cannot be extinguished with water, because water cannot cool it to a low enough temperature to prevent it from generating flammable vapors.[12] Although heavier than air, gasoline is lighter than water, which is another reason water cannot be used. With a specific gravity of 0.69, if water is applied to burning gasoline, the latter will simply float on top and spread about. That property is the basis for the "light water" foam concept in which carbon dioxide foam bubbles keep a water film on top of the gasoline.

On the positive side, gasoline has a narrow flammable range of 1.5% to 6% in air. Any concentration more than 6% is too rich to burn. However, ignition can occur even in diluted states; and when a rich mixture is dissipated, it passes through the flammable range as it is dispersed. The fact is that gasoline is easily ignited, and all ignition sources should be eliminated before venting.

Once ignited, gasoline fires burn with tremendous quantities of radiant heat and copious amounts of heavy, sooty smoke. The heat release rate—the amount of heat energy released in a given period of time—for a small pool of gasoline (2 sq ft [0.2 sq m]) is approximately 400 kW, compared with a heat release rate of 50 kW for a wastepaper basket of the same footprint. The radiant heat makes close approach to a gasoline tanker difficult, but not out of the reach of a properly charged foam nozzle. This high radiant heat also makes exposure protection a primary consideration whenever a tanker fire occurs in a populated area. Traffic must be stopped one-half mile in each direction and structures within this radius should be evacuated to maximize life safety and minimize the impact to the surrounding area. It is not uncommon for surrounding structures to be heavily involved in fire before the arrival of the fire department.

Tanker fire operations

Equipment needed:

- Foam nozzles, eductors, reservoirs
- Class B foam sufficient to the task
- Combustible gas detectors
- Shovels
- Sand truck
- Spill booms and absorbents

Supplemental equipment:

- Master stream foam equipment
- Small excavator
- Sandbags
- Dry chemical extinguishers

There is no single tactical plan that fits all gasoline tanker fires. Although life safety, exposure protection, spill control, and vapor suppression are primary strategies at all incidents, extinguishment procedures vary with the incident encountered based on the scene size-up. Critical factors include incident location, terrain, vehicle position (upright/overturned), the part of the vehicle involved in fire, and whether there is a large discharge of product associated with the fire.

The primary considerations for the incident commander to ascertain while responding are location, degree of involvement, and life hazard. (Is the fire on a remote stretch of highway, on a bridge, under an overpass, or in a crowded neighborhood? Is the terrain level or sloped?) If sloped, are there downhill exposures that must be evacuated? What part of the truck is on fire: the cab or cargo tank area? If the fire is confined to the engine or cab area, can hoselines be directed between the cargo tank and the cab to prevent fire from spreading to it? Has the fire spread to nearby exposures already causing a rescue priority? Is there an immediate life hazard in or near the vehicle? If so, can immediate steps be taken to rescue the driver/passenger before the fire extends to the passenger compartment?

Another important early consideration is the position of the vehicle. Is the vehicle upright or on its side? Is it leaking fuel through the dome covers? Can the leak be controlled and the vapors contained? If the vehicle is upright and the vents are showing fire, sufficient quantities of Class B foam and dry chemical must be brought to the scene immediately, before an attempt to extinguish the fire can be made. An operation that runs out of foam solution while extinguishing a fire burns back to its original size and ends up having no net effect. Sufficient quantities means having enough **foam concentrate** and water to both blanket and reblanket the burning product and to suppress vapors from spills. Water streams can be directed to cool the sides of the tank to keep the aluminum shell from melting too quickly. Cooling the sides of the tanker with water in conjunction with applying foam to the burning liquid can slow the rate of burning somewhat, thus assisting the foam in successfully extinguishing it.[13] When using water, take care to prevent water from being directed onto the flames or entering the tank. This only displaces gasoline and may cause the tank to overflow product, spreading the fire to exposures. The same goes for the foam stream. It must be aimed in an arc so that the foam is laid on top and not driven beneath the surface. Even with careful application, spills and slop over occur and additional foam lines and booms are necessary to control fuel spills.

Life hazard

As previously mentioned, most tanker fires result from accidents in transit. Potential victims include the driver, occupants of a vehicle that collided with the truck, or people trapped in an occupied structure into which the truck collided. Because gasoline fires ignite and spread so quickly, in most well-involved tanker fires, driver survival often depends on the ability to self-evacuate. Few rescues are made, unless the fire is small on arrival, in which case an attempt to extinguish it with Class B foam and/or dry chemical may resolve the problem. However, often by the time the fire department arrives, the level of radiant heat prevents close approach by rescue crews. Nevertheless, in situations where victims are at risk, an attempt should be made to stop the fire from spreading to them with an exposure line, if the fire has not become too large to do so. Aside from those in the immediate vicinity of the tanker, life safety obliges the immediate evacuation of all persons from the area 1,000 ft (305 m) downwind and the eventual isolation of an area of one-half mile in all directions along with the elimination of ignition sources in that area. To accomplish this, a unified command structure must be set up to include police to assist in the evacuation.

Tanker fire strategies

Option A. Defensive strategy: Do not attempt to extinguish the fire. Letting the fire burn off is a legitimate tactic in some cases. If there is no life hazard, available water/foam is insufficient, crews would be placed at unwarranted risk, or the fire is in a remote location with no exposures, the preferred tactic is to stop traffic, set up perimeters, protect exposures and let the fire burn itself out. Even in a moderately populated area, if exposures can be safely protected from igniting, and no critical infrastructure is threatened, the safest procedure is to let the fire consume the product. Even though gasoline is an expensive commodity, the fire should not be fought simply to save the product or the vehicle. The gasoline will be contaminated with foam and offloading it can be a costly and hazardous process. The runoff of foam/gasoline solution into nearby waterways may cause environmental damage far in excess of the value of the saved product. When a defensive strategy is employed, cooling streams may still be directed from a safe distance to cool the outer shell and adjoining tank compartments to impede further involvement.

Allowing the fire to burn off is the only option when insufficient Class B foam is available to extinguish it. Although most vehicle fires, including fuel-oil trucks, can be fought with either water fog or foam; however, a gasoline tanker fire can only be extinguished with Class B foam. Once initiated, foam application must be continuous to be effective; so if the tanker is well involved (one or more tank compartments), the foam operation should be curtailed until sufficient foam can be brought to bear (fig. 18–30). As mentioned earlier, the sides of the tanker shell can be cooled with water streams in the interim, to prevent failure of the aluminum skin and the escape of product. This is a defensive strategy. Whenever water is used to cool the sides of the tank, care should be taken not to direct the stream onto the burning gasoline. If water splashes into the burning tank opening, flaming gasoline can overflow the sides and travel to exposures, particularly those downhill. Similarly, no attempt should be made to direct a hose stream onto flames venting from a pressure reducing valve.

Fig. 18–30. A fully involved tanker can place a heavy demand on foam supplies. A defensive strategy aimed at exposure protection should be initiated until sufficient supplies of foam are on the scene to support a continuous application. (Courtesy of Brent Perkins, Shelby County Tenn. F.D.)

Option B. Mount an offensive attack on the fire. If life safety is at risk, buildings are exposed, infrastructure is threatened, and sufficient foam can be brought to the scene quickly, an offensive attack on the fire can be mounted. Whenever there is life safety involved, firefighters must act to save a life by attempting a quick knockdown (if the fire is small) or by placing a hose stream between the fire and the endangered people (if the fire is too large to extinguish quickly).

A quick knockdown is also advantageous for a tanker truck fire that does not involve the cargo area. A fire involving the engine or cab area of a gasoline tanker is essentially a routine truck fire until the cargo tank gets involved. Quick water application may prevent the fire from spreading and developing into a full blown tanker fire. Handlines should be directed to extinguish the fire and an exposure line should be leveled at the space between the cab and the tank shell to keep it cool. If the saddle tanks below the cab are involved, water fog or Class B foam may be needed to complete extinguishment. Similarly, a fire under the cargo tank (a tire on fire, for example) should be quickly extinguished before the contents become involved.

If the fire is located under a bridge, in a tunnel, or affects a populated building or other infrastructure, every effort should be made to protect exposures and control the fire before it causes significant damage. Flame plumes can extend vertically 50 ft (15 m) or more. Master streams can be directed to cool the steel girders with water, taking care not to displace the gasoline. A larger fire threatening exposures may require water, foam, or a combination of streams to confine the fire.

Because of the intense heat they generate, gasoline tanker fires can be slow to respond to foam application, and close approach can be impeded. Generally, when operating at a tanker fire, nozzles should be located at the furthest distance that will still reach the target. The use of monitors and master stream foam equipment can extend the reach and keep members in safer locations.

Estimating the amount of foam needed. The use of foam, while covered in the context of tanker fires here, is described in greater detail in chapter 25, Implementing the Planned Response to a Hazardous Materials Incident as well as chapter 31, Advanced Fire Attack. Refer to those chapters for foam terminology, foam equipment, and foam application techniques.

In estimating the amount of foam needed, an involved tanker fire can demand the application of several hundred gallons of Class B foam concentrate to bring under control. The application rate must be proportionate to the intensity of fire development. If the tanker is fully involved, several hand lines or a master stream may be called for. Additional foam is also necessary to blanket pools of spilled gasoline in order to prevent ignition. Such operations demand team work and should be practiced beforehand, during training exercises.

When deciding whether to make an offensive attack, it is important to determine if you have enough foam to complete the job. Table 18–2, based on NFPA 11, *Standard for Low, Medium, and High Expansion Foam,* provides a reference that can be used to determine the

Table 18–2. Foam application rates for spills, based on NFPA 11

Foam type	Minimum application gpm per sq ft	Minimum discharge time (minutes)	Types of spill
Protein or fluoroprotein	0.16	15	Hydrocarbon
Aqueous film forming foam (A.F.F.F.), Fluoroprotein film forming foam (F.F.F.P.) and alcohol-resistant AFFF or FFFP	0.1	15	Hydrocarbon
Alcohol-resistant foams	Check listing criteria provided by the manufacturer	15	Flammable and combustible liquid spills necessitating alcohol-resistant foam

minimum amount of foam needed. Remember the difference between **foam concentrate,** which typically comes in 5-gal (19-L) pails, and **foam solution,** which is the mixture of foam concentrate *and* water.

Here's an example: Let's say that on arrival, you have a tanker on its side with a burning spill area of approximately 40 ft × 40 ft. How much total foam solution will you need for the initial application period of 15 minutes?

- 40 ft × 40 ft = 1,600 sq ft
- 1,600 sq ft × 0.10 (from the table) = 160 gpm for 15 min
- 160 gpm × 15 min = 2,400 gal of foam solution

Now, to determine how much foam concentrate you need to bring to the scene, you must know what percentage concentrate you are using. So, let's say your department purchased 3% foam. That means that 3% of those 2,400 gal of *foam solution* is going to be *foam concentrate* (with the remaining 97% water).

- 0.03 × 2,400 = 72 gal of *foam concentrate* (15 pails) for initial 15-minute attack
- Additional foam concentrate to maintain foam blanket until picked up by environmental recovery firm (foam blanket will degrade over time)

Controlling runoff. Containment of spilled product is a crucial challenge in tanker fires. Streams of gasoline can escape from the damaged tank structure and quickly find an ignition source. Flowing gasoline travels rapidly and can quickly spread fire to nearby exposures. Dry chemical quickly extinguishes streaming gasoline, but vapors can reignite. Several members should be given dry chemical extinguishers to quickly douse any ignited gasoline on the ground. Gasoline spilling, pooling, or running along the roadway should be contained by a dike and blanketed with foam. Diking can be done with

commercial booms, sandbags, or shovels and dirt. For large releases, excavators and earth moving equipment should be requested to form dikes and berms in an effort to control the spillage. Once contained and covered with a blanket of foam, the vapors must be monitored with combustible gas detectors and foam reapplied whenever vapors return. Building a barrier around sewer grates and manholes can prevent gasoline from entering subterranean conduits where it is likely to find a source of ignition and spread the fire. If gasoline does enter a sewer, a unit should be assigned to flood the sewer with foam, and the wastewater treatment plant must be notified. To minimize environmental damage, efforts must be made to prevent **runoff** from entering waterways. If this cannot be avoided, the local Health Department and the Coast Guard should be advised.

Safety management. Clearly, tanker fires require a large number of personnel to control. Multiple alarms or mutual aid are commonly necessary. Many different tasks must be completed simultaneously involving numerous groups and divisions coordinated by means of the Incident Command System (ICS). Essential tasks may include rescue, evacuation, exposure protection, fire attack, foam management, water supply, runoff containment, air monitoring, hazmat control, medical, traffic control, and utilities. The safety officer has a critical role to play in all of this.

Safety of personnel is paramount at these incidents. A rapid intervention crew (RIC) should be established at the beginning of the incident. Firefighters intent on their mission can get tunnel vision and unwittingly find themselves standing in a pool of gasoline or otherwise put themselves in jeopardy. The principle of approaching the vehicle from uphill and upwind is especially important when attempting to extinguish a gasoline tanker fire. Wind can direct the thermal plume toward firefighters advancing from downwind, decrease the reach of the hose streams, and disrupt the application of the foam blanket. Crew members operating downhill are in danger of flowing gasoline or explosive vapors collecting in low areas, and the safety officer must keep crews positioned safely.

Once the fire is extinguished, there may be several hundred gallons of gasoline remaining in the tanker that didn't burn. This product must be off-loaded with specialized equipment before the vehicle is towed away. The trucking company and/or petroleum transporter are responsible for the cleanup and should provide the necessary apparatus for safe removal. The process of removing the remaining product can be time consuming and hazardous. Fire department units must remain on the scene until this process has been completed. Every effort must be made to prevent vapors from reigniting. Combustible gas detectors help determine when the foam blanket must be refreshed to control the vapors.

LPG tanker fires

Liquefied petroleum gas (LPG) tank trucks can carry up to 11,500 gal (45,532 L) of liquefied fuel under pressure when full. Smaller, local delivery trucks known as **bobtails** carry between 2,000 and 3,000 gal (7,571 and 11,356 L) of LPG. Bobtails also have hose reels and pumps to transfer the LPG at delivery points. The fuel is plentiful, with approximately 18 billion gal (68 billion L) are transported and used annually.[14] LPG is used more prevalently in rural areas where gas mains are limited. The tanks on LPG trucks are cylindrical with rounded ends that resemble a SCBA cylinder. They are constructed according to DOT MC-331 and NFPA 58 specifications (fig. 18–31). They have a steel exterior shell that is usually painted white and are placarded with the number 1075. Knowing the shape of the various DOT vehicles gives the responding firefighters an idea of the potential cargo even when the placard is not visible. Because of the possible hazards associated with a spill or fire, propane tank trucks are also designed under Department of Transportation (DOT) and

American Society of Mechanical Engineers (ASME) standards that reduce the hazard during transportation. These features include fusible closure valves and remote emergency valve controls.

The most significant safety device is the pressure relief valve located on top of the tank either at the center or toward the rear. To keep the LPG in liquid form, the tanks maintain an internal pressure of about 250 psi (1,750 kPa), and the relief valve is calibrated to open when the pressure exceeds this level by a specified margin. However, if the relief valve is damaged during an accident, it may not work properly. The biggest hazard associated with fires in LPG tank trucks is the danger of a BLEVE. A propane cargo tank involved in a fire could cause a violent BLEVE in as little as 5 minutes if flames are impinging on the steel shell above the level of the liquid.[15] This does not give firefighters much time to intervene in the incident and incident commanders must consider this time frame when deciding whether on not to employ an offensive attack.

Chemical properties. LPG refers to a category of petroleum-based fuels that include propane, butane, isobutane, methane, and propylene. Propane and butane are similar in chemical structure and characteristics. The term LPG can mean either propane, butane, or a combination of the two with butane use more prevalent in warmer climates. LPG is used in home heating systems, barbecues, warehouse forklifts, and as an alternative fuel in some motor vehicles. It is also used in stoves found in campers, RVs, and boats; making a BLEVE a possibility at fires in those vehicles. All of these fuels are volatile, highly flammable gases. Like gasoline, vapors that find an ignition source will flashback violently.

Although it is a vapor at ambient temperatures and atmospheric pressure, LPG becomes liquefied when placed under pressure. This allows for easy transport in liquid form. When compressed, propane gas shrinks to ¹⁄₂₇₀ of its original volume. Because of its high compression/expansion rate, propane tankers are never filled all

Fig. **18–31.** MC-331 tanker

the way, but they maintain a vapor space above the liquid to allow for expansion during normal warming. This vapor space is significant to firefighting operations because the steel tank shell above the level of the liquid will heat and weaken much more quickly than below the surface.

LPG is colorless, odorless, and nontoxic. Although invisible, a whitish cloud of condensed water vapor may be visible near the leak site. However, given its expansion rate, an explosive mixture extends well beyond the visible area. Therefore apparatus should be staged well outside the vapor area and only intrinsically safe radios and flashlights should be operated. To make allowance for detection when seeping into the atmosphere, an odorant known as **ethyl mercaptan** is added to the fuel. Ethyl mercaptan gives LPG a pungent aroma that can aid in early discovery and prevention of an explosion.

Propane has a flashpoint of −156°F (−104°C). In contrast to CNG, propane is 1.5 times heavier than air. This property keeps it from dissipating readily into the atmosphere unless there are breezy conditions. Instead, it collects in low areas in much the same way as gasoline; and as such, it is subject to detonation when an ever-present ignition source is found. Its flammable limits are 2.2%–9.5% in air. Although the flammable limit is narrow, only a small amount is needed for ignition. During a leak situation, a combustible gas indicator can be used to determine whether the released product is within the flammable range. However, even when too rich to burn, there is a mixture gradient as the vapors dissipate through which the flammable limit is entered. This hazard can be reduced by the use of water fog. LPG is water soluble. An LPG leak should be handled by evacuating the area, eliminating sources of ignition, and dispersing the vapor cloud with water fog. Members operating the stream should approach from uphill and upwind to stay out of the vapor cloud.

Fire operations. Whenever a propane truck is involved in a fire, it is a serious matter. The primary strategies in a fire situation are to evacuate the area and to cool the tank so that no hot spots develop. Propane tanks are constructed of steel, and steel weakens at 1,100°F (593°C). The combination of a weakening steel shell with an increasing internal pressure from a boiling, highly compressed gas in liquid form can lead to a BLEVE in which the tank separates, explosively propelling flames and fragments over a wide area. Hazmat guides recommend the evacuation of all individuals for 1 mile in every direction when an LPG vehicle is involved in fire. Fire operations involve setting up operations from the sides, not the ends of the vehicle. Although the tank can go in

any direction, if a BLEVE occurs the ends tend to travel the greatest distance.

Before initiating an offensive attack on a propane fire, the incident commander should know the length of time the fire has been impinging on the tank and the amount of LPG being carried. If a tire or engine compartment fire can be extinguished expeditiously, a disaster may be prevented from occurring. If the fire cannot be extinguished quickly, or it is unknown how long the tank has been heating, a defensive approach is necessary. Depending on the specific circumstances, the primary tactic may either be to evacuate the area or to cool the tank from both sides. Cooling streams should be directed from unmanned monitors using smooth bore nozzles to obtain the greatest reach possible. The upper part of the tank is the most vulnerable because that is where the vapor space is. Lacking liquid to dissipate the heat, this part of the shell weakens the fastest. Therefore streams should be directed toward the top of the tank, allowing water to roll down the sides (fig. 18–32).

The emptier the tank is, the faster the steel weakens. If the driver reports that several deliveries have been made and the tank is near empty, the window of opportunity to control the situation is greatly reduced. Sometimes a frost line can be seen on the side of the tank. Formed by condensation inside the tank, this line indicates the level of LPG inside. As soon as the monitors are set up, firefighters should withdraw to a safe location, approximately one-half mile (0.8 km) back. If copious amounts of water are not quickly available, or if flames have been impinging on the tank for an unknown period of time and there are no rescues, crews should withdraw from the area immediately.

Relief valves dissipate internal tank pressure up to their capacity if working properly. On arrival it is important to determine whether the relief valve is operating. If the tank pressure increases faster than the relief valve can disperse it, the internal pressure builds. Cooling the tank can assist the relief valve to do its job. The dispersal of pressurized vapor from the relief valve is accompanied by a rushing sound. If the pitch or volume increases, it is a signal to retreat to a safe location. If flames show from the relief valve, the propane has either found a source of ignition or has reached its auto ignition temperature of 842°F (450°C). Care must be taken to not extinguish flames coming from a venting pressure relief valve. Doing so allows rapid emission of unburned gas into the surrounding area and could lead to an explosion. It is important to note that an overturned LPG tanker's relief valve may be below the liquid level and thus not operable.

Fig. 18–32. Unmanned water monitors are used to cool a LPG tanker truck.

Bus fires

During the 5-year period of 1999–2003, fire departments across the country responded to an average of approximately of 2,200 bus fires annually in total. These fires caused an estimated annual average of 3 civilian deaths, 30 civilian injuries, and $24.2 million in direct property damage per year. Bus fires (including school buses) accounted for only 1% of the total reported vehicle fires, 1% of the vehicle fire deaths, 2% of the total vehicle fire injuries, and 2% of the vehicle fire property damage. On average, six bus or school bus fires were reported daily throughout the country.[16] Most bus fires were ruled accidental and attributed to mechanical or electrical failure. Statistics show that most bus fires originate in the engine compartment or wheel/brake area. Engine compartment fires often extend to the passenger compartment when flames spread vertically up the exterior of the bus and compromise the windows above, allowing heat and smoke into the interior (fig. 18–33). Tire fires can burn through the wheel well and enter the passenger compartment from below. According to the National Highway Traffic Safety Administration (NHTSA) less than 0.05% of all reported bus crashes resulted in fire.

Fig. 18–33. Fire at the rear of an occupied bus presents a life hazard to passengers. (Courtesy of Boise, Idaho, Fire Department)

Although they are relatively infrequent, bus fires can present a high life hazard, especially when the passengers are the elderly or school children. One bus fire that involved the tragic deaths of 23 senior citizens received national attention, which may lead to the use of automatic fire detection and suppression systems on buses. The fire occurred September 23, 2005, on Interstate 45 in Texas, when a bus carrying the seniors caught fire while they were being evacuated from Hurricane Rita. Investigators found that the fire resulted from an overheated wheel bearing that ignited the right-rear tire of the bus.[17]

Bus fires present several challenges to responding firefighters. Rescue and evacuation are chief among them. A bus is a large vehicle with a potentially high life hazard that requires more than a single unit response. Bus capacities range from 25 passengers on minibuses, to 66 on intercity motor coaches and school buses. Bus fires spread quickly and may require a significant amount of water to control. Depending on the size of the pumper's onboard tank, a well-involved bus may require far more water than a single engine carries. A task force assignment of two engines, a ladder, a rescue, and a battalion chief would be needed to cover the initial assignments at an occupied bus fire. When the engine compartment is located in the rear of the bus, a fire originating there may call for two hand lines: one brought to the passenger area to protect occupants, and one directed onto the burning engine or tires. Hose crews may find it difficult to penetrate to the interior because the confined nature of the bus with its narrow center aisle and tight, high back seats. Advancing a hoseline is made more difficult when people are still on the bus. In most cases, passengers, if ambulatory, will self-evacuate before the fire department's arrival. Ventilation for life is another important tactic. The thick smoke generated by synthetic seats and trim on the interior can quickly asphyxiate passengers. Horizontal ventilation via the side windows is an immediate priority, and a ground ladder is needed to reach and open the roof hatch. The side widows are generally constructed of safety glass that can be broken with a tool. Most have an emergency release handle. If equipped with two doors, both must be opened to assist with evacuation. Bus doors are opened and closed by a pressurized air system. DOT standards require that each door is furnished with an emergency release valve that will dump the air pressure. These valves are red and located on the interior of the bus next to the door. Their location may vary, so it is a good idea to contact your local bus company and arrange a training exercise.

School buses. School buses are a special class of vehicle designed with the protection of children in mind, in the event of a collision or rollover. Every school day, approximately 450,000 yellow school buses transport more than 24 million children to and from schools and school-related activities.[18] Most up-to-date school buses are equipped with two emergency doors (one in the back and one on the side) and multiple emergency escape windows. The doors have handles on both the inside and outside of the bus. These emergency mechanisms work well; however, if the bus frame is torqued, children may not be strong enough to open the doors. In addition, newer buses have one or more roof hatches that can be opened manually from the interior. These hatches are designed to provide another means of escape if the bus has rolled over. At this time school buses are not equipped with self-opening roof hatches to vent smoke in case of a fire, though the technology exists.

Depending on the bus design, the location of the engine varies (fig. 18–34). In a traditional school bus, the engine is in the front, separated from the passenger compartment. A fire occurring in the engine compartment, if significant, may require the evacuation of the students via the rear and side exit. In modern passenger and school buses, the engine is in the back, beneath the rear passenger compartment. This configuration can affect the passenger area more directly, but passengers evacuate through the front exit where they are used to entering and exiting. The best strategy for an occupied bus is to

Fig. 18–34. Firefighters apply foam to a school bus fire that originated in the engine compartment and spread to the passenger compartment through the fire wall, where it quickly became fully involved. Note the proximity of the flame plume to overhead power lines. (Courtesy of Kyle Hastings, Mendham, NJ, F.D.)

stretch two hand lines, one to the passenger compartment and one to the engine compartment. Entry to the engine may require a key, or forcible entry through the side access door might be necessary.

According to the National Coalition for School Bus Safety, there is no federal requirement mandating that school bus seats have a higher horizontal flame spread rating or fire resistance than other vehicles, but some states may require one.[19] Many seats are constructed of urethane foam padding covered by vinyl. They can produce thick smoke and add significantly to the fire load.

A review of school bus fires reveals that many tragedies have been averted by alert, well-trained bus drivers who pulled over and got the kids off the bus at the first sign of smoke. At this time most school buses are powered by diesel fuel, which is mounted between the axles, beneath the passenger compartment in a steel enclosure to prevent damage in the case of a side impact. Some states are now allowing school buses to be powered by propane and other alternative fuels. The use of alternative fuels may affect tactics, and local fire departments should adjust tactics accordingly in areas where alternative fuels are used.

NOTES

1. U.S. Fire Administration, Topical Fire Report Series, Highway Vehicle Fires. 2(4). http://www.usfa.dhs.gov/downloads/pdf/tfrs/v9i1.pdf. October 9, 2008.

2. Gustin, Bill. "New Tactics for New Car Fires." Fire Engineering, April 1996, p. 5.

3. Prather Timothy G. "Storing Gasoline and Other Flammables." National Agricultural Database, Agricultural Engineering Department, Agricultural Extension Service. Knoxville, Tennessee: University of Tennessee. Available at http://www.cdc.gov//nasd/docs/d000701-d000800/d000760/d000760.html/, April 2002.

4. Junkins, Lee. "Is It Time to Change Our Training Yet? Part 2" Available at http://www.firelink.com/training/articles/332-is-it-time-to-change-our-training-yet—part-2/, September 6, 2007.

5. Hollins, Lee. "Airbag Inflator Explosion." Fire Engineering, December 1996, p. 34.

6. Automotive Engineering International Online, "Tech Briefs," http://www.sae.org/automag/techbriefs_06-00/.

7. Automotive Engineering International Online, "Tech Briefs," http://www.sae.org/automag/techbriefs_06-00/05.htm.

8. Emery, Jason D. "Compound Factors." Fire Chief, August 2007, p. 92.

9. Emery, p. 94.

10. www.seattle.gov/fire/publications/CNGAutoFire/CNG%20Auto%20Fire%20May%202007.ppt/.

11. Wilen, Saul B. "Countering Terrorism Threats: Trucking Industry and Multi-Modal Distribution Network Vulnerabilities." San Antonio, TX: International Horizons Unlimited. Available at www.intlhorizons.com/article-trucking.htm/, February 10, 2003.

12. Fried, Emmanual. "Fireground Tactics." HM GINN Corp., 1983, p. 199.

13. Fried, Emmanual. "Fireground Tactics." p. 202.

14. Suburban Propane. Available at http://www.suburbanpropane.com/propane.html/.

15. Hermann, Stephen L. "Haz Mat Studies." Firehouse, March 1991, p. 22.

16. Ahrens, Marty. "Vehicle Fires Involving Busses." NFPA Journal, Sept/Oct. 2006. Available at http://findarticles.com/p/articles/mi_qa3737/is_200609/ai_n17193680/.

17. Levin, Alan. USA TODAY. August 8, 2006. Available at http://www.usatoday.com/news/nation/2006–08–08-bus-fires_x.htm/.

18. School Bus Information Council. "School Bus Information Facts 2004." 2004. Available at http://www.schoolbusinfo.org/School%20Bus%20Fact%20Sheet%202004.pdf/.

19. U.S. Government Printing Office. "Title 49—Transportation." U.S. Government Printing Office. October 2002, CITE: 49CFR571.302, pp. 740–743. Available at http://a257.g.akamaitech.net/7/257/2422/14mar20010800/edocket.access.gpo.gov/cfr_2002/octqtr/49cfr571.302.htm/.

Vehicle Fires

FIREFIGHTER I

Chapter 18

LESSON FROM THE FIREGROUND

A call is received reporting an automobile fire on a city street at dusk. The dispatcher sends the nearest engine and ladder company to the scene. On arrival, the engine officer reports a heavy fire in the passenger compartment of the vehicle which is parked parallel to the curb with no other vehicles near it. As the engine company stretches a hoseline, one member of the ladder "takes the glass" using a 6-ft (2-m) hook while another walks to the front of the vehicle and prepares to force the hood open in order to cut the battery cable and check for extension. What is wrong with this picture so far? Water reaches the nozzle and the nozzle team approaches the vehicle at a 45 degree angle from the side, directing the stream into the passenger compartment and sweeping it beneath the vehicle to cool the gas tank and undercarriage.

Before the flames fully darken down, the vehicle's horn begins to sound, the headlights begin to flash and the sound of the ignition cranking can be heard. Realizing that the ignition wires have shorted and the car could start, the engine officer calls for a chock. A few seconds later, the motor turns over and lurches forward as the firefighter arrives with the chock. Although he places

the chock in front of the rear wheel, there is too much momentum and the flaming vehicle rolls over the chock and continues down the street. The truckman at the hood has been knocked down and is lying on his back, his legs under the vehicle holding onto the radiator as the vehicle drags him down the street. If he lets go, he will be run over! If he holds on, he will be crushed against a wall!

A routine car fire has just turned into rather hazardous incident. What happened next? A quick thinking member sees an old, discarded TV on the sidewalk in a pile of refuse, grabs it, and throws it under the front bumper. The TV is too large for a car to drive over. It lodges in front of the front tire on the passenger side, causing the car to come to a stop. The truckman was not seriously hurt, but could easily have been injured or killed.

Lessons Learned: expect the unexpected at auto fires, stabilize the vehicle as soon as it can be done safely, and avoid working in close proximity to a burning vehicle—especially in front of or behind it—until after all visible fire has been extinguished, and all surfaces have been thoroughly cooled.

QUESTIONS

1. Identify the specific automobile components likely to contribute to the ignition of a fire.

2. What are your priorities when a large motor home is heavily involved in fire and parked next to a convenience store? How will you prevent extension of the vehicle fire into the store?

3. Identify the eight probable locations of a motor vehicle fire and discuss the potential hazards associated with each location.

4. As the officer of Engine 7 you are responsible for the safety of your crew. Engine 7 is responding to a truck fire on the expressway. Off in the distance heavy smoke can be seen as you enter the on-ramp. Traffic continues to speed by the truck that is well involved with fire. The posted speed limit on the express way is 70 mph (113 kph). How far from your operation should visual warning devices be placed and why?

5. What are some of the products of combustion coming from today's vehicle fires?

6. Most fire engines carry 500–1,000 gallons (1,893–3,785 liters) of water onboard. Occasionally, additional water will be needed to fight specific vehicle fires. Identify five instances in which you would need to consider additional water supplies.

7. Explain the proper hoseline selection for a small car fire that is fully involved, a full size pick-up truck that is involved in the passenger compartment, and a semi truck burning in the engine compartment.

8. As a rule of thumb, the hoseline should be advanced from the _____ of the vehicle, at a _____ angle, and not directly from the front, back, or sides.

9. What is the recommended approach to fighting a fire resulting from a failed fuel tank?

10. Opening the hood and checking the engine compartment are standard procedure at vehicle fires. Opening the hood is necessary at automobile fires for two reasons. What are they?

11. List the differences in the way vehicle fires should be fought in hybrid or alternative-fueled vehicles as opposed to conventional automobiles.

12. Gasoline tankers can carry as much as _____ gallons of gasoline. What UN number placard would you expect to see on one?

Search and Rescue

by Mike Nasta with Joe Alvarez

This chapter provides required knowledge items for the following
NFPA Standard 1001 Job Performance Requirements:

FFI 5.3.9

FFII 6.3.2

This chapter contains Skill Drills. When you see this icon, refer to your Skill Drill book for step-by-step instructions.

OBJECTIVES

Upon completion of this chapter, you should be able to do the following:

- Identify the necessary tools required to perform a search of a building safely
- Identify the five search priorities in order of importance
- Describe a primary search
- Describe a secondary search
- Describe three primary search techniques
- Describe the three emergency procedures for firefighter safety and survival
- Describe six methods of victim removal

INTRODUCTION

The fire department's primary goal is to protect life (including our own) and property. As firefighters we must perform these actions in a safe and responsible manner. The object is not to win medals, but to protect the people we serve and safely return home to our loved ones. We accomplish these lofty goals through tactics that are well thought out and quickly executed. To the untrained eye it may seem that our actions are arbitrary, but in reality fighting fires is a well-orchestrated event carried out by a highly trained team. Make no mistake about it: The procedures and techniques that make up this chapter are critical for the survival of the rescuers as well as the victims. By definition, to search is to look for or seek out. In the world of the firefighter, it means to seek out or look for victims who require our help to remove them from danger, whether it comes from a fire or any other type of emergency to which firefighters may respond during the course of their duties.

Preparing for a search and search tools

Before beginning any search it is imperative that all firefighters are in full protective gear, including self-contained breathing apparatus. In addition, each firefighter must be equipped with a portable radio, not only to transmit information about search efforts, but also to transmit a Mayday message should the firefighter become trapped. All firefighters must be equipped with a tool such as a set of irons (flathead axe and Halligan) or a hook or pike pole (fig. 19–1). Additional tools may include thermal imaging equipment: ropes for rope guided searches, webbing, and a powerful hand light. Tools such as Halligan, axes, and pike poles should be used to extend the reach of the searching firefighters. Great care should be exercised when searching with these tools. Although these items greatly enhance our ability to perform searches, if used improperly they can injure or kill the very people we are searching for. The searching firefighter must swing the "light end" of whatever tool being used (the fork end of the Halligan tool, for example) toward the victim. The tool can also be used to extend your reach under a table.

The searching firefighter can also use these tools to sound floors for stability. It should be noted that when sounding a floor in a case such as entering a window, the area should be swept gently first in the event that a victim is in the area that the firefighter is sounding. Forcibly hitting a victim with the tool will injure or kill the victim. No firefighter should ever enter a structure without a tool. Whenever a firefighter enters a building without full personal protective equipment (PPE) and a tool, it is not only that firefighter who is in danger, but all other firefighters on the scene.

First in a long line of actions, the firefighter must safely arrive to the scene. Whether firefighters start the response from a fire station or from their homes, they must use some mode of transportation to arrive at the scene. All too often, firefighters are killed or injured in motor vehicle accidents en route to the emergency. The best way to prevent these occurrences is to obey all traffic laws, including using seat belts. No matter what type of policy your department has concerning emergency response, you should always take your safety into your own hands by using all available safety devices and procedures.

Fig. 19–1. Search tools come in a wide variety of shapes and sizes. Many commonly used tools were actually developed by firefighters looking for innovative ways to combine or improve standard tools.

SEARCH AND RESCUE

Search size-up and safety

FFI 5.3.9 FFII 6.3.2 Every firefighter must perform a task analogy or size-up for all events we respond to. These mental notes are critical in keeping us safe. We continually drill and train to hone our physical skills. Although it is imperative to maintain operational readiness, we tend to forget about the mental aspect of our jobs; part of this is taking a critical look at the entire scene as we approach it. Are there any barriers that may impede access or visible signs of structural failure? How well trained am I in building construction? Do I know the signs of failure? What are the fire or smoke conditions telling me? The answers to these and many other questions must be asked and answered long before stepping one boot into the structure.

Upon approaching an event, look for some indications of whether or not the structure is occupied. Some indicators are the presence of cars, time of day, closed window dressings, children's toys outside, air conditioning operating in windows, and the all-important, yet so often overlooked, relevant preplanning information. Every firefighter should have intimate knowledge of the response district. Every day as you travel through your response area and the areas nearby, make mental as well as written notes that you can use if and when the time comes to respond to an incident.

Every firefighter should make mental notes of window and door locations before entering a building. This information may be a lifesaver should that firefighter become disoriented or trapped and suddenly in need of an emergency escape route. The firefighter should be cognizant of how many floors they may have ascended or descended. This information is a must for two reasons:

1. It keeps the firefighter oriented.

2. This information may help a rapid intervention crew locate the firefighter if necessary.

Before entering the structure, pay attention to the smoke conditions. What color is the smoke? Does it contain any indicators that suggest an imminent backdraft or flashover? Is it drawn back into the building as you open the entry door? If so, this may be an indicator of backdraft. Is the smoke violently pushed out of the building as if under extreme pressure? This may be indicative of an ensuing flashover.

FFI 5.3.9 Once you're inside and beginning your search, pay strict attention to smoke, heat, and fire conditions. They can change rapidly, making a survivable atmosphere into a violent and deadly space that you must escape very quickly. Be ever mindful of construction type, layout, and how fire affects that type of construction (e.g., trusses, lightweight structural members, wide open spaces, and confusing layouts). Watch for missing or burned-through floor boards, or building features that have been purposely removed for whatever reason. Use a hand tool to sound the floor as you walk or crawl, to detect sponginess or weakness before placing your weight on it. Before opening a door to an adjacent room, look for signs of smoke or fire coming under the door, and check the temperature of the door. If it is hot there is likely fire on the other side.

Take notice of door swing. The rule of thumb is that doors that open away from you usually lead into living spaces such as apartments or bedrooms. Conversely, doors that open toward you usually lead into service areas such as utility rooms or can be indicative of an elevation change such as steps that lead to a basement or attic. Doors that lead to utility closets may have ventilation louvers built into them. Doors in places of public assembly, such as theaters, usually swing in the direction of egress for the occupants. Before opening a door, always check it for heat by first feeling the door from bottom to top, and carefully control the door as you begin to open it. Door control offers the opportunity to close it quickly should conditions in the room be untenable. Now where do we begin our search or what areas are our top priority?

Search priorities

- Fire room/fire floor

- Room above/floor above

- Top floor

- Floors in between

- Floors below and the building exterior

The most endangered occupants are in and around the fire room and fire floor. Now this may sound like common sense to most; however, firefighters are easily distracted if other victims cry out for help. We may tend to give those victims our attention first when they are not the ones who require our immediate attention. Of course, we don't want to minimize the fact that the victim calling for help needs it, too. However, firefighters must realize that the victims who can't call for help are the ones who are in the most need. So we must either address both victims simultaneously or prioritize and help the ones in the most danger.

The next area that needs attention is the room immediately above the fire. The room above directly receives all the products of combustion as well as a good amount of the heat. Keep in mind that the amount of heat the room and floor above receives depends on the type of building construction. These factors also determine how much danger the rescuer faces when searching the floor above. Obviously, the rescuer faces more danger in a balloon frame tenement than in a fire-resistive building.

Subsequently, the firefighter must address the top floor. The top floor is the next stop for all the smoke and gases rising through convection. The conditions on the top floor are affected by two factors: the location and extent of the fire, and whether the floor has been ventilated properly.

After the top floor, all the floors in between the top floor and the previously searched lower floors must be searched. In buildings that are more than two or three stories in height, searching all these areas will require multiple search teams and a great amount of coordination.

Lastly, and many times overlooked, are the floors below the fire and the building's exterior. Although people on the floors below the fire are rarely affected by the products of combustion, fire departments are always responsible for the well-being of all occupants within the structure. The outside of the building must also be thoroughly examined for victims who may have jumped from the structure. By this we mean all four sides of the structure must be searched to find any victims who may have exited the building by other than normal means. Victims have often been located in shrubbery and in other locations outside the structure.

After entering the room to be searched, there are several areas that the searching firefighter must pay strict attention to. The first area is the normal path of egress, in other words, the areas that are directly in line with the door or hallways. Behind doors is another area where victims are often found; any resistance a search team finds in trying to open the door once forcible entry has been completed is probably an indication of a victim located behind the door. Normally if the path to the door or the hallway is blocked the victim will choose to move toward the window. This fact makes it imperative that we check the area below and around the window. Firefighters that are assigned to search must keep all possibilities of victim location in their mind.

Search categories

FFI 5.3.9 Search can be divided into two different categories: primary and secondary searches. Primary search is a rapid search of high-priority areas. Primary searches are often conducted prior to control of the fire. Secondary search is slower and more methodical. Secondary searches are usually conducted after the fire has been controlled.

Primary search. **Primary searches** are a rapid check of a fire building focused on areas that are normal areas of egress for the occupants. These areas include but are not limited to doorways, windows, and all adjacent areas that lead to these locations. For firefighters to successfully search a structure, they must have an understanding of the mindset of the escaping victim. In times of stress, most people resort to leaving the building by the same routes they use during their everyday routine. In other words, if they normally use the side door daily, they are likely to use that same door during a fire. Humans are creatures of habit, which drives us to think in this manner.

Firefighters only have seconds to get into the heads of the victims and try to determine what they may think while they are in a state of stress and disorientation. For these reasons we search high-probability areas first. These also just happen to be the areas that we normally use for access to the building such as the front door, pathways leading to exterior doors, bedroom windows, and the paths leading to those areas. Because of the speedy nature of this type of search, firefighters must cover these areas quickly and aggressively to greatly improve the survivability of the victims.

Secondary search. **Secondary searches** are usually slower, more methodical, and more thorough than primary searches. These types of searches are often done after the fire has been controlled. During secondary searches firefighters must search for victims in every possible spot inside and outside the structure. Areas searched during the primary search are rechecked along with the areas that were not checked. These areas include but are not limited to closets, toy boxes, showers, and under beds or other furniture that could provide a hiding spot for a victim. Hiding spots differ for adult victims and child victims. It is at this point that firefighters must learn a little about how their victims think when they are under the extreme stress of being trapped.

The mind set of adults and children often differs during a chaotic state. Adults try to reason their way out or try to think the problem through; children resort to areas of comfort or protection. Adults may try to escape harm by going into the shower and turning the water on thinking that the water protects them from the fire only to find that the smoke kills them or they wind up steaming themselves to death. Conversely, children try to get to their parents thinking that mommy and daddy can protect them. Parents are often found trying to get to their children. It is for this reason that if a firefighter finds an adult victim that firefighter must also look for any children that may be with that adult. On many occasions firefighters trying to remove the adult victim to safety leave the child behind. In once such case, the child was right underneath the mother. The mother was removed, but the firefighters never saw the child and they left the child behind. So take an extra second and sweep around the found victim just in case a second victim is nearby. Children will also hide from the danger in areas that are comforting to them, such as in toy boxes, under beds, in closets, and any place that provided them refuge in the past.

Children may be frightened by the sight of the firefighter in full protective equipment and hide. The only way for the fire service to overcome these fears is through education. Your fire department must teach children how a firefighter looks when wearing full protective equipment. Fire departments should go to schools and allow children the opportunity to meet firefighters before they are attired in PPE and then again after that firefighter is fully geared. It allows children to face the person in full PPE.

Search techniques

- Light scan search
- Perimeter search
- Lifeline search

Search techniques are designed to keep a firefighter safe as well as oriented during searches. Searching firefighters are exposed to extreme risk, especially during primary search. Disorientation continues to be a deadly problem for firefighters. Each year many firefighters are trapped and either killed or severely injured during search efforts. Ideally, by using the proper search techniques, we can reduce or even eliminate these tragedies. The following techniques used under the correct conditions are designed to help firefighters efficiently search the building as well as keep the firefighter oriented in the structure.

Before beginning any search, it is imperative that all firefighters are in full protective gear as well as self-contained breathing apparatus. All firefighters must be equipped with a tool such as a set of irons (flat-head axe and Halligan) or a hook or pike pole. No firefighter should ever enter a structure without a tool. By entering a building without full PPE and a tool, a firefighter endangers him or herself as well as all other firefighters on the scene.

Light scan search. This technique can be used if the smoke condition in the room is several feet off the floor, allowing the searcher to quickly scan the room with a portable light to check for any victims located on the floor or on any furniture such as couches, beds, or chairs. To properly perform a **light search**, the firefighter must be in full PPE and equipped with a powerful portable light. The firefighter enters the room by first checking the door from bottom to top using the back of the hand. Once inside the room, the firefighter either crouches below the smoke layer or lies down flat on the floor below the smoke condition and uses the light to completely scan the floor area and any furniture for victims. This technique allows the area to be searched in a very short period of time so the firefighter can continue searching other areas. This technique is usually limited for use in rooms that are smaller in size because of the limitations of the light and how far the firefighter can see across the room (fig. 19–2).

Fig. 19–2. A light search involves using a flashlight to quickly and effectively search rooms with only a light smoke condition.

Perimeter search. It can be said that this search technique is the bread and butter of all search operations in the fire service. This technique lends itself well for use in private dwellings, apartments, and relatively small operational areas. Either a two- or three-person search crew can perform this technique (fig. 19–3).

Two-firefighter perimeter search. The two-person perimeter search always begins by checking the door in the same manner: from bottom to top with the back of the hand. The first firefighter enters the room and immediately places the right hand on the right wall and starts to crawl along the right wall. The second firefighter lies on the floor and performs a quick light scan search of the area. The second firefighter then places the light on the floor at the doorknob side of the door near the door jamb. This light serves as a beacon and additional orientation point for the searching firefighters. (Note: The light should not be placed in the path of the door swing in case another firefighter enters the room and knocks it away from the door.) The second firefighter then places a left hand on the left wall and continues to crawl along that wall until the two firefighters meet.

Fig. 19–3. The two firefighter perimeter search is one of the most common search methods.

Upon meeting, the two firefighters should pause momentarily and listen for any sounds such as a victim breathing, moaning, or crying. After listening for any victims, the two firefighters return to the door by following the beam of the light placed by the second firefighter (fig. 19-4). The two firefighters continue toward the light through the center of the room. Working side by side, the firefighters should stay in physical contact with each other while returning to the door. By following this pattern the firefighters can cover most of an average-sized room.

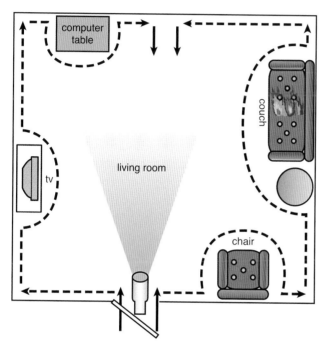

Fig. 19—4. Two-firefighter perimeter search

If the light is not visible to the firefighters from across the room, they should follow one wall back to the doorway. At this point the two firefighters follow the same wall: one firefighter remains in contact with the wall while the second firefighter, keeping contact with the first, stretches out into the middle of the room in an effort to cover as much of the room as possible. While searching, the firefighters should keep mental notes of all doors and windows but should not enter any other doors that would take them into another room. Rooms should be searched one at a time. Closet doors can be quickly swept with a tool to check for any victims. After completing the search of the room, firefighters should pause momentarily at the door of the completed room and quickly discuss any discoveries, such as doorways they may have found or any additional rooms that were encountered. This room is now completely searched and should be marked as such before the firefighters move on to the next room (fig. 19–5).

Marking a room after the search is completed can be done in many ways. For example using a marking pen to mark the door, leaving mattresses folded in half, or any other means dictated by your department's standard operating procedures (SOPs).

Fig. 19—5. In order to prevent a duplication of effort, it is necessary for firefighters performing a search to mark the room as "searched" in a conspicuous manner, according to local policy.

Three-firefighter perimeter search. When the situation arises and there are three firefighters available to perform a perimeter search, the procedure changes. After the door is properly checked, the first firefighter enters the room and starts the search by crawling along the right wall. The second firefighter then enters the room and crawls along the left wall. The third firefighter then enters the room and conducts a light scan search; however, this firefighter remains at the door with the light shining toward the middle of the room so the searching firefighters can use it as an orientation point (fig. 19–6).

FFI 5.3.9 Firefighters engaged in perimeter searches should communicate with each other on a regular basis during the search. This communication allows firefighters to keep check on one another and ensure that each firefighter is safe. Communication also gives each firefighter psychological assurance that they are not alone in the room. This assurance will help keep each firefighter calm during the search, as low visibility and extreme conditions can cause disorientation and panic. The communication does not necessarily need to be verbal at all times, the firefighters could track each other by listening for the other firefighters' movement, listening for sound from the other firefighters' breathing apparatus, or by tapping on the floor occasionally with a tool. The firefighters should guard against making noise or talking constantly because constant noise will make it harder for the search crew to hear any noises that possible victims may be making.

Fig. 19–6. When possible, using a three-firefighter perimeter search provides the best combination of firefighter safety and victim search methods.

Lifeline or rope-guided search. Lifeline or rope-guided searches should be used whenever it is necessary for firefighters to search large areas such as warehouses, supermarkets, or movie theaters. This type of search should also be used in basements or any place with confusing or mazelike floor plans such as office cubicles. Firefighters should not use any of the previously mentioned search techniques in these types of situations. Disorientation in large area buildings is a constant danger to firefighters. All too often a firefighter becomes complacent because most fires occur in dwellings and the main search technique is the perimeter search. Failing to use a lifeline search in a building with a large or confusing floor plan can and often has proved deadly for many firefighters.

Lifeline searches should begin with a fully equipped firefighter (full PPE, self-contained breathing apparatus [SCBA], and tools) and a search rope that is stored inside a rope bag. The average search rope should be approximately 200 ft (60 m) long. The rope may contain indicator knots that can be tied in the rope at 20-ft (6-m) intervals. These knots allow the firefighter to determine how far they have penetrated the structure by simply counting the knots as they move along the search rope (fig. 19–7).

Fig. 19–7. Search rope can be invaluable on the fire ground. Besides increasing firefighter safety, using a search rope can allow for a faster and more coordinated search. Indicator knots tied at intervals along a rope can help firefighters estimate their penetration distance into a building.

The search rope is tied to an unmovable or substantial object outside the building or fire area, but not a vehicle. Firefighters then enter the area to be searched, and the first firefighter holds the bag and allows the rope to deploy as they move forward into the search area. Any remaining firefighters, whether it is one or more, then guide themselves along the rope, never losing physical contact with the rope. Whenever the search crew takes a turn inside the structure, the rope should be tied off; this keeps the searching firefighters from dragging the rope into areas that the crew did not cover as they move further into the building (fig. 19–8). By dragging the rope across areas not searched on the way in, the search team runs the risk of endangering themselves on the way out. If the firefighters cross areas not covered previously, they may fall into an open shaft, become entangled in furniture, or be trapped by many other obstacles found in burning structures.

Fig. 19–8. To control the deployment of a search rope, it is recommended that the rope be tied off to a substantial object outside the structure.

Search crews performing a lifeline search can expand the search area by carrying personal **tether lines** that can be attached to the main search line by carabiners. The firefighter simply attaches the tether line to the main search line and searches off the main line to cover areas such as cubicles (fig. 19–9). It must be noted that tether line must be no longer than 10 or 15 ft (3 or 5 m) in length, thus reducing the possibility of the firefighter getting too far off the main line.

Safety is further enhanced by the use of an entry control officer who is positioned at the point of entry. This control officer must be equipped with a clipboard and a timing device (stop watch). The control officer records the names of the firefighters on the entry team, air cylinder duration time (e.g., 30-minute or 60-minute cylinder), and time of entry. The control officer as well as the entry team must be equipped with portable radios preferably on their own tactical frequency. The control officer records the entry time of each member. Following proper air management techniques (described in chapter 10, Self Contained Breathing Apparatus), the control officer reserves enough time for the team to exit the building. For example, a team equipped with a typical 30-minute rated cylinder is allowed a total operational time of approximately 16.5 to 18.5 minutes to enter the building, conduct search operations, and leave the building. This leaves 25% of bottle capacity, the level at which most SCBA low-air alarms activate, in reserve for safety purposes. In reality, a 30-minute cylinder does not last for 30 minutes—for the typical firefighter, they

last the 16.5–18.5 minutes cited above. Use of longer duration cylinders (larger size bottle) will increase these times accordingly. Firefighters must not wait until their low-air alarms activate—they need to be out of the building before alarm activation.

Fig. 19–9. Tether line

Upon being recalled, the firefighters simply reverse their direction on the line by 180° and follow the line out to the starting point. The firefighter maintaining control of the bag leaves the bag on the floor where he or she stopped and follows the rope out, leaving the bag behind. The lead firefighter should make a mental note of the last knot that was past so that he or she can let the control officer know how far into the search area has been searched. The control officer can then use that information to let the second team know where the first team left off, so the second team could proceed immediately to where the bag was left without researching the area that the first team already completed. Finally, lifeline searches are an important tool; all firefighters must be trained to maintain their orientation in large buildings or buildings with confusing layouts (fig. 19–10).

Fig. 19–10. Here firefighters use a search rope or "lifeline" to guide their search of a structure.

Thermal imaging equipment

Thermal imaging cameras (TICs) are devices that see through smoke by reading heat signatures, using very slight variations in temperature that exist between different objects to create an image on the camera's screen. In other words, cameras read the temperature difference between a victim and the victim's surroundings. By using this heat differential, the user can view outlines of the objects within the camera's range. Thermal imaging cameras are available in many designs. The camera can be handheld or helmet mounted. However, no matter what their differences, they all work on the principle of heat differential.

Thermal imaging must *never* take the place of any of the tried-and-true search techniques. Although thermal imaging technology has added a new dimension to how firefighters work on the fireground, the fire service must guard against becoming too reliant on this equipment. Remember, thermal imaging cameras can still fail unexpectedly, leaving any firefighter not using proven search techniques lost and disoriented inside a structure. Searching firefighters should use perimeter or lifeline search techniques in conjunction with thermal imaging cameras. Combining both standard search techniques and thermal imaging equipment optimizes the search safety. By doing this, both firefighters and the public will benefit (fig. 19–11).

Firefighters must know how to operate the controls on their thermal imaging camera and be completely competent in the recognition of different objects viewed through the camera (e.g., what a person, door, or different types of openings look like). The firefighter should be trained in what the different heat signatures look like when viewed through the camera. Some cameras read heat signatures on a black and white screen: the brighter the white, the hotter the object. Newer cameras read heat on a color screen using oranges and reds to indicate levels of heat. No matter how your camera operates, you should be thoroughly trained in its operation before trying to operate it in a hostile environment. The best training combined with the latest technology results in a safe and successful search. When the thermal imagining camera is assigned to the officer that is directing a search crew, the officer can use the advantage of the camera to direct the searching firefighters. The officer can direct them toward any victims that he sees and away from any encumbrances the searching firefighters will encounter. This will greatly reduce the amount of time required to search an area. It should be noted that the searching firefighters still must exercise great care to keep from becoming disoriented.

Fig. 19–11. Thermal imaging camera technology is arguably the most important innovation to search and rescue. The use of TICs has spread to nearly all fire departments, small and large. (Courtesy of Bullard)

Searching with a hoseline

A hoseline may be used in conjunction with firefighters' individual tether lines if a rope is not available. One advantage to this method is that the hoseline will protect the firefighters that are searching. A disadvantage is that the search will be limited to the area covered by the hoseline. In addition, a hoseline will be cumbersome and difficult to relocate, thus slowing the entire search operation to a slow crawl. However given a choice between no rope and searching off a hoseline, choose the hoseline every time. It's better to be safe than sorry.

MASK CONFIDENCE AND EMERGENCY PROCEDURES

Mask confidence or emergency procedures are techniques that each and every firefighter must learn and become highly competent in using. Techniques such as the reduced-profile maneuver, swim method, and the quick-release maneuver must be practiced and mastered by each and every firefighter. The use of these methods at a moment's notice may mean the difference between life and death. Every firefighter should also be intimately familiar with the emergency operation of the particular SCBA that they are using. All these procedures and methods must be mastered before a firefighter enters a hostile environment.

Reduced-profile maneuver

The **reduced-profile maneuver** enables the firefighter to move through areas that would normally be too small to fit through, such as stud channels (fig. 19–12). The normal spacing for stud channels is 16 in. (40 cm) on center, leaving the firefighter a little bit less than that amount to squeeze through. The firefighter executes the following steps:

- Start by loosening the waist strap of the SCBA.

- Loosen the SCBA's strap (the strap opposite the unit's regulator) and remove your arm from that strap.

- Reach back with one hand and grab the bottom of the unit's bottle near the valve. Then turn the SCBA unit in the direction of the strap that is still in use.

- Tuck the top of the air bottle under your armpit, thus aligning the bottle with the side of the firefighter.

- After the firefighter moves through the restricted area, reverse the previous steps and redon the SCBA.

Figs. 19–12. In emergency situations, firefighters may have to reduce their profile in order to fit through wall studs or other tight spaces.

Swim method

The **swim method** is used when firefighters encounter an entanglement hazard but are not yet entangled. Turn the SCBA unit toward the corner where the wall and the floor meet (fig. 19–13). This allows the air bottle to be directed toward an area and reduces the probability of it catching on the hazard. This also forces you onto your back and in the correct position for the next step in this maneuver.

Extend an arm with the palm facing the floor above the head, similar to the motion a swimmer would use to perform the backstroke. The extended arm then lifts the entanglement above your head as you continue to crawl forward under the entanglement. Continue this maneuver until you clear the area of the entanglement hazard.

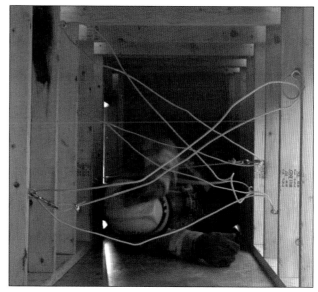

Fig. 19–13. The swim method is used to help a firefighter avoid becoming entrapped in an entanglement hazard. It is always preferred for firefighters to learn to avoid hazards rather than have to learn how to recover from them.

Quick release maneuver

To avoid entrapment, use the **quick release maneuver** (fig. 19–14). It should be employed if the firefighter has already become entangled and needs to escape.

1. Backtrack in a straight line. Drop down on your stomach try to move forward again. If you are still entangled, start over.

2. Fully extend both shoulder straps.

3. Slip your right arm through the right shoulder strap.

4. Grasp your left shoulder strap *and regulator hose* with your left hand.

5. Disconnect waist belt buckle with right hand.

6. Turn 180° *to the left* to face entanglement, maintaining *grip with left hand.*

7. Free yourself from the entanglement.

8. Redon unit.

Fig. 19–14. Entanglement hazards have caused serious injuries and deaths to firefighters over the last several decades. Because of this, it is essential that all firefighters learn basic disentanglement techniques.

VICTIM REMOVAL

Drags and carries

Victim removal is an important part of our job, which is often not practiced enough. Keep in mind that when performing these techniques, you must use your leg muscles, *not* your back, to prevent injury to yourself.

The goal of victim removal is to prevent further injury to the victims and remove them as quickly and safely as possible. It is easy to practice these techniques in a controlled environment; however, it is extremely challenging when firefighters are in a stressful situation with zero visibility, high heat, and limited knowledge of the layout of the building. Victims that are located by searching firefighters should be removed to a clean area or removed to the outside of the structure as soon

as possible. When removing said victim, the firefighters should make every effort to keep the victim's head as low to the floor as possible, thereby keeping the victim closer to the cleanest air.

FFI 5.3.9 The practice of a firefighter removing his/her face piece to give it to the victim is strongly discouraged. The reason for this is that the victim might not want to give it back and then the firefighter would be in a life-and-death struggle to get the face piece back from the victim. In addition, firefighters should try to remove victims to the exterior of a building by the path that gets the victim safely out of the "immediately dangerous to life and health (IDLH)" atmosphere to medical treatment as quickly as possible. For example, when a fire is located on the first floor of a single family home and has not yet been knocked down, it is usually better to remove a victim through a second-floor exterior window rather than down the stairs to the first floor and then to the exterior. Similarly, it may be advisable to take a victim to the public hallway in a multiple dwelling *when the hallway is relatively clear of smoke.*

There are multiple procedures for removing victims from an IDLH atmosphere and many carrying techniques, depending on your environment. Some carries are more feasible than others, depending on the conditions. These include the following:

- The blanket drag
- The seat carry
- The firefighters carry
- The extremity carry

The blanket drag. If the victim is laying on his or her back, spread the blanket next to the victim, fully opened. Roll the victim toward the rescuer and roll them back onto the blanket. Roll the blanket around the patient, supporting the head and neck. The patient should now be dragged head first, with head and shoulders slightly off the ground (fig. 19–15).

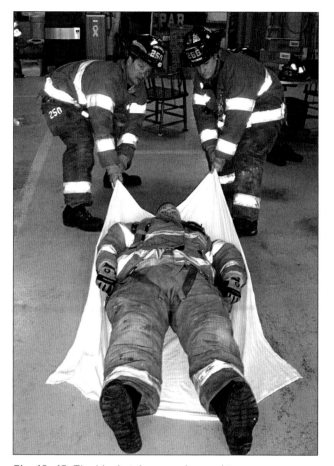

Fig. 19–15. The blanket drag can be used to move unconscious or heavy victims. This maneuver can be attempted by a single firefighter, but is most effective with two firefighters.

The seat carry. Two firefighters are required for this carry. The rescuers are to face each other. With your left hand, grasp your own right forearm just around your wrist. When both have done this, face each other. With your right hand grasp the other firefighter's left forearm firmly, and he or she should grasp yours. This forms a square seat (fig. 19–16).

The firefighter carry. The firefighter carry can be performed by one firefighter on either a conscious or unconscious patient (fig. 19–17).

This carry is not recommended for a smoke-filled environment because you may subject yourself and the victim to extreme heat and toxic gases. Firefighters performing this carry should make sure that the victim weighs less than their own weight.

Fig. 19–17. The firefighter carry can be used on a conscious or unconscious patient, but should *not* be used under smoke or fire conditions.

Fig. 19–16. The seat carry can be accomplished with two firefighters on a conscious victim.

The extremity carry. The extremity carry requires two firefighters and uses victims' extremities to carry them to safety (fig. 19–18).

Fig. 19–18. The extremity carry

The next set of carries should only be done when conditions warrant it:

- Clothing drag
- Webbing drag
- Downed firefighter drag
  - Using SCBA
  - Using turnout coat harness

Clothing drag. The firefighter should squat or kneel at the head of the victim grasping firmly on the clothing on each side of the victim's head. Drag the victim across the ground. Support the victim's head on your forearms when using this technique. It is important to stay as low to the ground as possible so that the victim's head does not push downward toward the chest and cause the victim to have difficulty in breathing (fig. 19–19).

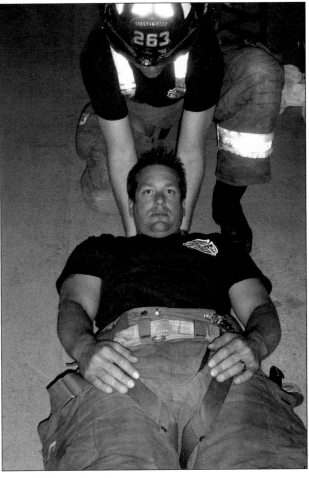

Fig. 19–19. Firefighters using the clothing drag to move a victim must monitor and support the victim's head.

Webbing drag. The webbing drag can be performed by either one or two firefighters. One-inch tubular webbing is one of the most important tools a firefighter carries. This webbing should be joined by way of the water knot to make a complete loop of the webbing and should be carried this way (fig. 19–20).

Steps for these and other drags and carries are in your skill drills book.

Search and Rescue

FIREFIGHTER I

Chapter 19

Fig. 19–20. Using 1-in. (25-mm) tubular webbing, one or two firefighters can assemble a makeshift harness and drag a victim to safety.

FIREGROUND NOTE

Search quickly; search thoroughly! We owe this to the citizens we are sworn to protect (if you forget this, refer back to the oath you took when you were sworn in). Remember to protect yourself, stay oriented, and, most of all, keep your head in the game. If you lose your cool, you may next lose your life!

LESSON FROM THE FIREGROUND

The time is 0230 hours. Your ladder company is dispatched to a report of a dwelling fire. As you step on the rig and try to shake the cobwebs from your head, you begin to run through a million scenarios. The radio breaks in, stating that a patrol officer is reporting a confirmed structure fire with possible entrapment. Your ladder company is riding with one officer and three firefighters. Per SOP, you and your partner are assigned to roof ventilation and the officer and remaining firefighter are to provide forcible entry and begin the primary search. As you approach the scene you find a three-story multiple dwelling with fire showing from the second floor and heavy smoke showing from the third floor and cockloft.

You and your partner position the aerial and begin to ascend to the roof position to open up the scuttle and provide much-needed relief to the firefighters trying to make the stairs. Suddenly the radio comes alive—it's your company officer ordering you to change tasks and place the aerial to the front bedroom window in order to vent, enter, and search for missing 7-year-old twin boys. You obey the officer's request and remove the bedroom window, allowing the smoke to vent. You sweep under the window before sounding the floor, just as you were trained to do. You enter the room, climbing over a box located under the window, and immediately proceed to the bedroom door and close it. As you begin the search, the heat becomes unbearable, so you quickly perform a perimeter search and exit back out to the aerial just before the room flashes. As you push yourself out the window onto the aerial you knock over the box that you climbed over on the way in—something that will change your life forever.

The engine company makes the room shortly after your exit and quickly knocks the fire down. As they enter the room, they find victim number one partially hiding under the bed. Remember the box you knocked over? A second victim is found under the box. It was a toy box that the child used to hide from the fire. You are still unaware of these tragic deaths as you return to the roof and complete your original assignment. Upon exiting the roof you hear the tragic outcome and begin to second-guess every move you made during that search. You wonder what you could have done differently. Did I search thoroughly enough in the amount of time I was in the room? Did I give those children every chance to survive that I could have? This author was that firefighter. This is an event that I will question for the rest of my life. Remember: You will not be able to save everyone, but you must give every victim the best chances possible.

Remember: Search quickly, but search thoroughly. We owe that to the people we protect and to the oath we took. My hope to all that read this is that you will never have to wonder whether you did a you can!

Stay safe, search well, and Godspeed.

QUESTIONS

1. When performing a size-up, what are possible indicators that could lead an emergency responder to believe a structure is occupied?

2. When searching a multi-story building involved with a fire, why would searching the floors above the fire be of a higher priority than the bottom floor?

3. When performing a primary search, it is helpful if rescuers are aware if they are looking for an adult or a child. What are some different reactions that adults and children tend to demonstrate?

4. Secondary searches are usually slower, more methodical, and more thorough than primary searches. Why are these attributes not exhibited during the primary search?

5. Before entering into a room or structure with a closed door, why is it recommended that the rescuer check the door prior to entering with the back of a closed hand?

6. How can door construction and direction of swing provide clues to the type of space located on the other side?

7. When performing a search for victims, why is it important to search the outside of the structure as well?

8. How do the stages of fire within a structure affect your choice on the technique to be used to perform a search?

9. What are some of the advantages for rescuers to occasionally pause when performing search operations?

10. Why is it important that marking procedures showing when a room search is/has been conducted are dictated in the standard operating procedures?

11. What are some of the risks of using a thermal imaging camera that a rescuer is unfamiliar with?

12. How does the fire stage affect the choice of drag or carry when removing unresponsive victims for heated atmospheres?

13. How can the dangers of using lifeline searches increase or decrease when searching large structures?

14. Why is it important for rescuers to train in using mask confidence or emergency procedure techniques before rescue situations?

Basic Fire Attack

by Jerry Knapp with Chris Flatley

This chapter provides required knowledge items for the following
NFPA Standard 1001 Job Performance Requirements:

FFI 5.3.5	FFI 5.3.11	FFI 5.5.1
FFI 5.3.8	FFI 4.3.12	
FFI 5.3.10	FFI 5.3.19	

This chapter contains Skill Drills. When you see this icon, refer to your Skill Drill book for step-by-step instructions.

OBJECTIVES

Upon completion of this chapter, you should be able to do the following:

- Define *strategy, tactics,* and *size-up* as they apply to firefighting
- Describe the 10 steps for a successful fire attack
- Describe offensive and defensive strategies use at a fire incident
- Describe the importance of command control and communications at a fire incident
- List the common responsibilities of engine company personnel at a fire incident
- List the common responsibilities of truck company personnel at a fire incident
- Describe the key considerations for hoselines, water supply, forcible entry, ladders, ventilation, and search at a fire incident
- Describe the importance of an after action review of a fire incident

Fig. 20–1. Aggressive interior firefighting saves lives and property and is at the heart of what we do best. (Courtesy of Tom Bierds)

INTRODUCTION

This chapter brings together all the knowledge, skills, and abilities you have gained in previous chapters. It will provide you with a basic overview of what is required for a successful fire attack operation at a structure fire. As a Firefighter I, you will be given specific tasks to perform by your company officer or a senior firefighter. You will execute your assignment as part of a team, your fire company. It is the coordinated efforts of multiple fire companies working together that result in a successful fire attack (see fig. 20–1).

You might be part of an engine company, delivering water, deploying hoselines, or executing other tactics to extinguish fires. Or maybe you are a truck company member, assigned to place ladders; perform search and rescue, ventilation, or forcible-entry operations; secure utilities;and perform salvage or overhaul.

While you are performing your particular duties, it is important to understand the overall "big picture." Your understanding of how all the pieces of fire attack fit together will help you see the importance of your role. While not every task may be as dramatic as rescuing a child or being on a nozzle and knocking down a rapidly spreading fire, every task at a fire is critical to overall success. Your proficiency in carrying out your assigned tasks will directly affect the outcome of the fire attack.

It is important that you understand two important terms: strategy and tactics. While used interchangeably by civilians, they mean two different things. **Strategy** is the development and implementation of a plan, incorporating specific goals, to bring a fire under control. **Tactics**, on the other hand, are specific actions taken to accomplish the goals identified in an overall strategy.

Take a fully-involved car repair shop, for example. The strategy may be to take a defensive stance and protect exposures with the specific goal of preventing fire from spreading to an adjacent exposure. Tactics would involve placing a hoseline between the fire building and the exposure flowing water directly on to the exposed structure.

In order to understand all the elements of a basic fire attack, we will use a series of scenarios to illustrate the important details. The first scenario will be relatively simple. After you gain an understanding of the basics, we will advance into other, more complex, scenarios.

It is important to note that this chapter will cover only the basics of a fire attack operation, from pulling up on the scene to returning back to quarters after your job is done. The first scenario will be an uncomplicated fire but will require techniques, skills, tactics, and strategies covered in almost every other chapter.

At the end of this chapter the firefighter trainee will understand the following concepts and, more importantly, how they fit together for a successful fire attack operation:

- Strategy: An overall plan, including goals, of a basic structural fire attack

- Tactics: The specific firefighting procedures performed by company officers and firefighters to meet the overall strategic goals

- Size-up: An evaluation of what is happening

- Doctrine for an aggressive interior fire attack: Critical steps used across the country for structural fire attack

- Type of fire attack operations: Offensive, defensive, defensive/offensive, offensive/defensive (and the conditions that cause the transition from one to the other)

- Command, control, and communication: On the fire scene and why they are important

- Fire-extinguishment methods: Direct, indirect, and combination methods of fire extinguishment

- Coordination of engine and truck company functions

This scenario is based on a house fire because house fires often require all of our knowledge, skills, and abilities to be successful and safe. The house fire is also a good example because it is the most dangerous and deadly type of fire for both civilians and firefighters (fig. 20–2).

2007 HOME FIRE DATA	
Annual civilian injuries	14,000
Percentage of all structure fires	78%
No. civilian deaths	2865
Annual fire loss	$7.4 billion
Percentage of firefighter deaths	50%

Fig. 20–2. NFPA Fire Data Block

Communication

FFI 5.3.5 There are a few basic levels of communication that will occur at a house fire. Communication is the lifeblood of any emergency operation. Without effective communication, the operation is doomed to failure.

First, the dispatcher will provide information about the location, type of alarm (automatic, telephone, witness, etc.), the alarm location, and other important information the dispatcher may have (fig. 20–3).

Fig. 20–3. A dispatcher

Messages received from dispatchers often hold clues to the fire condition. Words like "across from" or "next to" will indicate that the fire may not have been reported by someone inside the structure but by a passerby.

Generally, chief officers will arrive before the apparatus (though not always) and give a quick "on-scene report" confirming the address, providing a brief description of the fire, and giving orders for the responding units (fig. 20–4).

Fig. 20–4. Chief officer giving orders

Let's take a look at a typical communication from a first arriving chief at a house fire. A typical initial fire report would be: "Battalion 23 on scene, 20 Main Street, a 20×40, 1½ story single-family home fire showing on A and B side, report of victims trapped." This report provides valuable information to responding firefighters and confirms the correct address and gives dispatch an initial report.

Important points you should gain from the initial report:

1. Confirmed address—you are going to the correct place.

2. Type of occupancy—residential (general knowledge of the typical hazards).

3. Size and height—type of ground or aerial ladders needed.

4. Location of fire in building and severity (may determine tactics).

5. Report of victims reportedly trapped (clearly this is the priority). When a life hazard exists, all on-scene operation support the search and rescue operations.

The on-scene report paints the picture for incoming units so you can begin to consider what priorities, actions, and tools will be necessary at this call.

Command will communicate with engine and truck officers to give assignments, direct search and rescue, coordinate ventilation and fire attack operation, monitor progress of assigned crews, and ensure the safety of all firefighters on the scene.

Unit leaders (engine and truck officers) will report back to command via radio on the progress of their assigned tasks and other valuable information such as fire location, the location and status of victims, and other safety considerations.

Interpersonal communication among the company members and with the company officer is critical for success and safety. The company officer will give initial orders, for example, "stretch the 1¾-in. attack line to the front door," or "we have a report of persons trapped on the second floor." Company members will have to coordinate actions to ensure that the orders and tactical assignments are executed properly. The nozzle operator may ask the backup position to flake out the line or ask for more effort to pick up the nozzle reaction. Firefighters will use their portable radios to communicate with one another during the entire fire attack operation.

COMMON TERMINOLOGY

Firefighters use common terminology to describe different areas of the fire building. This allows firefighters to communicate quickly about strategy and tactics and to give orders. On larger fires it is a way to divide up areas of responsibility. For example, a chief officer may assign a subordinate officer to be responsible for a particular side of the building. That officer will coordinate all actions necessary for the operation on that side or area and report to and work for the incident commander (IC).

FFI5.3.10 It is important to clarify the location terminology here. In National Incident Management System terminology, we would use the terms *Division A, Division B, Division C,* and *Division D* (fig. 20–5). These are essentially geographic areas or parts of the entire fire area. The division chief (in the past, this position was termed the "sector" chief) is responsible for all activities in that area and how those activities impact all other **sectors**. These latter designations also help orient all on-scene firefighters to particular locations in a building where things may be happening: spreading fire, a trapped victim, or a localized collapse, for example. Exposures are designated by letters corresponding to the side of the fire building they face: exposure D is the building that faces the D side of the fire building. Exposure D1 is the next furthest exposure on the D side of the fire building (fig. 20–6).

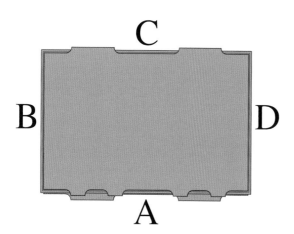

Fig. 20–5. Building sectors

The A side of the structure is usually the side of the building with the main entrance that faces a street, although not always. Sides B, C, and D are the other three sides assigned clockwise around the structure. Divisions can also refer to floors, such as floor 2, division 2. It is up to the incident commander to make the division designations.

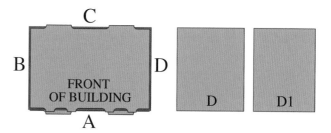

Fig. 20–6. Sector view with exposure designations

STEPS TO A SUCCESSFUL FIRE ATTACK

1. Size-up: the ongoing process of evaluating the situation before arrival, upon arrival, an during the incident

2. Develop a strategic plan (the incident commander's job)

3. Establish a reliable water supply

4. Force entry or exit into or out of the structure

5. Conduct search and rescue operations

6. Stretch and operate a hoseline; confine and extinguish the fire

7. Ventilate the fire building

8. Protect exposures

9. Fire control and overhaul

10. Pick up and return

YOU ARE HERE

1. Size-up

2. Strategic plan
3. Establish water supply
4. Force entry/exit
5. Search and rescue
6. Fire attack
7. Ventilate
8. Protect exposures
9. Fire control and overhaul
10. Pick up and return

Size-up

Step 1 in any emergency situation, size-up is critical for gaining awareness to develop an action plan. The ISFSI's 2013 *Position Statement on Fire Dynamics Research* states "Size-up must occur at every fire... A tactical plan for that fire must be developed, communicated, and implemented." Size-up is the ongoing evaluation of what has happened, what is likely to happen, and the available resources (in what priority order) needed to resolve the situation. Everyone on the fireground does an initial size-up and a continuing size-up as the situation changes.

Therefore, you must conduct your own size-up: evaluating the situation, determining what you know and what you don't know, and formulating what you think the situation really is, despite several unknown factors. As a Firefighter I, you will be given specific orders. However, you must continually conduct your own size-up of the situation to ensure your safety, to be sure you are performing the correct tactics, and to ensure the operation is having the desired result.

Dispatch time. Here is an example of how to use size-up and existing information. Assume that your dispatch time is early in the morning. Would you expect to find people sleeping? Where would these people be? In this case they are likely to be in the bedrooms in the rear of the house. Consider also that the victims may have attempted to escape and have collapsed by windows or on usual exit paths within the house.

You might think that the time of day of this call makes it unlikely that anyone is awake. Consider that people may work nights and be coming home or just going to work. Was someone cooking, and was this the cause of the fire? Don't discount any bit of information; you may not initially see how it fits in the overall understanding of the situation.

On-scene information. Bystanders, civilians, and police officers may have valuable information about the fire or occupants. A neighbor may report that the family is all away on vacation, or report that one person was home alone. Not all civilian reports are reliable. No bad intentions intended, but they may be swept up in the excitement of the moment and provide bad information. Conversely, police officers may have good information. They may have been on the scene before the fire department and have had a few minutes to gather and possibly verify that information.

Location of fire building. From the dispatch information you know that you are not responding to the industrial side of town. The fire alarm was in a new development. Developments are usually built with the same or similar style. This fact may help you understand the floor plan of the house, even if you have never been in it.

Floor plan. Have you been in the houses before? Did you inspect them when they were being built, or does your neighbor live in one just like it? Knowing the layout of the fire building is one of the most important factors in a successful operation. For example, you can move quickly through the structure toward the sleeping areas when you know where to go.

If this were a two-story home, what rooms may you expect to find on the first floor? Kitchen, living room, dining rooms, and maybe a utility room if there is no basement. What does that tell you bout what type of fire you may be encountering? What and where are the utilities? Electric, natural gas, or is it bottled gas or propane? Will that affect operations?

Construction hazards. If the housing development where the fire is located were described as new; how new? The words "new construction" now almost always means "lightweight" construction. Lightweight construction has been around long enough to almost not be considered new. If this home is built with trusses, laminated beams, or other composite materials, those factors will hasten fire spread and early collapse.

Lightweight construction is now very prevalent in our country. It is critical to understand that lightweight construction (trusses, laminated beams, metal studs, etc.) often has little or no fire resistance. Expect early and catastrophic structural failures that will cause floors to collapse, sending firefighters into the burning basement; second and third floors to drop firefighters a floor or more, trapping those below; and roofs to collapse, trapping firefighters in burning rooms on upper floors. Prefire intelligence and planning are your best survival tools.

Resources available. You also know what other resources are responding with you. You know that another engine, a truck, and chief are on the way. Is this the typical response to a fire that is reported by telephone? Based on the report of a confirmed fire, the dispatcher may have dispatched additional units. The police department, whose unit may be on the scene before you, may also provide valuable information either directly or through dispatch.

You know what the staffing is on your engine; do you know what your assignment will be when you pull up? The ride to the scene is a time to make those assignments if they are not dictated by department policy.

Weather may also play an important part in your size-up. Will very high or low ambient temperatures limit the time firefighters can work? Will the doors and windows be closed or locked, delaying entry, confining the fire? Is there a high-wind condition that could drive fire quickly or unnaturally through the building immediately after the ventilation is completed?

The dispatch information reported a fire on the first floor. Did the caller give the address or say "next to" or "across from"? This may indicate that the call was made by someone not in the house but a person passing by or nearby. Could this indicate the possibility of an advanced fire on arrival? Are you receiving several calls reporting the same fire? Does this indicate that the fire is large enough to be seen by others? Or does it confirm a working structural fire?

At this point in your career many of these strategic decisions are not made by you. They are offered to give insight into what you will come to understand later in your career. You will do well if you control your anxiety and follow orders. When you put on your facepiece, try to control your breathing and keep your head.

Size-up upon arrival. The following are seven specific size-up points that must be considered to complete your size-up upon arrival:

1. Location of the fire and type of construction

2. Life hazard

3. Fire control

4. Forcing entry

5. Ventilation

6. Stretching considerations

7. Water supply

Size-up begins with receipt of the alarm and is a continuing process until you leave the scene. Everyone on the scene must conduct a size-up of the initial situation and a continual size-up of the fire scene. Everyone on the scene must conduct individual size-ups of the initial situation and continue to conduct size-ups, since incidents change rapidly.

YOU ARE HERE

1. Size-up
2. **Strategic plan**
3. Establish water supply
4. Force entry/exit
5. Search and rescue
6. Fire attack
7. Ventilate
8. Protect exposures
9. Fire control and overhaul
10. Pick up and return

Developing a strategic plan

Although it is the chief or first-in officer who will determine the overall strategy based on his or her size-up, it is important to understand the four basic fire attack strategies.

Strategy is the overall rescue and fire attack game plan for this call. Strategy is determined by command level officers. One possibility is to conduct a rapid search and rescue operation, supported by forcible entry and ventilation, then rapid deployment of the initial hoseline to protect the rescue crews and to attempt to control and or extinguish the fire.

Tactics, on the other hand, are the supporting tasks necessary to accomplish the overall strategy. It will be up to the company officer (or, in some cases, a senior Firefighter II) who has to make some tactical decisions (what room to hit with the line during the advance, where to cut the roof, etc.). It will be the firefighter who will execute the tactical decisions made by the company officers.

Offensive strategy. Offensive strategy is used when an aggressive interior search or attack can save lives or property, and some or all of the following factors are present:

- Lives can be saved by rapid interior search and fire attack operations.

- The building has a limited amount of fire and has areas that are salvageable.

- The building is safe for firefighters to operate in for a short period of time or until complete extinguishment (fig. 20–7).

Fig. 20–7. Size-up of this fire reveals that the fire appears to be contained to one or two rooms on the second floor. An offensive attack could result in saving the building and contents with a reasonable risk to firefighters. However, if this building was built with lightweight construction materials, it could be a deathtrap for firefighters. Incident commanders must realize these dangers to firefighters. (Courtesy of Brian Duddy)

Defensive strategy. Defensive strategy is employed when it is determined that some or all of the following factors are present (fig. 20–8):

- There is no saveable human life present; it is not worth risking firefighters' lives for a futile rescue attempt.

- The building is so heavily involved in fire that it is not salvageable (there is nothing left to save, neither contents nor the building itself).

- The building is unsafe due to heavy fire involvement.

- The building is unsafe due to a fire load on the lightweight construction components.

Fig. 20–8. This fire calls for a defensive strategy. There is no salvageable human life inside and no saveable property, therefore no need to risk firefighters' lives.

LESSON LEARNED

Rock Hill Missouri Fire Chief John Kriska had preplanned all commercial structures in his first due area. Heavy fire greeted the engine company. The Engine captain, following the preplan, established a defensive attack. Moments later, the metal bar joist (lightweight construction) failed under the fire load, sending roof HVAC units crashing to the floor, exactly where the engine company would have been if an offensive attack would have been chosen.

Defensive/offensive strategy is used when the firefighter cannot immediately enter the building because of an extremely heavy fire involvement or other hazards prevent you from getting close enough for an offensive attack. Defensive/offensive operations are employed when some or all of the following factors are present:

- Heavy fire upon arrival

- Hazards that must be controlled before firefighters can gain entry

- When the fire is knocked down quickly, allowing the IC to consider changing to an offensive operation

A common method to employ this strategy is to use the **blitz attack**. The blitz tactic uses heavy streams from a safe distance until the fire is controlled enough to safely approach for complete extinguishment (see fig. 20–9).

Fig. 20–9. Here, downed electrical wires prevented firefighters from making an offensive attack.

Offensive/defensive. When possible, we try to mount an offensive strategy to make an aggressive interior fire attack in an attempt to save trapped occupants or the building or contents. Sometimes we must fall back to a defensive strategy, giving up the interior fire attack for the following reasons:

- This could have been the intention of the incident commander: Mount an interior attack until a search can be completed, then back out due to the severe risks to firefighters.

- No headway has been made on the fire (fire not darkening down), and extinguishments with interior line will not be possible (fig. 20–10).

- If the fire is progressing faster than our ability to put water on it, we may need to shift to a defensive position (proper use of a limited water supply).

Fig. 20–10. a) This fire started out as an offensive attack. b) Heavy fire conditions inside combined with a large amount of accumulated materials inside the house prevented the interior attack lines from advancing and thus forced firefighters to change from an offensive operation to a defensive attack. c) The fire was contained with no injuries to firefighters.

YOU ARE HERE

1. Size-up
2. Strategic plan
3. **Establish water supply**
4. Force entry/exit
5. Search and rescue
6. Fire attack
7. Ventilate
8. Protect exposures
9. Fire control and overhaul
10. Pick up and return

Establish a reliable water supply

There is one inescapable truth in the fire service. To extinguish the fire, you must apply more gallons per minute to overcome the total heat the fire is producing to ensure extinguishment. To accomplish this, one of the first priorities is to establish a reliable water supply (figs. 20–11 and 20–12). The first-in engine company usually has two main options to establish a reliable water supply: forward lay from a hydrant or reverse lay to a hydrant. Fires in a rural setting will require drafting from static source such as a swimming pool or lake or using water from tenders. Tender shuttles may be required for large fires in a rural location. (See chapter 15, Water Supply for details.)

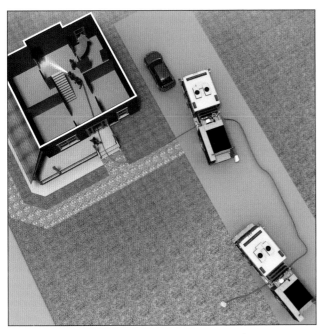

Fig. 20–11. Establishing a reliable water supply

Fig. 20–12. Establishing a reliable water supply is a critical step in the extinguishment process. (Courtesy of Brian Duddy)

YOU ARE HERE

1. Size-up
2. Strategic plan
3. Establish water supply
4. **Force entry/exit**
5. Search and rescue
6. Fire attack
7. Ventilate
8. Protect exposures
9. Fire control and overhaul
10. Pick up and return

Forcible entry

Firefighters conducting forcible entry are usually the first team to the building because they have only hand tools (Halligan, axe, hydraulic door opener, etc.) with them, as opposed to the engine company, which is slowed by stretching the hoseline.

Common tools carried by the forcible-entry team include the flat-head axe, Halligan, and/or a hydraulic door opener. The flat-head axe is often replaced with a maul or sledgehammer as a tool to drive the Halligan tool. However, the occupancy and characteristics of the response area will dictate other appropriate tools. For example, if the area has a lot of industrial occupancies tools selected, maybe a rotary saw and even a hydraulic spreader could be used on bars or reinforced metal doors with multiple locks. Metal foldout gates or roll-down security shutters also require a rotary saw for rapid forcible entry.

Basic Fire Attack

FIREFIGHTER I

Chapter 20

The forcible-entry team will make their size-up of the building and choose the most appropriate place to enter. At house fires, this is usually the front door (fig. 20–13). Choosing where to enter the building is an important tactical decision. In this chapter we will discuss residential fires, and in *Firefighter II* we will discuss other types of occupancies. It is important to note that where you enter the building may have significant consequences in terms of your effectiveness and safety. This is significant for several important tactical reasons:

- The front door is generally the fastest and most used way into and out of the home.

- Victims may be found near the door if they were overcome and unable to escape.

- Opening the door may allow victims to escape.

- Opening the door will allow the engine company members to move quickly to the seat of the fire.

Fig. 20–13. Firefighters from the truck company force the front door. Note that the officer is holding a piece of webbing on the door handle to control the door once it is forced open. (Courtesy of Jerry Knapp)

There are two important safety factors to consider when conducting forcible-entry operations. First, consider forcible exit, that is, how are you going to get out of the area you just got into if conditions suddenly worsen? Is there a window you can get out of? Is there a ladder at that window, or are there bars on the window? In a home or apartment, can you breach the gypsum board wall in time to save yourself and crew? If you are operating in a multistory apartment building and plan on using your bailout system, find your anchor point as soon as you enter the area. Trying to find it while the place is lighting up around you will be too late!

Second, when forcing the door to the fire area, always be able to control that door with a rope, piece of webbing, or tool. The sudden inrush of air could cause the fire to flashover or backdraft, trapping firefighters above the floor the door is on or in the public hallway.

YOU ARE HERE

1. Size-up
2. Strategic plan
3. Establish water supply
4. Force entry/exit
5. **Search and rescue**
6. Fire attack
7. Ventilate
8. Protect exposures
9. Fire control and overhaul
10. Pick up and return

Conduct search and rescue operations

There is no more important operation on the fireground than search and rescue. Saving the occupants of the building is always our first priority. We must remember that when we enter the building, we are equally valuable occupants. When a search and rescue operation is in progress at a scene, all operations must support the search and rescue. For example, the first hoseline must protect the means of egress for search team members. If the fire can be extinguished by this line, that's fine, but the primary purpose of the line is to protect the means of egress and the crew.

We must remember that search and rescue are two separate events. Entering the structure and searching for victims (and the location of the fire) is a dangerous task. When an entry team finds the fire, that information must be communicated to command and the engine, so they can bring the line to that location and extinguish the fire. When the team finds a victim, that ends the search and begins the rescue operation for that victim. This does not mean the search is over; other victims may still be in the structure.

When the victim is found, that information must also be communicated to the IC. Command will then be sure that medical treatment is available as soon as the victim has been removed from the structure. The egress route the team will be taking should also be communicated to other members operating in the area so they can clear the path to the exit.

This also allows the other fireground activities that are occurring simultaneously to support the rescue effort. When the rescue status is known, it greatly reduces the chances that the fire will be pushed on the search team by an advancing line or inappropriate ventilation. Ventilation will be performed to lift the heat and smoke and increase visibility. Forcible entry will be performed to remove obstacles and clear the path to the exit.

Search and rescue tools. It is important to select the proper tools to take with you for a search and rescue mission. Obviously, full personal protective equipment (PPE), including self-contained breathing apparatus (SCBA), are required. If you are going inside to work at any structure fire, a portable radio and handlight are also critically important. A thermal imaging camera will make your search much more rapid, effective, and—when used properly—safer for you and your crew.

Hand tools should be selected based on your department's SOPs. If the responsibility of the search and rescue crew is also forcible entry, then the Halligan tool and an axe are good choices. Your partner will have a 6-ft hook and possibly a water extinguisher, which are good complements to your search and rescue tools. Situations dictate specific actions, but this combination of tools provides a variety of options and good use of these tools to complement your search effort.

The Halligan and flat-head axe can be used in combination to force doors to gain entrance to the building. (See chapter 12 on forcible entry). The axe can be used to chock a door open after you force it. The Halligan can be used to sweep the floor as an extension of your arm to increase the efficiency of searching larger open areas (fig. 20–14).

The 6-ft (2-m) hook can be used also as a search tool. It can be used to take windows, if necessary (fig. 20–15). The power extinguisher can be used to hold a fire or extinguish a smaller fire found during the search.

When selecting tools, consider the number of personnel available and what specific task you will be accomplishing with that tool. Be wary of "do everything" tools because they may not function in any purpose with the effectiveness you expected. Also be suspicious of hooks shorter than 6 ft (2 m). Although seemingly a great idea, you selected a hook to provide an extended reach, and 3 ft (1 m) is not much of an extended reach. The standard time-tested tools described above have been successful in the fire service for many years. Learn to use these basic hand tools effectively and with mental agility, and they will assist you in the search and rescue mission.

Fig. 20–14. Sweeping with a tool

Fig. 20–15. Using a 6-ft (1.8-m) hook to open a window panel

LESSON LEARNED

We pulled up at about 0530 hours one morning, and the police officer met us as we stepped off the rig. He said there was a victim in the back bedroom, just below the window. When I asked him how he knew that, he said he saw him standing there, then collapse due to the smoke. Lesson learned: The police department maybe on the scene before you in enough time to collect valuable information about the status of victims or not inside the house.

Basic Fire Attack

FIREFIGHTER I

Chapter 20

The search and rescue plan. A standard search and rescue plan for single family dwellings uses the two-team approach (fig. 20–16). The two-team search plan at this fire will include one team entering the front door and the second team attempting to enter nearest to likely victim location. In two-story homes this will be the second floor for nighttime fires. The outside team does not necessarily have to enter through the second floor. One team forces the door at the most common entrance to the home, and the one most likely used by the occupants (usually the front door). This opens a door the escaping occupants might be using. The second team makes their way from the outside to rooms or areas where people are most likely be found. They may make use of portable ladders or porch roofs. You can see where knowledge of the layout of the house would be a huge benefit in this case.

Fig. 20–16. Two-team search plan. The second team can either enter above a porch or through a second story window.

The preferred means of removal (as taught by the New York City Fire Department [FDNY]) is to remove victims by interior stairs first, then through some horizontal exit or possibly an adjoining building, then fire escapes, then ladders (with an aerial being preferred to a portable ladder), and last being by a life-saving rope. All of these may not be an option in a private dwelling. Use the most practical method based on the situation and the best method to do no further harm to the victim.

LESSON LEARNED

I had the nozzle at a working house fire one night, and we were stopped at the locked front door. For some reason the truck company was delayed, so I decided to conduct the forcible entry operation with my foot. I leaned back and planted my size 10 boot on the door, missing the frame of the door and hitting a center wood panel. My foot went right through, and there I was with a charged line, fire blowing out, with my foot stuck in the door! Heavy fire or a large dog behind the door could have made this a painful lesson. Lesson learned: Use the forcible entry tools; the door provides protection from fire and other hazards if you control it!

The condition of the victims will have a great deal to do with how they are removed. With unconscious individuals, you may have limited options. Victims with burns and severe injuries may have to be moved as quickly as possible, risking other injuries to provide the best chance of survival.

Persons with lesser injuries may be "sheltered in place" until conditions improve to move them out of the building. A rescue should not place an individual at a greater risk than the current conditions.

An engine company with a charged hoseline can do more to effect the rescue of trapped or injured persons than any other small group of firefighters.

It is important to note that there are a variety of effective ways to protect lives of both civilians and firefighters. What does not change is that saving and protecting lives is always our first priority. Four of the most common ways lives can be protected are the following:

1. Immediate removal

2. Placement of hoselines to protect means of egress

3. Protection in place in areas of refuge

4. Fire extinguishment (if it can be achieved very quickly)

When a search and rescue operation is required at a fire, all other operations (fire attack, ventilation, forcible entry, and overhaul) must support the rescue operation. Putting the fire out and removing the bodies later is not a successful outcome. Hoselines can push fire onto victims or search crews. Inappropriate ventilation tactics can cause the fire to light up and trap and burn firefighters. It is up to the IC and the IC's division officers to ensure that these inappropriate and dangerous acts do not happen. All fireground actions must support the search and rescue.

Size-up is an important part of the search and rescue plan and operation. Evaluation of what you see during your size-up for your search operation will provide you with many clues that will help make your operation effective and safer for firefighters. It is important to note that these are only clues, not definitive answers. For example, does five days' worth of newspapers on the front porch mean that no one is home? Of course not; maybe the occupant is sick or simply has not picked them up. Here are few other considerations in your size-up for search and rescue:

- Does the house look occupied?

- Are there multiple mailboxes, utility meters, and so forth, indicating a multiple dwelling?

- Are there bikes or kids' toys outside the house?

- Are there cars in the driveway?

- Are TVs, air conditioners, or heaters running?

- Are there ramps that might indicate the presence of disabled people in wheelchairs?

Don't base your entire search and rescue strategy on one bit of information.

LESSON LEARNED

Peck street: Upon arrival, civilians told us that a person was trapped in this house. Firefighters entered the building and left the front door open, thus allowing the fire unlimited oxygen, which caused it to go to flashover very quickly, nearly killing three of the search and rescue crew. The victim was at a local bar. Lesson learned: Information from civilians at the scene may or may not be correct. Always ask, "Is everyone out?" But carefully evaluate the answer! Ask, ask again, and look for inconsistencies. Evaluate the answer, interrogate if you must, and remember that you are placing the lives of your firefighters on the line based on what people tell you!

YOU ARE HERE

1. Size-up
2. Strategic plan
3. Establish water supply
4. Force entry/exit
5. Search and rescue

6. Fire attack

7. Ventilate
8. Protect exposures
9. Fire control and overhaul
10. Pick up and return

Fire attack

This is the heart of what we do. Decisions will have to be made as to the size of the hoseline used in the attack, the positioning of the hoseline(s), and coordinating the hoseline attack with ventilation operations. It is not your responsibility to make these decsions—these decisions will be made by officers. You will, however, be expected to carry out the tasks dictated by these decisions (fig. 20–17).

Fig. 20–17. As the search and rescue team enters a structure, the open door provides the fire with needed air that allows the fire to continue in the free-burning phase.

A chief officer will coordinate the ventilation and fire attack operations. When the hoseline is in place, he will direct the ventilation team to break out or **take the windows** ahead of the hoseline, then direct the hose team to advance to the seat of the fire. These operations are important for the following reasons: Brother and sister firefighters have entered this building to conduct a primary search and rescue operation. The fire now can grow unrestricted until the engine company gets water on the fire. Controlling the fire minimizes all other problems and most other hazards on the fireground. Fire growth in compartment fires (inside a building) is often determined by the amount of oxygen available. The open door we enter provides an excellent source of the oxygen required to light up the building or room we are in.

Ventilation, entry, and search make up the fire service doctrine in North America. Although this doctrine provides the greatest opportunity for firefighters to make a successful rescue, it is very dangerous for firefighters. Rapid and effective engine company (fire attack) operations greatly reduce these hazards to firefighters that we have intentionally put in harm's way. Rapid and effective fire attack operations are the responsibility and mission of the engine company. It can be argued that this operation is the most important of all we do in terms of firefighter safety.

Knowing where to stretch the line is as important as what line to stretch. There will be times in your career where you will pull up to a fire and need a larger line than the standard 1¾-in. or 1½-in. (45 mm or 38 mm) hand line.

Large-caliber streams are produced by deluge guns, either apparatus-mounted or ground-based, ground-based rapid attack monitors, or the use of a 2½-in. (65-mm) hand line with a large tip to generate flows of 250 gpm (946 L/min) or larger.

For large fires, the FDNY has developed the acronym **ADULTS**. This is easy to remember by the phrase "ADULTS use big hose."

The **A** in ADULTS is for a fire that is *advanced* on arrival. Any fire that has surpassed the extinguishing power of your standard (1¾-in. [45-mm]) attack line calls for a larger attack line. Two ineffective hand lines will not have the reach and penetration as one large-caliber line. If the water cannot reach the burning material, it will have no extinguishing power.

The **D** is for the *defensive* positions. This means any line stretched for outside exposure protection should be capable of a large-caliber stream. This will allow the water to be applied alternately between the fire building and the exposure, providing fire-killing stream reach and penetration and good reach to provide excellent exposure protection, thereby minimizing damage to both with one stream (fig. 20–18).

The **U** is for fires where you are *unable to determine* the size of the fire area. If you can't tell how much is burning or how large the space it is in, you should not be going in without the protection and capability of a large line. This is not the firefight to be caught short of water!

The **L** is for *large* and uncompartmentalized fires. For example, the sales floor of a department store is no place to be without a large volume of water. The fire spread in a situation like that could easily overwhelm a small hand line.

The **T** is for the times when you need a *ton* of water to cool large amounts of burning material (fig. 20–19). For example, a lumberyard fire or building that has a lot of combustible contents, such as furniture. Another possible scenario is a flammable gas tank with flame impingement. For larger tanks you need a "ton" (500 gpm [1,893 L/min] minimum) of water to prevent a boiling liquid expanding vapor explosion (BLEVE). The much longer reach of the larger line keeps you much further away from the tank if it does explode.

The S is for *standpipe* operations. The FDNY has a policy that all lines stretched from a standpipe will be 2½-in. (65-mm) hose with a 1⅛-in. (30-mm) tip on a smooth bore nozzle. Most standpipe systems were not designed to supply the high pressures (100 psi [700 kPa]) required by a combination fog or automatic nozzle. The smooth-bore nozzle and large-diameter hose will deliver superior flow at low (design) pressure.

Fig. 20–18. This is a good example of a fire that needs large lines. There is a greatly advanced body of fire, necessitating a defensive operation, and at this point it is still undermined how much of this building the fire will involve. The high heat production will require tons of water to extinguish the fire. (Courtesy of Brian Duddy)

Stretching. We will now explore the stretching responsibilities of each position on an attack hand line. These positions include the officer, the nozzle operator, the backup position, and the door position. Each position is critical for a successful hose stretch (figs. 20–20 and 20–21).

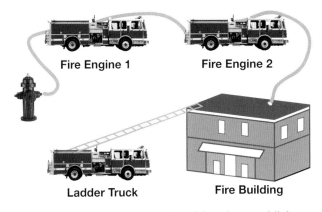

Fig. 20–20. Engine apparatus is positioned to establish a water supply and get the first hoseline in operation. Truck companies are positioned for search, rescue, ventilation, and other truck functions.

Fig. 20–19. Fires in industrial occupancies require the reach, penetration, and cooling effect of large lines. Here firefighters stretch a 5-in. (125-mm) line to a ladder truck. (Courtesy of Brian Duddy)

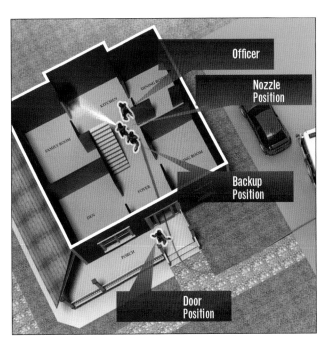

Fig. 20–21. Inside the fire building, each firefighter has a specific assignment and responsibility.

Officer duties in the stretch. The engine company officer (and, in some cases, a senior Firefighter II) is responsible for getting water on the fire as quickly as possible. Generally this officer will take direction from a chief officer on the scene. However, if the engine arrives before the chief, the engine officer will have to make some very important decisions and take decisive action. The engine officer can then pass command to any incoming officer or unit if appropriate. There are several subtasks the officer must accomplish to ensure water gets on the fire as quickly as possible.

1. Size up the fire (i.e., the size and number of lines).

2. Clearly order changes from the SOP.

3. Locate fire and tell the crew the best route to it (fig. 20–22).

4. Determine goal of line: exposure protection, fire attack, personnel protection, etc.

5. Be sure the line will not endanger others.

6. Keep members out of doorway "flue."

7. Keep members at floor level, below dangerous heat levels.

8. Coordinate timing of ventilation.

9. Be the eyes and ears of attack team.

10. Supervise the nozzle operator.

11. Call for relief when necessary.

12. Be responsible for the lives of the team.

Fig. 20–22. Here the engine officer directs the nozzle operator.

Nozzle operator duties in the stretch. There is a variety of ways to pack hose and an equal variety of methods get hose off the engine and to the fire. Described here are basic, universal skills that can be slightly modified to meet your department's specific attack line hose load. These are skills that will serve you and your company and department well if you learn, practice, and maintain them at a high skill level. In fire department terminology this is called **stretching the line**.

Nozzle operator duties

1. Carry the nozzle and the first 50 ft (15 m) of hoseline.

2. Work under command of the officer.

3. Know your department SOPs.

4. Get information from the officer.

5. Stop and wait for the backup position to shoulder the assigned hose.

6. "Bleed" air at door, check the flow, don facepiece.

7. Communicate with the officer and backup position during stretch and advance.

The nozzle operator is responsible for the first 50 ft (15 m) of hose, that is, to remove it from the engine or pumper and carry it to the point of attack (fig. 20–23). This length of hose is called the working line or lead length. It is the hose you will advance into the fire area with to kill the fire.

The nozzle operator shoulders the first 50 ft (15 m) of hose and carries it toward the fire. While moving toward the fire, an important step is to stop and wait for the backup position to shoulder his or her amount of hose. The nozzle operator should stop about 40 ft (12 m) away from the engine and wait just a couple of seconds for the backup position to grab the hose and carry it from the engine (fig. 20–24). Now moving together, you and your backup are stretching the initial attack line! If this is a 200-ft (60-m) preconnected hoseline, then you are carrying 50 ft (15 m), there is about 50 ft (15 m) between you, the backup is carrying 50 ft (15 m) and he or she is dragging the remaining 50 ft (15 m) off the engine. Properly executed, you two can stretch 200 ft (60 m) of hoseline (fig. 20–25).

Fig. 20–23. The nozzle operator has the working length on his shoulder and is moving away from the engine.

Fig. 20–24. The nozzle operator must wait a few seconds for the backup position to shoulder the load of hose. These few seconds will save a lot of time in the overall stretch.

Fig. 20–25. The door position clears the bed of any remaining hose, or if the load is not preconnected, will determine how much hose is needed and connect it to the pump discharge.

The **point of attack** is the point at which you as the nozzle operator will drop your working length, flake it out, and request to your officer that the line be charged with water. This is termed **calling for water**.

You will have to use your size-up observations to determine where to drop your working length. In this case, because you don't know exactly where the fire is behind the front door, you will charge the line just outside the door.

Preparing to charge your line requires you to flake out your working length (fig. 20–26). Dry hose can be literally thrown to allow water to flow through it easily and to minimize kinks that can reduce water flow and pressure.

Fig. 20–26. The nozzle operator and backup firefighter flake out their line in the direction of their advance.

Basic Fire Attack

FIREFIGHTER I

Chapter 20

It is at this point that you don your facepiece from your SCBA (figs. 20–27 and 20–28) and await the water in the line. When the hose is being charged, open the nozzle to allow the air that is trapped in the hose to bleed out. When the line is solid and fully charged with water, flow the nozzle fully to ensure that the pump operator has given you adequate pressure and volume of water. If you only open the line a small squirt, that is all you know you have, a small squirt. Flow the line for about 10 seconds to be sure you have full flow, correct pressure, and pattern selection for combination nozzles.

Fig. 20–27. Firefighters don their hoods and facepieces. Note they are holding their helmets between their knees so they don't get kicked around or lost.

Fig. 20–28. Firefighters must be able to don SCBA facepieces and hoods with gloves on. This reduces the preparation time needed to attack the fire and prevent injuries. Firefighters must learn to conduct all necessary actions (full escape, reduced profile maneuver, etc.) with gloves on. Burned hands cannot help you save your own life.

All the while you are stretching, flaking out, and advancing the line, you should be listening for a variety of things on the fireground. First, you should be listening to the radio to hear that coordination has been done for ventilation and that it is being planned or accomplished. Listen for the sound of glass breaking and/or the ventilation saw running. Good, timely ventilation will reduce the possibilities of flashover and backdraft that could injure or kill you. Listen also to reports from the search and rescue teams. Ensure that you will not push fire or superheated products of combustion onto them, causing injuries, burns, or death.

Listen for the sound of the line as you operate the line inside. The sound of the line will indicate if the stream is bouncing off the walls or ceilings. The sound will also indicate openings like doors and windows and also holes in floors.

Backup position's duties in the stretch

1. Second firefighter in stretch.

2. Carry second 50 ft of line and drop it at appropriate time and place.

3. Communicate with nozzle operator.

4. Relieve the nozzle reaction for nozzle operator during the advance.

5. Watch the nozzle operator's body and head positions during the advance.

FFI 5.3.10 The backup is the second firefighter in the stretch, responsible for carrying 50 ft (15 m) of hose and dropping the hose as the line is laid out (fig. 20–29). The door position drops his or her line first. Like the nozzle operator, door position must be continually be evaluating the position of the engine relative to the fire building location. From this observation, door position will determine where and when he or she will drop the length and assist in the stretch.

In our example, the point of attack is going to be at the front door. The backup firefighter will drop the hose and flake it out in a position such that it does not kink and allows for an easy advance into the fire area if the 50 ft (15 m) of working hose the nozzle operator has is not enough. Once the backup position has flaked the hose out so that it will not kink, he or she should quickly move toward the nozzle operator and assist him or her in flaking the line and preparing to attack the fire.

The primary responsibility of the backup firefighter is to relieve all the nozzle reaction from the nozzle operator. As water is discharged and flowing from the nozzle, an equal and opposite reaction is realized by the nozzle operator. This is called **nozzle reaction**. Generally, the higher the nozzle pressure and greater the flow, the greater the nozzle reaction. During the advance into the fire area, the backup position must push the hoseline forward to counter this nozzle reaction so the nozzle operator does not tire and continues to advance and attack the fire.

Fig. 20–29. The backup position, moving in conjunction with the nozzle operator, carries one length of hose.

Each member should be able to carry approximately 50 ft (15 m) of hose and drag the same amount, allowing them both to efficiently stretch 200 ft (60 m) of hose. In our example, the point of attack will be at the front door. The backup will drop the hose and flake it out so that it does not kink. This will allow for an easy advance into the fire area if the nozzle operator's 50 ft (15 m) of working hose is not enough (fig. 20–30). Once the backup's hose is flaked out, the backup should quickly move toward the nozzle operator to assist in flaking that line and preparing to attack the fire.

Fig. 20–30. The backup position drops the hose first, allowing the nozzle operator to continue the advance to the fire.

Door position duties in the stretch. The door position is the third firefighter in the stretch. In our example, the door position is responsible for making sure that the preconnect bed is clear of hose, following the line

quickly to remove any kinks, and feeding hose to the nozzle operator and the backup firefighter.

As the officer, nozzle operator, and backup position prepare to advance into the fire, it is important that the door position be very mobile (move back and forth along the line) and ensure that there are no kinks in the hoseline and that he or she can quickly supply the team with the amount of hose they need to advance to the seat of the fire.

Third person in stretch clears preconnect bed (fig. 20–31), carries the last 50 ft (15 m) of line toward the fire, chases kinks, feeds the line from edge of the fire area outside the "immediate danger to life and health (IDLH)" atmosphere, can relieve the nozzle operator, backup firefighter, or officer, because the third person has conserved air by being outside of the IDLH environment. The third firefighter also has a safety link to outside, and knows how far and where the team has advanced

Fig. 20–31. The door position makes sure the hosebed is clear of all hose during the first part of the stretch.

When the nozzle operator advances into the smoke, the door position must be careful to push just the right amount of hose to him or her. Since the line is rigid, the door position can push the nozzle operator into areas he or she may not want to go or push the nozzle out of his or her hands. A good technique is to push up a bow of hose onto a door frame or wall and allow the backup position or nozzle operator to pull it in as needed. This causes less physical exertion on them and provides hose only when needed, and doesn't push into dangerous areas.

The door position is responsible to see that every foot of hose needed by the nozzle team is provided to them so they can control their advance (fig. 20–32).

Fig. 20–32. One of the door position's responsibilities is to keep the hose advancing. This may require him to move hose around objects that snag the line. These include car tires, fence posts, trees, door frames, and saddles.

Advancing charged hoselines

Officer duties during the advance. The officer will be the eyes and the ears for the nozzle operator. Often the stream blocks the view of the nozzle operator. The company officer can be off to the side of the nozzle operator and provide a better view of the progress of the fire attack, for example, if the stream is hitting the desired target. As the officer controls and monitors the progress of the company, the officer has two hands free to send important radio transmissions and other important tasks. The officer will monitor the level of fatigue for the company and request additional firefighters, companies, or hoselines to assist if required. The officer's other duties include pulling the company out when possible as they become less combat effective. Tired firefighters are dangerous firefighters and are prone to injuries. In the end, it is the company officer who is responsible for the overall safety and accountability of the company members.

Nozzle operator techniques during the advance.

There are a variety of ways to position yourself when you advance. There is no right way, and it is important to note that you may use many or all of these during your advance into the fire area until final extinguishment. Fatigue, speed of fire control, and other conditions will determine your speed of advance and subsequent positions while operating or backing up the nozzle operator.

In figure 20–33, the nozzle operator demonstrates good technique, with the nozzle out in front at about arm's length where he can rotate it around and distribute the water into the fire room. He has it under his armpit, using the large muscles of his shoulder to hold it. His

right elbow is braced against his knee to help counter the nozzle reaction.

Another nozzle operator position that provides a great deal of stability while advancing is demonstrated in figure 20–34. It allows the nozzle operator flexibility to direct the stream in almost any direction and to move in quickly when necessary. This position provides a great degree of overall flexibility, allowing one leg to be out in front confirming that the floor is safe. The knees can be switched to allow the bunker pants insulation to cool and reduce the chance of burns. Having only one knee on the floor instead of both reduces, by 50%, the chance of contacting nails, hypodermic needles, and dangers such as broken glass on the floor.

The two-knees-down method has the following disadvantages: It does not allow for rapid movement of the nozzle inward toward the fire, or for the firefighter to feel to see if the floor is intact ahead. Also, the thermal insulation in the knees of the bunker pants is compressed and can lead to painful burns if the floor is hot, if the floor covering is melted or was burning, or if hot water soaks through. Also note that the backup position is holding the hose too high, causing the nozzle operator to fight the spring action of the charged line (fig. 20–35). Firefighters should consider the charged line a solid pipe from the nozzle back 12 ft (3 m). Keeping this "pipe" straight will reduce fatigue on both the nozzle operator and the backup position.

The backup is a key position in the aggressive interior fire attack (fig. 20–36). The backup takes a firm grip on the hose and pushes forward to relieve all the nozzle reaction. This makes the nozzle operator's job much easier and more effective. The backup position can also use an alternate grip to relieve the nozzle reaction to assist the nozzle operator (fig. 20–37).

Fig. 20–33. Proper nozzle handling technique while stationary

Fig. 20–34. Proper nozzle handling technique while advancing

Fig. 20–35. Improper two-firefighter hose-handling technique while advancing

Fig. 20–36. Proper two-firefighter hose-handling technique while advancing

Fig. 20–37. Alternative two-firefighter hose-handling technique while advancing

The position in figure 20–38 allows the most rapid advance and provides a high degree of safety for the nozzle operator because both knees are off the floor. It puts the nozzle operator in a little higher position, which helps detect high heat levels that may precede flashover, thereby preventing advance into deadly conditions. Being higher also allows the backup to be in better position to relieve the nozzle reaction. This position is favored by experienced nozzle operators.

Fig. 20–38. Alternative nozzle position hose-handling technique

As the advance begins, the nozzle team must remain low in the door (fig. 20–39). This will allow the smoke and heat to vent over their heads as they enter. Some experienced firefighters have professed that you should wait to see what the smoke does when the door is initially forced. The theory is that after the door is forced, if the smoke gets drawn back in, this may be a warning sign of backdraft. This is potentially difficult to see as it may be caused by the natural convection of air into the fire area. Remember the warning signs of backdraft, and look at what the smoke is doing before you force the door. Smoke is always a reliable indicator of the fire condition when you learn to read it.

Fig. 20–39. The hose team needs to stay low as they make entry to the fire building.

As you enter the structure, move into the room and out of the door opening. When you operate the stream, rotate the nozzle and listen to the sound of the water splashing off the ceiling, walls, and the floor. The sound will indicate any openings, including windows, doors, and holes in the floor (fig. 20–40).

It is important to remember that the hoseline will be charged with 50–100 psi (350–700 kPa) of water pressure. When the line is first charged, it will quickly straighten out. Hold it firmly and crack the nozzle to release the air. Flow the nozzle at full volume to ensure that you have proper water pressure and volume. If you crack the nozzle and release a squirt, you only know that you have a squirt, but you need to know you have full volume.

Fig. 20–40. Sweeping the floor with the line will wash debris away from you; this can be any type of hazard, whether biological, sharp, or other. Sweeping the floor will also cool the floor, reducing the potential for burn injuries.

Water hammer. The hoseline is pressurized, and when the nozzle is open the water has significant velocity as it flows through the line and nozzle. Always open and close the nozzle slowly to prevent water hammer. Water hammer is pressure that is created when a flow of water is rapidly stopped and the pressure is redirected to the path of least resistance. Water hammer can increase pressure by as much as six times the pressure contained in the hose. This obviously can cause a burst length or damage to the pumper and other appliances.

Door position duties during the advance. The door position is the third member of the engine company and has an important role in the advance of the hoseline (fig. 20–41). The door position remains at the door during the advance and is responsible for chasing kinks from the door outward and supplying hose as needed by the nozzle operator and backup position.

The door position must be careful not to push in too much line because it will kink or could push the nozzle team into areas where they do not want to go.

Figures 20–42 and 20–43 show good techniques that the door position can use to supply the appropriate amount of hose to the nozzle team.

Fig. 20–41. The door position assists in the advance by feeding line in from just outside the fire area. He tries to maintain a full tank of air so he can assist and relieve the nozzle team when they become fatigued.

Fig. 20–42. Making a loop of hose on the floor allows the nozzle team to advance quickly and easily.

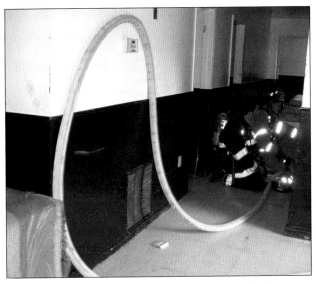

Fig. 20–43. Putting a loop of hose up on the wall allows the nozzle team to very easily pull the hose in as they move down the hallway. This is not always possible but is an excellent method.

The well hole stretch. This is a special type of stretch commonly used in older apartment buildings. It can be used whenever you encounter a well hole in the stairwell.

The well hole is the space between the stairs and the edge of landing of the public hall in a multiple dwelling. Using the well hole will reduce the number of lengths required in the stretch, speeding the stretch and reducing friction loss (fig. 20–44). On average, one length of hose will reach from the base of the stairs to the fifth floor.

After dropping the folded hose at the base of the stairs, the second firefighter will proceed up the stairs, assisting with the stretch. When sufficient hose has been hauled up to the point of attack, the line must be secured by hose straps to the railing before the line is charged. When the line is charged, there is a possibility that the weight of the water could cause the line to fall back down the well. Having sufficient line at the point of attack cannot be overstressed. When the line is secured and charged, it is extremely difficult to haul up more line.

Additional firefighters can assist in the stretch, making sure that enough line has been brought into the building and properly flaked out. When the line is charged, they can chase kinks as they move up on the line.

If the well is wide, the nozzle operator may opt to carry a length to the drop point before hauling the line up the well. If a second line is required to be stretched up the well, the nozzle operator has no option but to take only the nozzle up the stairs. When advancing the line up the stairs, the nozzle operator must pass the second line

Fig. 20—44 (a,b, c, and d). Well hole stretch

around the first to prevent the two lines from becoming twisted around each other.

Often companies will store utility ropes in empty bleach bottles or other plastic jugs to facilitate rope stretches or hauling tools to the roof. If the well is wide enough for the jug to fall down it, a utility rope stretch can be used to get the first or the second line up the stairs.

Standpipe stretch. Standpipe stretches are another type of important stretch. Standpipe systems are covered in greater detail in chapter 30, Fire Protection Systems, but is also covered here as an introduction.

Simply put, a standpipe system is a fixed set of water supply piping with hose valves that is typically installed in high-rise and large area buildings. Standpipes avoid the necessity of stretching hose all the way from a fire engine in the street to a remote part of a building; firefighters simply attach their hand line to a hose valve close to the fire area to attack the fire. The standpipe system is usually pressurized with water (but not always); a fire department connection (FDC, also known as a "Siamese") at street level allows firefighters to pump water into the system to supplement it. In a high-rise, hose valves are most often located in the stairwells.

Operating hoselines from standpipe systems can be challenging. It requires close coordination on many levels to be not only safe but also effective. It requires the pump operator on the street to supply the correct pressure to the system for the floor the nozzle will be operating on. Simple friction loss calculations don't apply. It is important to coordinate the efforts of the firefighter at the floor outlet where the line is hooked up who maintains the correct pressure and an experienced nozzle team that ensures the nozzle is flowing properly.

Whenever a hoseline is stretched from a standpipe outlet, a pumper must supply the FDC to ensure an uninterrupted water supply. The hookup location must be out of the IDLH environment and never run the risk of being exposed because if there is any problem with the line, the firefighter controlling the outlet must be able to make corrections without the stresses of heat and smoke. The closest location that satisfies both criteria is often an enclosed stairway on the floor below. That stairway should be designated the **attack stair**, and all firefighting efforts should be started from that stair. If building occupants can be alerted of this stair's designation, escaping occupants can be directed to an **evacuation stair** and thus will not be subjected to heat and smoke.

When the hookup site is selected, based on fire conditions, closest to the fire and providing access to the fire area, sufficient hose must be brought to the location. In addition to lengths of hose, a standpipe kit is required. This kit must consist of items to facilitate the hookup with some contingencies. When operating from standpipes, the apparatus can be many floors away, so a complete kit can save a great deal of aggravation.

Some equipment that may be necessary in the kit includes, but is not limited to, a pipe wrench large enough to remove stubborn caps or pressure-reducing devices; spanner wrenches to tighten hoselines, to prevent excess water from accumulating on floors and creating slip-and-fall hazards or unnecessary water damage; and any specific adaptors that may be required for your location (fig. 20–45). Often adaptors are required to convert from pipe thread to hose thread or between municipal threads. Door chocks are always useful when stretching lines, and they take up little room and add little weight to the kit.

Every standpipe kit must include either a pressure gauge or flow meter to ensure that the correct pressure or flow is being supplied to the line. A firefighter must hook up the gauge after the standpipe has been tested, so that any

debris flushed from the pipe does not damage the gauge. A firefighter must be positioned at the outlet when the attack begins to make any corrections to pressure or flow when water is flowing. If available, this firefighter should remain in this position in the event of an emergency, burst length, and so forth.

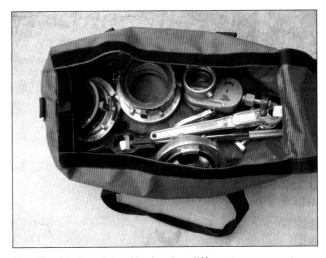

Fig. 20–45. Standpipe kit showing different components

Once the hookup has been made and the fire attack is to begin, charge the line and bleed the line as you would at any other fire operation (fig. 20–46). But when stretching from a standpipe, a final check of the stairs must be made before the door to the fire area is opened. Occupants' floors above the fire will be exposed to the toxic smoke. *A fire attack must never be commenced with civilians above the fire floor in the stairwell.* If a firefighter is available to be posted as a sentry on a floor above the fire floor that provides access to the other stair, this firefighter can remove any occupants from the attack stair to the evacuation stair.

Fig. 20–46. Hoseline attached to a standpipe Siamese connection

When the door opens and the line is advanced in to the fire area, firefighters will be needed to advance the line down the hall. Flaking the line up to the next landing in the stairs will aid in the advance due to the weight of the line being pulled down the stairs.

Buildings that require standpipes are typically office buildings, high-rise apartment buildings, and "projects." They are built of steel and concrete, and the combination of the two will produce some of the hottest fires you will ever feel. Exacerbating the situation, these buildings have limited means of ventilation. These "brick ovens" will require a skilled team of firefighters with knowledgeable leadership to extinguish the fire and reduce injuries.

Methods of aggressive interior fire attack. There are four methods of structural or aggressive interior fire attack: combination, indirect, direct, and modified direct (as described in chapter 16, Fire Streams). Note that before an interior attack is initiated, several factors must be considered. Here are a few basic thoughts to consider:

Is the building safe to enter? Advances in lightweight construction have resulted in buildings that simply will not tolerate a fire load and will collapse rapidly, trapping and killing firefighters.

Heavy fire in any building should be carefully analyzed before firefighters are committed to entering the building and attempting an aggressive interior fire attack.

Are there salvageable human lives inside the building? "Risk a lot to save a lot; risk a little to save a little" is something a wise old fire officer once said. If fire is blowing out of every window in the house and through the roof, the odds of someone surviving are near zero. Firefighters are occupants also, so we must be careful not to unreasonably endanger the "new occupants" (firefighters) if the old occupants are already dead.

Similarly, if there is a reasonable chance that we can make a rescue, and we are not assured that everyone is already out of the building, a search and rescue operation is the key event at this fire. It is of the utmost importance to recall that trapped occupants cannot wait until the fire is extinguished to be rescued. After the fire is out, this operation is in fact a recovery (of a dead body), not a rescue operation.

Is there any property left to save? We don't have to get inside on every fire. Consider the outcome of many fires: heavy fire upon arrival, firefighters make an aggressive attack, one or more firefighters die or are injured, the fire is extinguished, and the insurance company pays huge sums of money so the building is built back better than it was before!

The point is this: We must take risks on the fireground to save lives and property. We must ensure that these are manageable and reasonable risks for ourselves and our members.

Recall that the doctrine for aggressive interior fire attack generally follows this sequence: Truck company members or other firefighters will force entry into the building to conduct search and rescue operations. Engine company members will establish a reliable water supply and stretch a hoseline to fire building to the seat of the fire or between the victims and the fire. Other truck company members will ventilate the fire building just before the engine crews push in to attack the fire. Officers will plan, direct, and coordinate these actions. Because firefighters will enter the building before water is applied, and the fire is at its most dangerous time (it now has an unlimited amount of oxygen causing it to grow unchecked), rapid, aggressive, and proper fire attack operations often will make the difference between life and death for other members inside. It can be argued that nothing is more important than extinguishing the fire because it minimizes all other hazards on the fireground.

Modified direct method of attack. The modified direct method of fire attack is the most common type of attack used. It is used when the fire has gone through the flashover phase or extended beyond one room to several rooms or fire areas, heavy smoke has obscured visibility, and/or conditions are impossible to make a direct attack (fig. 20–47). The room may literally be filled with fire from floor to ceiling. A good sign that these conditions are present is fire pushing out a door or window or heavy smoke throughout the fire area (fig. 20–48).

Fig. 20–47. This room has gone to flashover. The chair on the left and sofa on the right are fully involved almost to the floor level, and flames fill the entire room from floor to ceiling. Ceiling temperatures reach 2,000°F (1,093°C) or more.

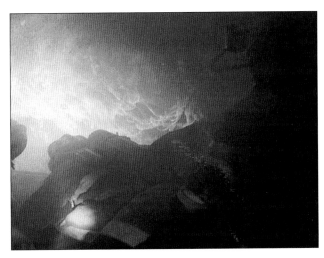

Fig. 20–48. Heat from flashover will force firefighters to the floor and make conditions impossible for firefighters to operate in until the fire attack begins. Turnout gear will become saturated with heat and not protect you from flashover conditions. The modified direct attack will help cool the atmosphere and extinguish the fire, allowing firefighters to enter, attack the room, and move through to the next room or fire area.

When these conditions are present, the modified direct method of fire attack (as described in chapter 16, Fire Streams) is the most appropriate. This is an aggressive interior fire attack. The nozzle operator operates the nozzle in a straight stream or "zero degree fog" position if using a fog nozzle. Preferably, a smooth bore nozzle would be used for this type of attack.

The nozzle operator directs the stream in circles, starting at the ceiling level and moving the nozzle in a clockwise or side-to-side motion. The water bounces off the ceiling and is broken up and distributed in large drops of water that hit the burning fuel and extinguish it. The nozzle is rotated around, and the fire stream will directly hit the burning fuel (direct attack effect). This water will also cool the ceiling and walls. This reduces the heat that is radiated back into the room. It also helps cool the upper atmosphere in the fire area.

Note that cooling the fire area does not extinguish the fire. By cooling the room, in effect, you are treating the symptom (heat) and not the disease (fire). The large water droplets that are bounced off the ceiling and land on the burning fuel are large enough to extinguish that bit of fire, which contributes to the overall extinguishment process.

The nozzle operator uses the reach of the stream to put water on the fire, not only to first control some of it, but to see how the fire was going to react to the application of water. Live electrical circuits, flammable liquids, and **water-reactive chemicals** in the room may react

violently with the application of water. Better that this happens when the nozzle team is outside the fire area rather than in it!

FFI 5.3.12 There are several important facts to understand when using the modified direct method of attack. According to The United States National Institute of Standards and Technology (NIST) report NBSIR 80-2120, *Fire Development in Residential Basement Rooms,* tests that were conducted utilizing 16 full scale burn tests of living room fires resulted in ceiling temperatures reaching 2,000°F. The room you are entering to extinguish the fire has very dangerous products of combustion near the ceiling that you do not want near you. It is therefore vital to maintain the thermal balance of the fire room during the attack (fig. 20–49).

Fig. 20–49. Thermal layering simply means that the hottest air is in higher levels of the room, and cooler air is in the lowest level, near the floor.

Nozzle choice for modified direct attack. The most proven fire stream (and the safest for firefighters) for interior fire attack is a solid stream from a smooth bore nozzle or a combination nozzle set to a straight stream pattern from a fog nozzle.

Because of the dangerous conditions inside during a modified direct attack, it is important to choose the correct nozzle and stream pattern. Since we are inside during the combination attack, it is important not to disturb the thermal balance that the fire has established. In essence you want to leave the bad (superheated) air up and away from you and keep the good (coolest) air down near you at the floor level.

The modified direct method of attack pits us against a fully involved fire inside the fire building where it is the most dangerous. Using a straight stream from a fog nozzle or a solid stream provides us the most fire-killing power and the least danger as proven by both experience and laboratory testing.

All fire streams will move air into the fire area as a result of their water movement. Firefighters usually enter through a door directing the stream into the fire area. Thus there is an unlimited amount of air that can be pulled into the fire room or area.

From actual air measurements, we know that a straight stream or solid bore nozzle will move about 725 cubic feet per minute (cfm) (20.5 cubic meters per minute [cmm]) into the fire area. This small volume of air can be adequately vented via a window or door ahead of the nozzle team. The result is that the thermal balance in the room where firefighters are operating is maintained as much as possible. The hottest air remains at the ceiling, and the coolest remains at the floor.

Maintenance of the thermal balance allows firefighters to move through this room that has just been extinguished and into other fire involved areas.

Fog streams: combination and indirect attacks. If you choose a fog nozzle and select a spray or fog pattern, huge amounts of air will be drawn into the fire area. In tests conducted at the Rockland County, NY, Fire Training Center, air volumes of 2,000 cfm (57 cmm) (were measured when a fog stream was used. Estimates of air moved range as high as 6,000–10,000 cfm (170–283 cmm) from 1¾-in. (45-mm) fog nozzles. The 30°–60° fog pattern from a combination nozzle moves so much air into the fire area that it completely disturbs the thermal balance.

It is also important to remember that liquid water expands into steam at an expansion ration of 1,700:1. This further mixes and pressurizes the fire room and its superheated air and smoke.

Use of fog or spray patterns inside for an aggressive interior fire attack is dangerous for another reason: the massive amounts of steam they create. The water droplets are a much smaller size and therefore provide a greater surface area to absorb heat from the fire. To the inexperienced this seems to be a good characteristic. However, the reality is that once the heat is absorbed by these small water droplets, they turn into steam, vastly increasing their volume and adding to the **overpressurization** of the room. More importantly, this steam is stirred up by the air movement returning to the nozzle and backup position, which may burn the backup position and prevent advance into additional rooms of unchecked fire.

Since these small drops of water were vaporized, they did not make it to the burning fuel to extinguish the fire. Although the symptom (heat) was partially removed, the fire (disease) continued to burn, spread, and threaten occupants' (civilians' and firefighters') lives.

A particular hazard created by fog streams when used for interior firefighting is that they can actually push the fire with the massive amounts of air they introduce. These streams can drive fire into void spaces (walls, ceilings, and truss spaces). They can also drive fire from one room to another or through an entire building, much like a poorly placed ventilation fan. This is possible because the reach of the fog stream is very limited. The limited reach, coupled with the massive air movement, results in fire being moved throughout the building because the water does not reach the seat of the fire. Often firefighters do not know the full extent of this disastrous effect because it is often concealed by smoke and steam.

A similar and equally dangerous effect created by fog nozzles when used inside a fire building is that if a nozzle team inadvertently moves down the hall past a room of fire, then operates a fog stream, it is very likely that the fire and superheated products of combustion will be drawn back onto the attack team, creating the potential for injuries and cessation of the fire attack (fig. 20–50).

Fig. 20–50. Firefighters have disturbed the thermal balance with a fog stream inside causing superheated steam to envelope them, creating the potential for injury and stopping the fire attack in the first room.

Further confusing the issue is that a fog stream appears to be a very successful technique for firefighting, especially from the nozzle operator's limited point of view. Holding the fog nozzle, you have a wall of water in front of you. The water spray leaving the nozzle, usually at 100 psi (700 kPa), makes considerable noise and nozzle reaction. Essentially the nozzle operator is fooled into thinking there is a significant strategic weapon in his or her hands.

LESSON LEARNED

We responded to a garden apartment that had fire blowing out one window. The assistant chief told me to take the nozzle and move into the left. After several attempts at operating a fog pattern in a circular motion, and with the heat increasing each time, we retreated. We found that we were drawing superheated air from the room adjacent to us. We did not make the sharp turn into the fire room, and our fog stream pulled fire onto us from the next room.

Additionally, when demonstrating the use of fog nozzles in a parking lot, the fog stream appears to provide protection from the fire by the massive amount of air that is moved past the nozzle operator toward the fire area, thereby "pushing" all the dangerous heat and smoke away from the operator. This "parking lot experience" is in fact exactly the opposite of what happens when a fog nozzle is used inside, as described earlier in the nozzle selection section.

A myth developed that you can "breathe off the nozzle" if you put your face close to the stream. Used frequently before SCBA became a part of our personal protective equipment, air was available here because it was being drawn in from a clean air source behind the nozzle team. Some firefighters even incorrectly believed that oxygen was being broken off the water molecules. If this were true, the remaining hydrogen atoms would have created a very explosive condition in the fire area.

The fog stream in reality has little reach and penetration to reach the seat of the fire. Many a nozzle operator and backup position have been burned by using a fog stream inside a fire room.

It is important to understand the limits of a fog hand line and its dangers for interior firefighting. Do not base your fire attack strategy and techniques on your experience with one-room fires or parking lot experience.

The fog streams of the indirect and combination methods of fire attack (described thoroughly in chapter 16, Fire Streams) prevent firefighters from entering the compartment/building for search and rescue. Recall that the indirect method of attack was developed for shipboard firefighting where no one was occupying the cargo hold areas. The combination method is an extension of the indirect method, with a rotating fog stream in a compartment. The indirect and combination methods doom anyone still inside to certain death by scalding steam and toxic products of combustion. It also allows fire that the steam cannot reach in void spaces to continue to grow and spread unchecked.

YOU ARE HERE

1. Size-up
2. Strategic plan
3. Establish water supply
4. Force entry/exit
5. Search and rescue
6. Fire attack

7. Ventilate

8. Protect exposures
9. Fire control and overhaul
10. Pick up and return

Ventilate the fire building

FFI 5.3.11 Ventilation is often described by experienced firefighters as the key to success for any aggressive interior fire attack operation. If ventilation is performed in the right place at the right time, it allows the engine company to rapidly advance on the fire and extinguish it, which will minimize all other problems on the fireground. Ventilation, or opening up of the fire room or building allows the products of combustion, heat, and smoke to exit the building, raising the thermal layers, raising the smoke layer, increasing visibility, and decreasing the potential for flashover. See chapter 14, Ventilation, for a detailed explanation of ventilating different types of buildings. There are four types of ventilation: horizontal, vertical, positive pressure, and hydraulic ventilation.

Horizontal ventilation. As its name implies, horizontal ventilation consists of using or making horizontal openings (doors or windows) to ventilate the fire area or building. Horizontal ventilation will provide more efficient venting when doors and windows are opened opposite the advancing hoseline. The hoseline can drive smoke and heat from the building through the horizontal openings. A single firefighter with a tool (hook, pike pole, Halligan, or portable ladder, depending on whether it's a first- or second-floor fire) can create a great deal of ventilation (fig. 20–51).

Fig. 20–51. a)Horizontal ventilation is most often accomplished by removing windows. b) When ventilating a window, remove all glass, screens, curtains, shades, and blinds. Remove the window sashes as well, so firefighters can escape quickly if necessary (make a door out of a window). (Courtesy of Tom Bierds and Brian Duddy)

Vertical ventilation. Vertical ventilation is the opening of a hole in the roof to allow the products of combustion, smoke, and heat to leave the building via the newly created opening. As with horizontal ventilation, vertical ventilation will allow the products of combustion, heat, and smoke to exit the building, raising the thermal layers, raising the smoke layer, increasing visibility, and decreasing the potential for flashover. The purpose is the same; the tactic is different (see fig. 20–52).

Fig. 20–52. Vertical ventilation

If fire has penetrated the attic space due to failure of the gypsum board ceiling or walls, opening the roof will draw the fire through the opening instead of allowing the closed up roof to cause the fire to mushroom and spread horizontally inside the attic (fig. 20–53).

Coordination of the venting is required. As the line is charged and is moving into the fire area, the windows should be removed. Venting prior to that can cause the fire to increase in intensity. This could cause more damage to the building, thus increasing our fire problem or causing more injury to the victims who may still be inside.

In figure 20–54, truck company members have done an excellent job by cutting the roof allowing smoke and heat to escape. This prevented the fire from spreading into the main part of the house. When possible, ladders should not be positioned over windows. If fire erupts out these windows, firefighters could be trapped on the roof. In this case firefighters could escape safely with a short jump to the ground level.

Fig. 20–53. Fire drawn up through vent hole. (Courtesy of Tom Bierds)

Fig. 20–54. Firefighters exit the roof after successfully venting the fire.

Positive pressure ventilation. Positive pressure ventilation (PPV) is generally considered to be the use of large fans (upwards of 30,000 cfm [850 cmm] for typical PPV fans), positioned outside the building to create an increased or positive pressure inside the building (fig. 20–55). These large-volume fans force clean air from outside the building through the building and drive contaminated air outside via a second ventilation opening. For many years firefighters used smoke ejectors, which were smaller fans (10,000 cfm [283 cmm]) to create a suction or negative pressure from inside the building to move contaminates from inside to outside the building.

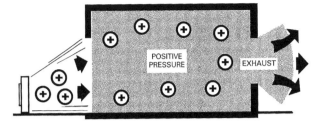

Fig. 20–55. Positive pressure involves placing a blower outside a room to force pressurized air inward, driving contaminants to the exterior.

PPV is very effective and can be used on small structures or very large commercial structures, high-rises, and other large buildings. The effectiveness of PPV comes from the basic physics principle that one only needs to increase the pressure a small amount to create an air flow in the direction desired.

There are two main ways to successfully use PPV. First, the fan can be positioned by the front door before the fire attack commences. The theory behind this use is that it will force heat and contaminates out as firefighters move in with the hoseline. Many fire departments use this method, while others prohibit it during fire attack. The obvious danger to this is that the increase in air supplied to the fire causes the fire to grow very, very rapidly and also be driven into voids and concealed spaces as well as *at* trapped victims. Additionally, if the fire does grow rapidly, it can cause firefighters to be trapped and killed. *Extreme caution must be exercised when using PPV during a fire attack.*

Another successful application of PPV is to position the fan after the fire has been knocked down to blow out contaminates—heat, visibility, and toxic gases—in order to improve conditions so firefighters can conduct overhaul operations (fig. 20–56). This has proven very successful in many fire departments. The danger of this tactical use of ventilation is that firefighters must be sure the fire is sufficiently under control, to prevent the building from "lighting up" because of the introduction of fresh air (rapid fire growth), creating danger for firefighters inside.

Basic Fire Attack

FIREFIGHTER I

Chapter 20

Fig. 20–56. A PPV fan placed at the front door will drive smoke and heat out horizontal ventilation openings created by firefighters. By controlling what windows are opened and closed firefighters can control the air flow through the building ventilating specific rooms as needed.

PPV has significant applications, especially in high-rise buildings, where it can be used to pressurize stairwells and keep them smoke free for occupants to escape through. By opening doors on specific floors, entire floors can be positively pressurized and cleared or kept clear of smoke and products of combustion.

Like all tools in the fire service, PPV has to be used under the right conditions, at the right time and as part of a fire attack system. There are no magic bullets in the fire service.

Communications. Fireground communications are critical to this ventilation. The firefighter assigned to vent should be listening for the engine officer to order the hoseline charged. This should serve as a warning that they will be ready to move in shortly. If any doubt exists about when to vent, ask the officer directly. The FDNY has a written procedure that only the ladder company officer can order horizontal ventilation of the fire area. This ensures that members in an apartment are not exposed to the increase in fire from premature venting.

YOU ARE HERE

1. Size-up
2. Strategic plan
3. Establish water supply
4. Force entry/exit
5. Search and rescue
6. Fire attack
7. Ventilate
8. **Protect exposures**
9. Fire control and overhaul
10. Pick up and return

Protecting exposures

FFI 5.3.10 Confine, then extinguish is the overall strategy to limit fire spread. Protecting exposures is the first step in confining and limiting the spread of fire, and ultimately extinguishing the fire. Confining the fire essentially means cutting off the fire spread and not allowing it to extend to other areas or buildings.

Exterior exposures. An **exterior exposure** is a building that, left unprotected, will be ignited by radiant, convected, or conducted heat from the original fire building or room.

When a fire attack operation is going to be defensive, one of the most common goals of a hand line is exposure protection. Remember that this goes back to the main goal of firefighting—to confine and extinguish the fire. By confining the fire to the building on fire, you are protecting the exposure. Protecting the exposure may involve placing the hand line between the fire building and the exposure, in this case, the neighboring structure (fig. 20–57).

When officers order a line to be stretched for exposure protection, they must make it clear what the goal of the line is going to be. A large hand line or ground-based monitor will probably be in a fixed position outside. A large hand line may be advanced into the exposure to direct their stream on the fire building. These are important distinctions that must be clear to the firefighters on the line.

An important note: When selecting the exposure that needs protection, the rule is to protect the exposure with the greatest value, not necessarily where the fire is going to spread.

Fig. 20–57. A hoseline is positioned between the fire building and the exposure building to protect the exposed building. (Courtesy of Brian Duddy)

To properly protect this exposure, a large-caliber hand line should be positioned between the fire building and the exposure. In this way the line can be used alternately on the fire building and the exposure. Water is applied *directly* to the exposure; water should be applied at the top of the wall so that it will cool the surface of the wall as it runs off.

Further exposure protection may involve getting into the building and removing any curtains or drapes from the windows and any flammable materials that could ignite from the radiant heat. Operating a hoseline from the exposure is often a tactic. But in this case, because they are so close, that may not be appropriate since it might only allow smoke and heat to damage the structure.

YOU ARE HERE

1. Size-up
2. Strategic plan
3. Establish water supply
4. Force entry/exit
5. Search and rescue
6. Fire attack
7. Ventilate
8. Protect exposures
9. **Fire control and overhaul**
10. Pick up and return

Fire control and overhaul

FFI 5.3.10 Once the fire has been knocked down (i.e., when all visible fire has been extinguished), it is important to let it blow. Letting it blow means allowing the heat and smoke vent from the building so that any unextin-

guished fire can be discovered. If a hoseline is operated too long, it will overcool the area and the smoke will not lift. When to shut down the line is generally an officer's decision. If the timing is left to the nozzle operator, be alert for changing conditions and the need to open the line again.

This may be a time when a hoseline can be used for ventilation. A hoseline set to a fog pattern, held 4–5 ft (1.2–1.5 m) back from the window and directed out, will move the heat and smoke out. The same may be accomplished with a solid stream nozzle; by taking the tip off and using a broken stream from the shutoff, similar effects can be felt.

At this point the members assigned to overhaul should be allowed into the fire area with their tools to open up the area and examine for extension.

The process of opening up means that the interior wall, ceiling, and other burned surfaces must be removed. The idea is to expose the concealed spaces behind them until the unburned areas are exposed (fig. 20–58).

Fig. 20–58. Opening walls and ceilings after the initial fire attack must be done quickly to search for hidden fire. Fire can travel undetected in void spaces and is a serious threat to firefighters. (Courtesy of Tom Bierds)

Once the walls, floors, or ceilings are open, the engine company can come back in and wash down any hot spots. The hoseline should be directed on any charred surfaces until they are cooled. Particular attention should be paid to the areas where structural members are attached. Where floors lay on beams and where boards are nailed together can hold heat and continue to smolder. These members should not be removed, but instead the stream should be directed to drive the water between them until completely cool.

Some of this work may be performed by relief crews from other companies. If the first units must perform this work due to personnel shortages, officers may allow the work to be performed without SCBA. Carbon monoxide levels must be monitored, and the physical condition of the firefighters must be the prime consideration in making this decision.

LESSON LEARNED

We responded mutual aid one night to a fully involved house. The chief met me on the front sidewalk of the involved home and directed my line to put water on the exposure. My line operating off tank water, which saved the home next door and was not wasted on the fully involved, nonsalvageable home.

YOU ARE HERE

1. Size-up
2. Strategic plan
3. Establish water supply
4. Force entry/exit
5. Search and rescue
6. Fire attack
7. Ventilate
8. Protect exposures
9. Fire control and overhaul
10. **Pick up and return**

Pick up and return

Generally, by the time we have made an aggressive interior attack on a working fire, we are all pretty well exhausted. Repacking hose and replacing ladders and tools now seems to take on a low priority. Resetting for our next alarm is, however, very important.

How well we reset and recover our equipment from this alarm may well determine how our company, or maybe even another group of firefighters, will perform next time. Like packing your own parachute, take time to do it right because lives—firefighters' lives—will depend on it.

When repacking hose, inspect it for damage. Worn jackets can indicate that the hose is compromised and may fail when pressurized. All firefighters should be familiar with their department's procedure for reporting damaged hose. If there is any doubt as to the serviceability of any length of hose, it must be tested before it is returned to service. Steps should be taken to prevent a damaged length from becoming mixed with serviceable ones.

Hose should be repacked when it is clean and dry. Mild soap and water is usually enough to clean the hose. Follow the manufacturer's recommendation and department SOP.

When the hose gets repacked, the important thing is not that it goes on but how it will come off. This has been compared to packing a parachute.

Tools. **FFI 5.5.1** Preparing your tools for your next alarm is also very important. Hand tools should be inspected for damage, cleaned, and placed back in their proper places on the rig according to your company and department policies. There is nothing that looks less professional and competent than a firefighter going from cabinet to cabinet looking for a tool at an emergency.

Power tools such as saws need to be refueled, oiled, and sharpened if necessary. All blades must be inspected to determine whether the blade is the correct one for the saw, has the required teeth, and is in generally good condition. Damaged or worn blades and saw chains can be swapped out to put the saw back in service quickly.

SCBA also needs to be inspected, serviced, cleaned, and tested before you put it back on the rig. Remember that this is life-saving equipment that you or other firefighters will depend on at the next alarm. Be sure to read and comply with manufacturers' instructions for cleaning and servicing. Harsh cleaners and cleaning methods should never be used. Simply reading the directions and properly maintaining SCBA will save your life one day. Improperly maintained SCBA may result in your death.

After action review. Before you leave the scene, maybe even before you recover your equipment and repack hose and ladders, your officer should conduct the **after action review (AAR)**. The purpose of this informal review, often held on or near the back step of the rig, is to capture any lessons learned from this fire. It is a time to review what SOPs you used or deviated from, how successful the operation was, what actions you want to sustain because they were successful, and what actions you want to improve or change.

It is important to do the AAR as soon as possible because we all want to "sanitize" our memory of the fire. That is, we want to dwell on what we did well and forget what we did that was not so effective or sometimes even just incorrect. Remember, this is not a critique of the fire or firefighters! It is a time to review the scenario you pulled up to, the size-up (was it really what you thought?), the tactics and strategy used, and what unknowns made this fire unique. It is also a great time to praise actions that were appropriate or outstanding.

A good technique to conduct the AAR is to look for three things you did well and three things that you would change. Ask firefighters first for three "ups"—what they did right. Then ask for three "downs"—what they did wrong. Additionally, a great question to ask is: What would you do differently at the next similar fire? Often you will get answers such as: "Well, I did this and it worked OK, but this other technique may have been better." This kind of discussion is noninflammatory and fosters the concept of what could we have done better, not what did we do wrong.

Above all, remember this is an after action review, not a critique of personal actions. In the end, it should help share information and develop the team, not criticize individual actions.

SCENARIO: FIRST FLOOR FIRE IN A ONE-AND-A-HALF-STORY HOUSE

Here are the details of your fire scenario:

This scenario assumes that you are familiar with your rig or apparatus (engine or truck) and its hose loads, ladders, hand tools, and all other equipment. This scenario is not intended to replace your department's standard operating procedures (SOPs) but to offer a good introduction to fire attack. As always, operate according to your department's guidelines.

It is 0223 hours, and you are dispatched to a one-and-a-half-story house fire with reported fire on the first floor (figs. 20–59 and 20–60). It is a prosperous neighborhood, a relatively new development with a lot of young families with children. To provide an overall understanding, we will keep this scenario simple and understandable: Only four units are responding: Engine 1, (your unit), Engine 2, Truck 1, and a battalion chief

on the first alarm. The engine companies have a driver, an officer, and two firefighters. Truck 1 has a driver, an officer, and two firefighters.

Fig. 20–59. The house

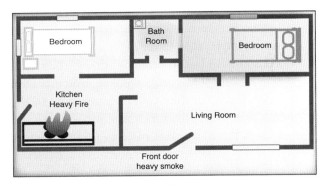

Fig. 20–60. Diagram of scenario

Description of scenario: Heavy fire out kitchen window, heavy black smoke out front door, fire out side door, rear windows seeping smoke, and heavy smoke from the gable vent at the roofline. Occupants outside in their pajamas report that their teenage son did not get out.

To conduct a safe and effective response to this alarm, we will individually examine the necessary steps for success. In this scenario, as in most structure fires, these are the large steps or **benchmarks** that must be considered and dealt with. It is important to note that these steps may be accomplished concurrently or in sequence or not at all depending on the specific situation. Firefighting is not a cookbook type operation. It is one-third training, one-third experience, and one-third art and science. Firefighters and fire officers must be mentally agile to adapt to the situation and conduct the most critical operations and prioritize others, if personnel is insufficient to do all of them at once. For the purpose of this scenario, we will have adequate personnel.

So let's go step by step at this fire.

Size-up

Let's consider size-up in the context of our 1½-story house fire scenario and how it will affect the tasks you may be assigned:

1. *Location of fire* and *type of construction*. Fire is on the first floor. It will be easily accessible to both search and rescue crews and engine company members. The fire is exposing the unfinished attic (this is the uninhabited half story), but vertical extension is not a top priority right now. If this house was built with lightweight construction, wooden I-beams or trusses collapsing would always be a concern. Collapsing roof rafters, wiring, and attic contents have killed firefighters inside. Since this is a house, it is likely fully open and unenclosed inside.

2. *Life hazard*. You have reliable information that at least one person is still in the home. Immediately this puts emphasis on the need for search and rescue operations. The last reported position of the victim was in his bedroom, but the smoke alarms may have awakened him, and he could be anywhere in the home. Based on this information, you will start the search in the most likely place to find the victim, then move on to the most dangerous place (closest to the fire), and finally, if there were upper floors, above the fire (which is not the case in the particular fire since there are no occupied floors above the first floor).

   Due to the confirmed life hazard at this alarm, truck company emphasis will be on forcible entry, search, and ventilation. Since the aerial device will not be used due to the low height of the building, the truck company members may be assigned like this:

   The inside team: Two members with forcible-entry tools are assigned to force the front door if necessary, enter, and search. The outside team: Two members are assigned as a second search team and will attempt to gain access via a different manner from the first team. The remaining two truck company members will perform ventilation from the outside of the building to vent hot gases and smoke to make the engine company's push-in easier, safer, and faster.

3. *Fire control*. The fire building is a home, and we are making an aggressive interior fire attack so 1¾-in. hoselines will be adequate because the fuel load is not excessively high. A good general rule is two rooms of fire per hoseline. Even though your size-up reveals that one line should be sufficient, always stretch a backup line. Engine 1 has laid a supply line from the nearest hydrant, following their SOP. The driver has stopped the engine just past the building, leaving room for the ladder truck. Engine 1 has left one member at the hydrant who will charge the line when the driver is ready for water. Engine 1 officer has received orders from the chief on the scene and has told the crew to stretch an attack line to the front door and make a modified direct attack (described below) on the fire. Engine 1 officer has requested Engine 2 officer to send personnel to Engine 1, stretch a second attack line as a backup line to the first attack line, and assist with advancing the initial line.

4. *Forcing entry*. This is a home in a good neighborhood, so forcible entry should not be a problem. It is likely that there will not be excessive locks or security devices. Homes generally have wooden doors and frames and can be forced easily and quickly with hand tools.

   This function will be taken care of by the truck company crew who forced entry for their search mission and at the same time paved the way for the engine company to stretch and advance the attack line.

5. *Ventilation*. Rapid ventilation will greatly assist the search team and the engine company pushing the line in. Windows provide excellent sources of horizontal ventilation openings. This important function was taken care of by two members from the truck company. Their initial actions will be horizontal ventilation to support the search and fire attack, then vertical ventilation of the roof if necessary.

6. *Stretching considerations*. Stretching at this fire will be relatively easy. The first line will go to the front door across the lawn from the engine parked just past the fire building. Stretching off the rear of the engine is unobstructed by fences, hedges cars, and so forth. The working length of line at the front door should be enough hoseline to reach all parts of this building. A four-person engine company can establish a water supply and rapidly stretch the first attack line. The second engine company can assist with the first line if necessary and add a second backup line.

7. *Water supply*. Your size-up shows active fire that may extend into the attic of the structure. Where is your hoseline's water supply coming from? Are you oper-

ating solely with water from your engine's booster tank, or is the water supply coming from a hydrant, drafting source, or tanker shuttle? Standard operating procedures vary from department to department, but a good choice here is for the driver to provide water to the single attack line from the 500-gal (1,893-L) booster tank. This gives the driver about 2 minutes to hook up the supply line and get a reliable water supply from the hydrant.

Strategic plan

In our 1½-story house fire scenario, we have chosen the offensive strategy for the following reasons:

- The building is safe for us to enter.
- There is or may be a need for search and rescue operations.
- Properly placed hoselines can cut off the fire spread.
- Property can be saved with a manageable or reasonable risk to firefighters.

It is very important to note at this point that we know several factors, but several others we do not know.

What we know (or think we know):

- Where is the fire?
- What and how much is burning?
- What will it take to extinguish it?

What we don't know:

- Are there victims in the house, and if so, where are they?
- How far has the fire spread inside?
- What hazards await us inside?
- Are there backdraft conditions inside?

Establish a water supply

Your engine company has chosen to lay a supply line from the hydrant (forward lay) to conduct the first phase of your mission: Establish the reliable water supply. Engine 1 stops near the front of the building but leaves the actual front for the ladder company.

In rural settings it may be necessary to establish a tanker shuttle or drafting operation. For urban fires there may be a hydrant at the corner of each block. No matter

where you are, a high priority is establishing a reliable and adequate water supply.

Force entry/exit

Forcible entry is usually accomplished by the search and rescue crew as they enter the building. In this case, firefighters from Truck 1 will be conducting this important task. However, engine companies should assign someone to bring forcible-entry tools in the event the truck's arrival is delayed.

Search and rescue

In our scenario, members of Truck 1 will force the front door and search for those in the most danger first, usually closest to the fire or above it (is it possible the teenager has a bedroom in the unfinished attic?). A second team will attempt entry into a bedroom window in the rear of the house, near the Division B and C corners. This provides them direct access to a bedroom where there is a good chance the teenager will be found and provides an escape route for firefighters if they are trapped by worsening conditions.

How does this affect the engine company with the hoseline? Consider all the moving parts. Members of the truck company are out ahead of you searching; members of the outside team are in remote areas, possibly out of sight, moving through rooms for victims. How can you protect them with your hoseline? There are three critical options for the engine company:

1. Place the line between the truck team and the fire.

2. Protect the means of egress (and interior stairs).

3. Don't drive the fire toward the truck team. The nozzle team needs to maintain awareness of everything that is going on around them. At first this may seem chaotic and arbitrary, but as you gain understanding and experience, you will see that this is a well-choreographed performance.

Fire attack

The engine company is responsible for stretching the attack lines to the seat of the fire in this offensive fire attack. Getting water on the fire quickly is their most important task. Consider what has happened to the fire environment. As the search crews entered the 1½-story single-family home, they moved through an open door or window. Both of these access points were left open as previously described to provide ventilation and immediate exit points if needed. This has allowed an unlimited amount of air for the fire. Most structure fires are controlled by the amount of air they have available. More air means more free burning fire.

In our example, we are conducting an aggressive interior fire attack based on the officer's size-up and strategy. The heart of the fire attack is stretching and operating the first hoseline. Although other hoselines will be stretched for this fire, let's focus on the all-important first line. As you approach the scene, your Engine 1 officer turns and tells you the company will be stretching a line directly to the seat of the fire.

This is a residential fire, so a 1¾-in. (45-mm) hose will provide the required water volume to begin our attack and possibly extinguish the fire. The recommended water flow is 180 gpm (681 L/min). This target flow provides for a margin of error incase of kinks in the line, inadequate pump pressure, or other real-world issues that happen on the fireground. This flow will also provide some extra flow to knock the fire down quickly and provide for an adequate amount of water for possible encounters with special hazards such as a broken gas main, leaking propane tank, or leaking and burning fuel oil tank. Using a 1¾-in. (45-mm) line is the SOP for your department for residential fires. Your officer should have sized up the fire and determined that the best route to the fire is through the front door. Your line will go directly to the fire or fire room and conduct a modified direct attack. Your officer's size-up will continue and will do his or her best to determine that this line will not push fire onto other members or into unburned areas

After the line is stretched to the front door, the engine officer will call for water, and the line will be charged. At this time this officer will call command and advise that the line is in position; command will direct that ventilation be accomplished so you can push in. Also, among the engine officer's many responsibilities is to verify that the company members are down near the floor below the heat level and out of any door ways during the attack.

A modified direct attack is selected for this fire. The nozzle operator directs the solid/straight stream into the fire area from outside the room to darken down the fire. The nozzle operator will use the reach of stream to begin to extinguish the fire. This firefighter will then move into the room or down the hallway to complete extinguishment.

Ventilate

In our 1½-story home fire scenario the proper ventilation to support the fire attack is horizontal ventilation of the windows in front of the hoseline. In reality, it is very likely that windows in and near the fire area or room will be broken out by firefighters. Other windows in areas that are not severely exposed can be opened normally by firefighters. Often sashes and storm windows can be removed, limiting damage to the property. However, as previously stated, rapid and effective ventilation is often the key to success at fire attacks, resulting in rapid fire suppression and saving significant property. Conversely, by not taking the windows, the push-in by the engine company due to untenable conditions results in excessive dangers to firefighters (flashover, backdraft, burns) is delayed, and often the building dies a slow death, consumed by fire in void spaces concealed by smoke and steam.

In our example, vertical ventilation of the roof is likely not required by first-in companies. Assuming the fire has not breached the walls or reached the upper level of the home (the uninhabited ½ story attic), cutting a hole in the roof to vent out fire gases will do no immediate good. It will cause additional damage to the building that may not be necessary.

If, however, fire has reached the unfinished attic above the first floor, it will be necessary for firefighters on the roof to cut the roof shingles and sheathing, opening up the roof. The ideal place to cut the roof, of course, is directly over the fire.

Protect exposures

In our scenario, we have interior exposures, adjoining rooms, adjacent rooms, and rooms above the fire room. Hoseline placement was designed to push the fire back into the room of origin and prevent it from extending to exposed areas outside that room. There are no exterior exposures since the home is not close to adjacent buildings.

Fire control and overhaul

Since we were able to contain the fire to the kitchen and adjacent bedroom area, we can focus our efforts on checking for extension in these areas. We can use a hydraulic vent out the kitchen window with our hoseline to clear the area of smoke, exposing any pockets of fire. We must also open up the walls and check for extension into the unfinished attic. A thermal imaging camera can be used to "see" any hot spots.

Pick up and return

While this was a "bread and butter" fire, fought routinely by any department, there are always things to learn. What did you learn at this fire? Did any unusual things happen? How well-coordinated were the firefighting operations? Your officer will often take a few moments after picking up to go over the fire and discuss any important issues. Take this time to ask questions while the fire is still fresh in your mind.

Ensure that all of your tools and equipment have been picked up and returned to the apparatus. When you get back to the fire station, perform any equipment maintenance (including SCBA) or tool refueling tasks so they are ready for the next fire.

ADDITIONAL FIRE SCENARIOS: SIZE-UP CONCERNS

Now that you have thoroughly analyzed a typical first floor fire in a 1½-story home, we will move on to other scenarios. The following examples of alternative locations for a fire in a single family home (in the basement, for example) and other types of occupancies build on your understanding of basic fire attack. Each of the succeeding examples reviews the size-up issues that may be encountered. However, only the size-up concerns that change are identified for brevity purposes.

Basement fires in a private dwelling

Basement fires provide some unique challenges to firefighters.

Location. The location of the fire makes this not a favorite among firefighters. For basement fires we often have to work above the fire, which is one of the most dangerous places. The key to safe and successful response to basement fires is to get below it or at least be on the same level with it during the fire attack.

The way to do this is to gain access to the outside doors if available and control the fire from that position (fig. 20–61). Attacking the fire by pushing the attack team down the interior stairs is the least viable option and the most dangerous. Consider the condition of interior basement stairs before the fire and after they have been exposed to fire.

It is often difficult to determine where the fire is in the structure since smoke may be rising and filling the entire structure. A good way to determine if the fire is in the basement is to take out a small basement window with a tool. You will immediately be able to determine if the fire is down there or not.

Fig. 20–61. Access a basement fire from outside. (Courtesy of Ryan Hart)

Once you have determined that the fire is in the basement, check to see if it has extended to the first floor or attic. If this is a balloon frame home (see chapter 7: "Building Construction"), a fire in the basement will rapidly extend to the attic and often other floors. If the fire is extending vertically for any reason (pipe chases, balloon construction, floors burned through, etc.) you must get lines into position on these areas rapidly.

Before committing firefighters to these dangerous areas, always check for structural integrity. If trusses or wooden I-beams were holding up the first floor and the basement fire has involved them, expect an early collapse and use defensive tactics (fig. 20–62).

Fig. 20–62. Wooden I-beams

Utilities in the basement may provide a heavy fire load and rapid fire development. Oil tanks, natural gas lines, and meters will result in heavy volumes of fire if they are involved (fig. 20–63).

Further complicating a basement fire may be the huge fuel load from stored materials. Simply said, more stuff equals more fire.

Fig. 20–63. A gas meter inside a building

Life hazard. Basement fires can threaten occupants of the building in ways described above. In apartment buildings, upstairs occupants may not be aware that there is a fire in the basement, which will complicate your search and rescue operations. With real estate prices escalating across the country, basement apartments have become more and more common.

It is very important to remember that we are occupants too! It cannot be overemphasized, if the first floor is being supported by lightweight construction (trusses, glue-lam beams, etc.), keep members out from underneath and from on top of this very dangerous type of construction.

Fire control. Controlling the fire in a basement is an extreme challenge to firefighters because of its lack of accessibility. The least desirable method of accessing the basement is by using the interior set of stairs within the home—this point of access is like descending a fireplace chimney. Some basements have exterior access through a set of "clamshell" bulkhead doors or a set of exterior stairs in a well—these are the more desirable ways of accessing a basement fire because it minimizes the punishment firefighters must take while descending the stairs (fig. 20–64).

Fig. 20–64. Clamshell doors provide exterior access to basement.

When using the interior stairs to attack the fire, first position a hose line at the top of the interior stairs. When ready to move as a single unit, the hoseline team begins its descent down the stairwell, paying particular attention to the condition of the stairs. Moving down the stairs must be done swiftly and in a coordinated fashion so that no one stays on the stairs more than is necessary to move down them. The goal is to get the hoseline team out of the "chimney" and onto the basement floor.

If a very large body of fire exists in a basement (heavy fire is showing at most or all of the window/door openings), and it has been determined that no one is in the basement or there is no savable human life there, consider putting the nozzle in the window you broke to see if there was fire in the basement. Often knocking down the fire this way prevents firefighters from having to enter this very dangerous fire building which may be on the verge of floor collapse (particularly for exposed wooden beams, and especially for lightweight wooden trusses or wooden I beams). *Note that hoselines are never directed into windows when the building is occupied by civilians or firefighters as this can result in serious injury or death.*

Because basements are frequently not finished, exposed wood joists and subflooring will be involved in fire, creating more of a fire load. Also remember to shut off utilities from the outside before firefighters enter for any fire attack.

Force entry. Remember that the goal is to get even with or below the fire if possible. The outside doors to the basement often provide this access. If there is a full-size personnel door in a well, by all means use it, forcing with standard techniques. Be prepared for a face full of fire when you open this door, because you are on the fire floor—it is now just below grade.

As described above, basements often have clamshell doors leading down a few steps that end at the basement floor level. These doors cannot generally be forced by standard means and require cutting with metal-cutting saws.

Gaining access to the basement is only part of the issue with basement fires. Planning your secondary means of egress is the more important part. Generally, for many types of occupancies, there are two ways into and out of the basement: the interior stairs and, if present, the outside stairs. If you make your advance through the exterior stairs and it becomes blocked, your only other egress option is via the interior stairs. Attempting to conduct an emergency egress via the interior stairs has the following problems: First, is the door locked from the first floor? If it is, forcible-entry tools will be necessary. It is important to note that the area at the top of the stairs is usually very constrained space and may not allow forcible entry tools to be used, causing you to become trapped. Interior stairs are generally not well maintained, may be weakened by rotting due to previous or exiting water in the basement, and may not have handrails or other safety items.

Since this area is the highest part of the fire area, it will collect the most heat and densest smoke and will likely flashover first; certainly this is not a good place to be, especially during an emergency egress!

Windows to basements are generally small, too small for a firefighter to exit, and often placed high in the exterior walls to allow some light and ventilation. Although windows may be present, they are of little value as a secondary means of escape.

Ventilation. Ventilation of basement fires requires special tactics. First, use what the building has made available to you, the windows above the exterior grade, high in the foundation. These are in a very good place, high in the fire area, and will be a good first step. Usually these windows are small and therefore provide limited capability to release heat and smoke. Often basements have low ceilings, further trapping heat and smoke, so ventilation may be a critical step in gaining access for firefighters.

An alternative tactic for ventilation of basement fires is to cut a hole in the floor above and vent smoke out through the first floor then out a nearby window (fig. 20–69). Be wary of fire-weakened floors when performing this tactic. Be especially careful in newer buildings of lightweight construction; it is important to recall how rapidly trusses and laminated wood joists fail under even moderate fire loads. Working above or below a floor constructed with these lightweight members must be performed with extreme caution—they are easily capable of quickly killing firefighters when they collapse.

Stretching considerations. Basement fires present unique challenges to engine company members as well. Because you are in a confined space with the fire, you must ensure you have enough line to fight your way all the way to the seat of the fire. Delays and interruptions in flowing water will cause the fire to light up, possibly trapping you and your team. By the same token, basements are generally cluttered and mazelike areas, so too much hose will cause problems like kinks that will delay or cease your attack, again endangering you and your crew. Using the floor above to lay out hose is a good tactic to help you advance.

No matter which access to the basement you are using, interior or exterior, remember that your advance will have to be rapid as heat and smoke will be pouring out of the upper levels of that door way. Get below it fast.

Water supply. A basement is the worst place for a fire in the building because it will expose and threaten the entire building above it. When considering water supply, simply have enough in case the fire finally involves the whole structure. If the fire building becomes fully involved, make sure you have enough water to protect exposures as well.

FIREFIGHTING CONSIDERATIONS IN OTHER TYPES OF OCCUPANCIES

Now that we have an understanding of the basic fire attack principles using our single family dwelling example, let's move on to fires in other types of buildings. We will not examine every phase, but rather focus only on the different and specific size-up challenges faced by firefighters in these common structures. In this "basic" *Firefighter I* chapter, we examine these different types of building occupancies from your perspective as the firefighter. As mentioned at the beginning of this chapter, you, as a Firefighter I, will be asked to perform a specific task, under an officer or senior Firefighter II's direction. Firefighter I training instructs you *how* to perform these specific tasks.

In the future, if you enroll in a Firefighter II training program with this textbook, you will use these same set of buildings and occupancies to examine the fire problems from a leader's perspective. Firefighter II training emphasizes the "decision-making" aspects of firefighting—specifically *where* and *when* to ventilate, search, and attack the fire.

Wood frame garden apartments

Garden apartment type buildings have become common in suburban and even rural areas. They are economical to build and provide residences for substantial numbers of people that can either rent or own them if the co-op ownership method is used (fig. 20–65).

In a sense, garden apartments are simply a group of single family homes put together both horizontally and vertically, and many of the same issues must be dealt with by firefighters in much the same way as detached single family homes. Let's take a look at some of the important differences for firefighters.

Fig. 20–65. Garden apartment. (Courtesy of Tom Bierds)

Location of fire and type of construction. Garden apartments are usually set back off the road or parking lot. This causes firefighters to have to carry ground ladders, tools, and hoseline greater distances than to fight a single family dwelling. It is important to pace yourself in walking to the fire building so you are not too fatigued to fight the fire when you get there. Resist the temptation to run to the scene. When you don your mask to enter the building, you will quickly deplete the air supply because of the stress of the run from the rig to the building.

Construction of the garden apartment will affect the overall strategy. Lightweight construction often has no level of fire resistance; no protection is provided for the structural members holding the building up (in the form of gypsum board covering the individual floor and roof beams, for example). This lack of fire resistance will often cause incident commanders to quickly abandon offensive operations and move to defensive operations for the safety of firefighters. Defensive operations use larger hoselines, portable monitors, and water tower operations.

Life hazard. As a result of the dense population in garden apartments, search and rescue operations often require many more firefighters than a single family dwelling. A fast moving fire, especially in a lower unit, will rapidly endanger people in units above and adjacent to the fire apartment. Simultaneous search and rescue will often be necessary to save lives. For firefighters, occupants rescued from apartments and brought out to the public hallway will need to be carried or at best assisted down the stairs and out of the building.

Fire control. Fire control can be very challenging in garden apartments simply because there is so much to burn. Lots of people mean lots of furnishings, beds, clothing, computers, and the like. Also, items such as bicycles and outdoor toys are stored in living areas. Firefighters on hoselines can get caught and trapped and die during what was thought to be a routine fire attack in a couple of rooms of fire.

In addition to all the furnishings and property inside a garden apartment, there is a tremendous amount of fuel in the wood framing, flooring, sheathing, and interior trim of garden apartments. Since the entire building and contents are combustible, often a huge fire load results in a huge fire. When fires in these buildings gain control of the building and involve the wood structure, it is difficult to get enough water on the fire quickly enough to stop it. When attacking fires in garden apartments, consider the use of big lines quickly.

A good technique for fire control if the engine company cannot get in the fire apartment is to breach the wall in the adjoining unit or next to the front door and apply water through this hole. This firefighting technique may hold the fire to a room and contents fire, thus preventing it from extending to the void spaces, which would lead to eventual destruction of the building.

Forcing entry. Gaining access to a residence is generally not a problem unless it is in an urban area or one plagued by crime. In areas where residents have fortified their apartment doors, firefighters should come armed with more effective and possibly hydraulic tools to speed entry.

Ventilation. Ventilation of garden apartments is very similar to that for single family homes. Taking windows in front of the hoseline is always a good technique. This may be a bit more difficult because windows can be two or three stories above the ground. Use of ground ladders (carried around the building because of the set back) will be required.

Roof ventilation will be necessary for fires that have entered the attic void space. Often the attics are not divided and provide a rapid lateral and vertical fire spread opportunity. Since the building is usually wood frame and the roof is sheathed with plywood, firefighters can use rotary or chain saws effectively.

Stretching considerations. Stretching hoselines at garden apartments can be very challenging. In order to make the units appealing and supply the garden appearance, U-shaped or zig-zag layouts are used in the design. This means that hose stretches have to be very long. If your engine company uses preconnected hoselines, these will almost always be too short.

Many engine companies that have garden apartments in their fire due area use a thief line. A **thief line** consists of 200–300 ft (60–90 m) of a 2½-in. (65-mm) hose, with a wye or water thief at the end to reduce the friction loss and supply the required volume. Smaller-diameter attack lines can be attached to the wye or thief and used for interior fire attack. Preconnected lines can be detached from the engine, shoulder carried, and used; or apartment packs can be carried in canvas bags or tied together with webbing or quick-release straps.

Water supply. Multiple reliable and high-volume sources are necessary for these types of fires. Experience has shown that if fire walls or interior gypsum board partitions and ceilings are breached by fire, it will turn into a fast moving and large body of fire requiring huge amounts of water.

Taxpayers

Location of fire and type of construction. Taxpayers are a general classification of buildings that contain a business on the first floor and apartments or living space on the upper floors. These are typical Main Street–type buildings.

Compared with strip malls (below), these buildings are usually of ordinary construction and are relatively fire resistant. However, basement fires in these occupancies often present a problem because of stock or storage items from the business.

For firefighters, access to fires in taxpayers are relatively easy. Large front windows and front doors for customers provide good access directly off the street. Beware, however, of the parapet (a decorative set of brick or other masonry unit that is constructed on top of the front wall of the taxpayer), as it is often not well supported laterally and can easily fall during a fire (fig. 20–66).

Life hazard. Life hazard in the storefront is usually minimal. Store patrons or employees are awake and alert when the store is occupied. Residential occupants upstairs can be a real problem. Frequently a door to the side of the storefront leads up a set of stairs to the upstairs apartments. In older buildings, these stairs are steep and narrow. Fires originating down below can cut off access to these stairs, trapping occupants on upper floors.

Fire control. Controlling the fire can be a challenge in taxpayers as the storefront may contain anything from a candy store to a hardware store, a pharmacy and general goods, a toy store, or an auto parts store. Firefighters should consider using large, 2½-in. (65-mm) high-flow hand lines for these fires. Ladder towers placed near the front of the building with buckets placed near the ground can direct master streams effectively up into the ceilings of the stores (to get at hidden fires) with excellent results. The large-caliber streams make fast work of the fire and prevent the hazards to engine company members from making an interior attack.

Fig. 20–66. This taxpayer's parapet is leaning and may be unstable.

Forcing entry. Forcing entry can be a very challenging process. Roll-up gates, sliding gates, and other heavy security measures often are present. Rear doors may have been bricked up or, at a minimum, contain very strong security measures. Heavy-duty tools and power tools will be required to gain access to these doors, which are critical as a secondary means of egress for horizontal ventilation.

Ventilation. Since these stores are usually side by side, ventilation in the front and rear is essential for first floor fires. Display windows can provide large openings in the A side of the building. These are readily available at ground level.

Large fires in one-story taxpayers may extend in to the **cockloft**, the combustible void space above the ceiling of the store. In such cases, vertical ventilation will be necessary to prevent the fire from moving in this concealed space and spreading to other parts of the building above the other stores. This will typically require a large primary vent hole directly above the store, and, in some cases, a trench cut to cut off the fire's horizontal movement in the cockloft.

Stretching considerations. Although hoselines can be easily stretched to the front of the building, and large windows provide excellent access if the first floor is involved, stretches to the rear can be difficult. A good firefighter decision is to stretch the hoseline through an adjacent building to gain access to the rear of the fire building.

Fire escape stretches, rope stretches, and other advanced methods may be required to get hoselines in proper position.

Water supply. As with any nonresidential structure, always stretch big lines right from the start. Big lines obviously require large amounts of water, so a reliable and redundant water supply is important.

Strip malls

Location of fire and type of construction. Strip malls are the modern version of the taxpayer (fig. 20–67). They are constructed cheaply and quickly of materials that do not maintain structural integrity under a fire load. Like taxpayers, they contain stores on the first floor. They may be one or more stories and are subject to early and deadly collapse from burning contents (fig. 20–68). Some strip malls are of non-combustible construction with metal bar joists and metal deck roofs. Other strip malls are of ordinary construction with wood joists or (more commonly) lightweight wood trusses or wooden I-beams.

Often, security issues that create limited access (fig. 20–69) or cost considerations during construction, such as leaving structural members unprotected (figs. 20–70 and 20–71), factor into firefighter safety concerns.

Fig. 20–67. The front of the strip mall shows it contains a variety of different occupancies.

Fig. 20–68. This strip mall has two floors on part of the building.

Fig. 20–69. The rear of the building provides limited access and usually high security. Note the roof-mounted HVAC units. (Courtesy of J. Knapp)

Fig. 20–70. Unprotected steel structural members will fail rapidly under a fire load.

Fig. 20–71. Note the lightweight and unprotected C channel members holding up the roof.

The location of the fire in the structure is of major significance to the firefighter. Fires are often in the rear of these buildings in storage or work areas. This means firefighters must push through the building, generally from the front to rear to attack the fire or conduct search operations. These firefighters are directly under the collapse zone of the unprotected steel trusses and beams supporting the HVAC units and the dead load of the roof itself. High security of rear doors ,if they even exist and are not bricked up, usually prevent rapid attack or access from the rear.

Life hazard. The life hazard of strip malls can vary depending on the occupancy.

Fire control. Fire control operations should be attempted from outside the structure if significant fire has attacked the unprotected structural steel components. Because of the small front-to-back distances of these structures, firefighters can use the reach of the stream to extinguish heavily involved areas. This tactic keeps firefighters out of the most extreme danger zone. Staying out from under this building and using the reach of the stream may be a life-saving tactic for you and your crew one day.

Force entry. Again, like taxpayers, strip malls may have extreme forcible-entry challenges, especially in bad neighborhoods. High security on doors and windows may necessitate cutting locks and gates with rotary saws. Barred and or bricked-up doors and windows in the rear are formidable challenges. Consider breaching interior walls as an alternative, especially if life safety is an issue.

Ventilation. It is very tempting to vent the roof of these buildings. The roof is easily accessible by ground ladder, usually flat and inviting to the aggressive truck company. A "traditional" roof of solid sawn wood joists offers the possibility of vertical ventilation, if necessary. However, other types of roofs are dangerous for firefighters attempting vertical ventilation. Firefighters must be aware of these critical dangers:

1. In the case of non-combustible construction, the structural steel joists are usually unprotected (bare steel without any fire resistance). Weakening and failure of the steel joists is a distinct possibility with a moderate or large fire below. Cutting the metal deck itself between joists can leave the portion of the deck where the firefighter is standing unsupported, resulting in the deck bending and sending roof firefighters into the fire. Ventilate using the front and rear doors and windows if possible. Stay off of the roof.

2. In the case of lightweight wooden trusses and wooden I-beams, firefighters must stay off the roof. In addition, a fire in the wood trusses or I-beams themselves results in the very real potential of collapse onto firefighters below. This happened in 1989 to two firefighters in Orange County, Florida who were killed when the wooden trusses collapsed. The smoke condition in the stores was light while there was a raging fire above their heads in the truss void. Use hooks to open up the ceiling and thermal imaging cameras to determine the extent of fire above the ceiling.

Stretching considerations. It is tempting to use small interior attack lines for fires involving these structures. The fire appears small because stores in strip malls are often small square footage. What firefighters must recall is that there is likely a very high amount of combustible material, which will require a high flow. Stretch and use a 2½-in. (65-mm) hoseline for these fires. The reach, penetration, and flow will make quick work of the fire from a position of safety outside the collapse zone.

Water supply. In the case of ordinary construction, a large combustible cockloft/void space will add tremendously to the fuel load in addition to the combustibles in the store itself. A large volume of water is necessary. Another problem with the Orange County, Florida fire cited above was the lack of a continuous water supply; the firefighters were relying solely on the water in the fire engine's tank rather than being connected to a fire hydrant. Fire can quickly get above the ceiling and spread laterally.

Big box retail

Location of fire and type of construction. Big box retail buildings are very much like a large strip mall that is undivided and has a higher ceiling (fig. 20–72). Many types of businesses may occupy these type buildings: pharmacy, toy store, hardware, housewares, grocery, and other retail businesses. The construction weaknesses under a fire load are similar to strip malls, though the size, square footage, and height vary.

The location of the fire plays a key role in firefighter safety and responsibilities. Fires may be in high-rack storage, hazardous materials may be stored in the building, or HVAC units may be on top of or under the roof surface. All of these are very dangerous type fires.

Fig. 20–72. Note the lightweight construction, unprotected steel, and large size of this building.

Life hazard. Big box stores may contain a relatively high life hazard. Occupants may not evacuate if there is not a perceptible danger (fig. 20–73). Fire alarms often go unheeded. Fire may grow in storage areas or void spaces, then flashover and spread, rapidly trapping or killing occupants who did not escape.

Fig. 20–73. Here a big-box-type construction building houses a retail outlet.

High ceilings in these buildings allow combustible gases to accumulate high above firefighters' heads, possibly igniting the roof deck. Use the thermal camera to check over your head to be sure you are not in danger from a fire in the roof itself or accumulating hot gases that could lead to flashover.

Fire control. These are generally large unenclosed (inside) buildings. Hose streams may not reach into all areas from outside the building. Consider using master streams from tower ladders or deck pipes off engines to obtain the necessary reach. Roof ventilation like the strip mall is very dangerous. Roof vents and scuttles can be used if available for ventilation. Sometimes these buildings are protected by automatic sprinklers; if they are, by all means use and support the systems.

There are lots of products to burn in these buildings. Always use a 2½-in. (65-mm) hoseline if you are going inside and have any significant fire. This size line will provide the reach and flow you will need to extinguish the fire.

The good news is that many of these buildings contain sprinkler systems. Sprinkler systems (discussed in greater detail in chapter 30, Fire Protection Systems) are your best ally. They work in the dark, don't need an SCBA, extinguish fire only when necessary, and function until we shut them off.

Force entry. Generally front entrances are the easiest to force. Large windows may be present for ventilation or entry. Rear access may be limited by security concerns similar to strip malls.

Ventilation. Retail stores make a profit by selling a volume of products. One advantage available to you may be a large loading dock door. This may provide excellent horizontal ventilation.

Stretching considerations. Parking lots usually provide good access to the front of the building. Stretching will be relatively easy until you get into the store. The building may be very deep from front to rear and require a long stretch similar to garden apartments. Always consider using big lines at these fires.

Water supply. Since this is a big box building that has big volume and big contents, a robust water supply must be established. If the building has a sprinkler system, be sure not to steal water from the system by using a nearby hydrant that may be trying to supply the sprinkler system.

Office buildings

Location of fire and type of construction. The location of the fire in office buildings is important because these buildings often are divided up into small offices or cubicles (fig. 20–74). The floor layout can become a deadly maze for firefighters. If it is an open office type floor plan, fire can spread rapidly from cubicle to cubicle quickly.

Office occupancies can occupy a variety of construction types, too many to be discussed here. Refer to chapter 7, Building Construction, for specific construction hazards.

Fig. 20–74. Office building

Life hazard. Typically occupants will be awake and alert in office buildings. Accounting for occupants can be easy if there is a fire plan and they are well schooled in its use. However, this is more the exception rather than the rule, so plan for an extensive and extended search and rescue operation. Use of life lines and large area search procedures may be necessary.

Disabled persons working in the office may provide special challenges to firefighters. Many multi-story office buildings have designated "areas of rescue assistance" or "areas of refuge" for disabled people (fig. 20–75). These rooms and areas are typically separated from other areas by a one-hour fire rated wall (sometimes these locations are actually inside stairwells) and will be provided with a two-way communications system with the building's lobby. These areas are designated with special signage identifying this area and may be equipped with a communications system that connects to a building's lobby. Refuge locations will be a high priority search area.

Basic Fire Attack

FIREFIGHTER I

Chapter 20

Fig. 20–75. Disabled people who are incapable of evacuating the upper floors of a multistory building on their own may be waiting for you in an area of rescue assistance such as this one.

Fire control. Most modern buildings will be protected with automatic sprinklers. As previously stated, these are a firefighter's best friend. Support the system with hoselines as early as possible. If the fire building is not equipped with a sprinkler system, plan for long hoselines and high fire volume because of a high fire load.

Force entry. Forcible entry concerns for offices are similar to any other building and are usually dependent on the level of crime in the area and need for security in the particular occupancy. Obviously, banks and financial institutions will have more security than a general purpose office. Some office buildings may have secure areas with the main office area or complex.

Ventilation. Ventilation considerations depend on the type of building construction.

Stretching considerations. As previously stated, office buildings and layout can vary. Good preincident intelligence can go a long way in making your stretch successful. Some offices have a large open lobby or waiting areas. These areas will consume a large amount of hose before even reaching close to the fire area. Other offices with cubicles or highly divided floor space will present equally challenging and hose-consuming stretches.

Water supply. As with any structure fire, establish a reliable water supply.

Restaurants

Location of fire and type of construction. This category of building fire is really dependent upon the type of building construction the restaurant is housed in, how big or small the building is, and the type and size of cooking equipment in the kitchen (fig. 20–76). A common important factor you will deal with is something that has little to do with fire attack operations: how often and how well the hood ventilation system is cleaned and serviced. Grease builds up from frying of food in these systems and can trigger fast-moving and dangerous fires.

Fig. 20–76. Restaurant

Fast-food restaurants are special hazards that must be recognized by firefighters. In order to minimize cost and maximize profit, these restaurants are often built of lightweight material, with minimal fire protection systems and with no regard or minimal regard for firefighter safety. This is a class of "disposable" buildings that should never be paid for with a firefighter's life. Sadly, these buildings have taken several firefighters' lives in recent years. It is critical to remember these are designed by the chain owners as disposable buildings, built with the cheapest material and construction methods available solely to sell, sell, sell and maximize profit.

A common hazard in these disposable buildings is a lightweight truss supporting roof-mounted heating, ventilating, and air conditioning (HVAC) units. Under the roof deck are HVAC distribution systems; deep fat fryer duct work; and electrical, gas, and plumbing utilities. From the inside, all this is hidden by a drop ceiling. If fire invades the truss space and has attacked the trusses, expect a rapid and fatal collapse. Obviously, firefighters can be trapped and burned to death in this common fire scenario.

Life hazard. The life hazard can be high during busy times when the restaurant is in operation. However, occupants, customers, and employees will be awake and alert and usually exit the building if they perceive danger.

If the fire occurs after business hours, check for maintenance or cleaning people in the building. However, always consider the risk to firefighters in these dangerous buildings. Another consideration is that you may be able to conduct a "search" from outside the building. Fast-food restaurants often have lots of windows and doors. If you open all these and simply look inside, because of the small floor space, you may be able to visually search the building from outside in a position of safety.

Fire control. Some restaurants will have built-in fire-extinguishing systems, especially in hoods and deep fryers. If these appliances are involved, activate the built-in fire-extinguishing systems if they have not already been automatically or manually tripped.

There is a very good possibility that the fire actually started in the cooking hood and ductwork due to the accumulated grease—these are very hot fires which can spread beyond the sheet metal ducts. Look for fire spread to surrounding combustibles (wood studs, stored paper goods, etc.) with the use of thermal imaging cameras and by opening up suspected fire extension locations.

Force entry. Forcible-entry considerations are similar to other structures. Large restaurants may have exit doors with panic hardware on the inside. After the initial team gains entry, these doors may provide excellent access for other firefighters.

Ventilation. Especially for kitchen fires, consider turning on the hood ventilation system to exhaust smoke from the building. *Make sure, however, that the fire is not in the cooking hood and duct system, a common fire location.* Other than this, usual ventilation considerations apply.

Stretching considerations. It is important to recall that restaurants come in a variety of shapes and sizes. We have all been in the mom and pop restaurant that is squeezed into a long narrow building, sometimes with a dining area up one or more floors. On the other side of the restaurant scale are large catering halls that seat hundreds. Obvious stretching considerations are

associated with each of these varieties and everything in between.

Water supply. As always, establish a reliable water supply.

Vacant buildings

A wise old fire officer once asked, "What is in a vacant building to save that is worth the life of a firefighter?" Sure it is a challenge to attempt to put the fire out using an aggressive attack, but what are you saving? Never forget, whenever you enter a burning building, there are a lot of things, some of which we considered here and others, that in the end can kill you. If the building had enough fire in it that you need to aggressively attack it, how much damage is being done to that building, and what will it be worth after the fire? The answer is probably not much. Risk a little to save a little. A vacant is a vacant until the occupants (us) arrive and enter (fig. 20–77).

Fig. 20–77. Vacant building

Location of fire and type of construction. Vacant buildings are very dangerous. For the safety of members you must assume that the structure could be compromised. Here is an example: an old, heavy timber building can withstand a small fire for a relatively long time (due to the massive nature of the wooden structural members) before it becomes structurally unsafe. Simply put, these massive timbers provide us with time to get inside and extinguish the fire. That statement assumes the building is well maintained and the structural members have not been compromised. Since many heavy timber buildings have been around for a long time, they often are not well maintained and have had numerous occupancies during their long and storied lives.

If the building is vacant, how long has the hole in the roof allowed in rain and snow to help rot the wood or rust the connections? Have insects attacked the heavy timber to further weaken it? What types of changes were made by each occupancy over the years?

The point is, even the most fire-resistive structures and structural members may be compromised by forces during the time it has been vacant.

Some other safety concerns with vacants

- Have expensive conveniences been removed? Elevators and dumb waiters may have been removed or vandalized. Did the previous owner leave barrels of leftover hazardous materials or hazardous waste inside?

- Are heavy items left on shelving that may fall on interior teams?

- Were stairs and holes cut in the floor to allow the removal of large machinery?

- Were inexpensive repairs like tar paper put over holes in the roof made by the previous or current owner?

- Are windows and doors boarded up for security, thus limiting egress of the new occupants? (That would be us, firefighters, as we are occupants too!)

- Are there multiple fires in the building? Did the owner want it to burn?

Life hazard. A false report of squatters in an abandoned cold storage building caused the death of six Worcester, Massachusetts, firefighters in 1999. Consider the hazard to firefighters and the lack of reliability of on-scene reports before committing members to search this dangerous type of building. If you have to search the building, use search ropes and thermal imaging cameras. Be aware of the numerous hazards this building presents.

Fire control. Attempt work from the outside. Use the reach of the hose streams to darken down the fire from positions of safety. Use large-caliber streams with high volumes of water and long reach and penetration. Attack the fire if necessary from positions of safety.

Force entry. In vacant buildings, this usually means taking the plywood off the windows and doors. If truck company members get the door open and accessible, wait until they get a couple of other openings available to you to use before making entry. Vacants often have bricked-up or window security devices that are difficult to remove from the outside. Obviously, whatever prevents or slows down the mal-intentioned vandal slows down the well-intentioned firefighter.

Ventilation. Standard ventilation practices apply to vacant buildings—with one important caveat: You never know how sound the structure is, so assume it is not safe; for example, the roof is not safe to vent unless you are supported by a ladder or tower bucket. Consider the use of horizontal ventilation (windows) and not risking firefighters on the roof. Horizontal ventilation may be difficult, as noted previously.

Stretching considerations. This is not an aggressive interior fire attack so leave the 1¾-in. (45-mm) hose on the rig. Bring the big lines, and overwhelm this fire from the outside. Water damage is not an issue. Consider the use of portable monitor nozzles and large-caliber streams. The sooner you put the fire out, the less danger it is to everyone on the scene.

Water Supply. As always, establish a reliable water supply for the size of the fire you are fighting.

EXPOSURE PROTECTION

When protecting exposures, apply water directly on the exposed surfaces, as this is much more effective at absorbing heat and delaying or preventing ignition due to radiant or convective heat (fig. 20–78). Application of water on the exposed building is not only more effective but can be done with less water than other means. Water curtain nozzles were used for a number of years. Recent scientific evidence has determined that these water sprays are not as effective as applying water directly to the exposed surfaces (fig. 20–79). The water curtain is simply not dense enough to absorb all the radiant heat from the source fire. Water curtains have enjoyed success because they inadvertently apply water to the exposed surface. Additionally, these nozzles are supplied with 2½-in. (65-mm) lines, which require significant personnel to stretch and copious amounts of water, which may be in short supply on the fireground.

Fig. 20–78. Water curtains aren't as effective at absorbing heat than direct application of water to the exposed building.

Fig. 20–79. This is a good example of a firefighter with a properly positioned hoseline protecting a heavily exposed building. A good sign an exposure is getting ready to light up is paint discoloring and peeling, bubbling, and beginning to smoke. (Courtesy of Brian Duddy)

"SMELL OF SMOKE" CALLS

Often you will be called to respond to a "smell of smoke in the building" with only this vague information: odor of smoke in the building, 20 Main Street. This call presents unique and challenging situations to firefighters. The most important consideration at these calls is this: is there significant fire in the void spaces of the building that is hidden from you? Void spaces can be the truss space between floors of a building, the space above a drop ceiling, in the walls of a balloon frame home in attic or cockloft spaces, in utility chases or even

in soffits above kitchen cabinets. If there is significant fire, follow standard firefighting practices. Always have hose lines in place when opening void spaces where you suspect there is fire. If you are looking for hidden fire and you find it you had better have something to extinguish it with. Firefighters have been killed after they opened a space and heavy fire was driven out by a flashover in that space caused by the newly introduced oxygen. Never underestimate the potential of hidden fire.

After you have determined that there is not significant fire in these void areas, it is often a challenging detective game to find the source of the smell or visible smoke. Ask the occupants obvious questions first: where did you smell it? Where was it the strongest, when did you smell it? What were you doing and what was happening in the building when you smelled/saw it? These questions will help you eliminate some potential sources and highlight potential suspected areas to concentrate your search. As employees enter the building for the first time that day or occupants return home, they may notice the odor or haze of smoke. If you can't find the source ask them to retrace their steps to determine what appliances or circuits they energized and eliminate these as possible sources.

In multi-family residential buildings, a "food on the stove" run is very common. Forgetful people leave a pot of food cooking on the stove after they leave the premises. Working fires can erupt in these situations. Overheated food on the stove has a distinctive odor; you will come to know the smell very well in your career.

Frequently it is electrical appliances or lighting fixtures that are the source of the odor. Always check the breaker panel to determine if an appliance, motor, fan, or lighting circuit has shorted or burned out, tripping a breaker or blowing the fuse. A tripped breaker may point directly to the source of the smoke. In addition, use the thermal imaging camera to scan circuit breakers in a panel—hot breakers (indicating an electrical circuit that is at capacity) will glow brightly.

In occupancies that have fluorescent lighting, check to see if one light fixture is not as bright as others. If you find one of these, the ballast or starter mechanism in the light maybe the culprit and the source of the smoke (fig. 20–80). An overheated ballast has a particular odor; you will recognize it once you've experienced it.

Especially early in the heating season, dust on heating appliances may burn off and cause an odor or some visible smoke. New appliances of any kind may emit odors when used for the first time. Ask occupants if there is anything new in the building.

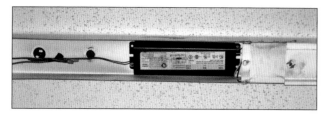

Fig. 20–80. Starter and ballast

Use of the thermal imaging camera can be a great assistance in determining the source of the alarm. Use it to scan suspected appliances, motors, fans, and lighting fixtures you think maybe the cause. This is often the definitive step in determining the cause of the odor or light smoke.

Smoke detectors are another cause of fire department responses similar to odors of smoke. Typically a smoke detector will sound for a short time causing the occupant to call the fire department. By the time we arrive on the scene there is no apparent cause. Again this is a detective game to determine the cause similar to "odor of smoke" responses. Always rule out active or past fire as the first step.

Common non-fire causes of smoke detector alarms are: steam from a shower or other source, dust, cleaning or air fresheners sprayed in or near the detector, insects, or cooking.

In all these cases always remind the occupant to call the fire department again if the odor returns, the alarm sounds again or if they have any reason to suspect a dangerous condition. The last thing we want as firefighters is to respond to a working fire because of a delayed alarm.

OUTSIDE FIRES

FFI 5.3.8 One of the most common types of outside fires is the dumpster or trash fire (fig. 20–81). If these fires are small in size or contained to a small bin, they can easily be extinguished with a booster line or preconnected "trash line." Larger containers, larger piles of trash, and construction debris should be overwhelmed with an 1¾-in. (45-mm) line, or in case of a large debris pile, a 2½-in. (65-mm) hoseline or master stream device. When choosing the size line to extinguish the fire, always remember that you want to overwhelm the fire. A fair fight only exposes us to unnecessary dangers for extended periods of time. Take a cannon to the gunfight and you will win decisively.

Fig. 20–81. Dumpster

Most often with these types of fires, there is nothing to be saved, so no one and nothing should be risked. Use the reach of the stream to apply water to the fire from a distance. Once the fire is knocked down, firefighters will have to pull apart the debris to reach smoldering pockets for final extinguishment. Pike poles, commonly referred to as hooks, are used to pull apart debris to ensure final extinguishment.

Safety at outside fires is often deceiving. The fire is visible and easily accessible, and apparently will be easy to extinguish. We must always remember that closed containers or other hazards may be contained in the trash or garbage container. First, consider that if something started the fire, it could be a hazardous material that may produce toxic fumes. Possibly an arsonist started the fire to cheaply dispose of trash or to dispose of evidence or even a body. Disposal of hazardous waste is expensive. A common practice by unscrupulous persons may be to hide it in common trash. At construction sites or even in household waste, closed containers such as propane torch cans or 20-lb (9-kg) propane tanks may be found. Exposed to fire, they can explode (BLEVE), exposing firefighters to rocketing tanks and lethal shrapnel from tank fragments. Chemical hazards such as unused or outdated pesticides and used or unused cleaning chemicals and construction material can often be found in trash.

At a recent fire in the northeastern United States, a small propane cylinder became a projectile at a dumpster fire. It hit the building with such force that it set off the automatic alarm in the structure.

You never know what is burning in a trash or dumpster fires. For this reason it is important to wear full PPE and SCBA. A shift in the wind or a sudden flare-up of fire or smoke can expose firefighters to dangerous chemicals or other hazards. If you always wear your PPE and SCBA, these are two decisions you don't need to think about on the fireground.

A good tactic for dumpster fires is to fill the container with water. Often dumpsters will have a drain hole in lowest part of the side of the container. Plug this with cone shaped wooden plug by tapping it in with a hammer or flat-head axe, then simply flood the container with water (fig. 20–82). This tactic reduces the time and hazards for firefighters. However, be careful when flowing water into them. Be wary of the weight of water that you are adding and the possibility that the dumpster will move with added weight. Occasionally, it may be necessary to remove the contents of the dumpster to properly extinguish the fire (fig. 20–83).

Fig. 20–82. Dumpster plug

Fig. 20–83. Here a large dumpster had to be unloaded to be extinguished. Trash fires are a common call for firefighters. Here firefighters extinguish a large fire in a container. Remember to always be aware of hazardous materials illegally concealed in trash fire. (Courtesy of Tom Bierds)

Junkyard fires

Junkyard fires are outside fires that pose unique and special hazards to firefighters. Junkyards and scrap metal recycling sites are often large and wandering areas, forcing us to make long supply hoseline lays. Frequently on the outskirts of town or rural areas, water supply may be limited to nonexistent.

Automobile junkyards often stack cars to save space, creating unstable stacks of cars that can fall on firefighters. Obviously, sharp metal, burning plastics, and piles of hot and possibly molten metal dripping down from stacked cars all present us with serious hazards at these fires.

Although these fires may be spectacular, resist the urge to conduct an offensive attack. There is nothing to be saved, so nothing should be risked. Use master streams right away, because they have greater knockdown and can be applied from a distance away, thus providing a margin of safety. It sounds simple but is an often underused method, using the reach of the stream to provide some standoff distance for yourself at these fires (fig. 20–84).

Fig. 20–84. At large outdoor fires, like this one in an automobile junkyard, the use of master streams is required. Note how far the streams reach providing a good margin of safety for firefighters. (Courtesy of Brian Duddy)

Outside tire fires

Rubber automobile tires are sometimes stacked in huge piles, either awaiting disposal or recycling. When these mountains of rubber catch fire, they are very difficult to extinguish (fig. 20–85). They are generally stacked to conserve storage space. This stacking provides just enough space for air and oxygen for combustion, but not enough accessibility for effective stream application. Because they produce huge quantities of heat and black smoke, it is difficult and sometimes impossible to provide and effectively apply enough water to effect extinguishment. These fires often burn for days. Experience has shown that the most effective extinguishment method is to physically separate the unburned tires from the burning tires. This is usually accomplished with contracted or on-site heavy equipment while firefighters control the fire spread for safety. Class A foams have some effect on increasing the ability of water to penetrate these difficult fires.

Fig. 20–85. Tire fire. (Courtesy of Robert Ladd)

Outbuilding fires

Another common type of outside fire is a shed or small storage building (fig. 20–86). These fires can be deceptive and often contain hazards to unsuspecting firefighters. A shed or detached garage may be referred to as an outbuilding, garage, shop, or barn. These buildings may contain products, chemicals, and processes that the home or business owner does not want in his main house or business. Common hazards found in outbuildings include pesticides, pool chemicals, herbicides, flammable liquids, and gases. Recently, a fire in an outbuilding sent eight firefighters to the hospital. The owner ran a seamless linoleum floor business and had a variety of toxic chemicals that were burning. Strategy for these types of fires is to prevent them from extending to surrounding exposures, which may include the main house, business, or storage building, other nearby buildings, cars, trucks, or wildland. Always use full PPE and SCBA.

Fig. 20–86. Firefighters prepare to extinguish a shed fire. Note that they are going to use the reach of the stream to apply water, thereby keeping themselves at a safe distance. There is nothing to be saved, so nothing should be risked. (Courtesy of Tom Bierds)

Groundcover fires

Small brush fires. FFI 5.3.19 A very common type of response involves small fires in vegetation, including leaves and grass. These brush fires often occur along roadways and railroads, sometimes sparked by improperly disposed cigarettes or hot exhaust systems in cars (a car's catalytic converter can ignite leaves and grass when it is parked on top of these combustibles). Other brush fires are caused by campers who leave campfires unattended. Brush fires can grow in size to become wildland fires, described below.

Small brush fires are usually controllable with a single fire company and small hand lines (1½-in. or 1¾-in. [38-mm or 45-mm]). A key to extinguishing these fires is to determine the direction of spread, anticipating where it is headed. These fires tend to move as a linear front and can be knocked down in a sweeping side-to-side attack along the front.

Be extremely careful of even small brush fires burning in windy conditions. These fires can grow exponentially in size, erupting into a full-blown wildland fire. Also, be wary of fires burning near buildings. In these situations, it is best to call for additional fire companies quickly, before the fire gets out of hand. Since many brush fires occur in locations where there are no fire hydrants, the available water supply—onboard water tanks on the fire engine—may not be enough to deal with the fire if it grows too large.

Wildland fires. FFI 5.3.19 Large fires involving vegetation have come to be known as wildland fires. Some of these fires occur in the "urban-wildland interface," locations where residential development has penetrated into forests and heavily vegetated areas. Some of these wildland fires involve large responses of hundreds of pieces of firefighting equipment from many states, much more equipment than even the biggest building fires.

While a complete discussion of wildland firefighting is beyond the scope of this textbook, it is important for you to have a basic understanding of the terms and equipment used in wildland firefighting.

The use of proper terminology in wildland firefighting is just as important as it is in structural firefighting. Some of the more important terms to describe a wildland fire are the **head**, which is the portion of the fire with the greatest rate of spread (usually the edge of the fire opposite from which the wind is blowing; a fire may have multiple heads); **fingers**, which are long narrow strips that extend from the main body of fire; **pockets**, which are unburned areas between the main body of fire and the fingers; the **rear** or **heel,** which is the end of the fire opposite from the head; **flanks,** which are the sides of the fire; and **islands**, which are unburned areas within the fire's perimeter (fig. 20–87). **Spot fires** are small fires started by flying embers far ahead of the main body of fire. *Green* is an area that has not been burned (the material may be live or dead vegetation). *Black* is burnt area.

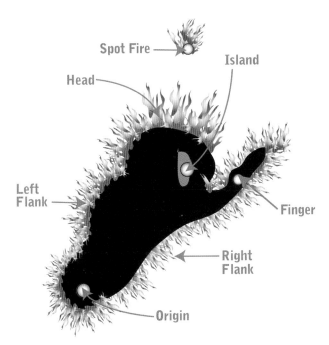

Fig. 20–87. A wildland fire

In terms of fire spread, creeping fires move very slowly. A running fire is one that spreads quickly with a well-defined head. A backing fire moves away from the head, downhill, or against the wind. A **crown fire** consists of serious fires that move across the tops of trees or shrubs, often independent of the fire at ground level (fig. 20–88).

Blowups occur when there is a sustained, rapid increase in the rate of spread, preventing control of the fire. A blowup will often necessitate changing the plan of fire attack. A **flare-up** is any sudden acceleration in the rate of spread for a short period of time.

Firefighters should be constantly aware of ground fire behavior, as well as changing weather and wind conditions when fighting ground fires. Escape routes and areas of safety should be identified and kept in mind throughout the firefighting operation in case of a sudden change in fire behavior.

When fighting a wildland fire, certain techniques are used. **Control lines** are "constructed" or natural fire barriers used to contain the fire. Firelines, on the other hand, are cleared strips or portions of a control line where flammable material has been removed by scraping or digging down below vegetation to mineral soil. An anchor point is the starting location for a fireline. A fire barrier is a safe anchor point. Using anchor points helps reduce the possibility of being outflanked by the fire while the fireline is being constructed. **Slopover** is fire that crosses the control line or natural barrier.

The primary methods for perimeter control of wildfires are direct and indirect attack. Direct attack is achieved through establishing control lines either at or close to the burning edge of the fire. Control lines for indirect attack are established at a distance from the fire, when the fire is too large or intense to use a direct attack.

When fighting a wildland fire, proper wildland PPE is required (refer to chapter 9, Personal Protective Equipment, for specifics on wildland PPE). In addition, the wildland firefighter carries a fire shelter (fig. 20–89). Shelters are used as a last resort when a firefighter becomes trapped and in danger of being overrun by the fire.

Fig. 20–88. A crown fire in Yellowstone Park

Fig. 20–89. Wildland shelter. (Courtesy of Andoni Kastros)

Wildland firefighters also use special tools and equipment. The most common hand tool is the Pulaski (fig. 20–90). It is a combined axe and mattock (a mattock is a chisel-like shape), which is capable of chopping down trees (the axe) and breaking up ground to create a fireline (the mattock). Large wildland fires necessitate the use of heavy equipment such as bulldozers, as well as air resources such as tankers and attack aircraft.

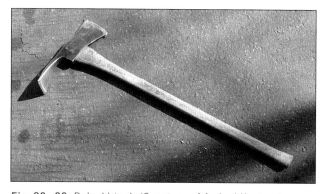

Fig. 20–90. Pulaski tool. (Courtesy of Andoni Kastros)

Specialized training is required for wildland firefighting. Such training includes safety procedures (LCES: lookouts, communications, escape routes, safety zones), constructing and maintaining firelines, wildland fire behavior, and tool use among many other specialized topics.

FIRES IN STACKED MATERIAL

Fires in stacked material, whether inside or outside a building, present two major challenges for firefighters: water application and collapse hazards. Common occupancies where you may find stacked material are lumberyards, junkyards, recycling plants, and warehouse or storage areas. Applying water to stacked material is difficult because extinguishment requires water to be applied on all six sides. Pallets of raw materials, parts, fabric, or other items are stacked on top of another to save space. As a result of this method of storage, fire can be on all four sides and the top and bottom. Bins or pallets of materials usually have access for storage, and retrieval from only the front side and may be stacked several deep. Further complicating water application is the fact that shelving may prevent water from dropping down onto the top of the burning material. In-shelf sprinkler systems are required to apply water to stored materials and are a good option. If these systems are in place in the building, always supply the system with one or more hoselines.

In the case of warehouses with automatic sprinklers, water application can be compromised by shelving in storage racks, blocking water from dropping down onto the top of the burning material. Rack sprinkler heads are required in such situations to apply water directly on to stored materials.

As the packaging material burns away, as in the case of a cardboard box or carboy container, its contents may spill out or fall. Wooden pallets that are the base for many types of container systems burn, and they may lose structural integrity and cause contents to shift and fall onto firefighters making an interior attack.

Falling debris from stacked material presents several hazards to firefighters. Obviously injuries can occur from this heavy material falling on unsuspecting firefighters. The falling debris will not be seen by firefighters below, because it will be obscured by smoke and can be initiated by lateral forces applied by hose streams. Falling debris can cover exit ways and hoselines, trapping firefighters or at the very least making a tactical withdrawal a very dangerous and time-consuming operation. Depending on the type of material stored in stacked fashion, the collapse or opening of containers by physical collapse or burning of containers can result in rapid fire progress, killing or injuring firefighters.

Extinguishing stacked material fires helps create an additional hazard that may kill or injure firefighters. Water will be absorbed by both packing and packaging materials and will therefore increase the weight of the stacked material. The weight of water, at 8 lb per gal (1 kg/L), can cause catastrophic failure of the shelving system. If the material is stacked without shelves (e.g., large rolls of paper or bailed materials such as hay or recycled materials), water can soften it, causing it to sag or become unbalanced and fall on firefighters. Firefighters have been injured and killed in this exact scenario. Remember to stay out of the collapse zone for stacked material.

Foam use on stacked material

Class A foam can be used to increase the effectiveness of water on stacked material fires. (Foams are discussed in greater detail in chapter 31, Advanced Fire Attack.) These foams lower the surface tension of water and therefore make it more effective. The water penetrates baled materials with greater effectiveness because of the reduced surface tension of the water, thus increasing the cooling effect of the water applied. Essentially, the water is allowed to penetrate deep in the material instead of beading up like raindrops on a car hood because the water's surface tension is reduced. This is caused by the foam concentrate, which is a detergent-based synthetic foam. These concentrates are not designed for use on flammable liquids but rather on any Class A combustible.

When **aspirated** much like Class B foams, Class A foam has a cooling and smothering effect on Class A combustibles. Class A foams are generally used at less concentration than Class B foams; 0.1–1% and can be proportioned a number of ways. Used as a wetting agent, standard solid bore or combination nozzles can be used. When used for pretreatment (before the fire) or as a mop-up tool, air aspirating nozzles or compressed air systems are needed.

NOTES

1. The United States National Institute of Standards and Technology (NIST) report NBSIR 80-2120, *Fire Development in Residential Basement Rooms,* October 1980, (Fang and Breese).

QUESTIONS

1. What is some of the basic information that can be gained from a proper communication report of a fire officer that has arrived on scene?

2. List at least five steps to a successful fire attack.

3. What is the purpose of size-up?

4. There are seven specific points to size up that must be considered upon arrival. List all.

5. What are the primary differences between an "offensive vs. defensive" type of strategy?

6. Which type of strategy is the "blitz attack" method employed?

7. Why are doors the primary entry and egress points to initiate a fire attack?

8. What is the primary purpose of the fire attack line?

9. When performing a rescue of trapped occupants, what is the preferred means of removal?

10. An engine companies operations can do more to effect the rescue of trapped or injured persons than any other group of firefighters. What are the common ways this is accomplished?

11. List the primary responsibilities for the nozzle operator during the initial stretch.

12. List the primary responsibilities of the backup position during the stretch.

13. Which position of the fire attack line is responsible for monitoring fatigue levels of the crew, communicating with command, and requesting additional assistance during the advancement of the hoseline?

14. What type of building will most likely require the use of a standpipe stretch to get the initial attack line into operation?

15. When utilizing the direct or modified direct method of attack, the nozzle should always be set on which pattern?

16. What are the dangers of opening up a fog stream during fire attack?

17. What are some of the basic duties firefighters will perform during the pick up and return part of an incident?

18. What is one of the most challenging types of fires to control, and why?

19. When sizing up a garden apartment for fire attack, what must often be considered when making the hoseline stretch?

20. Taxpayer buildings present a unique combination of occupancy during firefighting operations. What types of occupancies can typically be expected?

21.   Big box retail structures should always have what size of line deployed?

22.   When sizing up a vacant structure for fire attack, what are some of the general considerations for this type of building?

23.   Outside tire fires prove to be extremely difficult to extinguish and often burn for days on end. What is the most effective way to combat tire fires?

24.   List some of the hazards firefighters face when combating fires in stacked material.

Salvage and Overhaul

by Jeff Shupe

This chapter provides required knowledge items for the following NFPA Standard 1001 Job Performance Requirements:

FFI 5.3.13

FFI 5.3.14

This chapter contains Skill Drills. When you see this icon, refer to your Skill Drill book for step-by-step instructions.

OBJECTIVES

Upon completion of this chapter, you should be able to do the following:

- Define the term *salvage*
- Identify types of damage done by fire
- List the tools and equipment needed to effectively perform salvage operations
- Describe methods of grouping furniture in order to protect them from damage
- Describe two methods of deploying salvage covers
- Describe two methods of storing salvage covers
- Identify two methods of removing standing water from a structure
- Identify two methods of stopping water flow from an activated automatic sprinkler system
- Describe different methods of securing a building after firefighting operations
- Define the term overhaul
- List the equipment needed to effectively perform overhaul operations
- List four ways of detecting hidden fires
- Describe two devices that are used to detect hidden fires
- Identify methods for opening walls, floors, and ceilings
- Identify techniques for overhauling roofs and building contents
- Describe overhaul's role in conducting a fire investigation

INTRODUCTION

Salvage can be defined simply as "the art of saving property." It is a process whereby firefighters try to minimize damage to a structure and its contents when a fire or other emergency takes place. During firefighting operations, the basic way to save anything from harm is to either extinguish the fire and stop its destruction, or remove items of value from affected areas. This effort helps fire departments keep property loss down and achieve the stated goals of the American fire service, which are to save lives *and* property.

Sometimes known as **loss control**, salvage is a component of firefighting that can go a long way toward building good public relations between a fire department and the community it serves. Many fire departments have received praise and accolades for jobs well done at saving someone's property from fire. Some fire departments have even benefited from this financially and in other ways. Even though firefighters learn the importance and value of good salvage techniques early in their careers, it is one of the things that probably receives the least amount of attention on the fireground until after the bulk of the fire has been knocked down. This lack of attention may be partly because it is not truly associated with the excitement of actual fire-suppression efforts or other closely related *action* work at a fire. However, it is truly gratifying when someone acknowledges that you have done a commendable job of saving someone's property from loss.

KINDS OF FIRE DAMAGE

Generally, there are two classifications of fire damage: **Direct** (or primary) and **indirect** (or secondary). Direct fire damage is that which is caused by the actual combustion process, where there is physical destruction from flame, heat, or smoke. Indirect damage is all other damage caused from suppression efforts and other activities. An example of indirect damage is opening up of ceilings and walls to check for fire travel. There may not be any fire, but the job must be done, because if overhaul is not done and fire is left unchecked, the results will show later with more damage and the need for more overhaul.

SALVAGE OPERATIONS AND PROPERTY PROTECTION

FFI 5.3.14 **Salvage** is one of three incident priorities of firefighting. It falls under the heading of *property* conservation. It is also considered one of the basic steps of firefighting. With these points in mind, the importance of saving what we can or what we must save cannot be overstated.

Salvage begins with fire attack. It can take place in many forms, ranging from suppression efforts to the actual removal of property or the grouping and covering of property from threat of damage. An example of salvage from suppression action takes place when firefighters make a quick, aggressive knockdown of a fire followed by efficient ventilation to rid the building of heat, smoke, and gases. The size of attack, the point of approach, and the type of ventilation used in this scenario all affect the total outcome of damage. To illustrate this point, think of a working fire in the living room of an occupied two-story single-family residence. A quick and well-placed attack line, discharging the right volume of water, may be just what is needed for a rapid knockdown of a fast spreading fire while confining it to its area of origin. This effective method of attack can prevent the fire from spreading to uninvolved areas of the house, which will help to limit fire spread and damage. This effort relates to stopping direct and indirect fire damage. Quickly attacking the fire this way can stop greater loss from happening. Other fireground actions such as ventilating the building will also help the salvage effort by relieving the interior of heat, smoke, and gas accumulation.

Planning for salvage

For salvage operations to be efficient, there needs to be prior planning and training. Procedures should be developed to deal with the different kinds of salvage operations that might be needed for the different building types and occupancies found in a particular community. For example, special preplans might be needed for an office building that has especially valuable contents or documents in the offices. Preplans can tell firefighters where these contents are located and what measures should be taken to protect them.

Industrial manufacturing businesses might have materials on-site that are important to the company's survival or may require special handling or salvage techniques. Firefighting history has shown us that some small towns have existed because of their dependence on a large industry or business. Many of the town's citizens were employees of this business, and when a major fire took place, there was not enough saved to keep the operation going. The end result was jobs lost and a faltering local economy that led to scaled-back town services. That loss eventually caused a loss in the quality of life for the community. There could also be a threat to firefighter safety or a much larger problem if fire control in a particular type of facility was not protected properly and created a larger, more complex safety and salvage concern.

Sprinkler systems are a valuable asset to protecting buildings from the threat of fire. Their ability to control or hold fires until the fire department arrives has been proven over time. However, when a sprinkler system is activated, it has the ability to control a fire or hold it in check, but after that, it has the potential to cause extreme water damage. Because of that, fire departments must know from preplans, walk-throughs, and training where sprinkler systems' riser control valves and piping are found in a structure.

Salvage tools and equipment

FFI 5.3.13 Tools and equipment used for salvage should be carried on fire apparatus in compartments where they are easily accessible. In years gone by, ladder or truck companies were generally responsible for carrying this type of equipment and taking care of salvage operations. In larger cities where there were numerous businesses requiring property protection, salvage or **fire patrol** companies were established. These were crews who were paid by insurance companies, and their only job was salvage on the fireground. The equipment carried in their apparatus was strictly for that purpose. These companies no longer exist in our cities, so all salvage operations depend solely on the efforts of the local fire departments.

Nowadays, even though certain units may carry salvage equipment, it is generally accepted that everyone has a hand in salvage operations. Many departments have some basic salvage equipment on all of their fire apparatus. Because of this, every firefighter should know where the tools and equipment are located and know how to use them.

The following is a list of tools and equipment that might be needed to perform salvage duties (fig. 21–1):

    Shovels
    Brooms
    Mops
    Squeegees
    Pike poles
    Floor runners
    Polyethylene plastic sheeting
      (e.g., Visqueen brand)
    Salvage covers—canvas type
    Roll roofing paper
    Buckets
    Sprinkler head kit and sprinkler tongs
    Wooden wedges of different sizes
    Submersible pumps
    Water vacuums
    Hand tools
    Hammers
    Electric or battery-operated drill

    Supply of nails and screws
    Wood lath strips
    Duct tape
    Assortment of rags and towels
    Sawdust—carried in large bags
    Debris carryall bags
    Polystyrene or wood blocks
    Linoleum or carpenter's knife

Fig. 21–1. A wide variety of equipment is used to protect property during salvage and overhaul operations.

Where and when to begin salvage operations

When beginning salvage, first determine where the initial salvage efforts will have the greatest impact on saving property. If operations start in a room below the fire floor, then you will most likely arrange or group furniture into piles. Furniture or items located below a dripping ceiling should be moved to another area of the room or removed from the area all together if necessary. Where there is a tall piece of furniture like a chest of drawers, place it in the center of the pile or group so that when a salvage cover is thrown over everything, it acts as a pole draping the salvage cover over everything while allowing water to run off and away (fig. 21–2).

Fig. 21–2. Vinyl covers protect valuable contents from hot embers and water damage. Grouping contents together allows for the most efficient use of salvage covers.

If a floor is collecting water, then it will be necessary to use blocks or even something like soup cans to lift the furniture or objects off of the floor to prevent water absorption and damage (fig. 21–3). Where fires occur in industrial or commercial occupancies, skids can be used to pile items on and lift stock items off of the floor to keep them away from water pooling.

Fig. 21–3. Sometimes simply lifting valuables up off the ground can prevent them from being damaged from water runoff.

Generally, salvage operations begin on the fire floor or the floor directly below. It is these two areas that are likely to sustain the most amount of damage from fire, smoke, heat, and water. Just after a fire is extinguished, water most likely will collect on the fire floor, then quickly find its way to areas below. If a large amount of water has been used for the fire, then operations should start directly below the fire floor as soon as possible. If the area below

the fire floor has ceilings, then firefighters must check them to see if they are accumulating water and might possibly collapse. It may be necessary to puncture the ceiling to relieve built-up water in the ceiling space.

Before water is relieved, it may be necessary to figure the best way to channel water out of the area. Also, water in the ceilings may affect electric wires and fixtures. Perhaps water chutes (see later in this chapter) can be devised to get water out of the building. Floor runners may need to be placed for firefighter traffic and or water droplets falling from above.

As stated earlier, salvage operations should begin as soon as possible. They can begin immediately during a fire attack in an indirect manner or as soon as firefighters are able to initiate a more formalized effort.

Throwing salvage covers

FFI 5.3.14 The most common salvage tool is probably the salvage cover. Typically made of canvas, salvage covers are cut or made into different sizes (fig. 21–4). Some have coatings or treatments applied to them to help shed water. Nowadays, covers vary in size, including 10×12, 12×12, 12×16, and 14×18 ft (3×3.7, 3.7×3.7, 3.7×5, and 4.3×5.5 m).

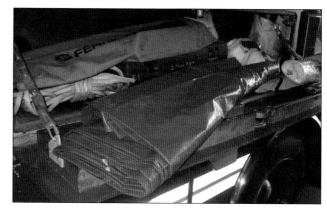

Fig. 21–4. While canvas salvage covers are found in most fire departments, they are being replaced by vinyl covers such as these.

If possible, salvage covers should be thrown over furniture piles and tucked in at the bottom of the pile to prevent water splashes from damaging the furniture.

After the salvage covers are used at fires and taken back to the fire station, the maintenance work begins. They are washed and hung up to dry. When they are completely dry and free from any chance of mold developing, they are checked for any holes or tears, then folded (fig. 21–5).

Fig. 21–5. Salvage covers must be properly folded and cleaned after each use.

A new material that is being used for salvage covers is polyethylene plastic sheeting (fig. 21–6), commonly the Visqueen brand. It has several advantages over canvas covers and tarps. One advantage is that it is economical. One roll can be 120 ft (37 m) long by 20 ft (6 m) wide. It is disposable, so there is no maintenance of cleaning, drying, and folding. It is also quick and easy to use on the scene, and it can be cut to fit the situation. The only item necessary to make it work is a utility knife or other type of cutting tool. On an apparatus, it is easy to store and can fit in any apparatus.

Fig. 21–6. Polyethylene plastic sheathing is a popular alternative to traditional salvage covers because of its low cost and the ability to manipulate its size.

Water chutes and catchalls

Salvage covers are primarily used to protect furniture and other valuables but can also serve other uses, such as **water chutes**, where a trough is made using covers, pike poles, and ladders to catch dripping water and divert it away (fig. 21–7). Covers can also be used for holes left in the roof of a building. They can be used as catchalls after the sides have been built up or rolled up, using pike poles once again (fig. 21–8).

Fig. 21–7. Creating a water chute from a salvage cover can be necessary to divert water away from valuable belongings.

Fig. 21–8. Conventional salvage covers can have the sides rolled up to manufacture a catchall.

Removing water and dewatering equipment

Getting water out of a building is often great concern for firefighters. As you know from chapter 15, Water Supply, water weighs 8.34 lb per gal (1 kg per L). Considering that a 2½-in. (65-mm) hand line can flow upwards of 250 gpm (946 L/min), the use of such streams can add more than a ton of weight every minute to the structure. This puts an additional stress on an already compromised building. In addition, we may need to remove water from a structure to aid in a postfire investigation or to find fire victims in a flooded basement. Finally, some cities assist homeowners in pumping out basements after a flood as a public service. Whatever the reason, firefighters are often expected to use dewatering equipment in such situations.

It may be possible to remove water by clearing floor drains, if present. Additionally, it may be necessary to cut holes in floors to allow water to drain to lower levels. Toilets can be removed from their attachment to the floor in bathrooms to allow drainage as well—make sure that the toilet is replaced or the drain is sealed after such actions (fig. 21–9).

Fig. 21–9. To facilitate draining, a toilet can be removed. This tactic can be especially important in multi-story buildings where creating chutes and catchalls isn't feasible.

Although not found too often on fire apparatus, the water vacuum is a useful device for removing water from areas that are not easily accessible with mops or squeegees. Some water vacuums are made like a backpack and are carried on a firefighter's back, making it very portable, but also limiting the amount of water it can pick up (fig. 21–10). However, if there is a large amount of water that needs to be removed and there is limited capability to do it, then the services of professional cleanup crews should be called to the scene because of their larger water vacuum machines.

The use of dewatering pumps is sometimes called for. These pumps range in capacity from a few gallons per minute to several hundred gallons per minute. Some are electric powered, while others have their own generators. Ironically, some dewatering pumps use water (hoselines) to power them. A key to the efficient use of these pumps is to select a low point location where water will flow to the pump (fig. 21–11). Ensure that the outlet of the pump is located outdoors in a location where the discharged water will not find its way back into the structure.

FFI 5.3.13 Safety is of prime importance here. Ensure that all electricity has been shut down before entering an area with standing water. Never stick your hand or any body part near any floor or roof drain; use a tool with a long handle to clear drains.

Fig. 21–10. Using a vacuum to remove water is effective at small fires or incidental discharges of sprinkler systems.

Fig. 21–11. Dewatering pumps should be placed at the lowest collection point so that the water will drain toward the pump.

Stopping water flow from a sprinkler system

FFI 5.3.14 When ordered by the incident commander (and only the incident commander [IC]) once a fire has been extinguished, an operating sprinkler system will be shut down to avoid additional water damage. The firefighter at the riser control valve (most often an outside stem and yoke valve, or OS&Y valve) will shut off the valve (figs. 21–12 and 21–13). After closing the OS&Y valve (the stem is now completely inside the valve), the firefighter can open the main drain and drain out the water from the system (fig. 21–14).

Note: After the water is drained from the system, the sprinkler system will no longer be capable of extinguishing a subsequent fire or rekindle because the water supply will have been shut off to the sprinkler heads.

Fig. 21–12. An outside stem and yoke (OS&Y valve) in the "open" position

Fig. 21–13. An outside stem and yoke (OS&Y valve) in the "closed" position

Alternatively, a firefighter may be asked to insert a **sprinkler wedge** or wood chock into an operating sprinkler head (if it is still flowing water) (fig. 21–15). Firefighters who perform this function will get very wet—a consideration when cold temperatures would cause the firefighter's gear to freeze. The advantage of this technique is that

the sprinkler system will remain in service, and the other heads that have not been activated will remain capable of extinguishing a subsequent fire or rekindle.

Fig. 21–14. The main drain of a sprinkler system is normally labeled and easy to locate.

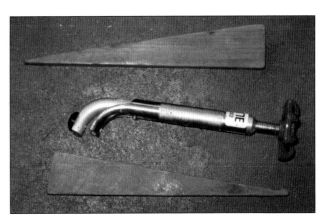

Fig. 21–15. Sprinkler wedges or tongs come in a variety of sizes.

After a fire, most fire departments have their fire prevention bureau follow up to make sure the sprinkler system has been properly restored; some establish a **fire watch** until the system has been restored by a licensed contractor. Other fire departments actually restore sprinkler systems to full operation by replacing heads and resetting **dry-pipe valves** (the alarm valve on a dry-pipe sprinkler system in which the pipes are normally filled with air to avoid freezing) under nonfire conditions. When performing such procedures, ensure that exactly the same sprinkler head is used to replace the head that activated.

For detailed information on total sprinkler system operations, see chapter 30, Fire Protection Systems.

Securing a building after firefighting operations including forcible entry

FFI 5.3.14 In many fire situations, postfire salvage operations require the fire building to be secured before the fire department leaves the scene. During the course of firefighting, there might have been structural damage caused from forcible-entry work to doors and windows. Forcible entry methods for salvage can include anything from forcing doors of rooms adjacent to the fire area to cutting holes for drainage or other types of wall or floor breaches. Firefighters should try to consider the least damaging methods for forcible entry during salvage, to reduce property damage and minimize the tasks of securing the structure before leaving the scene.

If the building is one where it is going to be reoccupied after repairs, then the fire department should close any openings in the building made from firefighting or fire damage. This is to prevent any environmental damage that might occur.

For example, if the fire department had cut a hole in the roof of a house during fire operations, then it should cover the hole with a tarp or other material that will keep the elements out of the building. Generally, canvas tarps will work fine because they are heavy enough to resist wind forces and can keep the elements out also as long as they are secured to the roof. Visqueen or other plastic film sheeting can also be used; however, it may need to be double-layered to resist wind forces. The outer edges of the plastic sheeting should be folded over two or three times to give strength where it will be attached to the structure, so it won't tear from high wind forces. Also, it will be necessary to use long pieces of wood or lath strips to anchor the perimeter of the sheeting to prevent wind forces from getting under the plastic covering and tearing it off the roof decking. Another reason for attaching it this way is to stop rain or other elements from being blown underneath the covering and getting inside the building by that route.

If the roof being covered is a flat roof like that found over a commercial store or "taxpayer," it may be necessary to build a little frame with a pitch to direct the rain off the cover, so the water won't be able to collect and pool in the cover, which would cause the cover to hang down into the vent hole. Firefighters will need to figure out the best direction to pitch the runoff to.

When there has been any substantial fire damage to the first floor or lower level that will cause the building to be vacated during rebuilding, then security will be an issue. If doors or windows have been damaged from forcing, then it may be necessary to cover them with plywood sheeting or oriented strand board (OSB) (fig. 21–16). In many cases, all that is necessary to attach the sheeting is a hammer and nails and pieces of sheeting cut to the size needed to cover the window. Usually, it can be nailed to the perimeter of the window. If the building's exterior walls are of brick, then the sheeting can be attached to the top, bottom, and side rails of the window creating a now secured structure.

Fig. 21–16. Plywood can be used to secure broken windows.

If the building has sustained damage beyond repair and will need to be demolished, then firefighters will need to establish a safe perimeter with barrier tape around the property that will let people know their limits.

Floors with holes in them from cutting operations or from fire damage can be secured by simply putting a door over them and nailing it in place. In extreme cases in which much of the floor is too weak to support anyone, barrier tape over the door can serve as a warning device or nailing the entrance door shut to that area.

OVERHAUL

A simple definition of **overhaul** is "making sure the fire is out and leaving the building in as serviceable a condition as possible." Overhaul is a learned process that is extremely important to the outcome of the incident and should be carried out in a systematic way to minimize the chances of rekindles happening. The process of overhaul generally begins after the fire is extinguished or brought under control, and firefighters are able to move into fire-damaged areas and finish extinguishment by examining burned contents and opening the building's suspected void spaces, typically the walls, floors, and ceiling spaces, to search for hidden fire.

Safety first!

Firefighters must always keep personal safety in mind, even after the bulk of the fire has been extinguished. During overhaul, it is necessary to use complete personal protective equipment, including self-contained breathing apparatus (SCBA), unless the atmosphere has been determined safe to operate in without it (fig. 21–17). A company-level officer should be assigned the responsibility of supervising safety and the overhaul effort in each area where it is performed. The officer should watch for any problems and also monitor all radio communications. If fire is found to be spreading quickly to other areas of the structure, it is that officer's job to alert other crews and the IC about changing conditions or fire travel, or anything that might affect the safety of others working.

Before overhaul begins, it must first be determined if the building is safe to be operating in. In situations where there has been severe fire damage to the building's structural components, it will be the IC's responsibility to determine if it is safe to work in. This decision should be based on reports from company officers, firefighters, and the IC's own personal observations of the structure's condition. Fire service history has taught us that it is this time of a fire incident that is very dangerous and in some cases deadly to firefighters. In other situations where firefighters have had a tough, punishing fire, they can be fatigued from physical stress and effort. It can be times like this when firefighters lets their guard down about the building or fire conditions and just want to get the rest of the job done and get back to quarters. Perhaps there are obvious safety hazards, but they are not being recognized or considered. Here is where we can get into trouble.

Fig. 21–17. Numerous toxic gases are produced during the decay stage of a fire, when overhaul takes place. Therefore it is imperative that firefighters always wear SCBA.

Some points to consider before overhauling a structure are the following:

- Building construction type and type of materials used in its construction: Is there any fire damage to them?

- Occupancy of the building and its contents: Are there any unsafe or hazardous materials involved?

- What is the volume of fire and the length of time the fire has been burning?

- What is the actual damage to the building's structural system?

- Length of time for extinguishment process, namely water: How much was used and for how long?

- Are there any telltale signs of a weakened, unsafe structure that may be a collapse hazard, like any sagging roofs or exterior walls that may be bowing outward?

- Is there any water running out from any part of the building?

- Are there unstable chimneys that may topple?

- Is there enough lighting to see inside the building? Do lights need to be brought in?

If firefighters are already operating inside the structure, are there any reports of water pooling or building up on floors? Do any of the floors feel springy or spongy? Are firefighters reporting any unusual sounds or occurrences within the structure, such as ceilings dropping or wall plaster falling to the floor, or sounds like cracking or stressing noises? Is there a buildup of water on any flat roof surfaces, indicating a weakened roof that is developing a new concentrated, live load? If any of these points is happening, it may be prudent to remove firefighters from the area or building until a further determination can be made concerning the structure's stability. Firefighters noticing any of these signs or other things need to make sure everyone on the scene is alerted to the possibility of an unsafe environment.

Having a plan and where to begin

Just as every fire should have an attack plan, the overhaul process should have a plan, too. Generally, the fire's location within a building is the starting point for the process, and more than likely, that is where overhaul will begin. Remember, that while fires have six sides—front, rear, both sides, top, and bottom—so too does the overhaul process. Firefighters need to remain proactive during overhaul and be suspicious of fire travel. To illustrate this point, picture a fire that has been localized and confined to one or two rooms on the third floor of a four-story garden apartment building. Firefighters need to check if the fire has extended beyond these rooms. Fire remaining unchecked in any wall, floor, or ceiling void spaces or pipe chases could eventually find its way to the cockloft space over the entire structure and cause tremendous damage. The best way to know for sure is to have a crew go above, below, and around the fire area to examine for fire extension. Visual investigations or observations along with good radio reports will help keep everyone aware of the fire's activity—its location, what it is doing, and where it might be going.

If the fire building itself is large and has sustained a substantial amount of fire damage, or if it has a large amount of contents that will require considerable attention, there will probably be extensive overhaul efforts. The IC might consider making a request for more firefighters to the scene to set up and rotate overhaul crews. This move serves to gives those who have already been working at the fire a break, and it helps to spread the workload by bringing in fresh, alert personnel.

Before beginning overhaul, it is important for firefighters to be fully aware of the damaged area(s) and to be looking for possible causes of the fire. In some cases, burn patterns will give clues as to damage and ignition sources. If these are detected, everything should be done to preserve evidence and not destroy or remove any evidence until fire investigators arrive and are able to determine its importance to the fire's cause. In many instances, firefighters begin overhauling and destroying evidence or end up throwing it out of the building.

Attack hoselines

Attack hoselines should not be removed from any areas needing overhaul. Where there is suspected fire travel, hoselines should remain charged and in place until overhaul has been completed and the IC has approved it. In far too many instances, fire departments have placed too much reliance on a single hoseline to extinguish a fire and cover all the potential points of fire travel and extension. After fire has been discovered extending to different areas, the time and effort used to reposition this line might let a fire gain great headway, growing more than the single line of hose can handle. Incidents like this have resulted in greater loss and, in some cases, firefighter injuries. Fire departments should know when and where multiple hoselines should be stretched for efficient coverage. An old adage of the fire service says where fire extension is suspected, don't send a crew to investigate ... send a hoseline and tools!

Tools and equipment

The task of overhaul is generally one of manual labor, meaning hard physical work. The tools used most commonly to accomplish this are hand tools of the pushing, pulling, striking, and cutting variety, but in some cases power tools are used also. Some of the more common tools are axes—both pick-head and flat-head axes; pike poles of different styles and lengths depending on the amount of reach or pulling needed; Halligan and Kelly tools for prying or leverage; shovels; and power saws, both chain and rotary. Other useful tools include rubbish hooks, carryall bags, and even wheelbarrows.

Detecting fire

After the main body of fire or flames have been knocked down or extinguished, it may be hard to actually know if there is any remaining fire due to poor visibility—all that is visible might only be the blackened, charred remains. Many firefighters have been fooled after a fire has been knocked or extinguished and the smoke has been removed from the room, only to have the room fill with smoke and heat minutes later from fire burning behind the walls or ceilings. In these cases, firefighters might have to use their own senses to find hidden flames, such as in the following examples.

Sight. Look for the following:

- Discoloration of paint or wall coverings

- Blistering or bubbling of paint or varnish or shellac finishes

- Heavily damaged or severely burned areas showing extreme amounts and depth of charring

- Smoke coming from around window or door frames or moldings, or registers

- Small sparks or cinders dropping from ceiling areas

- Smoke arising from floors, especially finished floors with subfloors

- Openings (vents, shafts, etc.) near the fire that may be allowed heat and smoke to travel to other parts of the building

Touch and feel. Use the back of your hand to touch suspected hot surfaces, first sensing for heat without pressing your skin to the suspected surface.

Hearing. Listen for the following:

- Any sounds of crackling or snapping as so often happens when wood burns

- Sounds of pressure building from pipes or other vessels

Smell. Use your sense of smell to detect the odor of fresh wood burning or other fresh smoke. If odors are noxious or smoke appears to be building in volume, then redon your face piece for personal safety.

Technology for detecting fire or heat. In the past, firefighters had only their learned principles of techniques and good instincts to help them search out hidden pockets of fire. Many times, firefighters worked extra hard trying to find the source of odors of smoke, only to find nothing, and so they would leave the building to return to quarters, only to return an hour or two later to find a fire roaring out of the windows and through the roof. Nowadays, there is a great tool that employs modern technology that most fire departments have or at least have access to. It is the thermal imaging camera, commonly called TIC (fig. 21–18). Using this device allows firefighters to detect heat or fire in hidden spaces without having to tear a room completely apart to find it. This saves time, effort, and guess work. The TIC is especially useful for the scenarios already described in this chapter, and it has many other uses where any amount of heat greater than the ambient area temperature can be identified through observation on the camera screen.

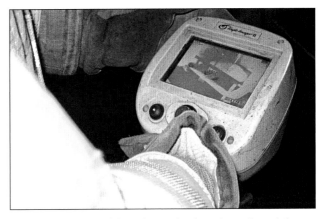

Fig. 21–18. Thermal imaging technology has allowed the overhaul process to be less damaging to property and more time efficient.

Opening walls, floors, and ceilings

Before any wall, ceiling, or floor enclosure is opened, first determine if there is a real need to do so! In far too many cases, firefighters have caused needless damage to occupied buildings during overhaul by opening areas where there was no fire, nor was there any threat of fire extension. This makes firefighters and their fire departments look less like the professionals they want to be. And their community will perceive that, too. However, when done properly, the overhaul process will leave the building with no fire remaining, and a structure that will sustain minimal damage.

Ceilings need to be opened whenever there is a concern of hidden fire. In obvious situations where there has been substantial fire damage to a room, there will be no question about the need to open the ceiling, especially above the area where the fire burned. When ceilings located below cockloft or attic spaces are opened and there is a large volume of fire found, the burning area should be opened completely for extinguishment and further examination. If the fire is found to be extending horizontally, firefighters may need to get ahead of the fire's direction of travel and begin pulling down the ceiling in that area to cut off or limit the fire's spread. Once the fire is stopped, the entire ceiling will now need to be opened because of the threat of sparks or embers remaining. When fire is found in a ceiling space, the firefighters who found it should make sure this condition and the need to get above it are communicated immediately to everyone.

A special technique for opening walls and ceilings has been developed by Lt. Michael Ciampo of the New York City Fire Department (FDNY). Called the punch technique, the firefighter uses a hook on ceilings and a Halligan tool on walls to create a series of initial perforations in the gypsum board to precut the surface, before removing the gypsum board. Once the perforations have been made, the firefighter can easily and effectively remove the gypsum board in large sections (figs. 21–19 and 21–20).

When it is time to open walls, it should be done completely from stud to stud and floor to ceiling (fig. 21–21). Doing this will expose the channel(s) and allow firefighters to see if there has been any charring inside the wall space. Remove the baseboard to expose the bottom of the wall and edge of the floor. If fire is found in several wall bay spaces, they must be opened completely. A concern here is if the fire in the wall spaces is extending either up or down vertically, especially in balloon frame construction. If a wall is opened and fire jumps out, it should be extinguished by the hoseline, and then the nozzle should be pushed into the wall space to direct water up and down the space to knock down any possible extension. Once again, the officer supervising should contact everyone by radio or verbally to let them know about extension and that crews should be ordered to check for it. Fires in outside walls will need to be checked on the outside of the structure, also. Fire traveling up an outside wall can extend to the upper parts of a building and may reenter the structure.

Fires hidden in floors or floor spaces can require extra effort, depending on the type of floor. In many residential structures, the floor is plywood laid over wood joists or trusses. There may be a layer of carpeting or linoleum on top of that. For others, there may be a subfloor of plywood or floor planks, then a hard wood floor on top of that. Still other residential floors have this supporting system with ceramic tiles for the finish. In any event, the firefighter must first understand the type of floor and the strength of its supporting system in order to determine the safest method to open the floor (fig. 21–22). For example, where there is carpeting, it may be best to cut carpet away with a utility knife before any tool use. If it is a wood floor, it may be best to use a power tool for cutting, as an axe may bounce away or glance off the floor boards when struck. Ceramic tiles may need to be struck with a maul or sledgehammer first.

Fig. 21–19. The ceiling punch technique involves using a pike pole to weaken gypsum board so that it can be removed more easily in large pieces.

Fig. 21–20. The wall punch technique works in a similar manner to the ceiling technique. However, the tool of choice for this evolution is the Halligan.

Fig. 21–21. Firefighters must expose the interior of a wall surface to prevent rekindle during the overhaul process.

Fig. 21–22. When opening up floor assemblies, firefighters must be careful not to cut through the beam below, compromising its load-carrying capability.

Roof overhaul

Different kinds of buildings have different kinds of roofing systems. Because of that, it is important for firefighters to recognize different types of building construction and roofs. Structures have different types of roof-supporting systems and roof-covering materials. Anytime fire or heat has reached the roof area, the roof must be examined for fire (fig. 21–23). In many cases this means the roof decking and covering must be removed. Appropriate methods and proper tools should be used, as this task is labor-intensive.

Fig. 21–23. The roof assembly must always be analyzed and opened up if it has been involved in fire.

Some structures have roof systems that are totally combustible, meaning the rafters, ridge boards, decking, and shingles can burn, whereas others may have a metal deck and an insulation covered by roofing materials, finished with an asphalt-type coating. In these cases, hand tools are most likely to be used along with hose

streams. Sometimes power saws can be used to cut away portions of the roof to make less work. If necessary, the job can be done from a roof ladder, aerial ladder, or tower platform.

Techniques for overhaul

Once the flames are knocked down and overhaul has started, the manual work with hand tools begins. It is best for firefighters to have an assortment of tools with them in the structure to deal with the different overhaul needs. Here is where another old fire service adage applies: "The firefighter should let the tools do the work." Firefighters who do not have the right tool for the job will end up working harder to get things done. Firefighters should first examine the type of structure they will be overhauling and take the right tools in the first time. Many times firefighters have tried to make up for not having the right tool for the job and have worked extra hard to do a task, only to receive an injury for their effort.

An example of proper tools for the job is where fire is found in the first floor of an older two-story multiple-occupancy structure that has 12-ft (3.7-m) ceilings that need to be opened to check for fire extension. Firefighters generally carry 6-ft (2-m) pike poles for residential structures, but in this case, the firefighter needs at least an 8-ft (2.4-m) pike pole or ceiling hook.

The firefighter should hold the hook or pike pole so the hook end faces away. As the firefighter pierces the ceiling with the point, it may be necessary to turn the pole at a quarter turn so the business end punches past the lath or ceiling surface. The pole is then turned so the hook once again faces away. The firefighter should locate the joist to which the lath or ceiling is attached, then position the hook along side of it. As the firefighter pulls downward and to his or her front area, the connections between the two are broken, releasing bigger pieces of the ceiling area. The firefighter should open up as much as is necessary to get to clean wood.

Overhauling building contents

When overhauling the contents of a structure, sometimes all that is necessary is to use a stream of water from a hoseline. But in some situations, other methods are necessary to get the job done. For example, a bedroom has sustained heavy fire damage, and there was some extension into the hallway. There will probably be extensive overhaul needed. There might be clothing hanging in a closet that is still smoldering. There might also be window drapes or shades that need attention to be sure they are extinguished. Instead of using the force and volume from the attack hoseline to do the job, firefighters can pick up the clothing articles and take down the shades and drapes, and remove them all to the outside or into the bathtub for a dousing (if the tub is still in service). There may be piles of clothing in the room also smoldering. In some cases, a bucket of water or a tub nearby with water in it can serve the purpose.

If you find it necessary to remove the contents from the structure, ensure that proper safety procedures are followed. Never just throw things out of a window—make sure the area below is clear before dropping the objects. In tall multistory buildings, never use the elevator to remove mattresses and the like—they have been known to flare up inside the elevator, endangering firefighters. Roll up and tie mattresses with rope before bringing them down through the building stairs.

There will be fires in occupied structures where the owner or occupant has smaller, valuable items found after the fire, such as items on a dresser or shelf. It may be best to get a box or other container to put them in for safe keeping while they are returned to the owner. Care should be taken to minimize any breakage by firefighters. This action can serve three purposes: (1) it helps to save something that might be very valuable to someone; (2) it helps firefighters to minimize property loss; and (3) it can build positive public relations between the fire department and its community and make a positive situation from a bad experience for someone.

When overhauling, there is a natural tendency for firefighters to use water heavily for final extinguishment. Firefighters may be tired and want to get done quickly, especially if there was a well-involved fire situation necessitating a lot of hard, physical work. There is always the belief that insurance is going to pay for the loss to the owners anyhow! If the structure is not going to be rebuilt and will be demolished, then by all means use as much water as needed to make sure a rekindle does not happen. But where fire damage is limited in size and if the building is going to be repaired and reinhabited, then firefighters should be careful about the amount of water used during overhaul. If there is any question in this case, then maybe overhaul efforts were not thorough enough to open all areas of potential fire spread, and water is being used to flood it out. This will lead to unnecessary water damage, and it could lead to an uninhabitable building. Officers and firefighters should always be aware of the amount of damage caused *after* overhaul efforts.

Tips for overhauling

- Determine that the building or structure is safe for personnel to operate in.

- Maintain communications and control of the task (company officers).

- Have a plan on where to start and where to suspect likely fire travel.

- Make sure firefighters use the proper tools and techniques for the task at hand.

- Keep hoselines charged and in place until they are no longer necessary.

- Ensure that holes in the floor or other safety hazards are identified, and proper barriers are placed to protect firefighters operating in the area.

- Perform overhaul in coordination with other operating crews.

- Remove debris to the outside to be completely extinguished.

- Look for any possible signs of how the fire may have started.

- Cover any windows or openings in an occupied structure to prevent any further damage.

- Before leaving the premises for the final time, conduct a walk-through of the structure to ensure there is no remaining fire. You must avoid an embarrassing and dangerous **rekindle**—a situation in which a hidden smoldering fire reignites after your departure, setting the building on fire again. Use all of your senses and the thermal imaging camera to search for any hidden fire.

Preserving fire scene evidence and arson

FFI 5.3.13 During the entire incident—from dispatch to picking up and returning to quarters—firefighters should be aware of any unusual signs or clues that might lead to an explanation of what may have started the fire. (Fire investigation is covered in detail in chapter 32.) During overhaul, firefighters are likely to come across things that might point to where the fire started and what may have caused it. Signs of origin can include:

- Location of fire or point of origin

- Single or multiple fire locations

- Direction of fire spread

- Faulty wiring or electrical equipment

- Signs of accelerants

- Cans or container

- Unlocked doors or signs of forcible entry

When signs are noticed, firefighters should be careful not to destroy any evidence or throw anything out that fire investigators might find useful in their probe. If possible, notify investigators and stop the overhaul process as long as the fire is under control. Should firefighters discover the cause or perhaps find something that might point to a crime, do not disturb any evidence if possible—notify investigators immediately and protect the scene.

Arson is the intentional setting of fire to a building or object for the purpose to destroy it. There are many reasons why someone would perform this crime, and that is why it is so popular. Arson can be a very costly crime when all things involved are considered, including firefighter health and safety. Sometimes a building is rigged to burn quickly, and that could lead to a structural collapse that might injure firefighters.

Because firefighters never know when an arson fire will happen, they must be alert to signs that point to arson. For example, if you are a member of the first due company on the scene of a structure fire that is well-involved, and your response time was very good, that might be a clue. If you are stretching in your initial attack line, and it is an occupied house, but the owners are not on the scene and the side door was found open, there might be another sign. As you have knocked the fire down and are beginning overhaul and you smell an odor like that of gasoline or another flammable liquid, then you very possibly have an arson fire to deal with. All this information should be given to the IC, who will then notify the fire investigators. During your overhaul, be on the lookout for anything unusual or any container or flammable liquid stains. Be careful not to disturb anything that looks out of place in a normal living environment. Remember not to destroy this crime scene.

QUESTIONS—SALVAGE

1. How do you think you and your department can be prepared for preventing extensive water damage to property with minor fire conditions?

2. In a multi-story occupancy, on what floors will the salvage operations generally begin?

3. When the fire has been knocked down and the fire floor is measuring inches of water, what are a few techniques learned in this chapter that you as a firefighter can use to alleviate the excessive weight of the water condition?

4. Discuss some ways you can cover holes in the floor or warn others of potential risks resulting from fire suppression efforts.

5. Why is it important to secure a building or door after firefighting operations have been concluded?

6. List some tools you believe would be essential in the preservation of people's property after the main body of fire has been knocked down.

7. Why is it important to follow through with the shut-off of all the utilities before entering an area with standing water?

8. How would you clear a flat-roof drain to allow water to run freely and remove the added weight caused by water on the roof?

QUESTIONS—OVERHAUL

1. When searching for extension of fire in an adjoining room or attached structure and a minor fire has been knocked down, why is the use of thermal imaging cameras a good practice to follow?

2. In a multi-story building, do you think it is safer to remove smoldering mattresses down the interior stairs, creating a tripping hazard to firefighters, or to quickly bring it down an elevator?

3. Is it helpful to the fire investigators to remove suspicious items or appliances that may have caused the fire?

4. If you are responding to a commercial occupancy, which size of pike pole would you take? Answer the same for a two-and-a-half-story private dwelling.

5. How would you prepare to check for extension in the floor before actually getting down to the plywood for various flooring types, and what tools would you use?

6. When the main body of fire is knocked down by the firefighters, should the hoseline stay in place while overhaul takes place, or should it get out of the way of members performing overhaul? Why?

7. What must be done next if fire is found in wall bay spaces?

8. When is it safe to remove SCBA during overhaul?

9. If you can summarize the definition of overhaul, what would it be?

Introduction to Hazardous Materials/WMD

Edited by Jason Emery

This chapter provides knowledge items for the following NFPA Standard 472 requirements. For more detail, see the Knowledge Correlations on p. xxxvi.

Awareness	Operations	Product Control
4.1.1	5.1.1	6.6.1
4.2.1	5.2.2	
4.4.1	5.4.3	

OBJECTIVES

Upon completion of the chapter, you should be able to do the following:

- Describe the difference between hazmat/WMD incidents and other emergencies.

- Identify different locations through which hazardous materials are either stored or shipped.

- Describe the capabilities and limitations of the operations-level responder at a hazmat/WMD incident.

- Describe the impact hazardous materials laws and regulations have on emergency responses.

- Describe how the local emergency response plan (LERP) and department SOPs guide the operations-level responder at a hazmat/WMD incident.

- Define commonly used hazardous materials terminology as covered in this chapter.

- List the three main phases of a hazardous materials/WMD response.

INTRODUCTION

As discussed in chapter 3, Fire Department Organization, the fire service has evolved over the years into an all-hazards organization. Simply put, if it endangers the public, the fire department typically plays some role in the response. Along those lines, in most communities it is the responsibility of the fire department to handle the release of hazardous materials (fig. 22–1). In most cases these incidents are unintentional and the result of human error or container failure. In some cases, however, we encounter situations where the release is intentional and is classified as a criminal or terrorist incident. In either case, it is important that firefighters handle the response at the level their training allows. Because hazardous materials are used in or transported through every community, proper training prevents unnecessary and potentially dangerous exposures to these materials (fig. 22–2). Additionally, training is required by OSHA 1910.120, which states that employees who participate—or are expected to participate—in emergency responses be given training in hazardous materials.

Fig. 22–1. Fire departments are expected to handle all types of emergencies, including those involving hazardous materials. (Courtesy Tom Lenart)

Fig. 22–2. Hazardous materials are transported through every community. (Courtesy Emergency Training Solutions)

Historically, firefighters tend to be less comfortable handling hazmat responses than structural fires, rescue, or EMS runs, primarily because of the potential complexity of these incidents. The focus of the next four chapters in this text is to address the responsibilities of firefighters operating at the hazmat operations level and provide a clear picture about how to handle these types of incidents. The material is covered using the same simple and systematic approach that is employed on scene. The basic steps include analyzing the incident, developing the response plan, and then implementing the plan. These concepts can be applied to any hazmat scenario and will ensure an effective and orderly response, especially when multiple response agencies are involved.

HAZMAT/WMD INCIDENTS VS. OTHER EMERGENCIES

Hazardous materials/weapons of mass destruction incidents are different from other emergencies because they can be far more pervasive and severe than, say, a large structure fire. A release of a hazardous material can endanger responders and the public as well as the environment and property if proper actions are not taken to control or stop the release. Also, depending on the material, a release can affect a much larger geographical area, which increases the potential for injury or death. Depending on the scale, these incidents can become more complex than standard emergency responses and may require specially equipped and trained personnel to respond (fig. 22–3). The potential for long-term effects on people, the environment, and property should also be considered. Incidents involving terrorist activity also bring the additional danger of secondary attacks and armed resistance coupled with the fact that these releases are often designed to inflict the greatest amount of damage (fig. 22–4). Terrorist incidents also require that crime scene management, evidence preservation, and unified command be employed to work closely with the needs of law enforcement.

Fig. 22–3. Hazmat incidents are often more complicated than standard emergency responses. (Courtesy U.S. Air Force)

Fig. 22–5. Some communities have facilities that manufacture hazardous materials.

Fig. 22–4. Terrorist incidents such as the Oklahoma City bombing are designed to inflict great damage. (Courtesy U.S. Department of Defense)

Fig. 22–6. Hazardous materials are transported by rail through some communities. (Courtesy Emergency Training Solutions)

COMMON HAZARDOUS MATERIALS LOCATIONS

As mentioned, hazardous materials are used, stored, and transported in every community. It is important that responders recognize both the obvious and not-so-obvious locations where these materials may be found. Some response districts have facilities from which hazardous materials are produced and shipped (fig. 22–5). Others may use the materials in manufacturing facilities, and some may deal only in consumer quantities and vehicles that travel on their roadways and railways (fig, 22–6). The bottom line is that no matter how small the community, it is always possible to encounter a hazardous material.

Response personnel should conduct preplans of those facilities in their response area that utilize hazardous materials in quantity. Table 22–1 lists some of the locations where responders should expect to see hazardous materials.

Table 22–1. Locations where hazardous materials are found

Methods of Transportation

Roadways	Railways
Waterways	Pipelines
Airways	

Fixed Facility Locations

Large manufacturing or storage plants	Photo processing laboratories
Service stations	Fuel storage facilities
Doctors' offices	Agricultural stores
Hardware stores	Tank farms
Dry cleaners	Weapons depots
Paint supply stores	Warehouses
School laboratories	Laboratories
Farms	Maintenance facilities
Residences	Flight line areas
Pool supply stores	

Transportation Terminal Locations

Docks or piers	Airplane hangers
Railroad stations	Truck terminals

HAZMAT RESPONDER LEVELS AND RESPONSIBILITIES

As discussed in the introduction, responders must operate within their level of training and never above it. To do so would put both first responders and the public at risk. The **National Fire Protection Association (NFPA)** and the **Occupational Safety and Health Administration (OSHA)** both recognize the following levels of training and responsibility as they relate to hazardous materials incidents.

Awareness-level responder

Awareness-level responders are expected to recognize the presence of hazardous materials, secure the area, protect themselves and others, and request the response of appropriately trained personnel to the scene (fig. 22–7). These responders include those individuals who may arrive first on the scene of a hazmat incident in the normal course of their duties. This group includes law enforcement, emergency medical service (EMS) providers, and security personnel. Awareness-level responders do not typically train to play an active role in offensive or defensive operations. Their duties generally stop at protecting others from further harm and requesting the appropriate assistance needed such as fire, EMS, and law enforcement. These actions need to be performed in a manner consistent with departmental SOPs and the LERP.

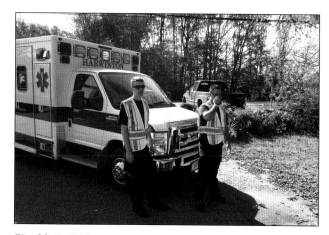

Fig. 22–7. EMS personnel typically operate at the hamzat awareness level.

Operations-level responder

Operations-level responders operate above the awareness level and are expected to respond to a hazmat incident in order to protect people, the environment, and property from the effects of the release. This response is carried out using a defensive approach to control the release from a safe distance and to prevent it from spreading. Operations-level responders are trained to act in a defensive manner only, without attempting to stop the release of the material at its source unless it can be done from a remote location (fig. 22–8). The role of the personnel operating at this level is based on the department's SOPs as well as the community's LERP.

Table 22–1. Important elements and their symbols

Element	Symbol	Element	Symbol
Hydrogen	H	Helium	He
Lithium	Li	Beryllium	Be
Boron	B	Carbon	C
Nitrogen	N	Oxygen	O
Fluorine	F	Sodium	Na
Magnesium	Mg	Neon	Ne
Aluminum	Al	Silicon	Si
Phosphorus	P	Sulfur	S
Chlorine	Cl	Argon	Ar
Potassium	K	Calcium	Ca
Arsenic	As	Selenium	Se
Bromine	Br	Krypton	Kr
Rubidium	Rb	Strontium	Sr
Iodine	I	Xenon	Xe
Cesium	Cs	Barium	Ba
Radon	Rn	Chromium	Cr
Manganese	Mn	Iron	Fe
Cadmium	Cd	Nickel	Ni
Copper	Cu	Zinc	Zn
Germanium	Ge	Cobalt	Co
Bismuth	Bi	Tin	Sn
Antimony	Sb	Mercury	Hg
Lead	Pb	Radium	Ra
Uranium	U	Plutonium	Pu

Fig. 22–8. Operations-level personnel can operate in a defensive manner only.

Although NFPA 1001 requires that operations-level training be part of the Firefighter I curriculum, there are numerous other reasons to be trained to this level. Although hazmat responses do not typically make up the bulk of runs for a fire department, hazardous materials are used in or transported through every community, which means there is always an opportunity to respond to that type of incident. Operations-level training prevents unnecessary and potentially dangerous exposures to response personnel and civilians alike. Lastly, OSHA 29 CFR 1910.120 requires this level of training for responders conducting defensive operations at a hazmat incident. The responsibilities of operations-level responders include analyzing the incident, planning a response, and then implementing the planned response. These actions are conducted with the guidance of a technician-level responder, an allied professional, or departmental SOPs. Per the NFPA 472 standard (2008 ed.), operations-level responders must receive additional training to perform any of the following mission specific operations: personal protective equipment (PPE), mass decontamination, technical decontamination, evidence preservation and sampling, product control, air monitoring and sampling, victim rescue and recovery, and responses to illicit laboratory incidents. In addition to the core competencies for the operations level, this text covers PPE and product control.

Technician-level responder

Technician-level responders are trained to a greater level and operate using offensive tactics to control and stop the flow of the hazardous material at its source. They utilize equipment and techniques that are above the level of the operations-level responder to enter the hot zone or area of release to complete this task (fig. 22–9). It is important to note, however, that operations-level personnel play an important support role for technician-level responses. They often staff the technical decontamination portion of the incident and assist with the donning and doffing of PPE. In addition, they can assist by collecting information and conducting research.

Fig. 22–9. Technician-level responders operate with a higher level of training and equipment. (Courtesy U.S. Navy)

HAZARDOUS MATERIALS LAWS AND REGULATIONS

There are numerous federal laws that are related to hazardous materials response, planning, and operations. It is key that the emergency response community understands these laws and the requirements set for them. Federal laws are created by the U.S. Congress, while rules and regulations are created by federal or other governing bodies to provide for ease of interpretation and compliance. The following is a synopsis of the laws and their basic requirements.

OSHA HAZWOPER

- In states that have OSHA plans, the **Hazardous Waste Operations and Emergency Response (HAZWOPER; 29CFR1910.120)** regulations are enforced by OSHA compliance officers. In the remaining states, these same regulations have been adopted by the federal **Environmental Protection Agency (EPA)** under 40CFR311. This law with its accompanying regulations applies to all emergency responders whether public or private and includes hazmat teams, police officers, firefighters, and industrial emergency responders. For emergency responders, this law contains the following levels of competency: awareness, operational, technician, specialist, and on-scene incident commander. It also includes requirements for skilled support personnel (e.g., heavy equipment operators) and specialist employees (e.g., an on-site scientist in a research facility). In fixed facilities, one may find emergency response teams that are trained to the various levels of competency along with skilled support personnel and specialist employees. During pre-incident planning of fixed facilities, it is imperative that fire departments, hazmat teams, and other emergency response agencies seek out these groups and understand their roles during a site emergency.

Comprehensive Environmental Response Compensation and Liability Act

- The **Comprehensive Environmental Response Compensation and Liability Act (CERCLA)**, also known as the Superfund, covers unattended, abandoned, or inactive hazardous waste disposal sites. This law also requires that the "responsible party" (who caused the hazmat release) be held liable and must contact the National Response Center upon release of a "reportable quantity."

Superfund Amendments and Reauthorization Act

- The **Superfund Amendments and Reauthorization Act (SARA-1986)** amended CERCLA and also added sections on planning, preparedness, training, and response, which in turn had the most influence on "the way we do business" of most laws pertaining to hazmat. This law, in turn, led to the development of OSHA 1910.120 HAZWOPER. In addition, SARA Title III (Emergency Planning and Community Right to Know Act) led to the development of state and local emergency planning committees known as SERCs and LEPCs, respectively.

- The **Resource Conservation and Recovery Act (RCRA)** requires the proper management and disposal of hazardous waste in treatment, storage, and disposal facilities and establishes installation, leak prevention, and notification requirements for underground storage tanks. Most large industrial facilities have storage areas for their waste, known as RCRA pads, which may or may not have fire protection.

Clean Air Act

- The **Clean Air Act (CAA)** was enacted to control airborne emissions to protect the environment. When amended in 1990, it addressed emergency response planning at certain facilities that produce highly hazardous or toxic materials. In addition, it authorized the creation of the Chemical Safety and Hazard Investigation Board, which is now known as the **Chemical Safety Board (CSB)** and operates similarly to the **National Transportation Safety Board (NTSB)**. The CSB is dispatched to major chemical incidents, mostly at fixed facilities, to investigate the cause and report back to the federal government.

Oil Pollution Act

- The **Oil Pollution Act (OPA)** amended the original federal Water Pollution Control Act. It covers fixed facilities and carriers (barges, tankers, railcars, deep-water terminals, vessels, pipelines) and requires emergency plans, drills, exercises, and the verification of spill response contractors and their capabilities. Where a coastal zone may be affected, area committees and **area contingency plans (ACPs)** are required.

Community Emergency Planning Regulations (40CFR 301–303)

- These regulations were developed for SARA Title III, and they require that state and local emergency planning groups develop and/or review hazardous materials response plans (fig. 22–10). The SERCs do this on the state level, and the LEPCs do it on a local level. LEPCs typically include the local fire department, law enforcement, emergency medical service, government representatives, health department, nonprofit assistance agencies, and perhaps local industry.

Fig. 22–10. Local officials and emergency responders play a vital role in the LEPC.

HAZARDOUS MATERIALS RESPONSE GUIDELINES

Two valuable resources to hazmat responders are the LERP and department SOPs. These documents can provide valuable guidance on how to handle a hazardous materials release in the community.

Local Emergency Response Plan (LERP)

A good place for the responder to learn about hazardous materials/WMD response is the local incident response plan. Your community likely has an emergency response plan already developed. Many times an annex specific to hazardous materials is included in that plan. Plans for terrorism events are also are also annexed in local emergency response plans, as the personnel responding to these types of incidents must have the same training as a hazardous materials responder.

The LERP addresses how the local response will occur, and, if necessary, how that response becomes elevated to the state and even the federal level. The LERP is usually maintained in the local communications center or the 9-1-1 center. A copy should be located in each station so that department members can become familiar with its contents.

Standard operating procedures

Progressive departments have standard operating procedures (SOPs) or standard operating guidelines (SOGs) for all types of department operations, including hazardous materials responses. These documents are designed to give responders guidance on how to handle different types of incidents they may encounter in the field. Responders should be familiar with and know how to access their department's SOPs or SOGs. A copy of these documents should be provided in each station.

COMMON TERMINOLOGY

It is important that all hazmat responders be familiar with basic terms that are referenced in hazmat standards and responses. This familiarity enables responders from various backgrounds to speak the same "language" at the scene. It is important to understand that, although all of these substances fall into the general classification of hazardous materials, there are several terms used based on which agency created the definition.

Hazardous materials definitions

A **hazardous material** is defined by the U.S. Department of Transportation (DOT) as any substance or material capable of posing an unreasonable risk to health, safety, and property when transported in commerce, and which has been so designated. In Canada the term used for these materials is **dangerous goods**.

Hazardous substance

A **hazardous substance** is a substance designated under the CERCLA as posing a threat to waterways and the environment if released. In OSHA 29 CFR 1910.120 the term is used to describe all the chemicals that are regulated by the EPA as hazardous substances and by the DOT as hazardous materials.

Hazardous chemical

A **hazardous chemical** is defined in OSHA 29 CFR 1910.120 as any chemical that poses a physical or health hazard.

Dangerous goods

Dangerous goods, as defined by the Canadian Transport Commission (CTC), describes any product, substance, or organism included by its nature or by the regulation in any of the United Nations (UN) classes of hazardous materials.

Hazardous waste

A **hazardous waste**, as defined by the DOT, includes any material that is subject to the hazardous waste manifest requirements of the EPA listed in 40 CFR, part 262.

Weapons of mass destruction

A **weapon of mass destruction (WMD)** is a material or device designed to inflict great harm on people or property. It can be an explosive device, a toxic or poisonous chemical, a disease organism, or radioactive device (fig. 22–11).

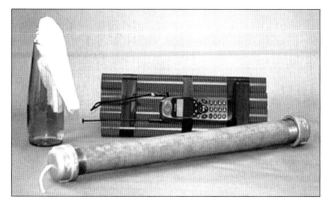

Fig. 22–11. Explosive devices are considered weapons of mass destruction.

MANAGING HAZMAT/WMD INCIDENTS

Due to the potential complexity of a hazmat/WMD incident, it is important that responders follow a logical and standardized course of action to ensure that all response objectives are met and the safety of the responders and civilians alike is addressed. The following steps are used to guide response personnel through the response.

Analyze the incident

Like a standard emergency response, this phase begins the moment the emergency is dispatched. The information given to the responder from the dispatcher on the initial assignment, as well as updates given en route, will be used to make initial decisions about how to approach the scene (fig. 22–12). Information such as the location and, if possible, the materials involved provides a solid base to build upon. Additional information collected will be used to further analyze the incident and to plan and implement the response. The key steps in this process are to survey the scene, collect hazard and response information, and determine the likely behavior of the material. During this response phase, personnel isolate the area and deny entry to prevent any additional exposures as they collect information (fig. 22–13).

Fig. 22–12. Size-up begins with the information provided by the dispatcher. (Courtesy J. Rains)

Fig. 22–13. The collection of information is used to plan the appropriate response.

Plan the response

After the data on the material(s) involved is collected and analyzed, it is used to plan the proper response. It may be determined that the resources currently on scene are appropriate or that more advanced equipment and training is required. Issues such as scene control and safety are considered closely based on the material(s) involved. The incident command system branches and divisions are filled out in order to support the options chosen. The response objectives are defined along with the means by which to accomplish those objectives, including selection of PPE (fig. 22–14).

Fig. 22–14. The information collected in the initial phase of the response is used to determine the level of PPE required.

Implementing the response

During this phase, the chosen response objectives are implemented and product control or rescue operations are conducted (fig. 22–15). This phase should be continuously evaluated to ensure that the objectives are being met, and adjustments should be made if they are not. Personnel should be decontaminated at the end of this phase to ensure that there is no potential for the material to spread outside of the containment area.

Fig. 22–15. The response objectives are implemented during the response phase of the operation.

INTRODUCTION SUMMARY

The modern fire service includes hazardous materials incidents in the many types of incidents they are responsible for. These incidents are often more involved than a standard emergency response and require special training and equipment. Hazardous materials can be found in any community, regardless of its size, in households, commercial and industry facilities, or in transportation. Response personnel trained to the operations level are tasked with taking a defensive approach to handling a hazardous materials release in any of those locations (fig. 22–16). There are many laws that govern the use and accidental release of hazardous materials to which responders can look for guidance. Additionally, the LERP or department SOPs provide direction to emergency responders handling the incident. Responders should remember the three major phases of a hazmat response when managing the scene of a hazmat release:

- Analyzing the incident

- Planning the response

- Implementing the response

Fig. 22–16. Operations-level personnel are tasked with taking a defensive approach only.

QUESTIONS

1. Which training level has the primary duties of protecting others from harm and requesting assistance?

    _____

2. How are hazmat incidents different from other emergencies?

    _____

3. What type of hazardous materials location would a photo processor be?

    _____

4. What are the three levels of training recognized by NFPA and OSHA related to hazardous materials
    incidents? _____

5. Which NFPA Standard applies to a hazmat response? _____

6. Name three federal laws that relate to a hazardous materials response.

    _____

    _____

    _____

7. Community Emergency Planning Regulations call for each state to form what type of group, and what is
    the group's primary responsibility?

    _____

    _____

    _____

8. What are the three steps to ensuring all hazmat response objectives are met?

    _____

    _____

    _____

Analyzing the Hazmat/WMD Incident

Edited by Jason Emery

This chapter provides knowledge items for the following NFPA Standard 472 requirements. For more detail, see the Knowledge Correlations on p. xxxvi.

Awareness		Operations	
4.1.2	4.2.3	5.2.1	5.2.4
4.2.1	4.4.1	5.2.2	
4.2.2		5.2.3	

OBJECTIVES

Upon completion of the chapter, you should be able to do the following:

- List and define the three different steps of the *analyzing the incident* process.

- Describe how the senses are used during an initial scene survey and the limitations associated with them.

- List the types of scene conditions operational-level responders should be aware of when responding to a hazmat/WMD incident.

- List the different types of transportation and facility markers that may be encountered by response personnel, and describe the type of information each provides.

- Recognize the different types of container shapes found in fixed facilities and in transport and the types of materials they hold based on visible construction features.

- List the different hazard classes in the Department of Transportation (DOT) classification system, and identify the class(es) involved in an incident based on placards displayed on the container.

- List and define the common terms used to describe the chemical and physical properties of a material.

- Describe the different health hazards associated with a hazmat/WMD incident.

- Define the different routes of entry into the body associated with hazardous materials.

- Describe the information that can be provided by material safety data sheets (MSDSs) and shipping papers.

- List additional hazardous materials resources available to emergency responders and the type of information provided by each one.

- List the factors that are involved in determining the behavior of the material being released from its container.

- Describe the steps involved in using the Department of Transportation Emergency Response Guide (DOT ERG) to determine the size of the endangered area.

- Describe the difference between the initial isolation zone and protective action distances as listed in the DOT ERG.

SECTION I:
SURVEYING THE SCENE

INTRODUCTION

Surveying the scene is arguably the most important phase because it forms the basis for all decisions made for the remainder of the incident. Effective decisions can be made only if the effort is made to collect all available information on a release and then consult available resources to determine the correct actions (fig. 23–1). Great care must be taken during this process; even something as simple as misspelling the chemical name can result in major problems.

Fig. 23–1. Effective decisions require the collection of information on the product released.

The three basic steps in this phase are:

1. *Surveying the scene* to collect clues on the type(s) of materials involved

2. *Collecting the hazard and response information* regarding those materials

3. *Determining the behavior of the material* based on what the physical properties are determined to be

Surveying the scene can be done in conjunction with the *isolate the area and deny entry process* that will be addressed later.

USING THE SENSES

Upon arrival on the incident scene, the responder's senses provide the first clues that the incident involves some type of hazardous materials release. The senses of sight, smell, and sound can provide valuable clues to response personnel.

For example, liquids pooling on the floor or the ground, chemical reactions taking place, a vapor cloud or fire, injured persons in the area, condensation lines on pressurized tanks, corrosive reactions taking place, and the boiling of unheated substances are all visual indicators that a release has occurred. The hissing sound of a pressurized container releasing its contents or the banging/creaking from overstressed containers are other indicators of a pending release or a release that has occurred. Lastly, the odor of a gas leak or burning materials can also be an indicator.

Unfortunately, using the senses is limited in that the closer a first responder gets to the hazmat incident to identify the product, the greater the risk of exposure. Some materials can be deadly at the amount required to smell them, so by the time they are detected the responders have already been exposed to a lethal dose. Other materials are odorless, tasteless, and colorless, thus providing no warning to those being exposed. In addition, it is possible for some materials to deaden the senses so that, although it is still present in the air, it can no longer be smelled by a responder who may wrongly determine that the material has dissipated. It is always best to conduct scene surveys from a distance using binoculars or other visual aids to stay out of the exposure area (fig. 23–2).

Fig. 23–2. Always maintain a safe distance when collecting hazard information.

SCENE CONDITIONS

Good observation skills play a key role on the initial response and size-up. If responders fail to take a good look at the incident as a whole, they often miss important pieces of information. As with any emergency scene, tunnel vision can be dangerous and must be avoided at all costs. When arriving on scene, consider some of the following questions and make note of what is occurring or will potentially occur:

- *What type of container is involved?* Is it a rail car, cargo tank, intermodal, or fixed facility tank?

- *What is the container size?* Is it a small cardboard box, a 55-gal (208-L) drum, or a 50,000-gal (189,271-L) fixed-facility tank, and how much potential release of product is there?

- *Is the container marked?* Are there visible markings such as DOT placards, UN/NA numbers, NPFA 704 symbols or product names, and ID numbers that can be used to determine the product or general hazards (fig. 23–3)?

Fig. 23–3. Container markings can help identify the product and/or its hazards.

- *What is the physical state of the material?* Is it a solid, liquid, or a gas?

- *How badly is the container damaged?* Is it a large tear, a small hole, or broken piping or valving, and what is the rate of product release?

- *How long has the container been leaking?* Is it a few minutes, several hours, or a few days, and how much product was potentially released?

- *Is the container on fire?* Is extinguishment necessary, or would it be better to let the material burn off?

- *Are there any injuries involved?* Are they minor or serious, and will victims need emergency decontamination (fig. 23–4)?

Fig. 23–4. If there are any victims, determine if they require emergency decontamination.

- *What is the topography like?* Is it flat, allowing for minimal product spread, or are there hills, facilitating the flow of the product away from the source of the leak?

- *How is the land used?* Is it industrial, farming, residential, or a highway, and how will the release potentially impact the area?

- *How accessible is the release?* Will response personnel and vehicles have access to the scene, or will extra equipment be needed?

- *What are the weather conditions?* Is it hot or cold? Is it raining or snowing? What is the wind speed and direction? How do these conditions impact the spread of the material?

- *Are there any bodies of water nearby?* Is there a danger of the material reaching a reservoir, lake, pond, river, or stream, thus spreading the contamination?

- *What, if any, are the public exposure risks?* Was the release in an urban or rural area, and how much of the population is at risk (fig. 23–5)?

Fig. 23–5. Hazmat releases in urban areas can provide greater challenges than in rural areas because of the dense population.

- *What types of utilities are in the area?* Are there any above- or below-grade wires in pipelines in the area that could provide a potential ignition source or a path for the material to flow along?

- *Are there any storm or sewer drains nearby?* How close is the product to flowing down the drains, and where do those drains lead?

- *Do potential sources of ignition exist?* Are any of the following present in the area: lighting equipment, chemical reactions, electric motors and controllers, open flames, cutting or welding operations, smoking materials, or portable heating equipment?

- *Is the incident inside a structure?* Are there people inside of the building? Are there any floor drains or an HVAC system involved that could inadvertently lead to a spread of the material?

- *Is anything out of the ordinary occurring?* Is there evidence that this release could involve some type of criminal or terrorist activity based on the material and location or by visible clues on scene?

After making an initial observation of the scene, the firefighter can obtain a better idea of the incident scope and determine whether additional resources are needed, or if the first-due assignment can properly mitigate the situation. Additionally, the responder can determine the number of potential exposures in the area and establish other valuable pieces of information that can be used when planning the response phase.

FACILITY AND TRANSPORTATION MARKINGS

Container markings can play a key role identifying the hazards of a particular product, and potentially even the identity of the material involved. The goal is to identify these markings as early in the incident as possible so that the firefighter can make informed decisions about how the release should be handled. These markings should be identified from a distance to ensure that the responder stays out of the exposure area. Sometimes, in addition to placarding, the container itself will be marked with the name of the material that it holds (fig. 23–6).

Fig. 23–6. Container markings play a key role in product identification.

Facility markings

Various types of markings can be found on hazardous materials containers in fixed facilities. They can range from placarding that indicates the general hazards of the substance to the name of the product listed on the tank. The following are different types of markings found on fixed facility containers.

National Fire Protection Association (NFPA) 704. NFPA standard 704 is a marking system used for fixed bulk storage tanks and vessels in fixed facilities. Many state and local fire codes require that the NFPA 704 system be used at all fixed facility locations within their jurisdiction. It has four diamond-shaped sections joined to create one large diamond placard-type marking (fig. 23–7). This placard system provides information about the general hazards and degree of severity for flammability, toxicity, and reactivity.

Fig. 23–7. The NFPA 704 marking system consists of color-coded diamonds with a number system to indicate the level of danger for specific hazards.

The numbering system ranges from 0 to 4, 0 being no hazard and 4 being the worst hazard. The left diamond section (blue) denotes the health hazard of the material; the upper diamond (red) denotes the flammability of the material; the right diamond section (yellow) denotes the reactivity of the material; and the bottom diamond section (white) denotes any special hazard associated with the material.

Tables 23–1 through 23–4 illustrate the hazards associated with each number given in the different sections of the diamond. This system does not identify the product; identification must be made through other means. Also, this system does not provide specific information on the hazards; it only provides a general estimate of how dangerous the hazard is in the context of each of the categories.

Table 23–1

Health Hazard			
Symbol/ Number	Level	Danger	Definition
4	Extreme	Highly toxic	Short-term exposure may be fatal. Special protective equipment may be required.
3	Serious	Toxic	Avoid inhalation or skin contact.
2	Moderate	Moderately toxic	May be harmful if inhaled or absorbed through the skin
1	Slight	Slightly toxic	May cause slight irritation
0	Minimal		All chemicals have some degree of toxicity

Table 23–2

Flammability			
Symbol/ Number	Level	Danger	Definition
4	Extreme	Extremely flammable gas or liquid	Flash point below 73°F
3	Serious	Flammable	Flash point from 73°F to 100°F
2	Moderate	Combustible	Requires moderate heating to ignite Flash point 100°F to 200°F
1	Slight	Slightly combustible	Requires strong heating to ignite
0	Minimal		Will not burn under normal conditions

Table 23–3

Reactivity Hazards

Symbol/ Number	Level	Definition
4	Extreme	Explosive at room temperature
3	Serious	May explode if shocked or heated under confinement or mixed with water
2	Moderate	Unstable, may react with water
1	Slight	May react if heated or mixed with water
0	Minimal	Normally stable, does not react with water

Table 23–4

Special Hazard Symbols

Symbol/ Number	Definition
W̶	Water reactive
OX	Oxidizer
COR	Corrosive
☢	Radioactive

Hazardous Materials Identification System (HMIS). The HMIS provides clear, recognizable information to facility employees by standardizing the presentation of chemical information. This system was designed to inform workers of the dangers posed by exposure to hazardous materials they work with under normal conditions. This is accomplished with color codes corresponding to the hazards of a product, assigned numeric ratings indicating the degree of hazard, and alphabetical codes designating appropriate personal protective equipment (PPE) employees should wear while handling the material.

In many respects the HMIS is similar to the NFPA 704 marking system. The color and number coding are identical for fire, health, and reactivity hazards. But instead of the diamond, the HMIS uses a color bar system (fig. 23–8). In this system, the white section is used to indicate what level of protective equipment is required instead of the special hazard denoted by white in the 704 system. This is indicated by a letter, with each letter specifying a different level of protection. Another feature that differs from the NFPA label system is that HMIS allows an asterisk (*) to designate a material as a carcinogen (cancer-causing material) or for materials known to have an adverse effect given chronic exposure.

Fig. 23–8. In many ways the HMIS is similar to the NFPA 704 marking system.

Miscellaneous container markings—fixed facility. In addition to the placards and symbols discussed previously, the first responder will often encounter other markings on fixed facility tanks that can help determine the contents of the container and provide other valuable information. For example, the product name and/or the capacity of the tank may be labeled or stenciled directly on the tank. Another helpful piece of information is the tank or site identification number (fig. 23–9). This ID number can be used in conjunction with site preplans or emergency operations plans to determine the contents of the tank as well as its volume.

Fig. 23–9. Site identification numbers or the material name stenciled on the tank aids in the identification process.

Transportation markings

Transportation markings can be found on all modes of transport and can include placarding indicating the hazard class to which the material belongs, pipeline markings, package labeling, and other container markings. These markings can aid in understanding the general hazards associated with the loads as well as more specific information, depending on how well it is marked.

United Nations Numbering System (UN). This international system of identifying hazardous materials and dangerous goods has been adopted by most countries around the world. The four-digit **UN** numbers are required for shipment of hazardous materials. The DOT regulations require all vehicles to apply placards using this numbering system as well as the hazard class. North American (NA) numbers are identical to UN numbers and can be assigned to a material if it does not have a UN number.

There is a two-part system to UN/NA identification numbers: the first part divides hazardous materials into nine hazard classes that form the basis for the DOT hazard classes; the second part assigns a four-digit number to specific materials for identification purposes.

The UN/NA identification system utilizes the UN hazard classes list in table 23–5.

Table 23–5. UN hazard classes

1	Explosives
2	Gases
3	Flammable liquids
4	Flammable solids
5	Oxidizers
6	Poisons and infectious substances
7	Radioactive substances
8	Corrosives
9	Hazardous materials not otherwise defined
ORM-D	Other regulated materials

The four-digit UN/NA identification number is required only on tank cars, cargo tanks, and portable tanks. It may be found on the face of a standard DOT placard (fig. 23–10), or it may appear on its own panel. The DOT requires that if the UN number appears on its own panel, it must be accompanied by another placard that indicates its hazard class. When hazardous materials are being transported in bulk containers, this four-digit ID is required to be displayed on all four sides of the vehicle. Note that a single four-digit ID number is not necessarily specific to one chemical. For example, *UN 1993* is commonly displayed on many tanker trucks. This number is used when transporting diesel fuel.

Fig. 23–10. The UN/NA ID number can be included on the DOT hazard placard or on its own.

DOT placarding system. The U.S. DOT under CFR49 sets rules and regulations for marking vehicles that transport hazardous materials. These placards are also found at fixed facilities, because many tank trucks, railcars, and bulk intermodal tanks are parked or sited at these locations. The placarding system allows first responders to approach the scene of an incident and have a basic idea of what the materials involved could be. The DOT utilizes the United Nations (UN) hazardous materials classification system, which is discussed in greater detail in chapter 24, including the numbering and color system that is employed. For now, it is more important that the responder recognize the components of the placard. The following items are represented on the placard: hazard class symbol, hazard class designation or four-digit UN/NA number, a background color that represents the class, and the UN hazard class number (fig. 23–11).

Fig. 23–11. There are different pieces of information contained on the DOT placard.

Special situation transportation markings.

The **marine pollutant** marking is displayed on bulk shipping packages containing materials designated as marine pollutants. This marking must be displayed on both ends and both sides of the container unless it has been properly placarded as corrosive, flammable gas, etc. (fig. 23–12).

Fig. 23–12. Marine pollutant marking

The **elevated temperature materials** marking is displayed on each side and each end of bulk containers with the word HOT. The word HOT can be placed directly on the container or written in black letters and placed on a placard with a white background (fig. 23–13).

Fig. 23–13. Elevated temperature marking

Elevated-temperature materials are those materials that, when transported in bulk containers, are:

- Liquids at or above 212°F (100°C)

- Liquids with a flash point at or above 100°F (37.8°C) that are intentionally heated and then transported at temperatures at or above their flash point

- Solids at a temperature at or above 464°F (240°C)

All bulk containers containing materials that meet these requirements must be marked with the word HOT unless they contain molten aluminum or molten sulfur. These containers must be marked MOLTEN ALUMINUM and MOLTEN SULFUR, respectively.

The **inhalation hazard** marking is used on materials considered to be hazardous when inhaled (fig. 23–14). An example is anhydrous ammonia.

INHALATION HAZARD

Fig. 23–14. Inhalation hazard marking

Pipeline markings. A large network of pipelines runs throughout the United States, and millions of gallons of hazardous materials are transported through it each year. Like other transport methods, these pipelines fall under the jurisdiction of the DOT. Although primarily underground, they can pass over or under roads, railroads, and waterways. Typically, gas pipelines are used for one specific product only. Liquid petroleum pipelines, however, may carry several different petroleum products at the same time. It is imperative to recognize pipeline markings inside and adjacent to fixed facilities and throughout your response district. Pipeline markings may not always mark the exact location of the pipeline, and they are typically found at intersections with roads and railroads. They are required to display the following information (fig. 23–15):

- Contents of the pipeline (product class)
- Signal word: *caution*, *warning*, *danger*
- Operator of the pipeline
- Emergency contact telephone number

23–15. Pipeline markings are required to contain several pieces of information.

Military markings. Military markings are used to identify detonation, fire, and special hazards on military transport vehicles and at U.S. military installations. Because military ordinance is designed to create bodily harm and property damage, extreme caution should be practiced upon approach. Responders should remember that drivers may be under orders not to identify cargo that is sensitive in nature. The military should always be contacted immediately if one of their transport vehicles is involved in an incident, as they can provide valuable assistance in handling the product. Tables 23–6, 23–7, and 23–8 illustrate the symbols used by the military for hazardous materials as well as a general description of their properties.

Table 23–6. Explosive/fire symbols

Symbol	Hazard
1	Mass detonation hazard
2	Explosive with fragmentation hazard
3	Mass fire hazard
4	Moderate fire hazard

Table 23–7. Chemical hazard symbols

Symbol	Hazard
	Highly toxic
	Harassing agents
	White phosphorus munitions
	Apply no water
	Wear protective breathing apparatus

Table 23–8. Chemical warfare agents

Symbol	Hazard
G	G-type nerve agents
H	H-type mustard agents
L	Lewisite
VX	VX nerve agents

Radioactive labels. Radioactive labels contain several key points of information about the material being shipped and the level of danger associated with it. Responders need to be able to recognize and understand the importance of this information when coming in contact with a radioactive material that is being shipped. Figure 23–16 illustrates the different types of information presented on a radioactive label.

Fig. 23–16. Radioactive package labels contain key information about the radioactivity of the material being shipped.

The radioactive label identifies the following:

- The *visual hazard* symbol indicates a radioactive material as does the *UN class number* at the bottom.

- The *vertical bars* indicate the shipping category as either radioactive I, II, or III.

- The *contents* line identifies the material being shipped in the package.

- The *activity* line indicates the level of radiation emitted by the package.

- The *transport index* is the maximum level of radiation at a point 1 meter away from the surface of the package.

- There are three different shipping categories for radioactive materials. These are based on the level of radiation emitted by the material and the hazards associated with it. Additionally, fissile labels are used on packages containing fissile material. The fissile label will be displayed with one of the three radioactive category labels (table 23–9). The criticality safety index on this label is used by the shipper to indicate the maximum number of packages or containers allowed in a single shipment.

Table 23–9. Radioactive material and fissile labels

Category	Symbol	Color	Definition
I		White	Almost no radiation
			Maximum allowable radioactivity on the package surface is 0.5 mrem/hr.
II		Yellow/White	Low radiation levels
			Maximum level of radioactivity of the package surface is 50 mrem/hr and 10 mrem/hr at a distance of 3 ft (1 m) from the package.
III		Yellow/White	Higher radiation levels
			Maximum allowable radioactivity of the package surface is 200 mrem/hr and 10 mrem/hr at a distance of 3 ft (1 m) from the package.
			Vehicles carrying Yellow III packages must be placarded on both sides and ends.
Fissile			Fissile material label will be added to category I, II, or III labels.

Miscellaneous container markings—transportation. In addition to the placards and labels used in transportation discussed previously, there are other markings that provide helpful information. Identification numbers on the container can be compared to the shipping papers to ensure that they match; they also allow the responder to contact the shipper directly and confirm the material being shipped against the tank ID number.

On highway cargo tanks, in addition to the standard DOT placards, the shipper's ID or trailer number may be found (fig. 23–17). Other markings may include the company name and logo, a specially colored tank designated for the material being transported, and the manufacturer's specification plate.

Analyzing the Hazmat/WMD Incident

FIREFIGHTER I

Chapter 23

Fig. 23–17. Shipper's ID or trailer number can aid in the identification process.

On rail transport cars, the name of the material or commodity may be stenciled directly onto the tank for specific tank cars. These dedicated rail cars will have the product name stenciled on the side and are only used to transport that particular material. Reporting marks and volume/specifications markings can also be found (fig. 23–18). The seven-digit standard transportation commodity code (STCC) may be stenciled on the tank. Numbers starting with 48 indicate a hazardous waste.

Fig. 23–18. Reporting marks or volume specifications can be stenciled on the tank.

Lastly, on intermodals, additional markings can be found on the tank or tank frame. These markings indicate the ownership of the tank, the standards to which it was built, and a data plate indicating the size, type, and country codes (fig. 23–19).

Fig. 23–19. Intermodal container markings

Miscellaneous markings. Pesticide labels fall under the category of miscellaneous markings. They are used on containers that store chemicals designed to kill insects; these can be found on materials in fixed facilities or in transport. Pesticides can be found in all types of occupancies ranging from commercial to residential and in varying quantity, depending on their use. These labels contain the name of the pesticide and the following information (fig. 23–20):

- A *signal word* is used to indicate how toxic the materials are. They are broken into the following categories:

  - *Danger/poison* means highly toxic.

  - *Warning* means moderately toxic.

  - *Caution* means relatively low toxicity.

  - The label may also contain a *precautionary statement*, such as *keep from waterways* or *keep out of reach of children*.

- *Hazard statements* list special flammability, explosion, or chemical hazards as well as if it is an environmental hazard. For example: *Extremely Flammable—flash point below 80°F (27°C)*.

- The *active ingredient* section lists the names and percentage of the active chemicals that make up the pesticide. Inert ingredients are listed as a percentage only.

- Finally, the *Environmental Protection Agency (EPA) registration number* can be found on the label. The EPA regulates the manufacturing and labeling of pesticides and requires a registration number on the label. Additional information can be obtained by contacting the Chemical Transportation Emergency Center (CHEMTREC) and providing it with this number. The Canadian version of this number is the pest control products (PCP) number.

The label may also contain information on the mode of entry into the body, storage and disposal requirements, first aid information, and, if known, an antidote in the event of poisoning.

Fig. 23–20. Pesticide labels contain the name of the material and hazard level.

HAZARDOUS MATERIALS CONTAINERS

Hazardous materials can be stored and transported in containers of all shapes and sizes. From small laboratory containers to large tank farms holding thousands of gallons of product, operations-level personnel must be familiar with the types of fixed facility and transportation containers found in their district.

Container shapes

The container shape can provide valuable insight into the type of material contained inside. For example, containers with rounded ends and protected valving are most likely carrying a pressurized load, whereas containers with flat ends are typically nonpressurized. Containers with external stiffening rings may indicate a more dense substance, such as a corrosive. These simple clues can assist responders very early on in making

educated decisions about the contained materials until more specific data can be located.

Bulk packaging and containers (transportation)

There are many mobile tanks and vessels used to transport hazardous materials over roadways, railways, and waterways. The DOT defines bulk packaging as anything that meets the following requirements:

- Liquids: capacity greater than 119 gal (450 L)
- Solids: net weight greater than 882 lb (400 kg) or capacity greater than 119 gal (450 L)
- Compressed gas: water capacity in excess of 1,001 lb (454 kg)

They can be part of the vehicle, such as a cargo tank, or they can be placed on the vehicle, as in the case of intermodals. They are constructed of steel and aluminum; some are insulated and some are not. Some carry cryogenic materials (extreme cold), and some carry molten materials (extremely hot). First responders must have a basic understanding of what these tanks and vessels look like by shape so they can develop an action plan from a distance upon arrival at a transportation incident. Placards as required by DOT may not be visible after a crash or while the tank is burning; however, shapes sometimes tell the story. What follows is a review of the most common types of tanks, vessels, and railcars you will encounter in your work as a responder. Pay strict attention to the shapes of the containers, which can assist you with identifying the hazard class of the materials.

Over-the-road carriers. Millions of hazardous material shipments are made over highways and streets each year. From gasoline deliveries to the local service station to hydrogen deliveries at manufacturing plants, hazardous materials are all around us on our roadways. Recognition of the different types of container shapes and the materials they carry is important when responding to incidents involving these vehicles.

DOT 406/MC306 nonpressurized. These types of tank trucks are used commonly to transport gasoline, fuel oil, kerosene, and other flammable and combustible liquids (fig. 23–21). They can be constructed of steel or aluminum and run to a normal maximum capacity of 9,000 gal (34,069 L) and an internal pressure of 3–5 psi (21–35 kPa). They are usually compartmented (different grades of gasoline, e.g., regular, premium), have recessed manheads for rollover protection, and are normally egg-shaped or elliptical from the front or rear. Emergency shutoffs are located in the front and rear of the trailer. These tanks may contain gasoline, fuel oil, alcohol, other flammable/combustible liquids, and class B poisons. The main hazards are fire and environmental damage.

Fig. 23–21. DOT 406/MC306 trailer

DOT 407/MC307 low-pressure. These tanks are constructed of steel and may be rubber lined, with a normal capacity of 2,000 to 7,000 gal (7,571 to 26,498 L) and a pressure of under 40 psi (280 kPa) (fig. 23–22). They are also typically double-shelled (tank within a tank) for leak protection and have recessed manheads for rollover protection. Uninsulated tanks have a round cross section with external stiffening rings and a single compartment. Insulated tanks have a horseshoe cross section with one or two compartments. You may find flammable liquids, combustible liquids, poisons, and many other chemicals in these tanks. The main hazards are fire and environmental damage.

Fig. 23–22. DOT 407/MC 307 trailer

DOT 412/MC312 corrosive liquids. These tanks run with pressure under 75 psi (525 kPa) with a normal capacity of up to 7,000 gal (26,498 L) (fig. 23–23). The tank cross section is round, similar to the MC307 but with a smaller diameter compared to its length. They

have numerous rings around the tank shell for strength and stiffening purposes and have built-in rollover and splash protection. The loading area is usually covered with a corrosive-resistant materials. Typically, they will be constructed in one large compartment and contain acids of different varieties. The main hazard is chemical burns.

Fig. 23–23. DOT 412/MC 312 trailer

MC331 high-pressure tanks. These tanks contain gases or liquids under pressure starting at 100 psi (700 kPa) (fig. 23–24). They have capacities ranging from 2,500 to 11,500 gal (43,532 L) and have a bolted manway at the front or rear. The cross section is circular, and it has rounded or dome shaped endheads indicating a pressurized container; the front or rear is round as well. The emergency shutoffs are located in the front and rear of the trailer. These will also be typically painted white or some other heat-reflective color. These tanks carry propane, liquefied natural gas (LNG), anhydrous ammonia, and other gases that have been liquefied. The main hazard depends on the chemical; however, rapid expansion should be expected.

Fig. 23–24. MC331 trailer

MC338 cryogenic liquids. These are heavily insulated steel tanks that have a round cross section at the front and a squared-off cabinet or compartment at the rear where the valves are (fig. 23–25). Most often they are marked "refrigerated liquid," and you may often see puffs of vapor coming off the tank where the pressure-relief valve is operating. These cryogenic tanks usually carry liquid oxygen, nitrogen, carbon dioxide, and other gases that have been converted to a liquid by refrigeration. The main hazards are frostbite and burns.

Fig. 23—25. MC338 trailer

Compressed gas tube trailer. These units run with pressure between 3,000 and 5,000 psi (21,000 and 35,000 kPa). They are a series of steel tubes or cylinders banded and manifolded together and will typically have an overpressure device for each cylinder (fig. 23–26). The valves are protected with a compartment found at the rear of the trailer. These trailers often carry helium, hydrogen, and other gases under pressure, and can be found at construction or industrial sites. The main hazard depends on the gas; however, high pressures should be expected.

Fig. 23—26. Compressed gas tube trailer

Dry bulk cargo tanks. These tanks are not typically under pressure, but if so, the pressure would be under 22 psi (154 kPa) (fig. 23–27). From the side the tank may look like a series of inverted cones connected together. They use air to assist with loading the dry powders, and the discharge valves are located at the bottom of the hoppers. Dry bulk tanks carry a wide variety of materials, for example bakery flour, plastic pellets, fertilizers, and

even slurry-like concrete in bulk. The main hazard depends on the material contained, but toxic materials can also be carried.

Fig. 23—27. Dry bulk trailer

Railcar and tank cars. Railcars are used to transport hazardous materials throughout the country in large quantities. Any department with a railway that passes through its district should be aware of the potential need for a hazmat response. These incidents can range from a leaking container or valve to a large-scale release due to a train derailment. The following are the most common types of rail cars encountered, their characteristics, and the types of materials they carry.

Nonpressure tank cars. Also known as general service cars, these tank cars have a typical capacity of 4,000 to 45,000 gal (15,142 to 170,344 L) and operating pressures between 35 to 100 psi (245 to 700 kPa) (fig. 23–28). Older cars can have an expansion dome with visible fittings. These cars can carry a wide variety of materials including flammables, combustibles, oxidizers, organic peroxides, poisons, irritants, reactive liquids, and other similar materials. The valves and fittings are visible and accessible, and the tank car has flat or nearly flat endheads compared to a pressure tank car. The main hazard depends on the material contained.

Fig. 23—28. Nonpressure tank car

FIREFIGHTER I

Pressure tank cars. These tank cars can range in capacity from 4,000 to 45,000 gal (15,142 to 170,344 L) and operate at pressures between 100 and 600 psi (700 and 4,200 kPa) (fig. 23–29). They are constructed of steel or aluminum and are of a cylindrical noncompartmented design. The valves, gauges, and pressure relief valves are located inside a protective housing on the top of the tank.

Flammable liquids and toxic gases are usually found in these types of cars. These tanks have rounded endheads that are more pronounced than nonpressure tank cars. The main hazard depends on the material contained.

Fig. 23–29. Pressure tank car

Cryogenic tank cars. These are heavily insulated steel tanks of a double wall design that contain liquids refrigerated to –150°F (–101°C) or less, at a pressure of 25 psi (175 kPa) or less (fig. 23–30). The fittings on these tank cars are at ground level at either the ends or in the center side of the car in a cabinet. They carry the same cryogenic materials often carried on the MC338 (e.g., liquid oxygen, nitrogen, carbon dioxide, and other gases that have been converted to a liquid by refrigeration).

Fig. 23–30. Cryogenic tank car. (Courtesy Doug Stark)

Dry hopper cars. These cars vary in configuration and come in three different models: the pneumatically unloaded car, the covered hopper car, and the open-top hopper car (fig. 23–31). The pneumatically unloaded car uses compressed air to assist with unloading what may be dry caustic soda, nitrate fertilizers, plastic pellets, or other fine powders. The open-top hopper is used for heavy coarse material like gravel, coal, and the like. The closed-top hopper transports cement, grains, and similar medium-granulated materials.

Fig. 23–31. Closed top dry hopper rail car

Box cars. With these cars, identification of potential hazardous materials is typically not possible by the car's outer appearance (fig. 23–32). Instead, responders should look for hazard placards. Also, consider that refrigeration and heating systems may pose a hazard.

Fig. 23–32. With box cars, the type of material carried is not readily apparent.

Intermodal containers. An intermodal container consists of a tank container that is placed in a frame (fig. 23–33). This protects the container and allows for easy stacking, lifting, and securing. The frame can be of two types:

- Box type—encloses the tank in a cage

- Beam type—consists of frame structures at the ends of the container

Fig. 23–33. Box type Intermodal container

They are called intermodals because they can be used on ships, railways, or highways and are used to transport the same types of products as rail and highway containers. They can also be found in fixed facilities and in nonpressurized or pressurized configurations.

Nonpressurized intermodals can be found in two types—IM-101 and IM-102—and are the most common type of intermodal used in transportation. They typically have a maximum capacity of up to 6,300 gal (23,848 L) and can be used to carry liquid or solid materials. Despite being listed as nonpressure, some of these intermodals can be pressurized up to 100 psi (700 kPa). They may contain products such as nonflammable liquids, mild corrosives, foods, and other miscellaneous materials, flammable materials, corrosives, and miscellaneous industrial materials.

Pressurized intermodals (Type 5) typically have a maximum capacity of 5,500 gal (20,820 L), and can operate at a pressure of up to 500 psi (3,500 kPa). They may contain products such as liquefied gases, LPG, anhydrous ammonia, and bromine.

Cryogenic intermodals (Type 7) are designed as a tank within a tank separated by a layer of insulation, with the area between the tanks normally containing a vacuum designed to keep the contents cold. The construction is similar to that used in rail and cargo trailers designed for cryogenic materials. These intermodals may contain products such as helium, nitrogen, and oxygen.

Tube module intermodals contain several cylinders 9 to 48 in. (23 to 122 cm) in diameter permanently mounted in an open frame with a compartment at one end that encloses the valving, similar to those trailers seen in rail and highway use. Tube module intermodal containers may contain products such as helium, nitrogen, and oxygen.

Miscellaneous bulk packaging

Intermediate bulk containers (IBC). These containers are commonly found in industry to transport product around an industrial site and for moving bulk chemicals between processing facilities (fig. 23–34). The IBC is usually square in shape and can hold up to 500 gal (1,893 L) of liquid product or an equivalent amount of powders, slurries, or other forms of materials. They can be fabricated of aluminum, stainless steel, or a heavy gauge plastic. The plastic IBCs are often inside a heavy-gauge wire cage for stability and rigidness.

Fig. 23–34. Intermediate bulk containers (IBCs) are used to transport materials between facilities.

Bulk bags. These have capacities from 500 to 5,000 lb (227 to 2,268 kg). They contain solid materials such as pesticides or fertilizers (fig. 23–35).

Fig. 23–35. Bulk bags are used to transport solid materials.

One-ton cylinders. These are capable of transporting one ton of chlorine (fig. 23–36). These cylinders are 3 ft (1 m) in diameter and 8 ft (2.4 m) long with convex or concave heads. They are transported on railcars and trucks and contain liquefied gases such as chlorine, phosgene, and sulfur dioxide.

Fig. 23–36. One-ton cylinders are used to transport chlorine.

Non-bulk packaging or containers

Non-bulk quantities of hazardous materials can be transported using a variety of containers. These can carry many, if not all, of the same materials that the larger containers carry, so the hazards remain similar, but the materials are typically in smaller quantities. The DOT defines non-bulk packaging as containers meeting the following definition:

- Liquids: capacities less than 119 gal (450 L)

- Solids: capacities less than 882 lb (400 kg) or 119 gal (450 L)

- Compressed gas: water capacity of 1,001 lb (454 kg) or less

The following are the most common examples of non-bulk packages.

Bags. Many dry materials come in bags for transport and use in industrial fixed facilities (fig. 23–37). The contents could be pesticides, oxidizers, organic peroxides, and the like. Sometimes they are simple powders or granule materials. The bags can be made of woven materials, plastic, or paper and are sealed by heat, glue, ties, or stitching. Bags are normally transported and stored on pallets.

Fig. 23–37. Bags can contain various types of hazardous materials.

Boxes. These may be fiberboard (cardboard) or wood (fig. 23–38). They may contain almost any type of hazardous material such as liquids, solids, radioactive materials, and so on.

Fig. 23–38. Boxes can be used to transport virtually any type of hazardous materials.

Small containers. Common small containers of chemicals range in size from a few milliliters to 5-gal (19-L) cans (fig. 23–39). These types of containers are most often found in laboratories and research facilities where smaller containers are easy to store and easy to handle by the research staff. They are used for flammable liquids (solvents), corrosives, acids, and other lab materials needed in small quantities. These smaller containers can be made of metal, plastic, or glass.

Fig. 23–39. Small containers are often found in labs.

Carboys. These containers can be made of glass, metal, or plastic (fig. 23–40). Glass carboys can be found in a fiberglass or wood box for protection from breakage. Carboys are designed to hold liquids and can have a typical capacity of 5 to 15 gal (19 to 57 L). They may contain water, caustics, acids, or flammable/combustible solvents. The type of material the carboy is constructed of depends on the material carried.

Fig. 23–40. Carboys are designed to carry various liquids.

Dewar flasks. Liquid substances that must be kept cold can be shipped or stored in a Dewar flask (fig. 23–41). It is a double-walled container with a vacuum between the layers to provide thermal insulation, essentially a tank within a tank. One of the more common uses in a laboratory is to hold liquid nitrogen.

Fig. 23–41. Dewar flasks carry cryogenic liquids.

Drums. Drums are used to store and transport the entire gamut of hazardous materials (with a few exceptions), including but not limited to flammable liquids, combustible liquids, corrosives, water-reactive chemicals, oxidizers, acids, and the like (fig. 23–42). They can be constructed of metal, plastic, or a fiberboard material. It should be noted that not all drums are 55 gal (208 L) in size, although that's the most common. The 33-gal (125-L) drum can be found in fixed facilities as well. Also used to pack powders and liquids are fiber drums in various sizes, which look like cardboard but are treated and constructed of a tougher material than normal corrugated cardboard used in a standard delivery box. Getting it wet, however, may lead to container failure. Common industry practice when using fiber drums is to line them with heavy plastic bags or inserts.

Fig. 23–42. Drums come in various types and sizes and are used to carry just about any type of material.

Compressed gas cylinders. These cylinders are as common as storage tanks and drums in fixed facilities, and in certain industries they are more common (fig. 23–43). The semiconductor, electronics, pharmaceutical, and medical industries are some examples of industries in which compressed gases are used on a daily basis. Cylinders can range in size from a few pounds to several thousand gallons. Common household use of cylinders can range from a 20-lb (76-lb) gas grill propane cylinder to a 250-lb (946-lb) cylinder used to heat a home. Cylinders can hold flammable gases, toxic materials, poisons, corrosives, or mixtures of these at pressures between 40 and 900 psi (280 and 6,300 kPa). Cylinders are outfitted with an operation wheel for opening and closing and, with the exception of those storing poisons and similar toxins, have some type of relief plug or frangible disk to prevent overpressuring. This will operate when heated to relieve the pressure on the cylinder when impinged upon by fire or other heat source. The relief should allow the pressure to blow off to the atmosphere, rather than causing a catastrophic failure of the cylinders, which are constructed of rolled steel. This prevents flying shrapnel, which could cause injury or death.

Fig. 23–43. Compressed gas cylinders come in many sizes.

Radioactive packaging

There are several types of packages specially designed to transport radioactive materials. Each of these packages has different requirements depending on the type of radioactive materials being transported.

Excepted packaging is used to transport materials with extremely low levels of radiation (fig. 23–44). It is used for limited quantities of materials, instruments, and items such as smoke detectors, and consists of fiberboard boxes and wooden or steel crates. Packages and shipping papers do not indicate a hazardous material.

Fig. 23–44. Excepted packaging is used for materials with extremely low levels of radiation. (Courtesy of DOE)

Industrial packaging is used to transport materials that present a limited hazard (fig. 23–45). They may contain contaminated equipment or radioactive waste encapsulated in concrete. There are three different categories of industrial packaging based on strength ratings.

Fig. 23–45. Industrial packaging is used for materials that present a limited radiation hazard. (Courtesy of DOE)

Type A packaging is used to transport low-level radioactive wastes and radiopharmaceuticals with a higher concentration than is allowed in excepted and industrial packaging (fig. 23–46). Generally, type A packages have an inner containment vessel of glass, plastic, or metal and packing material of polyethylene, rubber, or vermiculite.

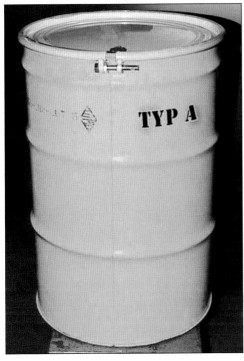

Fig. 23–46. Type A packaging is used to transport low-level radioactive wastes. (Courtesy of DOE)

Type B packaging is used to transport spent fuel, high-level radioactive wastes, and high-concentration radioisotopes (fig. 23–47). They range in size from a small radiography cameras to 55-gal (208-L) drums to heavily shielded steel casks that weigh 98 tons or more.

Fig. 23–47. Type B packaging is used to transport high-level radioactive wastes. (Courtesy of DOE)

Type C packaging was created for the transport of more highly radioactive material by air and is designed to withstand severe air crashes. It has the same basic shape as Type B package. This type of packaging is rarely used.

Fixed facility containers

Much like transportation containers, fixed facility containers come in a variety of shapes and sizes and are designed for the materials they hold. Many of the same concepts regarding tank design presented in the previous section will apply to these containers as well. Fixed facility storage is found in low or nonpressure, pressurized, and other types.

Low pressure or nonpressure storage. Low pressure or nonpressure fixed facility storage includes the following types.

Cone roof. The roof is an inverted cone welded to the tank side with weak seams so that the roof could easily blow off if the tank explodes or overpressurizes (fig. 23–48). This type of facility could contain any combination of flammable or combustible liquids and may have a fixed foam system.

Fig. 23–48. Cone roof tank

Horizontal tanks. These tanks sit on legs, usually a steel frame on a cement pad (fig. 23–49). Horizontal tanks can contain any combination of flammable or combustible liquids and may have some form of fixed protection (e.g., deluge or foam spray system).

Fig. 23–49. Horizontal tank

Floating roof tanks. The roof is set on floating pontoons that float up and down on the surface of the product contained therein (fig. 23–50). These are mostly used for gasoline storage where the floating roof eliminates vapor space, lessening the hazard.

Fig. 23–50. Floating roof tank

Covered top floating roof tanks. This type of tank looks similar to the cone roof tank, except that there are eye vents around the top rim of the tank (fig. 23–51). Like the floating roof tank, there is an internal pan that floats on the surface of the product. These tanks are mostly used for bulk storage of gasoline. A similar design to this type of tank consists of a roof shaped like a geodesic dome, also used for bulk gasoline storage.

Lifter roof tanks. The roof slides up and down on tracks, and when the contents pressurize, the roof lifts slightly to relieve the pressure. This tank is used for gasoline and other high vapor-pressure flammable liquids.

Underground storage tanks (nonpressure). These are found mostly in gas stations where the tanks are buried below grade, and the materials are pumped to the surface for dispensing.

Fig. 23–51. Covered top floating roof tank

Dome top/dome roof. These are low-pressure tanks for flammable and combustible liquids stored up to 15 psi (105 kPa) (fig. 23–52).

Fig. 23–52. Dome top/dome roof tank

Pressurized fixed facility storage. Storage types for pressurized fixed facilities include the following.

Spherical pressure vessels. High-pressure storage for up to 600,000 gal (2.3 million L), these vessels are used mostly for liquefied petroleum gas (LPG) and vinyl chloride (fig. 23–53). It is a single shell tank of noninsulated design with operating pressures ranging from 100 to 500 psi (700 to 3,500 kPa). Like water storage tanks, these tanks are often sited on large steel support legs.

Fig. 23–53. Spherical pressure tank

Horizontal pressure tanks. These are high-pressure storage tanks with capacities from 500 to 40,000 gal (1,893 to 151,416 L) of product at 100 to 500 psi (700 to 3,500 kPa) (fig. 23–54). Its rounded ends indicated a pressurized container. They are typically of a single shell, noninsulated design and are usually painted white or a highly reflective color to reflect light and heat. These tanks are used most often for propane, ammonia, butane, ethane, compressed natural gas (CNG), and similar materials.

Fig. 23–54. Horizontal pressure tank

Other types. Additional types of fixed facility storage include the following.

Cryogenic liquid tanks. Pressures vary from product to product and can range up to 250 psi (1,750 kPa) with a typical capacity of up to 1,000 gal (3,785 L) at most fixed facilities (fig. 23–55). As with cryogenic transport containers, they are insulated and vacuum jacketed. They can be found at hospitals, gas processing plants, and industrial plants. They are used for carbon dioxide, liquid oxygen, liquid nitrogen, and similar materials.

Mounded above-ground tanks. In older terminals, usually fuel oil depots and the like, tanks that are half in-ground and half above-ground may be found, mounded over with dirt and grass or gravel. These tanks are connected to a fuel oil truck loading rack and are protected with a bulk foam system.

Fig. 23–55. Cryogenic tank

SECTION I CONCLUSION

To make educated decisions about the types of materials encountered at an incident and their dangers, the operations-level responder must carefully observe scene conditions to gather information. Upon arrival, a proper scene condition assessment starts the process by identifying the potential extent of the release as well as how it will affect the surrounding area and exposures. Additional information can be gathered by recognizing facility and transportation markings that, at the very least, will identify the hazard class or dangers associated with the material and, at best, may include the very name of the material. Likewise, recognizing the different types of container shapes used in transport and fixed-facility applications and understanding how the design can assist in identifying potential contents is also very important. It is, however, only the first step in the analyzing-the-incident phase. The initial observations must be backed up through the collection of hazard and response information.

Section II:
COLLECTING HAZARD AND RESPONSE INFORMATION

INTRODUCTION

After conducting the initial scene survey to determine the potential scope of the incident, the first responder must begin collecting more information about the product. This process may start with determining the hazards class of the material using the DOT placards and proceed to using other resources to determine the exact chemical and physical properties of the material. Responders should be aware that in some instances determining the name of the product may be relatively easy, whereas in other situations it can take some time to locate the name. There are six basic types of information gathered in this phase: material identification, physical properties, chemical properties, physical hazards, health information, and response information. Depending on how much information is readily available, this can be a time-consuming process.

DOT PLACARDING

The Department of Transportation's hazard classification system can provide valuable response information at a hazmat incident. The placards required to be displayed on transportation containers allow emergency response personnel to recognize potential response hazards early in the incident and before more specific information can be collected.

DOT hazards and divisions

As discussed earlier in this chapter, the U.S. DOT sets placarding requirements for hazardous materials being transported from one location to another. Materials are placarded according to their primary danger based on the UN hazard classification system. Responders should be aware, however, that a material grouped in one class may have other hazards associated with it that are not immediately apparent because there is no placard for it. The classifications are broken up into nine classes, with several having subcategories or divisions to account for specific issues. For example, Class 2 is for gases, but there is a division for flammable, nonflammable, poisonous,

and so on. There is no division for refrigerated liquefied gases and cryogenic liquids, and they are placarded based on the primary hazard of the substance. These materials have boiling points colder than –90°C (–130°F) at atmospheric pressure.

Table 23–10 illustrates each hazard class, the divisions that make up that class, the representative placard, the hazard, and examples of materials found in the particular class/division.

Placarding requirements. The U.S. DOT requires that hazmat loads of 1,001 lb (454 kg) or more be marked with the appropriate placard indicating the material's primary hazard. The placards must be visible on all four sides of the vehicle. The following materials, however, must be placarded if they are transported in any quantity:

- 1.1, 1.2, 1.3 explosives
- 2.3 poisonous gas
- 4.3 dangerous when wet
- 5.2 organic peroxide (type B, liquid or solid, temperature controlled)
- 6.1 poison (material poisonous by inhalation)
- 7 radioactive (radioactive yellow III)

A *dangerous* placard is used when the weight of two or more categories of hazardous materials exceeds 1,000 lb (454 kg) (fig. 23–56). With this placard, identification of the specific hazard is not readily apparent.

Fig. 23–56. With the dangerous placard, identification the specific hazard is not readily apparent.

Non-bulk shipments (not exceeding 1,000 lb [454 kg]) of two or more categories of hazardous materials that require placards may use the *dangerous* placard instead of the individual placards for each material. The placarding rules require that if 1,000 lb (454 kg) or more of one category of material is loaded at one facility, then the placard for that specific material must be used.

An additional category, *other regulated materials* (ORM-D), are consumer commodities that present a limited hazard during transportation due to form, quantity, or packaging. A placard is not used, only labels (fig. 23–57).

Fig. 23–57. Other regulated materials (ORM-D) label

A consumer commodity is a material that is packaged or distributed in a form intended or suitable for sale through retail sales agencies, or a material used by individuals for personal care or household use. This term also includes drugs and medicines. Examples include small arms ammunition and furniture polish.

Limitations of placards. Responders arriving on the scene of an incident involving hazardous materials need to be aware that there are limitations to the placarding system. The first thing to remember is that only the primary hazard is placarded, and there may be other dangers associated with the material not indicated by the placard. If the vehicle or tanker was involved in a collision or engulfed in flames, the placards may not be visible. In some instances response personnel may not be able to get close enough to see the placards. Human error can always play a part as well. Some shipments may be unmarked or improperly marked, and hazards may not be immediately apparent. For example, if the placards were never applied, applied incorrectly, or if they were never changed from the last load hauled in the container, the responder will have difficulty determining the hazard associated with the load. In the case of a dangerous placard, the primary hazard associated with the load may not be apparent.

Another limitation to consider is the fact that there is essentially no difference in danger between a 1,000-lb (454-kg) load of a hazardous substance and a 1,001-lb (454-kg) load of the same substance, even though the first one doesn't need a placard and the second one does. Responders must understand there may be instances in which they encounter unclassified materials or materials with exemptions. Always cautiously approach containers with shapes that commonly indicate hazardous materials while collecting response information.

CHEMICAL AND PHYSICAL PROPERTIES

For responders to make educated decisions about the materials involved in a hazmat incident, they must understand the properties that govern the material's behavior. For example, a chemical that could present a significant hazard when released on a hot summer day may be relatively inert on a subzero winter day. Understanding the physical properties of the material will allow operations-level responders to develop an appropriate and safe defensive response plan based on available personnel and equipment. During the information collection process, it is important that personnel understand the data provided by the various research resources that will be discussed later on in this chapter. The hazmat responder will likely come in contact with the following terms.

Chemical reactivity

Chemical reactivity is the ability of a material to undergo a chemical reaction with another substance. During the reaction process, increased temperature and pressure buildup can result in catastrophic failure of a container.

Exothermic and **endothermic** are two types of chemical reactions. The first type is a reaction that causes a release of heat. Exothermic reactions occur with most chemical reactions. An endothermic reaction is a chemical reaction that is accompanied by the absorption of heat. An example of this is the reaction that takes place inside an ice pack.

Unstable materials can react violently with little or no outside interaction. Unstable substances are those capable of undergoing spontaneous change. For example, nitroglycerin may explode if jarred, heated, or otherwise contaminated. Examples of unstable materials include compounds that crystallize or deteriorate such as picric acid, ether, organic peroxides, and dynamite.

Hypergolic materials ignite when they come in contact with each other. Hypergolic reactions occur when a fuel and an oxidizer are mixed.

Pyrophoric materials are those elements that react and ignite upon coming in contact with air.

Corrosivity (pH)

Corrosives are substances that destroy or burn living tissues and have destructive effects on other types of materials. Containers can be damaged and lose structural integrity if they are not designed to contain corrosive materials.

Corrosives are divided into acids and bases (alkaline).

Contact with acids can cause severe chemical burns and permanent eye damage. Usually a person who comes in contact with an acid feels pain. Common acids include hydrochloric, nitric, and sulfuric. All acids have a pH value of less than 7. Another property of acids is that they dissolve metals and react with bases.

Bases break down fatty skin tissues and penetrate deeply into the body. Coming in contact with a base does not normally result in immediate pain. Rather, a greasy or slick feeling on the skin is indicative of an exposure. This is the result of the base breaking down the fatty tissue in the skin. Common bases include caustic soda, potassium hydroxide, and other alkaline materials. A base has a pH value greater than 7.

Particle size

Particle size is a term that refers to the size of a solid particle and is usually measured in microns.

Persistence

Persistence refers to the ability of a material to remain in the area of release for long periods of time. It is intended to prevent responders from reentering an area in which concentrations of the material remain high for an extended period of time.

Physical state

Physical state refers to the form a material exists in: gas, liquid, or solid. **Gases** are substances that have no definitive shape or volume. **Liquids** are substances that have no definite shape, but do have a specific volume. **Solids** are substances that have both a specific shape and volume. The severity of the release and methods of control vary based upon the physical state of the product. Solids tend to be the easiest to control because they remain in place unless acted upon. Liquids are more difficult to control than solids because they flow with gravity. Gases are the hardest and may require extensive evacuations.

The physical state of a material can also determine the most likely method of exposure. Solids generally enter through contact, ingestion, or the inhalation of particles such as dust. Liquids are typically ingested, absorbed through the skin, or inhaled if they are evaporating.

Gases can be inhaled, absorbed through the skin, and possibly ingested.

Specific gravity

Specific gravity is the weight of a substance compared to the weight of an equal volume of water at a given temperature (fig. 23–58a & b). It determines whether a substance sinks or floats in water. Water is given a value of 1; materials with a value greater than 1 will sink in water, and materials with a value less than 1 will float.

Fig. 23–58a. Materials with a specific gravity less than 1 will float in water.

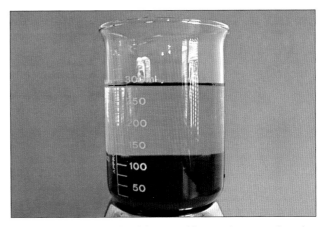

Fig. 23–58b. Materials with a specific gravity more than 1 will sink in water.

Specific gravity is important when determining the effectiveness of pads and booms. Most hydrocarbons have a specific gravity of less than 1 and will float on water. Materials that sink are more difficult to contain and clean up. Water solubility is a concern with materials that have a specific gravity greater than 1.

Table 23–10. Hazard classes

Class	Division	Placard	Hazards	Examples
Class 1—Explosives				
1	1.1	EXPLOSIVE 1.1 1	Mass explosion	Black powder TNT Dynamite Blasting caps
	1.2	EXPLOSIVE 1.2 1	Projection hazard	Detonating cords Aerial flares
	1.3	EXPLOSIVE 1.3 1	Fire hazard Possible minor blast or projection hazard	Propellant explosives Liquid-fuel rocket motors
	1.4	1.4 EXPLOSIVE 1	No significant blast hazard	Practice ammunition and signal cartridges
	1.5	1.5 BLASTING AGENT 1	Very insensitive blasting agents	Prilled (pelleted) ammonium nitrate fertilizer and blasting agents
	1.6	1.6 EXPLOSIVE 1	Extremely insensitive detonating articles	Fertilizer/fuel oil mixtures.
Class 2—Gases				
2	2.1	FLAMMABLE 2	Flammable gas	Acetylene, hydrogen, methane, and propane
	2.2	NON-FLAMMABLE GAS 2	Nonflammable gas	Carbon dioxide and anhydrous ammonia
	2.3	INHALATION HAZARD 2	Poisonous gas	Phosgene, chlorine, cyanide gas, arsine, methyl bromide
	2.4	2	Corrosive gases	Ammonia, hydrogen chloride, chlorine, methylamine
		OXYGEN 2	Oxygen	

Class	Division	Placard	Hazards	Examples
Class 3—Flammable and Combustible Liquids				
3			Flammable liquid	Gasoline, kerosene, and acetone
			Combustible liquid	Mineral oil and no. 6 fuel oil
Class 4—Flammable Solids				
4	4.1		Flammable solid	Magnesium
	4.2		Spontaneously combustible materials	Phosphorus
	4.3		Dangerous when wet	Calcium carbide, sodium hydride, magnesium powder
Class 5—Oxidizers and Organic Peroxides				
5	5.1		Oxidizers	Calcium carbide, sodium hydride, magnesium powder
	5.2		Organic peroxides	Ethyl ketone peroxide and peroxide
Class 6—Toxic and Infectious Substances				
6	6.1		Poisonous	Arsenic
	6.2		Infectious substances	Rabies, HIV, and hepatitis B
Class 7—Radioactive				
7			Radioactive	Cobalt, uranium, and plutonium

Class	Division	Placard	Hazards	Examples
Class 8 – Corrosive Materials				
8			Corrosive	Sulfuric acid and sodium hydroxide
Class 9 - Miscellaneous				
9			U.S. miscellaneous	Dangerous goods Environmental hazardous substances Dangerous wastes
			Canadian miscellaneous	

Water solubility

Water solubility (also known as miscibility) is the ability of a liquid to mix with water. It is difficult to remove water-soluble materials from a body of water. Corrosives, poisons, and alcohols tend to be water soluble. Water-soluble materials are difficult to extinguish when burning.

Vapor density

Vapor density is the density of a gas compared to the density of air (fig. 23–59a & b). It determines whether a vapor will rise or fall. Air is given a value of 1; gases with a vapor density greater than 1 will sink, and those with a vapor density of less than 1 will rise. For example, propane is a gas with a vapor density greater than air. With a vapor density of 1.56, it will accumulate in low spots; potential ignition sources should be considered.

Vapor pressure

Vapor pressure is the pressure at which a liquid and its vapor are in equilibrium at a given temperature. Liquids with high vapor pressures evaporate rapidly. It is important that the first responder consider a material's vapor pressure when deciding evacuation routes or other tactical plans. The higher the vapor pressure, the more dangerous the chemical. Higher vapor pressures also translate into lower boiling points. Chemicals with high vapor pressures emit vapors at lower temperatures than chemicals with low vapor pressures. Examples of substances with high vapor pressures include gasoline, acetone, and alcohol. Substances with low vapor pressures include motor oil, diesel fuel, and water.

Boiling point

Boiling point is the temperature at which a liquid changes to a gas at normal atmospheric pressure; reaching the boiling point results in a rapid change from a liquid to a gaseous state. The lower the boiling point, the more volatile a material is. A liquid with a low boiling point has a high vapor pressure and a low flash point. At temperatures below the boiling point, evaporation takes place only from the surface of the liquid; during boiling, vapor forms within the body of the liquid.

Flash point

Flash point is the minimum temperature at which a liquid gives off sufficient vapors to create an ignitable mixture with air near its surface. At its flash point, a fuel source gives off sufficient vapors to ignite momentarily and will not continue to burn unless additional heat is introduced. The flash point is important in determining the temperature at which a flammable liquid is giving off sufficient vapors to ignite. A liquid with a low boiling point has a high vapor pressure and low flash point.

Ignition temperature

Ignition temperature is the minimum temperature that a fuel in air must be heated to in order to ignite without an independent ignition source being present. It is also known as the autoignition temperature. The ignition temperature of a substance is significantly higher than its flash point. All flammable materials have an ignition temperature, and it is an important factor when determining the potential of ignition of a flammable substance.

Fig. 23–59a. Gases with a vapor density less than 1 will rise.

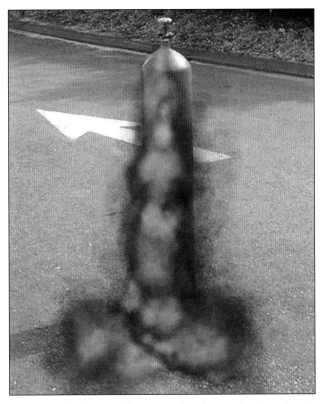

Fig. 23–59b. Gases with a vapor density greater than 1 will sink.

Flammable (explosive) range

Flammable (explosive) range is the percentage of the gas or vapor concentration in air that will burn if an ignition source is introduced. The flammable (explosive) range has the following limiting concentrations:

- Lower explosive limit (LEL): if the concentration is below the LEL, it is too lean to burn.

- Upper explosive limit (UEL): if the concentration is above the UEL, it is too rich to burn.

These measurements are given as a percentage in air (fig. 23–60). Concentrations between the upper and lower limits will burn rapidly if ignited, and any concentrations above 10% of the LEL must be considered to have potential for ignition. Containers can be damaged by an explosion if the contents are in their flammable range and an ignition source is introduced. Responders should always consider that ventilating an area above the UEL will eventually bring it back down into the material's flammable range. Caution should always be taken to control potential ignition sources when dealing with flammable atmospheres.

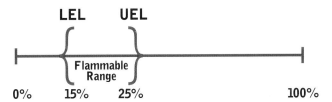

Fig. 23–60. The flammable range of anhydrous ammonia

Toxic by-products of combustion

Toxic by-products of combustion are given off by all substances when they are burning. Responders should keep in mind, however, that substances classified as hazardous materials will often produce more toxic by-products than a fire burning natural materials such as wood. There is also the potential that the hazardous materials could be consumed in the combustion process. The first responder should research the material to determine how it will react under fire conditions.

Radiation

Radiation is energy released in the form of particles or electromagnetic waves. There are two types or groupings of radiation: ionizing and nonionizing.

Ionizing radiation. Ionizing radiation has enough energy to cause a physical change to atoms by triggering them to lose electrons and become **ions**. When first responders refer to radiation in a hazardous materials response, they are usually referring to ionizing radiation. Examples include alpha, beta, gamma, and neutron (fig. 23–61).

Alpha particles are relatively heavy and slow moving. They have poor penetrating power and can be stopped by a piece of paper or skin. Alpha particles consist of two protons and two neutrons.

Beta particles are fast and can move at speeds of $\frac{9}{10}$ the speed of light. They can penetrate up to 1 to 2 cm of water or human flesh. Beta particles can be stopped by a sheet of aluminum a few millimeters thick. Because they consist of an electron, they have very little mass compared to an alpha particle.

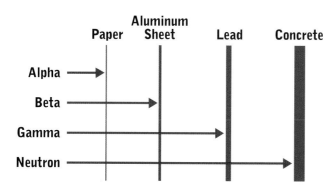

Fig. 23–61. Alpha, beta, gamma, and neutron radiation require different levels of shielding.

Gamma rays are electromagnetic rays that move at the speed of light and can kill living cells. Thick barriers of concrete, lead, or water are used as shielding materials for gamma rays.

Neutron radiation consists of penetrating particles and is much harder to shield against than alpha, beta, and gamma radiation. This type of radiation is not as common as the other types discussed, and it primarily results from the fissioning or splitting of certain atoms within a nuclear reactor. Large quantities of water and concrete are most commonly used to shield the reactor against neutrons. Unlike other types of radiation, neutron radiation can cause some materials, such as alloy steels, to develop an induced radioactivity after absorbing neutron energy. However, the absorption of neutron radiation does not always lead to a radioactive atom.

Nonionizing radiation. Nonionizing radiation has enough energy to cause molecules to move or vibrate, but not enough to change them chemically. Examples include radio waves, microwaves, ultraviolet and visible light, and magnetic fields.

HEALTH HAZARDS

Because the top priority of all hazmat responders is the preservation of life, it is important to understand the effects a product may have on human physiology. As such, responders must be familiar with the terminology used to describe health hazards, the effects different classifications of materials have on the body, typical routes of entry, and the threshold limits of potential exposures. This information plays a crucial role in making informed decisions about the incident response and understanding the level of danger faced by those in the exposed area.

Health hazard terminology

When collecting response information it is also important that responders understand the different terms used to describe health hazard concerns. For example, it is important to understand the difference between acute and chronic effects of a material. Responders should be familiar with the following terms and be able to describe the differences between them.

Infections vs. contagious. Contagious substances can be transmitted between a person or animal to another through some manner of contact, typically through bodily fluids. **Infectious** refers to a type of disease that is the result of exposure to a harmful microorganism. This microorganism reproduces within the body and begins to attack its organs and cells. Just because a disease is infectious does not necessarily mean it is contagious.

Acute effects vs. chronic effects. Acute effects will present their symptoms immediately, whereas **chronic effects** can take a substantially longer time to appear, even years after the exposure.

Acute exposures vs. chronic exposures. An **acute exposure** is typically considered a large dose in a short period of time, whereas a **chronic exposure** occurs when someone is exposed to a lower dose over a longer period such as days, weeks, or years. Acute exposures can often have both short-term and long-term effects, depending on the substance involved.

Health hazards associated with a hazardous materials release

Responders should have a general idea of the health hazards associated with a release, even before they may know the exact name of the material. Using the basic hazard class information, as well as the physical attributes of the material, certain dangers and health effects can be considered. Additionally, physical hazards associated with the container and working in appropriate personal protective equipment must be assessed. The following are health hazards that may be encountered at a release.

Thermal—heat. Responders should be aware that operating in protective clothing can cause a body to overheat. Exposure to heat can lead to one or more of the following:

- **Heat cramps** result from heavy exertion and exposure to high heat. They are caused by dehydration and excessive loss of salt in the extremities.

- **Heat exhaustion** is a mild form of traumatic shock resulting from prolonged physical exertion in a hot environment when the body becomes incapable of releasing excess heat.

- **Heatstroke** is a serious medical condition that can become life-threatening if it is not treated promptly.

Table 23–11 lists the symptoms of each heat-related condition.

Table 23–11. Symptoms of heat-related conditions

Heat Cramps	Heat Exhaustion	Heatstroke
Heavy perspiration	Heavy perspiration	No perspiration
Skin moist to the touch	Skin cool, pale, and moist	Hot, dry skin
Physical weakness	Dizziness	Weakness and confusion
Muscle cramps	Mildly elevated temp	High body temp
	Weak pulse	Rapid pulse
		Convulsions
		Shallow breathing
		Headache

To prevent overheating, personnel should take preventative measures such as drinking plenty of fluids, utilizing mobile showers or misting setups, setting up rest areas in the shade or an air conditioned area, rotating personnel, and avoiding coffee and caffeinated drinks (fig. 23–62). If response personnel display any symptoms of these heat-related injuries, they should be removed from the response operation and treated according to local medical protocols.

Fig. 23–62. Response personnel should drink plenty of water to prevent heat-related injuries.

Thermal—cold. Responders have the potential for cold-related injuries when dealing with cryogenic or liquefied gases such as liquid oxygen (LOX), hydrogen, nitrogen, and liquid natural gas (LNG).

These materials can freeze objects and human tissue instantaneously upon contact. Clothing saturated with a cryogenic material must be removed immediately because many of these liquids are flammable, and their vapors pose a serious flammability problem.

Table 23–12 lists the conditions that can result from exposure to cold.

Table 23–12. Symptoms of cold-related conditions

Superficial Frostbite	Frost Nip
Waxy or white skin	Whiting or blanching of skin
Outer layers of skin are firm to the touch	
Tissue underneath is still flexible	
Deep Frostbite	**Hypothermia**
Cold and pale skin	Shivering
Skin hard to the touch	Slow pulse and respiratory rate
	Sleepiness, apathy, or listlessness
	Glassy eyes
	Unconsciousness
	Freezing of extremities
	Core temperature of 95°F or less
	Death

If response personnel display any symptoms of these cold-related injuries, they should be removed from the response operation and treated according to local medical protocols.

Mechanical hazards. Mechanical injury may occur if the responder is struck by an object or rubs up against one. The failure of a pressurized container may also result in serious mechanical injury. The failure of such a container can result in serious bruises, lacerations, or puncture wounds.

Friction injuries are most commonly caused by contact between the skin surface and protective clothing, causing blisters and brush burns. Friction injuries are less common than striking injuries in hazardous materials incidents.

Poisons. Poisons can cause death or serious bodily injury to responders. There are many different types of poisons, each having certain effects on the human anatomy (table 23–13). The type of damage caused to the body depends on the poison involved in the incident.

Table 23–13. Effects of poison types

Poison	Targeted Organs or System
Halogenated hydrocarbons	Kidneys
Benzene, nitrates, arsine	Blood
Parathion	Central nervous system
Ammonia, phenols, carbon tetrachloride	Liver

Etiological exposures. An **etiological exposure** is an exposure to a microorganism that could result in a disease. Most of these diseases are transmitted by blood or body fluids. Simple protective garments provide protection against these diseases. Examples of diseases resulting from etiological exposure include AIDS, tuberculosis, hepatitis, and typhoid.

Radiation. **Radiation** exposure may result in damage to individuals and future generations. Radiation sickness or poisoning cannot be transmitted to someone else; however, contaminated individuals may carry dangerous material on their bodies, posing a threat to those around them. Radiation may be present in medical centers, nuclear power plants, research facilities, and industrial processes.

The following are protection methods for ionizing radiation:

Alpha particles. Personal protective gear along with SCBA will be sufficient to protect responding personnel from alpha radiation (fig. 23–63).

Fig. 23–63. Turnout gear and SCBA are sufficient to protect responders from alpha radiation.

Beta particles. The use of personal protective gear and SCBA provides only limited protection against beta radiation, which is more powerful than alpha particles. Further shielding can be provided by using heavy plastic, wood, or thin metal.

Gamma rays. Gamma rays require dense materials such as lead to shield a person from their effects. Personal protective equipment provides no protection against this type of radiation.

Neutron. Neutron radiation requires large quantities of water and concrete to shield against its effects, such as is used in the core of a nuclear reactor. Personal protective equipment provides no protection against this type of radiation.

Exposure to radiation can have varying effects on the body, depending on the intensity and duration of the exposure. Large doses can cause extensive cellular damage and result in death, whereas smaller doses can cause cellular damage that increases the risk of cancer. Often the evidence of injury from low or moderate doses may take months or years to appear.

A **chronic exposure** is continuous or intermittent exposure to low levels of radiation over an extended period of time. Effects of chronic exposure to radiation include:

- Genetic effects
- Cancer
- Benign tumors
- Cataracts
- Congenital defects
- Skin changes

Chronic exposure only produces observable effects some time after the initial exposure occurs.

An **acute exposure** is an exposure to a large single dose of radiation or a series of doses over a short period of time. High levels of exposure can result in death within a few hours, days, or weeks. Effects of acute exposure results in the rapid development of radiation sickness and include the following:

- Gastrointestinal disorders
- Hemorrhaging
- Anemia
- Loss of body fluids

- Bacterial infections
- Electrolyte imbalance

Delayed effects of an acute exposure can include the following:

- Cataracts
- Temporary sterility
- Cancer
- Genetic effects

Responders must consider the following when radiation is present: type of radiation, amount absorbed by the body (dose), route of exposure, and length of time exposed.

Radiation exposure reduction methods. The first responder can use time, distance, and shielding to reduce the exposure risk.

- *Time.* As the amount of time spent near a radiation source decreases, the overall exposure is reduced (linear reduction). This results in a proportionate reduction in the dosage received.

- *Distance.* As the distance from a radiation source increases, the amount of exposure decreases. Radiation intensity varies inversely with the square of the distance from the source. As your distance from the source of the radiation doubles, the amount of radiation you are exposed to is decreased by the square of the distance; therefore, doubling your distance decreases your exposure to a fourth of the dose at the original distance. Likewise, tripling your distance reduces the exposure to a ninth of its original strength. For example, increasing your distance by a factor of 2 reduces the intensity of the exposure to ¼ of its original strength (fig. 23–64).

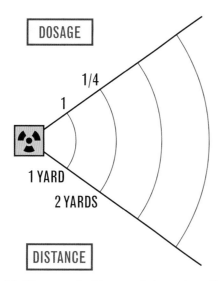

Fig. 23–64. When you double your distance from the radioactive source, you have ¼ of the original exposure.

- *Shielding.* A first responder should use the appropriate type of shielding for the radiation present. Barriers of lead, concrete, or water provide good protection from penetrating radiation such as gamma rays. As discussed previously, the thickness and the type of materials required to protect from radiation depends on the type of radiation. Keeping substantial objects such as vehicles, dirt mounds, or other obstructions between the source and the responder will help decrease the amount of overall exposure.

Asphyxiants. Simple asphyxiants are typically inert gases that displace the oxygen required for breathing. They dilute the oxygen content of the atmosphere to less than the minimum required for sustaining life. In addition, heavier-than-air gases can pool in low-lying areas such as basements and simply displace the air (fig. 23–65).

Fig. 23–65. Propane, transported by this vehicle, is a heavier-than-air gas.

Chemical asphyxiants are chemicals or substances that prevent the body from using oxygen. They operate in one of three ways: They may tie up the blood's oxygen-carrying hemoglobin and prevent it from carrying the oxygen. They can also remove the hemoglobin from the blood so that there is no longer any transport vehicle for the oxygen. Finally, they may cause other malfunctions in the blood's ability to carry oxygen.

Carcinogen. Carcinogens are materials that are known to cause or are suspected of causing cancer in people.

Convulsants. Convulsants are drugs or chemicals that cause convulsions in exposed individuals. Muscle spasms may start soon after the exposure and may continue for 3 to 30 minutes. Exposure results in dyspnea (difficulty breathing), suffocation, and muscular rigidity. Death can result from asphyxiation or exhaustion. Injury can also be sustained from falling or striking an object on the ground. Examples of convulsants include strychnine, carbamates, organophosphates, and picrotoxin.

Corrosives. Corrosives are chemicals that have destructive effects on materials and burn or destroy living tissue. When they come in contact with combustibles, they may result in fire or explosion.

Corrosives are divided into two groups: **acids** and **bases**. Contact with acids can result in severe chemical burns to the skin and/or damage to the eyes. Generally, pain is felt upon contact with an acid. Bases react with the body by breaking down fatty tissue and penetrating deep into the body. Contact with bases does not typically result in immediate pain. A greasy or slick feeling on the skin is an indication of contact with a base. This is a result of the fatty tissue breaking down.

The following are symptoms of contact with corrosives:

- Nausea and vomiting
- Burning around the nose, eyes, and mouth
- Difficulty breathing, coughing, or swallowing
- Burning or skin irritation in a localized area

If the potential for exposure to these products exists, first responders should remove themselves from the area and reassess the situation to determine the cause of the symptoms. Any deterioration or discoloration of equipment should alert the first responder to the potential safety issue.

Toxic materials. Some chemicals by their makeup can be extremely lethal at very low levels. Toxic materials can be broken up into two general categories: **toxic** and

highly toxic. The following measurements can determine which category a particular material is assigned to.

Lethal dose (LD50). This is an indication of the lethality of a given substance or type of radiation. The most commonly used lethality indicator is the LD50, the dose at which 50% of subjects will die.

Lethal concentration (LC50). This is the median lethal dose of a toxic substance or radiation. It is the dose required to kill half the members of a tested population. LC50 figures are frequently used as a general indicator of a substance's acute toxicity.

Table 23–14 shows toxicity levels of some common chemical substances. The fire codes International and National Fire Protection Association (NFPA) have provided definitions as to what constitutes a toxic and a highly toxic chemical. The following are the definitions from the 2009 edition of the International Fire Code, chapter 37.

Toxic. A chemical falling within any of the following categories is considered toxic:

- A chemical that has a median lethal dose (LD50) of more than 50 milligrams per kilogram, but not more than 500 milligrams per kilogram of body weight when administered orally to albino rats weighing between 200 and 300 grams each

- A chemical that has a median lethal dose (LD50) of more than 200 milligrams per kilogram but not more than 1,000 milligrams per kilogram of body weight when administered by continuous contact for 24 hours (or less if death occurs within 24 hours) with the bare skin of albino rabbits weighing between 2 and 3 kilograms each

- A chemical that has a median lethal concentration (LC50) in air of more than 200 parts per million but not more than 2,000 parts per million by volume of gas or vapor, or more than 2 milligrams per liter but not more than 20 milligrams per liter of mist, fume, or dust, when administered by continuous inhalation for 1 hour (or less if death occurs within 1 hour) to albino rats weighing between 200 and 300 grams each

Highly Toxic. A material producing a lethal dose or lethal concentration that falls within any of the following categories is considered highly toxic:

- A chemical that has a median lethal dose (LD50) of 50 milligrams or less per kilogram of body

weight when administered orally to albino rats weighing between 200 and 300 grams each

- A chemical that has a median lethal dose (LD50) of 200 milligrams or less per kilogram of body weight when administered by continuous contact for 24 hours (or less if death occurs within 24 hours) with the bare skin of albino rabbits weighing between 2 and 3 kilograms each

- A chemical that has a median lethal concentration (LC50) in air of 200 parts per million by volume or less of gas or vapor, or 2 milligrams per liter or less of mist, fume, or dust, when administered by continuous inhalation for one hour (or less if death occurs within 1 hour) to albino rats weighing between 200 and 300 grams each

- Mixtures of these materials with ordinary materials, such as water, might not warrant classification as highly toxic. While this system is basically simple in application, any hazard evaluation that is required for the precise categorization of this type of material shall be performed by experienced, technically competent persons

Table 23–14. Toxicity levels of common chemical substances

Chemical	LC_{50} (ppm)	PEL	STEL	IDLH (ppm)
Ammonia	4,000	25 ppm	50 ppm	300
Chlorine	293	Ceiling 1 ppm	—	10
Hydrogen chloride	2,810	Ceiling 5 ppm	—	50
Hydrogen cyanide	—	10 ppm	4.7 ppm	50
Phosgene	5	0.1 ppm	—	2
Sulfur dioxide	2,520	5 ppm	5 ppm	100

Irritant. Irritants cause temporary inflammation of the eyes, skin, or respiratory tract. Symptoms of exposure to irritants include redness, itching, discomfort, and irritated eyes or skin. In addition, coughing or difficulty breathing results from respiratory exposure.

An irritant gives off vapors that target mucous membranes. Although the effect of an irritant is often temporary, it can cause severe inflammation. An irritant may produce permanent damage if exposure is repeated over time.

Sensitizers/allergens. Sensitizers and **allergens** can cause allergic reactions after repeated exposures. The immune systems of some people believe the material is dangerous and attack it, whereas in other people no reaction takes place. The reaction may be severe or mild and may not occur until several hours or days after the exposure, although most occur within seconds or minutes of exposure. Repeated exposures may cause a rash on the skin or an asthma-like reaction.

Reactions to irritants vary, depending on the means of exposure and individual susceptibility to the material. Some persons may not be affected by the first exposure to the material, but may suffer dangerous effects the next time an exposure occurs. For example, someone stung by a bee for the first time may suffer no ill effects, but upon being stung again may experience severe anaphylaxis or allergic reaction.

Target organ effects. These are signs and symptoms of a chemical exposure that by their nature affect a specific organ or organs rather than the entire body. For example, neurotoxins affect the nervous system, hepatotoxins affect the liver, and nephrotoxins target the kidneys. Upon determining the name of the material and researching its chemical and physical properties, responders should determine the health effects, such as a tendency to affect a target organ, and pass this information to EMS responders.

Psychological. This is mental harm from being exposed to, contaminated by, or even just being in close proximity to an incident. Factors include response to incidents that are devastating to a community, or involve the death of a friend, colleague, or child.

TRACEM-P

When addressing the different types of harm that potentially occur at a hazmat incident, the acronym TRACEM-P can be used to categorize the most common types of hazards that are addressed.

1. Thermal
2. Radiation
3. Asphyxiation
4. Chemical
5. Etiological
6. Mechanical
7. Psychological

Routes of entry

Individuals may be exposed to hazardous substances through inhalation, ingestion, injection, or absorption. The physical state of matter often determines the mode or route of entry into the body.

Inhalation. Inhalation is the most common route of exposure. Individuals may inhale material such as vapors, gases, fumes, smoke, or aerosols through the nose or mouth. The first responder should protect against this method of exposure by wearing appropriate respiratory protection.

Ingestion. Individuals may ingest materials through the mouth, which commonly occurs when eating, drinking, or smoking contaminated materials. Poor hygiene after handling hazardous materials is the primary cause of this type of exposure. First responders should be completely decontaminated before they are allowed to eat or drink. In addition, no food, drink, or tobacco products should be allowed in the hazmat area.

Injection. An individual may be exposed via injection when materials are taken in through a puncture or needle stick. This mode of exposure is primarily a hazard for emergency medical personnel who handle syringes or IV needles.

Absorption. An individual may absorb materials through the skin or eyes. Many poisons can be absorbed in this manner. The eyes, neck, wrists, groin, hands, underarms, and areas of broken skin are particularly susceptible to exposure by absorption because they are the areas on the body where the skin is the thinnest. Also, any breaks or damage to the skin can allow materials to be absorbed more readily. As a precaution, first responders should always wash their hands prior to touching their face.

Health data terminology

During the research process, responders will encounter the following threshold quantity measurements that indicate the level and types of exposure deemed safe for a given period of time. These values should be compared against the measurements collected on scene to get a benchmark as to how hazardous the level of concentration is. Threshold limit values (TLV) are developed by the American Conference of Government Industrial Hygienists (ACGIH). These values are revised on a regular basis. Threshold limit values can be measured in parts per million (ppm) or in milligrams per cubic meter (mg/m^3) of air.

Threshold limit value/time weighted average (TLV-TWA). The TLV-TWA is the maximum concentration of a substance a person may be exposed to for eight hours a day, 40 hours per week without suffering harmful effects. It is designed primarily for exposures in the workplace. The lower the TLV, the more toxic the material.

Threshold limit value/short term exposure limit (TLV-STEL). TLV-STEL is the maximum exposure time, limited to 15 minutes no more than four times a day without suffering harmful effects. This includes a minimum one hour rest period between exposures.

Threshold limit value/ceiling level (TLV-C). TLV-C is the maximum concentration that should never be exceeded for any period of time.

Immediately dangerous to life and health (IDLH). IDLH identifies any concentration of a toxic, corrosive, or asphyxiating substance that poses an immediate threat to life. Exposure to these materials can result in irreversible or delayed adverse health effects and may interfere with a person's ability to escape from a dangerous atmosphere. Positive-pressure SCBA is required for entry into an IDLH atmosphere.

Recommended exposure limits (REL). REL is similar to the TLV-TWA and is the occupational exposure limit recommended by the National Institute for Occupational Safety and Health (NIOSH) for a 10-hour work day during a 40-hour work week. These are recommendations based solely on scientific data. It is measured in ppm or mg/m^3, just like the TLV.

Permissible exposure limit (PEL). PEL is similar to TLV-TWA and is the maximum allowable exposure in an eight-hour day. This system is adopted by OSHA and is subject to the rule-making and political process. It is measured in ppm or mg/m^3, just like the TLV.

INFORMATION RESOURCES

There are various information resources that can be used on scene to identify the hazardous material involved and determine the chemical, physical, and health hazards associated with it. These can range from shipping papers to the U.S. DOT Guidebook (which is designed to give responders initial guidance on response procedures), to more advanced computer software that can be used to find more specific information. Additionally, local industry; academic institutions; and local, state, and federal hazmat responders can provide valuable information and resources. Several of the basic methods are covered in this section. The information obtained from these resources allows the responders to make educated decisions on the defensive options that can be performed safely given the equipment they have on hand. It also helps determine the need for additional resources.

People

When an emergency responder comes face to face with the uncertainties of a hazardous materials emergency, a familiar face with knowledge of hazardous materials can be especially reassuring. Local hazardous materials specialists are ready and willing to help and are available in almost any community. The emergency responder should get to know these assets and their areas of expertise. The following are some examples.

Hazardous materials teams. Does your community have a hazardous materials team? If so, give them a call and arrange for a visit. Hazardous materials teams often designate themselves as defensive or offensive. Defensive teams generally provide decontamination assistance or spill control for fuel leaks. Most defensive hazardous materials teams are trained to the operations level as described in NFPA 472 and OSHA 29 CFR 1910.120(q). Offensive teams are usually fully staffed and equipped to mitigate a spill at the source. These teams undergo intense training (fig. 23–66) and are trained to the technician level of the NFPA and OSHA standards mentioned earlier. Hazardous materials teams may have many reference resources on hand to assist you during an emergency or when preplanning.

Fig. 23–66. Technician-level responders are trained to a higher level than operations-level responders. (Courtesy of Pullman FD)

Industry representatives. Local industries likely have safety officers on staff, or even hazardous materials specialists if the company uses hazardous materials in its operations. If the company is in your response area, telephone them and ask to speak to their safety representative. Another good way to reach and meet the industry experts in your area is to attend the local emergency planning committee (LEPC) meetings. LEPCs were developed to create plans for response actions to hazardous materials incidents. Many LEPCs have expanded and now take an "all hazards" approach to also include terrorism incidents. Industry representatives located at fixed facilities are also an important resource when an incident occurs in their facility.

Academic institutions. Chemists from local colleges and laboratories are often an overlooked asset to the emergency responder. They understand the chemistry of a hazardous materials situation, especially if multiple chemicals are involved. Many chemists enjoy the opportunity to assist local responders with their planning efforts. Ask around your neighborhood and see if you have a chemist nearby who is willing to help out if needed.

State and federal emergency responders. All states have organizations that plan for hazardous materials incidents. These agencies generally can be reached by contacting the state emergency response center. Most state hazardous materials responders interact closely with the local hazardous materials response teams. If you do not know who your state hazardous materials responder is, contact the state emergency response center or the state emergency planning commission.

In the event of a terrorist incident, the National Guard has several assets that may be used. The civil support teams and CERF-P teams are located throughout the country. These National Guard assets are specially trained to respond to incidents involving chemical, explosive, radiological/nuclear, and biological terrorism, and are continually training with their equipment. They often can characterize a sample of unclassified material or decontaminate mass casualties. Although their primary mission is to respond to incidents of national significance, these specialists may also be available to you for other hazardous materials responses.

The U.S. Environmental Protection Agency (EPA) and the U.S. Coast Guard also have responders trained in hazardous materials. These responders are known as federal on-scene coordinators (FOSCs) and may be able to provide resources not immediately available locally.

FOSCs are available 24 hours a day and can be reached by contacting the National Response Center at 1-800-424-8802.

Print resources

U.S. DOT Emergency Response Guidebook. *The U.S. Department of Transportation Emergency Response Guidebook* (commonly referred to as the ERG) is the most common and widely used resource by emergency responders at hazardous materials/WMD incidents (fig. 23–67). It outlines the general concerns of the product as well as recommended initial actions to take, and is the first source of information used by responders in hazardous materials transportation incidents. The ERG is intended to give the first responder quick information regarding the hazards and protective actions in a hazardous materials incident. It is meant as an initial reference guide, but its usefulness is limited to the first few minutes of the incident. Other resources need to be referenced for more specific product information.

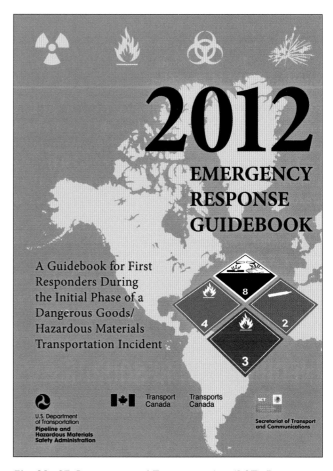

Fig. 23–67. Department of Transportation (DOT) Emergency Response Guidebook (ERG)

The ERG is released every four years. Copies are provided by the U.S. Department of Transportation to the State Emergency Management Agency, and are then distributed to the local responders for use in each vehicle assigned to those agencies. *Every fire department response vehicle should have a U.S. DOT Emergency Response Guidebook.* If you do not have one in your apparatus, ask your senior officer to have one placed in the vehicle. The ERG is available for download from various Web sites, and can be found by a Web search for "DOT Emergency Response Guidebook."

The ERG is organized into five distinct color-coded sections designed to make the guide simple to use. The white section contains important reference material, the yellow section can be used to look up a material by its four-digit UN/NA ID number, the blue section references the material by its name, the orange section contains the emergency response guides, and the green section provides the initial isolation and protective action distances for toxic by inhalation materials. The following covers each section in greater detail.

White section. Found at the beginning of the book, the white section provides valuable information on how to use the ERG as well as how the information is compiled. A list of important phone numbers as well as the UN/NA hazard classifications can be found in this section. The following can also be found:

- *Table of placards.* This information is designed to allow the responder to determine the appropriate guide number based on the placard displayed on the road trailer or rail car (fig. 23–68). The first responder is able to match the placard on the vehicle to the one in the table and reference the appropriate guide number. This table is utilized when access to the shipping papers, number placards, or identification number is not possible, but the placard is visible.

  The number in the circle near each placard indicates the appropriate guide number found in the orange section. For example, the guide number 118 is shown next to the flammable liquids placards. The responder should use the response information found in the orange pages under Guide 118 for a response to a release of an unknown flammable liquid.

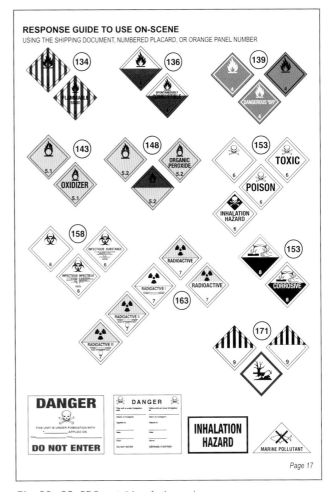

Fig. 23–68. ERG—table of placards

- *Railcar and road trailer guide.* In the absence of a placard or other identifying marks, this reference can be used to determine the appropriate guide based on the container type (fig. 23–69). The number in the circle near each placard indicates the appropriate guide number. Because container designs vary greatly, the suggested guides should be used only as a last resort if no other means of identification is available.

- *Intermodal identification codes.* This section lists the codes used to identify different types of materials shipped in intermodal containers.

- *Pipeline transportation.* This section reviews the markings used to indicate the presence of a pipeline as well as indications of a potential leak.

The back of the book contains another section, color coded white, that contains general information about personal protective equipment, fire and spill control procedures, responses involving terrorist incidents, as well as a glossary and additional contact phone numbers.

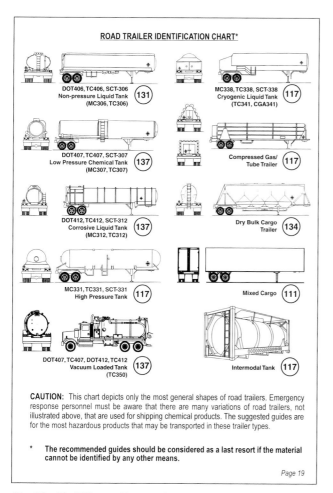

Fig. 23–69. ERG—railcar and road trailer guide

ID No.	Guide No.	Name of Material	ID No.	Guide No.	Name of Material
1493	140	Silver nitrate	1544	151	Alkaloid salts, solid, n.o.s. (poisonous)
1494	141	Sodium bromate	1545	155	Allyl isothiocyanate, stabilized
1495	140	Sodium chlorate	1546	151	Ammonium arsenate
1496	143	Sodium chlorite	1547	153	Aniline
1498	140	Sodium nitrate	1548	153	Aniline hydrochloride
1499	140	Potassium nitrate and Sodium nitrate mixture	1549	157	Antimony compound, inorganic, n.o.s.
1499	140	Sodium nitrate and Potassium nitrate mixture	1549	157	Antimony compound, inorganic, solid, n.o.s.
1500	140	Sodium nitrite	1549	157	Antimony tribromide, solid
1502	140	Sodium perchlorate	1549	157	Antimony tribromide, solution
1503	140	Sodium permanganate	1549	157	Antimony trifluoride, solid
1504	144	Sodium peroxide	1549	157	Antimony trifluoride, solution
1505	140	Sodium persulfate	1550	151	Antimony lactate
1505	140	Sodium persulphate	1551	151	Antimony potassium tartrate
1506	143	Strontium chlorate	1553	154	Arsenic acid, liquid
1506	143	Strontium chlorate, solid	1554	154	Arsenic acid, solid
1506	143	Strontium chlorate, solution	1555	151	Arsenic bromide
1507	140	Strontium nitrate	1556	152	Arsenic compound, liquid, n.o.s.
1508	140	Strontium perchlorate	1556	152	Arsenic compound, liquid, n.o.s., inorganic
1509	143	Strontium peroxide	1556	152	MD
1510	143	Tetranitromethane	1556	152	Methyldichloroarsine
1511	140	Urea hydrogen peroxide	1556	152	PD
1512	140	Zinc ammonium nitrite	1557	152	Arsenic compound, solid, n.o.s.
1513	140	Zinc chlorate	1557	152	Arsenic compound, solid, n.o.s., inorganic
1514	140	Zinc nitrate	1557	152	Arsenic sulfide
1515	140	Zinc permanganate	1557	152	Arsenic sulphide
1516	143	Zinc peroxide	1557	152	Arsenic trisulfide
1517	113	Zirconium picramate, wetted with not less than 20% water	1557	152	Arsenic trisulphide
1541	155	Acetone cyanohydrin, stabilized	1558	152	Arsenic
1544	151	Alkaloids, solid, n.o.s. (poisonous)	1559	151	Arsenic pentoxide

Page 38

Fig. 23–70. ERG—identification by UN/NA ID number

Yellow section—identification by UN/NA ID number. The yellow-bordered pages of the ERG list the UN/NA ID numbers in numerical order and should be used when the product ID number is known (fig. 23–70). The ID number is the four-digit number displayed on all four sides of a vehicle or container transporting hazardous materials. This section provides the shipping name and the guide number assigned to the product. Highlighted chemicals indicate a poison or inhalation poison risk and require referencing the Initial Isolation and Protective Action Distances information found in the green section. This is addressed in greater detail shortly.

Blue section—identification by name. The blue section lists material names in alphabetical order and should be used when the product's name is known (fig. 23–71). The names of materials in this section are listed as they appear on shipping documents. The responder should carefully double check the spelling. This section provides the UN/NA ID number and the guide number assigned to the product. Highlighted chemicals indicate a poison or inhalation poison risk and require referencing the Initial Isolation and Protective Action Distances information found in the green section. This is addressed in greater detail shortly.

Name of Material	Guide No.	ID No.	Name of Material	Guide No.	ID No.
Chlorodinitrobenzenes, solid	153	3441	Chlorophenates, solid	154	2905
1-Chloro-2,3-epoxypropane	131P	2023	Chlorophenolates, liquid	154	2904
2-Chloroethanal	153	2232	Chlorophenolates, solid	154	2905
Chloroform	151	1888	Chlorophenols, liquid	153	2021
Chloroformates, n.o.s.	155	2742	Chlorophenols, solid	153	2020
Chloroformates, poisonous, corrosive, flammable, n.o.s.	155	2742	Chlorophenyltrichlorosilane	156	1753
			Chloropicrin	154	1580
Chloroformates, poisonous, corrosive, n.o.s.	154	3277	Chloropicrin and Methyl bromide mixture	123	1581
Chloroformates, toxic, corrosive, flammable, n.o.s.	155	2742	Chloropicrin and Methyl chloride mixture	119	1582
Chloroformates, toxic, corrosive, n.o.s.	154	3277	Chloropicrin mixture, n.o.s.	154	1583
Chloromethyl chloroformate	157	2745	Chloropivaloyl chloride	156	9263
Chloromethyl ethyl ether	131	2354	Chloroplatinic acid, solid	154	2507
3-Chloro-4-methylphenyl isocyanate	156	2236	Chloroprene, stabilized	131P	1991
			1-Chloropropane	129	1278
3-Chloro-4-methylphenyl isocyanate, liquid	156	2236	2-Chloropropane	129	2356
			3-Chloropropanol-1	153	2849
3-Chloro-4-methylphenyl isocyanate, solid	156	3428	2-Chloropropene	130P	2456
			2-Chloropropionic acid	153	2511
Chloronitroanilines	153	2237	2-Chloropropionic acid, solid	153	2511
Chloronitrobenzenes	152	1578	2-Chloropropionic acid, solution	153	2511
Chloronitrobenzenes, liquid	152	1578	2-Chloropyridine	153	2822
Chloronitrobenzenes, liquid	152	3409	Chlorosilanes, corrosive, flammable, n.o.s.	155	2986
Chloronitrobenzenes, solid	152	1578			
Chloronitrotoluenes	152	2433	Chlorosilanes, corrosive, n.o.s.	156	2987
Chloronitrotoluenes, liquid	152	2433	Chlorosilanes, flammable, corrosive, n.o.s.	155	2985
Chloronitrotoluenes, solid	152	2433			
Chloronitrotoluenes, solid	153	3457	Chlorosilanes, n.o.s.	155	2985
Chloropentafluoroethane	126	1020	Chlorosilanes, n.o.s.	155	2986
Chloropentafluoroethane and Chlorodifluoromethane mixture	126	1973	Chlorosilanes, n.o.s.	156	2987
			Chlorosilanes, n.o.s.	139	2988
			Chlorosilanes, poisonous, corrosive, flammable, n.o.s.	155	3362
Chlorophenates, liquid	154	2904			

Page 109

Fig. 23–71. ERG—Identification by material name

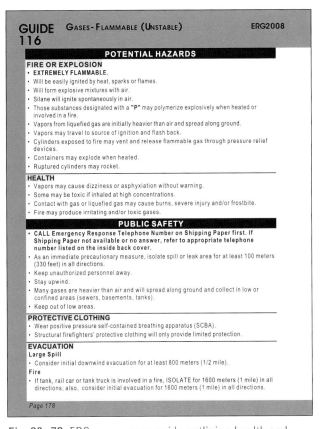

Fig. 23–72. ERG—response guide outlining health and safety information

Orange section—initial action guides. The orange section identifies the most significant hazards and informs first responders of initial actions to be taken to protect from immediate hazards. Each guide is broken down into three sections. The first section lists the *potential hazards*, listing the product's health effects and fire/explosion hazard. The hazard listed first represents the more serious danger. The next section outlines the *public safety measures* that should be taken in the event of a release and addresses isolation distances as well as personal protective clothing and respiratory recommendations. The protective clothing options include street clothing and work uniforms, structural firefighting protective clothing, positive-pressure SCBA, and chemical protective clothing and equipment. These protective clothing options are addressed in greater detail in chapter 24. Finally, the emergency response section covers actions to be taken in the event of a fire, spill, or leak, as well as first-aid information. Each guide is two pages with health and safety information included on the left page (fig. 23–72) and emergency response information on the right page (fig. 23–73). Each guide covers a group of chemicals with similar properties.

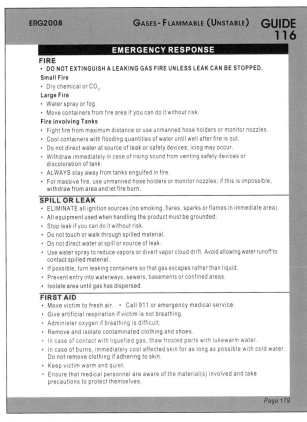

Fig. 23–73. ERG—response guide outlining emergency response information

This section should be used when the entry in the yellow or blue section is *not* highlighted. If product identification cannot be made by any of the index methods, the first responder should refer to Guide 111, which is the first guide in the orange section. The responder should use this guide only until the product is identified.

Green section—initial isolation and protective action distances. The green section should be used to look up the highlighted entries found in the yellow and blue sections. It is designed for materials that present a toxic-by-inhalation hazard. Specific isolation and protective action distances have been established for this group of hazardous materials. This section is organized by ID number.

The highlighted entries in the blue and yellow sections indicate that the material presents a poison and/or poison inhalation risk. If the material is highlighted and *not* on fire, go directly to Table 1 in the *Guidebook*'s green section. If the material is on fire or a fire is involved, also consult the given orange guide page and use the evacuation information under the public safety section. This is a very important instruction to follow because there are some highlighted products that become a greater hazard when involved in fire, and the evacuation distance may need to be increased to the distances noted in the orange guide.

Table 1 in the green section contains a *first ISOLATE in all directions* column (fig. 23–74). This distance indicates the area where an immediate hazard may be present. The next column indicates the *protective action distance*. This information should be used by emergency responders to make recommendations regarding the potentially affected populations. These distances, however, are valid for a period of only 30 minutes following the release. If the spill has passed the 30 minute mark, then the orange guide should be referenced for the evacuation distances. The protective action distances are further broken down based on whether the spill is during the day or at night and also whether the spill is large or small. A small spill is considered 200 L (53 gal) or less, or approximately the size of a 55-gal (208-L) drum. Large spills are considered anything that exceeds this amount. The process of using the DOT ERG to determine the correct isolation and protective action distances is covered in greater detail later in this chapter.

Table 2 lists the chemicals that will produce large amounts of toxic-by-inhalation (TIH) gases when spilled in water (fig. 23–75). This table is also arranged by the materials' ID numbers.

TABLE 1 - INITIAL ISOLATION AND PROTECTIVE ACTION DISTANCES

		SMALL SPILLS (From a small package or small leak from a large package)			LARGE SPILLS (From a large package or from many small packages)		
		First ISOLATE in all Directions	Then PROTECT persons Downwind during-		First ISOLATE in all Directions	Then PROTECT persons Downwind during-	
ID No.	NAME OF MATERIAL	Meters (Feet)	DAY Kilometers (Miles)	NIGHT Kilometers (Miles)	Meters (Feet)	DAY Kilometers (Miles)	NIGHT Kilometers (Miles)
1815	Propionyl chloride (when spilled in water)	30 m (100 ft)	0.1 km (0.1 mi)	0.1 km (0.1 mi)	30 m (100 ft)	0.3 km (0.2 mi)	0.8 km (0.5 mi)
1816	Propyltrichlorosilane (when spilled in water)	30 m (100 ft)	0.1 km (0.1 mi)	0.2 km (0.2 mi)	60 m (200 ft)	0.6 km (0.4 mi)	2.0 km (1.3 mi)
1818	Silicon tetrachloride (when spilled in water)	30 m (100 ft)	0.1 km (0.1 mi)	0.3 km (0.2 mi)	100 m (300 ft)	0.9 km (0.6 mi)	2.9 km (1.8 mi)
1828	Sulfur chlorides (when spilled on land)	30 m (100 ft)	0.1 km (0.1 mi)	0.2 km (0.1 mi)	60 m (200 ft)	0.7 km (0.5 mi)	1.2 km (0.8 mi)
1828	Sulfur chlorides (when spilled in water)	30 m (100 ft)	0.1 km (0.1 mi)	0.2 km (0.1 mi)	30 m (100 ft)	0.4 km (0.2 mi)	1.2 km (0.8 mi)
1828	Sulphur chlorides (when spilled on land)	30 m (100 ft)	0.1 km (0.1 mi)	0.2 km (0.1 mi)	60 m (200 ft)	0.7 km (0.5 mi)	1.2 km (0.8 mi)
1828	Sulphur chlorides (when spilled in water)	30 m (100 ft)	0.1 km (0.1 mi)	0.2 km (0.1 mi)	30 m (100 ft)	0.4 km (0.2 mi)	1.2 km (0.8 mi)
1829 1829 1829 1829 1829 1829	Sulfur trioxide, inhibited Sulfur trioxide, stabilized Sulfur trioxide, uninhibited Sulphur trioxide, inhibited Sulphur trioxide, stabilized Sulphur trioxide, uninhibited	60 m (200 ft)	0.4 km (0.2 mi)	1.0 km (0.6 mi)	300 m (1000 ft)	2.9 km (1.8 mi)	5.7 km (3.6 mi)
1831 1831 1831 1831	Sulfuric acid, fuming Sulfuric acid, fuming, with not less than 30% free Sulfur trioxide Sulphuric acid, fuming Sulphuric acid, fuming, with not less than 30% free Sulphur trioxide	60 m (200 ft)	0.4 km (0.2 mi)	1.0 km (0.6 mi)	300 m (1000 ft)	2.9 km (1.8 mi)	5.7 km (3.6 mi)

Page 310

Fig. 23–74. ERG—Initial isolation and protective action distances

TABLE 2 - WATER-REACTIVE MATERIALS WHICH PRODUCE TOXIC GASES

Materials Which Produce Large Amounts of Toxic-by-Inhalation (TIH) Gas(es) *When Spilled in Water*

ID No.	Guide No.	Name of Material	TIH Gas(es) Produced
1898	156	Acetyl iodide	HI
1923	135	Calcium dithionite	H_2S SO_2
1923	135	Calcium hydrosulfite	H_2S SO_2
1923	135	Calcium hydrosulphite	H_2S SO_2
1929	135	Potassium dithionite	H_2S SO_2
1929	135	Potassium hydrosulfite	H_2S SO_2
1929	135	Potassium hydrosulphite	H_2S SO_2
1931	171	Zinc dithionite	H_2S SO_2
1931	171	Zinc hydrosulfite	H_2S SO_2
1931	171	Zinc hydrosulphite	H_2S SO_2
2004	135	Magnesium diamide	NH_3
2011	139	Magnesium phosphide	PH_3
2012	139	Potassium phosphide	PH_3
2013	139	Strontium phosphide	PH_3
2308	157	Nitrosylsulfuric acid	NO_2
2308	157	Nitrosylsulfuric acid, liquid	NO_2
2308	157	Nitrosylsulfuric acid, solid	NO_2
2308	157	Nitrosylsulphuric acid	NO_2
2308	157	Nitrosylsulphuric acid, liquid	NO_2
2308	157	Nitrosylsulphuric acid, solid	NO_2
2353	132	Butyryl chloride	HCl
2395	132	Isobutyryl chloride	HCl
2434	156	Dibenzyldichlorosilane	HCl
2435	156	Ethylphenyldichlorosilane	HCl

Chemical Symbols for TIH Gases:

Br_2	Bromine	HF	Hydrogen fluoride	PH_3	Phosphine
Cl_2	Chlorine	HI	Hydrogen iodide	NO_2	Nitrogen dioxide
HBr	Hydrogen bromide	H_2S	Hydrogen sulfide	SO_2	Sulfur dioxide
HCl	Hydrogen chloride	H_2S	Hydrogen sulphide	SO_2	Sulphur dioxide
HCN	Hydrogen cyanide	NH_3	Ammonia		

Use this list only when material is spilled in water. Page 345

Fig. 23–75. ERG—materials producing toxic gases when mixed with water

Miscellaneous entries. Some hazardous materials listed in the ERG, such as styrene monomer, have a P listed after the guide number (128P). The *P* indicates that the material may *polymerize*. A chemical that polymerizes builds on itself, creating a chain of molecules, which could potentially become unstable. Usually an inhibitor is added to a monomer in transportation. Nevertheless, responders should be *extremely cautious* when responding to this type of material.

Shipping papers. Shipping papers are a valuable resource in determining the type of material involved as well as the quantity that responders have to contend with. Shipping papers can provide response personnel with the following information:

- Shipper's name and address
- Receiver's name and address
- List of shipped material(s)
- Proper shipping name of the material
- Emergency response telephone number

Shipping papers are required for all modes of transportation, although the name of the document, the person responsible, and the location differ depending on the mode of travel. When searching for the shipping papers, it may be necessary to check the entire area of each location. In airplanes and trucks, the shipping papers are located near the pilot or driver. In an emergency, shipping paper information can be obtained from the shipper/manufacturer or through CHEMTREC. Table 23–15 shows the various types of shipping papers and their names, locations found, and who is responsible for the papers based on the mode of travel.

Table 23–15. Types of shipping papers

Mode of Transportation	Title of Shipping Papers	Location of Shipping Papers	Responsible Person(s)
Highway	Bill of lading	Cab of vehicle	Driver
Rail	Waybill/consist	Engine or caboose	Conductor
Water	Dangerous cargo manifest	Bridge or pilot house	Captain or master
Air	Air bill	Cockpit	Pilot

After accessing the shipping papers, the first responders will be able to determine if the load contains any type of hazardous materials by looking for the following information:

- First-listed order of hazardous materials on the shipping papers
- "X" in the HM column indicating hazardous materials. Note that "RQ" may replace the "X" in the hazardous materials column if the material is considered a reportable quantity.
- Material's hazard class
- UN/NA ID number

Figure 23–76 is an example of what a hazardous materials entry would look like on a shipping paper.

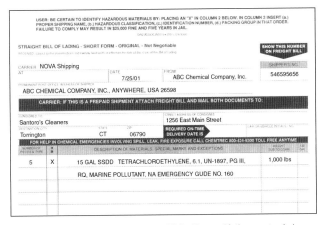

Fig. 23–76. Shipping papers will indicate if the material being transported is hazardous.

Material Safety Data Sheets (MSDS). MSDSs are designed to provide comprehensive information on a material. It is required by OSHA 1910.1200—Hazard Communication Standard that employers provide an MSDS for every hazardous chemical at their facility that is found in greater than "household quantities." The firehouse you work or volunteer in is required by the same standard to keep MSDSs on everything from cleaning supplies to fuel to foam. MSDSs contain specific information about a particular hazardous material produced by an identified manufacturer. Because it is designed to provide information about a specific chemical, it is more useful to the responder in providing specific properties about the chemical. The MSDS also lists contact information for the manufacturer, who can be a very valuable resource during an incident response. If possible, the responder should try to access the chemical's MSDS as soon as possible. Do not compromise responder safety, however, to access this or any other document during a response.

MSDSs can typically be obtained from the following:

- Facility hazard communications plan
- Facility manager/employer
- Sometimes attached to shipping papers
- Manufacturer of the material
- Supplier of the material
- Local emergency planning committee
- Central location at the facility

Fire departments may maintain MSDSs for high-quantity, high-use items in their response area.

MSDSs can vary in the amount of information they provide, but OSHA requires the following information to be provided at a minimum (fig. 23–77):

Section I—Contact Information

- Manufacturer's name and address
- Emergency telephone number
- Information telephone number
- Signature and date

Section II—Hazardous Ingredients

- Common name
- Chemical name
- Chemical Abstract Service (CAS) number
- Permissible Exposure Limit (PEL; a term used by OSHA)
- Threshold Limit Value (TLV; a term used by ACGIH)
- Other exposure limits

Section III—Physical and Chemical Properties

- Boiling point
- Specific gravity
- Vapor pressure
- Vapor density
- Corrosiveness (pH)
- Melting point
- Evaporation rate
- Water solubility
- Appearance and odor

Section IV—Fire and Explosion Hazard Data

- Flashpoint and autoignition temperatures
- Flammable limits (LEL, UEL)
- Extinguishing methods
- Special firefighting procedures
- Unusual fire and explosion hazards

Section V—Reactivity Data

- Stability of the material, which addresses conditions to avoid
- Incompatibility issues
- Hazardous decomposition or by-products
- Hazardous polymerization, listing conditions under which this may not occur

Section VI—Health Hazard Data

- Routes of entry
- Health hazards
- Signs and symptoms of exposure
- Medical conditions aggravated by exposure
- Emergency and first aid procedures
- Lists whether or not the material is a carcinogen

Section VII—Precautions for Safe Handling

- Steps taken in the event of a spill
- Waste disposal methods
- Handling and storage precautions
- Other safety precautions

Section VIII—Control Measure

- Respiratory protection
- Ventilation
- Protective gloves
- Eye protection
- Additional PPE

ABC CHEMICAL

Proton 451 - Chemical Resistant Epoxy Coating   MSDS No. 59659
Date of Creation: 10/11/1995   Date of Update:01/24/2002   Date Printed:01/24/2002   Revision: 18

Section 1 - Chemical Product and Company Identification

Product/Chemical Name: Proton 451 - Chemical Resistant Epoxy Coating
Chemical Formula: N/A
CAS Number: N/A
Other Designations: N/A
Manufacturer: ABC Chemical   Phone: (555) 123-4567
              200 Main Street   Fax: (555) 123-6789
              Anywhere, USA 12345 -6789

HMIS	
H	1
F	2
R	1
PPE †	
† Sec. 8	

EMERGENCY TELEPHONE NUMBER: Use only in the event of an emergency involving a spill, leak, fire, exposure, or accident involving chemicals. Within the U.S, Canada, or the U.S. Virgin Islands, call CHEMTREC at 1-800-424-9300, 24 hours a day. Or, outside these areas, call (703) 527 -3887. Collect calls are accepted.

Emergency Overview
Proton 451 - Chemical Resistant Epoxy Coating:
- Is flammable
- Is a clear oily liquid
- Has a ketone odor

Section 2 - Composition / Information on Ingredients

Ingredient Name	CAS Number	% wt
Methyl Ethyl Ketone (MEK)	000078-93-3	60

Chemical Name	OSHA			NIOSH			ACGIH			Canada			NIOSH IDLH
	TWA	STEL	Ceil.	TWA	STEL	Ceil.	TWA	STEL	Ceil.	TWA	STEL	Ceil.	
	ppm / mg/m³	ppm / mg/m³	ppm / mg/m³	ppm / mg/m³	ppm / mg/m³	ppm / mg/m³	ppm / mg/m³	ppm / mg/m³	ppm / mg/m³	ppm / mg/m³	ppm / mg/m³	ppm / mg/m³	
Methyl ethyl ketone (MEK)	200 / 590			200 / 590	300 / 885		200 / 590	300 / 885		200 / 590	300 / 885		3000

Section 3 - Physical and Chemical Properties

Physical Appearance: Clear, oily liquid
Odor: Ketone odor
Vapor Pressure: Not Determined
Vapor Density (Air=1): >1
Specific Gravity (H$_2$O=1, at 4°C): Not Determined
pH: Not Determined

Water Solubility: N/A
Other Solubilities: None Known
Boiling Point: 147 – 321 °F
Freezing/Melting Point: N/A
% Volatile: Not Determined
Evaporation Rate: <1

Section 4 - Fire – Fighting Measures

Flash Point: 137 °F
Flash Point Method: SCC
Autoignition Temperature: Not Determined
LEL: Not Determined
UEL: Not Determined
Flammability Classification: Flammable
Extinguishing Media: Dry chemical, foam, or CO2.
Unusual Fire or Explosion Hazards: heat or contamination may lead to fire and explosive decomposition. If confined during exposure to fire, may decompose with force.
Hazardous Combustion Products: Oxides of carbon
Fire -Fighting Instructions: water should be used to keep fire-exposed containers cool. If leak or spill has not ignited, water may be used to disperse the vapors and to protect persons attempting to stop a leak. Water spray may be used to flush spills away from exposure. Do not release runoff from fire control methods to sewers or waterways.
Fire -Fighting Equipment: Because fire may produce toxic thermal decomposition products, wear a self-contained breathing apparatus (SCBA) with a full face -piece operated in pressure-demand or positive-pressure mode.

NFPA
2
1   1
—

Fig. 23–77. MSDSs contain valuable information about the properties of the hazardous material, including physical/chemical properties, firefighting measures, stability and reactivity, hazards, disposal procedures, protective equipment information, and other data.

Although this information represents the minimum required, OSHA encourages the ANSI MSDS standard and the additional information it provides. As such, responders may encounter MSDSs set up in the following format:

1. Substance identity and company contact information
2. Chemical composition and data on components
3. Hazards identification
4. First aid measures
5. Firefighting measures
6. Accidental release measures
7. Handling and storage
8. Exposure controls and personal protection
9. Physical and chemical properties
10. Stability and reactivity
11. Toxicological information
12. Ecological information
13. Disposal considerations
14. Transport information
15. Regulations
16. Other information

National Institute of Occupational Safety and Health (NIOSH) Pocket Guide to Chemical Hazards.
The NIOSH *Pocket Guide to Chemical Hazards* is also an excellent reference to have for hazardous materials responses (fig. 23–78). Although the NIOSH guide is designed primarily for a facility employee, many responders use it as well. The NIOSH guide is small, portable, and is also available free online.

Fig. 23–78. The NIOSH Pocket Guide contains useful information for operations-level responders.

The NIOSH Pocket Guide contains information that is more specific than the ERG. Although the ERG is the best initial reference for fire, spills, and response, the NIOSH Pocket Guide contains additional information such as exposure limits, symptoms of exposure, and synonyms as well as detailed chemical and physical property information. The *NIOSH Pocket Guide* is organized alphabetically.

Telephone resources

Many hazardous materials experts may not be located in your area, but they are only a phone call away. There are several 24-hour hazardous materials emergency resources available to the first responder.

Chemical Transportation Emergency Center (CHEMTREC). CHEMTREC is a 24/7/365 emergency call center that provides immediate information and assistance to anyone involved in a chemical or hazardous material incident. It can be contacted by calling 1-800-424-9300.

Today, CHEMTREC is the most widely used resource for emergency responders dealing with hazardous materials incidents. The service is free to all responders and anyone who deals with hazardous material emergencies. CHEMTREC is staffed by trained and knowledgeable personnel who have access to over 3 million MSDSs. CHEMTREC staff can fax or email an MSDS to you on scene.

CHEMTREC's emergency service specialists (ESS) can provide immediate guidance and links to technical expertise, as well as medical and toxicological advice and information through MSDSs and other resources. Also, information about the contents of tank cars, trucks, or other containers is routinely provided during emergencies through carrier contacts, shipping documents, and other systems and resources available to CHEMTREC ESS.

According to law, companies that ship hazardous materials must provide a 24-hour emergency contact number. CHEMTREC provides this service to its members. CHEMTREC then maintains a database of the company's MSDSs as well as emergency points of contact. Responders today can call CHEMTREC at any time, even when the company whose product has been released is not registered with them. CHEMTREC emergency service specialists will still try to assist the responder with information about the chemicals and the shipper. For additional information, visit http://www.chemtrec.com. There are versions of CHEMTREC that exist in Canada and Mexico that provide a similar service. In Canada the service is known as CANUTEC (Canadian Transport Emergency Center), in Mexico it is called SETIQ (Stema de Emergencia

para la Transportacion de la Industria Quimica). When contacting any of these agencies, it is important for the responder to provide the following information. This information should also be provided to local, state, and federal resources when requesting their response to a hazardous materials incident:

- Full name and title of caller
- Callback telephone number
- Location and description of incident
- Time of incident and weather conditions
- What actions have been taken thus far
- Type or description and number of containers or packages involved
- Product info from shipping documents
- Name of shipper
- Name of carrier
- UN, NA, and/or STCC number of the product
- Trade name or chemical/DOT shipping name
- Shipper and point of origin
- Consignee and destination
- Amount of material involved
- Identification numbers on the container
- Any fatalities, injuries, or exposures
- Specific information requested or type of information that is needed as a priority
- What resources are on scene or en route

Response personnel should be aware of the limitations of the CHEMTREC system because not all chemical manufacturers provide information to these organizations. The relevance of the information provided by CHEMTREC depends upon the information given to them by the caller. The first responder must understand that the response procedure information given is general in nature.

National Response Center. The National Response Center, located in Washington D.C. and staffed by the U.S. Coast Guard, is the single point of contact for reporting spills of oil, hazardous materials, and terrorism incidents. The National Response Center is also staffed 24/7 and can be contacted at 1-800-424-8802.

Many hazardous materials have a **reportable quantity (RQ)**. If the amount of material spilled is more than the RQ, the spiller is required to notify the National Response Center. The National Response Center then notifies the U.S. Coast Guard and/or the EPA, depending on the spill location, as well as state agencies and other government entities. This is how the state and federal governments learn about some of the spills that occur in your area.

Centers for Disease Control. If a victim is involved in your incident, you need to quickly find out what care must be administered. Your local poison control center may be this first call. If your local center has limited expertise in hazardous materials, you can also contact the Centers for Disease Control and Prevention, which has a division known as the Agency for Toxic Substances and Disease Registry (ATSDR), composed of a team of toxicologists who specialize in environmental health and hazardous materials. ATSDR can be reached 24 hours a day at 404-498-0120. If a contaminated victim is transported for treatment, responding medical personnel may want to use this resource to gain additional information regarding treatment and decontamination.

Computer resources

Many computer resources are available to the emergency responder responding to a hazardous materials incident. Two of the most common resources are discussed in the following sections.

WISER. Wireless Information System for Emergency Responders (WISER) is produced and distributed by the National Library of Medicine (fig. 23–79). WISER is a free download that can be accessed at http://wiser.nlm.nih.gov. WebWISER is also available for PDA use. A responder can subscribe to WISER and receive information on updates and online training exercises. WISER is one of the most commonly used tools by hazardous materials responders. WISER contains information on more than 4,700 hazardous substances. Furthermore, WISER also has extensive search capabilities, which can be especially helpful in an incident where limited information is available.

Fig. 23–79. Wireless Information System for Emergency Responders (WISER)

CAMEO. Computer-Aided Modeling for Emergency Operations (CAMEO) was developed by the National Oceanic and Atmospheric Administration (NOAA) and the U.S. EPA (fig. 23–80). CAMEO consists of three modules that can be useful to the emergency responder. CAMEO contains a chemical database with more than 6,000 chemicals. The user can access the response information data sheets (RIDS) that contain similar information to that on an MSDS. CAMEO also contains a chemical reactivity worksheet that predicts possible outcomes when chemicals are accidentally mixed together, such as at a transportation incident. CAMEO is available for free download at www.noaa.gov. It takes some practice to master, but CAMEO can provide valuable information for planning and response.

Another module of CAMEO is Areal Locations of Hazardous Atmospheres (ALOHA). A plume model that can estimate hazard zones for a chemical that becomes airborne, ALOHA requires the user to input information about the incident such as type of spill, weather conditions, and surrounding environment.

The third module of CAMEO is a mapping tool known as the Mapping Application for Response, Planning, and Local Operational Tasks (MARPLOT). MARPLOT allows the user to map the incident directly on a location where the incident is occurring. The user can then use ALOHA for a visual estimate of the plume of the released hazardous materials.

Analyzing the Hazmat/WMD Incident

FIREFIGHTER I

Chapter 23

CAMEO Home provides easy access to the CAMEO data management modules (such as Facilities and Contacts) and other programs in the CAMEO suite (CAMEO Chemicals, ALOHA, and MARPLOT). CAMEO is available for free download at www.noaa.gov (do a site search for CAMEO).

Fig. 23–80. CAMEO provides a comprehensive computer-based resource for responders.

SECTION II CONCLUSION

The collection of hazard and response information is a vital component to any hazardous materials response. The ability of the hazmat responder to make sound decisions depends on having as much information to draw from as possible. Before specific decisions can be made, the responder needs to understand the chemical and physical properties of the material as well as the potential health hazards. There are several different sources available to obtain this information about a product and additional resources such as people, telephone contacts, printed materials, and computer applications to confirm the information collected.

Section III:
DETERMINING THE BEHAVIOR OF THE MATERIAL

INTRODUCTION

When the responder has identified the material and determined its physical and chemical properties, the next step is to begin to estimate its likely behavior as it is released from the container. The type of damage to the container, topography, and environmental conditions are just a few of the additional factors that affect how the material will behave during the release. With this information it is also possible to begin to estimate the potential harm resulting from the leak.

CONTAINER BREACHES

In the mid 1970s Ludwig Benner Jr. created the General Emergency Behavior Model (GEMBO) with the intent of helping responders limit the effects of a hazardous materials release. This model is designed to aid in the threat prediction process and accounts for the various factors involved in predicting the behavior of a release. It is broken down into the following sections: stress, breach, release, engulf, contact, and harm.

Stress

Different types of stresses can be applied on the container, depending on the situation. It is also possible to have more than one of the following stresses acting on a container at any given time. For example, heating a container may weaken it and cause a chemical reaction to take place, or a mechanical stress may cause damage to a container and initiate a chemical reaction. The following are examples of common types of container stressors.

Thermal stress. Thermal stress can be the result of radiated, convected, conducted, or direct heat exposure (fig. 23–81), as well as exposure to cold. Heat or cold can result in the expansion, contraction, and weakening of the container. Thermal stress may increase internal pressure and reduce container strength simultaneously, resulting in sudden failure.

Fig. 23–81. Fire can place a thermal stress on a container.

Always be on the lookout for stressed containers when responding to a hazardous materials incident. If the material has been released before arrival, not only should responders address that release, but also determine the potential for other containers in the area to be stressed. Always be on the lookout for indications of thermal stress, such as the operation of a safety relief valve or the bulging of a container.

When heat is applied to a closed container, a boiling liquid expanding vapor explosion (BLEVE) may occur. This starts with the liquid inside boiling and exerting pressure on the container. The internal pressure increases until the container fails, which may result in an explosive release of the material (fig. 23–82).

Fig. 23–82. A BLEVE can result in catastrophic container failure.

The release of pressure may result in a violent rupture, causing fragments of the container to be projected significant distances. There is also a shock wave associated with a BLEVE. If the liquid is flammable, the container failure will be accompanied by a fireball.

Mechanical stress. Mechanical stress is the physical application of energy that results in container or attachment damage. It may cause the container to become deformed, cracked, penetrated, lose some of its thickness, or damage valves or piping (fig. 23–83). Mechanical stress is the result of a collision between two objects.

Fig. 23–83. Containers can become damaged due to mechanical stress.

Indications of mechanical stress:

- The container may become deformed or penetrated.
- It may also be punctured, gouged, scored, broken, or torn.

Responders should be aware that it is possible for a container to be damaged or weakened by a mechanical force without any visible signs of a potential release.

Chemical stress. Chemical stress results from an uncontrolled reaction or interaction of the container and/or its contents. The onset of container deterioration may occur suddenly or over a long period of time. Chemical reactions taking place in a container may also result in excessive heat and/or pressure that may result in container failure. The following are indicators of chemical stress:

- Containers that display visible corrosion
- Pressure or heat resulting from the reaction of the substances

Breach

After the container has been stressed to the point where a breach occurs, responders can expect the container to fail in one of the following manners.

Disintegration. Disintegration results in the total loss of container integrity. An example of this type of breach is a glass container shattering (fig. 23–84).

Fig. 23–84. Disintegration is the failure of a container.

Runaway cracking. Runaway cracking is the rapid expansion of a small crack in a closed container. The result is a container violently breaking into two or more pieces. This type of breach generally occurs in closed containers such as liquid drums or pressure vessels.

Attachment failure. In this type of breach, attachments may open up or break off. For example, safety relief valves, fusible plugs, discharge valves, and so on, may break.

Puncture. Punctures are generally caused by mechanical stresses and result in container failure. For example, a forklift may pierce a 55-gal (208-L) drum (fig. 23–85).

Fig. 23–85. A puncture in a container can result the release of a material.

Split or tear. A split or tear is commonly associated with fiber drums or plastic bags and can also refer to, for example, split 55-gal (208-L) drums and seam or weld failures.

Release

After the container becomes breached due the stresses placed on it, the material can be released in several different ways depending on the material involved and other factors. The following are examples of different types of releases.

Detonation. Detonation is an instantaneous and explosive chemical reaction that releases pressure and extreme heat. It results in the fragmentation, shattering, or disintegration of the container. Detonation occurs in $^1/_{100}$ of a second or less; the speed of this reaction affords first responders no time to react. Examples of materials that can detonate include military ammunition, mining explosives, and organic peroxides.

Violent rupture. Violent ruptures are chemical reactions that have a release lasting less than one second. It is also known as deflagration. It is associated with runaway cracking and overpressurization of closed containers. Containers and their contents may become projectiles as a result of the reaction. Like detonation, the speed of violent rupture affords first responders no time to react.

Rapid relief. Rapid relief is the fast release of a pressurized hazardous material. It may take several seconds to several minutes to release. The speed of the rapid relief depends on the size of the opening in the container, the properties of its contents, and the type of container.

In the case of rapid release, the pressure is released through:

- Relief valves
- Broken or damaged piping/valves
- Punctures
- Tears or splits

These types of releases typically give time for first responders to react and move to a safe location.

Spills and leaks. Spills and leaks result in the slow release of hazardous materials. The duration of release varies from minutes to days. Slower release rates from spills and leaks allow adequate time to develop countermeasures. Spills and leaks are nonviolent low-pressure flows resulting from the following:

- Broken valves/piping
- Tears, splits, or punctures in a container

Engulf

After the material is released from its container, it begins to engulf the area around it. The extent to which this occurs depends on the amount of material, the physical state of material (solid, liquid, gas), weather conditions, topography, type of container breach, control efforts of emergency responders, and the type of release and its duration. The following are examples of different engulfing events.

Hemisphere. The hazardous material is airborne in a semicircular or dome shaped pattern (fig. 23–86). It may be partially in contact with ground or water. The hazardous material initially rises and spreads outward symmetrically and falls equally in all directions. This type of event generally occurs when the winds are calm.

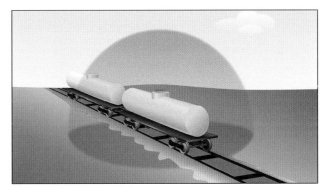

Fig. 23–86. A hemisphere engulfing pattern

Cloud. The hazardous material is airborne in a ball-shaped pattern (fig. 23–87). The material rises above the ground or water.

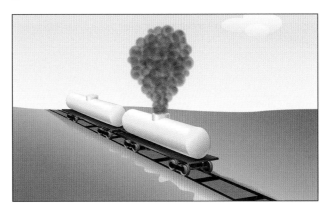

Fig. 23–87. A cloud engulfing pattern

Plume. The hazardous material is airborne in an irregular pattern (fig. 23–88). The material drifts with the wind. The trajectory of the substance is determined by wind and topography.

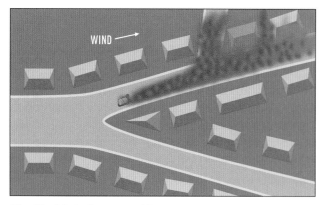

Fig. 23–88. A plume engulfing pattern

Cone. The hazardous material is airborne in a triangular pattern flowing away from the release point (fig. 23–89). The material flows with the topography and widens as it gets further away from the source.

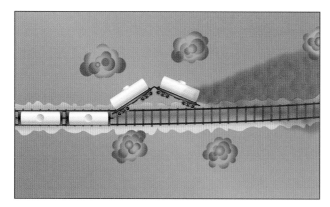

Fig. 23–89. A cone engulfing pattern

Stream. The hazardous material follows a path determined by gravity and ground topography (fig. 23–90). It can be a liquid or a gas.

Fig. 23–90. A stream engulfing pattern

Pool. A liquid hazardous material follows a flat, circular pattern (fig. 23–91). The spill spreads equally in all directions and may be present on the ground or on the surface of a body of water.

Fig. 23–91. A pool engulfing pattern

Irregular. Hazardous materials are deposited in an irregular pattern (fig. 23–92). For example, materials may be carried by contaminated personnel.

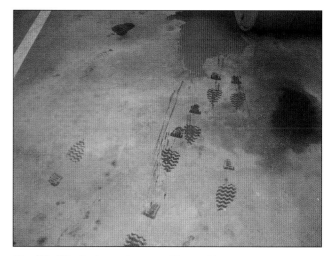

Fig. 23–92. An irregular engulfing pattern

Contact

As the released material begins to engulf the area around the container, a contact event can occur. A contact event refers to the amount of time an exposure (person or object) is in contact with the hazardous material. The factors influencing the duration of contact are the quantity of material released, the dispersion method, and the speed of release. There are four general time periods associated with a contact event: immediate, short-term, medium-term, and long-term.

Immediate event. In an immediate event, durations are measured in seconds and milliseconds. Examples include explosion, detonation, or deflagration.

Short-term event. A short-term event has a duration of minutes to hours. The event is characterized by a lower hazard, small (short) releases, and is quickly brought under control. Examples include transient vapor clouds.

Medium-term event. A medium-term event occurs over a period of days, weeks, or months. The event is characterized by a moderate to high hazard. First responders have a lengthy or difficult decontamination and moderate cleanup is necessary. Examples include lingering pesticides resulting from a fire or spill.

Long-term event. A long-term event extends over years or generations. It results in heavy contamination and has a lengthy and difficult decontamination. In the case of a long-term event, extensive cleanup is required. Examples include permanent radioactive sources such as Chernobyl.

Harm

Harm is the injury or damage resulting from exposure to the hazardous materials release and subsequent exposure. The three factors that determine the potential harm caused by an exposure are as follows:

- Timing of release: refers to the speed at which the material is released as well as the amount of time spent in contact with the material

- Size of release: refers to the size of the area which is covered by the material

- Toxicity of the material: refers to the relative level of harm that exposure to it causes

ESTIMATING POTENTIAL HARM

The focus of emergency response personnel at the operations level is to make general estimates regarding the area that will be affected by the release by using the hazard and response information collected. Responders have a number of tools at their disposal to estimate the potential harm that a hazmat release will have on the surrounding area. When these estimates are made, evacuations can begin, and defensive operations can be safely initiated. If the situation warrants it, the response of a technician-level team or other high-level resources facilitates more detailed estimates of potential harm.

Determining the size of an endangered area

One of the easiest and most readily available tools for estimating the size of an endangered area is the DOT ERG. As discussed previously, both the orange emergency response guide section and the green tables of isolation and protective action distances contain information on isolation and evacuation distances. Although this may seem redundant, this system accounts for the fact that some materials present a toxic-by-inhalation hazard (TIH) whereas others do not. The distances for TIH materials can be found in the green section, whereas the other ones are determined by looking in the orange guide section. Use the flow chart in figure 23–93 to choose the appropriate section of the ERG to use in determining the size of the endangered area.

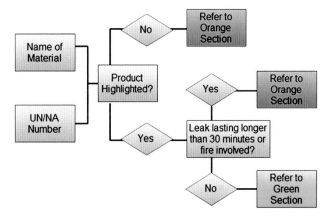

Fig. 23–93. Determining the size of the endangered area using the DOT ERG

If the only method of identification visible is a placard or a container shape, use the white section of the ERG to reference the appropriate guide number in the orange section (fig. 23–94).

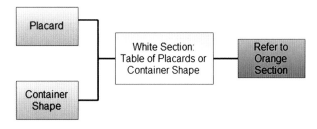

Fig. 23–94. Determining the size of the area using the container shape or placard and the DOT ERG

To control the endangered area, the hazmat responder should:

- Isolate the area of the spill using the initial isolation distances listed in the ERG.

- Remove people from the initial isolation area.

- Deny entry to the isolation area by unauthorized persons.

- If required, evacuate or protect-in-place those people found within the protective action zone.

Initial isolation and protective action distances

Determining the initial isolation zone. The first responder should reference the proper section of the ERG to determine the initial isolation zone. The public safety section in the orange guide should be used to determine the isolation zone for materials that are *not* highlighted. Evacuation distances are listed for materials involved in fires as well as spills. Materials that are highlighted use the initial isolation recommendations given in the green section. The initial isolation zone is established by creating a circle around the spill using the minimum isolation distance, as shown in figure 23–95.

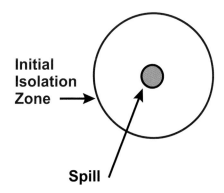

Fig. 23–95. Initial isolation zone layout

Determining protective action distances. The protective action distance is the area that is adjacent to and downwind of the initial isolation zone and in imminent danger of becoming contaminated within 30 minutes of the material's release (fig. 23–96). Responders must either evacuate or protect-in-place the people found in this area. Isolation distances for highlighted materials can be found in Table 1 of the green section of the ERG. Materials that are *not* highlighted do not have specific protective action distances given. The ERG suggests that you increase the initial isolation zone distance given in the orange guide in the downwind direction as necessary.

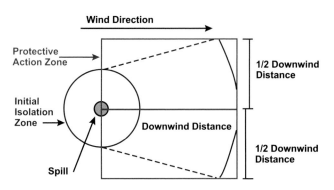

Fig. 23–96. Protective action distances layout

The protective action zone is shaped like a square and provides downwind protection.

Also, CHEMTREC and/or the manufacturer or shipper can provide additional information to supplement what is gathered from the DOT ERG. Other methods available to response personnel, depending on their level of training and equipment available, are computer plume modeling and metering capabilities to determine the extent of the release.

Estimating the potential exposures

After the size of the endangered area has been determined, response personnel must look at what types of exposures are in that area. In order of importance, exposures consist of people, the environment, and property. Responders should consider the potential extent of physical harm that can be anticipated in the area and what would be accomplished by taking action or not taking action before making any determination on an appropriate response. Factors in that decision include the number of exposures, to what extent they are exposed, and the concentration of the released material in the area of the exposures. Also, factors such as whether it is a rural or urban area, time of day, and the general occupancy in the area will all play a role in that estimation. Additionally, the size of the container, the size of the breach, as well as wind direction and speed will also be important factors to consider. Responders should be keenly aware of the scope of potential exposures that exist within the danger area and be sure to request adequate response resources that will support minimizing the effect on those exposures. This includes additional evacuation assistance and technician-level responses to potentially reduce the amount of product released.

Determining the concentration of a material

The two primary methods of determining the concentration of a chemical in a given area is the use of appropriate monitoring or metering equipment and computer-based dispersion model programs. These resources are not typically available to operations-level responders, so access to this equipment and personnel trained to use it should be arranged prior to an incident. Responders should be sure to train with these additional resources prior to ensuring that their capabilities are understood.

Atmospheric monitoring. Atmospheric monitors are used by firefighters to detect and measure the concentration of airborne health and fire hazards that may be present following a chemical release, a structure fire, or a confined space release. These hazards exist both as gases and vapors and may be produced by liquids or solids. Remember, liquids and vapors are readily inhaled, and those that are flammable are easily ignited when mixed in the appropriate concentration with air.

Most atmospheric monitors provide responders with a numerical reading that measures the concentration of products in the atmosphere. These numbers are then compared to standards that define concentration levels considered safe. Many atmospheric monitors are already programmed with these levels and include both audible and visual alarms that sound when unsafe concentrations are reached.

The devices used most often by responders have four separate sensors and are, therefore, usually referred to as **4-gas meters**. A typical atmospheric monitor includes a small electric pump that draws in a sample of the atmosphere. Today, most fire department monitors have four sensors: a lower explosive limit (LEL) sensor that detects flammable atmospheres, an oxygen sensor to monitor oxygen levels, a carbon monoxide sensor to determine carbon monoxide levels in parts per million, and a hydrogen sulfide sensor to monitor levels in parts per million. Each of these sensors is designed to detect and measure only one chemical. Figure 23–97 shows a typical 4-gas meter.

Fig. 23–97. A typical 4-gas meter

For most toxic atmospheres, measurements are usually read as **parts per million (ppm)**. Oxygen content is measured as its percent concentration in air, normally 20.9%. Monitoring for oxygen is important, and the alarm values of 19.5% and 23.5% are set by OSHA regulation, but the reality is that responders can be in danger before the alarms sounds. An oxygen drop to 20.8% from 20.9% can be a dangerous situation depending on the contaminant that has caused the drop. It may be only 0.1%, but that is a significant change. A drop to 19.9% would not result in an alarm, but it indicates considerable contaminants in the air. The concentration of flammable gases and vapors is typically measured as a percentage of the material's LEL, which is the lowest concentration when mixed with air that allows the material to burn once ignited. There are standard set points for the meter's alarm to sound when it detects unsafe levels of the monitored materials. Figure 23–98 provides alarm set points for an atmospheric monitor.

Atmospheric monitors do not *detect* immediately when exposed to an atmosphere. The manufacturers determine in advance the **response time** of the device, which is the maximum amount of time it may take to obtain a reading. The use of probes or flexible tubing can increase this time. Most manufacturers list the response time for each sensor in the manual. To use the device appropriately, make sure that the response time is understood.

Gas	Ceiling	TWA	STEL
CO	35 ppm	35 ppm	100 ppm
H_2S	10 ppm	10 ppm	15 ppm
SO_2	2 ppm	2 ppm	5 ppm
O_2	Low: 19.5% High: 23.5%		
LEL	10% LEL		

Fig. 23–98. An example of alarm set points for an atmospheric monitor

The ability of an atmospheric monitor to provide accurate readings must be checked on a regularly scheduled basis. This check is referred to as **bench calibration**, and is performed by exposing the atmospheric monitor to a predetermined concentration of gases. If the readings obtained are inaccurate, adjustments or repairs may be necessary. Calibration must be done usually every 30 days or based on the manufacturer's recommendation, and only by those with the proper training to conduct these tests safely.

Remember that the type of gas used to calibrate an atmospheric monitor influences readings that measure the concentration of flammable gases and vapors. Although there are many different flammable gases and vapors responders could encounter during a salvage and overhaul or a hazmat emergency, the atmospheric monitor is only *calibrated* to read *one* type of flammable gas. Readings obtained when attempting to detect and measure the concentration of other types of flammable gases may be higher or lower than their actual concentration. Such readings must be adjusted using a **relative response factor** provided by the manufacturer of the detection device.

For example, if an atmospheric monitor is calibrated using methane gas, readings when measuring the concentration of this gas are correct. However, when attempting to measure the concentration of another gas such as propane, the manufacturer of the atmospheric monitor may indicate that the reading must be *corrected* by multiplying it by 1.5. It is important to remember that each gas or vapor has its own response factor that is specific to each type of device. Always refer to the manufacturer's manual for your instrument.

When using atmospheric monitors, responders must protect themselves from the hazardous atmosphere they are in. Products of combustion from structural fires or gases and vapors from a hazmat incident are not always visible. Precautions for toxic and flammable atmospheres include the use of structural firefighter's protective clothing and SCBA. Some toxic materials may be absorbed through the skin despite wearing structural firefighter's protective clothing, as these garments are not airtight. Remember, readings that exceed the safe limit for the concentration of flammable gases and vapors demand the immediate evacuation of personnel and equipment to a safe area.

Responders using atmospheric monitors must take into consideration the physical state (gas, liquid, or solid) and chemical properties such as flammability, corrosiveness, toxicity, and high energy of chemicals. For example, some gases and vapors, such as methane, are lighter than air, whereas others, such as propane and gasoline vapors, are heavier than air. Because of a product's vapor density, a responder holding an atmospheric monitor at waist level may not obtain accurate readings.

Many atmospheric monitors have adjuncts that help sample the atmosphere. These adjuncts may include probes or flexible tubing that can be inserted into openings above or below grade. When using these probes, responders must be careful not to place the probe or tubing into liquids or unknown areas without a filter provided by the manufacturer. Figure 23–99 shows a typical probe used with atmospheric monitors.

Fig. 23–99. Typical probe used with atmospheric monitor

SECTION III CONCLUSION

Using the information collected during the scene survey and research phases of the response, the responder should take that information and begin to make educated decisions about how the material will behave as it is released from its container. Using the GEMBO model, they can determine what type of release is occurring and, in conjunction with the different resources available, begin to estimate the potential harm caused by the release.

CHAPTER CONCLUSION

As indicated in the introduction to this chapter, this phase of the hazmat response is arguably the most important because it forms the basis for all decisions made for the remainder of the incident. Without a diligent effort to collect all available information, it will not be possible to plan for all potential contingencies or to determine what additional resources are necessary. Use the methods outlined in this chapter to conduct a thorough scene survey, collect appropriate hazards and response information, and determine the behavior of the material. After those steps are complete, the same information will be used by the responder to plan the response to the hazmat/WMD incident.

QUESTIONS

1. Name the three steps for surveying a hazardous materials incident scene.

   _____

   _____

   _____

2. Why is recognizing container shape a vital skill for identifying hazards when responding to hazardous materials incidents?

   _____

3. What types of information do fixed facility marking systems provide to responders?

   _____

4. List three methods of identifying the hazards associated with a hazardous material in fixed facilities.

   _____

   _____

   _____

5. List three methods of hazard identification in transportation emergencies.

   _____

   _____

   _____

6. List the nine DOT Hazard Classes.

   _____

   _____

   _____

   _____

   _____

   _____

   _____

   _____

   _____

7. What types of materials are most commonly transported in a DOT406/MC306 trailer?

   _____

8. A material with a specific gravity of 1.2 would be expected to _____ in water.

9. What are the three best methods to reduce exposure to radiation?

   _____

   _____

   _____

10. List three print resources available to hazardous materials responders.

    _____

    _____

    _____

11. When looking up a chemical by name, what color section in the DOT Emergency Response Guide should be referenced?

12. MSDS stands for _____

13. List three locations you would anticipate to find an MSDS at a fixed facility.

    _____

    _____

    _____

14. What is the most widely used information resource for emergency responders dealing with hazmat incidents?

    _____

15. Name two computer database resources for hazardous substance identification.

    _____

    _____

QUESTIONS

16.   What does GEMBO stand for and what is its purpose?

_____

17.   A breach caused by a collision between two objects is called a _____ breach.

18.   Name three engulfing patterns of a hazardous materials release.

_____

_____

_____

19.   The area in imminent danger of becoming contaminated within 30 minutes of the material's release is called:

_____

20.   Atmospheric monitors are used to detect what types of hazards?

_____

Planning the Hazmat/ Weapons of Mass Destruction (WMD) Response

Edited by Jason Emery

This chapter provides knowledge items for the following NFPA Standard 472 requirements. For more detail, see the Knowledge Correlations on p. xxxvi.

Awareness	Operations			PPE
4.2.1	5.2.1	5.3.1	5.4.1	6.2.3
4.4.1	5.2.2	5.3.2	5.4.3	6.2.4
	5.2.3	5.3.3	5.4.4	

OBJECTIVES

Upon completion of the chapter, you should be able to do the following:

- Describe the methods to provide scene control at a hazmat/weapons of mass destruction (WMD) incident.
- Identify the protective action options available to the operations-level responder.
- Describe how to establish control zones around a hazmat/WMD incident.
- Describe how the incident management system is integrated into a response to a hazmat/WMD incident.
- List and identify the different levels into which a response can be categorized.
- Describe the process of determining the response objectives at a hazmat/WMD incident.
- List the different types of personal protective equipment (PPE) available to operations level responders.
- Describe how to choose appropriate PPE.
- List and describe the different signs that a terrorist event has occurred.
- Identify the different devices and/or materials that can be used at a WMD incident.
- List scene safety practices that should be considered at a WMD incident.

INTRODUCTION

After the product and hazard information has been collected, the responder must then take that information and, combined with assessing the potential behavior of the material, determine the proper course of action. From there, decisions regarding scene control, the incident management system, response objectives, and PPE are made. For incidents involving terrorist activities or WMD, additional concerns must be integrated in the planning and decision-making model.

SCENE CONTROL

Scene control operations are designed to protect both the public and responding personnel. To protect the public, responders should isolate the area, deny entry, and begin to institute protective actions such as protect-in-place or evacuation. In addition, to provide protection for emergency responders, access should be limited to the area, and control zones (hot, warm, and cold) should be identified and established.

Scene control priorities

Upon arrival on scene and after the initial size up determines that a hazmat incident is involved, responders should immediately begin the process of determining the size of the endangered area, isolating that area, and denying entry. This means that anyone not directly involved with the response should be removed from the immediate area, and civilians and unprotected responders should not be allowed into the isolation area. Determining the size of the endangered area is most easily accomplished by using the Department of Transportation Emergency Response Guide (DOT ERG) as discussed in chapter 24 (fig. 24–1). As more information is gathered about the product, decisions will need to be made regarding the additional protective actions that should be used (protect-in-place and/or evacuation) to protect the public, and control zones (hot, warm, and cold) will need to be set up for the protection of emergency response personnel.

Fig. 24–1. The DOT ERG can be used to determine the size of the endangered area.

Public protective action options

Protecting the public will depend largely on the fire department and other responders and the local emergency planning committee (LEPC) to develop an effective emergency plan. This plan needs to have a risk analysis of the potentially affected population. Because responders in the early stages are small in number and possibly overwhelmed, the need for accurate and up-to-date information is essential in developing an action plan that will include steps needed to protect the public.

When a hazardous material event occurs, the following options need to be considered when developing a plan to protect the public:

- Isolate and deny entry
- Evacuation of threatened populations
- Protect-in-place for all at-risk populations
- A combination of evacuation and protect-in-place

Isolate area and deny entry. The first responder should first isolate the area and deny entry based on information collected in the DOT ERG (fig. 24–2). Everyone not directly involved in emergency response operations must be kept away from the area. Unprotected emergency responders are not allowed entry into the isolation area. This "isolation" task is done to establish control over the area of operations. It is the first step for any protective actions that may follow.

Fig. 24–2. One of the first steps at a hazmat incident is to isolate the area and deny entry.

Evacuation. Evacuations are needed if the situation is such that the at-risk population is at a greater risk by remaining near the incident site. If there is enough time, evacuation is the best protective action. First responders should begin by evacuating people nearby and those outdoors in direct view of the scene. Evacuees should be sent to a definite place by a specific route, far enough away so they will not have to be moved again if the wind shifts. When conducting an evacuation, responders should instruct evacuees where to go, move evacuees to a safe location, provide evacuees with basic needs, and keep them informed of the incident's status (fig. 24–3).

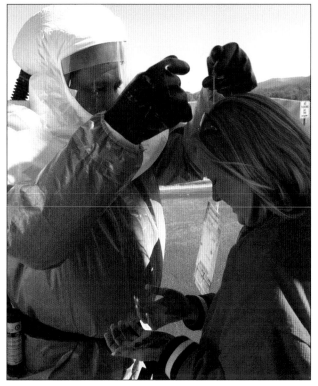

Fig. 24–3. Responders need to advise evacuees on the best place to relocate.

Evacuations should be conducted when the incident involves uncontrollable leaks, explosive materials, or unknown gas leaks from large-capacity containers. The following are factors to consider when making the determination to evacuate:

- The degree and severity posed by the hazard based on the risk analysis developed by response agencies and the LEPC

- The number of persons or the size of the population area that will be affected by the hazard

- The amount of resources (fire/police/EMS/private or public buses/mass transit) needed to effectively evacuate the population at risk

- The available resources needed to notify and provide instructions to the public, including radio and television media, mobile public address systems, reverse 9-1-1, door-to-door contact, cell phone text messaging, and recent technologies, such as social media

- The identification of safe passage routes and refuge centers for evacuated populations

- The identification of special-needs populations and how to effectively and efficiently move them

Protective actions—protect-in-place. This decision is based on the previous risk analysis determined by response agencies and the LEPC. This principle is grounded on the assumption that keeping the affected population in place as opposed to evacuation will provide a safer environment for them. During a protect-in-place action, people are directed to stay in a building, close all doors and windows, shut off HVAC systems, and not exit the structure until told to do so. This type of protective action may not be the best option if the vapors are flammable, it will take a long time for the gas to clear the area, or if the building(s) cannot be sealed tightly.

Protect-in-place is typically used during the following scenarios:

- The material is spreading too quickly, or it is too dangerous to risk exposure.

- There is a moderate- to low-hazard hazmat release.

- There are leaks that can be controlled quickly.

- Vapor clouds are expected to disperse rapidly.

- Hazardous materials have been completely released from their containers.

Some factors that can assist in determining this method of protection include the following:

- What is the potential threat, such as an airborne chemical or biological hazard?

- Will evacuation or protect-in-place provide the lesser danger to the public?

- Are there sufficient resources available to conduct a large-scale evacuation? If not, is protect-in-place the better option?

- Has the affected population been trained on the proper conduct when they are required to be in a protect-in-place situation?

Combination of evacuation and protect-in-place. Some instances may require a combination of evacuation and protect-in-place operations. This could be because some segments of the population would be safer being evacuated, whereas others are better off remaining indoors. This method is also used when on-scene resources are not sufficient to support a large-scale evacuation.

Methods to isolate area and deny entry

After determining the size of the endangered area, the first responder should take the following actions to secure the affected area and the indicated isolation distance:

- Position a responder in each area of approach.

- Direct traffic away from the scene.

- Use physical barriers such as barricades, vehicles, scene tape, and/or ropes; close doors and gates (fig. 24–4).

- Transmit warnings over vehicle or facility PA systems.

- Ask the media to make announcements to notify people to avoid the area.

Responders, especially those first on scene, must determine what methods of securing the scene will work best with the resources they have on hand. If additional resources are needed to properly secure the area, they should be requested immediately. Law enforcement can play a key role assisting with this process.

Fig. 24–4. Use physical barriers to prevent access to the area.

Establishing control zones

Control zones provide necessary scene control at hazardous materials incidents by regulating the movement of responders, thus reducing the potential for contamination.

Zones are set up to divide the levels of hazard at an incident and should be clearly marked (fig. 24–5). The size of each zone is based upon the degree of hazard that the material presents and requires the identification of the involved products. The zones may be adjusted based on changes in the incident. For example, wind should be considered when making the zone boundary determination.

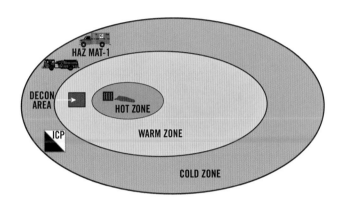

Fig. 24–5. Control zones are used to regulate the movement of emergency responders.

Similar to the methods used to determine the initial isolation areas and protective action distances, the initial determination of the scene control zone is based on information from the ERG, Chemical Transportation Emergency Center/Canadian Transport Emergency Center (CHEMTREC/CANUTEC), and scene observations and assessments. Long-term determinations are made by monitoring and sampling the materials and evaluating the extent of contamination, plume and dispersion models, and changes in weather or other conditions.

Hot zone. The hot zone is the contaminated area immediately surrounding the release. It should be large enough to prevent persons outside the zone from being exposed to the material, typically the size of the isolation distance and possibly including the protective action area. The hot zone should include all areas exposed to any gases, vapors, dusts, or runoff of the hazardous material.

Work in the hot zone is performed by hazmat technicians wearing chemical protective clothing (CPC) designed for the substance released (fig. 24–6). Only essential personnel who are required to control the incident should be allowed to enter this area.

Fig. 24–6. The hot zone is restricted to properly trained responders wearing appropriate PPE.

Incident control within the hot zone includes:

- Stopping the release
- Containing the released materials
- Triaging, removing, and decontaminating victims

Warm zone. The warm zone is the area between the hot and cold zone. It is used to support responders in the hot zone. Appropriate PPE may be required for responders working within the warm zone. Decontamination operations are conducted in this zone (fig. 24–7).

Cold zone. The cold zone encompasses the warm zone. Personnel are not required to wear any special PPE in this area. The cold zone contains the command post (fig. 24–8), staging area, and treatment/triage area.

Fig. 24–7. Decontamination operations take place in the warm zone.

Fig. 24–8. The command post is located in the cold zone.

INCIDENT COMMAND SYSTEM

An **incident command system (ICS)**, also known as an **incident management system (IMS)**, is a crucial component in the organization of emergency incidents, including hazmat responses. It allows for more efficient operations and a more effective span of control (fig. 24–9). It can be developed locally or adopted from a nationally recognized system, and should become part of the local emergency response plan (LERP). The ICS should specify the roles and responsibilities of each position during various emergency responses. The ICS is discussed in more detail in chapters 3 and 27 of this text.

For the purpose of this section, only basic ICS components and those aspects related to hazardous materials responses are addressed. While NFPA Standard 472 uses the IMS term and acronym in discussing the relevant requirements, we will use the ICS term throughout this section to maintain consistency with National Incident Management System (NIMS) terminology.

Elements of ICS

To be an effective scene management tool, the ICS must include the following components:

- **Common terminology**. Terms used to describe organizational elements, resources, and facilities must be consistent.

- **Modular organization**. The system should be designed from the top down with various branches/sections added, depending on the size and complexity of the incident.

- **Integrated communication**. Communication systems must allow the various agencies involved to communicate with each other.

- **Unified command structure**. Each agency with jurisdictional responsibilities needs to be represented in the command structure.

- **Manageable span of control**. The recommended span of control is five to seven people per supervisor.

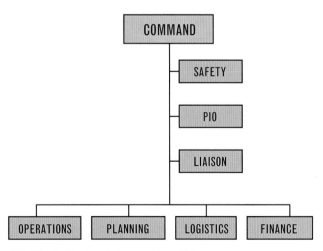

Fig. 24–9. The basic layout of an ICS

The actual size and complexity of the ICS is dependent on the size of the incident it is designed to handle.

Hazmat ICS positions, groups, and branches

Depending on the complexity of the incident, not all positions, groups, or branches in the incident command system may end up being filled. For hazardous materials incidents, however, there are some that must be filled. The following positions are all crucial to a hazmat response.

Incident commander. The incident commander is responsible for the overall operations at the scene of all incidents including a hazmat response. Incident commander duties are as follows:

- Designate a safety officer.
- Establish the site safety plan.
- Implement a site security and control plan.
- Identify the materials and conditions involved in the incident.
- Implement appropriate emergency operations.
- Ensure that proper protective equipment is used at all times.
- Set up a decontamination operation.

Safety officer. A safety officer is required at all hazardous materials incidents. The officer is responsible for the following:

- Monitor and identify potentially hazardous or unsafe situations.
- Stop any operation deemed unsafe immediately.
- Maintain communications contact with IC.
- Assist in incident planning.
- Identify potentially hazardous situations on the scene.
- Review incident action plan for safety concerns.
- Identify and correct unsafe situations immediately.

Hazardous materials branch or group. Most incidents will benefit from a standard application of ICS. Other types of incidents, such as hazmat, mass casualty, and so on, may require the use of more specialized functions within the operations section of the ICS organization. The specialized functions include the following:

- Hazardous material group supervisor
    - Entry unit leader
    - Decontamination unit leader
    - Site access control unit leader
- Assistant safety officer, hazardous materials

Any resources directly involved with the hazardous material are supervised by one of the functional leaders or the hazardous materials group supervisor. When the incident is more complex, a hazardous materials branch director may be required for proper span of control and organizational management.

The three functional positions within the hazardous materials group (entry leader, decontamination leader, and site access control leader) require a high degree of control and close supervision.

Hazardous materials group supervisor. The hazardous material group supervisor is assigned to the operations section and reports to the operation section chief or the branch director (if activated). The hazardous materials group supervisor is responsible for:

- The implementation of the phases of the incident action plan (IAP) dealing with the hazardous materials group operations
- The assignment of resources within the hazardous materials group
- Reporting on the progress of control operations and the status of resources within the hazardous materials group
- Direction of the overall operations of the hazardous materials group

Entry leader. The entry leader supervises all companies and personnel operating in the exclusion/hot zone along with directing all tactics and control of the positions and functions of all personnel in the exclusion/hot zone.

Decontamination leader. The decontamination leader supervises all operations in the contamination reduction/warm zone (with the exception of those handled by the safe refuge area manager). The decontamination leader also ensures that all rescued citizens, response personnel, and equipment have been decontaminated before leaving the incident (fig. 24–10).

Fig. 24–10. The decontamination leader supervises decon operations in the warm zone.

Site access control leader. The site access control leader controls the movement of all personnel and equipment between the control zones. This position is also responsible for isolating the exclusion/hot and contamination reduction/warm zones and ensuring proper routes and responsibility for the control, care, and movement of people in the safe refuge area.

Assistant safety officer–hazardous materials. The assistant safety officer–hazardous materials reports directly to the incident safety officer and coordinates with the hazardous materials group supervisor or hazardous materials branch director (if activated). This position is also responsible for the overall safety of assigned personnel within the hazardous materials group. In incidents involving multiple emergency activities, the assistant safety officer–hazardous materials does not act as the safety officer for the overall incident. An assistant safety officer–hazardous materials should be appointed when the scope of the incident requires it.

Locating the command post

The incident command (IC) post may be the first-responding vehicle until a formal location can be established. The IC post can be established in a conveniently located building, a specialty equipped vehicle, or a predetermined location in the facility preplan (fig. 24–11). The command post is always located in the cold zone. Always relay the location to dispatchers and responding units.

Fig. 24–11. A command post using a specialized vehicle

The following are factors to consider when locating a command post. It should:

- Be clearly marked

- Allow for controlled access to the site

- Be located uphill and upwind

- Be set up with the intention of not having to relocate it

- Allow for a view of the scene, if possible

Incident levels

The response plan for a hazardous materials incident is based on the severity of the incident; for example, a response to a car leaking gasoline is less than an overturned tanker truck leaking chlorine. Hazardous materials response levels are usually designated Level I, II, and III and are based on the level of risk an incident involves. The LERP and department standard operating procedures (SOPs) should dictate the resources necessary for each level as well as mandatory notification procedures to other agencies.

Level I: potential emergency condition. Level I incidents are the least serious and most easily handled of the three levels. They can be controlled by the organization having jurisdiction without additional assistance. These incidents do not require evacuation outside of the structure or facility, and there is no immediate threat to life, health, the environment, or property.

The following are examples of Level I incidents:

- Gas leaks on the consumer side of the meter (fig. 24–12)

- Small diesel fuel or gasoline leaks from an automobile

- Leaks involving consumer commodities such as thinners, paint, bleach, swimming pool chemicals, and so on

Fig. 24–12. Natural gas leaks on the consumer side of the meter are typically considered Level I incidents.

Level II: limited emergency condition. Level II incidents are beyond the capabilities of the first responders and require the response of additional resources, such as a hazmat response team. These incidents may require a limited evacuation of neighboring residents or facilities. They are not confined to a facility, but remain within a confined limited evacuation of the surrounding area. First responders at a Level II incident are required to use chemical PPE.

Response actions include the following:

- Diking and confinement of the material

- Plugging and patching operations

- Sampling and testing of unknown substances

- Implementing decontamination operations

The following are examples of Level II incidents:

- Leaks or spills requiring large-scale evacuations

- Incidents involving extremely hazardous substances

- Fire with a potential boiling liquid expanding vapor explosion (BLEVE) threat

- Major incident involving a flammable liquid spill or overflow (fig. 24–13)

- Spill or leak of unidentified or unknown substances

- Underground pipeline rupture

Fig. 24–13. Major incidents involving flammable liquid spill are typically considered Level II Incidents. (Courtesy of William Seward)

Level III: full emergency condition. Level III incidents are the most serious of the three levels and require large-scale evacuations. These incidents may require resources from state and federal agencies as well as private industry, and may necessitate the effort of several agencies to mitigate the incident. It is not confined or has moved past its confined geographic area and is an actual or perceived threat to life, health, and environment.

Response actions include the following:

- Use of specialized spill and leak control techniques
- Sophisticated sampling and monitoring equipment required
- Government and industry specialists required
- Use of large-scale decontamination setups

The following are examples of Level III incidents:

- Train derailment involving a leaking chlorine car
- Incidents resulting in the activation of the federal response system
- Incidents exceeding the capabilities of the local hazmat response team(s)
- Incidents requiring the evacuation of people extending across jurisdictional borders

Requesting additional resources

The first responder trained to the operations level should be familiar with available resources such as hazmat response teams; mutual aid fire, police, and EMS agencies; environmental protection agencies; and so

on (fig. 24–14). He or she should also understand each department or agency's response objectives and the role they play in the hazmat responses in their jurisdiction. A list of these available resources should be established, maintained, and included with the resource listing in the LERP.

Fig. 24–14. First responders should be familiar with available resources such as a hazmat team.

RESPONSE OBJECTIVES

To achieve the most favorable results possible, it is necessary for the incident commander to clearly define the objectives of the response. When responders are given a clear picture of the goals to be achieved, they can then determine what type of response action to employ as well as the resources, personnel, and PPE needed to accomplish the task. The objectives must be realistic based on the available resources as well as specific and measurable. The creation of these objectives should be one of the first steps taken by the incident commander. These objectives should keep the standard fire service incident priorities—life safety, incident stabilization, and property conservation—in mind. They should also reflect the limitation of operations-level personnel to defensive operations only.

Types of response actions

The three types of response actions include nonintervention, defensive, and offensive.

Nonintervention response. Nonintervention responses are implemented when the incident is beyond the capabilities of the responders, an imminent explosion is probable, there is a potential for a massive release, or the LERP or facility plan dictates this approach as determined by a site preplan.

The first responder should take the following actions when a nonintervention response is appropriate:

- Relocate responders and other personnel to a safe area.

- Relay conditions to dispatch and request additional resources.

- Establish scene control and an incident management system.

- Evacuate or protect-in-place as necessary.

Defensive responses. Defensive responses are implemented when personnel have adequate training and equipment to confine the product or the LERP or facility plan dictates this approach as determined by a site pre-plan of the hazards (fig. 24–15). This is the primary response action for the operational-level responder. The first responder should take the following actions when a defensive response is appropriate:

- Relay incident conditions to dispatch center.

- Set up an incident management system and control zones.

- Evacuate or protect-in-place as necessary.

- Use defensive operations to control and confine the product.

- Request additional resources as required.

Fig. 24–15. Defensive operations can take place when responders have adequate training and equipment.

Offensive responses. Offensive response is limited to technician-level responders because first responders at the operational level are not trained to initiate offensive operations. The exception to this rule involves materials such as gasoline and propane when the operations-level

responder has received specific training on handling the hazard.

Strategic considerations

When materials are identified, the first responder should determine the possible threat to life, health, the environment, and property. In the case of unidentified materials, the first responder should assume the worst, control sources of ignition, confine runoff, and avoid contact with the material. In addition, an effort should be made to protect the material from any external stressors such as heat, shock, or contamination that may cause it to react.

The first responder should utilize the General Emergency Behavior Model (GEMBO) model discussed in chapter 23 to determine the potential behavior of the material. Also a quick survey of the container can determine its general condition and what issues can potentially be expected. Examples include:

- Container not damaged

- Damaged with no release of material

- Damaged with a release of material and no fire

- Damaged with a release of material and fire

Strategic priorities

It is impossible to determine the overall objectives of the response without first looking at the strategic priorities that will define the tactics used to handle the response. As mentioned previously, the fire service's incident priorities in any emergency are life safety, incident stabilization, and property conservation. The following, in order of importance, is a more specific breakdown of these priorities when responding to incidents involving hazardous materials:

1. Rescue operations

2. Protect exposures

3. Extinguish fires

4. Confine the product

5. Contain the product

6. Recover the product

Rescue operations. Rescue operations should be the first priority at any incident (fig. 24–16). The first responder should analyze the risk versus benefit and establish an escape plan prior to entry.

Fig. 24–16. Rescue operations should be a first priority at any incident.

In multiple-victim situations, the first responder should rescue victims who can be easily saved first. During rescue operations, a thorough primary search should be conducted quickly if conditions allow. The first responder must also be aware of the potential for rapid deterioration of conditions.

During rescue operations, consider the following:

- What is the nature of the material involved and the severity of the incident?

- Is appropriate PPE available?

- How many victims are there? What are their conditions?

- How long will rescue operations take?

- Is the necessary equipment available to complete the rescue?

Assessing risk in rescue operations. When assessing the risk involved with making a rescue, the responder should consider the general properties for each of the hazard classes. Always weigh the risk against the benefit, and do not place responders in danger if there is no potential for the victim(s) to survive. Understanding the physical and chemical properties of the material will aid in this decision-making process. At a minimum, before performing rescue operations be sure to determine the specific hazards of the material(s) involved.

- *Class 1—explosive materials.* Potential injuries include thermal injury due to the heat from detonation as well as mechanical injury from the blast or objects thrown by the blast. The potential for chemical injuries also exists. If an explosive material has completely detonated, it may not pose an additional risk to first responders; however, rescuers should consider the possibility that there may be additional explosive materials in the same area, or in the case of a criminal or terrorist incident, that a secondary device may be present. Etiological concerns can arise from the victims' bodily fluids, and there is always the possibility that asphyxiation could be an issue due to depleted oxygen levels in the blast area.

- *Class 2—gases.* If the gas is stored under pressure, failure of the cylinder can result in mechanical, thermal, chemical, or asphyxiate hazard, depending on the material's hazard. If the contents are cryogenic in nature, a thermal hazard is present, and in confined areas asphyxiation, either simple or chemical, is a concern. If the gas is an inhalation hazard, full PPE and positive-pressure SCBA may provide sufficient protection for the rescuers. If the gas presents absorption, corrosive, or other hazard, however, standard PPE may not provide adequate protection. Potential ignition of flammable gases should also be a major consideration.

- *Class 3—flammable liquids.* The risk associated with flammable liquids is that they can present a thermal and chemical hazard as well as a mechanical hazard if an explosion were to occur. The rescuer should determine if the material is on fire and if ignition sources have been controlled. Water streams or foam should be provided to protect the victim or rescuer. An attempt should be made to keep runoff to a minimum. The rescuer must ensure that the material(s) involved are not water-reactive when using fire streams.

As mentioned, the primary hazard of flammable liquids is that they burn. Structural PPE and SCBA provide some protection from the heat (fig. 24–17). The rescuer must remember that flammable liquids burn hotter than an average structural fire. The first responder should also consider secondary hazards of the specific material(s) involved.

- *Class 4—flammable solids.* Flammable solids, including materials dangerous when wet and spontaneously combustible materials, all can cause thermal, chemical, and mechanical hazards. As with flammable liquids they can burn hotter than the average structure fire, and appropriate extinguishment methods for the material involved should be employed to protect the rescuer.

- *Class 5—oxidizers.* Oxidizers are materials that may react violently and without warning. They present a thermal, chemical, and mechanical harm concern. Due to the inherent instability of these materials, rescue operations need careful evaluation. If the incident appears to be worsening, first responders should be removed from the area.

- *Class 6—poisonous/infectious materials.* PPE specific to the hazard must be used. These materials present a hazard by inhalation, ingestion, absorption, or injection. Certain substances may also present a thermal hazard due to their flammability.

  By their nature, poisonous and infections materials pose a danger to life. Rescue attempts should be delayed until specific dangers can be assessed to determine if the available PPE on the scene is adequate. Structural firefighting PPE and SCBA may not provide adequate protection against all materials in this class.

- *Class 7—radioactive materials.* The first responder should assess the type of radiation present and ensure that the proper monitoring and protective equipment is available before attempting any rescues. The radiological hazard is relative to the dosage rate received over time. Use the time, distance, and shielding approach to reduce harm to responders. Some radioactive materials may also present a chemical hazard.

- *Class 8—corrosives.* Structural firefighting PPE may not provide adequate protection against corrosive materials. As a result, rescue operations should not bring responders into direct contact with corrosive materials. Corrosives may also present a vapor hazard that may compromise or penetrate the structure of PPE. Additionally, corrosives present a chemical and potential thermal hazard. They can also present a mechanical hazard if they weaken the structure of a container or building.

- *Miscellaneous materials.* Identification of specific material(s) involved is necessary in order to determine the specific hazards to responders. Responders should be prepared to contend with any of the listed types of harm.

Fig. 24–17. Structural PPE will provide some protection from the heat of a flammable liquid fire.

Protection of exposures. When attempting to protect an exposure, the first responder should determine the number of exposures involved in the incident and decide how many have already been lost. The first responder must also determine the best manner of protecting people, the environment, and property from further damage. Depending on the material released and its chemical and physical properties, it may be necessary to request additional resources to mitigate the release and/or isolate people in the area involved.

When protecting people, the most important consideration is life and health. The first responder can evacuate or protect-in-place to protect potential victims from the hazardous material.

Environmental concerns such as the atmosphere, surface water, wildlife, water table, and surrounding land should also be protected from exposure. Note that it may take years to fully realize the effect of an incident.

To protect property from exposure, the first responder should consider the extent of contamination of exposed items. Dilution or diversion of hazardous materials may be the best option. Do not risk life or the environment to save property. It may be necessary to write it off if the danger is too great.

Extinguishment of fire. The first responder may have to extinguish fire in order to conduct rescue operations. This tactical priority may be moved up in its importance if necessary to rescue people or to protect them from exposure. Careful evaluation is necessary prior to committing emergency personnel to extinguishing fire, as it may worsen the situation. Allowing the material to burn may be a viable alternative (fig. 24–18).

Fig. 24–18. In situations where extinguishing the fire can make things worse, allowing the material to burn is a viable alternative.

Confinement. Confinement is a defensive action in which the flow of the hazardous material is controlled (fig. 24–19). The methods used for confinement of hazardous materials are covered in detail in chapter 25.

Fig. 24–19. Confinement is a defensive action in which the flow of the hazardous material is controlled.

Containment. Containment is an offensive action that prevents additional releases from a container (fig. 24–20). It is not considered a first-responder skill and is performed by technical-level responders.

The following are factors affecting containment:

- The condition of the container
- Chemical/physical properties of the material
- The material's rate of release

Fig. 24–20. Containment is an offensive action that prevents additional release from the container.

Recovery. All defensive actions should be planned with future recovery operations in mind. This reduces the amount of time needed for cleanup and limits the number of exposures. Recovery is often conducted by companies specializing in this field.

PERSONAL PROTECTIVE EQUIPMENT (PPE)

Types of personal protective equipment

Personal protective equipment is an important component in any hazmat responder's inventory. More important, however, is the knowledge of how to pick the appropriate level of protection for the incident. Failure to understand how to interpret hazard and response information and use it to choose the correct PPE can result in significant injury to response personnel. Responders should also be trained in the use of any specialized hazmat/WMD PPE issued by the authority having jurisdiction (AHJ). The two major categories addressed here are respiratory protection and personal protective clothing. While operations-level responders are not necessarily expected to use specialized chemical protective equipment, they must know the differences between the various levels of protection and understand how to choose the appropriate level of PPE for a given material and how the available level of protection affects the options for defensive operations. If there is a lack of appropriate equipment, a request for personnel with the proper level of training and equipment should be transmitted immediately.

Respiratory protection. Respiratory protection equipment protects the first responder against the inhalation of toxic substances. The various types of protective breathing equipment are open-circuit self-contained breathing apparatus (SCBA), closed-circuit SCBA, supplied-air respirator (SAR), air-purifying respirator (APR), powered air-purifying respirator (PAPR), and particulate respirator. Respiratory protection is covered in more depth in chapter 10, Self-Contained Breathing Apparatus, but the more specific hazmat applications are addressed here. Each type of respiratory protection has its advantages and disadvantages. Because the respiratory risks for first responders at the operational level can range widely, the best course of action would be to use positive-pressure SCBA. It is readily available to fire service personnel and provides the highest level of respiratory protection.

Open-circuit SCBA. The open-circuit SCBA is the most commonly used breathing apparatus in the fire service (fig. 24–21). Only positive-pressure SCBA should be used. Positive-pressure units provide the wearer with a greater level of protection by maintaining a slightly-higher-than-atmospheric pressure in the mask. This substantially reduces the potential for contaminants to enter the facepiece. In an open-circuit system, air for breathing is compressed and stored in a cylinder carried on the wearer's back. Exhaled air is vented to the outside atmosphere through the regulator-mask assembly.

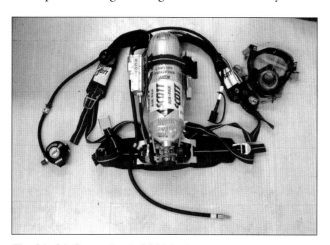

Fig. 24–21. Open-circuit SCBA is the most common type used in the fire service.

Air supply duration is dependent on the wearer's fitness, the degree of physical exertion, and the design of the unit. Always remember to include decontamination time when calculating the length of time a responder can work.

The advantages of SCBA are that it allows for a greater range of mobility and provides the responder with the highest level of protection. The disadvantages include limited usage time, weight, and difficulty to use in confined spaces. Most open-circuit SCBAs are designed to allow for 15–20 minutes of heavy labor. Some units use higher pressures and larger cylinder sizes to increase the time up to 45–60 minutes.

Closed-circuit SCBA. A closed-circuit SCBA consists of a cylinder of oxygen, a filtering system, a regulator, and valves. The system works by cleaning and filtering exhaled air and then adding oxygen. Usage time for a closed-circuit SCBA ranges from 30 minutes to 4 hours.

The advantages of a closed-circuit SCBA include the duration of air supply that exceeds the open-circuit model. Also, it typically weighs less than open-circuit SCBA. A disadvantage is that it is more complicated to use than open-circuit SCBA and requires special training.

Supplied-air respirator (SAR). In a SAR, the airline is attached to a regulator assembly containing one or more cylinders (fig. 24–22). The SAR is not commonly used by the fire service for hazmat applications. The air line is connected to a unit consisting of an open-circuit facepiece, a regulator, and an emergency egress cylinder.

Advantages of SARs include increased working time, the ability of a first responder to work without a cumbersome backpack assembly, and that it is lighter than SCBA. Disadvantages include a maximum travel distance of only 300 ft (90 m) away from the regulated air source, the potential for the wearer to become entangled in the air line, and the hose material possibly coming in contact and reacting with the hazardous material.

Fig. 24–22. The supplied air respirator is not commonly used in the fire service for hazmat applications.

Air-purifying respirator (APR) and powered air-purifying respirator (PAPR). Both APRs and PAPRs work by filtering ambient air (fig. 24–23). As such it does not necessarily provide adequate protection for emergency responders working at a hazardous materials incident, and is not typically used in emergency situations. Because it provides protection only against those substances for which the filter cartridges are designed, it has limited uses in emergency situations. Emergency responders should always use a respiratory protection method that does not use ambient air. In additional to particle filtering respirators, there are also vapor- and gas-removing respirators.

Fig. 24–23. Air purifying respirators work by filtering the ambient air and are not typically used in emergency situations.

The advantages of APRs and PAPRs are that they are lightweight, easy to use, and allow for greater mobility. There are, however, several disadvantages that include the fact that they cannot be used in oxygen-deficient atmospheres (levels below 19.5%), they have a limited usage time, and they can be used only for specific products.

Particulate respirator. Like APRs and PAPRs, particulate respirators are not designed for emergency responders at hazardous materials incidents. The advantages and disadvantages are the same, as well.

Types of personal protective clothing (PPC). As with respiratory protection, PPC is a key component in a responder's protective ensemble. Operations-level responders need to be aware of the different levels of PPC available to them as well as the purpose, advantages, and limitations of each of the options. Always keep in mind that no single type of PPC will protect a responder in all situations. PPC is necessary to protect the skin and the body from contact hazards such as chemical burns and the potential for absorption of toxic materials through the skin.

Work uniforms. Work uniforms are worn on an every-day basis and offer the least amount of protection in a hazardous materials emergency (fig. 24–24). Work uniforms may prevent day-to-day dirt and grime from getting on skin, but they offer no chemical protection.

Fig. 24–24. Work uniforms offer the least amount of protection at a hazmat incident.

Structural firefighting protective clothing (SFPC). SFPC is used every day for firefighter responses (fig. 24–25). When worn in combination with SCBA, it offers protection from thermal and mechanical harm. Structural firefighting protective clothing is not recognized as chemical protective clothing but may be used for specific duties during a hazardous materials incident. SFPC may be used while performing support functions in areas where the levels of toxicity are very low. SFPC usually consists of SCBA, personal alert safety system (PASS) device, helmet, bunker coat, bunker pants, boots, gloves, and protective hood.

Fig. 24–25. Structural PPE provides thermal protection to the responder but is not considered chemical PPE

High-temperature protective clothing. High-temperature protective equipment is a level above structural firefighting protective clothing (fig. 24–26). This type of protective clothing shields the wearer during short-term exposures to high temperatures. High-temperature protective clothing consists of approach suits, proximity suits, or fire entry suits. An approach suit allows firefighting operations to take place with high levels of radiated heat. A proximity suit allows for close approach to fires for rescue and suppression operations. Fire entry suits allow the wearer to work in total flame environments for short periods of time. High-temperature protective suits do not provide chemical protection. They are bulky and cumbersome to use and require specialized training.

Fig. 24–26. High-temperature protective clothing shields the wearer during short-term exposures to high temperatures. (Courtesy United States Air Force)

Chemical-protective clothing (CPC) and equipment. CPC is designed to prevent chemicals in solid, liquid, or gas form from coming in contact with the wearer. Each ensemble is designed for a specific level of protection, and the material that it is constructed of offers varying levels of resistance. The golden rule of chemical protective clothing is very simple: there is no one chemical protective ensemble or material that will protect you from everything.

The U.S. Environmental Protection Agency (EPA) established the Level A, B, C, and D standards for chemical protective equipment. These levels are also recognized by NIOSH, OSHA, and the U.S. Coast Guard. The NFPA recognizes Levels A, B, and C.

The four levels of chemical protective clothing are summarized in table 24–1.

Table 24–1. Chemical protective clothing levels

Level A	Encapsulating suit that covers both the wearer and SCBA
Level B	Consists of a garment designed for splash protection and an SCBA
Level C	Level B splash protection garment with a respirator instead of SCBA
Level D	Ordinary work clothes or uniform and no respiratory protection

Level A ensemble. The Level A suit is fully encapsulating and covers both the wearer and the SCBA (fig. 24–27). It affords the highest level of protection for the wearer. The Level A suit is designed to be used when working with liquids, vapors, or gases that present a severe threat of injury from contact. It is also advisable for a hazmat responder to wear Level A protection when the potential exists for the responder to be in contact with a toxic or corrosive material. This ensemble also meets the requirements that are described in the NFPA 1991 standard. This type of protection is not used by response personnel at the operations level.

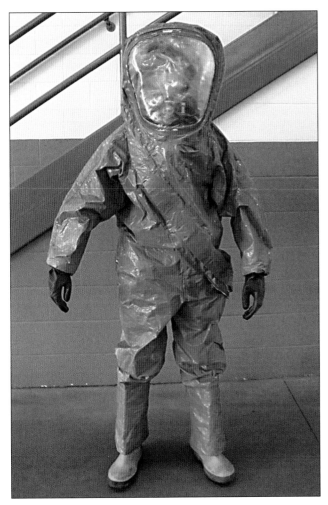

Fig. 24–27. Level A ensemble

The following are the typically recommended components of Level A protection:

- Fully encapsulating vapor-protective chemical-resistant suit

- Inner and outer chemical-resistant gloves

- Hard hat

- Communications system

- SCBA or SAR

- Chemical-resistant safety boots (including steel shank and toe)

- Overboots

The advantage of Level A protection is that it provides vapor protection for the wearer. Disadvantages include a potential for heat stress and impaired movement, communication, and visibility.

Level B ensemble. A Level B ensemble consists of a garment designed for splash protection and SCBA (fig. 24–28). This type of protection is used when it is unnecessary to provide protection from vapors. Potential areas of entry such as wrists, ankles, facepiece, and hood are sealed to prevent exposure from splashes. Responders will often use Level B protection during product confinement operations and while staffing decontamination areas. There are three types of Level B suits: two piece, coverall, and encapsulating. The encapsulating suit is the type most commonly used by hazmat teams. It provides protection against splash hazards but not against chemical vapors or gases. This ensemble also meets the requirements that are described in the NFPA 1992 standard and part of the NFPA 1994.

Fig. 24–28. Level B ensemble

Planning the Hazmat/Weapons of Mass Destruction (WMD) Response

FIREFIGHTER I

Chapter 24

The following are the typically recommended components of Level B protection:

- Chemical-resistant splash-protective suit

- Hard hat

- Inner and outer chemical-resistant gloves

- SCBA or SAR

- Communications system

- Chemical-resistant safety boots (including steel shank and toe)

- Outer boots

Disadvantages of Level B suits include impaired movement, communication, and visibility. Additionally, because SCBA may be located on the outside of the suit, chemical compatibility issues must be considered.

Level C ensemble. In a Level C suit, the same type of garment is used as in Level B protection. This level allows for respiratory protection other than SCBA (fig. 24–29). The respiratory protection used in this level consists of APR. The use of a respirator instead of SCBA changes the level from B to C. Air-purifying respirators cannot be used with encapsulating splash protection suits. A coverall suit is the style used in this application. This type of protection is not used unless the specific material is known and can be measured. Air purifying respirators have limited applications and should not be used in emergency response situations. This ensemble also meets the requirements that are described in the NFPA 1992 standard and part of the NFPA 1994.

The following are the components of Level C protection:

- Chemical-resistant splash-protective suit

- Hard hat

- Inner and outer chemical-resistant gloves

- APR or PAPR

- Communications system

- Chemical-resistant safety boots (including steel shank and toe)

- Outer boots

The advantage of the Level C ensemble is the increased mobility because SCBA is not required; the disadvantage is that it cannot be used unless the specific material is known and can be measured.

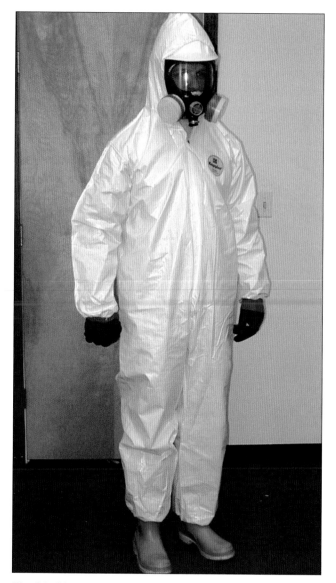

Fig. 24–29. Level C ensemble

Level D ensemble. Level D clothing, consisting of ordinary work clothes or uniforms, is not adequate for first responders at a hazmat incident (fig. 24–30). It provides protection against workplace hazards, but not chemicals. This level does not require respiratory protection. As a result, it should be used when respiratory protection is unnecessary and there is no splash hazard.

The following are the components of Level D protection:

- Work clothes or uniform

- Hard hat or helmet

- Chemical or work gloves

- Safety glasses or other eye protection

- Chemical-resistant safety boots (including steel shank and toe)

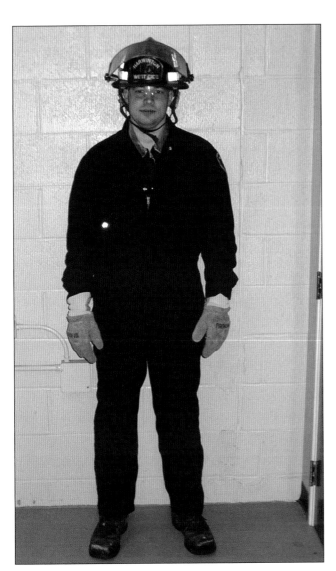

Fig. 24–30. Level D clothing

Personal cooling technologies

Working in personal protective equipment, especially chemical-protective clothing, can put a significant strain on the body, including the potential to overheat. Several different types of heat exchange units can be used to cool responders and reduce this risk. These include air cooled, ice cooled, water cooled, and phase-change cooling technology.

Air cooled. This is accomplished by supplying ambient or cooled air to the inside of suit through a hoseline. Advantages include cooling the surface of the skin. The disadvantages are a reduced mobility from the hose, limited range, and added weight

Ice cooled. This consists of ice packs worn in a vest on the inside of the suit. The advantage of this system is that it cools the skin. Disadvantages include added weight and unknown efficiency.

Water cooled. This uses a vest filled with chilled water worn on the inside of the suit. Some types utilize hoselines or tethers. Like air and ice cooled, the advantage to this method is that it provides cooling to the skin. The disadvantages are reduced mobility, added weight, and a short work cycle.

Phase-change cooling technology. This system uses a vest worn inside the suit and uses cool packs as a cooling medium. The cool pack material acts as a heat sink to draw heat away from the body. The material is designed to maintain a 59°F (15°C) temperature throughout the work cycle. Advantages include a lack of a shock to the system, such as when ice packs are used, a longer work cycle, and less time to regenerate than ice or gel packs.

Selecting appropriate PPE

When choosing the appropriate PPE, the first responder should determine the identity of the material involved and the exposure type (skin, respiratory, or ingestion). Remember that first responders at the operations level are not expected or trained to use special chemical-protective clothing. Local protocols and department SOPs will define the level of training, capabilities, and PPE available to operations-level personnel. The type of PPE available is an important factor in determining which type of defensive action to use. Response personnel should always use their department's SOPs or SOGs to dictate the selection of available PPE based on the task at hand. The proximity of the responder performing his or her duties to the release is also a factor. If the duties being performed are some distance from the release, such as building retention basins or building dams downstream to prevent the further spread of the material, then they need only to wear the appropriate safety equipment for that action (fig. 24–31). In other instances, such as responders operating closer to the spill to spread absorbent materials, additional PPE may be required.

There are several considerations that go into the selection of the correct CPC. The type of suit selected needs to provide chemical resistance to the materials the responder could potentially come in contact with.

Fig. 24–31. If the responder is operating in an area distant from the spill, chemical protective clothing is not likely to be necessary.

Chemical resistance is the ability of the garment to resist damage from direct contact with a chemical. As with chemical compatibility, several factors affect the resistance of the materials, such as time, temperature, stress, and reagents. CPC materials are specifically designed to resist the movement of chemicals into and through the material by one of three methods: permeation, penetration, or degradation.

Permeation is the process by which a hazardous chemical moves through a given material at the molecular level. Permeation occurs when the chemical absorbs into the material, moves at the molecular level through the material, and then de-absorbs to the interior. It then moves to the clothing or skin of the responder wearing the garment.

Penetration is the flow of a hazardous chemical through openings in the material such as zippers, seams, porous materials, pinholes, or other imperfections in the material.

Degradation is the physical destruction or breakdown of the material after being exposed to a chemical; it may consist of visible signs such as charring, shrinking, swelling, glazing, color changes, or dissolving. It may be at the molecular or nonvisible level and can be observed only by testing for weight of material, fabric strength, and other properties.

The PPE options for specific hazards

Thermal. For situations involving a thermal hazard, responders should select structural firefighting clothing, high-temperature clothing such as a proximity suit, or use flash protection for chemical-protective clothing. The type chosen depends on the level of thermal hazard present, available personal protective clothing, and whether there are any splash or vapor hazards associated with the material.

Radiological. Standard firefighting PPE offers only limited protection from radiological sources. The best protection is to determine the type of radiation present and use the time, distance, shielding concept discussed earlier to limit exposure and dosage.

Asphyxiating materials. For both simple and chemical asphyxiates, respiratory protection is the primary means of protecting response personnel. This can be worn in conjunction with structural firefighting gear and SCBA unless the material also presents a hazard requiring chemical protective clothing.

Chemical. Chemicals can present a splash hazard and a potential vapor hazard. Depending on the properties of the materials, the responder should select a Level A or B ensemble. Operations-level responders will be limited in their ability to address vapor hazards because they are not trained or equipped to operate in that environment.

Etiological/biological. Protection from microorganisms is based on the means by which they would enter the body, their physical state, and how dangerous they are. For example, anthrax in a powder form would present a different hazard from a substance in an aerosol form.

Mechanical. PPE used by hazmat responders provides minimal protection from mechanical hazards. The best method to protect against this hazard is to avoid situations where a mechanical injury may occur.

Care and maintenance of PPE

As with any equipment used in an emergency response, the regular care and maintenance of PPE is very important. Simply put, a responder's life depends upon this equipment functioning properly when it is needed. Manufacturer recommendations and department SOPs should dictate the procedures for cleaning, disinfecting, inspection, maintenance, testing, and storage. Personnel responsible for these procedures need to be well versed in the appropriate procedures.

Cleaning and disinfecting. Any PPE that becomes contaminated needs to be thoroughly cleaned, usually during decontamination operations. Additional cleaning and disinfecting, however, may be necessary depending on the material involved. The type of PPE will also dictate the cleaning process. For example, cleaning structural firefighting gear is accomplished differently from Level A CPC. Always follow the manufacturing recommendations, and if there is any doubt that the equipment has been compromised, it should be removed from service until it can be tested. Some PPE is considered disposable and is discarded after use, negating the need for additional cleaning.

Maintenance, testing, inspection, and storage.

As with cleaning and disinfecting, the procedures for maintenance, testing, inspection, and storage are largely manufacturer-dependent. All equipment should be maintained, tested, inspected, and stored according to department SOPs and manufacturer's recommendations (fig. 24–32). Maintenance and testing of chemical protective equipment typically involves training and equipment that exceeds the operations level. When inspecting CPC, be sure to look for any abrasions, discolored areas, cracks, or other physical damage that would indicate damage. CPC should be stored in a manner that does not create any stress points in the material and in a container or location that protects against physical damage. Structural firefighting clothing and SCBA should be inspected and stored consistent with department SOPs. Records should be kept on all maintenance, testing, usage, cleaning, and inspection activities per department SOPs as well.

Fig. 24–32. PPE should be maintained and inspected in accordance with department SOPs and manufacturer recommendations.

INCIDENTS INVOLVING TERRORISM AND WEAPONS OF MASS DESTRUCTION

The best way to look at this type of incident is that it is the *intentional* release of a hazardous material with intent *to do harm*. Unlike an accidental release, these releases are specifically designed to result in a maximum amount of damage from an explosive device or through the release of a chemical or biological agent (fig. 24–33). As such, the potential risks involved in responding to these types of incidents increases. The basic step-by-step methodology, however, of analyzing the incident, planning the response, and implementation remains largely the same. Incidents of this nature will likely place a much greater strain on available resources because of the potential for much greater damage and population exposure.

Fig. 24–33. The Oklahoma City bombing was designed to create maximum damage to the building.

Actions to be taken at terrorist incidents

In addition to standard precautionary steps taken by first responders at a hazmat incident, a response to a terrorist incident should take the following into consideration:

- Protect yourself and other responders.

- Relay any suspicious or criminal activity to dispatch upon arrival on scene.

- Isolate potentially exposed people or animals.

- Document initial on-scene observations.

- Establish control zones and control access to the scene.

- Take actions to preserve possible evidence.

- Watch for booby traps and/or explosive devices (fig. 24–34).

- Prevent secondary contamination, including from handling patients.

Additionally, because there is a law enforcement component involved with these responses, evidence preservation and documentation become key factors.

Fig. 24–34. Watch for explosive devices at the scene of a terrorist incident. (Courtesy of TEEX)

Potential criminal and terrorist targets

A terrorist/WMD event can occur anywhere. Even so, it is important for the fire department to consider what locations within their communities are most likely to be potential targets. The potential locations can be broken down into several general categories, including occupancy or location, types of events, and significant timing of an event.

The **OTTO** acronym developed by the U.S. Department of Justice can be used to show potential terrorist indicators. The acronym represents the following:

> **O**ccupancy and location
>
> **T**ype of event
>
> **T**iming of the event
>
> **O**n-scene warning signs

Occupancy or location. Certain types of occupancies can have a significant reason for being a target. It may be because of their symbolic or historical value or the purpose for which the building or location is being used. These can be further broken down into the following categories: symbolic and historical, public buildings or assembly areas, controversial businesses, and infrastructure systems.

Symbolic and historical targets represent an organization, idea, or event that is offensive in the mind of the terrorists. These can include structures of historical significance, such as the Washington Monument, Mount Rushmore, the Statue of Liberty, Yankee Stadium, Independence Hall in Philadelphia, or the U.S. Capitol Building (fig. 24–35). The structures can be symbolic, such as the World Trade Center; a building occupied by the Bureau of Alcohol, Tobacco, and Firearms; or the Internal Revenue Service.

Fig. 24–35. Historical buildings or locations can be terrorist targets.

Some terrorists who want to create property damage but not loss of life may strike government buildings such as ROTC offices or military recruiting offices on a weekend when they are typically closed.

Public buildings or assembly areas provide a means of letting the terrorists get attention through the possibility of causing mass casualties. These can include shopping malls, convention centers, entertainment venues, tourist destinations, and places of worship.

Controversial businesses attract the anger of extremist organizations. These can include abortion clinics, animal testing facilities, pharmaceutical companies, nuclear facilities, and furriers. Certain ecoterrorists also target controversial housing developments.

Infrastructure systems are any facilities that are necessary for the continuous operation of society. These include power plants, phone companies, water treatment plants, mass transit, hospitals, data storage facilities, financial institutions, and mass media communication facilities.

Types of events. A terrorist attack occurring at a certain type of event is a possibility. Some common events of concern are large sporting events such as the Super Bowl, the World Series, college and professional basketball playoffs, and racing events that include auto, horse, and marathon races (fig. 24–36). Political events to consider include Republican and Democratic national conventions and rallies for certain political causes. Visiting dignitaries can be another target. When members of the government, such as the president or vice president, attend events in different cities, or when the Pope visits the United States, they may become a target for terrorists.

Fig. 24–36. Popular sporting events can become a terrorist target.

Significant timing of events. Anniversaries of significant events can be triggers for terrorists. April 19 is a trigger for many antigovernment terrorist groups (both the fire at the Branch Davidian Compound in Waco, Texas, and the Oklahoma City bombing occurred on this day). Other event anniversaries can also be triggers, such as the Roe v. Wade anniversary on January 22 or the anniversary of 9/11.

On-scene warning signs. There are numerous signs that would indicate a potential terrorism event. Indicators include explosive devices, chemical labs, indication of biological agents, the release of chemicals into the environment or inside structures, and unusual odors or vapor clouds. Additional signs are addressed throughout this section.

Indicators of a terrorism event

Operations-level responders need to be aware of the signs of different types of terrorist or criminal activities to properly assess the dangers that are present. For example, the ability to differentiate between a chemical and biological release will allow the responder to make better decisions about how to initially handle the situation.

Chemical incidents. **Chemical incidents** are characterized by a rapid onset of medical symptoms, which may take minutes to hours. Indicators may include colored residue, pungent odors, and dead animal and plant life. The following may be observed at a chemical incident scene:

- Unexplained vapor clouds, mists, or plumes
- Abnormal number of sick or dead birds, animals, and/or fish
- Suspicious hazardous materials or lab equipment in the area of contamination
- Intentional release of a hazardous material
- Multiple individuals experiencing unexplained skin, eye, or airway irritation
- Unexplained odors/tastes not normal to the area
- Surfaces with unexplained oily droplets/film

Chemical agents may be present when multiple individuals have the following unexplained health problems:

- Nausea and vomiting
- Twitching, convulsions, or disorientation
- Sweating
- Pinpoint pupils or runny nose
- Tightness in chest, difficulty breathing
- Death

Biological agents. In cases of **biological incidents**, there are typically no indicators found because biological agents are generally colorless and odorless. In such incidents, the onset of symptoms may take days to weeks, depending on the agent involved. As a result of the delayed onset of symptoms, an affected person has a greater chance of transmitting the disease to others. The migration of these infected individuals may increase the area of the incident dramatically. Possible indicators of a biological release include:

- Multiple casualties with similar signs and symptoms reported by health care agencies
- Unscheduled or unusual spraying, especially at night
- Abandoned spray devices
- Unusual increase in the number of sick or dying people or animals

Radiological. The detonation of a large nuclear device or weapon would be readily apparent. Smaller or improvised devices may initially appear to be a very large conventional explosive device. Responders will not know if the device was radiological in nature until monitoring is completed. Some questions to consider when making the determination are:

- Was there a threat given?

- Is the area a potential target?

- Are there any suspicious packages, vehicles, or activities?

- Was there an explosion?

Illicit laboratories. Illicit labs may be used for the development of illegal drugs, weapons production, or WMD (fig. 24–37). When trying to identify an illicit lab, always look for indicators that do not fit the surroundings. Illicit labs can be found in the trunks of cars, motel rooms, trailer parks, hotel rooms, and self-storage buildings. Possible indicators include:

- Suspicious odors (pungent, sweet, bitter)

- Explosions/fires

- Blacked-out windows

- Unusual ventilation and drainage systems

- Stained soil

- Dead trees/vegetation

- Burn pits

- Propane tanks with corroded fittings

- Solvents (hexane, acetone, etc.)

- Multiple containers of over-the-counter medications

- Large quantities of hazardous materials not typical for the area

- Laboratory equipment
  - Beakers, tubing, and burners
  - Two-liter bottles, mason jars with tubing attached
  - Hot plates, electric skillets, slow cookers
  - Hand scales

- Bomb making equipment

Fig. 24–37. Illicit laboratories can be used to make illegal drugs or terrorist weapons.

Explosives. The signs of an explosion are obvious to response personnel. The determination that must be made is whether it was done intentionally. The following are some questions to consider:

- Was it a potential or logical target?

- Was there a threat given?

- Were there any secondary explosions?

- Were any pre-detonation indicators observed by witnesses?

In the event that personnel are on scene prior to the detonation, they should be on the lookout for suspicious packages that are left unattended, shipped or mailed with no return address, are misshapen or stained with an oily residue, or have protruding wires. They should also be aware of any suspicious activities such as people who are out of place, appear to be aggressive, or are taking photos or video of a potential target. Additional clues are suspicious vehicles parked in front of buildings, at hazmat storage areas, or in restricted areas. Unfamiliar vehicles loitering for long periods of time is also considered suspicious activity. The first responder should also note any type of device attached to containers such as storage tanks, pipelines, flammable liquid or chemical containers, and compressed gas cylinders.

DOT classification of WMD agents

Terrorists use many different weapons and means to achieve their goals. Some of them are very subtle; others meet their goal with extreme violence. Although WMD agents are often thought of as having the specific purpose of injuring or killing, therefore being outside of the standard DOT hazmat classification system, this is not the case. Every type of device or substance used as a warfare agent has a place in the DOT hazard classification system, allowing first responders to use many of the same informational resources to determine how to handle the response. However, after it is determined that a warfare agent is involved, it is always a good idea to seek out resources with specific information on that substance. Warfare agents include the following:

- Chemical agents
    - Nerve agents
    - Vesicants (blister agents)
    - Blood agents
    - Choking agents
    - Irritants (riot control agents)
- Biological agents and toxins
- Radiological materials

These weapons have been grouped into categories with similar properties. It is important to note that some weapons or agents do not easily fall into a single category. There are two common acronyms used to explain weapons of mass destruction. The first is CBRNE (chemical, biological, radiological, nuclear, and explosive); the other is B-NICE (biological, nuclear, incendiary, chemical, explosive). The major difference between the two is that B-NICE separates incendiary and explosives, whereas CBRNE does not. This section discusses the acronym B-NICE.

Biological agents and toxins. Biological agents and toxins are Hazard Class 6 toxic and infectious substances. They are most likely to be used in a terrorist incident because they are the easiest for a terrorist to produce.

Examples of biological agents include the following:

- Anthrax (DOT 6.2)
- Mycotoxins (DOT 6.1 or 6.2)
- Plague (DOT 6.2)
- Tularemia (DOT 6.2)
- Ricin (DOT 6.1)

Routes of entry depend on the compound and include skin contact, inhalation, or injection.

Anthrax is a naturally occurring bacteria found in dead sheep (fig. 24–38). Exposure occurs through skin contact or inhalation of the anthrax spores. Anthrax is relatively easy to obtain; however, the military-grade fatal type of

anthrax is difficult to culture and produce. It must be distributed under certain conditions to be effective.

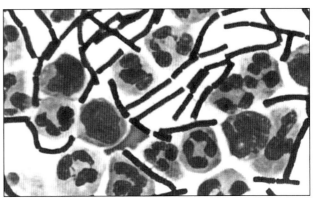

Fig. 24–38. Anthrax falls under Hazard Class 6.

Ricin is a widely available toxin that is easily produced. It is 10,000 times more toxic than sarin, a chemical weapon. However, unlike sarin, ricin is difficult to distribute and must be injected to be effective. People exposed to ricin via inhalation or ingestion will most likely become sick and recover. It is popular among domestic terrorists, second only to explosives.

Exposure and its effects. Effects of these agents on the body vary widely depending on the agent involved. In many cases individuals present with flu-like symptoms that get progressively worse. Hemorrhaging and the shutdown of various body systems can occur. In some instances, rashes on the skin are evident.

Detection. On-site detection methods at this time are very limited and in many cases not available at all.

Nuclear (radiological) agents. Radioactive agents fall under Hazard Class 7. There are three primary methods a terrorist group could use to distribute nuclear material in an attack. The first is to detonate a nuclear fission device (weapons grade). This method causes the most damage but is least likely to occur due to the difficulty in obtaining the device.

The second method would be to create a **dirty bomb** by using an explosive to scatter radioactive material. This would result in damage from the initial explosion as well as from the short- and long-term effects from the radioactive material.

The last method would be to target any type of facility that uses or stores radioactive material, such as a weapons facility, nuclear power plants, and so on (fig. 24–39).

Fig. 24–39. Nuclear power plants can be targeted by terrorists to create a radioactive release.

Fig. 24–40. Containers of flammable liquids can be a sign of accelerant use.

Exposure and its effects. These effects would be the same as discussed in chapter 23 regarding exposure to radiation.

Detection. Radiological material can only be detected by equipment such as a Geiger counter.

Incendiary devices. **Incendiary devices** fall under Hazard Class 3 flammable liquids and have been used by terrorist organizations for centuries. In fact, they are probably the easiest to obtain materials for and to build. These devices have been very popular in Europe for decades and have been on the rise in the United States since the mid-1980s. The Federal Bureau of Investigation (FBI) Bomb Data Center says that incendiary devices are used in 20% to 25% of all bombing incidents in the United States and are successfully ignited about 75% of the time. One of the major problems for investigators is determining whether an incendiary device was used for the purposes of terrorism or arson.

Signs indicating the use of incendiary devices for a terrorist event are similar to those found at a suspicious or arson fire. It is important to note that these following signs are not a guarantee that an incendiary terrorist event has taken place, but they are signals for the firefighter to be diligent and take precautions while operating at the incident. These include multiple points of fire origin, signs of accelerant use, containers of flammable liquids, splatter patterns indicating a thrown device, residue from the fusing material, signs of forced entry to the structure, common appliances out of place for the location, and so on (fig. 24–40).

Methods of detection. The use of incendiary materials can be detected using several different metering technologies, such as colorimetric tubes or combustible gas meters.

Means of protection. When dealing with incidents involving incendiary devices, firefighters should wear full PPE including SCBA. Avoid handling the device, and keep clear of any vapors, mists, or liquids until it is determined what they are. If unsure of the nature of the device, technical assistance should be called. To protect responders and civilians involved in the incident, proper decontamination procedures should be implemented prior to transporting to a hospital.

Chemical agents. **Chemical agents** fall under a broad category of materials that can be broken down into several types based on their composition and their effects on the body. These substances range from materials specifically designed to be used in warfare to those used in industrial applications.

Nerve agents. The following nerve agents are related to organophosphorus pesticides and fall under DOT Hazard Class 6.1. The two-letter abbreviations following each compound represents its military designation.

- Tabun (GA)
- Sarin (GB)
- Soman (GD)
- V agent (VX)

These nerve agents were designed for the sole purpose of killing people. The ability to kill large numbers of people is dependent on the dispersion device. To produce the desired effect, the nerve agent must be either touched in its liquid form or inhaled in its aerosol form. These materials do not remain in vapor form very long. Military warfare agents have vapor pressures lower than water. Vapors are not created from a pool of liquid, and it is generally not a major hazard unless the liquid form is touched or placed on the skin.

Exposure and its effects. Exposure to these agents can be via inhalation or skin contact with a liquid. The inhalation of a small amount can cause pinpoint pupils, runny nose, and mild difficulty breathing. If a larger amount is inhaled, it can cause sudden loss of consciousness, convulsions, temporary breathing stoppage, flaccid paralysis, copious secretions, and death.

Symptoms from exposure to a liquid type can range from localized sweating, nausea, vomiting, and a feeling of weakness, to a sudden loss of consciousness, seizures, breathing stoppage, copious secretions, paralysis, and death. Some of the warning signs that exposure has occurred are runny nose, difficulty breathing, and uncontrolled muscles and bodily functions. A fruity odor may also be reported. An easy way to remember the signs and symptoms of an exposure to nerve agents is to use the acronym SLUDGEM:

- **S**alivation
- **L**acrimation (watering of the eyes)
- **U**rination
- **D**efecation
- **G**astrointestinal upset
- **E**mesis (vomiting)
- **M**iosis (constricted pupils):

Methods of detection. Some common methods of detection are detection papers such as M8 or M9, colorimetric tubes, military detection kits, pesticide tickets, and electronic meters.

Means of protection. If during a response to an incident it is suspected that a nerve agent has been used, it is best to follow the procedures found in the **North American Emergency Response Guide (NAERG)**, Guide 153. Common antidotes are atropine and 2-PAM chloride.

Blister Agents (vesicants). Blister agents are designed to incapacitate the enemy. These compounds fall under DOT Hazard Class 6.1. Although these agents are toxic at high concentrations, the primary hazard is skin contact resulting in blistering and severe irritation. Blister agents pose less of a hazard than nerve agents.

Examples of blister agents include:

- Mustard agent (H)
- Distilled mustard (HD)
- Nitrogen mustard (HN)
- Lewsite (L)

A military weapon, blister agents are designed to incapacitate the enemy in two ways:

- The exposed person would be overcome with severe irritation and blisters of the skin (fig. 24–41).
- Several other people would be required to help treat the victim, tying them up and preventing them from fighting.

Exposure effects can be delayed from 15 minutes to several hours; quick identification is the key to patient treatment.

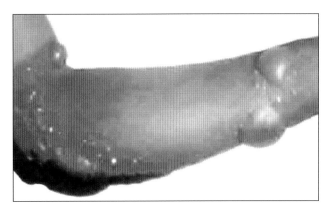

Fig. 24—41. Blister agents cause severe irritation and blistering of the skin. (Courtesy of the CDC)

Exposure and its effects. Vesicants can contact a person either as a liquid or a vapor. Vapors are more easily developed in warmer climates. Their primary effect occurs on the skin, the respiratory tract, the eyes, and the gastrointestinal tract. The mildest form is a reddening of the skin, similar to a sunburn with an itching or burning sensation. Blistering will occur later, and it can act like an acid on unprotected skin. These agents can cause respiratory failure, which can lead to death. Eyes are the most sensitive to vesicants. It takes less time from exposure to injury with the eyes than with the skin. The least affected is the gastrointestinal tract.

Its impact on the central nervous system seems to be minimal when persons are exposed to small amounts. Studies have shown that exposed persons appear to be sluggish, apathetic, and lethargic.

Detection methods. Similar to nerve agents; self-protection procedures can be found in the NAERG, Guide 153.

Blood Agents. Blood agents, otherwise known as chemical asphyxiants, disrupt the blood's ability to transport oxygen. Examples of blood agents include:

- Hydrogen cyanide (AC) DOT 6.1

- Cyanogen chloride (CK) DOT 2.3

Exposure and its effects. Contact with agents can be either from a vapor or a liquid. Liquids will vaporize quickly due to the chemical's volatility. These cyanides react with the hemoglobin in the blood and prevent it from carrying oxygen throughout the body. Its effect on the body is the same as asphyxiation, but more rapid. High concentration can lead to respiratory and cardiac arrest. Common signs that exposure has occurred are great difficulty in breathing and onset of cardiac symptoms. Some victims may report an odor of bitter or burnt almonds.

Detection methods. Similar to those used for nerve agents; firefighters should use the following procedures if they are at an incident and blood agents are suspected. If you have positively identified the substance as cyanogen chloride, use Guide 125. If the material is positively identified as hydrogen cyanide, use Guide 117. If a blood agent is suspected but not positively identified, use Guide 123. There is an antidote kit for blood agents called the Pasadena Cyanide Antidote.

Choking agents. Choking agents are common in industrial applications. They fall under DOT hazard class 2.3. One example is chlorine, which is used in water treatment facilities and swimming pools, thus making it present in almost any community.

Examples of choking agents include:

- Chlorine (CL) DOT 2.3

- Phosgene (CG) DOT 2.3

Exposure and its effects. Exposure to these chemicals is usually through inhaled vapors. The primary effect is pulmonary edema, or when the lungs fill with fluid and severe pneumonia sets in. Symptoms of this are eye and airway irritation, dyspnea, chest tightness, and delayed pulmonary edema. Pulmonary distress among victims is an outward warning sign. Other signs are odors such as

chlorine bleach or swimming pool odors and the smell of newly mown hay or grass, which is an indicator of phosgene.

Detection methods. Similar to other types of chemical agents; operating procedures when these chemicals are discovered can be found in NAERG Guide 124 for chlorine and Guide 125 for phosgene. If the material has not been determined then the procedures found in Guide 123 should be followed.

Irritants. Irritants are the most commonly used of all the potential terrorism agents. They are not extremely toxic. Symptoms generally dissipate within 15–20 minutes after the victim is exposed to fresh air.

Examples of irritants and their respective DOT class are as follows:

- Mace (CN) DOT 6.1

- Tear gas (CS) DOT 6.1

- Pepper spray (OC) DOT 2.2

As a point of consideration, pepper spray falls under DOT hazard classification of 2.2, but its subsequent hazard risk is 6.1.

Exposure and its effects. These agents cause discomfort and eye closure (fig. 24–42). They tend to render the recipient temporarily incapacitated. The major reason for their use is to cause pain, burning, or discomfort on exposed mucous membranes and skin. This occurs within minutes of being exposed. Initial signs of exposure are the smell of hair spray and pepper.

Fig. 24–42. Pepper spray causes discomfort and eye closure. (Courtesy of the DOD)

Detection methods. Detection of these sprays can be made through the use of laboratory testing using gas chromatography/mass spectrometry. Self-protection is accomplished by following the procedures in the NAERG Guide 159 if the material has been identified; if not, use Guide 153. For any victims affected by these agents, have them decontaminated and transported to a hospital.

Explosives. Bombs appear to be the weapon of choice for terrorists. Approximately 70% of all terrorist incidents involve the use of explosives. FBI bomb data reports that, on average, there are 3,000 bombings per year in the United States. The majority of these incidents are small bombings; however, the data shows that these explosions kill an average of 32 people per year and injure 277.

Improvised explosive devices (IED) can be designed to deliver an assortment of harm and destruction, and can also be used as a means of dispersing chemical, biological, incendiary, and nuclear agents (fig. 24–43). Explosives are defined as materials capable of violent decomposition. This decomposition often takes the form of extremely rapid oxidation. Explosions are the result of a sudden and violent release of gas during the decomposition of explosive substances. This release is followed by high temperature, strong shock, and loud noise.

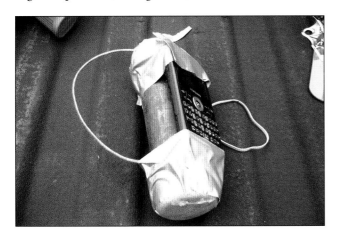

Fig. 24–43. IEDs can be designed to deliver an assortment of harm and destruction.

Scene safety

The first responder should consider the following safety issues when making an entry:

- There may be secondary events designed to incapacitate emergency responders.

- There is the potential for armed resistance and use of weapons.

- There could possibly be booby traps.

- There may be secondary contamination from handling patients.

It must be considered a possibility that the individual(s) who released the material or detonated the device will remain in the area to watch or plan to hinder emergency operations. Law enforcement may need to clear the area of any potential threats before any other operations can begin. There is also the potential for secondary explosive devices to be set in place with the intent to injure onlookers or emergency responders and further increase the chaos level. These devices can be triggered either by a remote device or by some type of a trip switch. Bomb squad personnel should be called in to ensure that there are no additional active devices before operations proceed.

Evidence preservation

It is vital that emergency responders consider the preservation of evidence. To properly preserve and collect evidence, the following actions should be taken:

- Do not move or touch anything that appears to be evidence unless absolutely necessary.

- Gently cover evidence that may be damaged by the weather or other external sources.

- Document all actions (fig. 24–44).

Fig. 24–44. Personnel operating at the scene of a terrorist incident should document all actions taken.

The collection of evidence should be conducted by law enforcement personnel only. Hazmat response personnel should collect evidence only if they have received proper training or if required to do so by law-enforcement personnel. It is vital to maintain a chain-of-custody record whenever it becomes necessary to collect or transport possible criminal evidence.

Additional assistance resources

The first responder should review the procedures outlined in SOPs and LERP for requesting state, federal, and military assistance at a terrorist incident. These incidents require a strong law enforcement component for crime scene preservation and security as well as evidence preservation.

At the federal/military level, the following resources are available for additional assistance.

FBI Hazardous Materials Response Unit (HMRU). The HMRU can provide assistance with the following:

- Identification

- Mitigation

- Evidence collection

Army's Technical Escort Unit (TEU). The TEU can provide assistance with the following:

- Identification

- Mitigation

- Assistance with chemical, biological, and explosive materials

Marine Corps Chemical Biological Incident Response Force (CBIRF). The CBIRF responds across the country and around the world to terrorist acts. It consists of three main sections:

- Decontamination

- Security

- Medical

This response force can also provide detection and mitigation assistance.

CONCLUSION

Upon arrival at a hazmat incident, controlling the scene to prevent additional exposures is a priority task. As this is being done, the incident command system needs to be established to better organize and implement the response. After sufficient information has been collected regarding the product release, the incident commander can set the response objectives for the operation. These objectives must be realistic in nature based on the available resources, and must be specific and measurable. After the product hazards have been identified and the response objectives defined, operational personnel can determine the appropriate PPE needed to meet those objectives. Lastly, although in many ways it is handled in the same basic manner as an accidental release, incidents involving criminal or terrorist activities require addressing additional concerns in the planning phase to ensure the safety of responders and civilians alike.

QUESTIONS

1. Name three reasons that a hazmat responder would choose to protect-in-place rather than evacuate.

    _____

    _____

    _____

    _____

    _____

2. In which control zone is the incident command center located?

    _____

3. Name the positions and groups or branches that are special to a hazardous response Incident Command System (ICS):

    _____

    _____

    _____

    _____

    _____

4. What are the three hazardous materials incident levels?

    _____

    _____

    _____

5. List the three different response actions.

    _____

    _____

    _____

6. List the six strategic priorities at a hazardous materials/WMD incident.

    _____   _____

    _____   _____

    _____   _____

7. Which type of SCBA provides the highest level of respiratory protection in a hazardous materials incident?

_____

8. Describe the four levels established by the Environmental Protection Agency for chemical protective equipment.

     _____

     _____

     _____

     _____

9. The process by which a hazardous material moves through PPE material at the molecular level is called:

_____

10. Responders might choose structural firefighting clothing for what type of hazard?

_____

11. Name five additional response actions that should be taken when a hazardous materials incident is the result of a terrorist act.

     _____

     _____

     _____

     _____

     _____

     _____

12. The U.S. Department of Justice acronym OTTO stands for what potential terrorism indicators?

    _____

    _____

    _____

    _____

13. What type of terrorist incidents are characterized by a rapid onset of medical symptoms?

    _____

14. Name five possible signs that an incendiary device has been used to start a suspicious fire.

    _____

    _____

    _____

    _____

    _____

    _____

15. The acronym SLUDGEM is an easy what to remember the symptoms of exposure for what type of mass destruction agent? What does the acronym stand for?

    _____

    _____

    _____

    _____

    _____

    _____

    _____

Implementing the Planned Response to a Hazmat/WMD Incident

Edited by Jason Emery

This chapter provides knowledge items for the following NFPA Standard 472 requirements. For more detail, see the Knowledge Correlations on p. xxxvi.

Operations		PPE	
5.2.3	5.4.4	6.2.3	6.6.3
5.3.4	5.5.1	6.2.4	6.6.4
5.4.1	5.5.2	6.2.5	6.8.3
		6.6.1	

OBJECTIVES

Upon completion of the chapter, you should be able to do the following:

- Identify the items that should be addressed in a safety briefing for personnel operating at the scene of a hazmat/WMD incident.

- Describe the safety precautions the entry team should take during a hazmat/WMD incident.

- Identify the limitations of personnel operating in personal protective equipment (PPE).

- Demonstrate the ability to don and doff PPE as issued by the authority having jurisdiction (AHJ).

- Describe and demonstrate the different types of defensive control operations available to operations-level personnel.

- Identify the most appropriate defensive control operation for a hazmat/WMD situation.

- Describe how to properly evaluate the progress of the planned response.

- Identify the different ways that a responder can become contaminated at an incident.

- Demonstrate the ability to perform emergency decontamination on an individual.

INTRODUCTION

The final phase of the hazmat incident involves implementing the response objectives outlined in the planning phase. As these operations are taking place, scene safety and the safety of response personnel are both of the utmost importance. Operations-level responders should never conduct operations that exceed their level of training and available equipment. During this phase, the incident commander (IC) needs to constantly evaluate the progress of ongoing operations and determine if the response objectives are being met. If the response is not successful, tactics must be modified accordingly. In addition, decontamination procedures must be implemented to prevent contamination outside of the hot zone.

SCENE SAFETY

Scene safety is a critical aspect to any emergency response, and a hazardous materials incident is no exception. It is crucial that the response plan include measures that promote the safety of all response personnel. All responders should be advised of these measures to ensure compliance.

Safety briefing

The initial **safety briefing** should evaluate what has occurred thus far as well as assess current conditions and what is likely to occur (fig. 25–1). The briefing should list the associated hazards, such as mechanical, respiratory, or skin absorption dangers.

Fig. 25–1. The initial safety briefing should evaluate what has occurred thus far and assess current conditions and what is likely to occur.

Following the incident, each responder should be briefed on the hazards involved with the product and give the information in a written format after the response is completed. Included should be any signs or symptoms of exposure to the product. The information should be maintained in each responder's medical records.

The safety briefing should include the following description of the site:

- Containers involved
- Topographical information
- Potential exposures
- Location of the control zones
- Location of the decontamination area
- Location of the command post
- Location of medical assistance area

Responders should utilize a map or sketch of the area to gain a better knowledge of the area's layout.

The safety briefing should review the tasks to be performed at the scene. This includes identifying the goal of the operation, describing each responder's duties, and determining task completion times. The briefing should also identify PPE requirements, including the requirements for entry, backup, and rescue teams, as well as decon personnel. Additionally, identification of monitoring requirements should also be presented. Communication protocols and contacts for emergency situations, escape routes, and precautions at incidents involving criminal or terrorist activities are also covered.

In the event of a terrorist incident or other criminal activities, responders should be reminded of the potential for secondary devices, armed resistance, booby traps, the use of weapons, and secondary contamination from the treatment of patients.

Entry team safety

The entry team is responsible for carrying out the response objectives as previously determined by the IC. They can be assigned to duties such as information gathering or defensive or offensive operations, depending on their level of training, available equipment, and the needs of the IC.

Buddy system and backup personnel. First responders should always use the buddy system when operating at a hazmat incident (fig. 25–2). In-depth or time-consuming tasks may require additional assistance to complete.

Fig. 25–2. First responders should always use the buddy system when operating at a hazmat incident.

The buddy system keeps an accurate count of responders operating at the scene. In addition, chemical protective suits reduce mobility and visibility, requiring multiple personnel to complete necessary tasks.

Backup personnel are crucial for emergencies involving entry personnel, especially because conditions can deteriorate quickly and unexpectedly. According to the two-in/two-out requirement found in the Occupational Health and Safety Administration's (OSHA) 1910.134 standard, there must be a backup team standing by whenever a team makes an entry. Backup teams should have identical PPE to the initial team's and should be suited up to the point where all they have to do is go on air. Backup teams must be in place before the primary team begins operations, and the team must be available for immediate response (fig. 25–3).

Fig. 25–3. The backup team must be available for immediate response.

Safety precautions to consider. When approaching the scene, the first responder at a hazmat incident must remember that the approach should be from the uphill/upwind side. Use binoculars and metering equipment (fig. 25–4) to assess the situation from a safe distance. The first responder should also be familiar with the topography before entry and should avoid all contact with the material.

Fig. 25–4. Use metering equipment to assess the situation.

During the initial response to the scene, consider the following:

- Response routes
- Potential human exposures and their proximity to the incident
- Water supply locations
- Access to the scene
- Wind direction

While working at the scene, additional factors to consider are current and expected weather conditions, the location of utilities, container integrity, behavior of the material, and appropriate PPE for the material. Also, if the product is venting or on fire, look to see if the conditions are getting worse, maintaining, or improving. In addition, responders should observe potential sources of ignition such as:

- Lighting equipment
- Chemical reactions
- Electric motors and controllers
- Open flames
- Cutting or welding operations
- Smoking materials
- Portable heating equipment
- Radios, flashlights, personal alert safety system (PASS) devices
- Fuel-powered equipment
- Sparks caused by static electricity or friction
- Flares
- Heated metal surfaces
- Internal combustion engines
- Lightning
- Radiant heat

In addition to the concepts discussed above, while using PPE, hazmat responders should also do the following:

- Complete a full safety check on the responder's PPE and SCBA prior to making entry.
- While working in PPE, avoid contact with hazardous material. Operations-level personnel

should not be operating in an environment where contact with the material could potentially occur, since they are only allowed to conduct defensive operations.

- Maintain a strict situational awareness and avoid contact with sharp objects and other hazards that could cause a tear or breach in the PPE.

As mentioned previously, the use of the buddy system and a backup team is also a key component in ensuring the safety of entry personnel.

EMERGENCY PROCEDURES WHEN WORKING IN PPE

In the event that entry personnel experience a failure in their PPE, the most important thing they can do is stay calm. The responder must keep a clear head in order to make sound decisions. There are several issues that can arise when working in PPE, such as loss of communications, a medical or other incapacitating emergency, loss of air supply, or a failure in the integrity of the suit.

In the event of a loss of communication with your partner and/or the entry supervisor, the best plan is to have an alternate form of communication, such as hand signals, prearranged. These signals will allow the entry personnel to indicate their status to one another and to other personnel if they are in visual range. This can be something as simple as a thumbs up to indicate everything is okay or a thumbs down to indicate a problem.

If a medical or other incapacitating event occurs to an entry member, the backup team would be activated to assist his or her buddy in the timely removal of the member from the area and to get them access to medical care. Depending on the severity of the problem, it may require emergency decontamination and immediate care. In the event of a cardiac arrest, it may be necessary to start lifesaving measures before decontamination has been fully completed in order to give the responder the best chance for survival.

As in a structural fire, the loss of air supply can be a major emergency and can be the result of anything from simply running out of air to a failure in the equipment. The immediate response should be to begin to move out of the area and toward a less contaminated location or directly to the decon area. At the same time

the safety officer or entry leader should be notified that an emergency has been declared. Entry personnel should never attempt to remove their suits, as it would expose them to the contaminants. In the event that the member is wearing a suit where the SCBA is worn on the inside, if possible, remove the regulator from the face mask and breathe the available but limited air supply inside the suit while making an exit from the area.

If there is a failure in the suit's integrity, the responder should exit the area immediately with his or her partner by moving toward the decon location or a less contaminated area. As with any air supply problem, this also requires the immediate notification of the safety officers or entry group supervisor. Determine the extent of the damage and potential level of contamination while attempting to seal the breach with a hand or other available resources to limit the contamination. Do not remove the facepiece until suit removal and decontamination of the responder can be accomplished.

Working in PPE

Responders working in PPE need to understand both their limitations and the limitations of their equipment. Additionally, it is important that they are familiar with proper donning and doffing procedures, as well as how to maintain the PPE.

Limitations of personnel using PPE. First responders must know and understand their own limitations and that of their protective equipment. Limitations of the wearer may be physical, mental, or medical.

Physical limitations. To maximize the amount of working time in PPE and SCBA, the wearer must be in good physical condition. The more work that needs to be accomplished, the greater the demands placed on the body. The use of this equipment may restrict the movement of the wearer, causing agility and balance limitations, as well as reducing dexterity and the ability to see (fig. 25–5). Finally, facial features may affect the first responder's ability to get a good seal with the SCBA mask.

Fig. 25–5. Use of PPE reduces the wearer's dexterity and ability to see. (Courtesy of Pullman FD)

Fig. 25–6. A medical exam needs to be completed before responders are allowed to wear PPE and SCBA.

Psychological limitations. Persons wearing PPE and respiratory protection should be able to handle themselves in a hostile and high-stress environment. First responders must have confidence in their ability to perform the necessary actions. Responders should also have the proper training and understand every aspect of their PPE. It should be noted that some individuals who are claustrophobic may not be able to wear a mask. The level of experience a responder has can also be a psychological limitation. Suit or respiratory protection failures can also present psychological challenges.

Medical limitations. Medical limitations can include wearers' muscular/skeletal condition as well as the condition of their cardiovascular and respiratory systems. The bodies of those who are in better physical condition will be strained less by the use of positive-pressure SCBA than those who are out of shape.

OSHA 1910.134 requires that any individual who is assigned a task requiring SCBA be medically cleared to wear the SCBA. A responder's medical history should be reviewed, and a physical exam (fig. 25–6) must be administered prior to being cleared to use SCBA. In addition, a fit test of the face mask is required.

Donning and doffing of PPE. Responders must be completely familiar with PPE donning and doffing procedures as dictated by their department standard operating procedures (SOPs) and manufacturer's recommendations. Different types of PPE may have different donning and doffing methods. Before any operations-level responder is allowed to participate in an actual hazmat response, he or she must have practical experience donning, doffing, and working in the PPE provided by the department (fig. 25–7).

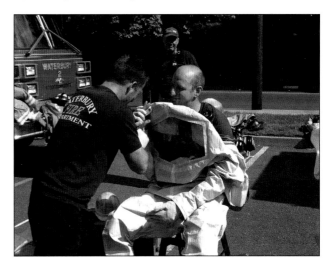

Fig. 25–7. Responders must have practical experience donning, doffing, and working in the PPE provided by the department.

Documentation of PPE usage. Following the use of PPE at a hazmat incident, the operations-level responder needs to complete the reporting and documentation requirements set forth by department SOPs and the local emergency response plan. Depending on local requirements, this can include a description of the actions that were performed, any problems or issues experienced with the PPE, any potential contamination that occurred, and decon measures performed on the PPE. Additionally, the final disposition of the PPE should be noted. For example, was it cleaned, inspected, and placed back in service, removed from service for repairs, or discarded? Local procedures may dictate that additional information is collected.

PRODUCT CONTROL (DEFENSIVE) OPERATIONS

The efforts of firefighters to contain the release of a hazardous material are intended to minimize environmental effects by confining the spill to the smallest possible area for later removal by commercial cleanup contractors. As with all other activities during these types of incidents, the safety of firefighters is vital, and those performing these tasks must make every effort to avoid contact with any hazardous material involved.

Hazardous materials can migrate from an incident scene. Spilled liquids move downhill where the product can then enter storm drains or other bodies of water; vapors from spilled liquids and dust from finely ground spilled solids move from the scene by air currents. Remember, anything used to contain a hazardous material must be compatible, meaning that the containment barrier cannot react with the hazardous material, which could produce dangerous fumes or perhaps even a fire. Another word of caution: avoid any contact with spilled hazardous materials during containment efforts.

Product control options

Defensive control methods are used to contain or confine a spill. These actions should be undertaken only if it is possible to perform the tasks without contacting the material. All responders must be wearing the appropriate PPE for the hazard. Responders need to be able to identify the purpose for and the procedures, equipment, and safety precautions associated with each of the following control techniques.

Absorption. **Absorption** is the physical process of absorbing or "picking up" a liquid product spill (fig. 25–8). In this process the liquid enters the interior of the absorbent material used and is trapped in that product. It is most effective on spills less than 55 gal

(208 L). Some absorbent materials can be used for liquid spills on both land and water. Booms and pads may be used to absorb materials on the surface of water. The absorbent material should be spread on top of the product or in the direction of its travel.

The following materials can be used for absorption:

- Dirt
- Sawdust
- Absorbent pads
- Socks
- Booms
- Speedy dry
- Absorbent particulate
- Pans
- Pillows
- Charcoal
- Kitty litter
- Product-specific absorbents

Fig. 25–8. Using absorbent materials to "pick up" a fluid spill

The first responder should consider the compatibility of the absorbent with the spilled product. For example, spreading sawdust on an oxidizer could result in a fire. The properties of different absorbent materials vary, and they are not necessarily interchangeable.

It is important to understand what types of liquids will be absorbed by the absorbent material being used. Some will not pick up water, whereas others will pick up any liquid they come in contact with. This information is helpful when determining what is needed to soak up an oil spill in a lake or stream. Because it is considered hazardous waste, the first responder must ensure that the absorbent material and the product is disposed of in accordance with environmental regulations.

The absorption method should not be confused with adsorption, which is when one material adheres to the outside of another.

Adsorption.
Adsorption is the chemical process by which the spilled product adheres to the surface of the sorbent. The absorbent must be compatible with the spilled product.

Because the process of adsorption is a chemical reaction, it can produce of large amounts of heat.

Confinement—diking.
Diking is the process of constructing a land-based barrier that controls the movement of liquid hazardous material. Dikes prevent movement of materials into areas where they can cause greater damage. They are constructed by forming an embankment. Construction should begin at the point farthest away from the spill and work back to the spill (fig. 25–9). The responder should ensure that it is far enough away from the spill that it can be completed before the material reaches it. Dikes can be constructed of materials available on site such as dirt, sand, clay, and other materials that may be found on the incident scene. There are two types of dikes commonly used to capture and control product releases:

- The **V-dike** captures released material by using the small end of the V as the collection point.

- The **circle dike** is used as a secondary containment to capture a released material that escapes or overflows the V-dike. It is a berm that is placed 360 degrees around a leaking container. It does not form a perfect circle but rather an enclosure for the product.

Fig. 25–9. A circle dike

Confinement—damming.
Damming is the process of constructing a barrier intended to slow or stop the flow of liquid into the environment. A dam or line dam can be constructed of any materials available that could prevent a liquid from moving down an incline. They are typically built in ditches, streams, or creeks. Additionally, dams may be used to act as accumulation points where product can be collected for cleanup. Overflow and underflow dams are used when constructing a dam in moving water.

Overflow damming.
Overflow dams should be constructed from materials with a specific gravity greater than 1. Hazardous materials with a specific gravity greater than 1 will sink in water and will be trapped against the base of the overflow dam. The pipes at the top of the dam allow the water that remains on top to flow freely over the dam (fig. 25–10). Pipes used in overflow dams should be a minimum of 4 in. in diameter.

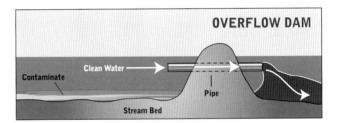

Fig. 25–10. An overflow dam

Underflow damming.
Underflow dams should be used for materials with a specific gravity lower than 1. Hazardous materials that have a specific gravity lower than 1 will float on water and will be trapped against the top of the overflow dam. The pipes at the bottom of the dam allow the water at the base of the dam to flow freely (fig. 25–11). Because most spilled hazardous materials float on water, this type of dam is most commonly used.

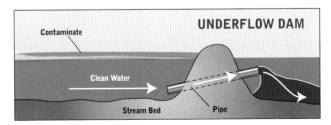

Fig. 25–11. An underflow dam

The following materials may be used to construct dams:

- Dirt or sand

- Pipes

When using pipes, note that they should have at least a 4-in. (100-mm) diameter. If the water flow is larger, it may be necessary to use either a larger pipe or multiple pipes. The responder should place enough pipes to cover two-thirds of the waterway. Hard suction can be used in an emergency.

Confinement—diverting. **Diverting** is channeling spilled materials into a containment area to an area where it poses less harm. It can be used on both land and water. A spill on land can be diverted by building a barrier made out of a material such as dirt, ahead of the spill. A spill on water can be diverted using booms to channel the material into an area where it can be absorbed or collected. Diverting allows the product to be directed to an area where it will cause less harm. For example, it may prevent a product from flowing down a storm drain (fig. 25–12).

Fig. 25–12. Spills can be diverted around an endangered area such as a storm drain using a diversion barrier.

The first responder should consider the angle and speed of the flow when constructing a diversion barrier. When dealing with fast moving spills, the barrier should be set up at an angle of no less than 60 degrees in order to be effective. As with dikes and dams, a diversion barrier should be placed far enough ahead of the spill so that it can be completed prior to the arrival of the material. This may require that some intermediate area between the spill and the barrier be sacrificed. Diversion barrier are generally built using the same materials as dikes.

Confinement—retention. **Retention** or **containment** can be broken down into two methods based on whether the physical state of the product is liquid or solid.

Liquid. When containing a liquid spill into water, booms are most commonly used. Booms are long tubular devices that float on top of the water and provide either a barrier or barrier/absorption (fig. 25–13).

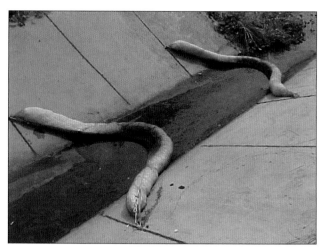

Fig. 25–13. An absorbent boom

Absorbent booms are made from various materials that can collect compatible materials released during a spill.

Retention or barrier booms are constructed of nonporous materials that float on the water and have a curtain extending below the surface to hold the product in place. The product is then removed using either absorbent pads or other manual devices, or it is vacuumed up by a cleanup contractor.

Solids. When containing spills of solid materials, the method most often used is covering the product. This involves placing tarps over the material to prevent movement. Movement may be caused by weather conditions such as wind and rain or by personnel walking through the product.

Dilution. **Dilution** reduces the concentration of the material to a nonhazardous or less hazardous state (fig. 25–14). This method has few practical applications at a hazmat incident, especially for first responders. This process can be used when dealing with small acid or base spills. There are disadvantages to using this method. Dilution is more likely to increase the volume of the product and create a runoff problem. It may also weaken the original product but not eliminate the hazard. In addition, fuels, oils, and other hydrocarbons are not water-soluble and cannot be diluted with water. Finally, this method should not be used on water-reactive materials.

Fig. 25–14. Dilution reduces the concentration of the material to a nonhazardous or less hazardous state.

Vapor dispersion. By moving gases or vapors using **vapor dispersion**, the hazard and concentration of the product are reduced, while firefighters are able to work from a safe distance. Vapor dispersion uses water spray to direct hazardous vapors away from a certain area (fig. 25–15). The turbulence created by the stream mixes up the air and reduces the material's concentration. Fans may also be used to prevent fewer problems with runoff and chemical incompatibility with water. However, fans should not be used with flammable materials unless a unit such as a water-driven positive-pressure fan can be used to reduce the risk of ignition. To be effective, the material must be water soluble or the vapor cloud must be moveable. Be sure to disperse the vapors into an area where they will not cause more harm.

Fig. 25–15. Firefighters dispersing a propane vapor cloud

When using this technique, first responders should confine the runoff and analyze it for contamination. When applying this technique to flammable vapors, such as LP gases, be aware that reducing the concentra-

tion in air may bring it into its flammable rage. Vapor dispersion is usually used to remove gases that are heavier than air from low-lying or enclosed areas. It is usually not a recommended practice except in life-threatening situations.

The first responder must know the identity of the product before using this tactic. Lighter-than-air vapors, which would normally dissipate on their own, may be knocked down by water spray.

Water-soluble materials such as anhydrous ammonia, when mixed with water, may produce another substance that could be dangerous. For example, anhydrous ammonia when mixed with water produces ammonium hydroxide, which is a corrosive liquid.

Vapor suppression. Vapor suppression is the reduction or elimination of vapors produced by a spilled hazardous material. Firefighting foams are effective when used on flammable or combustible liquids (fig. 25–16). This method significantly reduces the hazards associated with uncontrolled vapors. The selection of the proper foam for vapor suppression is an important decision. Transportation and industrial accidents, or even a mishap at the local high school, can result in a flammable liquid or hazardous vapor incident.

Fig. 25–16. Foam being applied to a combustible liquid

Foam extinguishes flammable and combustible liquid fires and protects liquid spills from ignition in four ways:

- Removes the air from the flammable vapors

- Minimizes or eliminates vapor release from fuel surface

- Provides a barrier between the flame and the fuel surface

- Cools the fuel surface and surrounding surfaces

The following are common types of foams used in hazardous materials applications:

- Aqueous film-forming foam (AFFF)

- Fluoroprotein

- High-expansion foam

Additional foam types are addressed in chapter 31, Advanced Fire Attack.

The following factors must be considered prior to using foam:

- The product must be compatible with the type of foam being used (water-reactive chemicals cause adverse reactions).

- Personnel should not walk through or disturb the foam blanket after it has been applied and established.

- After the foam is applied, monitor the integrity of the foam blanket.

Types of foam

Aqueous film-forming foam (AFFF). AFFF forms a thin layer of foam that floats on the surface of the fuel (fig. 25–17). It is a synthetically produced, detergent-based foam. There are several advantages to using AFFF:

- Extremely rapid knockdown

- Long shelf life

- Easy to foam and can be used with nonaspirating nozzles

- Self-healing foam blanket

Fig. 25–17. Aqueous film-forming foam (AFFF)

Among the disadvantages of AFFF include:

- Less overall burn-back resistance than fluoroprotein foam

- Effectiveness depends on the proper formation of an aqueous film

AFFF is self-healing after being disrupted and has good viscosity at low temperatures. It can also be purchased in an alcohol-resistant formula for use on alcohols and polar solvents.

Fluoroprotein foams. Although fluoroprotein foams are designed for hydrocarbon fires, protein foams can be formulated to be alcohol resistant by adding an additional mixture of materials. However, they generally only maintain their alcohol-resistant properties for about 15 minutes. Fluoroprotein foam can be injected into the base of a burning storage tank and be allowed to rise to the surface and extinguish the fire. This procedure is known as subsurface injection.

Fluoroprotein foam has the following advantages:

- Reasonably compatible with dry chemical extinguishing agents

- Better burn-back resistance than AFFF

- Not dependent on film formation

- Good fuel-shedding properties

- Nontoxic and biodegradable

Fluoroprotein foam has the following disadvantages:

- Does not provide as quick a knockdown as AFFF

- Requires aeration

- Not film-forming

This foam type is not affected by freezing and thawing and can be mixed with either fresh or salt water. In addition, fluoroprotein foams can be stored in temperatures ranging from 20°F (–7°C) to 120°F (49°C).

High-expansion foams. High-expansion foams are special-purpose foams with a detergent base. They are characterized by low water content and have poor heat resistance.

This type of foam is used for:

- Pesticide fires

- Suppression of fuming acid vapors

- Firefighting operations in confined spaces

Using high-expansion foam as a vapor suppression tool offers the following advantages:

- Good for use in basement fires or enclosed areas

- Low proportioning rate in conjunction with high-expansion ratios allow for large quantities of foam to be produced with a minimum amount of concentrate

- Not affected by freezing and thawing

High-expansion foams have the following disadvantages:

- Limited use on Class B fires because the thermal updraft causes difficulties in the formation of a thick blanket

- Does not heal itself when disrupted

- Generally not recommended for the outdoors because the foam blanket tends to blow off easily in the wind

Foam production. Foam is a specific agent for a specific type of material. As such, it must be used properly. Proportioning or mixing the right amount of foam concentrate with the right amount of water and air at the right pressure results in good quality foam. Foam is not just a collection of bubbles; it is a specific mix of concentrate, water, and air. It is also critical that there are sufficient quantities of foam concentrate to extinguish the fire and secure the spill.

Proper proportioning is important. If there is not enough concentrate in the finished foam, the overall quality and effectiveness will decrease. It may not extinguish the fire as expected, heat resistance decreases, and burnback resistance decreases.

If your finished foam has too much concentrate in it, foam will not flow around debris and obstacles. Additionally, limited foam concentrate will be depleted rapidly, not allowing enough for complete extinguishment and reapplication as necessary.

A common type of foam proportioning and delivery system is called an **inline eductor** (fig. 25–18). The eductor uses the venturi principle to pull foam concentrate from the foam container and mix it with the appropriate amount of water to make foam solution. Inside the eductor there is a restriction in the metering orifice that creates a **venturi effect**, causing the water to flow faster and creating a lower pressure area in the line, resulting in suction (fig. 25–19). The foam pickup tube is attached to the venturi area of the eductor and goes in the foam bucket. A metering device allows the passage of the correct amount of foam concentrate to enter the hoseline. Determining the appropriate ratio of foam to water depends on the foam being used and

the material it is used on. For example, an alcohol-resistant AFFF with a 1%/3% application ratio (fig. 25–20) would require 1% of foam concentrate and 99% water on a hydrocarbon spill and 3% of concentrate and 97% water on an alcohol spill.

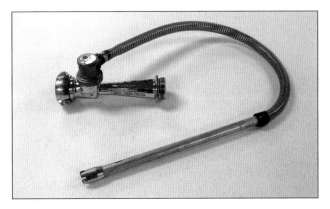

Fig. 25–18. Inline foam eductor

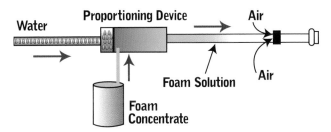

Fig. 25–19. The foam process introduces a set percentage of foam concentrate into the water supply and uses a foam nozzle to inject air into the foam solution.

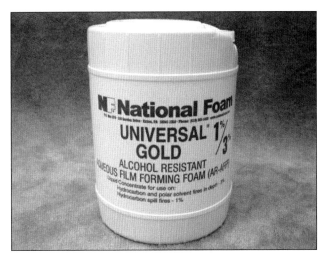

Fig. 25–20. Alcohol resistant AFFF (courtesy of National Foam)

The nozzle is the last step in the foam making process. Here the foam solution is aspirated, and finished foam is produced. The air is entrained in the foam by some type of mechanical means, usually directed at a baffle, or by foam solution streams directed at each other in the nozzle, then directed down the foam tube and out the end, forming the foam stream (fig. 25–21). The best quality foam blanket is generated with a nozzle designed for foam making and distribution.

Fig. 25–21. Foam nozzle

Application of foam. It is the nozzle operator's responsibility to apply the foam as gently as possible to allow the finished foam to form a cohesive but flowing blanket on the fuel to cover the product, allow the best development of the film-forming actions (stop vapor production), and maintain the security to prevent ignition. When applying foam, the operations-level responder should be familiar with local department SOPs on foam equipment and application methods. Different types of foam use different methods of application. The bank down, roll-on, and rainfall techniques are methods of applying foam.

Bank-down technique. In this technique, foam is bounced off a wall or object behind the spilled product. The foam then falls onto the hazardous material (fig. 25–22).

Fig. 25–22. Bank-down technique

Roll-on technique. In this technique, foam is applied ahead of the spilled product and gently rolled over it (fig. 25–23).

Fig. 25–23. Roll-on technique

Rainfall technique. In this technique, the foam is sprayed into the air above the product and allowed to rain down upon it (fig. 25–24).

Fig. 25–24. Rainfall technique

For additional information on foam types, compatibility factors, application rates, and methods, consult chapter 31, Advanced Fire Attack.

Remote valve shutoffs. This technique is not typically used by first responders at the operations level, but it is the best method of controlling spills for a limited number of situations. This process requires the firefighter, either manually or through engineering control methods (hydraulic, pneumatic, or mechanical), to stop the physical flow of product from a valve. This is done from a remote area, not at the leak. This should only be attempted if the responder will not be polaced in the hot zone and there is no danger of coming in contact with the material. This method will require the firefighter to interact with either the driver or facility personnel to determine where the control for the valve may be and what is the safest method to accomplish the task. Do not open or close any valve without understanding its implications.

Emergency shutoffs—transportation. There are three types of emergency shutoffs valves: mechanical, hydraulic, and pneumatic. Closing a mechanical valve closes all internal valves within 30 seconds of activation. Mechanical valves are constructed with corrosion-resistant cables and handles. Closing a hydraulic or pneumatic valve closes all internal valves when a loss of hydraulic or pneumatic pressure occurs. This typically operates off the tractor's system via a pigtail. Emergency shutoffs are usually well marked and located in easy-to-find areas. The shutoff valves are typically found behind the driver's side of the cab or near the control valves.

Figures 25–25, 25–26, and 25–27 are examples of shutoff valve locations on common trailers:

Fig. 25–26. Emergency shutoff in an MC307/DOT407

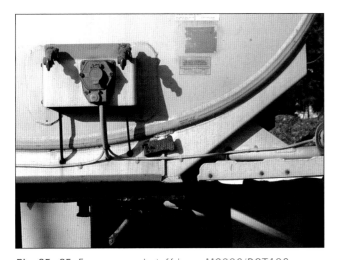
Fig. 25–25. Emergency shutoff in an MC306/DOT406

Fig. 25–27. Emergency shutoff in an MC331

Remote valve shutoffs—fixed facilities. Remote shutoff valves in fixed facilities are generally found in facilities with loading and unloading areas (fig. 25–28). They may be located near the entrance to provide easy access to emergency responders. Consult with facility personnel to determine the location. During facility preplans, the responder should look for remote shutoff valves and mark them on a site map.

Fig. 25–28. Remote shutoff valves are generally found in facilities with loading or unloading areas.

EVALUATING PROGRESS

As responders implement the tactics selected to meet the objectives of the emergency response, it is important that they evaluate the progress of their efforts. Without this continual evaluation process, it is impossible to determine if objectives are met.

Evaluating progress

When evaluating the progress to determine if the response is effective, the first responder should ask if the situation is stabilizing or worsening. If the situation is stabilizing, then the operations as implemented should be continued. If the situation is becoming worse, the action plan should be reviewed, and potential alternative approaches to the situation should be determined.

Throughout the emergency response, the responder should constantly be addressing the effectiveness of the response. Changing conditions may require a change in tactics to mitigate the incident. For example, the leak may become larger, the weather conditions may deteriorate, or responders may be injured (fig. 25–29). The action of emergency responders should be leading toward the ultimate goal of life safety, incident stabilization, and property conservation.

Fig. 25–29. An injured responder would require a change in the action plan.

Communicating the status of the response

The first responder should follow predetermined communications protocols to keep other parties informed about the response progress. The chain of command should be used to relay information, and dispatch must be kept appraised of the current situation. If possible, the transfer of critical information to the next level should be done face to face for the most effective communication of the situation.

First responders should be familiar with local emergency communications procedures as outlined in the organization's SOPs. For example, the SOP may require emergency communications message or tones, blasts on the appropriate air horn, or other predetermined methods. In an emergency situation where the situation becomes critical and personnel are threatened, the chain of command does not need to be followed. The first responder should avoid all delays in notifying the incident commander of an emergency situation.

Withdrawing from an incident

It may be necessary to remove responders from the incident area if conditions are too dangerous. For example, withdrawal may be necessary if the incident is beyond an operations-level response, there is imminent danger of explosion or boiling liquid expanding vapor explosion (BLEVE), or other potential for massive container failure exists. Keeping responders in the immediate area of a hazmat incident when there is nothing that can be accomplished serves no useful purpose. The incident commander needs to apply a risk-versus-benefit approach when determining whether operations should be allowed to continue or be suspended or modified.

DECONTAMINATION

Decontamination is a process of removing or neutralizing contaminants that have accumulated on personnel, equipment, and the environment (fig. 25–30). Decontamination protects responders from agents that may contaminate and permeate the protective clothing, SCBA, tools, apparatus, and other equipment used at the incident. It protects all on-scene responders by minimizing the transfer of harmful materials to clean areas and helps prevent the mixing of incompatible chemicals. It also protects the community by preventing uncontrolled transportation of contaminants from the incident. Decontamination operations can be hindered by the lack of a positive identification of the material, weather conditions, topography, and availability of equipment and trained personnel.

Fig. 25–30. Decontamination is the process of removing contaminants from people or equipment. (Courtesy U.S. Air Force)

Common terms related to decontamination

Response personnel should understand the following terms and definitions as they relate to contamination concerns and be able to differentiate between them.

Contamination. Contamination is the transfer of a hazardous material out of the hot zone in quantities greater than those deemed acceptable and which pose a risk outside the hot zone. It can be caused by direct contact with the hazardous materials present in the hot zone, tools used by hazmat technicians becoming contaminated, or vehicles driven through a contaminated area. It can also be the result of the movement of the dusts, particles, gases, vapors, fumes, mists, and runoff of the hazardous material and smoke and products of combustion spreading outside the hot zone.

Additionally, responders become contaminated by the following actions:

- Walking through a spill
- Touching the material
- Coming in contact with a vapor cloud

Among the basic methods of controlling the spread of contamination is setting up hot, warm, and cold control zones (fig. 25–31). People or equipment should not leave the hot zone without first being decontaminated. Access to control zones should be restricted. All contaminated items and clothing should be properly decontaminated or bagged and disposed of. The first responder should control all runoff from decon operations. If the release is indoors, the first responder should shut down HVAC systems to prevent other portions of the building from becoming contaminated.

When dealing with radioactive materials, in addition to the previously noted methods, the first responder should employ radiation detection equipment to monitor all personnel and equipment leaving the decontamination area.

Fig. 25–31. Control zones are set up to prevent the spread of contamination.

Secondary contamination. Secondary contamination is the contamination of people, the environment, and equipment outside the hot zone. It results from coming into contact with contaminated personnel, equipment, or property. Done properly, emergency and other decontamination operations prevent secondary contamination.

An example of secondary contamination is a victim of a hazmat incident who is transported to the hospital without proper decontamination. This endangers the EMS personnel and the emergency room staff, possibly resulting in their contamination.

Exposure. Exposure is the process that occurs when people, equipment, or the environment come in contact with a hazardous material. When exposed, a person has been subjected to a hazardous material via any of the various routes of entry into the body. This is different from contamination, in which any quantity of a hazardous material physically remains on people or objects. Exposure to a material does not necessarily cause contamination. For example, you may be exposed to a material in your workplace that meets the threshold-limit value for the time-weighted average (TLV-TWA) for that product. Being contaminated does not necessarily mean that you are exposed. For example, a responder's PPE may become contaminated at an incident; however, the responder is not exposed to the material unless the PPE fails or he or she is not properly decontaminated.

An exposure's hazard level depends on the material's concentration and length of exposure. Spills of a less hazardous substance require greater quantities to reach a harmful exposure level. Spills of **extremely hazardous substances** may only need a small quantity to cause a harmful exposure level.

Exposure from radiation can be either internal or external. Internal exposure is the introduction of radioactive materials internally to body cells, tissues, and target organs. Internal exposure cannot occur unless the victim has been contaminated. External exposure occurs when all or a part of the body is exposed to radiation from an external source. During an external exposure, the radiation may be absorbed by the body or it may pass totally through.

It is possible to be exposed to radiation but not be contaminated:

- Exposures can occur when a person is subjected to the particles or waves being emitted by the radiation source, without actually touching it.

- Contamination can occur when a gaseous, liquid, or solid radioactive material is released into the environment and deposits on people externally.

- Internal contamination can occur if the material is inhaled, ingested, absorbed through the skin, or injected through wounds.

Types of decontamination

Decontamination is the removal of hazardous contaminants from personnel, equipment, property, and the environment. NFPA Standard 472 indicates three levels of decontamination: emergency decontamination, technical decontamination, and mass decontamination. There is also a fourth that is not mentioned in NFPA 472, which is fine decontamination. The size of the incident determines what types will be used. For a small incident the use of emergency decontamination may be all that is required, whereas large-scale hazardous materials/ WMD incidents may require the use of all four types. Decontamination can be grouped into two large categories: wet or dry. Wet decontamination requires the use of some sort of liquid, primarily water. Dry decontamination does not require a wetting process. Because most decontaminations are chemical specific, there are no set rules, but at a minimum the firefighter should understand the procedures for emergency decontamination. Much of the information pertaining to decontamination is from the Environmental Protection Agency (EPA) and the chemical industry.

Emergency decontamination. Anyone contaminated at an incident needs to have the hazardous material removed as quickly as possible. Victims include those with dangerous contaminants on them who are in dire need of medical attention, or responders who have been accidentally exposed to the product as a result of chemical PPE failure. This process is essentially a gross decon and typically occurs before technical decon can be established. Any delay in this could have fatal consequences. For any type of hazardous materials–related incident, the IC should consider the use of emergency decontamination. In fact, this should be part of the response SOPs.

Emergency decontamination in its simplest form can be hosing down a victim or responder with a fire hose or garden hose, whichever is available (fig. 25–32). Washing down a person with water will usually be sufficient for most chemicals that firefighters encounter. The use of water will work as long as the victim's clothing is removed. In the case of airborne contaminants, allowing a person to be in a fresh-air environment can be a useful decontamination. During emergency decontamination, minimum protective clothing should include firefighting PPE, SCBA, and chemical protective gloves. In addition, depending on the substance, chemical protective clothing may be warranted.

When using water to remove the contaminants, it is important that every effort be made to control the runoff as soon as possible. There are various ways to accomplish this process. The most basic method is to use fire service salvage tarps and some ladders to create a catchall (fig. 25–33). Another method is to use a small inflatable swimming pool, available at many department stores. These small pools can be carried on the apparatus. Lastly, commercial decontamination pools can be used. Emergency decontamination, however, should not be withheld or delayed while waiting to set up containment. Life safety is the top priority.

Fig. 25–32. Responder preparing to perform emergency decontamination on a patient

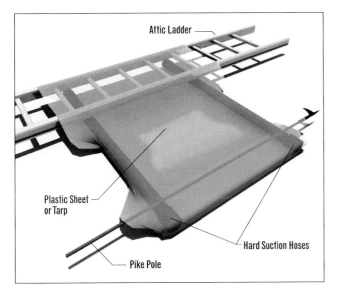

Fig. 25–33. A simple catch-all can be made with a ladder and a tarp.

The following procedures should be adhered to during the emergency decontamination process:

1. Remove victim from contaminated area.

2. Wash with flooding quantities of water.

3. Remove all contaminated clothing.

4. Continue to wash the victim.

5. Move victim to an uncontaminated area.

6. Begin first aid procedures.

7. Transport to the hospital as soon as the victim is decontaminated.

8. Advise ambulance and hospital personnel of the contaminant involved.

Some things to consider when performing emergency decontamination include the following:

- Avoid storm drains and any other areas where the environment could be compromised by the contaminants.

- If using safety showers in a facility, find out where the runoff is going. If it is going to the sanitary sewers, find an alternative.

- When removing chemicals that are corrosive in nature, use large amounts of water. Small amounts can cause a reaction with the corrosive.

- Make sure the flushing of water continues for at least 20 minutes when decontaminating corrosives.

Emergency decontamination is limited by the fact that it is considered a "quick fix" and some of the contaminants may not be removed completely. Also, some environmental damage may occur from the runoff before it is able to be contained. The need for immediate treatment of life-threatening injuries outweighs the potential disadvantages of emergency decontamination.

Technical decontamination. Technical decontamination is a more comprehensive approach to decon than emergency decon and usually consists of a four-stage process. The most important part of the decontamination process is to limit the amount of contamination possible. If responders don't get dirty, they don't have an excessive need for decontamination. Properly trained and equipped hazmat responders should avoid puddles and not kneel down or crawl, lie in the product, or put themselves in a position to be showered with chemicals.

When they are approaching the decontamination area, the less product on them, the less danger they are in.

Stage one of decontamination, also called gross decontamination, consists of a tool drop and a primary wash to remove the gross contaminants (fig. 25–34). This includes a full outer wash and rinse. Because the entry person is the dirtiest he or she can be at this point, this stage should be solo. This solo wash can be accomplished by a shower, polyvinyl chloride (PVC) washing stalls, a portable stall, or a garden hose.

Fig. 25–35. Step two is an assisted wash and rinse.

Stage three includes another wash and rinse followed by removal of the protective equipment (fig. 25–36). This is an assisted wash, rinse, and removal of equipment using decontamination personnel. It is important to note that respiratory protection should be the last item removed.

Fig. 25–34. Step one of a technical decon is designed to remove gross contaminants.

Stage two consists of a full outer wash and rinse (fig. 25–35). This is an assisted wash and rinse using decontamination personnel. This stage should concentrate on the boots and gloves of the individual. Many times they have received a high level of contamination from walking through or touching the product. With standard firefighting gear, a second wash and rinse are performed. In chemical-protective clothing, a wash and rinse followed by the removal of outer bands, tape, outer gloves, or boots is performed. Remember that a wash and rinse followed by a wash and rinse has proven to be very effective.

Fig. 25–36. Step three is an additional wash and rinse.

Stage four consists of a full body wash, drying, and dressing of the individual. This may be performed on site or off site. Supplies such as shampoo, soap, scrub brushes, cotton swabs, gowns, and slippers must be made available to adequately carry out this stage. On-scene medical examination and rehabilitation should be performed (fig. 25–37). An exam will compare vital signs taken before entry to vital signs taken after decontamination. This may be performed on site or off site. If the entry involved the use of chemical-protective clothing, heat stress reduction and hydration of the individual should be a priority.

Record keeping and exposure records should be completed at this time, along with discussion of the future effects of the chemical. Post-exposure discussions should include what to look for if there is a delayed effect of exposure. Incident stress should be discussed. Many of these chemicals may be reproductive toxins or carcinogens. There may be psychological stress that needs to be diffused.

Fig. 25–37. Step four includes a full body wash and medical evaluation.

Because decontamination is so equipment- and personnel-intensive, it is imperative that it be practical and practiced. Planning, contingencies, proper equipment, and training will prove to be the difference between failure and success. A hazardous material incident is no place to rehearse. All responders need to be familiar with the local emergency response plan and department SOPs as they relate to the technical decontamination process.

Mass decontamination. Mass decontaminations would typically be used at a terrorist event dealing with chemical/biological agents. In this type of event it becomes critical to get as many persons decontaminated as quickly as possible. The window of opportunity for decontamination to make a medical difference with victims is 10–15 minutes. Without decontamination some patients may die. In some cases standard triage

may not apply, as your local resources will dictate which patients may be salvageable. The key to saving lives is quick application of water in flooding quantities at a low pressure. Studies have shown that the use of bleach can actually make the situation worse. Do not delay the application of water. The setup of other equipment can be accomplished later as more resources arrive on the scene. This equipment includes tents, showers, etc.

Plan your decontamination setup to help the masses, specifically the victims that can be saved. Victims who are alive but unable to self-rescue are at the greatest risk. Victims who have removed themselves from the area have started the decontamination process by being in fresh air. Any symptomatic patients need decontamination within 10–15 minutes of contamination. Those, as well as victims who are contaminated, should remove their clothes. Victims who were in the vicinity of the incident and are not contaminated can be held for further evaluation at a later time. This may include persons on other floors or in other parts of a building.

Persons should be encouraged to stay in the water for as long as possible; this will be driven by the number of victims and the resources available. As resources arrive, the "bank teller" or "amusement park" line setup should be used to slow the process down and have the victims wait in the water. All persons, whether they are decontaminated are not, are to be held. They should be herded into separate areas to be further evaluated. Victims who initially are not symptomatic or contaminated can be decontaminated at another location if they so desire. A good location is a school or other building that offers privacy. They should be transported by emergency responders. In the event that they later become symptomatic, they can be run through the symptomatic line or taken to a facility for decontamination.

Attempts should be made to preserve privacy. Tents can be used as well as tarps. Tarps can be run along apparatus to provide some privacy. Children should stay with one of their parents. In many cases psychological decontamination may need to be performed. These types of victims can be transported to a fixed facility for final decontamination.

When using engine companies to provide water for the decontamination sites, use rear, side, and front discharges. The deck gun/pipe also should be used to create a water curtain. A staffed hoseline should be used at the end of the line after the victims have gone through the water, to further wash the victims off. As more resources arrive, a soap and water solution can be used to lightly scrub the victims (fig. 25–38a & b).

When possible, attempt to capture the runoff. Realistically, however, when confronted with hundreds of patients or in an emergency situation, runoff is a secondary concern to life preservation. If using one of the setups shown here, the amount of water is reducing the agent and in most cases rendering it harmless. The decontamination setups shown here are flowing a considerable amount of water, which would quickly cause all of the agents to break down. There would be little damage if the runoff enters the storm drain, as many contaminants already exist in that type of system.

CONCLUSION

Scene safety plays a major role in any emergency response, especially those involving hazardous materials. The use of the buddy system, understanding the limitations of PPE, and being familiar with emergency procedures while working in PPE are all critical components to a safe response. Failure to follow established safety guidelines can result in unnecessary and potentially dangerous exposure to the product.

During the response, the role of operations-level personnel at a hazmat incident is limited to defensive actions, in which there are several options available to help stabilize the incident. These options are designed to contain the product to the area already exposed in order to minimize potential harm, while at the same time prevent the responder from coming in direct contact with the material. During these operations it is very important to continuously evaluate the progress of the response and keep the incident commander updated. In the event that conditions begin to deteriorate, personnel must be prepared to withdraw from the area.

Decontamination plays a vital role in the prevention of the spread of the released material. Without the proper decontamination of people and equipment there is the potential for secondary contamination throughout the immediate area and beyond. There are several options available to responders based on the circumstances. Emergency decon operations should be conducted any time there is a victim or responder who has been exposed to the product and must be evacuated and treated promptly, whereas technical decon is used to systematically remove contaminants from responder personnel. Lastly, in the event that a large number of people have been exposed, a mass decon operation should be set up to handle the large number of victims.

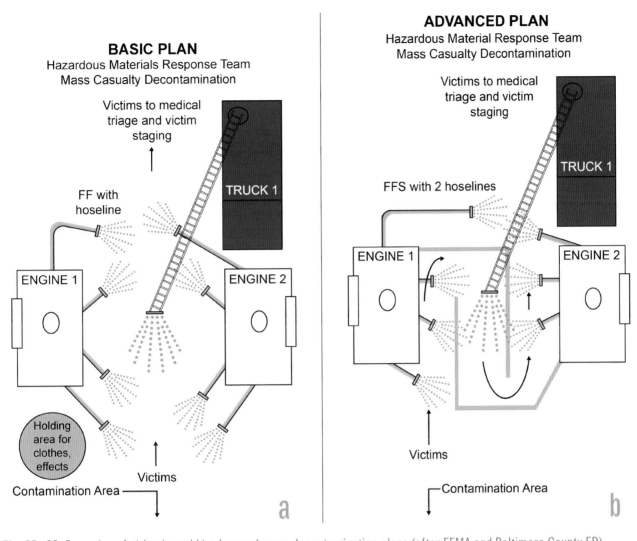

Fig. 25–38. Examples of a) basic and b) advanced mass decontamination plans (after FEMA and Baltimore County FD)

QUESTIONS

1. What seven items should be covered in the safety briefing regarding the hazardous materials incident site?

    i. _____

    ii. _____

    iii. _____

    iv. _____

    v. _____

    vi. _____

    vii. _____

2. Why is it important to use the buddy system when operating at a hazmat incident?

   _____

3. What backup communication plan is useful in the event of a loss of communication with a partner or supervisor? _____

   _____

4. Why is a firefighter's physical condition important to the effectiveness of working in PPE and SCBA?

   _____

5. Name five materials that can be used for product absorption.

    i. _____

    ii. _____

    iii. _____

    iv. _____

    v. _____

6. What is the difference between absorption and adsorption?

   _____

   _____

7. What are the two types of dams used for product confinement?

   _____

8. What are the three common foam types used for hazardous materials applications?

    i.   _____

    ii.   _____

    iii.   _____

9. Describe the differences between the "rain down" and "bank down" techniques of foam application.

    _____

    _____

10. What is "secondary contamination"? _____

11. Name three ways internal contamination can occur.

    i.   _____

    ii.   _____

    iii.   _____

12. Describe the difference between emergency and technical decontaminations.

    _____

13. What are the basic attributes of the four stages of technical decontamination?

    Stage 1: _____

    Stage 2: _____

    Stage 3: _____

    Stage 4: _____

14. In a mass decontamination situation, the key to saving lives is quick application of _____ in _____ quantities.

EMS in the Fire Service

by Victor Stagnaro

This chapter provides required knowledge items for the following
NFPA Standard 1001 Job Performance Requirements:

FFI 4.3

This chapter contains Skill Drills. When you see this icon, refer to your Skill Drill book for step-by-step instructions.

OBJECTIVES

Upon completion of this chapter, you should be able to do the following:

- Describe the role of the emergency medical system in the fire service
- Describe the role of the emergency medical service as it relates to firefighter safety
- Define the term "Standard of Care" as it relates to emergency medical care
- Identify the training requirements for emergency medical care in the United States
- Describe the basic rules of initial patient assessment
- List and describe the common types of medical emergencies encountered by firefighters
- Describe the proper procedures for the transfer of patient care

INTRODUCTION

The public has come to expect many things of their firefighters. When they don't know who to call, the fire department is often called to assist. From bringing a cat down from a tree to having a ring stuck on a finger, it is common for the fire service to respond to all types of emergencies.

Whether or not the fire department where you work or volunteer is fully integrated with an emergency medical service (EMS) system, it surely interacts as first responders work side by side with emergency medical technicians and paramedics. Whether called to vehicle crashes with injured people or an unconscious or unresponsive person at a local mall, firefighters are often the first to arrive and are expected to begin basic medical treatment until the arrival of personnel with appropriate training and expertise. Most fire department statistics show that 70%–80% of what they do is EMS related. Those are some staggering numbers; and as the baby boomer generation grows older, those numbers are more likely to increase. This chapter provides some introduction into the EMS service and covers some basic skills firefighters need to protect themselves from injury and disease as well as begin appropriate care of sick and injured patients. Just like in any emergency, the goal is to prevent further damage or injury and to stabilize the situation.

This chapter covers the basic steps needed to begin appropriate care after identifying some symptoms. Further training should be sought for more advanced care. Firefighters should *never* attempt to do more than their training has covered.

THE EMERGENCY MEDICAL SERVICES SYSTEM

EMS is part of a system generally initiated immediately after someone recognizes their need for service, regardless of whether it's after a motor vehicle crash, following a fall down a flight of stairs, or if they are having trouble breathing and feeling faint. When they call 9-1-1, or if a police officer calls in a request, the system goes to work. Through the work of fire chiefs, medical directors, and communications specialists working in a dispatch center, each jurisdiction determines what resources are sent for every type of call. The role of the new firefighters on an emergency medical incident is to learn from the more experienced firefighters and officers, but be careful to avoid causing more harm. Prepare a patient for the arrival of EMS crews and assist crews on the scene. The rewards of being a firefighter most often come from using your skills and training as well as seeing people's lives and property saved. Not everyone's belongings can be salvaged and not every life will be saved, but many are given the chance to survive through the efforts of the fire and EMS. As part of that EMS system, firefighters have the opportunity to positively affect lives.

FIREFIGHTER SAFETY

As in all aspects of firefighting, safety should remain among the highest priorities of every crew member. A firefighter would never enter a burning building without proper protective clothing and self-contained breathing apparatus (SCBA). Likewise, there are basic precautions and personal protective equipment (PPE) needed when providing emergency medical care. Issues related to infectious control include proper disinfection procedures to clean equipment prior to its use or just after it is used. Preventing contact and exposure to body fluids also is an important aspect of safety; and the use of PPE including gloves, eye protection or face shields, and respirators can help ensure exposures are limited or eliminated. Standard precautions mandate that gloves be worn during care and contact with all patients, regardless of their infection status. Additional measures should be employed for potentially infectious patients according to department and local protocols. Prior to and after wearing gloves and immediately after coming in contact with a patient's body fluids, firefighters should wash their hands and any other body parts that comes in contact

with body fluid, using a bacteria cleaning soap or other appropriate agent.

FFI 4.3 Every department should have policies in place to provide guidance on infection control. Firefighters should be thoroughly familiar with methods of isolating body substances. It should always be presumed that all body substances are infectious, and therefore appropriate PPE should be worn. Appropriate PPE may include gloves, protective eyewear, gowns, and masks. Always remember that handwashing is the first and best line of defense against infection.

Scene safety

An appropriate scene size-up should not be limited to building fires. One way firefighters can become proficient at completing a scene size-up is by doing so on every incident to which they respond, including an EMS incident. An EMS-related size-up includes determining where the exits are, establishing the best means for other providers to approach the building, and ensuring a safe working area.

You may need to call for apparatus to provide barrier protection or for law enforcement to move hostile citizens away from an injured patient. Assailants who attack their victims may still be on the scene. Be aware of your surroundings and be cautious, because it is likely that the assailant does not want their victim to be treated.

TRAINING AND STANDARD OF CARE

A single chapter on the role of a basic firefighter in EMS cannot provide enough training to cover the needed aspects of EMS care. However, because training is expanded and skills are developed, there is a duty to act as a trained firefighter or first responder. Determine the local fire department policies regarding a duty to act, and ensure an adherence to the policies. Failure to follow them may be cause for legal action against the provider and/or the department.

The U.S. Department of Transportation develops a national curriculum for EMS care. Each state and local jurisdiction adopts a set of patient care standards and treatment protocols and is required to operate under the license of a medical director. Regardless of your training, or whether you are paid or volunteer, treat every patient with respect. It is important to understand what is expected of you as well as your role in the local EMS system.

HEALTH INSURANCE PORTABILITY AND PRIVACY ACT

The **Health Insurance Portability and Privacy Act (HIPPA)** established a national standard for privacy of an individual's health information. Enacted into law in 1996, it defines and limits the circumstances in which an individual's health information may be released. Generally, there are three circumstances under which the law allows health care to be disclosed:

1. To the patient or persons the patient requests information be given to (e.g., a patient asks you to call his or her spouse)

2. For the purposes of health care operations, including providing pertinent information to other EMS providers and medical personnel rendering care to the patient or any individuals assessing care to improve quality

3. For the purposes of obtaining billing information, which is not generally done by firefighters

Essentially, firefighters only pass on a patient's health care information to another health care provider. A patient's health care information should never be shared with the public or media or discussed afterwards in a location where people not involved in patient care might overhear you. As a firefighter who treats injured and ill patients, it is important to understand the law and thoroughly know the policies and guidelines within the jurisdiction.

CRIME SCENES

Invariably, firefighters and EMS providers are called to the scene of a crime. The role of firefighters on any emergency scene is always life safety: the victim's and their own. Caring for a sick or injured patient is only secondary to your safety. If the scene is deemed unsafe, immediately call for law enforcement.

If the scene is safe, patient care is the first priority. Do not disturb anything more than is required to care for the patient. If you must move equipment or materials,

remember its initial location. Remember, local law enforcement must account for where everything is and how it got there; and you may be expected to describe what you saw, what you moved, and its location before you moved it. Restrict entry into the area to those required to be there. When you have finished taking care of the patient, check with the local law enforcement to see if there is anything they require from you before leaving the scene. You should write a narrative including the what, where, when, and how of the events to help you recall everything that occurred. Sometimes providers are called to testify in court up to months or years after the actual incident, and the narrative may be the only way to accurately remember the incident.

REPORTING TO LAW ENFORCEMENT

Federal and local laws require that certain cases be reported to local law enforcement, such as possible child abuse, elder abuse, domestic violence, and sexual abuse. Reporting should not be done in front of the patient, caregiver, or parent. Check with the local policies to ensure that you adhere to any existing regulations. Failing to report certain incidents may make you and your department liable.

INITIAL PATIENT ASSESSMENT

One of the basic rules of EMS is called the ABCs of patient care:

- A = Airway
- B = Breathing
- C = Circulation

When evaluating a patient, one of the first things to do is determine the patient's level of consciousness. This is done by checking to see if the patient is alert, able to respond to verbal commands, or unresponsive. If the patient is unresponsive, the provider must ensure the patient has an open airway. The airway of an unconscious patient can be obstructed if the head is tilted downward, blocking the airway passages. There are two different ways to open the airway: one is for a nontraumatic injury and the other is for a potential trauma patient. For a patient with a nontraumatic injury, the provider places his or her hand on the patient's forehead and the fingers of the other hand underneath the chin. Placing slight pressure on the hand and the fingers, the provider pushes the patient's head back to open the airway (fig. 26–1a).

If the patient may be suffering from a neck injury, the provider uses the jaw-thrust method of opening the airway. This time, the provider places his or her hands on each side of the patient's head, places the fingers along the jaw bone, and pushes the jaw open, which in turn opens the airway (see fig. 26–1b). If unsuccessful, revert to the head-tilt, chin-lift method previously described. Opening the airway is more important than the potential risk of a spinal injury.

Once an airway is established, it is necessary to ensure that the patient is breathing. One way to check for breathing is for the provider to place his or her ear near the patient's mouth and look, listen, and feel. The provider looks for chest rise and fall, listens for the breaths coming from the patient's mouth, and feels for the breath on their ear. If the patient is not breathing, the provider should be prepared to conduct rescue breathing.

Once the airway and breathing are completed, the provider should check for circulation. For an unconscious patient, the provider can check for a pulse by placing his or her index and middle finger on the patient's carotid artery in the neck. This can be done while looking, listening, and feeling for a breath (fig. 26–2).

For conscious adult patients, the radial pulse in the wrist is most often used to determine circulation. The brachial artery in the upper arm is used for infants younger than one year old. In addition to checking for breaths and circulation, knowledge of the rate of breathing and pulse rates can help the first responder determine treatment options. The Maryland Medical Protocol lists some average heart and respirations rates (table 26–1).

Once the patient's ABCs have been established, the provider should conduct a rapid primary patient assessment. This includes checking the patient beginning with the head and neck, moving all the way down to the bottoms of the feet and toes, and checking the patient for any major bleeding and/or deformities; generally only stop the assessment to deal with any major bleeding, which is covered in depth later in the chapter.

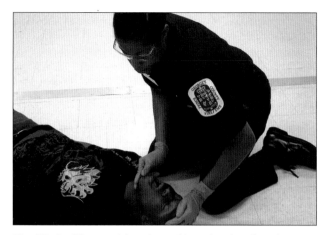

Fig. 26–1a. The provider places his or her hand on the patient's forehead and the fingers of the other hand underneath the chin.

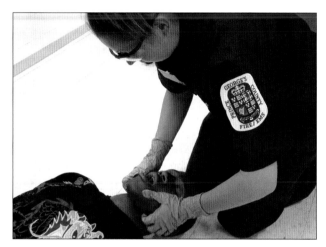

Fig. 26–1b. The provider places his or her hands on each side of the patient's head, places the fingers along the jaw bone, and pushes the jaw open.

Fig. 26–2. The provider is looking, listening, and feeling for a breath.

Table 26–1. Average heart and respiration rates

Age	Estimated Weight	Heart Rate	Respiratory Rate	Systolic B/P
Premature	< 3 kg	160	< 40	60
Newborn	3.5 kg	130	40	70
3 mo	6 kg	130	30	90
6 mo	8 kg	130	30	90
1 yr	10 kg	120	26	90
2 yrs	12 kg	115	26	90
3 yrs	15 kg	110	24	90
4 yrs	17 kg	100	24	90
6 yrs	20 kg	100	20	95
8 yrs	25 kg	90	20	95
10 yrs	35 kg	85	20	100
12 yrs	40 kg	85	20	100
14 yrs	50 kg	80	18	110
Adult	> 50 kg	80	18	120

TRAUMA PATIENTS

Firefighters most commonly see trauma patients who have been involved in motor vehicle crashes. A motor vehicle crash can include multiple injuries, including head and spinal injuries as well as injuries to the extremities and eyes.

For possible multiple injuries on a trauma patient that may occur as a result of a vehicle crash or long fall, injuries to the head, neck, and spine should always be suspected. To prevent further injury, immobilization of the head, neck, and spine is of the utmost importance. Improperly treating a patient with a neck or spinal injury can lead to more severe injuries and possible permanent paralysis.

Cervical collars are generally used to limit a patient from moving his or her head after an injury. Prior to the placement of the cervical collar, the head is kept from moving by holding the head with both hands, using only enough pressure to keep the head still. If the patient is lying down on his or her back, position yourself above the head or in the backseat of a vehicle if the patient is being extricated from the front seat of a vehicle. Hold the head still, as shown in figure 26–3, until the appropriate immobilization device is completely applied. Continue manual stabilization of the head after the cervical collar is in place, while other providers assist in further immobiliza-

tion by placing the patient on a backboard to immobilize the spine. ABC should be assessed and reassessed periodically. Talking to the patient and providing reassurance can help to keep the patient calm.

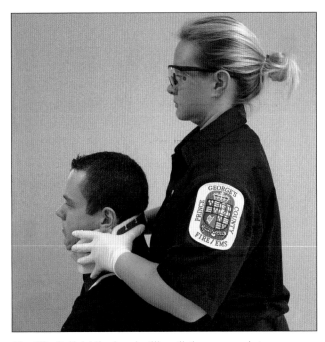

Fig. 26–3. Hold the head still until the appropriate immobilization device is completely applied.

Burns are also classified as trauma injuries. The first goal of treatment for burn injuries is to stop the burning. This is often done with copious amounts of water. The second goal is to protect the burned area from further injury and reduce pain by covering the area with a sterile dressing. According to the 2008 Maryland Medical Protocols for EMS Providers, moist dressings using a sterile solution are allowable for burns covering less than 9% of the body surface area. Do not place ice or ice packs on any patient with burns covering more than 5% of the total body surface area. Providers should become familiar with estimating the percentage of burned area and know their local protocols for treatment, which are usually based on the total body surface area burned (see fig. 26–4, a diagram for a body surface area rule of nines).

When treating a patient with multiple injuries, it is important to consider the injuries that are most life threatening and treat those first. The ABCs of patient care should be among the first considerations, followed by spinal immobilization and then the splinting of arms and legs that may show signs of a fracture.

EMS in the Fire Service

FIREFIGHTER I

Chapter 26

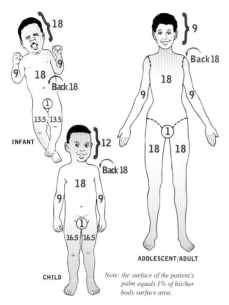

Fig. 26—4. The rule of nines

Fractures, dislocations, and sprains

It can be difficult for a field provider to distinguish the difference between a fracture, sprain, or dislocation. Without the benefit of an X-ray, even physicians may not be able to distinguish them. Regardless of the type of injury, the treatment is generally the same: They require splinting and immobilization. When examining an injured area, the provider should look for deformity, swelling, and bruising. It is possible to find a wound that suggests an **open fracture**, which is when a bone is broken and there is a wound through the skin in the same area as the break. The bone may be visible through the open surface of the skin. In this case take care to prevent contamination. In addition to splinting, the open area must be bandaged.

If the patient complains of pain when moving a possible fracture sight, do not attempt motion, unless it is necessary to prevent further injury to the patient. Prior to putting on a splint, check the extremity for a pulse to ensure that the fracture has not stopped the blood flow to the rest of the limb. Lack of blood flow between the injury site and the end of the limb may cause or be an indication of possible nerve damage. The patient should be transported to an appropriate medical facility without delay. Blood flow can be checked, as mentioned, by checking the pulse or by checking for capillary refill. It may be necessary to remove shoes, socks, and gloves to check appropriate blood flow. Capillary refill can be checked by gently pressing down on the fingernail or toe of the injured limb until the skin turns white. After

releasing the pressure, the nail bed should turn pink within 2 seconds, indicating that there is normal circulation. If it takes longer than 2 seconds, it may indicate a problem with circulation. Capillary refill should be checked before and after splinting. It should be noted that capillary refill is generally delayed in cold weather. In extremely cold weather, capillary refill may be an unreliable means of checking blood flow.

In addition to checking for a pulse or capillary refill, the provider should check the end of the limb for sensation and movement. Using the dull part of a pen or the eraser end of a pencil, gently rub the bottom of the foot or palm of the patient's hand, checking to see if the patient can feel it. Movement in the fingers and toes is a good indication that he or she has proper blood flow. As mentioned, if movement of the fingers and toes causes pain, it should be minimized.

Splinting can be done in a variety of ways, generally using commercially available splints secured with gauze. Splinting of long bones like arms and legs that don't involve joints can be a relatively simple task. Splinting shoulders, elbows, knees, and ankles can be complex and require more finesse, whereas pelvic and hip fractures as well as femur fractures (the long bone in the thigh) can be life-threatening injuries. A femur fracture, for example, can cause the large muscles (quadriceps and hamstring) to constrict, causing the two bone ends to draw inward. This type of fracture requires providers to put traction on the injury site and use specialized traction splinting to prevent further injury. Improper splinting, either too tight or too loose, can cause more damage. Therefore, providers should receive appropriate training in splinting before trying it. Unless you have been properly trained in splinting, simply make the patient as comfortable as possible and wait for the appropriate level of care to arrive.

MEDICAL EMERGENCIES

Medical emergencies can be caused by a variety of sicknesses and medical conditions. Providers are not trained to determine causes or diagnose medical conditions. That is why the main focus is to treat the symptoms displayed by the patient. After checking the ABCs of a patient and conducting an initial assessment, firefighters should attempt to determine the medical history of the patient. The SAMPLE format is the most common method of obtaining pertinent history from a patient, family member, or friend. **Signs and symptoms** reported by the patient are the first piece of information needed. Next, ask about any **allergies** to medications or foods. Obtain a complete list of medications the patient is presently taking. Gathering pill bottles or a current written list from the patient or family can expedite obtaining this information. Past medical history should be acquired. Important questions to ask include whether the patient has previously been hospitalized and, if so, for what conditions. Determine if the patient has a history of diabetes, seizures, high blood pressure, stroke, heart problems, or breathing difficulties like asthma or lung disease. Ask when the **last meal** the patient ate was and how much food he or she consumed. Finally, inquire about the *events* leading up to the current problem. Any information found during the assessment should be recorded and communicated to the incoming EMS units.

Seizures are among the more common medical emergencies to which the fire service responds. In addition to attempting to obtain as much information as possible about the patient, check the ABCs and wait for EMS personnel. For patients who are actively seizing, prevent them from further injury; do not attempt to restrain seizing patients, and never put anything in their mouths. Protect their heads from hitting hard surfaces, and move them to a safer location if possible. Often, when patients stop seizing, they are sleepy, confused, and may be hostile. Continue to monitor the ABCs until the transport unit arrives. If patients are unconscious or unable to stay awake, they should be placed in a side lying or **recovery position**.

Another common medical emergency is for a patient who is suffering from chest pains. A variety of things can cause chest pains, such as heart attack, heart failure, and angina pectoris. Regardless of the specific condition, the pains are generally caused by a lack of oxygen to the heart. If personnel have been trained in oxygen therapy, oxygen can be applied as soon as practical. Until more advanced care arrives, place the patient in a position he or she finds most comfortable, reassuring him or her as much as possible by talking to and learning more about the patient's medical condition, medications he or she takes, and any other medical history that can be obtained. Never give a patient anything by mouth. If the patient asks for assistance with taking medication, the provider is usually permitted to assist but is not allowed to administer medications. This means that the provider may be able to provide a drink of water, but putting a pill in a patient's mouth is beyond the scope of a provider's training.

Generally, the same steps can be taken for most medical emergencies. Always check the ABCs, obtain as much

medical history as possible, check for any medical alerts (fig. 26–5), and make the patient as comfortable as possible until EMS personnel arrive on the scene.

Fig. 26–5. A medical alert bracelet

Heat exhaustion and heat stroke

Heat exhaustion can result when the body loses water as a result of heavy sweating. After a prolonged condition of heat exhaustion, heat stroke sets in. **Heat stroke** is caused when the body's ability to release heat is overcome. Even when properly treated, heat stroke is often fatal. Patients who are suffering from heat exhaustion feel light-headed, dizzy, and/or nauseated. A heat stroke patient has flushed dry skin (because they have lost the ability to sweat), may be semiconscious or unconscious, and have a high temperature. These patients should be moved to a cool location. Encourage the patient to drink fluids unless they are vomiting. Heat stroke patients should be cooled immediately. This can best be accomplished by stripping them down to their underclothes and soaking them with water. There should be no delay in transporting a heat stroke patient to an appropriate medical facility.

Frostbite

Frostbite occurs when uncovered parts of the body are exposed to extremely cold temperatures. Frostbitten skin can look white or waxy and may be firm or frozen. Swollen and blistered skin may be possible as well. Never rub or massage a frostbitten area. Patients should be removed from the cold and protected from further injury. Rewarming is best done in a medical facility where there are controlled conditions and should not be attempted in the field unless transport is excessively delayed. Avoid using heating devices or stoves. Patients cannot feel the frostbitten area, and it may cause more damage by burning the area. Initially, frostbite can be treated by using body heat (i.e., putting frostbitten fingers under the arm). Jewelry should be removed; and if the patient is wearing wet clothes, they should be removed if possible.

BLEEDING

After determining the ABCs of a patient and conducting an initial assessment, it is important to stop and address any major blood loss of a patient. There are three main methods of controlling the loss of blood: direct pressure, elevation, and pressure points.

Direct pressure consists of placing a dry and sterile dressing on the injury site and applying pressure. To maintain the direct pressure, wrap the wound with gauze; it should be tight enough to ensure that pressure is maintained but not so tight it cuts of the circulation to the area beyond the injury. Elevation involves raising a wounded leg or arm above the level of the heart while maintaining direct pressure. Elevation is done in addition to direct pressure, if that alone fails to stop the bleeding. If bleeding persists and the bandaging becomes blood soaked, additional bandaging should be applied.

If the direct pressure and elevation fail to control the bleeding, the provider may need to apply pressure directly to the appropriate artery to restrict the blood flow, like a hose clamp restricts water flow on a fire hose. Figure 26–6 shows the two main pressure point areas affecting the arm and the leg. Bleeding that continues despite these attempts may require application of a tourniquet, so follow local protocols. Whenever there are open wounds to a patient—whether they are caused by an **open fracture**, an abrasion, puncture, laceration, or avulsion—it is always the goal to control the bleeding; prevent further contamination by wearing appropriate PPE; use sterile dressings; immobilize the affected area; and when dealing with an impaled object, stabilize the object to prevent further injury and discomfort (fig. 26–7).

Presume that all body fluids and substances are infectious. Therefore, standard precautions should be taken when encountering body fluids and substances.

Brachial Artery

Radial Artery

Femoral Artery

Popliteal Artery (back of knee)

Fig. 26–6. The two main pressure point areas affecting the arm and the leg

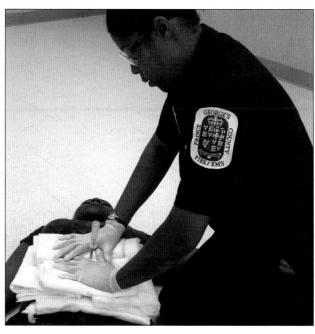

Fig. 26–7. When dealing with an impaled object, stabilize the object to prevent further injury and discomfort.

CHILDBIRTH

Commonly, the fire department is among the first to assist a mother in labor. Most events are not emergencies, but they may require some initial assistance to prevent a mother or child from becoming injured during labor. Actions should be taken until the arrival of personnel with greater training; transport of the mother should not be delayed.

The area where a baby develops in a mother's womb is called the uterus. The baby in the womb receives nutrients from the mother through the umbilical cord attached to the placenta. Attached to the wall of the mother's uterus and the baby inside the womb, the placenta is enveloped in a sac called the amniotic sac and is filled with amniotic fluid. There are three main stages of labor. Stage one is when the mother begins to sense initial contractions, indicated by typical labor pains. The provider should note the time and duration of the labor pain. When contractions begin to come approximately 1–2 minutes apart, and last for more than 1 minute each, the provider and mother should prepare for the baby's birth.

Sometimes the mother may announce that her "water has broken" meaning that the amniotic sac has released the amniotic fluid. This is nothing to cause alarm. The provider should check the mother's vaginal area and determine if the baby is **crowning**, which is when a part of the baby emerges from the vaginal opening (fig. 26–8). It should be noted that the average time of a mother having a first baby is more than 15 hours. Therefore, the provider should determine how long the mother has been having contractions, if this is her first baby, or if she has had multiple births. Labor and delivery times can be significantly shorter for a mother who has had multiple births.

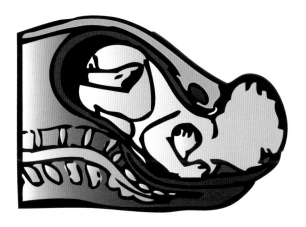

Fig. 26–8. A crowning baby

The provider should use a sterile sheet to drape the mother and prepare to wrap the baby on arrival. Keep the area clear of unnecessary bystanders and unneeded providers. Allow the mother to get comfortable, laying on her back; raise the buttocks, if possible, with her knees drawn up and spread apart. Make sure the mother is as comfortable as possible and ensure the vaginal area is clear of any obstructions, including clothing. Baby delivery is a natural process that can often be done with little assistance. The main role of a provider is to prevent injury and assist in the case of a complicated delivery, which would require immediate transport to an appropriate facility.

As the baby begins to emerge, place one gloved hand below the baby's head to provide support; avoid placing pressure on the baby's head and spread the fingers to avoid pressing down on the soft spots (known as fontanelles). If the amniotic sac has not broken, the provider can puncture the membrane around the baby's head and pull it away from the mouth and nose. Allow the baby to continue to come out naturally, never pulling the baby. When the head emerges, ensure that the umbilical cord is not wrapped around the baby's neck; if it is, gently unwrap the cord from the neck using two fingers to bring the cord forward and over the baby's upper body. After the shoulders and feet emerge, continue to support the baby and check the baby's airway.

Once the baby is completely delivered, place the baby on his or her side with its head slightly lower than its body. Check on the exact time of birth. Once the infant begins to breathe, tie the umbilical cord halfway between the baby and mother to stop blood flow through the cord. Although it is preferable to use a sterile umbilical tie or commercial clamp, a shoelace will suffice in an emergency. Assure that the tie is sufficiently tight to stop blood flow through the cord. Initially, only one tie is needed. Cutting the cord can await the arrival of providers with additional training.

Shortly after the baby is delivered, the placenta emerges from the mother's vaginal area; the placenta should be kept intact and wrapped in a plastic bag if possible. Keep the baby warm and dry and the mother as comfortable as possible.

If any complications arise during childbirth, the mother and baby should be transported to the closest appropriate medical facility. Complications could include significant bleeding, unusual presentations such as a foot or arm instead of the head, or appearance of the umbilical cord in the vaginal opening prior to seeing the baby's head.

TRANSFER OF PATIENT CARE

As a firefighter on an EMS call, one of your main jobs is to stabilize the patient until the arrival of personnel with a higher level of EMS training. A proper assessment is started when the call is dispatched, and evaluation of the scene and the patient begin on arrival. When the emergency medical technician and/or paramedics arrive on the scene, it may be your responsibility to advise them of pertinent information. Sometimes this is relayed via radio prior to their arrival.

Information about the current condition of the patient can help incoming EMS providers prepare their action plan to assist the patient. It prompts them to consider what equipment they need upon their arrival, particularly if it's different from what the initial dispatch information provided. When they arrive be prepared to give them a brief report of what you saw when you arrived, what actions you took, and any history of the patient you obtained (e.g., the patient advised that he took a nitro tablet, a common medication for heart patients, 5 minutes before you arrived).

Sometimes, the EMS providers request assistance in getting a patient loaded onto the transport unit. Every firefighter should become familiar with their local EMS providers and their equipment, how to take the stretcher out of the ambulance, and how to put it back in with a patient on it. Often a wheeled chair device (i.e., stair chair) is used to bring patients down stairs where a stretcher cannot fit. There are also several devices used to immobilize patients after a motor vehicle crash. The Kendrick Extrication Device (KED®) is commonly used. Providers should be familiar with the type(s) of devices used in their local jurisdictions. If used improperly the specialized equipment used by EMS providers can cause injuries; therefore, it is vital to become familiar with them (fig. 26–9).

Fig. 26–9. A wheeled chair device, or stair chair

Remember, it is not one person's job or one individual crew's responsibility to provide care. As a firefighter on an EMS call, you are part of a system designed to bring the best possible outcome to a person in need. The transition of care is a vital link in the EMS system. Your work is not necessarily over when the EMS crew arrives. Ask them if they have any questions or if they need anything before you leave the scene.

QUESTIONS

1. You are a member of an engine crew that arrives first to a bicyclist who has been hit by an automobile. The rider is lying in the road with an obvious open fracture to his left lower leg. What personal protective equipment will you wear to help your patient, and what universal precautions will you need to consider after the patient has been transported away from the scene?

2. The Health Insurance Portability and Accountability Act (HIPAA) was enacted into law in 1996. Under what three circumstances can you as a firefighter disclose information about your patient to others?

3. Discuss why the ABCs of medical care are three of the most important patient concerns you will have while treating your patient.

4. Discuss the procedures for checking a pulse in a patient. Include the differences for an unconscious versus conscious patient and adult versus small children patients.

5. You are on the first arriving engine to a bleeding call. Upon arrival you find a 29-year-old male sitting on the house porch with a deep bleeding gash in his left arm just above the elbow. Describe your actions in treating this patient.

6. Your engine crew is the first arriving units to an automobile that has run into a telephone pole. The only occupant is the 17-year-old male driver who is still seated in the car. He is conscious and speaking. He has an open fracture below the right knee. Explain how you will direct other crewmembers to provide neck stabilization and how you will splint the open fracture.

7. You are assigned to an engine company fighting a house fire on a hot July day. Upon exiting the house and going to the rehab area your partner states he does not feel well. How would you determine if he is suffering from heat exhaustion or heat stroke?

8. You are conducting your morning truck checks in the station when a car screeches to a stop at the station door the women driver gets out of the car asking for help. She explains to you that she is nine months pregnant, her water has broken, and her contractions are less than a minute apart. She was trying to make it to the hospital but the pain was too great. Discuss your actions to help this patient including actions to help birth the baby.

9. Upon arriving at the scene of a supposedly unconscious victim you realize the patient has in fact been shot. He is still alive. Describe your concerns from a safety standpoint and from an evidence preservation standpoint.

10. You are the first arriving unit to an altered level of consciousness call. Upon arrival you find a 50-year-old woman talking nonsense and is weak. She is surrounded by several family members who state this is not her normal behavior. What are some of the questions you will ask the family, and what are some of the things you are looking for to determine the patients needed treatment?

FIREFIGHTER

Incident Command System

Edited by Alan Brunacini, Forest Reeder, and Tim Flannery

This chapter provides required knowledge items for the following
NFPA Standard 1001 Job Performance Requirements:

FFII 6.1.1

OBJECTIVES

Upon completion of this chapter, you should be able to do the following:

- Identify the types of command systems
- Identify the five types of incidents developed by the National Incident Management System (NIMS)
- Describe the three organizational levels of command.
- Identify the command and general staff positions within the Incident Command System (ICS)
- Identify incident tactical priorities
- Describe how command is assumed and transferred
- List and describe the three command options
- Identify the ICS functions used at an incident
- Identify types of incident facilities
- Describe the purpose of a staging area
- Demonstrate the ability to function within an assigned role in ICS
- Demonstrate the ability to organize and coordinate ICS until command is transferred

INTRODUCTION

The simple truth is that a strong and functioning **Incident Command System (ICS)** will save firefighter lives. As in the military, organized command and control functions are essential to the success of every operation. Responder safety is always the first consideration, and the use of ICS is key to achieving this goal. In common with all systems or functions, the ultimate reason to use a command system is to provide for the safety of the emergency workers in the hazard zone.

From a single-company operation to a multilevel conflagration or mass casualty incident, a single person must be in charge. This person is identified as the **incident commander (IC)** and is responsible for establishing a set of predetermined outcomes and an overall plan of action to accomplish those goals. This is the guiding principle of incident command.

In this chapter you learn how an ICS functions and why the NIMS was created to provide a standardized-while-flexible ICS framework for emergency incidents across the United States. Standardization is crucial, but flexibility must exist to accommodate a vast array of incident types and levels as well as a broad spectrum of organizational types and makeups.

NIMS

After the 9/11 attacks, the federal government and local emergency response units discovered a disconnect when it came to adequate response to large-scale natural disaster or weapon of mass destruction (WMD) events. President George W. Bush issued **Homeland Security Presidential Directive 5 (HSPD-5)** in early 2003. The HSPD-5 directed the federal government and state and local agencies to work under a National Incident Management System, to be developed and administered by the Department of Homeland Security.

The purpose of NIMS is to create a framework for federal, state, and local agencies to work together effectively as may be required by the size of an incident. NIMS is now the national standard used throughout all 50 states, structured to manage situations of all sizes from large-scale national events down to small local incidents.

The NIMS is based on the principles of *standardization* and *flexibility*. These two components are required to create a scalable system that can be implemented for any incident from a small local fire to a large-scale natural disaster or man-made event.

By standardizing terminology and incident command structure and concepts, NIMS creates operational efficiency and unification among agencies when brought together for an emergency event. At the same time, by using incident command components that can be added, subtracted, or customized to a specific region or event type, NIMS maintains the flexibility to be applied to any incident response situation.

The principle of unified command

Unified command is the structure in which multiple individuals are cooperatively responsible for all strategic objectives of the incident. It is typically used when an incident is within multiple jurisdictions or managed by multiple disciplines.

For instance, a local fire event might require not only firefighters, but EMS and police responders for medical services and area control. Such an event would require a unified command structure in which representatives from each emergency service branch work together as a command team to implement a multi-branch response.

Common NIMS terminology

Some of the most common concepts and terms used in the NIMS framework include the following:

Unity of command. All persons in the operation have a designated supervisor to whom they report at the scene of the incident.

Span of control. The number of personnel one supervisor can effectively manage. The range is two to seven, with five being the optimal number.

Modular organization. An organizational structure where command components are used as needed and expandable according to complexity and size of the incident.

Freelancing. Uncommanded action, or operating outside of the established fire attack plan, operational guidelines, or operating protocols.

Resource management. A process to identify, acquire, mobilize, track, recover and demobilize, reimburse, and inventory necessary resources.

Incident categories

NIMS categorizes incidents as Type 1 through Type 5 (fig. 27–1).

HISTORY OF ICS

Incident Command Systems are nothing new to the fire service. Several variations of ICS have existed since the 1970s, but their importance cannot be underestimated because prior to this period, emergency event management and command structure differed from department to department, and sometimes even between chiefs in the same department. It was during the California wildfires of 1970 that the need for a standardized command structure, communication, and coordination became apparent. All of the following systems are varieties of an ICS.

FIRESCOPE

In 1972, the California-based command consortium **FIRESCOPE** (**FI**refighting **RES**ources of **C**alifornia **O**rganized for **P**otential **E**mergencies) was developed to manage firefighting efforts for large-scale wildfires that frequently plague the West coast. It was also later used to manage other large-scale disasters, including forest fires, floods, earthquakes, civil unrest, and so on. This system coordinates massive amounts of necessary resources during incidents that can last from weeks to months, require thousands of incident responders, and generally include federal and state resources.

Due to the effectiveness of the FIRESCOPE ICS, it was revised and adopted on a national level in 1982 to become the **Incident Command System/National Interagency Incident Management System (ICS/NIIMS)**.

Fire Ground Command

Also during the 1970s, a similar command system known as **Fire Ground Command (FGC)** was developed by Chief Alan Brunacini during his service with the Phoenix Fire Department. The FGC was a drastically scaled-down version of ICS used for the typical, fast-moving, high-hazard incidents that make up 99% of American fire service responses. These include fires in houses, apartments, and warehouses, as well as calls involving hazmat, multiple-victim motor vehicle accidents, and so on. FGC was similar to FIRESCOPE in application but used a slightly different organizational structure and terminology.

Incident Management System

Even with the development of FIRESCOPE, FGC, and NIIMS, the need was still apparent for a more common approach to incident command. This led to the 1990 creation of the National Fire Service Incident Management System (IMS) Consortium. The IMS Consortium was made up of fire service leaders and organizations across the nation, as well as FIRESCOPE, the National Fire Academy (NFA), Federal Emergency Management Agency (FEMA), and Phoenix Fire Department's FGC. The Consortium agreed to develop common protocols, pulling from aspects of both ICS and FGC, so it could be applied effectively from department to department in all regions of the United States. The new set of protocols was approved in 1993, and the new system was officially titled Incident Management System (IMS).

The IMS is used to apply local fire department resources to bring under control and mitigate local emergency events. The typical operational period for these incidents can last from 10 minutes to several days. Major objectives of an IMS are hazard zone management and protection of hazard zone workers.

In many areas, the terms *IMS* and *ICS* are used interchangeably to mean a local incident command structure with one individual in charge of the major decisions relating to the incident. Responders must remain current with locally and regionally accepted ICS practices.

Incident Command System

FIREFIGHTER II

Chapter 27

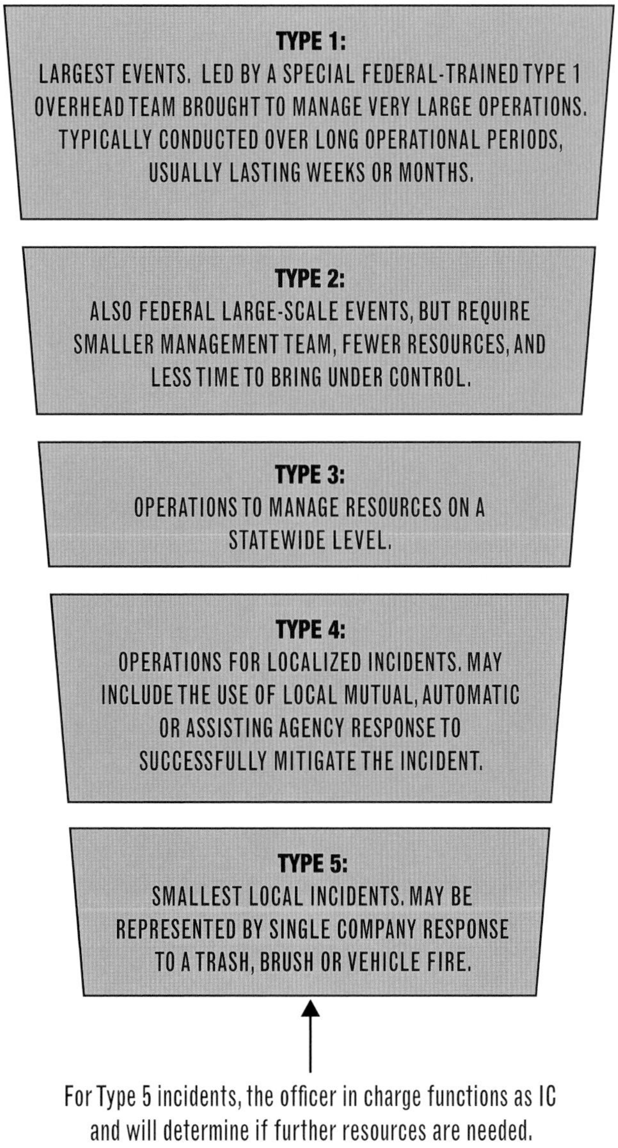

TYPE 1:
LARGEST EVENTS. LED BY A SPECIAL FEDERAL-TRAINED TYPE 1 OVERHEAD TEAM BROUGHT TO MANAGE VERY LARGE OPERATIONS. TYPICALLY CONDUCTED OVER LONG OPERATIONAL PERIODS, USUALLY LASTING WEEKS OR MONTHS.

TYPE 2:
ALSO FEDERAL LARGE-SCALE EVENTS, BUT REQUIRE SMALLER MANAGEMENT TEAM, FEWER RESOURCES, AND LESS TIME TO BRING UNDER CONTROL.

TYPE 3:
OPERATIONS TO MANAGE RESOURCES ON A STATEWIDE LEVEL.

TYPE 4:
OPERATIONS FOR LOCALIZED INCIDENTS. MAY INCLUDE THE USE OF LOCAL MUTUAL, AUTOMATIC OR ASSISTING AGENCY RESPONSE TO SUCCESSFULLY MITIGATE THE INCIDENT.

TYPE 5:
SMALLEST LOCAL INCIDENTS. MAY BE REPRESENTED BY SINGLE COMPANY RESPONSE TO A TRASH, BRUSH OR VEHICLE FIRE.

For Type 5 incidents, the officer in charge functions as IC and will determine if further resources are needed.

Fig. 27–1. NIMS event categories

Type 4 and Type 5 incidents represent more than 99% of all fire department incident activity. Each incident type may evolve into a higher, more complicated type. A Type 5 report of a car fire may turn out to be located inside the parking garage of an apartment building, requiring upgrading to a Type 4 response, bringing additional resources. In the same vein, a single localized Type 4 wildfire could grow to become a Type 3 statewide management incident.

Most U.S. fire departments use this type of system for the everyday management of their resources working in hazard zones. You will not typically hear of an incident being labeled as a particular type or classification; these labels are provided to illustrate the complexity of the incident and the resource management needed for it.

The ICS

The most familiar NIMS component for all incident types is the ICS, which is the basic management and command structure applied to all incident types. A Type 4 house fire will use ICS through the local incident commander and response team. A Type 1 multiagency overhead team uses ICS to manage the goals and objectives of the overall incident. At the same time, hazard-zone workers protect themselves using ICS while using the NIMS ICS structure to report back up into the Type 1 or 2 team chain of command.

The major goals of a local ICS are to ensure initial and ongoing firefighter safety at incident sites and to coordinate all command and operational action to bring incident hazards under control. **Resource management** of crews, apparatus, and other equipment needed to mitigate the problem can be achieved through the use of ICS.

The command system creates an organizational agreement among all incident responders that the incident commander is the overall site manager and that everyone on the scene will play their assigned roles in the IC's plan, reporting up to the IC through their designated supervisors (**unity of command**).

Command procedures give the IC responsibility for overall incident results along with the organizational authority to put responders to work with the same set of tactical objectives. For this basic incident management plan to be effective, responders must follow a set of command procedures that are agreed upon, written (in SOP form), and practiced prior to the event. This is particularly crucial in the typically fast-moving, dangerous incident conditions. *The ICS must be applied to every incident.* Saving the command system for "the big one" is just another way of saying that your department doesn't use, practice, or have an actual ICS. The ongoing everyday/every-event use of the system makes it a regular, habitual way to manage all emergency responses.

The dangers of uncommanded action. Some of the most serious, unsafe conditions on the fireground are those with **no command** or **multiple commands**. Without a strong, central IC from the beginning of emergency operations, the typical incident scene quickly deteriorates into an unsafe, out-of-control situation. These no-command beginnings often lead to uncoordinated action, commonly known as **freelancing.** Freelancing may eliminate the incident hazard on small incidents, but repetitively practicing uncommanded mistakes creates dangerous habits that can lead to serious injury or death on large, unusual, or time-consuming incidents. When an incident begins with uncommanded, fragmented freelancing, and the team grows as the incident progresses, it becomes impossible for all participants to safely support and coordinate actions to control the incident.

Uncommanded action causes duplicate searches of one area while exposed areas go without primary searches. Attack lines tend to congregate in the same location and leave concealed spaces and exposures uncovered. Salvage occurs after savable property has been unnecessarily damaged by later-arriving freelancers.

The most effective way to avoid these situations, provide firefighter safety, and stabilize an incident is to have a well-trained IC in place from the beginning of operations on *all* events. A strong IC with an operational team that understands and follows basic incident management procedures consistently outperforms a larger force of freelancing firefighters. Habits developed on day-to-day incident operations are the foundation for performance on bigger, longer, and more hazardous operations.

Organizational levels. There are three organizational levels for all incident operations (fig. 27–2):

Strategic level: The IC is responsible for managing the strategic level of the incident organization. The IC sets the overall incident strategy, develops and manages the **incident action plan (IAP)**, and assigns and controls the position and function of all incident resources.

Tactical level: Individual companies perform task-level work. When multiple companies operate at an incident scene, their coordinated tasks combine to make up the tactics. A classic tactical example is a ladder company performing vertical ventilation on a roof so engine companies can safely operate on the interior of a structure.

Task level: The task level is performed by firefighters and is where the work actually gets done. Engine companies stretch and operate hoselines while ladder and truck companies perform support work. These combined efforts complete the tactical priorities of rescue, fire control, and property conservation for the incident (for structural firefighting).

As an incident is managed, it is usually necessary to subdivide or organize the companies working into a more manageable **span of control**, usually no more than five to seven companies. When multiple units are assigned to the same geographic area of the incident scene (side A, the north side of the building, etc.), their actions should be coordinated, managed, and supervised by a tactical-level officer. Designations for these tactical-level company or command officers are sector, division, and group supervisors. In the ICS, divisions represent geographic locations where resources are assigned, whereas groups representing resources fulfilling specific functions don't have to be tied to specific geographical areas. An example is a refueling group that drives around in an ICS sector designation and refuels all of the division's apparatus.

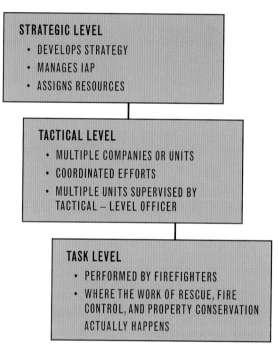

Fig. 27–2. The three organizational levels for all incident operations

Command staff positions

FFII 6.1.1 The command staff answers directly to the IC and provides him or her with essential information and assistance to operate on a strategic level. The IC activates these positions based on the needs of the incident. Only if determined necessary are these positions activated. The people filling these positions are called safety, information, and liaison officers (fig. 27–3).

Fig. 27–3. Command staff positions

Safety officer. The **safety officer (SO)** is responsible for keeping the IC advised on all operational safety matters relating to an incident. Although the ultimate responsibility of safety lies with the IC, the safety officer carries out necessary procedures to provide for a safe incident scene. He or she also has the emergency authority to stop and prevent unsafe acts during incident operations. Under OSHA regulation 1910.120, a safety officer is required by law at incidents involving hazardous materials. In addition, NFPA 1500 Standard for Occupational Safety and Health Program, NFPA 1521 Standard for Fire Department Safety Officer, and NFPA 1561 Standard on Emergency Services Incident Management System also require the designation of a safety officer at emergency incidents. If one is not directly appointed, the IC is responsible for all of the functions normally assigned to the SO, which can overwhelm an IC with decisions and information-gathering responsibility.

Information officer. The **information officer (IO)**, also called the **public information officer (PIO)**, is responsible for dealing with the news media and general public. He or she provides the media and public with accurate, complete information about an incident's cause, size, and current situation; resources committed; and other matters of general interest. There is only one PIO per incident, but he or she may have assistants. The IC must approve any information released by the PIO. Not all incidents require a PIO. Reasons for an IC to designate a PIO include working on a highly visible or sensitive incident, media demands interfering with the IC's ability to run the incident, and limiting the possibility of conflicting reports.

Liaison officer. The **liaison officer (LO)** is responsible for coordinating with any outside agencies that respond to an incident. These may be federal, state, or local government agencies; utility companies; and private organizations such as the American Red Cross. This position is established when the number of responding agencies begins to overwhelm the IC.

General staff positions

Typically, four general staff positions can be filled at an incident.

- Operations section
- Planning section
- Logistics section
- Finance/administration section

Sometimes a fifth section for intelligence or investigations may be filled, depending on incident type and scope.

General staff functions are more incident-specific. In other words, a mass-casualty incident may differ from a hazardous-materials incident. The incident drives this part of the command system. Certain functions that apply to a mass-casualty incident do not apply to a hazardous-material incident. Not all functional sections applicable to the general staff may be needed at an incident. The IC may need assistance with logistics, so a logistics section is established, but the IC may still handle the tactical aspects of the incident, making an operations section unnecessary. As the incident expands and the IC realizes that he or she is unable to effectively handle other functions, the IC hands those functions to general staff managers. Anyone assigned to run the operations, planning, logistics, or finance/administration section is called "chief," regardless of his or her official title within an organization (fig. 27–4).

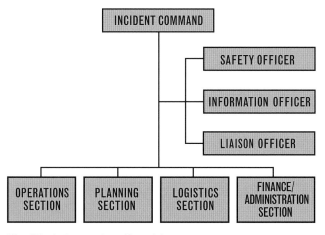

Fig. 27–4. General staff positions

Operations section. The **operations section** is responsible for all tactical operations relating to an incident. Operations at an incident can be set up depending on the following:

- Kind of incident

- Agencies involved

- Objectives and strategy

When the IC determines that he or she can no longer coordinate the strategic and tactical level of an incident, the IC designates an operations section consisting initially of those few resources first assigned to an incident. As additional resources are committed and the incident becomes more complex, a separate operations section may be established. The operations section expands or contracts based on the existing and projected needs of the incident.

The operations section develops from the bottom up by first establishing divisions, groups, and, if necessary, branches. Also, the operations section may have staging areas and, in some cases, an air organization.

The subordinate units of **divisions, groups, branches**, and **resources** within the operations section can be activated based on the needs of the incident (fig. 27–5).

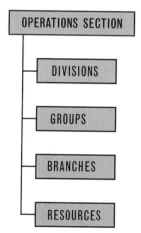

Fig. 27–5. General staff also report directly to incident command, as do command staff.

Divisions. A common method of organizing tactical operations at an incident is for the IC to first establish two or more divisions. Divisions always refer to geographically defined operational areas such as the area around a building, the inside or floors of a building, or an open area.

When defining an incident by division, there is a certain amount of latitude. An incident can be divided using compass points, such as east division, west division, and so on. It can be divided using letter-specific areas, such as side A, side B, side C, and side D. When using this format, the front of a structure indicated by street

address is always side A. The other sides are determined in a clockwise pattern around the structure.

An incident may also be divided by floors of a building, such as floor 1, division 1; floor 2, division 2; and so on (fig. 27–6). Initially, establishing divisions may be done to define the incident and may or may not include the designation of separate division supervisors. When the resources assigned within a division exceed, or will soon exceed, the recommended span of control guidelines of one to five, division supervisors should be designated. Division supervisors manage divisions not under the direct management of the IC or operations section chief.

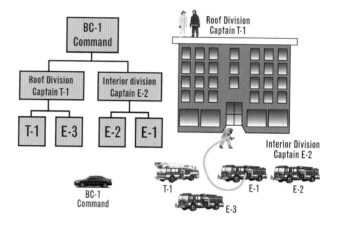

Fig. 27–6. Example of using divisions

Groups. Another common method of organizing operations at an incident is to establish functional **groups**. As the name implies, this form of organization deals not with geographic areas, but with functional activity. Examples of functional groups include fire attack groups, vent groups, search groups, evacuation groups, and so on. Groups, similar to divisions, are managed by supervisors.

A simple way to create groups at an incident is to look at the basic strategies to be used and then create a group to fill those strategies. For example, if the strategies are to search the building, vent the building, and control and extinguish the fire, then the groups become search group, vent group, and fire attack group (fig. 27–7).

Note: Divisions and groups are common designations used on the fireground. Within the command system, they fall between branches and task force/strike team. They are equal in authority, and each is overseen by a person with the title of supervisor. When divisions and groups are utilized at the same incident, the division and group supervisors must coordinate actions together.

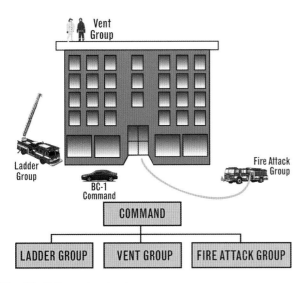

Fig. 27–7. Example of using groups

Branches. As a small incident escalates into a major incident, the span of control may become stretched as more divisions or groups are implemented. In addition, the IC can be quickly overwhelmed with various functions of command. The immediate need of the IC is support. **Branches** may be added to facilitate more effective incident management (fig. 27–8). The person in charge is called the **branch director**. Branches can be geographical or functional, similar to divisions and groups. Reasons to create a branch include the following:

- The span of control for the number of divisions/groups in place becomes unwieldy or unmanageable.

- The incident becomes more complex (e.g., multijurisdictional, worsening conditions).

- The incident has two or more distinctly different operations (e.g., fire, medical, hazardous materials).

Resources. Most incidents start small and grow based on type and severity. In these incidents, most of the resource's apparatus and personnel are committed to the operations section. This section almost always builds

from the bottom up. When an incident is small, there are few resources, so there is a small command system. As the incident grows, so does the command system as more resources arrive. There are several ways to organize resources: single resources, task forces/strike teams, divisions/groups, and branches.

- **Single resources.** Single resources are individual apparatus or a crew of firefighters with an identified supervisor that can be used in a tactical application on an incident. A single resource is the most common way of initially using resources on an incident. The person in charge of the single resource is designated by unit title, for example, captain, lieutenant, and so on.

Single resources can be typed to reflect capability. Unless a single resource is typed, its specific resource capabilities may not be clear to everyone. Examples of resources include a single engine company, truck company, rescue company, and so on. Because the operations part of an ICS normally develops from the bottom up (less to more), most of these incidents require only a small amount of resources. The following are some examples:

- Room and contents fire: two-engine and one-truck response

- Vehicle fire: two-engine response

Type 5 incidents can usually be handled by a single resource supervised by an IC. At times, the IC and single resource will be the same: for example, single engine for a dumpster fire, battalion chief called to smell of smoke. In each incident, the command structure looks like the image in figure 27–9.

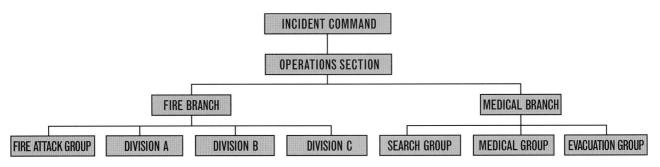

Fig. 27–8. Example organization of operations groups and branches

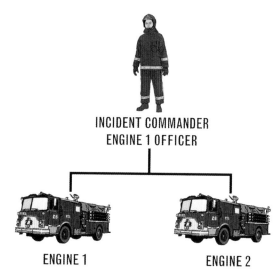

Fig. 27–9. Example of using single resources

- *Multiple resources.* One of the concepts under NIMS/ICS is the use of strike teams and task forces. Although similar in function, they are different. The difference is based on the kind and type. A *kind* of resource is what the resources is. Examples are an engine, truck, ambulance, rescue, and so on. A *type* of resource is a designation based on its size, capability, staffing qualifications, and ability to accomplish a task or function. For example, under engines you can have Type 1, Type 2, or Type 3. A Type 1 is larger and has more capabilities than a Type 2, and so on.

Strike teams are composed of resources of the same kind and type (fig. 27–10). They must have a leader and common communications between resources and the leader, have transportation, and operate within span of control limits. Strike team examples might include:

- Search team of five firefighters
- Ventilation team of three firefighters
- Strike team of four Type 1 engines

Task forces are any combination and number of single resources (within span of control limits) assembled for a particular tactical need (fig. 27–11). Task forces may be a mix of all different kinds of resources (of the same kind but different types, or of several resources of one kind mixed with other resources). Task force examples might include:

- Fire attack task force of four pumpers and two aerial ladders
- Water tender task force of five water tenders

As an incident becomes larger or more complex, the IC has additional options to use task forces, strike teams, divisions, or groups to increase the number of resources and still maintain a manageable span of control. For Type 5 and going into Type 4 incidents, an option for using more resources is to combine them into task forces or strike teams. In either of these, the IC can increase the number of resources substantially and still maintain span of control within acceptable limits. For example, one task force or strike team can have up to five resources. So an IC can have three engines and two trucks in a task force and have three of these task forces under his or her control. In reality, the IC has 15 resources under his or her command but only three subordinates reporting directly to him or her, thus maintaining span of control.

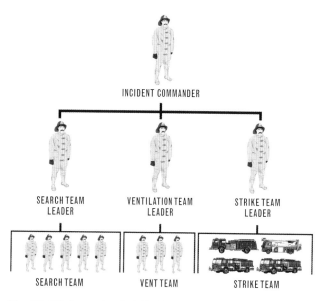

Fig. 27–10. Example of strike team

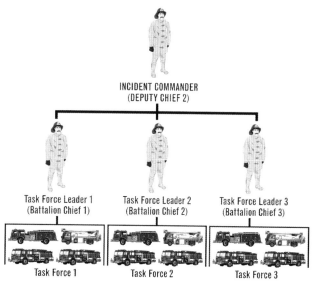

Fig. 27–11. Example of task force

Incident Command System

FIREFIGHTER II

Chapter 27

Planning section. The **planning section** is responsible for collecting and evaluating incident situation information, preparing situation status reports, displaying situation information, maintaining status of resources, developing an incident action plan (IAP), and preparing required incident-related documentation. One of the most important functions of the planning section is to look beyond the current and next operational period and anticipate potential problems or events. The planning section consists of four units: resources, situation, documentation, and demobilization units. The person in charge of these subunits is designated as a "leader" (fig. 27–12).

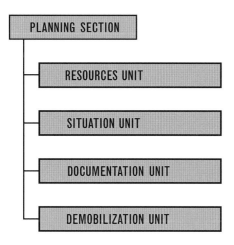

Fig. 27–12. Planning section positions

- **Resources unit.** The resources unit is responsible for checking in and maintaining status on all personnel, apparatus, and equipment assigned to the incident. It is the accountability unit for the incident that assists the IC and operations section in tracking all personnel and apparatus so they can determine where they are, if more are needed, and if certain resources can be released or sent home.

- **Situation unit.** The situation unit collects all current incident information and, based on this, prepares maps, displays, and projections. This assists the IC in determining future strategies and necessary changes.

- **Documentation unit.** The documentation unit is responsible for all documentation related to an incident, including distributing copies of the IAP, objectives, and strategies to all supervisory personnel involved in the incident. This provides responders with the IC's written expectations of them.

- **Demobilization unit.** On large or complex incidents, the demobilization unit works with the IC and operations section to develop a plan to release personnel and apparatus no longer needed at an incident, and it ensures that the incident is adequately staffed to meet the IC's objectives and strategies.

Logistics section. The **logistics section** is responsible for providing services and support to meet all incident needs. Early recognition of the need for a separate logistics function and section can reduce the time and money spent on an incident. There are six units within the logistics section: communications, medical support to responders, food for responders, supply, facilities, and ground support. The person in charge of these subunits is designated as a "leader." The logistics section chief may establish separate units for one or more of the logistics support or service activities (fig. 27–13).

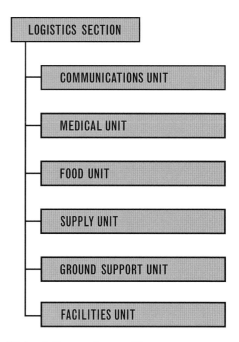

Fig. 27–13. Logistics section positions

Communications unit. This provides on-site communications at large incidents. It also ensures that there are adequate radios and the ability to repair them on scene. The unit is also responsible for developing a communications plan, for example, radio frequencies to be used and their purpose. An example is a mobile communications unit provided by the local, county, or regional emergency management coordinator.

Medical unit. The medical unit's functions include providing medical treatment for incident responders (victims are treated by medical personnel assigned to operations section) and developing an incident medical plan that includes transportation route, available hospitals, and EMS organizations. The unit is also responsible for implementing and maintaining the rehabilitation area at an incident.

Food unit. This unit ensures that incident responders have food and drinking water for a long-term incident. This can be accomplished by local organizations, the Salvation Army, American Red Cross, local canteens, or a ladies' auxiliary. (Note: In April 1995, the Oklahoma Restaurant Association maintained the food unit for the Oklahoma City bombing.)

Supply unit. At large incidents, the supply unit orders personnel, equipment, and supplies. It also stores and maintains supplies, services, and nonexpendable equipment.

Facilities unit. This unit sets up any fixed facilities that may be required for an incident. Typically, this unit is not established except on very large incidents. If a base needs eating and sleeping facilities for incident responders, this is the unit that accomplishes it. NIMS/ICS includes the following types of facilities: **incident command posts**, **staging areas**, **bases**, **camps**, and **helispots**. Other types can be implemented depending on the type of incident. For example, there are specialized facilities for mass-casualty, high-rise fire, and hazardous-materials incidents. A "manager" oversees all of these facilities except the incident command post.

- *Incident command post.* The **incident command post** is where the IC oversees the incident (fig. 27–14). Depending on the type and size of the incident, it may be located in a vehicle, trailer, tent, or building. The command post should be where the IC can view the incident, if possible, but not too close to danger. For large and complex incidents, the command post may be comprised of several structures that form a unified command of multiple agencies or jurisdictions. There may also be structures for command staff and communication centers. Examples of incidents and possible command posts include the following:

  – For a two-engine response to a vehicle fire, the command post would be the officer in charge located near one of the engines.

  – For a two-engine, two-truck response to a dwelling fire, the command post may be the back of the responding chief's vehicle.

  – For a mutual aid response to a hazardous-material incident, the command post may be a mobile trailer provided by emergency management.

Fig. 27–14. Internal view of a mobile incident command post

- *Staging areas.* Staging areas are where any resources to be used for a tactical assignment by the operations section go and remain until needed (fig. 27–15). The staging area is overseen by a "staging area manager." Depending on the size and complexity of an incident, there may be several staging areas. The staging area is normally under the operations section if one has been implemented by the IC. If not, then it reports directly to the IC. How large the staging area should be depends on the size and complexity of the incident. A staging area can range to two or three fire apparatus parked on a side street near the incident to a large fenced area capable of holding 30 or more pieces of apparatus.

Fig. 27–15. Staging area

Staging can be used several ways. Depending on the type, size, and complexity of the incident, two types or levels can be used. These are level 1 staging and level 2 staging. At a small incident or early in an incident, a level 1 staging may be more appropriate. For an incident that is escalating, it might be more prudent to use a level 2 staging. This concept first appeared in Chief Alan Brunacini's *Fireground Command* text.

For level 1 staging, arriving units radio incident command of their arrival and position. Incident command then determines which units are needed at the scene and instructs the rest to stop approximately one block from the scene in the direction of travel and report their unit number and direction. For level 2 staging, all additional responders other than first alarm report to the staging area and manager until requested by command.

- *Bases.* The base is where most of the logistics section and finance/administration functions are coordinated. This includes dispensing of food to responders, medical treatment for responders, and apparatus maintenance and repair. According to NIMS/ICS, there is to be only one base per incident. The person in charge of the base is a **base manager**. In many cases, this base may be located next to or near the incident command post. Most Type 5 and Type 4 incidents do not establish a base, but sometimes they provide logistical functions at a given area. Examples include the following:

  – A fire in a single-family dwelling may have EMS units establish a rehab unit near the scene to monitor responders' vital signs and provide them with fluids and a rest area.

  – A fire in a moderate to large warehouse may have a rehab unit established, the same as at the dwelling fire, and also have an area set up to provide food for responders. Providers may be a local canteen, the ladies' auxiliary of a volunteer fire department, or a local eatery.

  – For a large hazardous materials incident, the functions mentioned earlier are provided, and emergency management provides a communication unit to manage radio traffic. A sleeping area may also be established for responders who go off shift but will be needed the following morning.

- *Camps.* These are a carryover from the influence that forestry has had on the NIMS/ICS. These will not typically be used at Type 5 and 4 incidents. Camps are where resources may be kept to support

incident operations if a base is not accessible to all resources. Multiple camps may be established at an incident. The person in charge of the camp is a **camp manager**. An example is multiple agencies searching a large area for missing children. If the area covers several square miles, it would make sense to handle functions at a base that may be a distance away.

- *Helispots.* These are temporary locations where helicopters can safely land and take off. This is a term used under NIMS/ICS. Another term for it in the fire and EMS service is a **landing zone (LZ)**. This facility is supervised by a helispot manager. Helispots can be used to load or unload personnel, equipment, supplies, water, and so on. Medical helicopters often land at helispots to pick up victims injured at an incident.

Ground support unit. This maintains and refuels any vehicles assigned to the incident. It also provides transportation of personnel to and from the incident, if needed.

Finance/administration section. The **finance/administration section** is responsible for monitoring incident-related costs and administering any necessary procurement contracts. The IC retains responsibility for all finance-related activities until finance/administration units or the section is activated, and on most incidents it is not activated. Four units may be established: time, procurement, compensation/claims, and cost units. The person in charge of these subunits is designated as a leader (fig. 27–16).

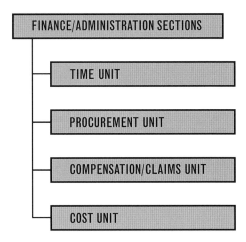

Fig. 27–16. Finance/administration section positions

- *Time unit.* This unit keeps track of personnel arrival and departure times at the incident to help with accountability and aids the resource unit in tracking personnel and apparatus.

- *Procurement unit.* This unit processes rental and purchase paperwork for specialized equipment to be used at an incident. The unit is also responsible for reporting when the equipment arrives, is used, and leaves.

- *Compensation/claims unit.* This unit is responsible for all workers' compensation claims reported at an incident. The unit also files all injury and illness reports associated with the incident.

- *Cost unit.* This unit is responsible for collecting all information relating to the cost of the incident and providing cost-savings recommendations.

COMMAND CONCERNS

Role of the incident commander

Successful incident operations require the application of a simple, straightforward management system that is effective for the incident and user-friendly for the responders. This ICS must start at the beginning of every event and only works when a strong IC performs the standard functions of command. The lack of understanding and application of this effective central-command role adversely affects incident outcomes more than any other incident challenge.

Tactical priorities

The IC must manage incidents around completing the basic tactical priorities present at all incidents. The tactical priorities in their completion order are life safety, incident stabilization, and property conservation. These standard priorities create a framework for the tactical operations required to conduct incident operations. Standard operational priorities create an accustomed order for the task-level work that must be done.

Life safety. The IC's primary responsibility on any incident is to ensure the safety of all members working on the incident scene. An effective ICS also serves double duty as the safety system the IC uses to manage firefighter safety for the strategic level of the incident organization.

The IC's safety routine becomes the foundation of effective incident operations and customer service.

Firefighter safety. The ultimate test for an ICS is whether the IC can always control the position and function of all operating resources. The IC's ability to change firefighter locations and actions is the most powerful strategic-level safety capability. As an example, when the IC determines that the truss roof attic is well-involved in fire and changes the strategy from offensive to defensive, it outperforms any other safety activity or system. The IC announces the strategy change over the tactical radio channel and orders everyone out of and away from the building. After the building is evacuated, the IC gets a roll call, or personnel accountability report (PAR), to ensure all troops are out of harm. Many times the roof collapses within the next several minutes, showing why the IC must always be in control of hazard-zone workers and bosses.

The IC uses the ICS to act out the standard **risk management plan,** which determines the level of risk firefighters can take. The risk management plan is simple and straightforward:

- We will risk our lives *a lot* to protect *savable lives.*

- We will risk our lives *a little* to protect *savable property.*

- We will *not take any risks* for lives and property that are *already lost.*

The risk management plan is the major tool the IC uses to determine the incident strategy based on the critical incident factors. The IC also uses the risk management plan as the basis for keeping the strategy and IAP current throughout the entire incident operation.

Victim safety. After firefighter safety, the life safety priority extends to the search and removal of viable, endangered victims in the hazard zone and the protection of any people exposed to hazardous elements of the incident. For offensive structural firefights, the life-safety priority is achieved by performing a search in the fire occupancy and any exposures threatened by the fire. The IC uses the standard rescue order to prioritize and manage the search:

- Most endangered

- Largest group

- Remainder of fire area or structure

- Exposures

Offensive structural firefighting operations are initiated with companies advancing attack lines to the interior of the burning structure. These initial lines are directly advanced to the most hazardous area of a building—the part on fire. These initial attack crews search the most hazardous area of a structure and attempt to control and eliminate the fire. The life-safety profile improves for firefighters and victims when the fire is extinguished. Putting out the fire greatly reduces everyone's risks and buys time to complete the search in the remainder of the structure. In these situations, early fire control supports search and rescue.

The IC is responsible for assigning all resources so that a quick, effective primary search of affected structures can be managed. The IC assigns companies to search specific areas. This eliminates duplicate searches while other critical areas go unsearched. The IC manages the initial IAP while getting a primary search completed. The primary search happens quickly during the compressed time periods in the beginning stages of the incident operation. After the fire is controlled, operations can slow down. Smoke, heat, and other hazards that can impede the primary search have been eliminated, allowing companies to perform a more thorough secondary search.

Because defensive fire areas can injure and kill fully-protected firefighters, any unprotected person in these areas is considered lost (see the risk management plan). For this reason, searches are not conducted in defensive fire areas and all-clears will not be given. After a fire has been controlled and the fire area deemed safe to enter, crews can search for victims. This is considered a secondary search and recovery, not a search and rescue activity.

Incident stabilization. For structural firefighting, stabilizing the incident problem revolves around controlling and eliminating the fire. The IC manages this tactical priority by getting companies around all seven sides of the fire and overwhelming it with water. The seven sides are the following:

- Interior/inside

- Top, including ceilings, attics, and floors above

- Bottom, including the floor below, crawl spaces, and basements

- All four exterior sides, including adjacent rooms, occupancies, or other buildings and concealed spaces of all those sides (walls, attics, utility chases, void spaces, build overs, etc.)

When the forward progress of the fire is stopped and no other resource is required for fire control, the IC transmits an "under control."

Defensive fire areas have been written off as lost because of fire involvement or some other type of hazard that makes them too dangerous to enter. In these tactical situations, the IC establishes collapse areas, builds an effective incident organization to keep firefighters operating in safe positions, determines cutoff points, gets all-clears in, and protects the exposures. In defensive situations, a fire is declared under control when the main body of fire has been cut off and all savable, exposed property is protected. Defensive fires are typically fought using master stream devices.

Property conservation. After fire control is achieved, all efforts on the incident scene must be directed toward controlling and preventing unnecessary damage to property. Offensive firefighting produces a certain amount of secondary damage. Primary damage results from the fire; secondary damage results from what we do while putting out fire. Ladder/truck companies often must force entry into fire areas, cut holes in roofs to vent smoke and heat from the structure, and open walls and ceilings to check for fire extension. Engine companies stretch attack lines into buildings and operate nozzles. The IC orders and manages these tactics at the correct times, places, and in proper amounts to keep fire from further damaging the structure and its contents.

After a fire is controlled and knocked down, a loss control plan that describes how salvage and overhaul will be performed should be developed. It should include lighting a building's interior to increase safety and reduce damage from firefighters stumbling in the dark. Attention should be given to the customer's personal and irreplaceable possessions, such as pets, pictures, family heirlooms, records, and medications.

All three organizational levels must be constantly aware that our actions are designed to protect savable property. The golden rule of loss control is to treat the customer's property as you would want your family's possessions treated.

Commanding effectively

Assuming command. **FFII 6.1.1** The first unit or member arriving at an incident scene, typically an engine company officer, is responsible for assuming the role of first IC. The standard assumption of command is performed by the first-arriving officer as part of the initial radio report. The initial IC must include the phrase, "I will be assuming [insert street name] command."

The standard initial assumption of command ensures that incident operations begin with a single IC and eliminates multiple, competitive ICs. The IC must assign all later-arriving units' personnel per standard operating procedures (SOPs).

Communications. The IC begins the communication process by transmitting a standard initial radio report. The report includes the following:

- Unit ID

- Arrival to the scene

- Description of the incident problem with action taken

- Declaration of the overall incident strategy

- The assumption of command

An initial radio report for a room and contents fire in an ordinary house would sound something like this:

> "Engine 1 is on the scene. We have a working fire in a medium-sized house. Engine 1 is laying a supply line and attacking the fire with a 1¾-in. attack line. This is an offensive fire. Engine 1 will be assuming Main Street command."

The IC must control communications throughout the incident. The radio is the only tool in the IC's arsenal to stay connected to all incident responders. If the IC gets knocked off the air, incident management goes down the drain.

The assumption of command automatically triggers staging procedures for all responding resources. Staging procedures cause later-arriving units to stop short of the incident scene and announce their staged location. Staging engine companies do not pass their last water source, while staged ladder and truck companies do not pass their last access point to the scene. This places incoming resources where the IC can actually assign them to the incident operation according to the IC's plan. Following staging procedures eliminates freelancing.

Situation evaluation. In most situations, the first-arriving company officer works and operates on all three organizational levels: strategic, tactical, and task. The company officer IC must assume command and perform the functions of command. This includes sizing up the **critical factors** for the incident; developing the incident strategy and IAP; directing and leading the crew to the

right places; and ensuring they take correct, safe, and effective actions (fig. 27–17).

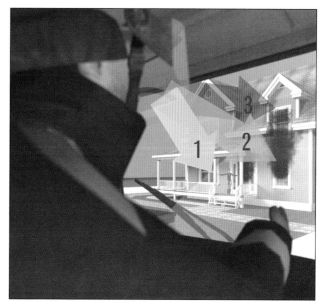

Fig. 27–17. Before employing a strategy, the incident commander must size up the critical incident factors.

Critical factors are a list of different aspects of the incident, along with the incident hazard, that have a major effect on completing tactical priorities. The critical factors also have a major impact on firefighter safety. Critical factors vary from incident to incident. They include:

- The size, age, and condition of a building

- Occupancy type

- Fire size, intensity, extent, and location

Deployment procedures describe the cycle companies follow regarding:

- Responding to the scene of an incident

- How they are assigned to positions around the scene

- How long they can safely operate in the hazard zone

- Methods to cycle companies in and out of the hazard zone (work-rest cycles, on deck, etc.)

Transfer of command. The incident command system is designed so the fast-attacking company officer IC has time to evaluate conditions, then effectively assign the next two or three companies to the most critical areas. The command system is supported and reinforced when the first-arriving response chief assumes command from the initial IC (using SOPs) and inherits an effective, safe, and controlled operation. This upgraded IC then sets up standard command functions.

Command is transferred when a higher-ranking officer arrives on the scene and goes through the SOP transfer-of-command process. Depending on your department's procedures, command may be transferred whether over the radio or face-to-face. Face-to-face transfer is considered the most effective, as it allows the most complete incident communication. Regardless of the method, the officer who assumes command should contact the dispatch center and announce that the specific unit is now in command. For example, "Battalion 2 to alarm. Battalion 2 has transferred command from E-1 and is now Main St. Command."

Incident management is designed and applied to support and manage task-level work. The system is built from the ground up. In many cases, the initial fast-attacking IC will solve the incident problem, eliminating the need to transfer command. Command should be transferred before the current IC becomes overwhelmed. Command is typically transferred from a company officer IC to the first-arriving response chief. For many fire departments, this is the only command transfer during an incident. After a strategically-positioned IC is in charge of the incident, command should be supported and reinforced by assembling a command team.

A key to effective incident management is building the properly sized incident organization and support staff. The command team uses the section positions to delegate functional and support responsibilities. This allows the IC and command team to focus solely on managing resources in the hazard zone (fig. 27–18).

Fig. 27–18. A command team consists of the IC, support officer, and senior advisor.

Termination of command. When command is terminated, the incident priorities have been met and companies are typically released from the incident to either return to service or to quarters for servicing. During this phase, final accountability of crews and resources take place, and the status of both are considered. Documentation of incident actions, injuries, and initial stages of critique processes can also occur. In some instances, termination of command may also include a radio message to dispatch advising of the final status of the incident and if any additional priorities are being handled by remaining companies. In this case, it is important to note that if companies remain, someone will be designated as in charge of the remaining support activities taking place.

Post-incident review

Command procedures also establish the framework for reviewing the effectiveness of incident operations. Before decommitting the working units involved in the incident, the IC should conduct a standard post-incident review. Here is a list of basic post-incident items to discuss:

- What were the most significant critical factors?
- Did the strategy and IAP match the critical factors?
- Were there effective incident communications?
- Were there adequate resources (on-scene, staged, response), and were the deployment procedures followed?
- Did the assignments match the IAP?
- Did the incident organization match the problem and the resources required?
- Was the IAP current throughout the entire incident?

The knowledge, reinforcement of good standard practices, and lessons from these post-incident reviews should be integrated back into the SOPs and training to continually improve performance for all emergency incident operations. Opportunities for organizational improvement and safety analysis also exist at almost every incident. Any accident or injury "near-misses" should be discussed as a chance to increase safety awareness in the organization. A national database exists, and individuals are encouraged to submit their reports through an anonymous system at www.firefighternearmiss.com.

FIREFIGHTER'S ROLE IN THE COMMAND SYSTEM

FFII 6.1.1 Typically, most firefighters work on the task level on the incident scene. An effective IMS protects hazard-zone workers and coordinates task-level work that solves the incident's problems. No command system can outperform the nonperformance of the task level. It is imperative that all hazard-zone workers (companies and firefighters) do the following:

- Follow deployment and safety SOPs

- Be assigned and fit into the IC's plan (no freelancing)

- Stay together as a company (voice, vision, or touch)

- Manage their air supply in a way that allows them to exit the hazard zone safely *every time* they enter a hazard zone

The ICS is as much about firefighter safety as it is about effective incident management. The most effective, well-managed incidents are also the safest. Firefighters must understand and fit into ICS to make it work because its goal is to provide the best possible service and ensure that all the workers are protected and go home at the end of their shifts. Understanding some basic management principles such as **unity of command** and **chain of command** helps us know where we fit within the system. Unity of command and chain of command tell us that a firefighter is responsible for reporting to their immediate supervisor for task assignments and who their company report to IMS/ICS. Respect for the chain of command allow for more effective assignments to be made and for safe and effective incident management to take place. Freelancing should not occur during an incident because it poses a risk to individuals and the entire team working in the hazard zone. A firefighter must report observations, considerations, and hazards encountered to their company officer to properly take necessary action and to communicate to the IC.

PUTTING ICS TO WORK

The ICS is part of the daily operations of the American fire service. We should use it on all response types and, as stated earlier, not reserve its use for actual working incidents. Routine responses can be the best places to use the communication processes and principles of ICS.

The principle of modular organization illustrates that the components are used as needed and expandable according to complexity and size of the incident.

Standardizing the functions of command allows for the IC's job duties to be covered initially by the first-arriving company officer, who is then supported by a designated incident commander, who is then supported by a functioning incident management team. If the incident requires multiagency response due to multiple objectives, then the full elements of a command system in a unified fashion are implemented tracking a wide variety of objectives and resources as well as the costs and administrative details needed to manage a massive response of emergency resources.

The individual firefighter's role in ICS is to work within the system as part of the task-level response to the incident objectives. You may be assigned to an engine company, truck company, or heavy rescue, and, at any given time, be responsible for performing tactical duties as varied as fire suppression to ventilation. You will report to and take orders from your company officer who, in turn, takes orders from a sector/division or group officer.

The IC will monitor the completion of the incident objectives and reinforce or modify task-level response based on the analysis of the standard functions of command and critical fireground functions. Maintaining crew integrity and communicating progress reports through the command structure keeps IC and other task-level groups apprised of your status and welfare. Companies needing support or reinforcement should request and receive it through the ICS. The safety officer should constantly monitor your position, condition, and activities, and you should always be aware of those facts as well.

A typical fireground illustration of ICS

A scalable ICS for a structural fire response may build as follows:

A fire department is dispatched to a fire in an apartment building. The first-in company officer arrives on the scene, positions the apparatus according to SOP and delivers a brief yet concise incident report on the mobile radio to inform dispatch and incoming companies of the conditions present, actions being taken, and the needs of the incident action plan. That company may assume a fast-attacking command position, moving to the interior of the building to meet a pressing incident objective, or stay in a command-mode position on the outside of the structure to assign resources as they arrive. Your SOP will determine which is appropriate for your agency.

As a dedicated incident commander arrives, a transfer of command will take place, and critical information including progress and needs are exchanged. An upgrade of the response is requested, and the incident commander will begin to build a command team to successfully manage the quickly emerging incident needs and priorities. Subdivision of the incident into manageable areas of supervision to track crews and assignments will be necessary. IC designates division supervisors in the four quadrants of the structure and assigns companies to them. Groups are formed with specific tasks such as ventilation, rescue, and water supply. A group supervisor may be assigned and could include a company officer to fulfill that objective. Crews will need to be rotated and rehabbed, and reinforcement of tactical positions will take place. The incident management team will monitor where companies are and what their assignments are.

During the course of the incident, the IC or SO will order periodic personnel accountability reports and, when the incident is stabilized, will begin to release resources to their quarters. Crew and resource management allowed this incident to be managed effectively, and the life safety, incident stabilization, and property conservation needs of the occupants were addressed by the correct selection of an incident strategy that was executed through proper task-level or tactical operations.

A statewide or regional incident response

In a small town in the central United States, an engine company is placed on alert for a possible tornado touchdown. The engine company officer responds to a residential area of the community to deal with multiple reports of damage from the storm.

The first-arriving officer considers crew safety and the capabilities not only of his or her company, but then of the department and surrounding communities. As they arrive at the incident scene, they view mass destruction including fire, injuries, and structural damage. The first-arriving engine assumes incident command and begins assessment of the situation. It is clear that this incident is well beyond the response capabilities of almost every fire department.

The company office has begun this response in Type 5 response and then requests mutual aid from the surrounding cities and counties. This incident has now become a Type 4 response. As the assessment continues, it is necessary to bring in even more assistance to staff an emergency operations center and field command post, and to determine many incident priorities. A Type 3 response is now active, bringing in the combined resources of the entire state and possibly even surrounding states. The incident runs for several days in a high state of operation but slowly stabilizes, and a systematic process of relieving the statewide companies down through the first-in engine company is drawn up and implemented.

Disaster aid and financial assistance from state and federal agencies is now possible thanks to the use of the NIMS, ICS, and all of the documentation of time, costs, and materials used carefully completed. A full incident debriefing can take place to identify and analyze the response to prepare for future deployments across the region.

CONCLUSION

Outside of any federal law or industry standard to use ICS, the responsibility to provide for the safety and welfare of all responders to an emergency incident falls directly to the incident commander. The standardization and modular approach used in ICS provides for a time-proven and effective solution to the safety and survival problems experienced by the fire service. A practiced and full-time utilized SOP on ICS should be a primary goal of every response organization. Each firefighter will work within the system under the direction of their company officer who is given direction and assignment at the task level of a single incident commander. As an incident expands due to size, complexity, or resource needs, the early use of the system makes it a smooth and effective expansion of the modules needed. The goal that *everyone goes home* can be achieved in great part through the effective use of ICS.

RESOURCES AND ADDITIONAL INFORMATION

Completion of NIMS training and certification at the levels of NIMS 100, 200, 700, and 800 levels may be required as part of many state firefighter training certificates. Online course work and information can be found at http://www.fema.gov/emergency/nims/NIMSTrainingCourses.shtm.

QUESTIONS

1. What is the purpose of utilizing an incident command system on everyday/every-event responses?

    _____

2. List the main difference between unified command and single command, and explain why all the other elements of NIMS/ICS remain the same._____

    _____

3. As incident operations escalate in time, size, and complexity, the strategic level responsibilities can overwhelm the command team. What can be done to address this problem?_____

    _____

4. List one similarity and two differences between strike teams and task forces._____

    _____

5. What are the six units under the Logistics section of the ICS?

    i.   _____

    ii.   _____

    iii. _____

    iv.   _____

    v.   _____

    vi.   _____

6. The size and scope of an incident determines if incident facilities are needed and what kind. List the five incident facilities that are recognized by NIMS/ICS and give an example of their physical locations.

    i.   _____

    ii.   _____

    iii. _____

    iv.   _____

    v.   _____

7. The IC's ability to change firefighter locations and actions is the most powerful strategic level safety capability. List one example of this._____

    _____

8. The IC manages the tactical priority of stabilizing the incident problem of a structure fire by getting companies around all seven sides of the fire and overwhelming it with water. What are the seven sides of the fire?

    i. _____

    ii. _____

    iii. _____

    iv. _____

    v. _____

    vi. _____

    vii. _____

9. When the IC determines that he or she can no longer coordinate the strategic and tactical level of an incident, what should he or she do? _____
    _____

10. In this chapter, there are seven post-incident items to discuss. List at least three of them, and give short examples of each. _____
    _____
    _____

This chapter provides required knowledge items for the following NFPA Standard 1001 Job Performance Requirements:

FFII 6.2.1

FFII 6.2.2

This chapter contains Skill Drills. When you see this icon, refer to your Skill Drill book for step-by-step instructions.

OBJECTIVES

Upon completion of this chapter, you should be able to do the following:

- Identify and describe how alarms are initiated by the public and received by the fire department
- Describe how fire departments are dispatched to emergency incidents
- Identify the types of emergency scene communication procedures and equipment
- Describe the term interoperability as it applies to incident management communications
- Describe the National Fire Incident Reporting System
- Identify standard forms and reports used by local fire departments
- Identify emerging technologies available to the fire department to improve emergency scene communications

UNDERSTANDING COMMUNICATIONS

Communications is an important but often overlooked aspect of fire services. It is so embedded in our routine activities that we often take it for granted. On a daily basis, proper understanding and use of communication equipment, policy, and procedures can ensure smooth operations. When errors or lapses occur, the results can be major, exposing the public and fire service personnel to risk and liability and can lead to unnecessary loss of life and property. Studies of major incidents have shown that well-managed communications are essential to achieving positive outcomes.

Shannon and Weaver are credited with developing the leading model of communications using technology (fig. 28–1). Their model consists of several components. First, an **information source** produces a message. This message is sent to a **transmitter**, which encodes the message. The transmitter then sends the message via a **channel** (**radio frequency**, telephone line, etc.). During this stage, noise is introduced into the transmission. This noise can be caused by static, interference, and reflects limitations of the technology being used. The message then reaches a **receiver**, which decodes the message, where it then is received at a **destination**.

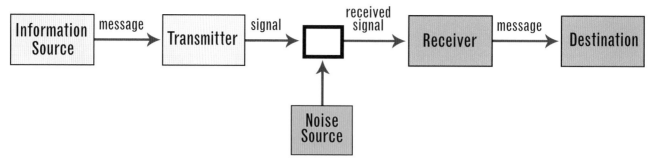

Fig. 28–1. Shannon and Weaver's model of communications

This model of communications can be very useful in understanding the limitations of communications via common methods used in the fire service—telephone, radio, even face-to-face. Poor connections, background noise, and related problems can impair the ability to communicate and cause introduction of errors. Methods to control for these most common errors will be discussed later in the chapter, but can include policies that require the person at the destination to repeat the message back to the information source, or requirements that dispatchers "spell out" numbers to avoid confusion (apartment "sixteen" versus apartment "6T" can be aided by saying "one-six or six-"thomas").

What is important to remember is that users of communications systems must be aware of the limitations of those systems, and allow for these limitations when communicating to ensure that their messages are properly transmitted and understood by the receiver at the other end of that system.

INITIATING AND RECEIVING ALARMS

The primary purpose of the public fire service communication system is to quickly and authoritatively accept reports of emergencies, and dispatch the appropriate units in a timely fashion. There are a number of technological aids that have come into use to facilitate the job of the public safety dispatcher or telecommunicator. Before we consider the entire system, we will focus on the initiation and receipt of alarms.

From the standpoint of the firefighter assigned to a company, perhaps the most fundamental aspect of fire service communications is initiating and receiving alarms.

There are several means of reporting alarms. These methods can include the following:

1. Municipal fire alarm

2. Telephone

3. Land line

4. Mobile

5. Private fire alarm

6. Still (walk-in) alarm

Each of these systems may be in use within a community. As technology progresses, the relative importance of each of these systems has changed over time. Each technology brings its own limitations and challenges. The earliest means for reporting of emergencies was the municipal fire alarm system. These systems, which originated in the mid-1800s, were widely used in urbanized areas, especially before the widespread utilization of telephones. They were based on telegraph technology (fig. 28–2). Many remain in service today, although almost no new systems are being installed because of the cost to maintain a dedicated network of wiring and infrastructure. In some areas, frequent false alarms led to removal of some boxes, or their replacement with voice-capable systems that could be used to potentially detect false alarms.

These municipal box systems reported a coded signal to the local receiving point (usually fire dispatch or even multiple fire stations). Personnel decipher the coded signal which translates back to an intersection or an address. These systems also permitted interconnection with fire alarm systems installed in major buildings. These systems were highly reliable and fast. Each box had the capacity to permit communication back to the dispatch center via telegraph, or later, voice. In many older areas of the country, these systems remain in service (fig. 28–3).

Fig. 28–2. Typical municipal telegraph-type fire alarm reporting box

Telephones have been a mainstay for the reporting of alarms in most of the country since the turn of the century. The community fire reporting system relies on people with telephones to report emergencies. Through the advent of 9-1-1 systems in 1968, a common emergency reporting number was established. Using this system enabled the development of technologies to improve the efficiency and effectiveness of emergency reporting. According to the National Emergency Number Association, approximately 93% of the U.S. population was covered by some level of 9-1-1 service in the year 2000. Improvements to 9-1-1 include the ability to route calls to a designated **public safety answering point (PSAP)** based on the location of the telephone number, and enhanced 9-1-1, which permits identification and location information to be associated with the a phone number to be displayed at the PSAP.

Wireless phones have grown from a luxury item to being commonplace. Because these phone numbers are not associated with a specific location, and because users are constantly moving, ascertaining the location of a cell phone caller and the emergency they are reporting can be challenging. The federal government has mandated that technology be implemented in phases—first to route 9-1-1 calls to a PSAP (done), and then permit the telephone number to be displayed at that PSAP, and finally, to permit the PSAP to know the location of the wireless caller. Until all these improvements are implemented, dispatch centers will continue to be frustrated by receiving calls from people who may not be in their service area, not know their location, or not know the location of an incident.

Fig. 28–3. A municipal alarm system using dedicated 9-1-1 phones

The recent adoption of "internet-based" telephones, operating on **Voice over Internet Protocol (VoIP)** has complicated the task of associating a location with a particular telephone number. Some of these phone numbers can be associated with a portable computer, and have the capability of "following" the user wherever they go. Requirements are in place to require identification of the callback number and "home' location of the VoIP number to a local PSAP, but these are not entirely complete.

Private fire alarm systems are used in commercial and multifamily buildings, but are gaining in popularity in private homes, as well. These alarm systems can range from simple smoke detectors to complex arrangements of smoke and heat detection, manual pull boxes, water flow alarms, and related equipment. Private fire alarms are privately maintained systems, whether required by local codes or not, that are monitored by a central station or other arrangement which in turn transmits the alarm to the fire services.

For many departments, automatic fire alarms are the most common type of fire-related incident. This increase in workload as a result of accidental, unintentional, and false alarms is offset by the early notification afforded by such systems. Earlier detection and reporting of fires leads to smaller, more easily controlled fires, this fulfilling a valuable public policy purpose. Some jurisdictions penalize owners of systems with excessive false alarms, which is a way of encouraging proper system maintenance and reducing the number of unnecessary responses.

The final method of reporting alarms is via a "still" or **walk-in alarm** reported directly to a fire company or personnel at a fire station. Often, people living nearby a fire station will go to the fire station rather than report an emergency by telephone. In other cases, passersby may walk in to report an incident near the fire station itself. The author vividly remembers one case in which a car on fire was driven up to the front of a firehouse—much to the surprise of personnel in the station.

Procedures must be in place for handling emergencies reported directly to personnel at a fire station or on apparatus. The same information that a dispatcher requests should be obtained to include the address, the nature of incident, and the identification or contact information for the reporting party. Members of the company or station must be alerted, and the dispatch center should be notified immediately that the company or units are out on service dealing with an incident reported directly by the public. Policies should spell out instructions for companies that encounter emergencies while en route to another call.

TRANSMISSION OF ALARMS AND ALERTING

FFI 6.2.2 In departments with multiple facilities, or on multi-jurisdictional dispatch centers, there is a need for a more elaborate method of directing units to reported emergencies. Depending on the nature of the emergency or its location, decisions must be made about which stations, units, and personnel to alert. Early municipal fire alarm box systems, which predated radio communications, transmitted a coded signal to the communications or dispatch center. These alarms were often monitored in fire stations as well. Personnel knew the location of each "box" and would know to respond to the appropriate location, where they would hopefully be met by the person who transmitted the signal. In volunteer organizations, these systems were often tied into large air-powered horns so that signals could be heard throughout a community. They were a very efficient way of alerting personnel because they both alerted and provided location information.

Because there were numerous "boxes" in most communities, a term known as a "box" card was used to describe both the physical location of the alarm box and the apparatus or resources that were assigned to respond.

In smaller communities, the listing may correspond with mutual aid departments that would be called if necessary. In larger departments, elaborate lists of units assigned to respond, usually based on distance form the box, would be developed. Commonly, box cards contain lists of resources through several alarms.

As municipal fire alarm systems were replaced, and computer-aided dispatch (CAD) systems were developed starting in the 1970s, specific locations throughout a community were selected and pre-determined apparatus response was designated for each such area. Even in communities that did not have such systems, areas created were referred to as "box areas." This information is incorporated into modern CAD systems to this day, as each address is associated with a geographic identifier or "phantom box" that contains a unique assignment of apparatus or resources at multiple levels of response. Figure 28–4 shows a diagram of a "typical" "box" or "run" card. Even the most modern dispatch facilities maintain a collection of physical cards to be used for this purpose in the event that their computerized system fails or is disabled.

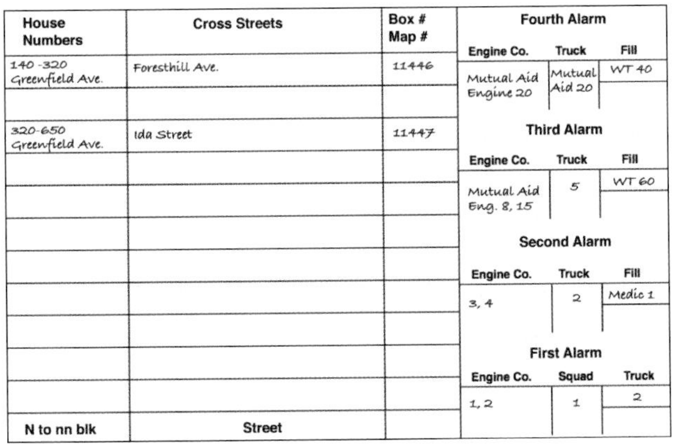

House Numbers	Cross Streets	Box # Map #	Fourth Alarm		
			Engine Co.	Truck	Fill
140 -320 Greenfield Ave.	Foresthill Ave.	11446	Mutual Aid Engine 20	Mutual Aid 20	WT 40
320-650 Greenfield Ave.	Ida Street	11447	Third Alarm		
			Engine Co.	Truck	Fill
			Mutual Aid Eng. 8, 15	5	WT 60
			Second Alarm		
			Engine Co.	Truck	Fill
			3, 4	2	Medic 1
			First Alarm		
			Engine Co.	Squad	Truck
			1, 2	1	2
N to nn blk	Street				

Fig. 28–4. A "box" or "run" card.

The number of units sent on an alarm is a function of local departmental policy. In smaller organizations, all available personnel and apparatus may respond on every alarm, regardless of type. As departments become larger, and alarms more numerous, specific numbers of units may be designated to respond based on the nature of the reported incident. This is necessary to conserve resources for additional alarms that may be reported, and to reduce unnecessary responses.

For example, emergency medical assists may receive a response from as little as one unit with a few personnel, while reported fires in buildings receive the highest level of response. Usually, a minimum of 2–3 engine companies and a ladder or service company are sent to any reported fire in a building. Structural firefighting requires a complement of personnel be on the scene, and if local resources do not meet the need, then other resources should be utilized through mutual aid, or preferably, automatic aid.

CAD systems make it possible to assign resources to specific addresses. Risk-related factors such as the presence of fire suppression systems, hazardous occupancies, or lack of equipment such as hydrants or standpipes can be used to trigger changes in the number and type of units that are sent to an alarm.

After a dispatcher determines the nature of an emergency and the appropriate resources to send, the next decision is how they will be notified (fig. 28–5). The most common means for alerting of fire service resources is over radio. Often audible or inaudible tones are used to activate speakers, pagers, and audible warning devices in fire stations. These tones, when audible, also serve to alert users monitoring the frequency that an alarm is being dispatched. These systems can be manually activated by the dispatcher, or can be automatically integrated into CAD systems. Other systems used included dedicated voice alerting systems that operate over leased or private lines or microwave links.

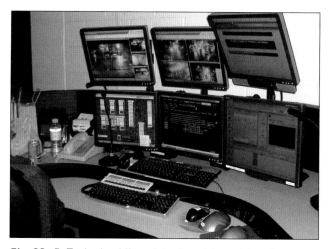

Fig. 28–5. Typical public safety dispatch position. Screens are for CAD system, radio system, and unit status. Manual fire station alerting capability is on the console on the right.

Operational communications

Use of communications requires a combination of procedures, policies, and training in the use of technologies. Many agencies neglect training in such basic areas as use of radios, techniques for interfacing with microphones, and use of alarm-reporting equipment.

Users should be aware of the technology they are using and be familiar with techniques for using the equipment. Practices such as holding the microphone at an appropriate distance from the mouth, speaking in a clear and forceful tone without shouting, and avoiding transmitting in areas that will contribute to feedback (standing too near other speakers) should be adhered to. If necessary, ask personnel standing nearby to turn down or cover their speaker/microphones. Appropriate language should be used at all times.

Physical positioning of the portable radio on the users body and in relation to protective attire can also affect the ability to transmit and receive clearly. Placing a radio in a dedicated pocket on the chest can improve transmitting capabilities over having the radio under a turnout coat at the user's waist level.

Additionally, users should always think about being succinct, calm, and clear in the verbal communication over the radio. Verbose messages, unclear language, and slang or jargon should be avoided in favor of well-considered, pointed messages. Once a report or message is given, it should not be necessary to elaborate unless asked for more information by the receiver.

Before transmitting, users should listen carefully to be sure that they are not interrupting a message between two other parties on the radio. This alone can make a great contribution to improving overall effectiveness of communications at an incident. If overloading of an operating channel is commonplace, then it is a sign of poor discipline or the possible need for additional frequencies.

Procedures for recognizing and establishing priority for urgent or emergency messages should be established in advance, and agreed upon by all agencies who will potentially be working on the same frequency at an incident. At any incident, radio channels will become overloaded, and the need to allow users to gain the attention of incident command will be critical.

Unit and personnel designations

The question of unit and personnel designations seems trivial, but can be very important to successful operations. Control of unit and personnel designations is usually maintained at the county or dispatch center level. Duplication of unit designations can lead to confusion, especially when those units may work together at an incident. Proper procedure for identifying units and personnel must be enforced.

For example, unit designations may be tied to a department, station, or unit type. Personnel assigned to a unit can be designated by their riding position. Usually, the designations of personnel are with letters, so that there is no confusion between personnel and equipment. That is, the officer can be designated as Engine 121-A, the driver as Engine 121-B, and other personnel as C, D, and so on. Some departments assign duties to personnel based on their riding position, which reinforces this system.

Personnel not assigned to a specific unit should be provided with a radio identifier, such as a badge number or rank and number (example: Lieutenant 7) to avoid the use of personal names on the radio. Once a person arriving at an incident is assigned, the designation should reflect the unit or function the person is assigned to.

Requesting assistance at an incident

When working on the fireground or incident scene, portable radios can be extremely useful in enhancing safety for personnel who may work apart from their crew. Often, when a member of a crew is assigned to a task away from the rest of their unit, they may encounter a situation or circumstances that require them to notify their supervisor, or on larger incidents, the operations section or incident commander. When such a situation is encountered, for example, the firefighter should formulate a message to notify others on the fireground of the information and request assistance, as appropriate.

For example, a firefighter assigned to operate a standpipe valve while the balance of his crew is advancing a line in preparation for forcible entry and fire attack, may receive information from a civilian evacuating the building about conditions on a higher floor indicating a smoke condition or people in need of assistance. While continuing to perform the assigned task, the firefighter should inform the highest ranking person on the channel "Engine 23-C, to operations—be advised I have a report from a civilian of a person overcome by smoke in the hallway of the sixth floor." The firefighter should wait for the message to be acknowledged for further instructions.

FIRE DEPARTMENT COMMUNICATIONS EQUIPMENT

This section of the chapter will address the "hardware" aspects of fire service communications. We will consider radio systems, system features, user equipment, and ancillary hardware.

Public safety radio systems

Public safety radio systems can be described as systems of radio transmission and reception infrastructure, mobile and portable user equipment, and dispatch or base station location integrated on a common set of frequencies for a defined functional purpose. This definition, while specific, does not address the numerous variations possible in public safety radio networks.

Understanding radio networks is important, although from the standpoint of a firefighter, we do not necessarily need to be concerned with all of the technical specifications, but rather the capabilities and intended purpose of the system and its components.

Radio systems can be characterized by the location of dispatching personnel, radio infrastructure, channel characteristics, number of channels, and the manner of operation. Dispatching and radio infrastructure can be centralized or dispersed; one or more frequencies may be in use; and the network may have multiple channels available.

Public safety radio systems operate on several different frequency bands:

- Very High Frequency—Low Band: 33 MHz–46 MHz

- Very High Frequency—High Band: 150 MHz–174 MHz

- Ultra High Frequency-UHF: 450 MHz–460 MHz

- 800–900 MHz

Following the scrutiny of public safety communications after the 9/11 attacks, and in response to the shortage of available frequencies for emergency response agencies, some new spectrum is being made available. In addition to these frequency bands listed above, the 700 MHz band is scheduled to become available for pubic safety as television stations (the current users) move to other frequencies.

The 4.9 gigahertz (GHz) band is available now, primarily used for data communication in support of public safety.

Each channel can be set up as **simplex** or **duplex** operation. Simplex operation means that only one frequency is used for both transmission and receiving signals. Duplex means that one frequency is used for transmitting while a second frequency is used for receiving. Duplex capability can mean that dispatchers may be able to hear transmissions from the field even while they transmit.

One desirable capability included in radio systems is **unit identifiers**, which display on the dispatcher's console and allow the dispatcher to know what unit is calling. Both mobile and portable radios can be equipped with this capability. Another function is the ability to remotely control a radio-coded squelch, which limits the ability to hear interfering transmissions from other organizations sharing the frequency. Distress or "man down" signals can also be sent from some radios. These capabilities are examples of **tone encoding**. These tones can be subaudible, meaning that users monitoring the channel cannot hear them.[6]

Radios have two distinct functions: transmitting and receiving. In mobile and portable radios, both functions are combined, which is why these radios are called **transceivers.** Transceivers have circuitry to accomplish both functions, and an antenna that works both in transmit and receive mode. When the transmit button is pressed, the antenna is dedicated to the transmitter. Likewise, when the transmitter is not active, the antenna works in the receive mode (fig. 28–6).

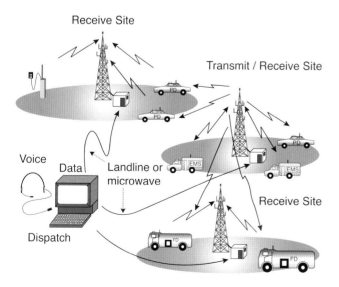

Fig. 28–6. Components of a conventional radio system

A major distinction in radio systems is the **conventional** versus **trunked** systems. A conventional system is what commonly comes to mind when describing basic radio system function (fig. 28–6). In a conventional system, channels are selected by the user, and switching of frequencies is not usually necessary to complete a conversation with another user. Channels are designated and function for a known purpose. For example, channel 1 might be Fire Dispatch, channel 2 is Fireground Operations, and channel 3 is Mutual Aid.

In a trunked system, the user selects a talk group, and the system selects the channel to be used for any given conversation. Over the course of a conversation between users, it is possible that multiple channels could be used. This would be done automatically and would not be apparent to the users.[8]

Trunked radio systems offer the ability to better utilize a limited number of frequencies by aggregating a large pool of users with the anticipation that peak demand for all user groups will occur at different times. Priorities are assigned to users, and, when a user keys their microphone, the system must give them access before they can transmit. Users are organized into **talk groups** that are usually organized by function and geography. For example, in a fire department covering a large area, talk groups may be assigned based on geography. Likewise, there may be talk groups for administration, fire prevention, and suppression. From the user perspective, each talk group behaves as though it was its own separate radio system.

Popularity of trunked systems grew out of the limited radio spectrum available, and the desire of some jurisdictions to create large, unified radio systems with the capability of linking multiple agencies. Because of their expense and sophistication, they are normally found only in large municipalities or County or metropolitan departments.

The other major distinction in radio systems is the nature of the signals being broadcast. Most systems use what is known as **analog technology**. This means that the radio signal being sent between parties on the system is the user's voice sent over the airwaves. Like an analog recording, noise or other issues can diminish the quality of the signal. The newer alternative is known as **digital technology**. In a digital system, the user's voice is converted to a digital data then converted back to voice when received. Digital signals have the capability for better transmission range, and are less susceptible to noise being introduced during the transmission process. However, software **algorithms** or programs are used to encode and decode the voice signal, and these algorithms can be affected by background noise when a user is transmitting. Microprocessors control digital systems, which require synchronization of transmitters and receivers.

Digital radio systems have a small time delay between the transmitting party's voice and the receiving party as encoding and decoding take place. This is typically not a major concern, but is perceptible when users are standing in proximity to one another. For fireground applications, there is considerable controversy regarding the applicability of digital voice radio technology because multiple users attempting to transmit are denied simultaneous access to the system. In analog systems, personnel receiving transmissions can detect multiple overlapping transmissions, which may occur, especially during critical fireground situations. For this reason, many organizations rely on direct (non-repeated), analog transmissions for tactical users.

There are numerous technologies available and widely incorporated into radio systems to increase or improve coverage. While range of a base station can be from 10 to 40 miles (16 to 64 km) depending on antenna height, topography, buildings, and output power, the transmitting power of mobile and portable radios is typically much smaller. Mobile radios typically operate in the range of 40–50 watts, while portable radios operate at 2–5 watts (figs. 28–7 and 28–8).

Multiple receivers may be distributed throughout the service area to enable lower-power **mobile** (vehicular mounted) or **portable** (hand held) subscriber units to be heard. This is especially important in fire service applications where transmissions from portable radios operating inside buildings are the norm. Radio systems use various technologies to select the best receive site to send the signal to the dispatcher.[5]

Repeaters are employed to receive transmissions from field units and rebroadcast them at higher power on the receive frequency of user equipment.

In systems covering large geographic areas, multiple transmit sites may be employed. These sites are managed using multicasting or simulcasting. **Multicasting** uses different frequencies on adjacent towers to increase range without interference. **Simulcasting** relies on a common frequency on multiple tranchangmit sites under computer control to ensure that their transmissions are synchronized in order to avoid conflicting with each other.

Fig. 28–7. Typical portable radio. (Courtesy of PMC Associates)

Fig. 28–8. Typical mobile radio (Courtesy of PMC Associates)

Other communications technologies

Mobile computer terminals (MCTs) are gaining in popularity in the fire service. While widely used in law enforcement, MCTs and many of their benefits are equally applicable to the fire service (fig. 28–9). They are becoming central to a number of technologies and software applications that are useful in the fire service.

From a dispatch perspective, CAD software can send messages directly to the MCTs, allowing them to be used for dispatching units. With incident information and the address on the screen, this eliminates the need to confirm the address over the radio. **Unit status** can be updated from virtual "buttons" on the MCT, again eliminating the need for verbal radio transmissions and improving accuracy of response times. Unit status includes messages useful to the dispatcher, such as "on scene," "in service," "on the air," and "on scene." This feature is critical to many busy departments, both to conserve radio channel availability and dispatcher workload in manually entering unit status changes into a CAD or other system.

Fig. 28–9. Arrangement of radios and MCT in a command vehicle. These radios are integrated through a common interface that can be used for interoperability.

As a functioning computer, the MCT has numerous capabilities, including storage of pre-plan information, reference material and contact information, incident command software, and related applications. Communications between the dispatch system and MCT is accomplished via radio, over commercial wireless networks, or on dedicated wireless broadband networks. A predecessor to the MCT was the **mobile data terminal (MDT)**, which is a "dumb terminal" that could only display unit status, incident, and other textual information. MDTs communicated almost exclusively over the local public safety radio system. As the need for bandwidth has increased, many agencies have turned to commercial wireless data networks to handle their data communication needs.

Automatic vehicle location (AVL) uses satellite or wireless phone signals to produce an approximate location of a vehicle or person. Early systems were constructed from dedicated infrastructure installed by the local community. AVL, when paired with geographic information system technology, can permit display of a map in the vehicle showing the path of the vehicle, and even recommendations on the route to take to a reported emergency.

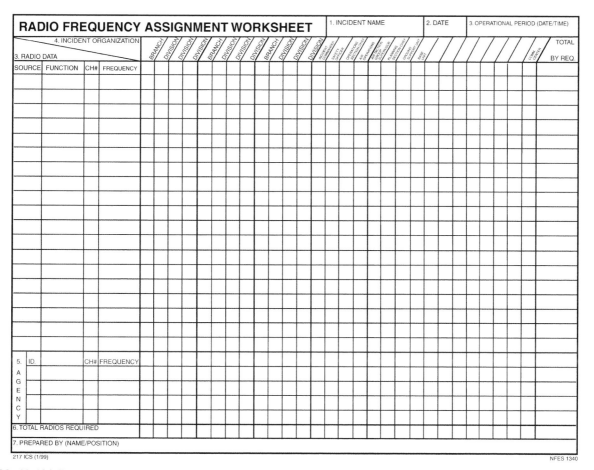

Fig. 28–10. ICS Form 217 shows radio frequency assignments for all units working an incident.

Advanced Communications

FIREFIGHTER II

Chapter 28

AVL is especially valuable in dispatching. The ability to see units located on a map of the service area can add to safety, enhance selection of the closest unit to alarms, and manage system-wide deployment in real time. The provision of AVL is becoming standard in busy systems or systems serving large areas.

Incident management

The National Incident Management System (NIMS) recognizes the importance of communications and provides guidance on how to establish communications at an incident (fig. 28–10). One of the key requirements of NIMS Incident Command is the establishment of common terminology and integration of planning for communications into the overall goals and objectives of the incident.[12]

NIMS advocates the use of plain text in radio transmissions. Ten codes or other esoteric codes, especially when they are unique to a single agency, will compromise communications at an incident with multiple jurisdictions.

Large-scale incidents, particularly those that involve multiple agencies, typically require multiple frequencies, with command functions being on a separate channel from tactical operations. Many smaller organizations fail to establish an adequate number of frequencies at operations, and do not plan to assign appropriate resources to manage complex communications at an incident. The outcome is usually overloaded frequencies, difficulty in communicating without cross-talk and interruption by competing units. Failure to move incident scene communications off a main dispatch channel has been implicated in numerous cases where dispatch covers scene operations, resulting in impaired scene communications and "stepping on" units who may be requesting assistance.[14]

Interoperability

Interoperability is defined as the ability of emergency responders to work seamlessly with other systems or products without any special effort. Wireless communications interoperability specifically refers to the ability of emergency response officials to share information via voice and data signals on demand, in real time, when needed, and as authorized.[16]

The local control of public safety radio systems often limits consideration of interoperability. Limited funding, aging equipment, and incompatible technologies already deployed in the field also hamper development of interoperability.

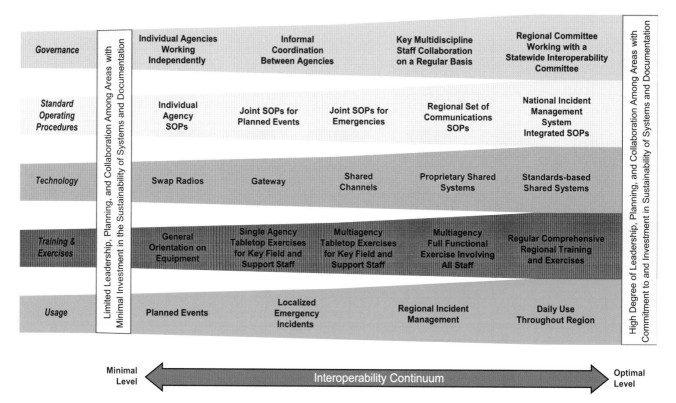

Fig. 28–11. SAFECOM's Interoperability Continuum provides a guide to assessing your organization's interoperability capabilities.

Solutions for communications interoperability can be as basic as providing radios for use by mutual aid partners, to programming of frequencies used by neighboring departments into your portable and mobile radios.

Gateways are devices that are used to link different frequencies together at a specific location. The gateway is often mobile, and carried in a command or communications vehicle. Gateways can link wireless phones and public safety radios so that they can speak with each other. There are gateways that are hardware and others that are driven by software. The most desirable solution is to develop regional radio networks with shared channels so that communication between agencies becomes effortless and routine (fig. 28–11).

Mobile communications vehicles

Many larger organizations operate some type of mobile communications facility incorporated into a vehicle. For small organizations, this may be as simple as a work surface and radio with mutual aid frequencies incorporated into a chief's vehicle. For larger incidents and in extreme climates, more elaborate vehicles are used for this purpose. These vehicles can range from converted cargo vans or ambulances to custom-equipped and constructed trucks or RV-type units.[18]

One important distinction is to keep the concept of a communications vehicle distinct from the notion of an incident command post. While they may be co-located, on larger or long-duration incidents, the communications vehicle will probably not be the best place for the incident commander and supporting staff to be working, as they will interfere with communications functions.

These vehicles have grown in sophistication as technology has advanced, and now such units should include radios, a link to the CAD system, mapping software, capabilities for receiving television and radio broadcasts, digital recording capability, telephone and fax capability, and channel-logging recorders for on-scene communications. Satellite communications, wireless broadband connections, ability to receive video feeds from helicopters, and computers are becoming common as well. Mechanically, these vehicles should be equipped with generators and portable lighting, and they should be capable of operating for extended periods (fig. 28–12a and b).

The future direction of these units is to be able to replicate the computer experience of being at a desk of a high-level administrator, with real-time access to enterprise software, e-mail, and data otherwise available in the office.

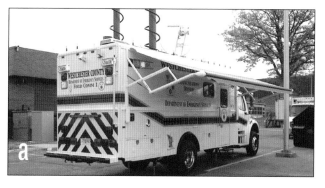

Figs. 28–12a, b. The Westchester County (NY) communications vehicle includes capabilities of receiving video feeds from helicopters, transmitting video, CAD interface, and ability to replicate the county government's network and computer applications.)

FIRE REPORTS

FFII 6.2.1 Documenting the activity of your fire company is an important component of communications. A basic incident report establishes such milestones as the time of alarm and time your company went en route, arrived on the scene, and went back into service. The location of the alarm, nature of alarm, and damage or casualties are also recorded. Units equipped with

MCTs may have the capability of completing reports from the field.

After an incident, it is important to be able to accurately record all of the important information about the incident.

The incident report can be handwritten or computerized. Record all of the important information such as the following:

- time of the call

- response time of the arriving apparatus

- incident address

- property owner information

- incident outcome

- any other information deemed important according to your observations or department procedures

To standardize reporting, incident report codes are often used to indicate information such as incident type, actions taken, area of fire origin, and property use. Written guides provide codes and explanation of those codes. Many incident report computer programs have code guides built into the reporting system. It is important to know where your department incident codes and regulation manuals are located, and whether they are in book form or incorporated into the computer system.

Many departments use an incident report based on the National Fire Incident Reporting System (NFIRS). Through state fire marshals' offices or their equivalents, state-specific versions of the NFIRS incident report are available for use throughout the United States. NFIRS-compliant reporting schemes are supported by numerous incident reporting and records-management software packages available for the fire services. The NFIRS Reference Guide can be found online at FEMA's NFIRS web page. Paper forms are also available for manual completion of these reports (fig. 28–13).

The use of NFIRS reporting allows departments to have consistent data for comparison with other organizations, and permits analysis of response times, staffing, and fire losses in one database. Fire protection systems and occupancy data are used by code writing bodies, and by the fire service for justification of code requirements. Some organizations elect not to participate in NFIRS, primarily out of a perception that there are no benefits or because completion of reports is thought to be too time-consuming. The adoption of computer software for reporting greatly reduces the effort involved, and speeds the collection of data, making information available on an almost "real-time" basis. Functionality of software such as "pull-down" menus and context-specific help greatly speed the reporting process. Progressive organizations report their information—failure to do so holds back the entire fire service.

NFIRS-based incident reports are required for recipients of federally funded FIRE Act grants. As a nationwide standard, they contain extensive information of value in establishing trends in causes of fires, identifying consumer products with potential safety issues, establishing performance, and gathering comparative data useful for management and in justifying resources. NFIRS data are used as the basis for the development of national statistics on the fire problem by the U.S. Fire Administration. The voluntary reporting system is administered by an organization called the National Fire Information Council, composed primarily of State and local representatives of fire agencies.

Perhaps most importantly to firefighters, NFIRS data is the basis for determining trends in firefighter casualties and can be used to target equipment, activities, or types of properties that are particularly hazardous or involved in accident scenarios. The absence of accurate and complete NFIRS reports is a major impediment to a better understanding of the fire problem and firefighter safety.

NFIRS reporting includes separate modules that can be used for various situations including civilian casualties, fire service casualties, hazardous materials, emergency medical services, wildland fires, and personnel, among others.

Other types of forms and reports

Besides NFIRS reports, members of fire companies often prepare other types of forms and reports. These include equipment maintenance forms, injury forms, supply requests, and drill schedules, among others. Most fire departments have specific forms to be filled out; with the introduction of the computer, many of them have been converted to an electronic format.

One of the more extensive reports prepared by the fire department itself is an after-action report. These reports are completed after a major incident which resulted in death(s) or major property damage. These reports usually contain extensive use of narratives: essentially detailed descriptions of what took place. For example, this could involve describing how and where hoselines were placed, the description of a flashover, or a description of how a wall collapsed. Firefighters may be asked

Complete this side for all fires

A

FDID ☆   State ☆   MM DD YYYY Incident Date ☆   Station   Incident Number ☆   Exposure ☆   ☐ Delete   ☐ Change

NFIRS - 2 Fire

B Property Details

B₁ ☐ Not Residential
Estimated number of residential living units in building of origin *whether or not all units became involved*

B₂ ☐ Buildings not involved
Number of buildings involved

B₃ , ☐ None   ☐ Less than one acre
Acres burned (outside fires)

C On-Site Materials or Products ☐ None

Complete if there were any significant amounts of commercial, industrial, energy or agricultural products or materials on the property, *whether or not they became involved*

Enter up to three codes. Check one box for each code entered.

On-site material (1)
1 ☐ Bulk storage or warehousing
2 ☐ Processing or manufacturing
3 ☐ Packaged goods for sale
4 ☐ Repair or service

On-site material (2)
1 ☐ Bulk storage or warehousing
2 ☐ Processing or manufacturing
3 ☐ Packaged goods for sale
4 ☐ Repair or service

On-site material (3)
1 ☐ Bulk storage or warehousing
2 ☐ Processing or manufacturing
3 ☐ Packaged goods for sale
4 ☐ Repair or service

D Ignition

D₁ Area of fire origin ☆

D₂ Heat source ☆

D₃ Item first ignited ☆   1 ☐ Check box if fire spread was confined to object of origin

D₄ Type of material first ignited   Required only if item first ignited code is 00 or <70

E₁ Cause of Ignition ☆

☐ Check box if this is an exposure report.   → Skip to Section G

1 ☐ Intentional
2 ☐ Unintentional
3 ☐ Failure of equipment or heat source
4 ☐ Act of nature
5 ☐ Cause under investigation
U ☐ Cause undetermined after investigation

E₂ Factors Contributing To Ignition ☐ None

Factor contributing to ignition (1)

Factor contributing to ignition (2)

E₃ Human Factors Contributing To Ignition

Check all applicable boxes   ☐ None

1 ☐ Asleep
2 ☐ Possibly impaired by alcohol or drugs
3 ☐ Unattended person
4 ☐ Possibly mentally disabled
5 ☐ Physically disabled
6 ☐ Multiple persons involved
7 ☐ Age was a factor

Estimated age of person involved

1 ☐ Male   2 ☐ Female

F₁ Equipment Involved In Ignition

☐ None → If equipment was not involved, skip to Section G

Equipment Involved
Brand
Model
Serial #
Year

F₂ Equipment Power

Equipment Power Source

F₃ Equipment Portability

1 ☐ Portable
2 ☐ Stationary

Portable equipment normally can be moved by one person, is designed to be used in multiple locations, and requires no tools to install.

G Fire Suppression Factors

Enter up to three codes.   ☐ None

Fire suppression factor (1)

Fire suppression factor (2)

Fire suppression factor (3)

H₁ Mobile Property Involved
☐ None

1 ☐ Not involved in ignition, but burned
2 ☐ Involved in ignition, but did not burn
3 ☐ Involved in ignition and burned

Mobile property model

License Plate Number   State   VIN Number

Structure fire? Please be sure to complete the other side of this form.

H₂ Mobile Property Type & Make

Mobile property type

Mobile property make

Year

Local Use

☐ Pre-Fire Plan Available

Some of the information presented in this report may be based upon reports from other agencies:

☐ Arson report attached
☐ Police report attached
☐ Coroner report attached
☐ Other reports attached

NFIRS-2 Revision 01/19/99

Fig. 28–13. A sample NFIRS incident report

Advanced Communications

FIREFIGHTER II

Chapter 28

to prepare such narratives since they actually experienced the things described in the report.

It is important for firefighters to ensure that all forms and reports are properly prepared. This responsibility includes using correct grammar and spelling. All documents must be proofread. Written documents are a reflection of the author and his professionalism.

EMERGING TECHNOLOGIES

New technologies hold great promise for improving fire service communications. New reporting methods will continue to evolve. Satellite phones, text-messaging devices, and **telematics** are likely to have major consequences for 9-1-1 systems in the future. For example, telematics, which is defined as the combined use of information technology and electronics (usually in mobile settings), is going to be used to generate reports of lost, stolen, or damaged vehicles directly to 9-1-1 centers.

These new devices will require investments in new technology for 9-1-1 centers, as well as changes to dispatching protocols and procedures to ensure that emergencies reported through these methods receive the appropriate responses.

Improved communications and tracking capabilities for fire service operations are likely to be introduced in the near future. These technologies include individual fireground text-messaging systems and even systems to determine the location of firefighters operating inside a building.

Some of these technologies are considered experimental, but could have a major impact on safety of firefighters if they prove to be practical.

BIBLIOGRAPHY

Desourdis, Robert I., Davis Smith, William Speights, Richard Dewey, and John DiSalvo. *Emerging Public Safety Wireless Communication Systems*. Boston: Artech House Publishers, 2002.

Fire Department Communications Manual: A Basic Guide to System Concepts and Equipment. FA-160. Federal Emergency Management Agency, U.S. Fire Administration, 1995.

Hawkins, Don. "Communications in the Incident Command System." *COPS Interoperable Communi-*

cations Technology Program: Issue Brief Number 2, May 2007.

McMillan, J. Rhett. *The Primer of Public Safety Telecommunication Systems, 3rd Ed.* Daytona Beach, FL: Association of Public-Safety Communications Officials, Inc. 2000.

Singer, Edward. *Land Mobile Radio Systems, 2nd Ed.* Upper Saddle River, NJ: Prentice-Hall, 1994.

Special report: Improving Firefighter Communications. USFA-TR-099. U.S. Fire Administration Technical report Series. Emmitsburg, Md.: U.S. Fire Administration, January 1999.

NOTES

1. Shannon, Claude E. and Warren Weaver. *A Mathematical Model of Communication.* Urbana, IL.: University of Illinois Press, 1949.

2. McMillan, J. Rhett. *The Primer of Public Safety Telecommunication Systems 3rd Ed.* Daytona Beach, FL: Association of Public-Safety Communications Officials, Inc. 2000. p. 77.

3. McMillan, p. 51.

4. Desourdis, Robert I., Davis Smith, William Speights, Richard Dewey, and John DiSalvo. *Emerging Public Safety Wireless Communication Systems.* Boston: Artech House Publishers, 2002, pp. 259–262.

5. Singer, Edward. *Land Mobile Radio Systems, 2nd Ed.* Upper Saddle River, NJ: Prentice-Hall, 1994, pp. 72–73.

6. Hawkins, Don. "Communications in the Incident Command System." *COPS Interoperable Communications Technology Program: Issue Brief Number 2,* May 2007.

7. *Special report: Improving Firefighter Communications.* USFA-TR-099. U.S. Fire Administration Technical Report Series. Emmitsburg, Md.: U.S. Fire Administration, January 1999.

8. SAFECOM http://www.safecomprogram.gov/SAFECOM/interoperability/default.htm.

9. *Fire Department Communications Manual: A Basic Guide to System Concepts and Equipment.* FA-160. Federal Emergency Management Agency, U.S. Fire Administration, 1995, Appendix C.

QUESTIONS

1. Name the five steps in the communications model developed by Shannon & Weaver.

2. What are the two new technologies that are making it difficult to determine the location of an emergency call?

3. What is a "still" alarm?

4. Why are unit and personnel designations important at an emergency operation?

5. In a "trunked" radio system, what makes "analog" technology superior to "digital"?

6. What is the difference between "multicasting" and "simulcasting"?

7. Name three advantages of a MCT.

8. What is NIFERS, and why is it important to the fire service?

9. There are several means of reporting alarms. Name four.

10. What is a CAD system and how does it improve dispatch procedures?

11. What is the most common means for alerting fire service resources?

12. Radios have two distinct functions. Name them.

Pre-Incident Planning

by Jack J. Murphy

This chapter provides required knowledge items for the following NFPA Standard 1001 Job Performance Requirements:

FFII 6.5.3

This chapter contains Skill Drills. When you see this icon, refer to your Skill Drill book for step-by-step instructions.

OBJECTIVES

Upon completion of this chapter, you should be able to do the following:

- Define the term *pre-incident plan*
- Describe the 10 occupancy types identified in the International Building Code
- Identify the five types of building construction types
- Identify the benefits of pre-incident planning
- Identify the critical items to consider when conducting an exterior building reconnaissance survey
- Identify the critical items to consider when conducting an interior building reconnaissance survey
- Identify the types and components of fire protection systems found in a target hazard
- Describe the proper method for conducting a hydrant flow test
- Describe the building tactical information point system (TIPS)
- Identify the proper symbols to use in a pre-incident planning sketch of a building

INTRODUCTION

The ability to successfully contend with a fire in a building is greatly enhanced by one critical factor: a **pre-incident plan**. Gathering detailed information about a specific building—known as a **pre-incident survey**—and formulating a plan of action *before an incident* gives a fireground commander *inside information* about the building and its contents, allowing the officer to anticipate problems and to best use his resources. A pre-incident plan that is implemented within the National Incident Management System (NIMS) structure will assist the incident commander with an incident action plan (IAP) to better reflect the overall fireground strategy, tactics, risk management, and firefighter safety.

Firefighters also benefit from gathering **building intelligence** in anticipation of preparing a pre-incident plan. By developing and improving their building intelligence-gathering skills, firefighters further enhance their tactical capabilities for actual specific buildings including anticipating fire behavior, water supply needs, search and rescue issues, forcible-entry challenges, proper hose and ladder placement, ventilation needs, and safety and survival concerns. Taking a closer look, we can see the particular benefits of this pre-incident information intelligence gathering and planning.

Pre-incident planning

Fire behavior. The basic principles of fire dynamics considers how the ignition, burning, and fire spread within a particular building relates to the characteristics of combustible materials present in the building. The need to understand building construction and the built-in fire protection features such as alarms, standpipe/sprinkler, fire-rated walls/partitions, fire doors, and so forth enable the firefighter to better understand the spread of fire and smoke within a structure.

Water supply. Water supply is a crucial component to controlling a fire. The best way to address a fire is by performing an exterior building reconnaissance to note the nearby water supply sources such as fire hydrants, the size of the water mains, and so forth. While performing an internal building reconnaissance, notice what built-in fire protection systems such as standpipe and sprinkler system can benefit to your response. We calculate the water flow requirements for a building and the actual water supply available later in the chapter.

Search and rescue. A vital component to performing a primary search for a quick investigation for victims is a good comprehension of the building floor layouts. Because the primary search is basically the first action taken on entry into a building, knowing a floor design ahead of time helps this specific phase of the search process.

Forcible entry. To carry out the fireground tasks to complete search, rescue, extinguishment, and so forth, firefighters must be able to access the structure. While performing a building reconnaissance, take a look at the various locking mechanisms, particularly new locking devices that offer more resistance to forcible entry. Take a minute and size up the situation for each; note on the reconnaissance from any locking devices that require more attention, especially multilock doors, metal gates, roll-up doors, window bars, interior security barriers, and so on.

Hose and ladder placement. Building intelligence obtained from conducting a pre-incident reconnaissance helps with proper hoseline selection, stretching, and placement within a particular building. It further assists in ensuring that the water discharge is of sufficient volume and that the line stretch can actually reach the seat of the fire.

Ventilation. When performing a building reconnaissance, look for easy paths of smoke travel to perform effective ventilation. Seek out ways to ventilate building smoke movement by vertical or horizontal means. Draw the fire away from the firefighters so they can access the building, perform a more effective search for victims, and suppress the fire.

Firefighter safety and survival. The firefighting tasks during the early fire growth stage have the highest degree of risk, and other fireground tactics that are being performed also present a level of risk. Hence, gathering building intelligence prior to an incident greatly helps in reducing firefighter death or injury.

Pre-incident planning involves evaluating the building fire protection systems, construction, contents, and operating procedures that could impact emergency operations. A pre-incident plan must address the structural integrity of walls, floors and the roof; live and dead loads; and obvious signs of deterioration or structural weakening.

The following are other conditions that could have an impact:

- Spread of the fire

- Ability of responding personnel to access the building's interior and to safely perform interior operations

- Potential for falling materials such as glass, curtain walls, exterior ornamentation, parapets, overhanging components and building exposures (fig. 29–1)

Fig. 29–1. Plenum areas above a drop ceiling may contain numerous multiple low-voltage cables that could entangle a firefighting crew in a collapse of the ceiling and its contents.

In deciding which building to target for a pre-incident plan, local fire departments typically target buildings in the community that present significant life safety concerns (for firefighters and occupants alike) or present a significant firefighting challenge. They are typically called **target hazards**.

The most important aspect of gathering building intelligence is to help responding firefighters effectively manage emergencies with available resources. This should not be confused with mandatory fire code inspections.

Accurate surveys and diagrams give firefighters the information needed to safely execute the most efficient operation. The pre-incident survey saves time during fire operations and helps firefighters prepare strategy and tactics to fight the fire.

Elements of the pre-incident survey

FFII 6.5.3 Department requirements for pre-incident surveys will vary. However, the common components typically found on the survey include the following:

- Date
- Owner/Manager Name
- Building name
- Floorplan
- Locations of
  - entrances/exits and internal accesses
  - utilities
  - water sources
  - fire protection systems
  - standpipes
  - hydrants
  - fire department connections (FDCs)
- Building construction
- Response hazards

Accurate diagrams will provide critical information for fire personnel in the event of an incident. Diagrams can include a plot of the building's interior and accesses, as well as locations of smoke alarms, sprinkler systems and water supply, interior and exterior building hazards, and any other factors that could affect firefighting operations at the location.

Gathering and distributing building intelligence

Building intelligence gathered during pre-incident survey of a structure can be accomplished by local fire companies, often accompanied by a chief officer. In the past, the plans that were subsequently developed often ended up in three-ring binders in the chief's car or on the dashboard of the fire engine. Although these **paper plans** continue to be used by many departments, electronic pre-incident plans offer quicker, more detailed information.

Today, local dispatch centers often have the ability to store and retrieve the building intelligence data and transmit the information to responding fire companies. This capability gives firefighters the necessary basic information concerning a building during a response and is followed by detailed diagrams/data and the actual pre-incident plan through mobile computer terminals in the apparatus.

TYPICAL TARGET HAZARD PROPERTIES AND OCCUPANCY CONSIDERATIONS

To conduct a reconnaissance survey and identify the key elements for a building intelligence plan, it is first necessary to identify the occupancy of the building. The following occupancy types are based on the *International Building Code, 2006 Edition*:

- The various *assembly occupancies (Group A)* are divided into five subgroups for the gathering of persons from theaters, night clubs, exhibition halls, arenas, stadiums, and so forth.

- *Business (Group B) occupancies* are used for office, professional, or service transactions, including the storage of records and accounts, for businesses such as animal hospitals, clinic outpatient, laboratories, print shops, and telephone exchanges.

- *Educational (Group E) facilities* cover two basic occupancies from six or more persons at any one time for educational purposes through grade 12 and a day care facility for more than five children older than 2½ years of age.

- *Factories (Group F)* are classified into two subgroups: industrial moderate and low-hazard occupancies. The use of the building or portion thereof is for assembling, fabricating, finishing, manufacturing, and the like. A moderate hazard occupancy may consists of aircraft, clothing, furniture, machinery, woodworking, and so on, whereas a low-hazard occupancy consists of beverages, foundries, gypsum, metal products, and so forth.

- *High-hazard (Group H) occupancies* are classified into three subgroups that include the manufacturing, processing, or storage of materials that constitute a physical or health hazard in quantities exceeding those allowed by the building and fire codes for occupancies, such as aerosol and compressed gas; combustible fibers and liquids; explosives, fireworks, flammable gas, and liquids; oxidizers; water-reactive materials; and so on.

- The various *Institution (Group I) occupancies* are classified into four subgroups in which people are cared for or live in a supervised environment, have physical limitations because of health or age, or are detained for penal or correctional purposes in assisted living facilities, halfway houses, alcohol and drug centers, hospitals, nursing homes, prisons, detention and correction centers, day-care facilities, and so forth (fig. 29–2).

Fig. 29–2. A fire in the area of the hospital where medical gases are stored may pose a threat to responding firefighters.

- *Mercantile (Group M) occupancies* are used for the display and sale of merchandise incidental to purposes that are accessible to the public for occupancy such as department stores, markets, and retail or wholesale facilities.

- The various *Residential (Group R) occupancies* are classified into four subgroups for sleeping purposes: boarding houses, hotels, and motels that are transient in nature; apartment buildings, dormitories, and hotels that are primarily permanent in nature; buildings with no more than two dwelling units and adult facilities for five or fewer candidates of any age for less than 24 hours; and residential occupancies arranged as residential care/assisted living facilities including more than five but not more than 16 occupants.

- *Storage (Group S) facilities* that are classified as not hazardous occupancies cover two basic groups: moderate hazard such as aerosols, books, furs, leather, and sugar; and low hazard for such occupancy as aircraft hangars, food products, glass, metal cabinets, and so forth.

- *Utility and miscellaneous (Group U)* are not classified in any specific occupancy but must conform to the building and fire codes as they pertain to fire and life hazard incidental to occupancies such as barns, carports, greenhouses, stables, tanks, and towers.[1]

CONDUCTING PRE-INCIDENT SURVEYS

SKILL DRILL

Performing pre-incident **building reconnaissance** necessitates gathering information about both the exterior and interior of the structure. Having information about a building's features—such as floor layouts, exits, and construction—enhances your ability to more effectively perform a search and rescue as well ensure your own safety and survival.

Prior to conducting a pre-incident survey, it is recommended that an appointment be made with the building owner. Remember, this is not a fire inspection to enforce the fire code. Enforcement of the fire code must be done in a separate visit—usually unannounced—to the facility and identified as such. Fire inspections have **due process** protections for the building owner, including the ability to refuse entry to the inspector. Fire inspections and pre-incident surveys are two different things.

Exterior

Preceding an interior building reconnaissance, an exterior site survey should be conducted by assessing the following:

- Building address and cross streets

- **AKA/vanity name** of building

- Primary and secondary entrances to the building

- Type of occupancy and construction

- Number of stories

- Primary/secondary hydrant locations as well as size of water mains; for rural area, nearest water supply

- Type of fire department connections, such as standpipe, sprinkler, combination sprinkler/standpipe; outside postindicator valves (PIV); outside stem and yoke (OS&Y)

- Obstructions to the building: trees, land depressions, overhead wires, roof setbacks, vehicle barriers, and so forth

- Exterior fire escape/fire stairs and exit discharge doors

- Window/door gates

- Key box location

- Basement exterior entrance and building exit discharge doors

- Fuel tanks, above and belowground locations

- Heating, ventilation, and air-conditioning (HVAC) air intake locations

The four sides to the building should be identified according to NIMS. The fireground sections are to be divided into four sides (A, B, C, D). The interior of a building is divided into divisions (floors, i.e., 7th division). For large buildings each division (floor) can be further reduced into subsector(s) (i.e., sectors 1, 2, 3, 4 and subsectors 1a, 1b, 1c, 1d). Identify the four sides of the building in figure 29–3, considering what is present on the various sides of the structure. Is the building attached or detached, a vacant lot or parking garage? Also note the topography of each side if different from side A, and so on.

Fig. 29–3. Building section identification in accordance with NIMS.

Design building descriptions

Side A: 236 Overlook Ave. Two-and-a-half story wood frame, two-family house

Side B: Three-story detached (20 ft [6 m] away) low-rise tenement building

Side C: One-story detached (50 ft [15 m] away) mercantile stores (4)

Side D: Two-and-a-half detached (10 ft [3 m] away) one-family house

Interior

Begin with a systematic building examination to evaluate the structure. For example, start from the roof level and work down to basement subgrade level(s).

Building statistics. Confirm the number of stories above and below grade, and identify the type of building construction (see chapter 7, Building Construction, for more details):

- A **fire-resistive** building is composed of structural members, walls, columns, beams, and divisions that are fire rated 2–4 hours with noncombustible materials.

- A **noncombustible** building is composed of metal frame, metal-clad, or concrete-block with unprotected or minimally protected metal bar joist (trusses).

- An building of **ordinary construction** is typically composed of masonry walls, while the interior framing system, including the roof and floors, are made of wood.

- A **heavy timber** building is composed of structural members that are large wooden columns and beams. They have masonry walls.

- A **wood frame** building may be composed of a balloon (vertical openings between exterior wall studs from basement level to attic) or a platform construction (floor joist and assembly are placed on top of the exterior bearing wall studs).

As shown in figure 29–4 (a, b, and c), from an ordinary construction foundation, a new addition constructed of pre-engineered cold-form galvanized steel is added to the upper levels. This will make it very difficult to identify where one section begins and the other ends. Adding a stucco exterior coating further obscures the different construction, making it more complicated for firefighters to determine how the building will react in a fire.

Fig. 29–4a. Top of building cold form steel addition

Fig. 29–4b. Lower portion of building/ordinary construction

Fig. 29–4c. Stucco exterior of the building

LIFE SAFETY FEATURES

Confirm the occupant load for the day (normal business hours), night, and weekend hours. Identify the building staircase(s) as being open or enclosed as well as which stairs lead to the roof and basement. If access stairs (an open stair that is located between two or more common floors and separated from the main building staircase) are present, indicate what floors they serve. Identify the side(s) of the building where an exterior fire escape and/or fire stairs may be present. Identify if windows and doors are protected by bars or metal gates.

Disabled people pose a challenge to firefighters. Knowing ahead of time the location of such a person within a building enables firefighters to help position themselves for a more effective evacuation. In many large new construction buildings, firefighters should note the **area of rescue assistance** that enables a physically challenged person to seek refuge and await instructions or assistance during an emergency evacuation. For existing buildings, local fire departments may create a safe haven area to implement an effective rescue for a person with special needs (fig. 29–5). Asking a person with special needs how best you can assist in their evacuation empowers them.

Fig. 29–5. Knowing where the areas of refuge assistance are located makes for a more effective evacuation for people with special needs.

The National Fire Incident Reporting System (NFIRS) identifies the property use as one of the following: assembly, educational, health care, detention and correction, residential, mercantile, business, industrial, utility, defense, agriculture, mining, manufacturing, processing, storage, outside or special property. If the building is a mixed-use occupancy, indicate the primary and secondary occupants.

WATER SUPPLY AND FIRE PROTECTION SYSTEMS

FFII 6.5.3 For your community water supply, if you are a suburban and urban area, identify the primary and secondary fire hydrants and the size of the water mains. Where private hydrants and private water tanks exist, identify the size of water main and tank capacity, as well as who is responsible to maintain the systems. For rural areas identify the main drafting water supply: lake, pond, pool, and river as well as the water shuttle travel time from the main water supply to portable water tanks. If your community has both types of water supplies, incorporate them into your plan. Conduct a water supply test on the hydrant system to establish the amount of water actually available. See the sidebar "Fire Flow Testing" on the following pages.

To access the water supply needed to control a fire, get an approximate structure measurement (length and width) of the building; this provides you with the needed water flows for a fire on a floor by multiplying the length by the width and dividing by 3 so as to get the total gallons per minute (gpm) per floor involvement. This also enables a fire officer and pump operator to effectively supply the water flow. If less of the total floor is involved in fire, reduce accordingly (i.e., if 25% of fire floor is involved, decrease the water supply needed; or if more than one floor is involved, increase the fire flow accordingly). For each exposure problem (building) add 50% of the 100% building involvement to the gpm figure.

When the building is equipped with a fire protection system, identify the types and particular system components that may be found.

Types of fire protection systems

Fire detection and alarm system (FAS). A building or local fire alarm system provides an audible and/or visual signal; it may range from single-station smoke detectors found in residential occupancies to a single-panel and multipanel hardwired fire alarm system. For the larger FAS systems, access the main building panel and see how the fire detection devices report to the panel so as to further assist the firefighters in locating the device that has been activated.

Sprinkler system. A building sprinkler piping system is a series of pipes that discharge water immediately from a sprinkler head once it is opened by heat from a fire. A sprinkler system may be a wet, dry, deluge, or a preaction arrangement. The system is fed from a water utility main. Identify what type of sprinkler system the building may have: full or partial. If partial, identify what area(s) it covers. A smaller **limited-area sprinkler system** consisting of 20 sprinkler heads or fewer may be tapped off the domestic water line.

Fire pump. A building fire pump is designed to increase water pressure. Where it is required, identify the fire pump's capacity in gallons per minute and the location of the pump that augments the building sprinkler and standpipe system (fig. 29–9a). For large buildings jockey pumps and pressure-reducing valves may be added to the system.

Standpipe and hose system. Standpipe and hose system are usually located within a building staircase. In

FIRE FLOW TESTING

Fire flow testing is a relatively easy procedure. To conduct a fire **flow test**, the following equipment is needed:

- Two fire hydrants with at least one 2½-in. (65-mm) nozzle butt on each

- A map of the water supply piping serving the hydrants

- Pitot gauge

- 2½-in. (65-mm) cap gauge with bleed-off cock

- Hydrant wrench

- Ruler accurate to ⅟₁₆ in. (2 mm)

- Pad of paper and pencil

To conduct a flow test, follow the steps below in numerical order. (For safety, always stand *behind* an open hydrant.)

1. Select the two hydrants nearest the property in question; designate one as a *pressure hydrant* and the other as a *flow hydrant*.

2. Sketch the location of the hydrants and the mains supplying them.

3. View the area around the flow hydrant to ensure that precautions are taken to avoid property, pedestrian, and vehicular damage from discharging water.

4. Take one 2½-in. (65-mm) cap off the pressure hydrant and tighten its other caps.

5. Attach the cap gauge to pressure hydrant.

6. Open the pressure hydrant fully and bleed off trapped air.

7. Record the pressure (psi) shown on cap gauge.

8. Remove one 2½-i. (65-mm) cap from the flow hydrant and tighten its other caps.

9. Measure the orifice size (inside diameter) to the nearest ⅟₁₆ in. (2 mm).

10. Feel the interior of the nozzle butt where it is attached to the barrel and compare it with those pictured in figure 29–6 to determine its discharge coefficient.

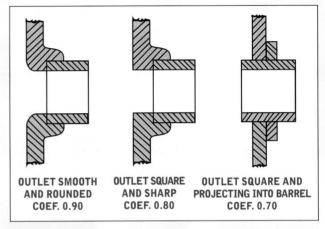

OUTLET SMOOTH AND ROUNDED COEF. 0.90   **OUTLET SQUARE AND SHARP COEF. 0.80**   **OUTLET SQUARE AND PROJECTING INTO BARREL COEF. 0.70**

Fig. 29–6. Coefficients of discharge for hydrants

11. Open flow hydrant fully.

12. Wait for constant *clear* and consistent flow (no trapped air) and then place the pitot tube in the stream following the placement criteria. Place the orifice on the pitot blade in the center of the stream, and place the edge of the pitot blade one-half the diameter of the nozzle butt away from the nozzle butt. Take the velocity pressure reading (psi) and record.

13. Take and record a second pressure reading (residual pressure) on the pressure hydrant while taking the pitot reading on the flow hydrant.

    a. Additional step to increase accuracy (if necessary): If the pressure drop of the residual pressure on the pressure hydrant is less than 25% of the original static pressure, shut down the flow hydrant and open two 2½-in. (65-mm) nozzle butts and take a new set of pitot readings. Continue opening 2½-in. (65-mm) nozzle butts on additional flow hydrant(s) until the 25% figure is reached. (A pressure drop of at least 25% is a commonly accepted practice for these tests.) Remember that each open nozzle butt represents flow. You must record pitot readings for every nozzle flow to determine the total water flow.

14. Slowly close both hydrants (at the same time, open the bleed-off cock on the pressure hydrant to allow for proper drainage).

15. Verify that both hydrants have drained fully by making sure water has passed below the level of the *steamer* (pumper connection).

16. Replace caps and tighten.

After you have performed the flow test and have recorded the information, the next step is to calculate the actual flow and plot the date.

To calculate the actual flow for each hydrant butt, first convert the velocity pressure reading(s) on the pitot gauge to gallons per minute by using the pitot gauge conversion chart in figure 29–7. Find the hydrant's pitot pressure reading on the left side. Next, move along the hydrant butt orifice diameter columns until the correct hydrant butt size is reached. Record the flow specified. Finally, multiply this flow by the nozzle butt discharge coefficient (determined earlier) to find the final fire flow for that nozzle butt.

Pitot Gauge Conversion Chart

Pitot Pressue (psi)	Hydrant Butt Orifice Diameters (in inches)							
	$2^{3/8}$	$2^{7/16}$	$2^{1/2}$	$2^{9/16}$	$2^{5/8}$	$2^{3/4}$	4	$4^{1/2}$
6	412	434	457	480	503	553	1169	1480
8	476	501	527	554	581	638	1350	1709
10	532	560	590	619	650	713	1509	1910
12	583	614	646	679	712	781	1653	2093
14	630	663	698	733	769	844	1786	2260
16	673	709	746	784	822	902	1909	2416
18	714	752	791	831	872	957	2025	2562
20	752	793	834	876	919	1009	2134	2701
22	789	831	874	919	964	1058	2239	2833
24	824	868	913	960	1007	1105	2338	2959
26	858	904	951	999	1048	1150	2434	3080
28	890	938	987	1036	1088	1194	2526	3196
30	922	971	1021	1073	1126	1236	2614	3309
32	952	1003	1055	1108	1163	1276	2700	3417
34	981	1033	1087	1142	1199	1315	2783	3522
36	1010	1063	1119	1175	1233	1354	2864	3624
38	1037	1093	1149	1207	1267	1391	2942	3724
40	1064	1121	1179	1239	1300	1427	3019	3820
42	1090	1149	1209	1269	1332	1462	3093	3915
44	1116	1176	1237	1299	1363	1496	3166	4007
46	1141	1202	1264	1328	1394	1530	3237	4097
48	1166	1228	1292	1357	1424	1563	3307	4185
50	1190	1253	1318	1385	1453	1595	3375	4271
52	1213	1278	1344	1412	1482	1627	3442	4356
54	1236	1302	1370	1439	1510	1658	3507	4439
56	1259	1326	1395	1466	1538	1688	3572	4520
58	1281	1350	1420	1492	1565	1718	3635	4600
60	1303	1373	1444	1517	1592	1747	3697	4679
62	1325	1396	1468	1542	1618	1776	3758	4756
64	1346	1418	1491	1567	1644	1805	3818	4832
66	1367	1440	1515	1591	1670	1833	3877	4907
68	1388	1461	1537	1615	1695	1860	3936	4981
70	1408	1483	1560	1639	1720	1887	3993	5054
72	1428	1504	1582	1662	1744	1914	4050	5126
74	1447	1525	1604	1685	1768	1941	4106	5196
76	1467	1545	1625	1708	1792	1967	4161	5266
78	1486	1565	1647	1730	1815	1992	4215	5335
80	1505	1585	1668	1752	1838	2018	4269	5403

Fig. 29–7. Pitot gauge conversion chart

If you opened more than one hydrant butt, add all the *converted* flows together for each residual pressure reading. This is expressed in gallons per minute as some specific residual pressure.

For example, let us say fire flow testing is conducted at a paper processing plant, and two nearby hydrants were selected. The static pressure in the *pressure hydrant* is found to be 80 psi (560 kPa). A pitot gauge reading from the one open 2½-in. (65-mm) hydrant butt (with a 0.8 discharge coefficient) on the *flowing hydrant* is 45 psi (310 kPa) and the residual pressure is 60 psi (420 kPa).

With the pitot reading pressure, the flow rate from a 2½-in. (65-mm) hydrant butt is found; for the pitot reading of 45 psi (315 kPa) the flow is roughly 1,250 gpm (4,731 L/min). This is multiplied by 0.80 to find the actual flow of 1,000 gpm (3,784 L/min).

Next, plot the static and residual pressures and corresponding flows on Q1.85, semiexponential paper (see fig. 29–8). Remember, a static pressure reading means a 0.0 gpm (0.0 L/min) flow.

Finally, draw a straight line through the points and extend the line to 20 psi (140 kPa). This is the available water supply line (curve).

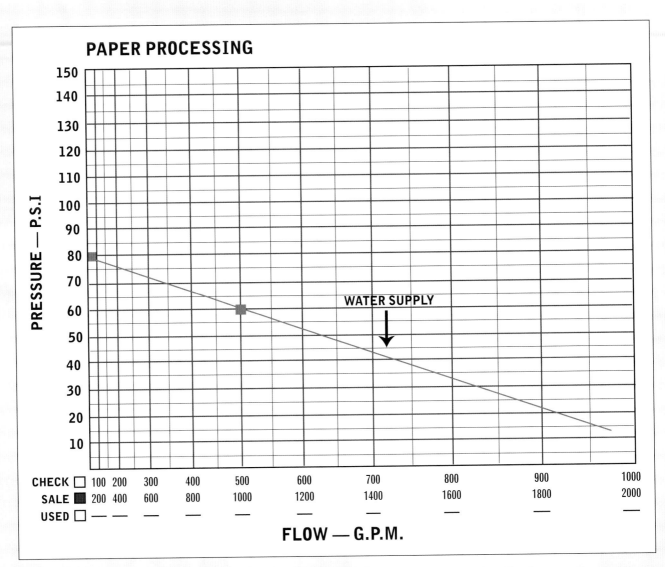

Fig. 29–8. Plot of statistical and residual pressures

Fig. 29–9. Building intelligence provides the firefighter with the fire pump gallons per minute and identifies the staircase where a standpipe connection can be found. (a) Fire pump (b) Standpipe connection

a larger building, some auxiliary standpipe connections may be found within the floor area (fig. 29–9b). In either case, identify the size of the hose thread connection so firefighters can deploy hoselines.

Fire department connections (FDCs). Other than a limited sprinkler system, when a building is equipped with FDCs, the fire department augments this interior fire protection system by supplying more water off one or more supply hoselines connected to an engine company pumper. This extra water pressure supplies one of three types of systems: sprinkler, standpipe or combination sprinkler/standpipe.

Chemical extinguishing systems. Fixed chemical extinguishing systems are designed to control flammable and combustible liquids hazards. Extinguishing agents may be dry or wet chemical, carbon dioxide, clean agent, and halon (no new halon systems are being installed; they are found in older, existing systems). They protect areas such as kitchen cooking hood system, computer data centers, dip tanks, and electrical and electronic equipment. Identify the type of system, the location within the building, and what hazard the chemical extinguishing system is protecting.

Fire wall and fire partition. A fire wall restricts the spread of fire and extends continuously from the foundation to the under side of the roof or through the roof. Fire walls essentially separate one building into two; it is the intent of a fire wall to allow complete burnout and possibly collapse on one side, but not allow fire to affect the other side of the wall. From the exterior at the roof level, fire walls will protrude no less than 18 in. (46 cm) above the roofline. However, a fire partition is a fire-rated assembly designed to restrict the spread of fire from one area of the building to an adjacent area. Openings in fire walls and partitions have openings (doors, etc.) that are protected.

HAZARDOUS MATERIALS

The use, dispensing, and handling of hazardous materials within a building should be kept on the premises at an approved fire department location. Note the location and amount of hazardous material in the building. For example, a building maintenance shop may contain flammable/combustible liquids, a fuel oil tank, and so forth.

Seek support from the fire department hazmat unit to assist in assessing the hazmat risk. Each hazardous material should have a material safety data sheet (MSDS) and other hazardous material documents as required by the authority having jurisdiction.

Hazardous Materials Management Plans (HMMP) and **Hazardous Materials Inventory Statements (HMIS)**, required under many fire codes, are particularly useful documents for pre-incident planning. They will tell you how the materials are stored/used and the quantities of the hazardous materials in the facility.

BUILDING TACTICAL INFORMATION POINT SYSTEM (TIPS)

Create TIPS to list the unique characteristic(s) within the building that are a potential threat to firefighters and/or occupants. Independently rank them according to their threat potential (i.e., truss roof: lightweight metal; 1,500 gal (5,678 L) aboveground oil tank in basement: side D, sector 4; an open vertical roof shaft: side B, sector 2, etc.).

Building data

Identify if the building is equipped with a fire department **key box** system for off-hour access or if a **master key** system is readily available as well as the following building components and features:

- The building's structural members should be identified according to the type: material supporting the horizontal load of the roof and floor (e.g., truss: metal/wood [light/heavyweight], cold-formed galvanized steel, poured concrete/re-bar, precast concrete, solid wood rafter/joist, laminated wood I-beams, and steel I-beams).

- How is the roof access achieved? Check the interior staircase or hatch. An exterior access may also be found via a fire escape gooseneck ladder. In some buildings, if a staircase does not enter into an attic space, look for an access port at the top floor level for entry into an attic or cockloft area (void space between the roof and the top floor apartment ceiling). When checking the roof area, look for automatic or manual roof vents, exhaust systems, the staircase penthouse door, and elevator

mechanical rooms that may assist with truck company ventilation. Note any heavy equipment on the roof such as refrigeration, HVAC units, and so forth.

- The floor decking may consist of precast or poured concrete, metal decking, wood such as tongue and groove planking, plywood, and oriented strand board (OSB).

- How is the basement access achieved? Check for an interior staircase(s) or an exterior access door. Access could be though both means. Note if the basement or other subbasement levels run the full length and width of the building or is partial. Also note any crawl space and entry locations.

- When a building is equipped with an elevator or a group of elevators, note the location of the **elevator mechanical room (EMR)**, the pit room (usually found below the elevator), and on what level the **firefighter phase II key** access control (described in chapter 31, Advanced Fire Attack) is located. For tall buildings, note if sky lobbies and blind shafts are present.

- A large building may have **mechanical equipment room (MER)** for the various motorized equipment such as HVAC, air compressors, chillers, and so on.

HVAC floor supply zones

Many buildings may be cooled or heated with either individual air-conditioning package units (IACPs) or an HVAC system. The IACP units usually cover a limited area or a floor. The HVAC units may cover either one floor or several floors via a duct system with fire and smoke damper to limit air movement. Some fire alarm systems may be equipped with a smoke management system to purge a smoke condition from the fire floor and pressurize the HVAC zones around the fire area. This can be achieved once the incident commander has received reports from the fire companies on the conditions in the affected areas. Other buildings may have a building management system (BMS) that automatically controls the warm and cool temperatures within a structure. The BMS system may assist the incident commander by shutting down the affected area from a remote location within the building. Understanding how the building IAPC/HVAC systems operate further assists firefighters in their efforts to control a fire.

Heating systems

Building heating systems may be powered by electric, natural gas, liquefied petroleum/gas, oil, high-pressure utility steam lines, or a combination gas/oil supply that gives the building owner an option to select the power supply source, solar power energy with high direct current voltage, and so on. Locating the building's main utility emergency shut-off valves and fuel tank locations helps the firefighter isolate the energy power supply source.

Building contact information

Emergency contract information for the building owner or management staff should be readily available to the fire department, particularly during the off-hour times.

COLLECTING DATA AND PREPARING PRE-INCIDENT PLAN

FFII 6.5.3 To begin collecting the data for the pre-incident plan, a local fire department should develop a standard recon form to gather the building information in the field, which enables the firefighters to collect the pertinent data for a fire department response. Collecting the data should include making quick sketches of the building plot plan, access into the structure for both primary and secondary, fire department connections, stair and elevator locations, taking photos of the four sides of the building, listing the unique characteristic(s) within the building that are a potential threat to firefighters and taking notes, etc.

For additional fire protection symbols representing detection and suppression systems, see Table 30-3 in chapter 30, Fire Protection Systems. Also refer to NFPA 170, *Fire Safety and Emergency Symbols* to make the pre-incident survey document easier for users, in particular chapter 7, Symbols for Use in Pre-Incident Planning Sketches (fig. 29–10).

FIRE PROTECTION SYMBOLS

SYMBOL	DESCRIPTION
⊗	Riser
 ⊳⊣	Public fire hydrant; two hose outlet & pumper connection
(AS)	Fully sprinklered space
(AS)	Partially sprinklered space
⟨NS⟩	Non-sprinklered space
FACP	Fire alarm control panel
⟨HD⟩	Heat detector
⟨SD⟩	Smoke detector

Fig. 29–10. Some NFPA 170 symbols for use in pre-planning

Complete building intelligence data (Section examples)

Once the pre-incident plan recon form is complete, the building data should be entered into a building intelligence format showing only the relative information that is pertinent to this building address (fig. 29–11). Depending on the fire department's data record capability (paper document or computer data base), the pre-incident planning information should be available for a fire department response.

OTHER BUILDING CONSIDERATIONS

Vacant buildings

While a vacant building may not contain threats to an occupant, it does present a high risk to responding firefighters. When permitted, perform an interior building reconnaissance, and if the risk is too great, conduct an exterior ground level recon as well as a tower ladder observation from above. On completion, mark the building accordingly.

Temporary conditions

Buildings under construction, renovations, and demolitions create a distinctive challenge to firefighters

Pre-Incident Planning

FIREFIGHTER II

Chapter 29

BUILDING INFORMATION

Address:	500 - 2nd Street / Hoboken, New Jersey	
AKA:	The Kliner Building	
Primary Entrance:	Side A	Sector 1
Secondary Entrance:	Side C	Sector 3
Cross Streets:	2nd St. & Jefferson St.	

WATER SUPPLY and FIRE PROTECTION SYSTEMS

Hydrant locations:	Primary: 213 Jefferson St.	Size of water main: 12-inches
Sprinkler system:		Wet: full building
Standpipe/hose system classification:		2½ National Standard thread
Location(s) standpipe riser and hose system connections:		Stair 'A'
FDC connections:		Combination spkr./standpipe
Location(s) of FDC:		Side A Sector 2
		Side D Sector C

BUILDING DATA

Key-box location:		Side A	Sector 1
No. of stories: 4 (Multi-family 6 units)		Ordinary construction	
Roofing structural members:		Solid wood rafter	
Roof access:	Interior: hatch off top floor corridor	Side A	Sector 1
	Exterior: fire escape	Side C	Sectors 3 & 4
Utility Mains:	Location of main shut-offs		
Electric	Div. # Basement	Side D	Sector 3
Natural Gas	Div. # Basement	Side D	Sector 4
Water	Div. # Basement	Side A	Sector 1

HAZARDOUS MATERIALS

No. 2 Diesel Fuel: aboveground tank
(1,500 gal. / enclosed room / 2-hour fire rating)

Div. # Basement	Side A	Sector 4

Emergency contact person(s): Martin Kenney
Emergency telephone numbers: 1-653-427-2224

Fig. 29–11. Sample of record of building intelligence card (fig. 29–12). The conditions are suitable for rapid fire spread both vertically upward and downward. During a building reconnaissance, firefighters should note vehicle access; the location and accessibility of the fire department connection; that the standpipe riser is within two floors of the highest level of work; that the top of the standpipe riser is not left open without a shutoff valve; that floor outlet valves are closed, especially at the below-grade level; the storage of flammable and combustible liquids/gases; explosive materials; temporary heating equipment; cutting and welding operations; and the floor level on which the staircase ends before encountering makeshift ladders to access upper floors.

Fig. 29–12. A building under construction (Jersey City, NJ) creates distinctive challenges to firefighters. Conditions rapidly spread fire both upward and downward. Wind conditions may create the need for ember patrols. (Courtesy of Ron Jeffers)

The danger of structural problems is heightened when the building is missing fire protection features such as spray-on fireproofing, fire walls and partitions, temporary erected wooden mold forms, steel bracing cables, and so forth.

Buildings undergoing floor renovations within an existing structure pose an even greater life safety threat to all occupants. Means of egress paths may also be temporarily altered but must be maintained during this phase of construction.

BUILDING INTELLIGENCE PLANNING FOR A FIRE DEPARTMENT RESPONSE

When a complete building intelligence planning program is incorporated into the fire department management system, the local dispatch center can provide more decision-based knowledge about the building while the fire companies are responding. This critical building information enhances the fire officer's **thinking-in-time** process with the initial size-up and also empowers firefighter crews with their assigned tasks within a specific structure. A dispatch communications center can provide incoming fire companies with key building essentials such as water supply, fire protection systems, life safety, and any potential threats to a firefighter. When the incident becomes a working alarm box, other building intelligence information are provided to the incident commander.

Because the fire service is a supportive organization by default, a department mission preparedness statement should include pre-incident building intelligence to further safeguard firefighter as well as occupant wellness.

PRE-PLANNING OF THE FUTURE

For future emergency responses, the fire service must wholeheartedly embrace a broad base-data entry and retrieval computer system that includes the following:

- Tracking systems not only for firefighters, but occupants as well

- Operational status of building management and fire protection systems, even before arrival at the building (transmitted to responding units)

- The ability for fire communication centers to dispatch building data intelligence in 3-D format showing digital blueprints of the structure that is also shared with local mutual-aid groups

- Mass casualty patient tracking and shared patient medical information

This collective emergency database will enable the fire department to provide real-time decision-based information to the fire and emergency services as well as the IC while responding to any incident and will continue to support fireground operations throughout the event.

NOTES

1. National Fire Protection Association. NFPA 1001, *Standard for Firefighter Professional Qualifications.*

2. International Building Code. 2006. *Use and Occupancy Classification.*

3. NFPA 170, *Standard for Fire Safety and Emergency Symbols*, 2006 Edition.

QUESTIONS

1. What is pre-planning? Why is it important to the incident commander?

2. What are some topics that should be included in a pre-incident plan?

3. Explain the difference between a "building reconnaissance" and a "building inspection."

4. When performing a building reconnaissance, you should look at both the _____ and the _____ of the building.

5. Name six items that should be identified while looking at the outside of the building.

6. When looking at the interior of the building, use a _____ approach to ensure that all areas are seen.

7. What are some unique concerns when pre-planning a building under construction or demolition?

8. A quick equation to determine the need fire flow is _____ times _____ divided by _____.

9. Describe the steps when fire flow testing a hydrant system.

10. Once a building pre-plan is complete, what agency should receive a copy to assist the fire department when responding to the building?

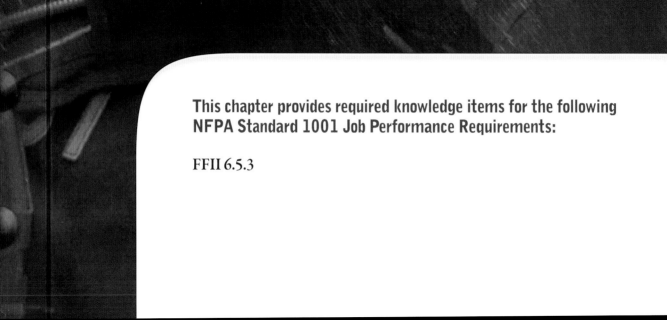

This chapter provides required knowledge items for the following NFPA Standard 1001 Job Performance Requirements:

FFII 6.5.3

OBJECTIVES

Upon completion of this chapter, you should be able to do the following:

- Identify the value of protective systems in protecting life and property and the reasons why firefighters should understand them
- Identify the common symbols used on drawings to diagram them
- Describe the basic functions and components of a fire alarm system
- Describe the basic types of fire alarm-initiation devices and how they operate
- Describe the basic types of fire alarm-notification appliances
- Explain the ways fire alarms can be transmitted to a fire department
- Identify types of sprinkler heads and how they operate
- Identify types of sprinkler systems and their main components
- Identify styles of indicating valves
- Identify standpipe classes and types of systems
- Describe problems firefighters encounter with standpipe valves in high-rise buildings
- Identify special hazard-extinguishing systems and how they work
- Identify specific problems specialized systems can introduce to responding firefighters

INTRODUCTION

Detection and suppression systems assist building occupants and fire departments. Detection systems warn occupants to flee burning buildings and can notify fire departments so fires can be safely controlled. Upon activation by a detection system, an automatic suppression system can limit fire spread and prevent unnecessary danger to building occupants by suppressing or controlling a fire before it gets large, thereby limiting smoke. These systems protect lives and property, and the public expects firefighters to know how they work.

Firefighters must know the names of detection and suppression system components. Not understanding them can result in communication breakdown between system designers and the fire service, and also within the fire service itself. These breakdowns can occur on the fireground or years before a fire when the system is initially designed. A firefighter can't speak with authority about a component or understand another's description of it if he or she doesn't know its name. Part of identifying components is knowing what they look like, but it's also important to know the different names they may be called. As with other areas of firefighting, communication breakdowns can cause injuries and death to firefighters and victims. Once you know something's name, you can get to how it works, and when it doesn't work properly, you can communicate that correctly.

FIRE ALARM SYSTEMS

FFII 6.5.3 Buildings protected by fire alarm systems are called **protected premises**. Without fire-detection systems, occupants might not discover a fire until they are overcome by smoke or heat, and fire departments might not arrive in time to save lives and property. Firefighters must know how systems work, the language to identify their components, and how to keep them reliably in service.

Fire alarm systems send and receive signals. An **alarm signal** indicates that an emergency condition needs immediate attention. The two basic kinds of alarm signals are the following:

1. Local alarm signals

2. Remotely transmitted alarm signals

A **local alarm signal** notifies a building's occupants of fire. A **remotely transmitted alarm signal** notifies the fire department directly or indirectly of fire (for example, indirectly through a separate monitoring facility such as a central station, described below). Fire alarm systems also generate trouble, supervisory, and annunciation signals. A **trouble signal** identifies system problems that can influence the system's reliability. A **supervisory signal** provides a way of monitoring an alarm system status and indicating abnormal conditions.

Fire alarm system components

Key components of fire alarm systems are described using a set of terms defined by NFPA 72, the *National Fire Alarm Code*.[1] These include:

Alarm-initiating devices: automatic or manual mechanisms that cause a system to indicate an alarm condition.

Alarm-notification appliances: mechanisms that make building occupants aware of an alarm condition.

Fire alarm control panel (FACP) or **fire alarm control unit (FACU)**: the brains of these systems that connect and supervise all of this hardware, or the main control unit for a fire alarm system.

The following three sections discuss how alarm-initiating devices work and activate the alarm-notification appliances through the FACP (fig. 30–1).

Fig. 30–1. Fire alarm control panel

Alarm-initiating devices

An **alarm-initiation device** is a hardware component used to determine if there is a fire. There are many kinds of alarm-initiating devices and technologies. People activate some, such as manual-pull stations, and others automatically activate when they detect smoke or heat. The method used to connect and control these devices helps determine what a fire department knows about the fire when firefighters arrive.

Some initiating devices use similar ways to detect fires but work in different areas. **Spot-type detectors** detect fire at a particular point or location. Typically, these devices are heat, smoke, or rate-of-rise detectors. A **linear detector** is a device in which detection is continuous along a path, essentially a cable that may run through a large portion of a building or loop around the ceiling of a room.

Manual-pull stations. Manual-pull stations are really just switches. Most of the time they are off, but if there is a fire, people flip them on to sound an alarm. NFPA 72 refers to them as **manual fire alarm boxes**, or equipment that activates a fire alarm by opening or closing a circuit. Even system designers, however, call them pull stations. There are two kinds.

Single-action pull stations (fig. 30–2) are manual fire alarm boxes that require only one step to activate, usually pulling down a switch or handle.

Double-action pull stations (fig. 30–3) are manual fire alarm boxes that require two steps to activate. Generally one step, such as lifting a cover or breaking a glass, exposes another switch that must be activated. The double action helps prevent **false alarms**, the activation of fire alarm systems in the absence of an emergency or fire condition.

One might be tempted to call a manual-pull station a form of spot detector. It can be difficult to pinpoint fire in a building based on the location of the activated pull station. Someone far from the fire might smell smoke and pull the station as he or she leaves the building.

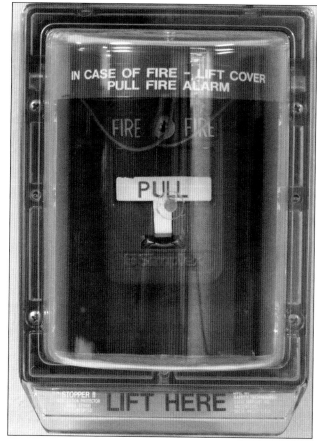

Fig. 30–3. Alarm-initiating devices—double-action pull station

Fig. 30–2. Alarm-initiating devices—single-action pull station

Heat detectors. A **heat detector** warns of a fire condition by sensing a high temperature, a high rate of rise in temperature, or both. A **fixed-temperature detector** activates when a predetermined high temperature is reached. Fixed-temperature detectors can be spot-type detectors or linear detectors (fig. 30–4). (The most common form of heat detector is the sprinkler head, which we will discuss later.)

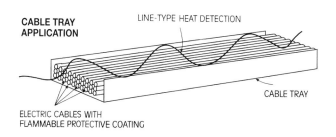

Fig. 30–4. Alarm-initiating devices—linear heat detector

Another type of heat detector, a **rate-of-rise** detector (fig. 30–5), activates when the temperature surrounding it rises faster than a predetermined value. Rate-of-rise detectors are almost always spot-type detectors, although some cutting-edge, fiber-optic, linear detectors can be put into a rate-of-rise mode.

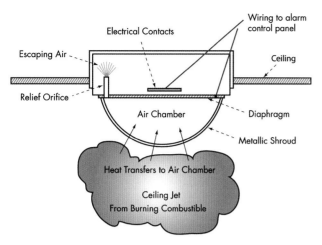

Fig. 30–5. Alarm-initiating devices—rate-of-rise detector. (Courtesy of John Morrison)

Fig. 30–7. A typical spot-type smoke detector

Another type of heat detector called a **rate compensation detector** (fig. 30–6) accurately senses surrounding air temperature regardless of temperature change in the air around it.

Fig. 30–6. Alarm-initiating devices—rate compensation detector

This kind of detector can be particularly useful in spaces where large temperature changes or cooling air movements occur.

Smoke detectors. A **smoke detector** (fig. 30–7) activates when it detects products of combustion, commonly called smoke. The most familiar is a **single-station smoke alarm device**, a combination smoke detector and alarm available in stores and used typically in existing private homes without detection-system code requirements. These units run on batteries and have built-in alarms. When they are activated, a local alarm sounds. They are commonly used in existing dwellings.

NFPA 72 has a number of requirements for new residences, including the following requirements for device locations:

- At least one device located on each level
- One device in each bedroom
- One device in the corridor outside each sleeping area

Newer residential systems are required to have all devices interconnected so that they can sound when one is activated. Newer systems also require a connection to household current.

Smoke detectors used in most modern buildings do not have built-in alarms. When they activate, they send a signal to an FACP, which then activates notification appliances throughout the building.

There are two basic types of smoke detector; ionization and photoelectric.

Ionization smoke detectors (fig. 30–8) use a small amount of radioactive material, usually americium, to charge the air passing through two oppositely charged electrodes. They are always spot detectors because the electrodes must be very close to each another. When the detector is powered, conductance between the electrodes is constantly measured.

Without smoke, this charge allows a constant current to flow between the electrodes. If smoke presents between the electrodes, this current drops. Circuits in the detector sense this, and the detector activates.

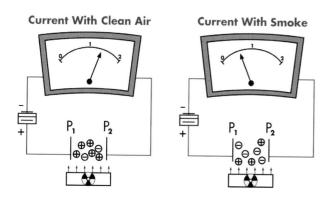

Fig. 30–8. Operation of an ionization smoke detector. (Courtesy of John Morrison)

Photoelectric smoke detectors use light beams to determine if smoke is present. There are two types of photoelectric detectors.

The spot-type generally uses **light scattering** (fig. 30–9). Smoke's deflection of the light beam sends the detector into alarm. Light normally projects inside the detector. Only when smoke is present does it reflect onto a sensor that activates the detector.

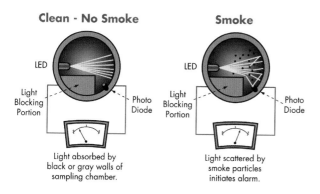

Fig. 30–9. Operation of a light-scattering smoke detector. (Courtesy of John Morrison)

The other type of photoelectric smoke detector is the **photoelectric light-obscuration smoke detector**, which measures how much of a light beam is blocked by smoke. This method is commonly used in a **projected-beam detector** (fig. 30–10), a type of linear photoelectric light-obscuration smoke detector in which a light beam is projected from a sending unit to a receiving unit. These detectors are not spot detectors. They are used to cover large areas such as an office building's atrium or a warehouse; the sending unit is mounted on one wall, and the receiving unit is mounted directly across on the opposite wall. When smoke blocks the beam, the receiver detects a reduction in transmitted light and actuates the alarm.

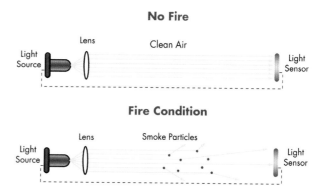

Fig. 30–10. Operation of a projected-beam smoke detector. (Courtesy of John Morrison)

An **air-sampling detector** (fig. 30–11), sometimes called a VESDA® system, uses suction tubes to draw air from different locations within a protected space. Air drawn into a smoke detector or gas-analysis device determines if fire is present (fig. 30–12). VESDA was one of the first innovators in this area, and the name sometimes describes the technology, although there are other vendors. Such systems are very sensitive, and often the tubes are mounted inside electrical cabinets and other spaces where rapid detection is necessary to prevent damage.

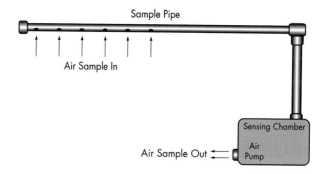

Fig. 30–11. Operation of an air-sampling detector. (Courtesy of John Morrison)

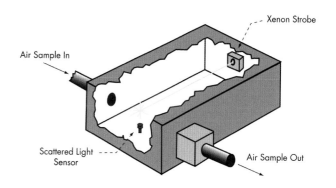

Fig. 30–12. Operation of an air-sampling detector sensing chamber. (Courtesy of John Morrison)

Fire Protection Systems

FIREFIGHTER II

Chapter 30

Gas detectors. **Gas detectors** detect dangerous chemical components a fire produces. **Single-station carbon monoxide (CO) detectors** are common in residential occupancies and detect the incomplete burning of solid, liquid, and gaseous fuels. They can detect CO exposure from cars running in connected garages and improperly vented appliances, such as furnaces and water heaters, as well as from fires. Vendors are introducing units to connect to building fire alarm systems as well.

Flame detectors. A **flame detector** activates an alarm when it detects radiant energy. There are two types: infrared, often called IR, and ultraviolet, often called UV (fig. 30–13). Sometimes, light from other sources causes unwanted alarms. Sunlight can accidentally activate an IR detector. Lightning, welding, and other electrical arcing can activate a UV detector. Combination UV/IR detectors ensure alarms activate only when they detect light from actual fires. The different kinds of flame detectors can look similar. Check a detector's information plate to determine its type.

Fig. 30–13. Alarm-initiating devices—UV detector

Alarm verification. If allowed by local authorities, some fire detection and alarm systems can reduce false alarms by allowing confirmation of smoke alarm operation. Sometimes alarms are confirmed by resetting smoke detectors that have activated and waiting for reactivation. If reactivation occurs within a given time, the system notification devices are activated. Another way alarms are confirmed is to require smoke detectors to be activated for a minimum time before accepting them as valid alarm-initiation signals and activating notification devices. Alarm verification is typically used on systems for commercial structures like office buildings. It can prevent frequent false activation of systems that can result in occupants ignoring alarms during an actual fire (the system crying wolf). However, they can also delay

fire department response. The use of alarm verification should be carefully considered.

Some systems use a **cross-zoned alarm system** in which two detection devices must activate before initiating a fire alarm condition. This is commonly used where a suppression system will be activated to avoid false activation of the system.

Notification appliances

When a manual- or automatic-detection device activates, there must be a way to notify the building's occupants of a fire and evacuate them. **Alarm-notification appliances** accomplish this. There are two types: Audible appliances that are heard, and visible appliances that are seen.

Audible appliances include bells, horns, sirens, and speakers (figs. 30–14, 30–15, and 30–16). A **temporal 3 pattern** is a standard audible alarm signal to alert a building's occupants to evacuate.

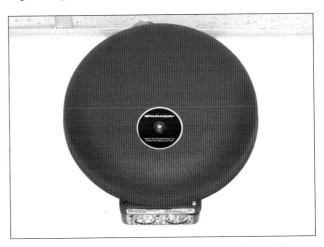

Fig. 30–14. Alarm-notification appliances—alarm bell

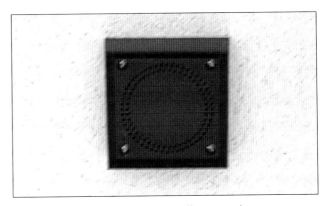

Fig. 30–15. Alarm-notification appliances—horn

Fig. 30–16. Alarm-notification appliances—siren

Visible-notification devices commonly called strobes (fig. 30–17) warn occupants visually of an emergency condition.

Fig. 30–17. Alarm-notification appliances—strobe

Types of fire alarm systems

NFPA 72 defines a fire alarm system as: "A system or portion of a combination system that consists of components and circuits arranged to monitor and annunciate the status of fire alarm or supervisory signal-initiating devices and to initiate the appropriate response to those signals."[2]

We just discussed "the components and circuits arranged to monitor and annunciate the status of a fire alarm." They are the alarm-initiating devices, alarm-notification devices, and FACP. We even discussed supervisory signals. We haven't discussed how everything ties together to "initiate the appropriate response to those signals."

1. How is the fire department notified of a fire? What happens to the signal when an FACP receives word that a detector has activated?

2. What happens if the FACP indicates a trouble condition? Who, if anyone, is directly notified, and where are they located?

Fire alarm systems can be configured a couple of ways to ensure these things happen. There are trade-offs in cost and reliability, and different protected areas have different requirements. The following are the basic types of fire alarm systems:

- Local fire alarm systems
- Auxiliary municipal fire alarm systems
- Remote supervising-station fire alarm systems
- Central-station fire alarm systems
- Proprietary supervising-station systems

Local fire alarm systems. A **local fire alarm system** only warns occupants of a building that there is a fire. It sounds an alarm within the building where it is activated but does not send a signal out of the building. Occupants learn of the fire when a detector activates. A local alarm system does not call a fire department. Building occupants must contact the fire department after they exit the building. Signs often located near or on fire alarm bells remind occupants to call the fire department.

Auxiliary fire alarm system. When a system transmits a fire alarm signal through to local fire service communication center using the same equipment and methods as alarms transmitted from street level alarm boxes, it is called an **auxiliary fire alarm system** (as described in chapter 28, Advanced Fire Department Communications). A system like this is usually created by connecting the set of fire detection devices inside the protected building to a "master box" located on the outside of the building. The master box acts in a similar manner to a manually activated municipal fire alarm system pull box. However, instead of being manually activated, it is activated by the building detection system. When activated it transmits a unique code through the municipal fire alarm system wiring to fire department headquarters when a fire detection device within the protected building is activated.

Remote-supervising station. When a system transmits alarm, supervisory, and trouble signals from a protected location to a remote location where suitable action is taken, it is called a **remote supervising-station alarm system.** It allows trouble and supervisory signals to go elsewhere than the alarm signals. With these systems, the supervising and trouble signals can be transmitted to a maintenance facility while the alarm signals go to an alarm-dispatch facility. These requirements are less strict than those required of a central-station system, described below.

Central station. A **central-station alarm system** is one in which the operations of the circuits and devices are:

1. Transmitted automatically to a central station

2. Recorded in a central station

3. Maintained by a central station

4. Supervised from a central station

The station is staffed by operators who receive a signal and take action as required by the National Fire Alarm Code, such as notifying the fire department. All the devices and their supervision and trouble signals going to one place make these systems different from remote supervising stations.

Proprietary. A system that transmits a signal from a protected facility to a monitoring station operated by the facility's owner is a **proprietary system**. These systems are common on college and office campuses, where the same group manages and is responsible for protecting many buildings.

Fire alarm annunciation systems

Fire alarm annunciation systems notify the fire department and others concerned of a fire's location (table 30–1). Some systems provide no information at the FACP about a fire's location within the protected building. These systems are called **non-coded alarms**. Other systems annunciate a fire's **zone**, the area within a protected facility in which a signal such as a fire alarm usually can be received or a form of control can be maintained, such as activating notification appliances. For example, a zone might be the third floor, or it might be more specific depending on the design of the system. A **zoned coded alarm**, according to NFPA 72, is "an audible or visible signal that conveys several discrete bits or units of information. Notification signal examples are numbered strokes of an impact-type appliance and numbered flashes of a visible appliance." In other words, a coded device creates a signal based on pulses of light or sound that indicate which zone is involved. A zoned non-coded alarm system tells a firefighter what zone it is in at the FACP or **remote annunciation panel**, a secondary FACP generally more conveniently located than the main panel such as at the main entrance to the building. A zoned coded system indicates what zone the

fire is in on the FACP and through a coded audio or visual signal.

Some newer systems have addressable devices. Again, using the NFPA definition, an **addressable device** is "a fire alarm system component with discrete identification that can have its status individually identified or that is used to individually control other functions." Think of each device, whether it's a detector, horn, strobe, some switch attached to the sprinkler system, or something else, as a simple computer on a large network. The computer isn't that smart, but it can continuously talk to the main computer on the network, which is the FACP. If it is a detection device, it can send a message that it has been activated to the FACP. If it is an initiation appliance, it may receive a message from the FACP to sound or light up. An addressable system has the following advantages:

1. Firefighters can quickly identify the specific detection devices that have activated when they arrive at a building.

2. The devices and appliances can continuously tell the panel they are working properly. In other words, the panel can supervise them.

3. Because each device or appliance has its own network address, the exact location of every activated device can be determined by looking at the FACP.

4. People servicing the system know which detectors need to be serviced because the detectors either report their own failures to the FACP or do not communicate with the panel.

5. If the designers want only certain appliances such as horns or strobes in specific areas of large buildings activated when the panel is in alarm, it is easily achieved because only certain network addresses can be activated.

Table 30–1. Types of alarm coding

Category	Description
Non-coded alarm	No information is given on the location of the activated device.
Zoned non-coded alarm	The fire alarm control panel shows the zone where the activated device is located, and it may indicate the specific device that was activated.
Zoned coded alarm	The fire alarm system indicates over an audible device the zone that has been activated. This type of system is often used in special occupancies like hospitals and prisons, where special evacuation strategies are used, and some occupants will not be evacuated.
Master coded alarm	The system is both zoned and coded, but the audible devices are used for a number of purposes, such as a change of class periods in a school. These systems are not installed in new buildings, and are being replaced.

Emergency voice alarm and fire department communication systems. Emergency voice alarm service is used when verbal instructions can be helpful to speed up evacuation and provide direction to building occupants. Voice alarm systems provide a recorded message that gives instructions to building occupants after receiving a detection signal. **Fire department communications systems**—often taking the form of a fixed, dedicated "firefighters telephone system" permit two way communications between firefighters in different locations, including stairwells, elevator cabs, and elevator lobbies in high-rise buildings for example.

Firefighting considerations for fire alarm systems

There are some things that should be thought about when working with fire alarm systems. These include:

- Making sure you don't reset the system until the device of origin has been determined. Modern smoke detectors usually have a solid red light on the individual detection device that indicates the device has been activated.

- Use the silence switch on the panel only if you are sure that the activation is a false alarm.

- Modern panels can usually store a history of alarm activations. You can usually scroll through them to see the history of activations.

- Systems with addressable devices will be able to tell you the exact device that has been activated at the FACP.

- Older zoned systems will only be able to tell you what zone has been activated. With zoned non-coded fire alarm systems you will only be able to find out what zone has been activated at the FACP. With coded fire alarm systems you can still tell what zone has been activated at the FACP, but you can also use the audio or visual signal provided to tell you what zone has been activated. You have to know how to interpret the code though— yet another reason to make sure you know the buildings in your jurisdiction.

FIRE SUPPRESSION SYSTEMS

FFII 6.5.3 Fire-extinguishing agents are liquid, solid, or gaseous materials applied to extinguish or control fires. All suppression systems in this chapter do nothing but ensure that a fire-extinguishing agent is put on a fire. Detection systems that work with suppression systems ensure an agent is applied as soon as a fire's existence is established.

Fire suppression systems can extinguish or control fires without firefighter intervention, and therefore, save lives and property. They can be an excellent first defense against fire. The public expects that firefighters understand how these systems operate. The most common automatic suppression systems are automatic sprinkler systems.

Water as an extinguishing agent

Water is the most common suppression agent applied by fire departments and activated sprinkler systems. Water puts out fires by removing heat from a fire, lowering the fire's temperature and thereby collapsing side one of the tetrahedron. Most of the temperature change is caused by water changing to steam; however the water temperature increases too, and that also removes heat from the fire.

Sprinkler systems

An **automatic sprinkler system**[3] is a system of pipes and sprinkler heads that, when activated, discharge water onto a fire without involving people. Most systems use

automatic sprinkler heads that open when heated to a certain temperature. Deluge systems use open heads and rely on valves to open when nearby detection systems activate. Sprinkler systems are designed and installed under NFPA 13, *Standard for the Installation of Sprinkler Systems*. All water-based suppression systems are inspected according to **NFPA 25, *Standard for the Inspection, Testing, and Maintenance of Water-Based Fire Protection Systems*.**[4]

Sprinklers and life safety. Sprinkler systems improve life safety by preventing flashover and fire spread outside of the room of origin.[5] This suppresses smoke, the number-one killer of people in fires. Even when a sprinkler system is not able to extinguish, the fire is usually confined to the room in which it started. This makes firefighters' jobs much easier.

Sprinkler heads. An **automatic sprinkler head** is essentially a heat detector that activates upon reaching a predetermined temperature. Unlike the heat detectors we have discussed, automatic sprinkler heads connect to piping. When the heads open, the pipes release water in them. Because sprinkler heads around a fire heat first, water flows to them and quickly controls and possibly extinguishes the fire.

Sprinkler operating elements. A sprinkler head that opens when the solder holding two pieces of metal together fuses or melts is called a **fusible link sprinkler head** (fig. 30–18). This fusing releases two levers that prevent water flow from the sprinkler head. Table 30–2 contains a list of sprinkler operating temperatures. A sprinkler head with a glass bulb works similarly. The glass bulb that prevents water from flowing breaks when it reaches the activation temperature. This type of sprinkler is called a **frangible bulb sprinkler head.**

Sprinkler deflectors. All sprinklers have **deflectors** to break the water stream into droplets and push them to cover an area larger than a straight stream of water would.

Sprinkler heads are not distinguished only by operating elements. They are also identified by mounting position, either upright or pendent. An **upright sprinkler head** (fig. 30–19) is mounted above sprinkler piping, so a large deflector must divert the upward-flowing water stream to the floor. Upright sprinklers have the gravitational advantage that any dirt, rust, or debris in the pipes probably will not accumulate in the head to block the flow of water.

A **pendent sprinkler head** (figs. 30–20 and 30–21) is mounted on the underside of sprinkler piping. As with all modern sprinkler heads, deflectors direct the water stream down. Deflectors tend to be much smaller than in upright sprinklers because they only break water into droplets to increase coverage and do not change flow direction. Pendent sprinklers are common. They mount to unseen pipes via ceiling holes often covered with caps. These caps, when heated, drop to expose the sprinkler heads.

Fig. 30–18. Operation of a fusible-link sprinkler. (Courtesy of John Morrison)

Fig. 30–19. Upright frangible-bulb sprinkler head. (Courtesy of Viking)

Table 30–2. Typical sprinkler head activation temperatures

Temperature rating °F	°C	Temperature classification	Color coding	Glass bulb colors
135–170	57–77	Ordinary	Uncolored or black	Orange or red
175–225	79–107	Intermediate	White	Yellow or green
250–300	121–149	High	Blue	Blue
325–375	163–191	Extra high	Red	Purple
400–475	204–246	Very extra high	Green	Black
500–575	260–302	Ultra high	Orange	Black
625	343	Ultra high	Orange	Black

Fig. 30–20. Pendent frangible-bulb sprinkler head. (Courtesy of Viking)

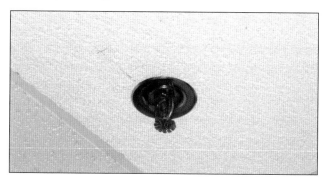

Fig. 30–21. Pendent fusible-link sprinkler head

Sidewall sprinklers are designed for installation on one wall of a rectangular room. The sidewall sprinkler has a distinct deflector that distributes water sideways along the length of a room. These types of heads are often found in hotel guest rooms.

In buildings where sprinklers were installed before 1953, you may encounter **old-style sprinkler heads**. This type of head directs some water toward the ceiling. These are different from modern sprinklers that direct the entire flow down. Old-style heads discharge about half the water to the ceiling and half on the fire. Newer sprinklers flow almost all water to the floor, where it can control fires.

Special sprinkler heads. Dry sprinkler heads are designed for installation in areas subject to freezing. An extension has a seal in the inlet end that prevents water from entering the extension until the sprinkler operates. A **dry pendent sprinkler** consists of a standard pendent sprinkler head attached to a section of pipe known as a drop nipple. A shaft inside the top of the drop nipple holds a cap that prevents water from entering. As a result, the inside of the drop nipple is normally dry, so it can't freeze. When the sprinkler head opens, the shaft holding the cap releases and allows water to flow through the nipple to the sprinkler head and the refrigerated room. Because water flows only through the drop nipples where the sprinkler head fused, only the activated sprinkler/drop nipple assemblies must be replaced.

Early-suppression, fast-response (ESFR) sprinkler heads quickly discharge a density of water droplet sizes that provide fast suppression. They are usually used in warehouse rack storage and other high-challenge areas. ESFR sprinkler heads are installed to specifically avoid the problems presented by sprinklers built into storage racks. In-rack sprinklers can damaged when stock is moved on and off the racks. In-rack sprinkler heads also make rearrangement of the racks extremely difficult, since rearrangement of the racks would require rearrangement of the sprinkler pipes as well.

A **deluge sprinkler head** has no release mechanism. This type of head is always open. They are used in special systems where all the heads flow at the same time. Deluge systems are uncommon because they require a lot of water, but they are used in special situations—for example when sprinkler systems are used to apply foam onto a hazard.

A **residential sprinkler** activates quickly to enhance occupant survivability in the room of origin. As residential spacing of heads is usually limited, they are designed to control fires with as few heads activating as possible.

Types of sprinkler systems

There are a few types of sprinkler systems. Each has its own purpose and uses a discussed sprinkler head:

- A **wet-pipe system** is a system of pipes filled with water that flow water onto a fire when an automatic sprinkler head is fused.

- A **dry-pipe system** is similar to a wet-pipe system except its piping system is filled with air or nitrogen instead of water. Water still flows from fused heads, but the pipes must fill with water first. These systems are commonly used when freezing is a consideration.

- A **deluge system** consists of pipes with open sprinkler heads. All heads flow when a deluge system is activated. Such systems are used in high-hazard areas where much water is necessary to extinguish a fire.

- A **preaction system** uses elements of deluge and dry-pipe systems and minimizes water damage. It resembles a dry-pipe system except it requires another detection system and a sprinkler head's fusing for water to flow.

- A **residential system** prevents flashover in rooms of origin, improves chances for occupant escape, and prevents fire spread to adjacent rooms.

Wet-pipe systems. The most common and simple sprinkler is the **wet-pipe sprinkler system** (fig. 30–22). A series of automatic sprinkler heads connects to a system of pipes. If the sprinkler head opens because it is near a fire, it flows water and suppresses the fire. An alarm system activates in two basic ways when a wet-pipe system starts to flow water.

The first method is from a water-flow indicator or **flow switch** that changes position when fluid such as water flows past it (fig. 30–23). A flow switch uses a paddle or vane to detect water flow in sprinkler pipes. These water-flow indicators normally contain a retard feature that prevents the water-flow indicator from sending a signal as a result of pressure surges in the system. It is distinct from a flowing sprinkler head.

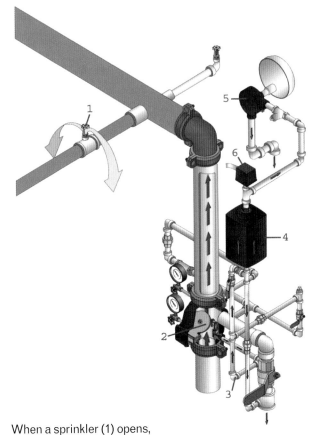

When a sprinkler (1) opens,
The discharging water lifts the alarm valve clapper (2) and flows through the alarm port (3)
to the retard chamber (4). When the retard chamber is filled, water flows to the water motor alarm (5) and/or the optional pressure switch (6) which signals an electric alarm bell.

Fig. 30–22. Operation of a wet-pipe sprinkler system. (Courtesy of Viking)

The second method is from a **sprinkler alarm valve** that indicates water flow. This is essentially a **check valve** that permits flow in only one direction and detects that flow into the full set of sprinkler system pipes. It can activate an electric alarm device or operate a **water motor gong**, a type of local **water-flow alarm** powered by water moving through a sprinkler system. A water-flow detector or alarm-check valve activates the water-flow alarm. Sprinkler alarm valves are also subject to pressure surges. A **retard chamber** between the sprinkler valve and water-flow alarm prevents false alarms by allowing pressure surges to dissipate before setting off the water-flow alarm.

Fig. 30–23. Flow switch

Dry-pipe systems. A dry-pipe sprinkler system (fig. 30–24) is similar to a wet-pipe system and is used generally where freezing is an issue. Without water, the pipes can't freeze. Instead of all the pipes in the system being filled with water, they are filled with compressed air or nitrogen. When a sprinkler head fuses, the gas leaks out and water flows into the pipe.

A dry-pipe sprinkler system uses a **dry-pipe valve.** Balanced forces of air and water on opposing sides of the valve prevent it from opening under normal circumstances. Usually the water pressure is much higher, but pressure is a force exerted on an area, and a larger area of the valve face is exposed on the gas side. The forces balance, and the valve opens only when the air pressure drops.

When a sprinkler head opens, the pressure on the gas side decreases because all the air in the system leaks out the sprinkler head. Because the force from the gas side decreases, the forces are no longer balanced and the dry-pipe valve opens. **Accelerators** and **exhausters** speed opening of the valve and expulsion of air from the pipes so water can flow. They activate when the system is activated.

Dry-pipe systems are supervised by measuring the gas pressure within the sprinkler pipes. Under normal circumstances a small amount of gas will leak from

the pipes over time. A pressure maintenance device (typically an air compressor) is used to add pressure back into the pipes when it drops below a certain level. This air is added so that the system will not discharge accidentally due to low pressure in the piping system. The device can add only a small amount of air and will not influence normal system activation.

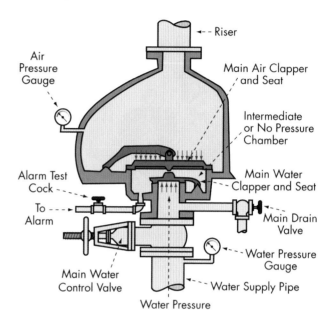

Fig. 30–24. Dry-pipe valve. (Courtesy of John Morrison)

Deluge systems. A **deluge sprinkler system** (fig. 30–25) uses open sprinkler heads called deluge sprinkler heads. The deluge system connects to a local detection system. The type of initiating device is based on the hazard being protected and so it might be a smoke, heat, or flame detector (the system can also be activated manually). When the initiating device is activated, it signals the fire alarm control panel, which in turn opens the deluge valve, allowing water to flow through the piping to the open sprinkler heads. Because all heads flow simultaneously, a large volume of water may be required to function properly, and fire pumps are often necessary to maintain pressure.

Preaction systems. **Preaction systems** (fig. 30–26) use elements of deluge and dry-pipe systems. A preaction system resembles a dry-pipe system, except it requires another detection system (typically using smoke detectors as initiating devices) for water to flow in addition to a sprinkler head's fusing. Water flows onto a fire only if the detection system opens the preaction valve and a sprinkler head fuses. In other words, two methods of detection, typically a smoke detector and a sprinkler head must, activate for water to flow, which minimizes the possibility of water damage.

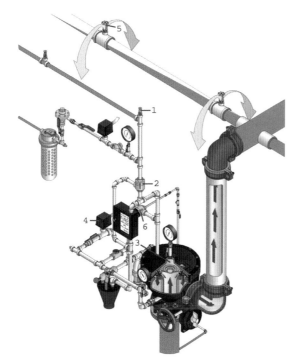

Fig. 30–25. Operation of a deluge system. (Courtesy of Viking)

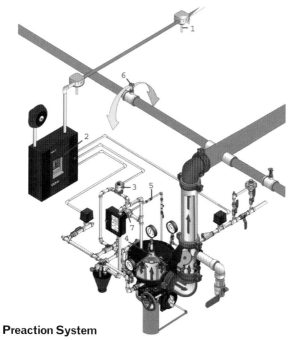

Preaction System

Single Interlock Electric Release
When the detector (1) is activated by fire, a signal is sent to the Release Control Panel (2). The panel sends appropriate alarm and trouble signals and, at the same time, signals the release of the solenoid valve (3). The deluge valve priming chamber (4) is then vented faster than water is supplied through the restricted orifice(5), allowing the deluge valve to open. The water enters the system piping, but until a sprinkler (6) activates, no water is discharged. When the deluge valve operates, pressure closes the PSOV (7) cutting off the supply of water to the priming chamber, latching the deluge valve in the open position.

Fig. 30–26. Operation of a preaction system. (Courtesy of Viking)

Residential systems. A residential system prevents flashover in rooms of origin, improves chances for occupant escape, and prevents fire spread to adjacent rooms in residential occupancies such as single- or two-family homes, as well as low-rise apartment buildings and hotels. **Residential sprinkler systems** (fig. 30–27) in homes and other occupancies are becoming more common. Their main objectives are to prevent flashover in rooms of origin, improve chances for occupant escape, and prevent fire spread to adjacent rooms. These systems have fewer heads compared with conventional sprinkler systems and an entire system can easily be seen in one figure. In one- and two-family homes, these systems often share a common water supply with the home's domestic water system (sinks, toilets, etc.). Sprinkler heads are omitted in small closets and bathrooms, as well as unused attics in residential systems.

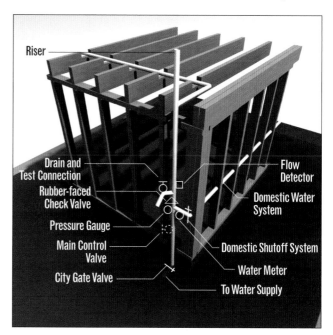

Fig. 30–27. Typical residential sprinkler system

Sprinkler system connections, piping, and control devices. Sprinkler systems need reliable water supplies. To ensure a supply is available, a continuous series of pipes from the source to the flowing head must be built and maintained. The main water supply may come from public or private companies, tanks on an owner's property, and local ponds, streams, or other bodies of water.

Fig. 30–28. Electric fire pump. (Courtesy of Paul Dansbach)

A fire pump might be necessary to maintain pressure within the activated system (fig. 30–28). This type of pump is permanently installed and connected to the sprinkler system. They are activated when a pressure drop caused by water flow is detected upstream of the pump. This type of fire pump is usually located in the basement of the building being protected. A much smaller capacity high-pressure pump called a jockey pump is sometimes installed next to the main pump. Its job is to maintain the pressure upstream of the pump so that small pressure variations don't cause main fire pump activation.

A fire department can supplement the water supply using a **fire department connection**, also called a **Siamese connection** (fig. 30–29). If the fire department supplements the water supply used by the sprinkler system, it is best to use a supply separate from the one the sprinkler system uses.

Fig. 30–29. FD connection

Every sprinkler system must have at least one main water supply control valve. In the United States, sprinkler systems fail about 5% of the time (one time out of every 20). The major reason for failure is that the main water supply control valve has been left shut accidentally. This valve must be an indicating type, meaning a firefighter can tell if the valve is open or closed just by looking at it. The two most common examples are the **outside stem and**

yoke (OS&Y) valve that exposes a stem to indicate it is open (figs. 30–30 and 30–31) and the **post-indicator valve** that reads either open or shut depending on its position (fig. 30–32). Similarly, **wall post indicator valves** also provide view panels with signs to indicate "open" or "shut" (fig. 30–33).

Fig. 30–30. OS&Y valve with tamper switch

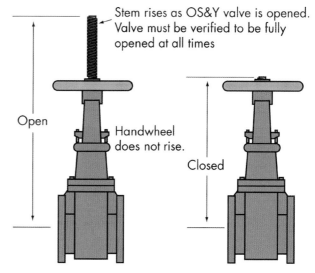

Fig. 30–31. Operation of an OS&Y valve. (Courtesy of John Morrison)

Fig. 30–32. Post-indicator valve

Supply-control valves are also supervised using **tamper switches** on valves that notify the FACP of a trouble condition if the valve is in the wrong position.

The main sprinkler system valve is found on all of the previously mentioned systems: residential, wet, dry, deluge, or preaction. Main sprinkler valves come in three types: alarm valve, dry-pipe, or deluge. The valve is attached to a riser that connects to the **sprinkler piping**, the network of pipes in a sprinkler system that delivers water to sprinkler heads. The sprinkler system has pipes called crossmains and branchlines if the system is a tree system (fig. 30–34); crossmains and branchlines if it is a grid system (fig. 30–35); and crossmains and loopmains if it is a looped system (fig. 30–36). Gridded systems and looped systems are used in many instances because they are more efficient than tree systems; they allow water flow to an outlet from more than one direction. All pipe systems except grid systems can be dry because the volume inside these grid systems takes too long to empty the air (or nitrogen in some cases) from the system.

Fig. 30–33. Wall post indicator valve. (Courtesy of Paul Dansbach)

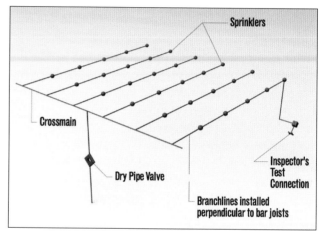

Fig. 30–34. Tree system

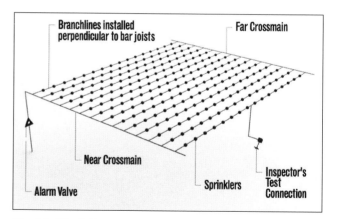

Fig. 30–35. Grid system

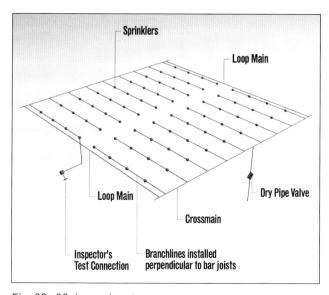

Fig. 30–36. Looped system

Firefighting considerations for operating sprinkler systems

There are some things that should be thought about when working with sprinkler systems. These include the following:

- Make sure that the fire department connection (FDC) is supplied.

- Make sure that the main riser control is open. This is usually an OS&Y valve.

- Make sure that, if there is a fire pump, it is working. Read the gauges on the pump and manually start it if you have to.

- Be sure to note the pressure on the main riser gauges on both side of the alarm valve, dry pipe valve or deluge valve. The gauges on the both the supply and discharge sides should provide appropriate readings. You shouldn't be seeing zero pressure for example—an indication that a valve may be closed somewhere and water isn't flowing.

- Make sure you don't close the riser control valve too soon! Only close the valve upon the order of the incident commander (the fire has been controlled) Leave a firefighter at the valve with a radio to quickly reopen the valve if it is necessary.

- Let a licensed contractor handle replacing fused sprinkler heads or resetting dry pipe valves. Post a fire watch if necessary until the system is fully restored.

Standpipes and standpipe classifications

Standpipe systems are systems of pipes and hose outlet valves used to deliver water to different building locations. These systems are designed and installed in accordance with NFPA 14, *Standard for the Installation of Standpipes and Hose Systems*. The following are types or classes of standpipes:

- Class I: designed exclusively for fire department use

- Class II: designed for occupant use

- Class III: designed for both fire department and occupant use

Most standpipe systems are supplied with a permanent water supply as well as a fire department connection; however, some dry systems will rely completely on the fire department connection for water (fig. 30–37). Some standpipes in tall buildings will have multiple fire department connections that serve different zones (groups of floors). It is important to supply the proper fire department connection.

Fig. 30–37. Fire department connections

Class I standpipes. Each **Class I standpipe** outlet has a 2½-in. (65-mm) male coupling and a valve to control water flow. They are usually designed so water accessible to fire department apparatus can be pumped to areas that need water within a building. Hose outlet valves connect to attack lines, and then personnel within a burning structure can deliver water.

Floor-to-floor openings are probably the most readily available fire paths for fire spread in tall buildings. Stairs are one of the primary reasons these openings are needed. It is clear that any stair in a high-rise building will need a fire-rated enclosure, often called a "fire-rated stair tower" to prevent this flame spread from occurring in the event of a fire. For high-rise fires, these standpipes are usually located within fire-rated stair towers so departments can have protected access to them. A hoseline can be connected in the protected area of the stair tower and then stretch the line from the stair tower to the fire floor.

Some taller high-rise systems have **pressure-control valves**, sometimes called **pressure-regulating valves**, that control pressure at the outlet of a standpipe to prevent excessive nozzle pressure in hoselines. Because **fire pumps** are often used to pump water to higher floors, a PRV keeps water pressure on lower floors manageable. The following are the three basic types of PRV:

- Pressure restricting
- Pressure reducing
- Pressure control

Pressure restricting devices restrict pressures in flowing conditions only so they don't control pressure in static conditions. They also don't compensate for changes in input pressure to maintain a constant discharge pressure. For these two reasons they are not always desirable. A commonly used pressure restricting device is an orifice plate. If they are used they should be installed at hose couplings so they can be removed. Other devices for regulating pressures are pressure control and pressure-reducing valves. A typical pressure reducing valve is shown in figure 3–38. These valves can regulate outlet pressures in both flowing and non-flowing conditions. They are required for outlets of systems where the static pressure can exceed 175 psi (1,225 kPa).

PRV operating pressure should reflect whether fog nozzles will be used because they often require higher pressure than straight bore nozzles. PRVs have caused difficulty in many major high-rise fires, usually because they restrict water flow when not adjusted properly. In newer systems they are designed so that the device can be frequently tested, and standpipe systems that use these devices have dedicated drainage systems with connections at every other floor. If buildings within your jurisdiction use PRVs, be sure to understand operation of their manual settings. If pressure restricting devices are used, be sure to know if they can be removed and how to remove them.

Class II standpipe. Although a **Class II standpipe** is designed for use by building occupant and firefighters, firefighters should not use them. They typically do not have an FDC and operate at pressures and flows that are usually too low to be of use to firefighters. Each hose outlet is usually preconnected with a 1.5-in. (38-mm) hose and nozzle. Because Class II standpipes require

water to flow before a fire department arrives, they often require additional fire pumps and water supplies to maintain volume and pressure. Preconnected hoselines are often not maintained, and their presence and serviceability should not be assumed. See an example of a typical cabinet used to store hoses in figure 30–39.

Class III Standpipe. A **Class III standpipe** combines the services of Class I and Class II standpipes. It has outlets for fire department use and a preconnected hose for building occupants.

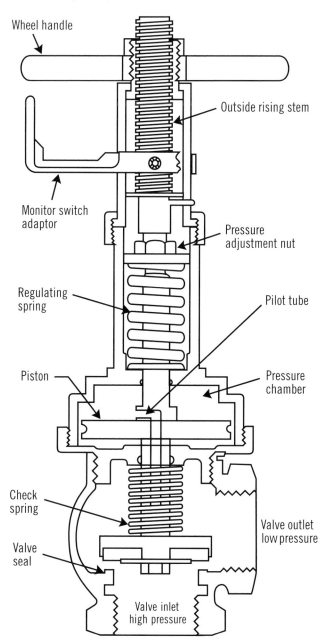

Fig. 30–38. Pressure control valve

Fig. 30–39. Hose cabinet

Firefighting considerations for operating standpipe systems

The following are some things that should be thought about when working with standpipe systems:

- Make sure that the FDC is supplied. If it is blocked or clogged, you may be able to pump back through a hose valve in a stairwell as a backup, although this won't work if the hose valve is a pressure-reducing valve.

- Make sure that the main control valve and riser isolation valve are open.

- Make sure that if there is a fire pump it is working. Read the gauges on the pump and manually start it if you have to.

- Be sure to note the pressure on the main riser gauge at the ground or basement level to make sure the system is working properly. There should be a pressure gauge at the top of the riser as well.

- Be wary of dry standpipe systems. They will take longer to fill, they may have been vandalized, or, depending on where they are, just plain neglected. Be wary of hose valves that have been opened by vandals before the fire.

Fixed-foam fire-protection systems. Although not found in all jurisdictions, it is possible to encounter fixed-foam fire-suppression systems. These locations include tank farms, bulk terminals, and flammable liquid storage warehouses.

At tank farms/bulk terminals, foam systems may be used to protect the storage tanks. These include systems that use **foam chambers** (also known as type 2 devices) that apply foam to the surface of the liquid (fig. 30–40).

Some tanks apply foam at the base of the tank using a **subsurface technique**. The tanks may also be protected with fixed foam nozzles on the ground, surrounding the tanks.

Loading racks are where delivery trucks are loaded with the flammable and combustible liquids (fig. 30–41). They are often protected with foam sprinkler systems. Flammable liquid warehouses use foam sprinkler systems as well (fig. 30–42).

Fig. 30–40. The use of foam chamber on a tank can help to rapidly and effectively introduce foam onto a working tank fire.

Fig. 30–41. Loading racks are often protected with foam suppression systems.

Fig. 30–42. Many standard sprinkler systems can be retrofitted to supply foam, such as this one. This type of system would be effective in a flammable liquid warehouse. (Courtesy of Buckeye Fire Equipment Company)

OTHER FIRE PROTECTION SYSTEMS

Other fire protection systems are generally applied locally or as total-flooding systems. A **total-flooding system** completely fills a room with suppression agent. A **local-application system** is a suppression system designed to protect only the area directly around a hazard.

Total-flooding gaseous systems

Halon. **Halon** is a fire-extinguishing gas that chemically interrupts the combustion reaction. In other words, it destroys the sustained chemical-reaction side of the fire tetrahedron. It is used in total-flooding systems, some local-application systems, and fire extinguishers.

Halon systems consist of a series of pipes and nozzles that connect to pressurized halon storage tanks. It is considered safe for humans.

New halon production is banned in most countries because it destroys the ozone layer. Recycled halon from systems taken out of commission is still legally available from halon banks, but it is expensive. The U.S. military still uses halon extensively. It has been used to protect large computer systems, telephone switches, and other electronic gear, as well as art and historical collections.

Clean agents. **Clean-agent gases** are designed to replace halon as total-flooding suppression agents without harming the ozone layer. These gases use a system of tanks, pipes, and nozzles to deliver the gas, just like halon. Because they have different properties than halon, however, the chemical tanks cannot be simply swapped for halon in existing halon systems. If a halon system is being replaced, a whole new set of pipes, tanks, and nozzles must be installed.

Halocarbons. One type of clean agent is **halocarbons**, which work by cooling the fire and chemically reacting with the fire. Halocarbon gases have a NOAEL concentration. The NOAEL acronym stands for "no observed adverse effect level." This is the concentration below which testing authorities consider safe. These systems should be designed so this concentration is never exceeded when the gas is discharged.

All halocarbons contain the element fluorine. When exposed to flame, they usually produce hydrofluoric acid, or HF, which is not safe for humans to breathe. While HF is also produced by halon systems, the volumes produced by newer halocarbon agents can be much higher. Newer halocarbon systems should use sensitive detection systems such as air sampling to activate quickly for small fires. This way, only a small amount of agent will be needed to extinguish a fire, and HF production will be kept as low as possible.

Inert gases. An **inert gas** doesn't react with most chemicals. Inert gas mixtures used as fire suppressants include helium, neon, argon, nitrogen, and carbon dioxide. They extinguish fires by lowering a room's oxygen concentration from the normal level of 21% to below 15%. The number of tanks to store enough inert gas to extinguish fires is usually much higher than the number of halocarbon tanks. In building designs where space is a consideration, this can be a concern.

Carbon dioxide. **Carbon dioxide (CO_2)** can be used in total-flooding and local-application systems. The colorless, odorless, nonreactive gas works well in extinguishing fires by reducing the oxygen concentration in a room to the point a fire can no longer burn. To do this, total-flooding carbon dioxide systems require agent application at concentrations above 30%. At this concentration, carbon dioxide kills very quickly by interfering with central nervous system functions.[6] Accidentally activated total-flooding carbon dioxide systems that have discharged into occupied areas have been responsible for many deaths.

The local-application systems work in a similar way to carbon dioxide fire extinguishers. It should be noted that while the CO_2 concentrations produced near activated local application systems may not be as high as those for total flooding systems, they might produce localized concentrations that are hazardous to humans as well.

Total-flooding water-mist systems

Water-mist systems use low quantities of water at very high pressure to suppress fires. Generally they are installed in total-flooding systems similar to deluge sprinkler systems, but the quantity of water applied is much lower. Piping diameter is also small, and the piping used is flexible, making for easy installation in existing buildings.

These systems are commonly installed on cruise ships in cabins and engine rooms because they can fight fires without flooding a ship. They have also been installed in other special applications, where avoiding interference with existing building features is an issue.

Local-application systems

Dry-chemical systems. Dry-chemical extinguishing systems use the same types of powdered agents as dry-chemical fire extinguishers. The powder is kept in pressurized tanks or systems in which nitrogen or carbon dioxide pressurizes the system when activated. Typical systems are used around gas pumps (fig. 30–43). These systems are essentially large, dry-chemical fire extinguishers attached to piping systems. They must be specially designed to ensure correct flow from the pipes.

Fig. 30–43. Dry-chemical suppression system

Wet-chemical extinguishing systems.

Wet-chemical extinguishing systems use a proprietary liquid agent, often a potassium solution. (The chemical symbol for potassium is the letter K, so sometimes these systems have "K" in their names.) They are usually local-application systems and are often used in restaurant hood systems to extinguish fires in deep fryers and other cooking equipment. When the wet-chemical agent is applied on top of a pool of grease, it chemically breaks down the grease by a process called saponification. Saponification refers to the formation of soap like layer of foam on top of the grease that smothers the fire and stops combustion. Restaurants like to use wet-chemical systems because they are much easier to clean up after than dry-chemical systems (fig. 30–44).

Fig. 30–44. Wet chemical system. (Courtesy of Joseph LoScalzo)

Smoke management systems

Smoke is responsible for the majority of fire deaths. In building fire situations, smoke often flows to places far away from the fire. A **smoke control system** uses air pressure differences to keep smoke away from building occupants so they can be evacuated safely. Systems that use fans are called mechanical smoke control systems. Other systems just rely on the "chimney effect" to move smoke out of an area. These are called passive smoke control systems. Hotel atriums, casinos, warehouses and other large areas often have built in systems for smoke extraction and smoke control.

A specific application of smoke control is the pressurization of stairwells. This is often used to prevent smoke infiltration of stairwells so that the public can evacuate safely. The concept of the "pressure sandwich," which is venting the fire floor and pressurizing the surrounding floors to prevent smoke movement from the fire floor, is yet another way that smoke control is frequently used in high-rise buildings. Smoke control systems are also used to remove smoke that may accumulate in the large atriums that are now frequently found in hotels and office buildings. Often such systems can be controlled locally from a panel such as the one shown in figure 30–45.

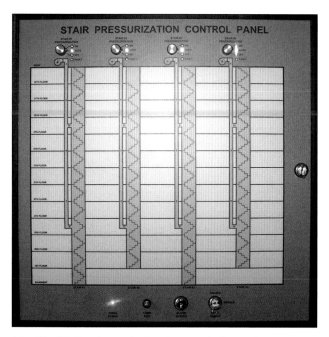

Fig. 30–45. Smoke control system control panel. (Courtesy of David Phelan)

It is important to know how a smoke control system for a building is activated. In the case of hotel atriums or casinos, they are usually connected directly to the fire alarm control panel and are activated automatically in the event that a detector in the protected area is activated. Generally in the case of warehouses the systems are activated manually.

Very large systems are used to clear the smoke out of train stations and rail or road tunnels. Often these systems are not under the direct control of the fire department. They are usually under the control of the operators of the rail or road system from a central control area. This occurs for a number of reasons. Like sprinkler systems, they often need to be activated before fire services personnel arrive. It may take the fire service a very long time to respond to a train stuck in a tunnel that goes under a river, for example. Passengers on the train may perish if they are not provided with clean air before the fire services personnel arrive.

Most of these systems also have more than one purpose. For example, in road tunnels the fans may be run every day to remove car exhaust from the tunnel—also a safety critical use. In rail tunnels they may also be run frequently to remove heat from the tunnels from train air conditioners and brakes. In all these cases the systems are designed to meet the requirements of both uses. The fact that the systems are used every day usually means that they are more reliable, since this means that they are tested every day; and if they break down, they must be fixed right away.

Clearly in these situations communications between the fire service and the system operators are very important. Joint training is critical so that, in the event there is an incident, the response will be properly coordinated. Fire department personnel should train with such systems so that they understand the design criteria (what it is supposed to achieve), how the system operates, and how to control the system.

Ammonia diffusion systems

Some cold-storage buildings storing food products use anhydrous ammonia as a refrigerant. Some hockey rinks also use ammonia. While many know that anhydrous ammonia is toxic, many do not know that it can be explosive under the right conditions (its explosive range is approximately 16%–25%). A 1984 anhydrous ammonia explosion in a Shreveport, Louisiana, cold-storage facility led to the death of a firefighter.

Ammonia refrigeration systems are required to be provided with ammonia diffusion systems under most fire codes. Basically, these systems allow firefighters to remove ammonia from the system, mix/dilute it by pumping water into a special fire department connection (specifically for this purpose), and finally discharge it down a sanitary sewer. While these diffusion systems perform the same function, they can differ in design. It is important to determine exactly how to operate the systems in your jurisdiction (fig. 30–46). When operating the system, it is imperative to notify the sewage treatment facility that will be receiving the ammonia mix.

Fig. 30–46. An ammonia diffusion system. You must understand how to operate this type of system before an incident occurs. (Courtesy of Ronald Spadafora)

COMPONENT AND MATERIAL QUALITY IN DETECTION AND SUPPRESSION SYSTEMS

We have simplified descriptions of some components of modern detection and suppression systems. For example, a manual-pull station was compared to a switch, but not any switch will do. All components connected to a detection or suppression system must be **approved**, meaning they must meet the requirements of the **authority having jurisdiction (AHJ)**. An AHJ is required to enforce local law concerning the construction or life-safety issues of a particular building or structure, including adopted building codes and standards.

The NFPA does not test devices itself but requires components of a detection or suppression system to be listed by an approved testing laboratory, such as Underwriters Laboratory or Factory Mutual. These labs deem equipment, materials, or services **listed**, or acceptable to the AHJ, in a document published by the laboratory stating they were tested. A **listed system** ensures that a system works as designed.

Common diagramming symbols

FFII 6.5.3 All elements presented in the previous sections of this chapter are represented in construction drawings by symbols. An extensive list of typical symbols is shown in table 30–3.

Table 30–3. Typical symbols used to represent detection and suppression systems in construction drawings.[7]

FIRE PROTECTION SYMBOLS

SYMBOL	DESCRIPTION	SYMBOL	DESCRIPTION	SYMBOL	DESCRIPTION
	RISER		FIRE DEPARTMENT- TWO HOSE OUTLET, FREE STANDING		TANK, ABOVE GROUND, VERT.
	VALVES (GENERAL)		FIRE DEPARTMENT-TWO HOSE OUTLET		TANK, BELOW GROUND, HORIZ.
	VALVE IN PIT		FIRE DEPARTMENT-ONE HOSE OUTLET		PUBLIC WATER MAIN
	POST-INDICATOR VALVE		FIRE PUMP WITH DRIVES		PRIVATE WATER MAIN
	KEY OPERATED VALVES		FREESTANDING TEST HEADER		UNDER WATER MAIN BUILDING
	OS & Y VALVE (OUTSIDE SCREW AND YOKE (RISING STEM)		WALL-MOUNTED TEST HEADER		SUCTION PIPE
	INDICATING BUTTERFLY VALVE		SCREEN/STRAINER		THRUST BLOCK
	NONINDICATING VALVE (NONRISING-STEM VALVE)	XXX	CONTROL PANEL (ATTRIBUTED) FCP FIRE ALARM CONTROL PANEL	Cx	FIRE SERVICE OR EMERGENCY TELEPHONE STATION A – ACCESSIBLE
	CHECK VALVE		FSA FIRE SYSTEM ANNUNCIATOR		J – JACK H – HANDSET
	BACKFLOW PREVENTER - DOUBLE CHECK TYPE		FTR FIRE ALARM TRANSPONDER OR TRANSMITTER ESR ELEVATOR STAUS/RECALL	XX	ABORT SWITCH HL – HALON
	BACKFLOW PREVENTER - REDUCED PRESSURE ZONE (RPZ) TYPE		FAC FIRE ALARM COMMUNICATOR HCP HALON CONTROL PANEL		DC – DRY CHEMICAL FO – FOAM
	PRESSURE REGULATING VALVE		HVA CONTROL PANEL FOR HEATING, VENTILATION. AIR-CONDITIONING, EXHAUST STAIRWELL PRESSURIZATION, OR SIMILAR EQUIPMENT.		WC – WET CHEMICAL CA – CLEAN AGENT WM – WATER MIST DL – DELUGE SPRINKLER
	PRESSURE RELIEF VALVE	XX	MANUAL STATION HL - HALON	CO₂	ABORT SWITCH (CO₂)
	FLOAT VALVE		DC - DRY CHEMICAL FO - FOAM	XX	HEAT DETECTOR (TERMINAL DETECTOR) R/F – COMBINATION - RATE AND FIXED TEMPERATURE
	METER		WC - WET CHEMICAL P - PULL STATION		R/C – RATE COMPENSATION F – FIXED TEMPERATURE
	PRIVATE HYDRANT, ONE HOSE OUTLET		CA - CLEAN AGENT WM - WATER MIST DL - DELUGE SPRINKLER		R – RATE OF RISE ONLY LINE OF TYPE DETECTOR (HEAT-SENSITIVE CABLE)
	PUBLIC FIRE HYDRANT - TWO HOSE OUTLET	CO₂	CARBON DIOXIDE	XXX	SMOKE DETECTOR P – PHOTOELECTRIC PRODUCTS OF COMBUSTION DETECTOR
	PUBLIC FIRE HYDRANT - TWO HOSE OUTLET & PUMPER CONNECTION		REDUCER		I – IONIZATION PRODUCTS OF COMBUSTION DETECTOR
	WALL HYDRANT - TWO HOSE OUTLET		ALARM GONG		BT – BEAM TRANSMITTER BR – BEAM RECEIVER
	PRIVATE HOUSED HYDRANT- TWO HOSED OUTLET		WATER MOTOR ALARM GONG TANK, ABOVE GROUND, HORIZ.		ASD – A/T SAMPLING

FIRE PROTECTION SYMBOLS, CONTINUED

SYMBOL	DESCRIPTION	SYMBOL	DESCRIPTION	SYMBOL	DESCRIPTION
	SMOKE DETECTOR FOR DUCT		FOR FIRES OF ALL TYPES (EXCEPT METAL) MANUALLY ACTUATED		MONITOR HOSE, DRY
	GAS DETECTOR		SYSTEMS UTILIZING A GASIOUS MEDIUM AUTOMATICALLY ACTUATED		MONITOR HOSE, CHARGED
	FLAME DETECTOR		SYSTEMS UTILIZING A GASIOUS MEDIUM MANUALLY ACTUATED		**AGENT STORAGE CONTAINER** FO - FOAM
	FLOW DETECTOR/SWITCH		HALON SYSTEM OR CLEAN AGENT EXTINGUISHING SYSTEM AUTOMATICALLY ACTUATED		HL - HALON
	PRESSURE DETECTOR/SWITCH				CL - CLEAN AGENT
	LEVEL DETECTOR SWITCH		HALON SYSTEM OR CLEAN AGENT EXTINGUISHING SYSTEM MANUALLY ACTUATED		DC - DRY CHEMICAL
	TAMPER DETECTOR	AS	FULLY SPRINKLERED SPACE		WM - WATER MIST
	VALVE WITH TAMPER DETECTOR/SWITCH	AS	PARTIALLY SPRINKLERED SPACE	CO_2	AGENT STORAGE CONTAINER CARBON DIOXIDE
	DOOR HOLDER	NS	NONSPRINKLERED SPACE		FUSIBLE LINK
	ALARM, MANUAL CONTROL	WS	WATER SPRAY SYSTEM	ETL	FUSIBLE LINK W/ ELECTROTHERMAL FEATURE
	SPEAKER/HORN (ELECTRIC HORN)		UPRIGHT SPRINKLER	SOV	SOLENOID VALVE
M	ALARM, MINI HORN		PENDENT SPRINKLER		
	ALARM, HORN/LIGHT SEPARATE ASSEMBLY		UPRIGHT SPRINKLER; NIPPLE UP		**UTILITY SHUTOFFS** E - ELECTRIC SHUTOFF
	ALARM, HORN/LIGHT, ONE ASSEMBLY		PENDENT SPRINKLER; ON DROP NIPPLE		W - DOMESTIC WATER SHUTOFF
	ALARM, LAMP/LIGHT, SIGNAL LIGHT STROBE		SPRINKLER WITH GUARD		G - GAS SHUTOFF
	WET CHARGED SYSTEM AUTOMATICALLY ACTUATED		SIDEWALL SPRINKLER		LPG - LP-GAS SHUTOFF
	WET CHARGED SYSTEM MANUALLY ACTUATED		OUTSIDE SPRINKLER		NG - NATURAL GAS SHUTOFF
	DRY CHARGED SYSTEM AUTOMATICALLY ACTUATED		PIPE HANGER		CNG - COMPRESSED NATURAL GAS SHUTOFF
	DRY CHARGED SYSTEM MANUALLY ACTUATED		ANGLE VALVE (ANGLE HOSE VALVE)	XXX	**DETECTION/EXTINGUISHING EQUIPMENT**
	FOAM SYSTEM AUTOMATICALLY ACTUATED		ALARM CHECK VALVE		DD - DUCT DETECTOR
	FOAM SYSTEM MANUALLY ACTUATED		DRY PIPE VALVE		HD - HEAT DETETOR
	WATER MIST EXTINGUISHING SYSTEM AUTOMATICALLY ACTUATED		DRY PIPE VALVE WITH QUICK OPENING DEVICE (ACCELERATOR OR EXHAUSTER)		SD - SMOKE DETECTOR FS - FLOW SWITCH (WATER)
	WATER MIST EXTINGUISHING SYSTEM MANUALLY ACTUATED		DELUGE VALVE		PS - MANUAL PULL STATION TS - TAMPER SWITCH
	DRY CHEMICAL SYSTEMS FOR LIQUID, GAS AND ELEC. FIRES AUTOMATICALLY ACTUATED		PREACTION VALVE		HL - HALON SYSTEM DC - DRY CHEMICAL
			CO_2 REEL STATION		WC - WET CHEMICAL SYSTEM
	DRY CHEMICAL SYSTEMS FOR LIQUID, GAS AND ELEC. FIRES MANUALLY ACTUATED		DRY CHEMICAL REEL STATION		FO - FOAM SYSTEM CA - CLEAN AGENT SYSTEM
	FOR FIRES OF ALL TYPES (EXCEPT METAL) AUTOMATICALLY ACTUATED		FOAM REEL STATION		BSD - BEAM SMOKE DETECTOR
			HOSE STATION, DRY STANDPIPE	CO_2	DETECTION/EXTINGUISHING EQUIPMENT CARBON DIOXIDE SYSTEM
			HOSE STATION, CHARGED STANDPIPE		

NOTES

1. NFPA. 2007. NFPA 72, *The National Fire Alarm Code*. Quincy, Mass.: National Fire Protection Association.

2. NFPA. 2007. NFPA 72, *The National Fire Alarm Code*. Quincy, Mass.: National Fire Protection Association.

3. NFPA. 2007. NFPA 13, *Standard for the Installation of Sprinkler Systems*. Quincy, Mass.: National Fire Protection Association.

4. NFPA. 2008. NFPA 25, *Standard for the Inspection, Testing, and Maintenance of Water-Based Fire Protection Systems*. Quincy, Mass.: National Fire Protection Association.

5. *Sprinkler Hydraulics*, Harold S. Wass, Jr.

6. "Review of the Use of Carbon Dioxide Total Flooding Extinguishing Systems," Robert T. Wickham, P.E., Downloaded from http://www.epa.gov/ozone/ snap/fire/co2/co2report2.pdf on 6/29/2009.

7. NFPA. 2006. NFPA 170. *Standard for Fire Safety and Emergency Symbols*. Quincy, Mass.: National Fire Protection Association.

QUESTIONS

1. _____ buildings are protected by fire alarm systems.

2. A _____ alarm system notifies only the building occupants of fire.

3. A _____ signal identifies system problems that can influence the system's reliability.

4. Automatic or manual mechanisms that cause a system to indicate an alarm condition are known as _____.

5. What types of manual pull stations exist? Which one helps prevent false alarms?

6. Which NFPA standard deals with fire alarm systems?

7. A _____ warns of a fire condition by sensing a high temperature, high rate of rise in temperature, or both.

8. List the types of detectors and how they react to different heat conditions.

9. What are photoelectric detectors and how do they work?

10. A flame detector activates when it detects _____.

11. What is the most common gas detector?

12. List the three basic types of fire alarm systems.

13. Discuss the components of a central-station alarm system.

14. A sprinkler head that opens when the solder holding two pieces of metal together fuses or melts is called a _____.

14. Discuss the difference between a pendant sprinkler head and an upright sprinkler head.

15. _____ sprinkler heads are designed to be in areas below freezing.

16. Which of the sprinkler systems use low quantities of water at very high pressure to suppress fires?

Advanced Fire Attack

by Chris Flatley

This chapter provides required knowledge items for the following NFPA Standard 1001 Job Performance Requirements:

FFII 6.1.1

FFII 6.3.1

FFII 6.3.2

FFII 6.3.3

This chapter contains Skill Drills. When you see this icon, refer to your Skill Drill book for step-by-step instructions.

OBJECTIVES

Upon completion of this chapter, you should be able to do the following:

- Identify the role of Firefighter II in carrying out assignments as team leader
- Describe offensive and defensive strategies used at fires involving flammable gases and liquids
- Define the five foam types as they apply to fire service operations
- Describe how firefighting foam is produced and applied to the surface of burning liquids
- List the different types of foam concentrate available to the fire service
- List the types of equipment used to develop foam that are available to the fire service
- List and describe the techniques for applying foam to a burning liquid
- List safety considerations when applying firefighting foam
- Describe the proper methods to determine a proper application rate of foam on a burning liquid
- Describe the two types of foam systems

INTRODUCTION

Now that you have received some training and gained experience as a firefighter, it is important to reinforce your basic firefighting skills. If you read fatal fire reports, (and you should) you will see that many injuries and deaths result from difficulties in fire company operations. Remember, other firefighters work in areas adjoining and above the fire, and their safety—as well as the safety of you and your crew—depends on your ability to execute your assignment. As you become a more seasoned firefighter, you will be tasked with greater responsibility. With that responsibility comes accountability. You will no longer be able to say "I didn't know" because at this point, you should. Firefighters *have to make it happen, not make excuses.*

This chapter builds on lessons learned from your training in Firefighter I. The new concepts introduced here guide you toward becoming a more experienced firefighter and advancing into the officer rank. You must thoroughly understand the concepts in this chapter before you complete the course. Once you complete the course, this manual will become an important reference. You will refer to it often during your career.

In Firefighter I you were taught how to perform specific firefighting techniques. Now in Firefighter II you learn how to decide which technique to employ as well as *where* and *when*. After a superior officer assigns tasks such as ventilation, fire attack, search, and so forth, you must be able to carry them out without immediate supervision. Although you do not yet have an officer rank, you are responsible for carrying out a variety of assigned duties as a team leader.

In many cases, your department's standard operating procedures (SOPs) will influence the decisions you have to make. For example, some departmental SOPs will dictate the size of a hoseline that has to be used for certain types of fires or their location. In cases such as these, your SOPs will help you make your decisions. This text is not intended to replace your department's SOPs. Any issues raised that deviate from departmental SOPs should be guided by the SOPs.

TYPES OF DUTIES

As a Firefighter II, you will be assigned tasks, and your responsibility is to complete them in a safe, efficient, and effective manner. Examine the tasks listed in the following text and consider the responsibilities and types of decisions you must make while completing each one:

- Coordinate an interior fire attack team given the appropriate amount of equipment and properly protected personnel.

- Identify and communicate hazards to your team.

- Decide the point of entry and the appropriate method to gain entry.

- Determine the method of fire attack based on its type, size, and location (basement, grade level, and upper levels of a building), as well as deciding on nozzle and hoseline selection and line placement based on conditions.

- Maintain proper communications between your team members, other teams operating in the fire area, and the incident commander. (Notify the incident commander of any changing conditions.)

- Maintain team coordination and ensure proper team integrity through communications and accountability.

- Constantly evaluate changes in fire growth and behavior, and anticipate fire spread.

- Decide the *priority areas* for search; and, should a victim be found, determine the most appropriate removal method.

- Decide where, how, and when to ventilate the building. Determine the need for proper ventilation and coordinate it with the fire attack.

- Monitor building structural conditions, paying particular attention to signs of structural distress or impending collapse.

- Scrutinize changes in fire conditions, including increase in fire intensity, impending flashover or backdraft, and other dangerous conditions.

SIZE-UP

As discussed in *Firefighter I*, size-up is a critical, basic function for incident commanders. Size-ups allow firefighters to make the best possible decisions on how to deal with the situation. However, it shouldn't be limited to officers. Firefighters, particularly those coordinating and carrying out tactical objectives, should also conduct their own size-up. There are seven specific issues a Firefighter II should consider when arriving on the scene to conduct a size-up:

Location of fire and type of construction: Where is the fire now, where is it spreading, and where will it ultimately extend? How does construction type confine the fire or allow it to extend?

Life hazard: What are the rescue priorities? Who might occupy the building given the time of day? Where are people located? Who is in the most danger and needs rescue first?

Fire control: What is the fuel load in the building, what are the extinguishing capabilities of the attack line(s), and is there fire protection equipment in place to control a fire?

Forcing entry: What is the best way to gain access to the building, support the rescue, and advance the hoseline?

Ventilation: What type of ventilation will have to be performed (horizontal or vertical, mechanical positive pressure ventilation, etc.) and at what location?

Stretching considerations: Where should the first and subsequent hoselines be placed?

Water supply: Where is your hoseline's water supply coming from? Are you operating solely with water from your engine's booster tank or is the water supply coming from a hydrant, drafting source, or tanker shuttle?

SINGLE-FAMILY HOME FIRES

Basement

FFII 6.3.2 As mentioned previously, the first step in developing any fire attack plan is an accurate size-up. The attack strategy may be based on the first arriving officer's size-up, but everyone on the fireground should conduct a size-up based on his or her assignment. For example, the nozzle firefighter may be concerned with stretching the shortest distance to the fire, while other firefighters may be concerned about whether there is enough hoseline to reach the fire. Estimating the stretch is a skill that all engine company members must be able to accomplish, even if hose loads are preconnected. You must be able to tell if the stretch will come up short and correct the problem.

Location of fire and type of construction. Some general points of basement fire size-up may include confirming the fire is actually in the basement. If fire is suspected in the basement, break a small pane of glass in one of the basement windows. This small opening either vents smoke or allows a clear look into the basement. It also restricts the amount of air that can enter, reducing the possibility of causing a backdraft. If the fire has extended to upper floors and there is a possibility of extension to the attic through voids in balloon construction, then more personnel are required to stretch additional hand lines to cut off the fire spread. Is this home built of lightweight construction? Does that affect how long firefighters can commit to interior operations before being withdrawn over concern of possible collapse? Time is the only thing we don't have control over on the fireground. We don't know how long the fire has been burning. We can't tell with any certainty how quickly the structure is being destroyed. The one thing we do know is that every minute the fire burns, more of the building is being compromised.

Also consider the contents of the basement. If it is packed with a family's lifetime accumulation of valuables, does that increase the fire load and reduce your ability to reach the seat of the fire? Could the fire have been started by defective heating equipment or damaged utilities in the basement? If the fire involves an oil burner, can it be remotely shut off? How does that impact on the fire attack? If the fire has affected the utilities, can they be controlled from the outside? Is the gas meter outside and can it be shut down? Can a utility crew be called to cut the electric service to the house? For firefighters in the basement, what clues would indicate a gas feed fire or a fire where electricity may be involved?

Life hazard. As in every fire or emergency, life safety is the most important consideration. Is the house occupied or vacant (figs. 31–1 and 31–2)? *Occupied* often refers to a home that someone lives in. If no one is home the house is *unoccupied*. An abandoned building has fallen into disrepair, and the owner no longer maintains the structure in a livable condition. Members should be aware of these important differences in the definitions. This does not preclude the possibility of vagrants or squatters occupying the house. All structures must be searched within the limits of safety. Determining if the structure is occupied or vacant is more art than science. In the long run, it comes down to your observations and experience. That is why every structure must be searched within the limits of safety. Vacant building fires are discussed later in the chapter.

Fig. 31–1. Abandoned structures can still be inhabited by vagrants or juveniles.

Fig. 31–2. Determining whether a structure is vacant can be a difficult task.

For our discussion at this time, answer the following questions: Is someone home right now? What time of day are persons sleeping, unaware of the conditions in the basement? Is the house a single-family dwelling, and where are sleeping areas? Is there a possibility of a basement apartment? What clues indicate a separate apartment? Generally, features like separate mailboxes or gas and electric meters may indicate a separate living unit or apartment in the home, but may not direct you to the basement. The lack of separate mailboxes or utilities should not rule out an apartment being present.

Even if you are unfamiliar with the room layout of the house, what clues can be gleaned from just looking at the house? What does the size and configuration of the windows tell you? Bathrooms generally have smaller windows; they may have frosted or obscured glass for privacy. Bathrooms may adjoin bedrooms. Larger windows next to these smaller ones may be the location of bedrooms. Air conditioning units in windows in warm climates or during the summer season can also indicate sleeping areas. Windows that are off height from others on the same side of the house may indicate the location of the half landing on stairs. Although this window would not be advantageous for entrance from the outside when conducting a primary search, it may be beneficial as a route to get an additional hoseline above the fire.

What is the risk to firefighters? Has the fire developed to the point where it is unsafe to allow firefighters to enter? Has the fire escalated to the point where it is unsafe for members to remain within the structure? When firefighters occupy the structure, they must be considered as part of the life hazard within the building.

Fire control. Controlling and extinguishing basement fires are some of the most difficult tasks you may face. Improper application of water creates large amounts of steam from which there is no relief. Yet, the inability to apply water to the burning material allows the fire to intensify and expose more of the structure to damage. The cramped conditions that often exist in basements require operations with a minimum number of personnel. This is physically demanding and leads to the need for frequent and timely relief of members.

Remember, a basement fire has the opportunity to vertically extend to all portions of the house: up the interior stairs; up pipe chases; and in the case of balloon frame structures, up the stud channels of the exterior walls. Knocking down the fire in the basement only controls the fire in that location; it is imperative to check for extension of the fire into the upper portions of the building.

Forcing entry. Generally, gaining entry into private dwellings is easier than commercial structures. But in all cases, the fire will not go out unless firefighters can get in to extinguish it. Gaining entry is also the way we enter the house to search for victims.

When confronted with a basement fire, what points of access do we have to the basement? Is our only access through the front door and down the interior stairs? These stairs are generally lightweight and narrow. The fire may have weakened these stairs, so do not bunch up and move quickly to the base of the stairs. Descending these stairs requires a determined crew of firefighters to *make the push* to the bottom of the stairs where conditions will be better.

If the line can't advance into the basement, another option is to consider any outside entrances. Does the house have an exterior entrance? Basements and cellars may have either a walk-out door or a set of stairs through a metal Bilco® door and down to the basement door below grade. These entries may provide another avenue for fire attack.

A word of caution: deploying lines from outside entrances may drive fire and smoke up through the interior, exposing interior crews to more heat and fire. A line must be stretched to the top of the interior stairs to prevent extension to the floors above. If the exterior line can knock down the fire, the interior line should advance to the basement for extinguishment. Before the interior line advances into the basement, be sure no fire has passed you; if fire is extending above, call for a third line. If a third line is required, consider bringing it in from either another door (rear or side) or through a window near the point of attack. Having three hoselines stretched through the front door or up the stairs clutters the stairs and complicates entry and exit.

If fire conditions are so severe that the nozzle team cannot make the push into the basement based on the stability of the first floor, a small hole can be cut in the floor over the fire or as close as possible. A cellar nozzle or distributor is placed in it to knock down some fire so hand lines can advance into the basement. This is a dangerous operation as well, but it may be necessary to gain control of the fire. After the fire has been knocked down and hand lines advanced into the basement, the hole can be expanded for ventilation, if necessary.

Ventilation. Basement fires are arguably one of the most difficult fires you will fight. Ventilation in these fires is limited. Small basement or cellar windows do not relieve the large amounts of heat generated by these fires, and normally low basement ceilings add to the amount of heat banking down on firefighters. A tactic that is sometimes employed is to cut a hole in the floor on the first floor near a window to vent the smoke and heat. A hole cut in the living room near the picture window could relieve the basement of heat. Compare it to cutting a hole in the roof when horizontal venting of windows is not enough to relieve the fire floor of smoke and heat.

As previously discussed, basement fires in buildings of balloon frame construction offer challenges as well (fig. 31–3). Fires that expose the base of the outside walls can allow heat and fire to travel up the stud bays to the attic (fig. 31–4). Any fire in the basement of a balloon frame building requires early and frequent inspection of the top floor and attic for extension. The heat and smoke enter the attic between the outside wall siding and the interior finished wall.

Stretching considerations. When stretching hoselines, the goals are as follows:

- Protect life
- Protect property
- Confine the fire
- Extinguish the fire

Fig. 31–3. In balloon frame construction, fire can travel vertically through the stud channel as seen above a basement window.

It has been said that the best life-saving measure is the prompt attack of the fire; put the fire out and many other problems go away. It has also been said that more lives are saved by the proper position and operation of a hoseline than any other life-saving technique. If we continue with that logic, the engine officer has the greatest influence on the outcome of the fire than any other firefighter on the fireground. Even

with the incident commander's best plan, it will fail without firefighters skilled and trained to execute it.

Fig. 31–4. The attic of a balloon-framed house must be examined during every fire.

On the fireground all effort should be directed to getting the first line into position before any other line is stretched. Communication between engine company officers as to the difficulties and need for assistance will ensure this happens.

The most important considerations when stretching are to select the correct size hoseline and to make sure you have enough hose to reach the fire before the line is charged. Adding length to a charged line, although not impossible, requires close cooperation between all members of the engine company. One of my best pieces of advice when it comes to stretching is as follows: *It is better to be a length over, than a foot short* (fig. 31–5). If considering a private dwelling fire, how much area is available to us on the front lawn to lose some hose even if we *overstretch*? If we can *lose* the extra hose on the front lawn this is not *overstretching*. If we have more hose in the street than we can manage, that is overstretching. If the pump pressure required for the stretch exceeds the limit of the line, that is overstretching.

Fig. 31–5. Keeping extra attack hose near the point of ingress aids in fire attack.

For a basement fire, the line must be able to get to the base of the stairs quickly, so enough hose must be nearby when the advance is made. Hose may have to be flaked out inside the house to be available for rapid deployment to the basement. Discuss with your company officers where the **drop point** (the point where the lead length of hose is dropped before it is charged to facilitate the advance) is located. Always refer to your own department's SOPs for clarification.

Ensuring there is enough hose to reach the fire involves several steps. Correct line placement is crucial. As a general rule, lines should be placed between the fire and those endangered by it. That can be either civilians or firefighters. That said, the line must protect the means of egress. In the absence of any life hazard, the line must protect exposures—in this case property. When protecting property consider its value. Protect the most valuable property first, even if it is not where the fire will likely spread. For example, you may need to give up the vehicle to save the house. Judgment is key when deciding where to deploy available resources.

Water supply. At this point in your firefighting career, you may think that water supply is someone else's problem. Maybe it is, but this is where your grasp of where you fit into the puzzle is the key. You may be the firefighter spraying the water, but shouldn't you know where that water is coming from and how much you have? Is the pump operator supplying you with the water from a limited booster tank or using a good hydrant with an unlimited supply of water? Is your water coming from a tanker shuttle? You must know this before you get face to face with the fire. To use a military analogy, is all the ammunition you have available to shoot merely the ammunition you brought with you? Do you shoot and then have to wait for resupply or is supply of ammunition unlimited? How engaged are you going to be in the firefight given those parameters?

Pump operators are the unsung heroes of the fire service. They are often left alone with the simplest instruction, "get me water," which is usually the most difficult thing to produce and produce *on demand*. One story from the New York City Fire Department (FDNY) tells of a resourceful pump operator who stretched a supply line from a high-rise building's standpipe system to supply his engine with water for a fire in the building next door because the hydrant in the street was frozen.

Kitchen

Considering our seven-point size-up, how would our attack plan need to be adjusted for a fire in the kitchen? Many of our considerations are similar, whereas some present different challenges. A fire in the kitchen most often begins on the stove. Defective stoves can cause fires. If the stove is gas or electric, it presents its own unique problems. Hot oils and such can be dangerous and may require specific extinguishing methods. If the fire has extended to the cabinets and affected the structure, the fire is more serious. Kitchens and bathrooms commonly have many void spaces for plumbing and lighting. If the fire has entered the void space, it must be completely examined. If unchecked, these voids can cause fire to extend to remote areas. A thermal imaging camera can be useful in reducing the damage, but it is no substitute for a thorough examination.

Living room

If the fire begins in some other location on the first floor, such as the living room, does the fire meet us at the front door? Do we have to push our way into the house? Is there a firefighter available to complete horizontal ventilation opposite the line and drive the heat and smoke out of the building rather than up the interior stairs? Can we get past the fire to the stairs to get above the fire and search the bedrooms? Will the hoseline be able to control the fire until we complete our search?

Bedrooms

A bedroom fire in a single-family dwelling is common. Fires in the bedroom can be caused by space heaters, electric blankets, and hot lamps contacting fabric surfaces. Victims are closer to the main body of this type of fire than any other. Rescue requires a rapid entry to the fire area, many times ahead of the hoseline. In spite of our best efforts, the results are not always successful. A large fire in a bedroom can extend into the attic, either from the failure of the gypsum board ceiling or through the eaves when the fire has vented out the windows (fig. 31–6). Once fire is in the attic, roof ventilation is required and ceilings must be pulled to allow a hose stream to apply water to the fire.

Fig. 31–6. Fire lapping through a window can extend into the attic and soffit space in wood-frame residential dwellings.

GARDEN APARTMENTS OF WOOD FRAME CONSTRUCTION

The discussion of a fire in a garden apartment- or townhouse-type building follows the same parameters as the private dwelling. From our perspective, garden apartments are typical modern apartment buildings (built since the 1960s), usually two to three stories high, set back from the street, and constructed of wood frame.

The size-up a garden apartment begins much the same way as a private dwelling: determining the type of construction and the location of the fire. The wood frame construction typically used in garden apartments plays a big role in the fire attack because void spaces are often large and run the length of the structure. A small fire that enters a void can quickly involve the whole structure, which leads to the question, "Where's the fire?" The fire must be located quickly, and the route of fire extension must be cut off. This often requires opening up in adjoining units or apartments to get ahead of the fire. Inspection holes made ahead of the fire must be large enough to determine conditions yet small enough to avoid introducing the oxygen necessary to intensify the fire. The hole must also be small enough so it does not draw the fire toward the hole, thus increasing the fire problem. Examination holes should be made with a charged hoseline in place. If you are looking for fire and your examination reveals fire extension, while you wait for the fire line, give the stream an opening large enough to operate in and drive the fire back toward the burned side. From this position the goal of the line is to contain the fire and not let the fire pass you.

Knowledge of the apartment layout helps determine avenues of fire travel. Are the apartments duplexes, or is there a different apartment above? If there is a separate apartment above, the layout is probably the same as the one below. This means the voids for plumbing and drains are above one another. If the unit is a duplex, the upper level of the unit consists of bedrooms and bathrooms, reducing voids that continue vertically into the attic.

Also consider whether the building has a public hall or if there are entrances to individual units from the outside (fig. 31–7). A public hall in the center of the building can act as a firebreak on floors below the attic (fig. 31–8). This hall may seal voids caused by the construction of stairs and other features and prevent extension across the hall.

Fig. 31–7. The use of party walls and private entrances can help eliminate concealed spaces in apartments.

Fig. 31–8. A common centralized entrance in this apartment complex can act as a fire break between individual apartment units.

Fig. 31–9. Firefighters must be prepared to extend attack lines to reach buildings with long setbacks from the roadway.

Fig. 31–10. Even a small fire in this building could necessitate several hoselines due to the number of concealed voids and exposures.

When assessing the life hazard in garden apartments, consider the six sides of the fire: the four sides on the same level as the fire and above and below. Fire can drop down in voids as well. Smoke and carbon monoxide (CO) can permeate a large area and effect many units; even low levels of CO require the area to be searched.

Gaining entry into multiple apartments can be time consuming. For a forcible entry, it is best to open any doors that may be necessary before being assigned other tasks. This ensures that doors are open if entry is needed quickly for an expanding fire situation or as an area of refuge.

When fighting fires in garden apartments, expect to find more people than a private dwelling. How do the escaping occupants affect your ability to stretch hoselines (fig. 31–9)? Your stretch must not interfere with the escaping occupants. Stretch the lines as close to the walls as possible to leave the area in the center of the hall clear. Where possible, avoid leaving hoselines on stairs. The line should be hauled up along side stairs and secured to newel posts and railings with hose straps.

The exact location of the fire must be known before a line is committed to the apartment. Just because there is smoke in the apartment does not mean the fire is in that apartment. When the fire apartment is found, engine crews must have enough hose to cover the entire fire area. Some apartments are large, and, as with a duplex, with entrances on the lower level; you may need to advance to the upper level via an interior stair. This may require more than one length of hose (fig. 31–10).

Stretches in garden apartments are often longer than those in private dwellings. Extending hoselines by adding rolled or folded hose as well as operating from a manifold or water thief may be necessary. Rope stretches and other alternative stretching methods may be employed to reduce the number of lengths in the stretch. Firefighters with garden apartments in their area must know their department's procedure for completing these long stretches. As the stretches become longer, the pump pressure must increase to overcome friction loss. The effects of kinks are even more dramatic. All firefighters must be aware of kinks and remove any and all kinks when they develop.

With these long stretches, there is a greater possibility of the line getting caught on obstacles. Turning corners and going up stairs with a charged hoseline can be difficult. The rate of advance into the fire area is directly related to the nozzle crews' ability to move the hoseline. Locating the drop point is critical. Having sufficient hose near the point of attack makes the difference in a successful fire attack. Having hose laid in the public hall or in an adjoining apartment on fire floor speeds the advance of the nozzle team. When every foot of hose that enters the fire area has to be dragged in from the sidewalk, the advance is slow and arduous.

Water supply in these complexes can be a challenge. Are there hydrants on site? Where are they located? Are they blocked by cars or shrubbery (fig. 31–11)? Are they privately owned and maintained, making their operability questionable? Do they provide the required fire flow if the whole structure became involved? Any delay in getting a reliable water supply established compounds the fire problem.

Fig. 31–11. Local codes must be strictly enforced to prohibit landscaping from obscuring fire hydrants.

Fig. 31–12. A typical tenement building

LARGER APARTMENT BUILDINGS OF ORDINARY CONSTRUCTION

Larger apartment buildings of ordinary construction, using brick load–bearing walls and wood joists, are often found in more urban areas than suburban or rural parts of the country. Two common types of these buildings are tenements and H-types.

Tenements

Tenements are smaller than H-types (fig. 31–12). They are usually three to five stories high and have two or four apartments per floor. There may be a store located on the first floor (fig. 3–13). Older tenements have four windows and no front fire escape. This indicates a **railroad flat** room layout. The rooms are arranged one behind the other front to rear, and the rear fire escape is the secondary means of egress. Larger tenements have four windows and a fire escape on the front and the rear. These generally have four apartments per floor and the fire escapes serve front or rear apartments. An exception to this rule may be corner buildings.

First-floor store fires. When a store occupies the first floor of a tenement, a door may lead from the public hall into the store. When these buildings were built, the store owner was generally a tenant of the building, and he would come down stairs and enter the store from this door. Now these doors may be sealed. From a firefighting perspective, this door provides a path for fire travel from the store in the occupancy above. When the store is heavily involved in fire, monitor conditions on the first-floor hall to ensure fire does not expose the public hall.

Fig. 31–13. It may be difficult for firefighters to determine the layout and compartmentation of mercantile aspects in tenement buildings.

Many first-floor stores have storage in the basement. A narrow stair may have been installed in the rear of the store for access to the basement (fig. 31–14). You may find that a one-story addition has been built in the rear of these buildings. If the store is a restaurant, this is where the kitchen is located. The refrigeration and pantry are in the basement. Many times, food preparation areas are located in the basement, so don't overlook the possibility of a life hazard in the basement.

The one-story addition creates a setback. Persons using the rear fire escape may come down on this setback. A firefighter should always be sent to the rear and relay observations to the incident commander.

H-Types. **H-type** buildings get their name from the fact that they are predominantly in the shape of an H (fig. 31–15). The apartments are in the **wings** of the H and are connected by a **throat** to form the H shape. They have brick masonry walls and wood joist floors and roofs. The larger (newer) H-types usually have incorporated some steel in the construction to increase the size of the building and provide a more open floor plan.

These buildings range in height from 4 to 7 stories. Pipe recesses and voids can run from the basement through the roof. Although these buildings are larger and the voids extensive, all the rules for examining voids still apply and may be even more critical because of the number of apartments that adjoin the void.

Fig. 31–15. A typical H-type building has pipe recesses and voids that can run from the basement through the roof.

Three different types of stairways exist in these buildings. The **transverse stair** allows occupants to transverse from one wing to another. This is the best from the fire department's point of view, because occupants can be directed away from heat and smoke and members can stretch hoselines while avoiding escaping occupants.

Wing stairs are typically a problem for firefighters in that the stairs only serve the wing. This reduces the number of occupants that may be on the stairs, but it does not allow members to cross over on each floor.

Isolated stairs only provide access to the individual apartments from a small landing. This landing can become crowded with firefighters trying to access the apartment. When these stairs are identified, the information must be relayed to all members on the fireground, and a hoseline should not be committed until the exact fire apartment is known.

Fire escapes are the most common form of secondary means of egress from these buildings. Some large buildings may have been built with **fire-rated doors** in the throat, making the stairs in the opposite wing the secondary means of egress.

The apartment layouts of H-types differ than tenements. In H-types, the layout is based on their position in the wing and proximity to the throat. Larger H-types can have an apartment in the throat with entrance doors on either side of the fire-rated doors.

Gaining entry into affected apartments is dependant on the number of apartments involved. It may require more than two teams to gain entry, search, and examine for extension. It is common to have to enter every apartment in the vertical line of apartments to examine for extension.

Fig. 31–14. Elderly or infirm persons may have limited means to exit the rear yard.

Success at fires in multistory multiple dwellings—both tenements and H-types—is often a result of proper ventilation. Vertical venting and roof operations are a key to that success. The interior stairs act like a chimney. Heat and smoke are carried up the stairs and start to bank down on the top floor. Venting skylights and bulkheads at roof level reduce the smoke and heat, making the stairway more tenable for escaping occupants and firefighters. In these buildings, vertical ventilation does not have to be delayed or coordinated with the hoseline advance.

For fires on floors below the top floor, good horizontal ventilation is normally sufficient to prevent extension. Often this is accomplished by a member with a hook or a Halligan tied to a piece of utility rope from the floor above.

For fire on the top floor, the combination of horizontal ventilation and a large vent hole in the roof reduces the chance of fire entering the cockloft. Extension to the cockloft is a major concern. The cockloft is the attic space above all the top floor apartments. Because of the size of the building and the need to achieve pitch on the roof for drainage, the height of the cockloft can vary from several inches to several feet. Once fire has entered the cockloft, it can race through the space fueled by the enormous amount of timber necessary for the roof support. Firestopping may be limited and ineffective. A trench cut may be used as a defensive measure (if the primary vent hole does not stop the spread) to prevent the fire from completely taking over the cockloft. A trench cut is a cut in the roof several feet wide that becomes a fire break between firewalls. If a trench is considered, it should be cut early in the operation and not pulled until it is evident that fire has entered the cockloft (fig. 31–16). A hoseline should be in position on the safe side of the roof and all members removed before the trench is pulled. The trench is not a second vent hole. A hoseline can be operated into the trench. By sweeping the stream side to side, you can prevent fire from crossing the trench.

Stretches in these buildings can require two or more engine companies to complete. Long stretches are common. Few were constructed with standpipe systems. Adaptation of SOPs may be necessary. Supply lines with water thief fittings or manifolds deployed in similar fashion to those used for garden apartments may be practical to reduce the number of lengths in the stretch, thereby reducing friction loss. To get the line into position quickly, take full advantage of opportunities to use **well hole**, rope (fig. 31–17), and fire escape stretches (fig. 31–18).

Fig. 31–16. A trench cut is a cut in the roof several feet wide that becomes a fire break between firewalls.

Fig. 31–17. A rope was deployed from the front apartment to haul the line to the fourth floor for the fire in the rear.

Fig. 31–18. A line was brought up the rear to the fourth-floor balcony and advanced to the fifth-floor apartment.

RETAIL COMMERCIAL BUILDINGS

Taxpayers and strip malls

The term **taxpayer** is used to describe an older, inexpensively constructed commercial building put up on a piece of land to generate income for the property owner (fig. 31–19). Strip malls are the modern descendent of the taxpayer. Although similar in outward appearance, the differences between them are a function of when they were constructed.

They were typically constructed of brick load-bearing walls and wood joist floors and roofs. Although some were built before 1920, most were built between 1920 and 1960. Some of the new taxpayers were two stories, with apartments or office spaces on the second floor. Many had basements with access through a trap door in the floor inside or sidewalk doors outside. The size of building and number of stores varied and depended on the size of the building lot. They are built directly adjacent to the street with no setback, unlike their modern descendent.

Fig. 31–19. Single-story taxpayers typically have 5–10 individual tenants.

Strip malls have been and continue to be built to accommodate the needs of people as they move from the city into the suburbs. These buildings are much larger than urban taxpayers because of the availability of land, with setbacks and contiguous parking lots. They are most commonly built of ordinary construction: exterior masonry walls of concrete block with wood joists/ lightweight wood trusses. They may also be constructed of concrete block walls or tilt walls with steel bar-joist roof trusses and a built-up metal deck roof. The roof structures are not typically fire-rated. As tenants come and go, alteration may have left the tenant separation walls in disrepair; most separations are non–fire-rated (fig. 31–20). (Commonly, the only fire-rated separations are between different types of occupancies that pose a life safety hazard such as places of public assembly—

restaurants and night clubs—and retail stores that deal in hazardous materials, such as swimming pool supply stores.) They are generally single story with relatively high ceilings. Heating, ventilation, and air-conditioning (HVAC) equipment is roof mounted and ductwork is run between the trusses and above the drop ceiling. Service areas and loading docks are in the rear, and customer parking lots are in front. They may have fire sprinklers, but the water supply is often from a supply pipe that also supplies private hydrates and may be a dead-end main. Carefully preplan to avoid disaster.

Fig. 31–20. Walls and partitions between occupancies in strip malls must not be trusted for their fire integrity without proper reconnaissance.

Big box retail stores

Big box retail stores are as the name implies: a big box, square, or rectangular shape for maximum efficiency of floor space. They include the national home centers and the warehouse clubs. In many ways the construction of big box stores is similar to strip malls, concrete walls, and steel truss roofs. They may have 100,000 sq ft (9,290 sq m) of retail space indoors and outdoor space of 20,000 sq ft (1,858 sq m). Typically, there is no fire-resistive rating to the steel bar joists; they are bare steel. A moderate or large fire impinging on the trusses will affect their structural integrity. The height of these stores is larger than strip malls, so expect inside ceiling heights of 30 ft (9 m) (fig. 31–21). HVAC equipment may be located inside the store. High-rack storage of a wide variety of products is the norm.

Fig. 31–21. High ceiling heights with truss components for roof construction are common in big box retailers.

Now that the types of retail stores have been identified, we begin with the size-up. How big is the store or stores? What is the occupancy? Is the store a high-hazard occupancy full of chemicals, flammable liquids, or paints? Do not be fooled; even a seemingly benign storefront may be full of hazards. Remember, these are commercial buildings built and operated for the sole purpose of making money. Life safety may not be a top priority, including the safety of firefighters.

So what *should* be considered in a life hazard assessment? Is the fire during the day? Is the store occupied? Does a retail store have a true and accurate accountability of the number of persons who may be in the store? They should know how many employees are working, but can they account for them all? This requires a thorough search of all building areas. Do not overlook bathrooms and stockrooms. Make sure all areas near exits are checked, even rear exits that may only be used by employees. Be aware that many big box stores have required exits along the sides of the store that are often illegally locked. Make sure people are not trapped behind these doors.

Firefighters entering commercial buildings should use a search line or hoseline when entering the structure. Conditions can change rapidly and the rope or the hoseline may be the only guide to the exit. Thermal imaging cameras are a critical life safety tool. High ceilings and large open areas may make detection of actual fire conditions difficult.

Can you determine what is actually on fire? Fires in commercial building often start in the rear storage areas and in service areas where utilities are located. There may be a maze of halls and corridors to reach these areas, so remember the search rope! A search rope also allows firefighters advancing a hoseline to follow your path. Would you be able to tell them how many right or left turns you made? Or is it easier to tell them to follow the search rope? The search rope also helps others find you if you become trapped or entangled in the stock or contents and can't free yourself.

One advantage in the newer, larger commercial buildings is that they are required to have a fire sprinkler system. Sprinkler systems can be valuable in controlling a fire at an incipient stage. They can also help you locate the fire. Water flowing out of an area or the sound of the sprinklers flowing can direct the search to the fire area.

If the fire is at night, entry into the store may be difficult. Store owners have a great deal of money invested in stock, and to protect it they lock the doors. Depending on their insurance rates, they may also have roll-down gates or other security devices to protect their investment. Store owners only want people in their store when

they can sell them something. Some commercial buildings have electronic fire detection systems—smoke and heat detectors—but even with these systems gaining entry into the store delays fire extinguishment. Be aware that some big box retail stores have cleaning and stock people in the store late at night.

An important point to emphasize is that when a store is locked and limits our way in, it also affects our way out. Rear doors may be bolted or barred. In the case of big box stores, the side exit doors may also be locked illegally. Firefighters assigned to forcible entry in commercial buildings may require additional tools to complete their tasks. When operating at commercial buildings, open all doors and advise all members of their location; if a firefighter must make an emergency exit, he or she can choose the closest exit. Also, rear doors often perform the critical function of serving as point for horizontal ventilation as a hoseline is advanced from the front of the store.

Ventilation in such commercial buildings is limited at best. Roof operations are restricted to removal of skylights and scuttles, *unless fire has heated the steel bar joist roof truss*. If fire has compromised the metal joists or is large enough to do so, conduct no roof operations, because the moment of failure cannot be predicted. These trusses warp, twist, and lose strength early on in a fire when exposed to heat. Unprotected steel lacks fire resistance. Switch to a defensive, **exterior attack**.

Tilt slab walls depend on the roof system to hold them upright. Any roof system warping or twisting that would lead to roof failure can allow the walls to lean. The entire structure could collapse.

If the structure is built with a corrugated metal roof deck, many fire departments avoid sending firefighters to cut the roof. The metal panels that make up the roof system do not always end on a roof beam or truss. When they are cut, sections can hinge inward and drop a firefighter into the fire. Review your department's SOPs to determine its policies for ventilation of metal deck roofs.

Other roof systems of gypsum plank and gypsum concrete should not be cut as well. These systems are prone to moisture and can deteriorate leading to failure. They can be identified during operations when the saw cut reveals a white powdery residue. In this case, notify the incident commander and prepare to evacuate the roof.

You may ask, "So how are we going to know this?" Buildings are built over a time of weeks and months. You need to be aware when new construction is going on in your area and get out and look at how these buildings are being built, when they are being built. Go to the job site, speak to the people who are putting it together, and find out how it is done. If you know how it goes together, you can understand how it will fall apart! Pre-incident planning is critical.

So how do you ventilate commercial building? It is usually best to remove the available windows. If the building is sprinklered and they are flowing, sprinklers cool the smoke, preventing it from lifting vertically. A fan may assist in horizontal ventilation once the fire has been knocked down. Positive pressure ventilation is popular in many areas of the country and requires close coordination to be effective.

In the case of sprinklered buildings, incident commanders do not order the sprinkler system shutdown until the fire has been knocked down and hoselines are in place. In all cases, a firefighter with a radio is positioned at the valve to reopen it if the fire rekindles.

When operating hand lines in commercial buildings, consider the fire load of the store. With all the material in the store, the fire quickly progresses past the extinguishing capability of a 1¾-in. (45-mm) line. Also, judge the reach of the stream; for all reasons just stated, an incident commander may not allow firefighters to enter the building. A 2½-in. (65-mm) hand line is usually required. In the case of a large fire, a rapid attack monitor may be required. These devices may have the capability to reach the rear of the store without placing firefighters in the collapse zone.

If the decision is made to enter, the exact location of the fire must be known and enough line stretched to reach the fire, as with all fires. Select the entrance point closest to the fire, which puts the shortest amount of hose inside the building. The firefighter following the hoseline to the exit is out of the building in the shortest time. Do not let firefighters come off the line if they may be unable to return to it. In commercial buildings with aisles, displays, and cubicles, landmarks and reference points may be difficult to establish. In commercial buildings the hoseline is a *lifeline*.

If the multistory, older department store has a standpipe system, what size is the riser supply pipe? Is the hose valve in a protected location such as an enclosed stairwell? Can the standpipe supply a large hand line? Is the system actually a class II occupant use–only standpipe system (fig. 31–22)? Are there 2½-in. (65-mm) hose valves in the stairwell? If the decision is made to stretch lines from the standpipe, carefully consider their use in a

large floor area store. How much hose is needed to reach the fire area given the layout of the sales area?

In the case of large big box stores, 1½-in. hose stations may be placed in the storage rack areas; these feed directly off of the sprinkler system, intended as mop-up lines. They are not considered a standpipe system. In large buildings with multiple sprinkler risers, each hose connection is typically fed with piping from an adjacent sprinkler riser (allowing shutdown of the sprinkler riser in the fire area while still maintaining a water supply to the hose connection from another *uninvolved* sprinkler system). These small hoselines are also designed to operate at the same pressure as the sprinkler system—typically insufficient for normal firefighting use. If 1½-in. (38-mm) connections are to be used by firefighters, the fire department connection must be supplied to provide adequate pressure.

Fig. 31–22. 1½-in. (38-mm) piping is inadequate to supply a large hand line; this hoseline is intended for occupant use.

When a commercial building has a sprinkler system or if the standpipe will be used for firefighting, a line must always stretch to supply the system through the fire department connection (Siamese). This should be one of the first lines stretched, ensuring that as additional heads fuse or the line is charged, enough water contains the fire and prevents the fire from over-running the sprinklers; however, it still could happen if the store owner has loaded the store with more stock than the system was designed for.

If the water supply for the sprinklers or standpipe comes from the same main as the hydrant to which the fire department pumper is connected, could you affect the others' water supply? Communications with interior crews on the performance of the sprinklers determine if it is so. Consult water district maps or public works employees if a problem exists.

COMMERCIAL OFFICE BUILDINGS

Low- and mid-rise commercial office buildings (structures up to seven stories) are being built throughout the country (figs. 31–23 and 31–24). They have all the same conditions as the taller urban predecessors, beginning with HVAC systems, firefighting operations from a standpipe systems, and large-area searches.

Fig. 31–23. Low-rise commercial office buildings are common throughout the country.

Fig. 31–24. Mid-rise offices pop up as a result of suburban sprawl.

Let's examine the construction of these buildings using our seven-point methodology. The construction of these building is generally a steel frame with poured concrete floors over a steel Q-Deck (fig. 31–25). The exterior walls can be prefabricated **curtain walls**, where the preassembled panels interlock with each other and are attached to the floor slabs (fig. 31–26). This installation method can produce a space between the outside wall and edge of the floor slab. If this gap is not properly fire stopped, it can allow extension to the floor above the fire. Walls can also be constructed of concrete block with a brick veneer or made completely of glass to meet the desires of the architect.

The floor layout often uses a **center core** design, where all mechanical/electrical equipment and stairwells are located. Elevator and stair shafts as well as bathrooms and electrical and communications closets are configured in the center of the floor plan, leaving maximum area around the perimeter for the tenant space. The tenant space generally has a perimeter of walled offices for executives, and the space between the offices and core contains cubicles for assistants and support persons.

Large office buildings, including all high-rises, have a fire command center near the main lobby of the building. The main fire alarm control panel, elevator status panel, emergency generator controls, public address system, and other firefighting equipment are located here.

Hundreds of people can be on each floor of an office building. Thus, accounting for missing persons during emergencies can present a challenge. Security-conscious firms may have some sort of electronic tracking system for employees that may provide some accountability; use it as a guide and search the fire area within the limits of safety.

Fig. 31–25. A steel frame supports the Q-deck.

Fig. 31–26. Before the concrete is poured into the Q-deck, the slab is reinforced with wire mesh and studs are welded to the deck to anchor the concrete to the decking.

A large-area search plan is crucial to maintain crew integrity. Reliable aids include search ropes and tag lines for firefighters who need to expand the search area into cubicles. A thermal imaging camera is important for the search team leader to look for victims, and it visually specifies the crew's location. A leader with a clear picture in a camera can guide a firefighter toward a victim or back to safety. The camera is an important tool while searching to monitor the heat conditions. Viewing the thermal layer in conjunction with a fixed object indicates whether the heat is banking down. Occasionally monitoring conditions overhead is also important.

Fire extinguishment in these buildings requires a high-volume, far-reaching hoseline. The rate of heat release by combustibles in this type of occupancy is much higher than in a single-family dwelling. You wind up with a hotter fire and more of it. Fire, heat, and smoke can easily be pushed around the core if the engine crew is not careful. The area overhead must be monitored to ensure the fire does not pass the advancing crew by means of the plenum area above the drop ceiling.

Entry into these buildings is unique. Some owners have provided the fire department with keys to lock boxes outside that contain master keys to the building for access during off hours. When these are unavailable, many locking devices can be encountered, from a simple tubular lock in an aluminum frame door to electronic magnetic locking devices. Many office buildings, particularly multitenant high-rises, use locks on stairwell doors to prevent reentry back into the tenant space. Buildings equipped with such locks are required to be outfitted with release devices that unlock the doors when they receive a signal from the fire alarm system or a *manual* signal from the fire command center.

Building service areas, mechanical equipment rooms, fire pump rooms, and the like are probably be locked and require forcible entry. *Note*: Just as you were taught to try the knob first, gaining entry is often not about force. A little finesse goes along way!

Access to upper floors of these buildings requires the use of elevators. Members walking more than several floors with all the required equipment is debilitating. The firefighters arriving on the fire floor must be prepared to commence operation quickly.

During a fire emergency, elevators are recalled to the first-floor lobby (or designated level), known as a **phase I operation**. The operational phase of elevator use by firefighters is called **phase II operation** or **fireman's service**.

Under phase II operation, the firefighter has control of all the functions of the elevator cab: up, down, door open, and door close, and so forth. Refer to your department's SOP on when the phase II operation's use of elevators is permitted. A thorough understanding of the function of phase II operation is required for the member operating the elevator to perform it safely. He or she is as responsible for delivering the firefighters to the upper floors as the driver of the apparatus that drove them to the building.

When operating elevators it is a good safety tip to look up the shaft before you get into the elevator. Shine a flashlight between the elevator car and the hoistway door to see if there is any smoke in the shaft. If the shaft is clear and you are ready to leave the lobby, select a floor, and as the car begins to move, press the *call cancel* button. This clears the floor selection and the car should stop at the next available floor. This verifies that the phase II operation function works properly. When selecting a floor to get off the elevator, two floors below the reported fire floor can be appropriate. If the elevator does not behave properly, *do not use the elevator.*

Be aware that many tall buildings use multiple **banks** of elevators that serve different groups of floors or **zones** (floors 2–20, floors 21–40, etc.). In many cases elevators serving the upper floors pass through **blind shafts**, which have no doors on the lower floors.

Using elevators during a fire can be dangerous. The key to safe firefighting operations using elevators is understanding the features of elevators, the potential hazards, and your department's elevator SOPs.

Beware of **access stairs**, which are open (unenclosed) stairs within a tenant space that serve adjacent floors. A smoke detector could activate on an upper floor served by the access stairs from a fire below, which could have you exiting the elevator on the fire floor. If the occupancy has access stairs, take the elevator two floors below the lowest floor served by those stairs. How would you know if access stairs exist? Ask building personnel. If they don't know, look at the tenant directory. If the same tenant has offices on two floors, it is possible that they installed an access stair. Law firms often install access stairs.

Usually, these buildings cannot be ventilated by breaking windows. Broken glass from floors high above the street can sail a great distance, injuring innocent bystanders. Glass dropped from lower floors can damage firefighters' operating apparatus and cut hoselines, leading to water loss issues. As a general rule, before any glass is broken in a high-rise fire the incident commander should be notified so the street below can be secured. Some high-rises, however, are equipped with safer, tempered glass, designed specifically for firefighting ventilation. Pre-incident planning is critical to establish the presence of such tempered glass windows.

Depending on the sophistication of the air handling equipment, fans can be turned on and dampers turned to an exhaust mode to clear out smoke. This should only be ordered by the incident commander and performed by qualified building personnel. Smoke detectors required by your local building code may be located inside the HVAC ductwork and prevent you from using the system. If the HVAC system is used for such operations, all firefighting units should be made aware so they can report any adverse effects. In some cases, the building may actually have a smoke control system. Make sure you gain an understanding of how the system operates *before the fire*, while conducting pre-incident planning.

Hoselines usually are stretched from a standpipe in the stairwell. Some jurisdictions have the standpipe connection in a hose cabinet on the floor itself. Never hook up to these outlets on the fire floor. The floor below the fire floor provides a safe place to hook up the initial line. If additional lines are required, they must come from floors below. The line must be flaked out up the stairwell; and, if the attack on the fire begins at the door to the occupancy, the line must be charged. Never enter the fire area with a dry hoseline. It is safer for the fire attack to begin from the protection of the stairwell as this will provide an area of refuge if conditions change on the fire floor.

Before the attack begins, position the line on the stairs for a rapid advance: Flake the line up the stairs so the weight of the line assists the advance. Be sure to check the stairs for escaping occupants before opening the door to the fire area. You don't want to expose people to the heat and smoke when the fire attack begins from the **attack stairwell**. Any occupants in the attack stairwell must be brought in on floors above and transferred to the other stair *before the attack begins*. If possible, with the building's public address system, alert occupants to use another specific stair for egress, called an **evacuation stairwell**. The evacuation stair door should never be opened on the fire floor to prevent contamination, and all entries on to the fire floor must come from the attack stair.

Do not overlook the possibility of stretching lines from the apparatus for fires on lower floors. Remember, the goal of the line is to get water on the fire as quickly as possible. A good expression to remember is that "everything is a possibility until it has been eliminated."

RESTAURANTS

Restaurants can be found in almost any type of building. The construction characteristics of the building do not change because of the restaurant; they are only compounded by it. Most restaurant fires are a result of issues from the kitchen, but smoking materials carelessly discarded into garbage cans can easily start a fire. We look at the kitchen in depth.

Commercial kitchens are an obstacle course of hazards: high-voltage electricity, high-volume gas piping, stoves with open flames with pots full of boiling liquids, fryers full of superheated oils, ovens, microwaves, and slippery floors. And that is all *before* the fire starts!

Before operating a hoseline in a commercial kitchen, control the utilities. Turn off the gas before you put the fire out. Fires involving the fryers may require the use of a specific extinguisher. They are no longer *deep fat* fryers; because of health concerns, restaurants cook in a light oil. Simply cooling the oil is not enough to extinguish the fire and prevent it from reigniting. A type K extinguisher should be available on premise for this purpose. If the fire-suppression system has not extinguished the fire, you may need to employ the K extinguisher.

All cooking equipment that produces **grease-laden vapors** is required to be located under the protection of an exhaust hood with an approved fire-extinguishing system. There are **filters** in the hood that are designed to trap the grease and oily vapor (fig. 31–27). These filters must be cleaned on a regular basis as set forth by the jurisdiction. Although the filters may be cleaned, some grease and oil can enter the exhaust ductwork. Exhaust ducts are a heavy-gauge welded design to prevent fire from breaking out of the ductwork. If a fire is not extinguished by the fixed system or is hot enough to ignite the grease build-up in the ductwork, they become very messy to put out.

Some fire codes require that a diagram of the ductwork be posted in the kitchen. A firefighter can use this diagram to trace the duct to its termination outside the building (fig. 31–28). These codes also call for an access panel to be provided every place the duct makes a turn, providing a point for contractors to clean the duct and remove any buildup. However, it works more effectively as a point for the fire department to apply water.

Fig. 31–27. The grease filters under the hood trap grease vapor, and the vents in the front are for the make-up air.

Fig. 31–28. The exhaust duct exits the building into a shaft. Note the access panel on the turn and the location of the make-up air louver above

Using a thermal imaging camera to determine if the fire has entered the ductwork can be challenging because almost everything in the kitchen is hot or giving off some heat. The duct may be naturally hot because it is exhausting the air from over a hot stove. It takes a skilled firefighter to interpret the thermal image correctly. It also provides an excellent training opportunity when the fire is under control.

The range hood of a commercial kitchen has another set of ductwork for **make-up air**, which replaces the air being sucked out by the hood's exhaust. The fans in this ductwork provide more volume than exhaust fans to create a positive pressure in the kitchen and keep the grease vapor under the hood. When following the run of the duct, do not get confused and follow the wrong duct. The make-up air duct may not terminate in the same location as the exhaust. The grease duct is made up of heavy-gauge welded steel and more resembles air-conditioning ductwork, lightweight assembled in sections with noticeable seams.

Commercial kitchens floors are notoriously slippery. Even the smallest amount of water on greasy floor creates a dangerous condition. Salt applied to the floor effectively improves traction. Dump out a few shakers of salt in the area where you are sanding; the effect will be noticeable. If more salt is needed, find the bulk items storage and use what you need. It is an easy way to prevent an injury.

VACANT BUILDINGS

Vacant building fires pose one of the most serious threats to firefighters. Fires in vacant building can occur in every community across America. With the ebb and flow of the economy, some areas see this more than others. The vacant building has been abandoned by the owner and fallen into disrepair. The extent of the damage is unknown. Floors, walls, and stairs are all of questionable stability.

So why do we fight these fires? Do we ever know if the building is truly vacant until it is searched? Does letting it burn create a hazard greater than the building's worth? Do we extinguish the fire so the property owner has more to haul away? The obligation to extinguish all fires must be balanced with the moral obligation to the safety of our firefighters.

Fires in vacant buildings should be considered suspicious: They happen for a reason. They may be set to cover up a crime, as an act of vandalism, or as arson for profit.

A fire investigator determines arson after the fire is extinguished and all accidental causes have been ruled out. The reason the building is on fire is of less importance than the fact it is on fire. In a fire of this type, the intent is to do as much damage in the shortest period of time as possible. Even if the fire department extinguishes the blaze, the damage would have been maximized.

How does that affect how to operate? Conduct a good, comprehensive size-up. Looking closely at the house may indicate several key elements in fire attack plan. If the building has been abandoned by the owner, the electric service wires may be cut, the meter may be removed and the gas service may be locked out. This may eliminate many *accidental* causes of fires, leading to a greater suspicion of arson.

Maximum effort must be directed to extinguishing the fire quickly. All firefighters must work to get water on the fire as quickly as possible. In addition, a minimum commitment of firefighters is assigned to the hazard area.

This is one type of fire where we adjust our aggressive interior attack methods in favor of a more cautious approach. Water may be prudent if it can be applied from the outside without exposing firefighters to the unknown dangers of an interior attack.

In many cases, it is simply too dangerous to commit interior forces to fight a fire in a vacant or abandoned building because of the size of the fire, the existing poor conditions of the building, and the lack of fire protection features. No firefighter's life is worth that of any building, particularly vacant or abandoned ones.

Firefighting operations in vacant buildings must be conducted methodically with an emphasis on safety, concentrating on the known life hazard, the firefighters. All the voids that are present when a building is occupied are still present while it is vacant. Additional paths for fire spread may be present from deterioration from elements, either natural or man-made. Vagrants and squatters may have taken shelter in the building and caused damage. Others may have vandalized the building by removing fixtures and other items strictly for their salvage value.

Every department should have a policy for firefighting operations in vacant buildings. The first arriving officer generally determines the fire attack plan, based on fire conditions, age and condition of the structure, exposures, and especially life hazard. Firefighters must remember that firefighting operations are conducted *within the limits of safety* with a minimal commitment of firefighters.

An important consideration in vacant buildings is what the previous occupant left behind. Take time in your own size-up to note the areas of concern. Maintain situational awareness: is this building now vacant for a reason? For firefighters with portable radios, listen to all the transmissions and try to piece together the puzzle, as the incident commander is doing.

FLAMMABLE GAS FIRES

FFII 6.3.3 Responding to flammable gas fires and emergencies are a part of your responsibility as a firefighter. You may be faced with several different gases. To effectively respond to these alarms, you must first understand the properties of the gas. As you will recall from your Firefighter I training, some gases are heavier than air and some are lighter than air, based on vapor density (air = 1). Obviously, this affects where vapors collect when they are released. Gases heavier than air collect in low areas, and vapors lighter than air tend to disperse in the air. Flammable gases are stored in cylinders or delivered by utility gas systems.

We are not discussing specific gas systems that may be found in hospitals or specific manufacturing facilities that may use gases in their processes. If these industrial facilities are in your response area, discuss the operating procedures with your company officers.

We will discuss the most common gases and where they can be found. One of the most common gases is natural gas. It is delivered to homes and businesses for cooking and heating. It may also be found as a compressed gas stored in cylinders as an alternative motor vehicle fuel. These vehicles are placarded as CNG (compressed natural gas) vehicles.

Natural gas that is piped into your community is made up almost exclusively of methane, but it may have trace amounts of other gases. Natural gas is lighter than air, colorless, and odorless in its natural state. For consumer use, the chemical ethyl mercaptan is added to give the gas a distinctive odor. The odor of mercaptan can be detected by our senses at a concentration of 20% of the lower explosive limit, well below the explosive range of the gas. The explosive range of natural gas is between 5% and 15%, so the odor can be detected by a person with a normal sense of smell at around 2% gas in air. However, do not rely on your sense of smell to determine the percentage of gas in a compartment.

Natural gas ignites at 1,163°F (628°C). The gas is considered a simple asphyxiant. Inhaling the gas (in higher concentration) can displace the oxygen in your lungs and cause asphyxiation.

Natural gas is delivered to homes and businesses through underground piping. Often the gas piping is steel, but some newer installations are using plastic gas pipes. The gas is supplied from a main to individual houses or industrial services. There are several points of control on the distribution system; firefighters do not shut down any gas valves that are in the roadway. These shutoff valves often have control of large portions of the distribution system and affect many homes and businesses.

Low-pressure gas is delivered to homes and businesses, except for some commercial facilities. Controlling leaks can be relatively simple. In attempting to control a gas leak, the first point of control is at the appliance. Typically, each appliance has a quarter-turn gas valve to shut the off the flow of gas. When the handle of the valve is perpendicular to the piping, the valve is closed (fig. 31–29). When it is in line with the piping, the valve opens, allowing gas to flow. Inside a structure the gas usually is in steel threaded pipe (black iron). There may be a stainless steel flexible connection to the individual appliance from this black iron pipe. The shutoff valve is located behind the appliance or in an adjoining cabinet. Note the position of the valve indicating the gas is on (fig. 31–30). This appliance connects with a flexible line to the stove.

Following the gas pipe back toward the street, the next point of control is a valve on the main line where the main enters the building (fig. 31–31). The size of the main and whether the building is residential or commercial dictates the gas valve style (fig. 31–32). The head of service valve is still a quarter-turn design. Generally, they are larger versions of the quarter-turn valve at the appliance.

Fig. 31–29. Two gas valves: the one on the left is open, the valve is parallel to the pipe; the one on the right is off, the valve handle is perpendicular to the pipe.

Fig. 31–30. The gas supply to any appliance is required to have a shutoff.

Fig. 31–31. A residential gas line is controlled by a quarter-turn valve.

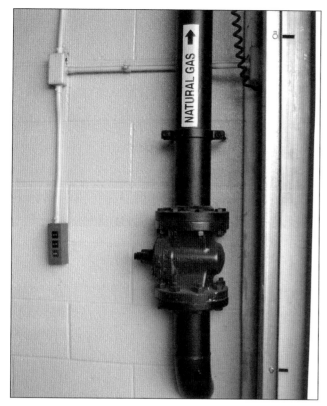

Fig. 31–32. Commercial gas lines distribute a much larger volume of gas and thus have much larger valves and piping.

Fig. 31–33. Firefighters should become familiar with residential gas meter since they may be called upon to control gas during emergencies.

Fig. 31–34. Commercial gas meters are more complex than the residential variety.

All gas services have a gas meter that can also be shut off. The meter also often serves as a pressure regulator. The meter may be located inside or outside the building. A valve on the meter can be used to shut down the gas, or it may be on the riser where the gas piping comes out of the ground (outside the building) or through the exterior wall (inside the building), before it enters the meter. Commercial and residential meter piping may be different in style but are similar in function. Note the gas valve where the riser comes out of the ground and the other before the gas meter (figs. 31–33 and 31–34). Both valves have rings, so the meter can be locked out by the utility. Note the size of the gas line as it comes from the ground. The smaller pipe indicates that the service line to this building is high pressure. Note the size of the pipe where it enters the building.

Valves located outside may be difficult to turn because of exposure to the elements. When these valves need to be closed, a small pipe wrench or the fork of a Halligan tool is generally enough to get the valve to turn. If it can't be turned, don't force it. Breaking off the valve at this location severely compounds the problem. Summon the utility crew for assistance.

The last point of control for shutting off the gas is the **curb valve**, located between the gas main in the street and the building. This is the fire department's last way of stopping the flow of gas to a building if all other options are impossible—it is located outside of the building. It is important to note that some fire department SOPs do not allow firefighters to operate this valve—this is left to the utility company. The curb valve is located under a steel cover and in a pipe casing. The valve is at the bottom. A long-handled wrench is required to operate this valve. In newer installations the valve body may be plastic and break easily when forced. Contact the local utility company in your area for more specific information on their underground equipment.

It is important to remember that whenever the gas is shut down to an appliance or building, the fire department does not reopen the valves. Some gas-fueled equipment has specific relighting instructions, and relighting must be done by licensed individuals. Other areas require that the utility be notified whenever the gas is shut off to any appliance. Check with the gas utility for local requirements.

When called to a natural gas leak, *ensure that the gas utility has been called to respond*. You must remember the properties of the gas. The gas is lighter than air and mixes easily in a confined space. In a confined space, the gas air mixture is explosive. For a suspected gas leak, firefighters should not turn on any lights, ring doorbells, or cause any sparks within the building. Turning off lights can cause a spark as well. If lights are on, leave them on; if lights are off, leave them off. Firefighter handheld radios and flashlights may also be a source of ignition. Turn on flashlights before entering, and do not speak on the radio until the atmosphere is deemed safe.

Obviously, when attempting to locate the source of the leak, never check for it with an open flame. Use a combustible-gas meter or detection equipment (fig. 31–35). Decide how to handle the incident based on the concentration of gas in the building and its ability to be controlled. With low concentrations, it is possible to locate the source of the leak and stop it. Uncontrollable leaks or leaks resulting in moderate or high concentrations of gas are too dangerous to allow firefighters to remain inside or near the building; firefighting units must be evacuated along with people in surrounding buildings and areas. In such cases, gas utility crews must shut off the gas remote from the structure (fig. 31–36). Liquid soap mixed with water to make soap bubbles can be used to check for small gas leaks on piping. When the solution is applied to a leaking pipe, the bubbles expand, indicating a leak.

Whenever the presence of gas is detected, full protective equipment is required. Self-contained breathing apparatus (SCBA) use is mandatory when investigating gas leaks within a structure. When the source of the leak is located, it is best to turn off the gas at the control point closest to the point of the leak. This minimizes the disruption to the home or business owner. Sealants and putty only slow the leak until it can be shut off at a valve. Necessary repairs may not be made if the leak can be controlled without turning off the gas.

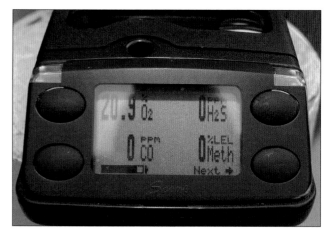

Fig. 31–35. Firefighters should learn how to operate all detection meters available in their department.

Fig. 31–36. Gas explosions can be extremely violent and destructive. (Courtesy of James O'Connell)

Once the leak has been controlled, the area should be well ventilated. Allow the area to vent naturally. Vent the upper floors first; this allows the gas to dissipate more readily, because the gas is lighter than air. Work your way down to the lowest level, allowing fresh air to enter. Do not use power vent fans unless they are intrinsically safe for explosive atmospheres. If it is necessary to use fans, they must be used in a positive-pressure mode to blow fresh air into the building and avoid a source of ignition.

Gas leaks located outdoors may involve the high-pressure side of the distribution system. There are important safety considerations when dealing with high-pressure gas. A relatively small pipe can dispel a large amount of gas, creating a large vapor cloud. When the gas leak is outside coming up through the ground, the odorant ethyl mercaptan does not pass as easily through the soil as the gas. The odorant is said to have been **scrubbed out**. In all cases, gas leaks must be verified by metering equipment.

Many times, outside gas leaks are the result of construction accidents, often from heavy equipment digging near underground utilities. When the gas line has been pulled out of the ground, resist the urge to plug it. The escaping gas causes static electricity to form on the piping. This small electrical charge may be enough to generate a spark and ignite. When the pipe was pulled from the ground, it may have created a void in the soil, which can cause gas to follow the pipe back into structures. Pulling the pipe may also have caused another break further down the line. Gas may be escaping into the ground undetected. If the gas leak runs under asphalt or concrete, the gas may travel great distances before being detected.

Utility crews have equipment to test for underground gas leaks. Firefighters must check all surrounding properties and areas below grade, because gas may permeate storm drains and septic systems. Eliminate all sources of ignition in the area of the vapor cloud. A fog stream may help disperse the vapor. If a hoseline is used near an excavation, use caution and prevent water runoff from entering the trench. This complicates the repair process.

If the outside gas leak has been caused by construction, evacuate as required. Stretch a precautionary line to protect exposures and possibly disperse the vapor. Remove all sources of ignition, staging apparatus upwind. As with all flammable gas, do not extinguish the fire until the flow of gas has been turned off.

Compressed natural gas can be used as a motor fuel in passenger vehicles, but identifying these vehicles may be difficult. Some states do not require these vehicles to be labeled, whereas others require a small CNG placard to be affixed to only the front and rear of the vehicle. If your response is to an alternative fuel vehicle powered by CNG, once you have confirmed that it is CNG-powered, the first task is to shut down the gas flow. There is a main shutoff located near the fuel cylinder. The cylinder may be located in the trunks of sedans and other cars or in the beds of pickup trucks. Another inline shutoff may be located under the **rocker panel** where the fuel lines run along the frame rails to the engine.

If the vehicle is involved in fire, let the fire burn off and protect exposures. The CNG cylinder is protected with a **burst disc** (for overpressures) and a **fusible plug** (which melts under fire attack, preventing cylinder overpressure because of heating from the fire). A hand line used from a safe distance prevents the disk from rupturing or the fusible plug from melting. If the vehicle is involved in an accident, control any fuel leaks and eliminate sources of ignition.

Propane is another common flammable gas. It is used for home barbecues, industrial forklifts, and other equipment. In rural areas propane may be used for home heating and cooking. It may be stored in large cylinders outside the house and piped to individual appliances. Controlling leaks is much the same as described for natural gas emergencies, except remembering that propane is heavier than air.

Propane is odorized much like natural gas. The cylinders for home barbecues are typically 20-lb (9-kg) cylinders, so there are 20 lb (9 kg) of propane by weight in the cylinder. A 20-lb (9 kg) cylinder contains approximately 4.75 gal (17 L) of liquid. One gallon of liquid produces 13,500 gal (51,103 L) of combustible vapor with a lower explosive limit of 2.15% and an upper limit of 9.60%. This means that it takes little propane to create an explosive mixture in air. One 20-lb (9-kg) cylinder can create an explosive mixture to completely fill a 1,100-sq-ft (102-sq-m) house. Thus the propane cylinders should never be stored indoors.

Newer propane cylinders are equipped with an **overfill protection device (OPD)** valve, which is built into the valve to shut off the valve when the cylinder has the correct amount of liquid. The float switch closes the valve when the proper liquid level is reached. The plastic tube is connected to the screw on the side of the valve. If the cylinder must be filled without a scale, the screw is removed and the cylinder is filled until liquid flows from the screw indicating the cylinder is full (fig. 31–37).

Fig. 31–37. Overfill protection devices (installed inside tanks) help ensure that propane cylinders are not overfilled.

Most liquefied petroleum gas cylinders are designed to accept 80% capacity as a liquid. This allows 20% of the gas to expand under normal temperature conditions. Propane gas expands approximately 1.5% for every 10°F (5⅝°C) rise in temperature. The pressure relief device on a barbecue cylinder is located in the valve, pointing in a direction opposite the hose connection. When approaching the cylinder, avoid approaching in a direction that places you in the path of the pressure relief device.

Cylinders equipped with the OPD device can be identified by the triangle hand wheel and the large external threads for connecting to the appliance (fig. 31–38). The older-style valves have a star-shaped wheel and internal threads. Some older cylinders can't be refilled based on the date of manufacture, so check with your local propane dealer for details (fig. 31–39). Outdated cylinders must not be discarded in the trash; check with the propane dealer or local government offices. Some municipalities have hazardous waste collections to accept this type of material.

Fig. 31–38. The triangular-shaped handle on this propane cylinder is indicative of it having an overfill protection device.

Fig. 31–39. Older propane valves without the overfill protection device (OPD) will have a star shaped handle.

Forklifts use 40-lb (18-kg) motor fuel cylinders. These cylinders are designed to be used and stored in the horizontal position and flow liquid to the vaporizer in the engine (fig. 31–40). Their pressure relief valves work

in much the same way, but there are important differences in the two types of cylinders. Because these cylinders are designed to contain liquid propane, a fire or emergency involving forklifts often involve a liquid leak (fig. 31–41). Escaping liquid is a more serious situation than escaping gas because of the vaporization rate.

Fig. 31–40. Forklifts use 40-lb motor fuel cylinders designed to deliver liquid propane to the vaporizer on the engine.

Fig. 31–41. Forklift cylinders have ports for liquid service as well as vapor. Note: The cylinder is equipped with a liquid level gauge.

It is important to note that, like all stored liquid cylinders, propane cylinders are susceptible to BLEVE (boiling liquid expanding vapor explosion). When heated, the liquid inside the cylinder increases the internal pressure (fig. 31–42). If the relief device cannot relieve the pressure, the cylinder could fail. Pressure relief valves in propane cylinders are spring-loaded, operate at 375 psi (2,625 kPa), and close when the pressure in the cylinder is reduced. If the cylinder is exposed to fire, the pressure relief valve could operate several times before the cylinder fails. Because the contents are flammable, a failed cylinder releases large quantities of an explosive mixture. That could result in an explosion and fire.

Propane should always be stored and secured outdoors (fig. 31–43).

Fig. 31–42. A BLEVE is a very dangerous situation, and all too common with the widespread use of portable gas grills. These are the remnants of a gas grill cylinder.

Fig. 31–43. Storage of propane cylinders must be in a marked secured location in compliance with applicable codes and standards.

Let's look at some general fires and emergencies you may be called to. This discussion is not intended to replace any standard operating procedures of your department but to give insight into successfully handling these situations. Consult your department policies for clarification if necessary.

The first involves a propane gas leak inside a home. As previously mentioned propane cylinders have no place in the home. If a leak is suspected by the distinctive smell of the odorant, confirm with combustible gas detectors.

How bad it smells is not an indication of the concentration of gas in the air or indicative of the explosive range.

For a leak with no fire, the procedure is as follows:

- Eliminate any sources of ignition
- Ventilate the house
- Find the leaking cylinder
- Close the valve
- Remove the cylinder from the house.

A leaking propane cylinder with *low concentrations of gas* in the house will also necessitate the stretching of a handline. Teams of two or more should enter the home and search for the cylinder. Remember all the sources of ignition. However, moderate or high concentrations of propane usually call for the evacuation of all firefighting personnel as well as surrounding areas, such as in natural gas leaks.

When venting the house, only a positive pressure method should be used. Air must be blown in so as not to pull the explosive mixture toward a fan that is not intrinsically safe. Remember, when venting a gas heavier than air in areas where the vapor collects, fans may be necessary to disperse the gas.

Note: Before approaching a flammable gas cylinder fire, firefighters should identify a safe haven or area of refuge that will provide protection from heat, concussion, or flying debris in event of a rupture or explosion. They should seek an area or shelter that can provide protection from heat, and far enough away from the failure areas of a cylinder to prevent or limit injury.

With all cylinders involved in fire, the best course of action is to use large mounts of water applied from a safe distance and allow the contents to burn off while protecting exposures. If the valve must be shut down or a rescue is required, approach under the protection of two properly flowing fog lines. Approach the cylinder to close the valve; otherwise stop the flow of the gas, or effect the rescue. Should the fire be extinguished before the valve is closed, the valve should still be closed completely as soon as it is reached.

Once the valve is closed and fire extinguished, the hose team can retreat by backing away. Firefighters should never turn their backs on a flammable gas cylinder or tank fire in the event the fire should suddenly reignite. Once the hose team has retreated, they should continue to cool the cylinder from a distance using a straight stream.

Fires are common in gas barbecue grills for several reasons. For example, spiders nesting in venturi tubes cause gas to back up in the tube and ignite when the grill is lit. The hose from the cylinder dry rots and leaks, and the escaping gas ignites. These types of fire are common at the beginning of the grilling season when the equipment has not be used for several months and been exposed to the elements.

If responding to a gas grill fire and the grill is 10 ft (3 m) from the house as recommended, you might allow the cylinder to burn off while protecting exposures. If the fire is exposing the house, this may develop into a structural fire and require two hand lines to control. Both hand lines should work in unison to advance firefighters close enough to shut down the flow of gas. Once the gas has been controlled, one hand line should continue to cool the cylinder while the other goes to work extinguishing the structural fire.

When attempting to shut down the valve, the hand wheel may be plastic or light white metal; they may have melted from the impinging fire. If attempting to shut down the valve, a pair of locking pliers may be necessary to turn the stem of the valve. The valves on these cylinders turn off as others turn them clockwise to shut them down. The fittings that attach to the valve's internal threads are left-hand thread. Fittings that attach to the large external threads of an OPD valve are right-hand thread.

Fires in forklifts can be handled in much the same way: two hand lines advancing to control the leak and extinguish the fire. Use caution not to extinguish the fire until the flow of gas has been shut off. If the fire goes out before the flow of gas is shut, use the hose stream to disperse the vapor. With forklifts a liquid release is more likely, but this liquid vaporizes quickly. Once the liquid vaporizes, use metering equipment to check for any concentrations of gas in surrounding properties.

Another common type of flammable gas is acetylene. Acetylene is often used by plumbers for soldering pipe and by ironworkers for cutting and welding operations. The acetylene gas is dissolved in acetone in the cylinder to make the gas more stable for consumer use.

Acetylene cylinders come in several sizes ranging from small *MC* tanks and larger *B* tanks used by plumbers to several larger size tanks for oxyacetylene welding or cutting torches (fig. 31–44). The important difference with these tanks is their relief devices. MC and B tanks have a fusible metal plug built into the valve assembly (fig. 31–45). Older cylinders for cutting and welding have

two lead plugs that melt out if the cylinder is exposed to heat, one on top and the other on the bottom. Newer models have both plugs on top (figs. 31–46, 31–47, and 31–48).

Acetylene torches have the gas dissolved into liquid acetone. The relief device for these tanks is in the valve assembly in the form of a burst disk. The significance is that these relief devices don't reset or close; a thin metal wafer melts open (figs. 31–49 and 31–50). Once they open, the gas escapes until the cylinder is empty. Cooling the cylinder does not stop the flow of gas, but it may prevent an explosion. The oxygen used in conjunction with the acetylene in these torches is not itself flammable, but it supports combustion (it is an oxidizer) and can make for a very intense fire.

Fig. 31–44. A collection of plumber's acetylene tanks. Note the larger B tanks on the left and the smaller MC tanks on the right.

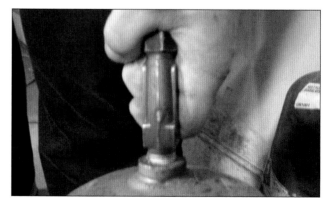

Fig. 31–45. On MC and B tanks, the relief device is a lead plug in the valve assembly. The small gray spot is the relief plug.

Fig. 31–46. Older torch cylinders have one plug on top and one on the bottom.

Fig. 31–47. The plug in the center is a lead plug, relief device.

Fig. 31–49. The relief device may be built into the valve assembly. Here the relief device is on the right.

Fig. 31–50. The thin metal wafer is all that protects the cylinder from rupture. The relief cap on the right has the copper intact while the one on the left has melted open. (Courtesy of Lampton Welding Supply)

FIREFIGHTING FOAM

FFII 6.3.1 Firefighters encounter class B fires—flammable or combustible liquids—on a fairly regular basis. We often see these fires where a product has been accidentally spilled, has ignited, and is burning vigorously. High radiant heat and large volumes of black smoke are common characteristics for hydrocarbon fuels such as gasoline and diesel fuel. Firefighting foams are used to control and extinguish class B fires. In addition, some special foams are used to fight class A fires.

NFPA 11 *Standard for Low-, Medium-, and High-Expansion Foam* covers the use of portable foam equipment, as well as fixed fire protection systems such as those that protect tank farms and **bulk terminals.**

A few important terms are common to all ignitable liquids:

Ignition temperature: The minimum temperature at which the fuel/air mixture must be heated to start self-sustained combustion

Fig. 31–48. Newer cylinders for cutting and welding torches have two relief plugs on top of the cylinder.

Lower flammable limit: The minimum concentration of vapor/air mixture below which propagation of a flame does not occur in the presence of an ignition source (measured as a percentage)

Upper flammable limit: Maximum concentration of a vapor/air mixture above which propagation of flame does not occur (measured as a percentage)

Flammable range: The range of vapor/air concentration between the lower flammable limit and upper flammable limit (measured as a percentage)

Flash point: The lowest temperature at which vapor pressure of the liquid is sufficient to produce a flammable mixture

Flammable liquid: A substance having a flash point below 100°F (38°C)

Combustible liquid: Any liquid having a flash point at or above 100°F (38°C)

Types of Class B fuels

Class B fuels are generally divided up into two types: hydrocarbon-based fuels and polar solvents. Each requires a unique type of foam for successful extinguishment. Hydrocarbons are oil based and include gasoline, motor oil, kerosene, jet fuel, and diesel fuel. Hydrocarbons do not mix with water and generally float on water. The old expression, "oil and water don't mix," holds true (fig. 31–51).

Polar solvents are the second major type of ignitable liquids we must understand. Polar solvents are distilled or synthetic products and will mix with water. Examples of polar solvents are alcohol, acetone, methanol, and ethanol. These polar solvent vapors are heavier than air and stay low to the ground and collect in low-lying areas. They burn with a pale blue flame and produce little smoke. Burning alcohol may not be easy to detect. Before approaching a spill of alcohol, look for heat waves or thermal currents rising from the spill. If a thermal image camera is unavailable, use a wooden pike pole or straw broom pushed out in front of you when approaching to confirm if the spill is on fire.

Alcohol-resistant foam must be used for fuels that contain polar solvents, since polar solvents are alcohol-based and will otherwise break down the foam. Full personal protective equipment, including SCBA, should be worn by all firefighters operating near an alcohol spill, even after the fire has been extinguished. Exposure to the vapors in sufficient concentration can produce dizzi-

ness, drowsiness, or apparent drunkenness. The effects of exposure may be delayed for many hours and could lead to unconsciousness or death.

Fig. 31–51. Oil and water don't mix.

Agents for extinguishing Class B fires

Several agents can be used to control and extinguish flammable and combustible liquid fires. We can use carbon dioxide (CO_2), dry chemical, or water on fuel with a high flash point such as diesel fuel. But each of these agents has major weaknesses: CO_2 simply blows away with the wind and is an asphyxiant in closed spaces; dry chemical has limited holding power; and water is unsuitable for low flash point liquids such as gasoline. Additionally, all are in limited supply (except water) on first-due apparatus. Specialty apparatus like those used at airports may have large quantities of specialty agents described earlier.

Class B foam is the agent of choice for flammable and combustible liquid spills and fires by engine companies. It is effective because it blankets the flammable liquid with an aerated, relatively stable foam blanket that extinguishes the fire, suppresses the vapors of the fuel, and most importantly provides a high degree of security to protect against reignition.

Class A foam lowers the surface tension of water molecules, which allows superior penetration into dense Class A fuel, but it is ineffective in fighting liquid fuel fires. In contrast to the penetrating qualities of Class A foam, Class B foam floats on top of the liquid hydrocarbon fuel, creating a barrier between the fuel and atmospheric oxygen, thus curtailing combustion. A Class B foam blanket must suppress fuel vapors for at least 15 minutes without reapplication.

Foam is an important tool in the fire service, and as such has specific uses (flammable liquids) and specific times when it should not be used.

Foam should not be used on electrical fires. Foam is 94% to 97% water, the remaining percentage is foam concentrate. Since water conducts electricity, so do foams. The chemicals in the foam can actually cause the foam to be more conductive than plain water. Electrical fires should be de-energized and treated as class A or B fires.

Foam is ineffective on **three-dimensional fires** (liquids that are spraying and burning at the same time) such as a broken pipeline or burning fuel leaking under pressure from an elevated tank. In a three-dimensional fire, dry chemical should be used to first extinguish the fire followed by foam which will cool and secure the situation.

Foam is ineffective on pressurized gas fires such as propane or butane. These fuels are normally vapor at room temperatures and are cooled and compressed for storage and transportation economies. Foam is not effective on products that are above their boiling point at normal temperatures and pressures.

Foam is also not effective on class D fires, combustible metals such as magnesium, titanium, sodium, or potassium because of the amount of water contained in the finished foam. A simple pneumonic summarizes this in general: "If the chemical ends in *ide* or *ium*, water is not their chum." It's silly but a great way to remember what *not* to use water or foam on.

Types of foam and foam terms.
Foam is a specialized agent for a specific type of fire. There are several types of foam concentrate available. In addition, there are specific terms used when dealing with foams. It is critical to know these terms to avoid confusion on the fireground.

Chemical foam: In the 1920s chemical foams were developed and relied on mixing of two powders in hoppers that were attached to a hoseline. Although successful, systems were difficult to use during emergencies. Chemical foam systems are no longer made or used in the fire service.

Mechanical foams: Developed in the 1930s for the U.S. Navy and are the type used today. Mechanical foams require four major components: foam concentrate, water, air, and mechanical aeration.

Foam concentrate: The chemical component purchased in 5-gal (19-L) buckets, 55-gal (208-L) drums, or bulk amounts.

Foam solution: Foam concentrate and water, properly mixed by the foam eductor before it reaches the nozzle.

Finished foam: Produced after the air has been injected (usually at the nozzle) (fig. 31–52).

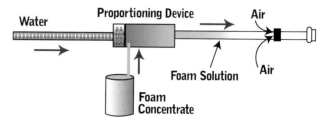

Fig. 31–52. The foam process introduces a set percentage of foam concentrate into the water supply, as well as utilized a foam nozzle to inject air into the foam solution.

Foam production. A common type of foam proportioning and delivery system is called an **inline eductor**. The eductor uses a venturi principle to pull foam concentrate from the foam container and mix it with the appropriate amount of water to make foam solution. Inside the eductor, there is a restriction in the metering orifice that creates a **venturi effect**, causing the water to flow faster and creating a lower pressure area in the line, resulting in suction. The foam pickup tube is attached to the venturi area of the eductor and goes in the foam bucket. A metering device allows the passage of the correct amount of foam concentrate to enter the hoseline. When water and foam concentrate are mixed it is called foam solution.

Many apparatus are being made with on-board foam systems. These systems can either incorporate an inductor in the piping of a particular discharge outlet or into the piping leading to the pump itself. Prepiped inductors have a disadvantage in that finished foam can only be discharged from that particular outlet. When foam concentrate is educted into the pump itself, foam can be delivered from any discharge outlet or apparatus-mounted deluge gun. All these systems require an increased level of cleaning and maintenance to ensure proper performance.

If an engine company needs to deliver finished foam and has no foam proportioning capability, foam concentrate in proper proportion (15 gal [57 L] foam to 500 gal [1,893 L] water) can be added to the apparatus booster tank to create foam solution. This is a crude method and depends completely on the mixing of the concentrate and water in the tank. The solution can be applied from an aerating nozzle to create finished foam. Foam solution flows to the foam nozzle where air is added to create finished foam.

Finished foam: How it works. It is important to understand several properties of finished foam. Like anything in life, these properties are a balance between several factors. In addition, there are several terms that you must know:

Knockdown: The foam blanket must spread across the fuel to control and ultimately extinguish the fire. The speed at which this occurs is called knockdown.

Heat resistance: How well the foam stands up to the heat of the fire. The blanket should be stable enough to withstand the extreme heat of the fire, hot metal, and debris that maybe in the spilled or burning area.

Fuel tolerance: The ability to shed any fuel that may be on top of the foam blanket as a result of the foam stream splashing the fuel. If the foam bubbles bring fuel to the surface, the fire can continue.

Vapor suppression: The ability of the foam blanket to keep fuel vapors from pushing up through the foam blanket where they can burn.

Burnback resistance: The foam's ability to withstand the heat of the fire without breaking down.

Drainage time: The time it takes for the water to separate from the foam blanket.

Types of foam concentrates. There are a variety of foam concentrates to choose from. Each has its advantages and disadvantages.

Protein foam was the first type of mechanical foam and has been used since World War II. It is primarily made from animal protein with other chemicals added to minimize corrosion and bacterial decomposition. It has excellent heat resistance and vapor suppression but is slow to spread over the fuel surface and it lacks fuel tolerance. It is inexpensive.

Fluoroprotein foam was developed by the addition of fluorochemical surfactants to protein foam. This foam flows better than protein foam, giving it a better knockdown speed and has better fuel tolerance. It is often used for **subsurface injection** at bulk tank fires. In this application, the foam is forced in under pressure below the liquid level of the tank using piping installed in the tank. The foam floats to the surface, creating a blanket and eventually extinguishing the fire.

Synthetic detergent foam is what we know as **high-expansion foam**. These foam concentrates are synthetic foaming chemicals and stabilizers. They are used in high-expansion systems for total flooding of basement fires and other large space fires that are difficult to enter to extinguish class A fires. High-expansion foams have limited use on class B fires because fuel vapors easily penetrate the lightweight foam, heat rapidly degrades the foam bubbles, and the reach of the streams is limited. High-expansion foams are considered unsuitable for class B fires.

Aqueous film-forming foam (AFFF) synthetic foaming agents replace the natural protein base and are designed for rapid knockdown (fig. 31–53). Developed for the U.S. Navy to rapidly extinguish shallow spill fires, AFFF sacrifices long-term heat resistance for rapid fire knockdown. This is one of the most common foams modern firefighters will use in day-to-day operation. The important additional capability of this concentrate is that it forms an aqueous film on the fuel surface. Rapidly spreading across the fuel surface, this thin layer of foam solution (that has drained out of the finished foam) results in rapid fire knockdown by vapor suppression. This is where the name *aqueous film-forming foam* is derived. Just as oil floats on water, AFFF floats on hydrocarbon fuels. AFFFs are effective on hydrocarbons such as diesel, kerosene, and jet fuels. The higher flash point of these fuels present less of a reignition hazard. Fuels such as gasoline and gasoline-alcohol blends require more frequent application of foam because of the lower flash point and the threat of reignition.

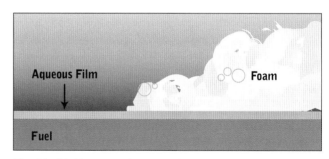

Fig. 31–53. Foam can be very effective when used properly.

Alcohol-resistant aqueous film-forming foam (AR-AFFF) was developed because fuels containing alcohol aggressively pull the water out of the foam, destroying it and reducing its fire-suppression effectiveness. These foams function much like a non-alcohol-resistant foam forming an aqueous film on the surface of the fuel. If alcohol is present in the fuel, the membrane is a bit more viscous and called a **polymeric membrane**. This type of foam is the most versatile in use today; and with the widespread use of oxygenated automobile fuels and alternate fuels with increasing amounts of alcohol, it is becoming the standard foam in use in first-response units.

Foam concentrates should never be mixed. Because of the differences in chemical composition of different brands of foam, mixing of concentrates can result in chemical reactions that congeal the concentrate. The congealed foam is semisolid and immediately clogs eductors and nozzles and stops your foam application operation.

Finished foams can be mixed on the scene without a negative effect. However, recall that each type of foam has strengths and weaknesses, which may result in confusion on the security and safety of the foam blanket.

Foam proportioning. Foam is a specific agent for a specific type of fire. As such it must be used properly. Proportioning or mixing the right amount of foam concentrate with the right amount of water and air at the right pressure results in good quality foam. Foam is not just a collection of bubbles; it is a specific mix of concentrate, water, and air.

It is also critical that there are sufficient quantities of foam concentrate to extinguish the fire and secure the spill. Running out of concentrate before the fire has been extinguished or has been secured allows the fire to quickly burn back to its original size and intensity—this is unlike a building fire. It is as if no attack had taken place at all.

Proper proportioning is important. If there is not enough concentrate in the finished foam, the overall quality and effectiveness will decrease. It may not extinguish the fire as expected, heat resistance decreases, and burnback resistance decreases.

If your finished foam has too much concentrate in it, foam will not flow around debris and obstacles. Additionally, limited foam concentrate will be depleted rapidly, not allowing enough for complete extinguishment and reapplication as necessary.

Proportioning may take place in one of several ways: induction (through eductors), injection, premixing, and batch-mixing. The most common method is induction using a portable inline eductor in conjunction with a hand line. Large, self-educting foam nozzles are also available with flows up over 2,000 gpm (7,571 L/min) (fig. 31–54). These larger flows must be supported with bulk (55 gal [208 L] or more) containers of foam concentrate. In addition, some foam is proportioned through eduction on apparatus using around the pump proportioners (fig. 31–55) and balanced-pressure proportioners (fig. 31–56).

Fig. 31–54. Large self-educting nozzles can supply streams of up to 2,000 gpm (7,571 L/min).

Fig. 31–55. The around-the-pump proportioner is one way to supply the correct mixture of water to foam concentrate.

Fig. 31–56. This balanced-pressure proportioner is mounted inside the apparatus.

Foam injection systems use specially designed foam pumps and are often found at fixed installations (fig. 31–57). Premixing is used in foam fire extinguishers where the foam concentrate is mixed, in specific measured amounts, with water inside the tank. Similarly, batch mixing is simply placing foam concentrate in a larger tank, an engine's tank, or a foam trailer (fig. 31–58). Although this type of proportioning is common for **compressed air foam systems (CAFS)**, described in the following text, take care when adding the foam concentrate, because it is corrosive to metal parts.

Fig. 31–57. A foam bladder tank

Fig. 31–58. Foam trailer

Inline eductors on hand lines. An inline eductor is the most common method for engine companies to proportion foam. As previously described, the eductor is placed in a hoseline. These generally have a flow of 65 or 95 gpm (246 or 360 L/min) for 1¾-in. (45-mm) lines. Two-and-a-half inch handlines will flow approximately 150 gpm (568 L/min).

Eductors are generally energy inefficient and consume approximately 65% of their inlet pressure to create the suction. Check your specific eductor, but generally the inlet pressure is designed to be approximately 200 psi (1,400 kPa). With about 70 psi (490 kPa) used to pick up concentrate, there is about 130 psi (910 kPa) available on the discharge side of the eductor. We know friction loss in 1¾-in. (44-mm) hose flowing 95 gpm (360 L/min) is 14 psi (98 kPa) per 100 ft (30 m), and we know we need 100 psi (700 kPa) at the nozzle to provide enough energy to aerate the foam and provide adequate stream reach; therefore 200 ft (60 m) is generally the maximum length of hose permitted after the eductor. When excessive back pressure occurs at the eductor, it causes incorrect proportioning and a less effective finished foam.

If a longer hose stretch is required, use 2½-in. (65-mm) hose to supply the eductor to ensure that proper inlet pressure is maintained. The position of the eductor in relation to the nozzle is another consideration. If the nozzle operates above the elevation of the eductor, the difference in height can slow the flow of foam solution and affect the proper aeration of finished foam. It is best to have the nozzle on the same level as or below the eductor.

Churning water from the pumps can affect the eductor's ability to draw foam concentrate. Churning water from the pumps may create turbulence that can affect the eductors ability to draw foam concentrate. To avoid this place the eductor one length from the apparatus. Firefighters encounter class B fires on a fairly regular basis. They are often the result of an accidental spill and when ignited can burn vigorously. There are some important points to consider when using an in-line eductor. If your in-line eductor setup is designed with the following critical factors in mind, you are likely be successful in proportioning and delivering foam at your next alarm:

- The eductor gpm must match the nozzle's rated flow in gpm

- Generally, pickup tubes are less than 6 ft (2 m) long, so don't modify or extend the pickup tube

- Avoid improper pump pressures to the eductor.

- Kinked hoses on either side of the eductor cause excessive friction loss and improper flows and pressures

- Nozzles should be fully open

- Air leaks suck in air instead of foam concentrate

- Keep your hands away from the air intake of the nozzle to ensure an adequate supply of air to make finished foam

- Always run clear water through the eductor for an extended period of time to flush it out after use

A bypass balanced pressure **proportioner** (eductor) works similar to the inline eductor (fig. 31–59). The bypass proportioner allows for a full flow of water if foam is not desired. This type of eductor is built into the plumbing of the engine. Along with such built-in systems, there is an additional foam tank as well with 25- to 100-gal (95- to 3,79-L) foam concentrate capacity.

Causes for poor foam generation can include the following:

- Not matching flow ratings between educator and nozzle

- Proportioning equipment that has not been cleaned, resulting in clogging

- Air leaks in fittings

- Excess back pressure resulting from too long hose lay on discharge side of the eductor

- Mixing different foams together, which can make foam too thick to pass through eductor

Fig. 31–59. The inline eductor is mounted after the first length of hose.

Foam application. The nozzle is the last step in the foam making process. Here the foam solution is aspirated and finished foam is produced. The air is entrained in the foam by some type of mechanical means, usually directed at a baffle, or by foam solution streams directed at each other in the nozzle, then directed down the foam tube and out the end forming the foam stream (fig. 31–60).

Fig. 31–60. The nozzle is the last determining factor in making foam. It can assist in entraining the foam with air.

The best quality foam blanket is generated with a nozzle designed for foam making and distribution. During the 1990s it was common to apply AFFF through standard combination (fog) nozzles. Now this is the exception rather than the rule, because all foams (other than AFFF) must be aspirated to be effective. Nonaerating AFFF was acceptable when applying AFFF for many applications. Because the foam solution was so effective

at extinguishing the fire by the film-forming component, the poor quality aspiration was acceptable. However with the advent of the addition of ethanol and the addition of alcohol to standard gasoline, NFPA 11 recommends aeration of all types of foams including AFFF and AR-AFFF.

It is the choice of the nozzle that determines the expansion ratio of the foam concentrate into finished foam (fig. 31–61). Standard fog nozzles produce 4:1 to 6:1, standard fog nozzle with low expansion foam attachment 10:1, foam nozzles with tubes 10:1, and mid-expansion foam nozzles 30:1 to 50:1. Remember, the foam nozzle must match the designed eductor flow and pressures. Additionally, the foam concentrate must be correct, matching the eductor and nozzle. Read the foam bucket label and manufacturer's instructions for specific details.

Fig. 31–61. This foam nozzle helps to introduce air into the stream, thus aspirating the foam.

Foam application techniques. It is the nozzle operator's responsibility to apply the foam as gently as possible to allow the finished foam to form a cohesive but flowing blanket on the fuel to smother the fire, allow the best development of the film-forming actions (stop vapor production), and maintain the security to prevent reignition. There are several techniques that make that possible:

- **Bank-down method:** Bounce the foam off an object or wall adjacent to the spill, allowing the foam to bank down gently onto the spill (fig. 31–62).

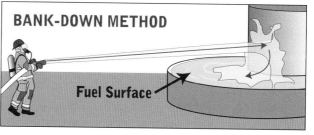

BANK-DOWN METHOD

Fuel Surface

Fig. 31–62. The bank-down method allows the firefighter to attack the flame from a different direction.

- **Roll-on method:** Roll the foam in by piling up finished foam in front of you and pushing or sweeping the foam onto the burning fuel (fig. 31–63).

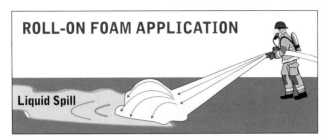

ROLL-ON FOAM APPLICATION

Liquid Spill

Fig. 31–63. The roll-on method is an effective way to push the foam onto a fuel spill.

- **Rain down (or snow storm) method:** The stream is directed almost vertically above the liquid's surface, allowing the finished foam to fall like rain or snow. An intense thermal column from the fire may prevent this method from being effective. If the foam stream is directed directly toward the fire, move rapidly back and forth horizontally to break up the stream and prevent it from plunging into the fuel (fig. 31–64).

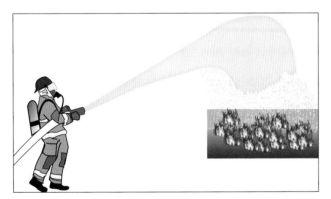

Fig. 31–64. The snowstorm method may not be effective if there is an intense thermal column.

Foam is often used on tank fires at bulk terminals. The key to extinguishing tank fires is to use a technique known as **over the top**, developed several years ago by the Williams Fire and Hazard Control Corporation of Texas. First apply the foam at the location where air is being drawn into the fire (determine this location by conducting a 360-degree survey of the tank). A cooling steam of water (not foam) is then applied to the side of the tank, just below the edge of the tank, to cool the tank shell and allow the foam applied in the tank to establish a **beachhead**. Finally, the foam is laid down like snow (fig. 31–65). Aim the master stream foam nozzle to let it fall just over the edge of the tank and onto the surface. This location known as the **sweet spot**.

Fig. 31–65. The "over the top" method was developed by Williams Fire and Hazard Control Corporation. It is an effective way to attack large petroleum tank fires.

To apply foam to a burning, running spill (and to attempt to contain it as well), work ahead of the spill. Direct foam in the path of the liquid so the liquid runs under the foam blanket, extinguishing the fire. Then work the foam blanket toward the source of the leak until the liquid is covered. Bouncing the foam off the ground or **pushing** the foam across the liquid prevents the liquid from splashing and breaking the foam blanket.

In many cases, a flammable liquid fire is the result of an accident. There may be obstacles in the spill. This may require additional hand lines or monitors to apply foam to cover the spill and extinguish fires within the voids. A combination of application methods may be required in this situation. Coordination is required to ensure the foam blanket is properly applied.

All these techniques are designed to prevent the nozzle operator from plunging the foam into the fuel. This could cause flaming liquid to be spread around the scene, possibly onto other firefighters, with deadly results. Never direct a stream into the spill or fire.

The nozzle operator must also be aware of when discharging water versus foam. When the eductor system begins flowing, water comes out first. Direct the water away from the spill or fire, it only makes it worse or spreads the fire. It takes a minute or so for the eductor to pick up foam concentrate, so that is flows through the hose to reach the nozzle. Listen to the sound: Water flows with a crackling sound, foam is softer and quieter. It also looks different. The nozzle operator must be aware when foam begins and when the stream turns back to water. The firefighter assigned to the eductor must communicate with the nozzle operator before running out of foam. A water stream focused on the foam quickly washes away the foam just applied, washing away all the fire suppression just achieved.

When flowing 95 gpm (360 L/min) of foam solution, (for easy math, let's say we are flowing 100 gpm [379 L/min]), at 1% that means for every 99 gal (375 L) of water, we are flowing 1% or 1 gal (3.8 L) foam concentrate. Thus the foam concentrate lasts approximately 5 min (at 1%). An officer should be assigned to the foam eductor to ensure that there is an adequate supply of foam concentrate available. Consider that if the foam is used at 3%, for every 100 gal foam solution flowing, 3 gal (11 L) foam is consumed each minute. Thus a 5-gal (19-L) foam bucket must be replaced every 2 min. This is a significant logistics challenge. How many foam buckets does your engine carry? How long will it last? It is important to do it right the first time; you only have one chance!

The firefighter assigned to the eductor must monitor the foam concentrate in the buckets to ensure the pickup tube is placed in the next full bucket before the concentrate runs out. Buckets positioned for use should have all caps removed prior to operation. The foam operation should not be interrupted because you cannot remove a cap. Some caps are difficult to remove, if this is the case and wrenches are unavailable, use the point of a Halligan tool to punch a hole in the cap to insert the pickup tube. Do not punch the hole directly in the container; if the foam from that container is not needed, there will be no way to secure the container. If the cap is punctured, it is possible to find a replacement cap.

As the foam stream leaves the nozzle, the stream begins to break up. This limits the nozzle operator's ability to see where the foam is landing. It is always a good idea to have a spotter off to the side to direct the nozzle operator and ensure that the foam reaches the appropriate area.

Foam blankets break down over time and must be reapplied, often in as little as 20 min. Ensure that you have enough foam concentrate to be able to reapply foam as necessary until the spill is cleaned up.

Foam safety. Flammable liquid fires are dangerous and dynamic. A structure fire will not move unless the building collapses or exposures are rapidly lighting up; however, a flammable liquid can flow down street or into storm drains endangering firefighters, apparatus, and numerous exposures. Always be aware of where the spill or liquid is and where it is or may be going to avoid being trapped and burned. Because of the possibility of reignition, always retreat facing the hazard or fire. Also be aware that when you stop application of agent, the advantage returns to the fire and the threat of it reigniting or becoming a more significant hazard gains momentum.

The threat of reignition requires that members operating near the spill or in the path of any vapor cloud be in full protective equipment, including SCBA (fig. 31–66).

If possible, avoid walking through a foam blanket. Your feet open the blanket and flammable vapors can rise around you. Should they ignite you will be standing in a flammable liquid fire. If you must walk through a foam blanket, be sure foam is reapplied to seal up any openings you made in the blanket. Do not direct the foam stream on other firefighters, but be aware of the danger you or they are in.

Fig. 31–66. It is important to wear full PPE at all times when applying foam.

Foam concentrates are not especially toxic, but they burn if they get in your eyes. Goggles or face shields *with* gloves are a good idea for those who may come in contact with foam.

Application rates. Just like structural fire attack, when water must be applied in sufficient quantity (gal/min) to overcome the heat produced by the fire, foam must be applied fast enough to extinguish the flammable liquid fire. An ignitable liquid must be applied at a rate per square foot of fire or spill. Using some simple calculations one can determine how much foam, water, and application rate is correct for any size flammable liquid fire.

When a foam hand line is required, it is important to understand the extinguishing capability of the foam operation. Before any foam operation is begun, an adequate volume of foam concentrate must be on the scene. If the foam blanket does not completely extinguish the fire or there is inadequate foam to reapply to overcome drainage and burnback, all of the foam applied will have been wasted.

Suppose there is a 40- by 50-ft hydrocarbon spill burning. NFPA 11 recommends an application rate of 0.10 gpm/ft²:

- $40 \times 50 = 2{,}000$ ft²

- Area × rate = gpm foam solution required
- 2,000 × 0.10 = 200 gpm solution flow

Note that this is the critical first step. This spill fire requires at least *two* 95-gpm eductors to meet this required flow, if you expect rapid extinguishment and lasting security from reignition.

Gallons of concentrate required:

- gpm × % concentrate = gpm concentrate
- × 0.03 = 6 gpm concentrate

To find rate of water needed (gpm):

- gpm × % water = gpm water
- 200 gpm × 0.97 = 194 gpm water

To find total volume (gal) of concentrate (*note:* per NFPA 11, standard recommended application time is 15 min):

- gpm concentrate × time = total gallons of concentrate
- 6 × 15 = 90 gal concentrate

To find total gallons of volume (gal) water:

- gpm × time
- 194 × 15 = 2,910 gal water

A good rule of thumb is that if you add a 0 to your eductor flow, it will give you an *estimate* of the maximum spill fire you can control with that one line in operation.

For example a 95-gpm eductor can handle a 950 ft² ignited hydrocarbon spill fire. Recall that 950 ft² is a fire less than 20 × 50 ft (1,000 ft²). To estimate the size of a spill fire of polar solvent, add a 0 and divide by 2. For example, a 95-gpm eductor and nozzle control a polar solvent spill fire of approximately 475 ft²: 950 ft² divided by 2 = 475 ft² or about 22 × 22 ft.

Controlled pit fires like the one shown here are excellent training for foam operations (fig. 31–67). It is important to note that this spill fire is not realistic. In a real scenario, such as a vehicle accident, there will be burning tires, hot metal, and other reignition sources. This training fire will be extinguished rapidly with minimum amounts of foam because the pit has no debris. Actual fires may take several times the amount of agent to control as training fires. The additional amounts of foam will be necessary to flow around debris and to replace what is being destroyed by the heat of the fire, hot metal, and so forth.

Fig. 31–67. Controlled pit fires like the one shown here are excellent training for foam operations.

Compressed air foam system (CAFS). CAFS are a relatively new class A firefighting capability. First developed for the **urban-wildland interface**, CAFS has found acceptance in structural firefighting nationwide. Essentially, CAFS uses a fire engine's centrifugal pump to provide a supply of water that is subsequently injected with foam concentrate (on the discharge side of the pump) and mixed with air through the use of an air compressor (fig. 31–68). The type of foam produced has the ability to stick to vertical surfaces (a great advantage in structural firefighting) and has been shown to have superior knockdown capability when compared with plain water (saving water in the process).

Fig. 31–68. CAFS has found acceptance in structural firefighting nationwide.

QUESTIONS

1. What is the first step in developing a fire attack plan?

2. What is the most important consideration at every fire or emergency?

3. What can happen if a basement fire is attacked from an exterior entrance into the basement?

4. When attacking a basement fire from an exterior entrance door, where should a second hoseline be placed to prevent extension of the fire to upper floors?

5. What piece of firefighting equipment can be used to knock down a fire if hoselines cannot enter into the basement to attack the fire?

6. What tactic can be used to ventilate a basement if basement windows and doors are not ventilating sufficiently?

7. What are the goals of stretching hoselines?

8. What is the most important consideration when stretching a hoseline?

9. As a general rule, where should hoselines be placed?

10. What hazards do the void spaces in townhomes present?

11. What tactic is used to locate the fire and route of extension in a townhome fire?

12. Generally, where do fires start in commercial buildings?

13. What are the benefits of having a search line when you enter a building?

14. What is an advantage commercial buildings have that is not normally found in residential buildings?

15. What are the limitations of roof operations when ventilating in commercial buildings?

16. What happens when steel bar joist roof trusses are exposed to heat?

17. What should firefighters do if they see a white powdery residue when cutting a hole in a roof?

18. When a commercial building has a sprinkler system or if the standpipe will be used for firefighting, what should be one of the first lines stretched to ensure there will be enough water to contain the fire?

19. What type of occupancy fire poses one of the most serious threats to firefighters?

20. What are the seven fireground priorities?

Origin and Cause Investigation

by Richard S. Wolfson

This chapter provides required knowledge items for the following NFPA Standard 1001 Job Performance Requirements:

FFII 6.3.2

This chapter contains Skill Drills. When you see this icon, refer to your Skill Drill book for step-by-step instructions.

OBJECTIVES

Upon completion of this chapter, you should be able to do the following:

- Describe the role of the firefighter in fire investigations
- List common sources of ignition
- Identify the parts of the scientific method used to investigate fires
- List at least three type of fire patterns
- Identify common causes of electrical fires
- Identify common ignition sources found at motor vehicle fires
- List at least three types of fire setters
- List the three types of evidence
- Describe the importance of maintaining the "chain of evidence"
- Describe the importance of documenting the fire scene
- Describe the importance of securing the fire scene

WHY FIRES ARE INVESTIGATED

Fire is a powerful force of nature. As such, it is capable of killing and injuring people as well causing extensive damage to property. Fires may be accidental or intentional. Thus it is important to find out how and why fires are started. This is why fires are investigated.

The investigation of fires has many benefits, including the identification of defective products such as electrical appliances, which can malfunction and start fires. Fire investigations often lead to changes in **fire and building codes** when it is determined that a particular code does not properly address a certain issue such as the flame spread of a particular **interior finish**. Finally, fire investigations sometimes uncover the crime of arson and lead to the arrest of an arsonist, removing the arsonist from society.

ROLE OF THE FIREFIGHTER IN A FIRE INVESTIGATION

FFII 6.3.2 Firefighters who understand the procedures of a fire investigation are valuable tools to the fire investigator. The observations of the firefighter are an integral part of the fire investigation. Although the role of the first-due firefighter is rescue and fire suppression, firefighters can provide information about their response and fire scene observations that will greatly assist fire investigators, including insurance and criminal or arson investigators.

Insurance investigators are independent investigators hired by insurance companies to determine how the fire started and if the insurance claim is valid. Criminal investigators, who hold state certification with authority to arrest people, determine if the fire was caused intentionally. Arson investigators are criminal investigators who gather evidence to lead to the arrest and prosecution of a suspect. Firefighters should document their observations to provide information to investigators as needed.

Document the date and time of the alarm and how the alarm was received, the name and address of the person reporting the fire, and any information received regarding his or her initial observations. The firefighter's observations should include the fire scene conditions on arrival (fig. 32–1). First, what were the weather conditions, including the wind direction and speed? Were there any persons or vehicles leaving the fire scene at the time of the first unit's arrival? Where was the initial first line stretched and what was the location of the fire? Was there any unusual difficulty in attacking the fire? Did the fire seem to actually spread during the application of the first line? Were there any unusual odors detected by the first arriving units?

Fig. 32–1. A gas can found in an arson fire

Multiple areas of fire should be noted and this information relayed to the chief officer, who will in turn notify the fire investigator. During fire suppression, document any unusual circumstances such as holes in the floor, difficulty in gaining access to the area of origin, and any evidence of vandalism or forced entry to the structure (fig. 32–2). The location of any victims should be fully documented.

If the occupants are out of the structure and awaiting the firefighters at the time of the fire department's arrival, firefighters should note the attire of the occupants. If the fire occurred in the early morning hours and the occupants are fully clothed, that is obviously out of place. This scenario should be documented and this information relayed to the chief officer and investigator.

Fig. 32–2. Vandalism was the cause of this fire.

OVERHAULING AND THE FIRE INVESTIGATION

During the fire suppression, firefighters should be aware of excessive overhaul procedures and refrain from causing any additional damage to the area of origin. During the overhaul procedures, it is imperative that all evidence be preserved. Minimizing the overhaul will help the fire investigator determine the cause of the fire occurrence; although all remaining hot spots of the fire must be extinguished, take care to avoid excessive overhaul. If possible, overhaul of the scene should be delayed if there is any evidence of the fire being **incendiary** in nature. If this determination is made, the area of origin should be preserved and treated as a crime scene. Upon the investigator's arrival, the observations of the firefighters should be relayed to the investigator through the officer in charge.

The chief officer may request the electrical utility within the structure to be shut off (fig. 32–3). The firefighter performing this duty should identify the **electrical distribution panel** and be familiar if the panel has a **main disconnect**. When put in the *off* position, the main disconnect will shut down the entire panel, and moving the individual branch circuits into the *off* position will be unnecessary. If the distribution panel has no main disconnect, the individual branch circuit breakers should be put in the *off* position; if electrical panel is older and uses fuses, individual fuses should be removed. Any circuit breakers that are tripped should be left in that position; fuses that have blown can be left in place. Firefighters must take note of the individual circuit breakers and/or the main disconnect that they shut off. This is important information for the investigator.

Fig. 32–3. An electrical panel after a fire

Additional observations during the suppression of the fire may include open doors and windows and any unusual openings within the structure. The blockage of any exit doors and/or passages should be noted. Are the smoke alarms activated and operating at the time of the firefighter's arrival? Is the sprinkler system operative or disabled?

FUELS

To have a fire, obviously, a fuel must be present. Fuels take various forms but can be generally grouped into one of following categories: *Solid materials* include things like wood, plastics, and even many types of metals when finely divided into powder form. *Liquids* include such materials as gasoline, acetone, and motor oil. Natural gas and hydrogen are examples of flammable *gases/vapors*. It is important to note that some materials will not support combustion, such as nitrogen (gas), concrete (solid), and water (liquid).

It is important that a fire investigator research the combustion traits of different types of fuels. When studying a particular fire, the investigator must establish the characteristics of the material in question such as **ignition temperature** for solid objects, flammable limits for gases and vapors, and **flash point** for **flammable** and **combustible liquids**.

SOURCES OF IGNITION

Sources of ignition are the different types of heat energy that initiate a fire by causing a fuel to ignite. These sources must be of sufficient heat energy and temperature (recall that heat and temperature are two different characteristics, as discussed in chapter 5, Fire Behavior) to be considered competent, meaning they are capable of causing ignition. Sources of ignition can take various forms, but they can be grouped into a variety of different types (fig. 32–4). These include open flames such as a matches, lighters, stove burner gas jets, or a water heater burner flame; hot objects such as a hot plate used for cooking, an exhaust manifold on a car engine, a car's catalytic converter, or a hot halogen lamp bulb igniting bedding materials; hot molten metals such as **slag** from a welding operation or sparks from a metal grinding wheel; frictional sources such as *locked* truck brakes or rotating objects such as a clothes dryer drum rubbing against a piece of clothing jammed between the drum and the dryer frame; and electrical system malfunctions such as a short circuit, an arc, or even static electricity.

Fig. 32–4. An ignition source

A handful of materials are subject to **spontaneous ignition**. According to National Fire Protection Association (NFPA) 921, *The Guide for Fire and Explosion Investigations*, spontaneous ignition is the "initiation of combustion of a material by an internal chemical or biological reaction that has produced sufficient heat to ignite the material." Therefore, spontaneous ignition is a chemical or biological process that allows certain materials to generate heat and ignite on their own, without the presence of an external heat source, such as a match. Examples of materials susceptible to spontaneous ignition are wet hay (where a biological reaction takes place inside the bale of hay over a period of time, generating heat, and sometimes igniting the hay as the heating process reaches the outside of the bale) and a pile of linseed-oil–soaked rags (where a chemical reaction takes place inside the pile of rags; the pile provides insulation for the heat, trapping it inside and not allowing it to escape).

BASIC FIRE INVESTIGATION PROCEDURES

An **origin and cause investigation** should be conducted using the scientifically established procedures set forth in NFPA 921, *Guide for Fire and Explosion Investigations*. An origin and cause investigation is just that: finding out what started the fire and where it started. This is the fundamental duty of a fire investigator. Additionally, fire reports submitted to the National Fire Incident Reporting System database (NFIRS is covered in chapter 28, Advanced Communications) must include information such as the source of ignition and the first material ignited.

The origin and cause investigation should also be conducted using the **scientific method**. NFPA 921 identifies the following as the scientific method:

1. Recognize the need (identify the problem).
2. Define the problem.
3. Collect data.
4. Analyze the data (inductive reasoning).
5. Develop a hypothesis.
6. Test the hypothesis (deductive reasoning).
7. Select final hypothesis.

Because a fire has occurred, indicating that a problem exists, the cause should be determined. Defining the problem, an origin and cause investigation should be conducted by the examination of the fire scene and the collection of data, which includes interviewing witnesses and the results of scientific testing.

CREATING A PLAN

Once assigned to investigate a fire, the investigator must develop a plan. There are several considerations:

- Site safety: Is the building stable enough to enter and is the atmosphere free of smoke, carbon monoxide, and other toxins?

- The number of investigators and equipment needed: Is this a large fire scene or one that requires large amounts of resources?

- The type(s) of investigator(s) needed: Are specialists in electrical systems, fire protection systems, forensic anthropologists specializing in dealing with fatalities, and so forth needed?

- The type of scene recording that will be performed: video, still photos, and so on.

Once the appropriate resources have been put in place, most investigators will begin the investigation. Most investigators approach a fire scene using a the same, systematic approach every time. For example, many investigators will move from areas of less fire damage toward areas of more fire damage. Many will also search the outside area of a building looking for evidence (such as studying exterior building fire damage around windows or finding an accelerant container) before they go inside the building. What is important is that investigators use a systematic method so they don't miss anything.

FIRE PATTERNS

Fire patterns can be considered the **fingerprints** of a fire. NFPA 921 defines fire patterns as "the visible or measurable physical changes or identifiable shapes formed by a fire effect or group of fire effects. Fire effects are the observable or measurable changes in or on a material as a result of exposure to the fire." Fire patterns tell a fire investigator about the movement of a fire.

There are a variety of patterns, the most common being the charring of wood and other materials as well as soot stains on walls and other surfaces. A specific, common type of char pattern is called the **V pattern**, a pattern often burned into a wall surface that is shaped like the letter V (fig. 32–5a). The base of the V points toward an object on the floor that ignited at some point on the fire. Sometimes the object has been moved during firefighting; the V pattern tells the investigator that a burning object was at that location. In some cases, the V pattern may be pointing at the object that started the fire!

Other patterns include **crazed** (cracked) glass, deformed objects such as light bulbs, spalled (chipped away) concrete, melted metals like aluminum, distortion like a twisted metal beam, and many, many more. Some patterns are actually created by the absence of heat such as a **protected** floor area underneath a piece of furniture that is shielded from the heat of a fire (fig. 32–5b). Although the details of what each pattern means is beyond the scope of this book, it is important for firefighters to understand that it is vital to try to maintain the fire scene as closely as possible as to how it was when the fire started. Fire patterns are very important indicators that, when taken collectively, tell the story of a fire.

Fig. 32–5b. Protected floor area underneath a bed

ELECTRICAL FIRES

Electrical services and electrical equipment in buildings sometimes cause fires. Electrical wiring can be overloaded (meaning the wire is carrying more electricity than it is rated to carry, causing it to overheat). A **short circuit** is a situation when the insulation around *two conductors* in a wire is broken and the conductors come in contact with each other, creating sparks and heat (fig. 32–6). In arcing, electricity *jumps* from one conductor to another when the conductors are not in direct contact, creating sparks and heat.

Fig. 32–5a. A V pattern on a wall

Fig. 32–6. A short circuited wire

For fire investigators to properly determine that fire was started by a piece of electrical equipment, he or she must have physical evidence to support the hypothesis. In the past, fires were often classified as *electrical* in nature if all other sources of ignition were eliminated. This is inadequate today—the fire investigator must prove how the fire started, using actual evidence.

As noted earlier in the chapter, a fire investigator may ask if you switched off a circuit breaker in an electrical panel for safety reasons during a fire. Having made a mental note of which breakers you changed may help the investigator determine whether a particular circuit was involved in starting the fire.

MOTOR VEHICLE FIRES

You will likely respond to a large number of vehicle fires in your career. Although many vehicle fires start in the engine compartment, it is not unusual for them to start in the passenger compartment or other areas (fig. 32–7). In addition to the obvious use of flammable and combustible fuels, the increasing use of synthetic materials provides even larger quantities of combustibles for a fire. There are a variety of ignition sources: overheated wires, hot surfaces such as exhaust manifolds and catalytic converters, mechanical sparks (metal-metal or metal-road surface contact) such as a broken drive shaft or a wheel rim that has lost a tire and is in contact with the roadway, and smoking materials.

Be wary of automobile fires with the presence of gasoline odors in the passenger compartment or trunk; this *may* be an indication of arson. Notify your company officer if you think this is the case.

ARSON

Arson fires, also known as **incendiary fires**, are intentionally set fires that are a crime in virtually every jurisdiction in the United States. Different states classify arson in slightly different ways, so it is important to understand the arson laws of your state.

People who set fires are called **arsonists**. People set fires for different reasons: for the excitement, as an act of vandalism, as an act of revenge, to gain insurance monies through fraud, or for **vanity** (fire setter starts a fire and extinguishes it to receive praise). Unfortunately, even a small number of firefighters themselves start fires to fulfill a need to respond to fires or because of some other deviant, behavioral reason. *If you suspect a fellow firefighter (or any one else for that matter) is starting fires, it is important to notify your local police.*

The evidence of arson may be visible after a fire has been extinguished. In addition to the brief discussion of some arson indicators identified in the beginning of this chapter, some specific things to look for are the presence of gasoline or other accelerant (either a gasoline can or the odor of gasoline in a location where it should not be expected), the presence of **trailers** (bed sheets or clothing tied into a long rope, which is soaked in gasoline and laid in such a fashion so as to spread the fire from one area of a building to another), multiple locations of separate fires without any logical connection, and fires in locations that typically lack an ignition source such as on stairwell treads and on top of beds (fig. 32–8). *If you suspect a fire may be intentionally set, you must notify your company officer who will, in turn, notify the incident commander. It is important not to disturb the suspected arson location once the fire has been extinguished.*

Fig. 32–7. Aftermath of an engine compartment fire

Fig. 32–8. A trailer is used to spread fire from one area of a building to another

EVIDENCE

FFII 6.3.2 There are three types of evidence: **demonstrative evidence** (tangible physical evidence such as a defective water heater), a fire pattern (described previously), or a photo of a fire scene. **Documentary evidence** is any evidence in written form such as an inventory list for a store or an insurance policy. **Testimonial evidence** includes such things as witness statements and expert witness testimony in a trial.

It is critical that the **chain of custody** be maintained for demonstrative evidence, meaning that an unbroken chain of possession is maintained. If a gasoline container is collected at a fire scene, for example, it is important that the container is never tampered with at any time. If the gasoline container must be transferred to a laboratory for testing, it must be *signed off* by the laboratory technician and so on as it moves from official to official. A chain of custody form accompanying the gasoline container will have the signatures of every person who has handled it. A piece of evidence must be protected from damage and alteration at all times.

When collecting evidence, proper precautions must be taken to protect the evidence from further damage. For example, gloves are worn when handling evidence which may contain fingerprints; precautions are taken to handle the evidence so that the fingerprints are not smudged. Delicate objects (like a water-soaked book of matches) must be handled appropriately. Evidence is then placed into labeled containers that are properly sized to protect the object (fig. 32–9). Containers should not allow evidence to "roll around" inside the container. In addition, the evidence must be compatible with the container—for example, chemicals which react with metal should be placed in non-reactive glass containers. All containers must be properly sealed to prevent contamination.

Fig. 32–9. Several evidence containers of varying shape, size, and material.

DETERMINING ORIGIN AND CAUSE

The collection of data is identified as the facts collected by observations, experiments, or other direct data-gathering means. This type of data is called **empirical data** because it is based on observation or experience and can be verified. When a fire investigator is investigating a fire scene, he is gathering a series of observable facts.

All the collected and observed information is analyzed by **inductive reasoning**, which should include only facts that can be clearly proven by observation or experiment. The development of a **hypothesis** is based on the data analysis. The investigator should now produce a hypothesis or group of hypotheses to explain the origin and cause of the fire. This hypothesis should be based solely on the empirical data that the investigator has collected.

The successful testing of the hypothesis (**deductive reasoning**) can only be achieved if it can withstand a careful and serious challenge. Test the hypothesis by the principal of deductive reasoning, in which the investigator compares the hypothesis to all known facts. If the hypothesis cannot withstand an examination by deductive reasoning, it should be discarded and a new hypothesis should be tested. If specific physical evidence from the fire scene contradicts the hypothesis that a fire investigator has developed, for example, the hypothesis must be rejected and a new hypothesis must be developed. In some cases, a hypothesis cannot be developed (because of lack of evidence, for example) and the fire is classified as **undetermined**. It is critical that an investigator never assign an origin and cause to a fire unless he can prove it using the scientific method.

DOCUMENTING THE FIRE SCENE

Every fire scene should be fully documented with photography (fig. 32–10). With today's digital media, the cost factor is negligible and should not be a concern to the investigator. When taking photographs, the investigator should use a **systematic approach**, identical to the systematic approach used to conduct the origin and cause investigation described earlier. First, the investigator will include overall views of the exterior of the structure, the structure's utilities including the electric service meter, distribution panel, heating systems, and any additional utilities identified within the structure. Fire protection systems—alarm systems and/or fire-suppression systems—should be photographed next. Finally, all rooms and areas involved in the fire should be documented (including the suspected room/area of origin) prior to the commencement of the investigation and the removal of debris. Photographs should be taken to document the actual removal of debris and reconstruction. The photographs will demonstrate to a jury how the investigation was conducted.

Fig. 32–10. A fire scene photographer

Fire investigators take large amounts of notes, recording all details of the investigation. This includes names and contact information of witnesses, observations about the building, details about fire damage, notes about photographs they take, and many other facts. Many investigators use a brand new newspaper-reporter-type note pad for each new investigation.

Investigators make sketches of the fire scene as well (fig. 32–11). These freehand drawings provide details on room layouts, furniture locations, and the like. Measurements are made of room dimensions and the distances between objects. Often, investigators are asked about details of a fire scene many years later while testifying in court about the fire. The investigator is permitted to use his notebook during the court proceedings to recall details of the fire scene for testimony.

Once the fire investigator has completed the investigation and has determined the origin and cause, he or she will prepare a final report. This report will be the *official* report of the fire, providing not only the origin and cause but many other details.

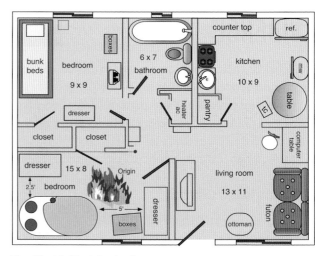

Fig. 32–11. Sketch of a fire scene

SECURING THE FIRE SCENE

It is imperative that a fire scene awaiting an investigation be properly secured, preventing the removal of evidence and alteration of the fire scene (fig. 32–12). Although building owners and occupants may want to enter the fire building, it is important that the investigators be allowed to do their work first.

Because investigators may not arrive while the fire is being fought, incident commanders may often leave a fire company to keep *control* of the building once the fire has been extinguished. Firefighters will be expected to secure the building and to keep an eye out for **rekindles** (smoldering fires which flare up back into a free-burning fire.)

An important 1978 United States Supreme Court decision, **Michigan v. Tyler (436 U.S. 499)**, affirmed a fire department's ability to maintain control of a fire scene, awaiting a fire investigator's arrival. This control means that a fire investigator does not need to get a **warrant** to conduct the investigation even though he or she arrives after the fire has been extinguished.

Fig. 32–12. This fire scene has been secured following an incident.

QUESTIONS

1. What is the most important benefit of investigating fires?

2. What is the role of the first-due firefighter in an investigation?

3. For what reason or reasons is it imperative to avoid excessive overhaul procedures as it pertains to fire investigations?

4. Why is it important for circuit breakers that are tripped to remain in the tripped position?

5. What could blockage of exit doors, and/or passages indicate?

6. What are some typical motives for arson?

7. What does the collection of data mean?

8. When documenting a fire scene using photography, what type of approach should be utilized?

9. Why is it important to use the scientific method to assist you in determining the origin and cause of a fire?

10. What does empirical data mean?

Fire Prevention and Public Education

by Tom Kiurski

This chapter provides required knowledge items for the following NFPA Standard 1001 Job Performance Requirements:

FFII 6.5.1

This chapter contains Skill Drills. When you see this icon, refer to your Skill Drill book for step-by-step instructions.

OBJECTIVES

Upon completion of this chapter, you should be able to do the following:

- Define the term fire prevention
- Describe the role of the fire department in fire prevention activities
- Define the terms building code and fire code
- Identify the major building and fire codes used in the United States today
- Identify the major features of a building code
- Identify the major feature of a fire code
- Describe the process for conducting a fire prevention inspection
- List organizations with fire safety interests
- Describe the procedure for conducting a Home Fire Safety Survey
- List common causes of fire found in a dwelling
- Describe the proper procedure for the placement of smoke alarms in a dwelling
- Describe methods of teaching fire safety to residents of the community
- Describe the proper procedures for conducting a tour of a fire station
- Describe the proper methods for presenting a talk on fire safety to community residents

INTRODUCTION

"Among the many measures that can be taken to reduce fire losses, perhaps none is more important than educating people about fire." This quote was taken from the landmark national report called *America Burning*, which was first published in 1973 (fig. 33–1). The document was a reaction to the high number of fire deaths and injuries in the United States, while other countries had a significantly smaller fire problem than we did. Members of the National Commission on Fire Prevention and Control, including top fire officials, educators, burn injury specialists, and researchers, were charged with finding out what could be done to reduce our fire risk factor, and the finished product was *America Burning*. This document told us that we had to shift our focus from suppression to prevention, a drastic change from what had been going on in this country (fig. 33–2).

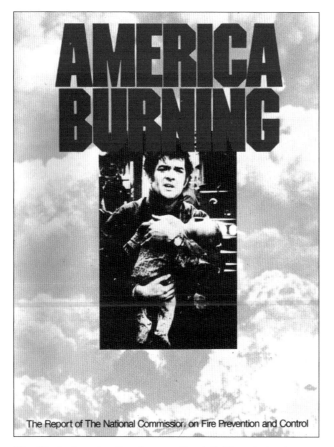

Fig. 33–1. *America Burning* was the definitive study of the American fire problem when published in 1973. It's publication led to the creation of the United States Fire Administration and the National Fire Academy. While some of its objectives were met, many others have yet to be fulfilled.

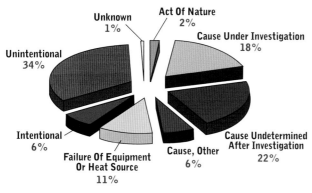

Fig. 33–2. Major causes of fires in structures

Although *America Burning* helped pave the way for fire-safety education in this country, this report also moved some of our thinking from the *reaction* phase of putting out fires to a more *proactive* phase that put more emphasis on fire prevention. Although there were fire departments back in the 1960s that did a great job at fire-prevention and fire-safety education, they were few and far between. *America Burning* suggested a U.S. Fire Administration (USFA; it exists today largely due to those recommen-

dations) that seeks out great programs and makes them available to the fire service to learn from and improve on. It is interesting to note that this report also outlined the need for a **National Fire Academy** (also in existence based on the recommendations of the report).

The results of that study are contained in the pages of *America Burning*. Although the forward has been updated several times to show how our fire statistics have declined, the body of the report remains unchanged. It is still available from the USFA. There were 90 recommendations made throughout the report, and it provides a basis for how our fire-prevention and fire-safety education efforts are grounded.

Throughout the remainder of this chapter, we will look at the topics of fire-prevention and fire-safety education separately. While they are often linked, they can be broken down into smaller elements for study. Fire prevention will look at the code enforcement efforts that are designed to control the hazards within buildings found through an inspection, while fire-safety education will focus on educating the community about the dangers associated with fire and how to make minor changes to be more fire safe where they live, work, and play.

FIRE PREVENTION

Entry-level firefighters have some dealings with fire prevention. Although they may not be immediately transferred or promoted into a fire department's fire-prevention division, they will be involved in issues pertaining to fire prevention in buildings in their community. Some fire departments hire entry-level firefighters and provide them with a fire inspector course shortly after hire. Once that course is completed, they may take part in regular building inspections, under the direction of their fire-prevention division. It takes one inspector a good portion of the day to inspect a standard strip mall, whereas a fire company with trained inspectors may divide up and tackle the businesses individually, and get done in less than an hour.

FIRE AND BUILDING CODES

FFII 6.5.1 Model fire and building codes are designed to ensure the safety of buildings. The first building regulations in this country were in reaction to fires by early settlers. These codes prohibited the building of fireplaces with wood and also did not allow covering roofs with thatch, which is highly flammable. With settlements that had houses built close by each other, the chance of a single fire destroying multiple buildings was a possibility. With the size and complexity of today's buildings, it is not acceptable to lose a building, or several buildings, in an area. The concept of fire-resistive construction, fire areas within buildings (the area enclosed by rated fire walls), and fixed fire-suppression systems are all in use today to contain or control fires within buildings.

Basically, building codes regulate how a building is to be constructed or renovated. Fire codes, on the other hand, regulate what activities take place inside the building in terms of fire safety. Building codes regulate how a fire wall should be built, while fire codes regulate such things as overcrowding in a nightclub or paint spray finishing in an auto body shop. Fire codes also ensure that the fire protection features built into a structure under the building code are maintained. There is overlap between these codes; they are a matched set of documents intended to be used together. As a firefighter, it is likely you will be expected to enforce a fire code.

The **National Fire Protection Association (NFPA)** and the **International Code Council (ICC)** both prepare models of building and fire codes. The NFPA produces **NFPA 5000:** *Building Construction and Safety Code* as well as **NFPA 1:** *Uniform Fire Code*. Similarly, the ICC produces the **International Building Code** and the **International Fire Code** (fig. 33–3). It is important for you to find out which of these codes is used in your jurisdiction—it is possible that your city or state does not have a building and/or a fire code at all, or uses a predecessor to these model codes. These codes are updated every three years by the NFPA and ICC.

Fig. 33–3. Publications of ICC and NFPA codes

These model codes are essentially ready for adoption and use; all that needs to be done is to fill in the name of the jurisdiction (city or state) that is adopting it. However, most jurisdictions make local amendments to the model code to customize it to their needs. When adopted at the local level by cities or counties, they are called ordinances; when adopted by a state, they are typically called statutes. Codes must be legally adopted by a jurisdiction to be enforceable.

Model **standards** are documents that are prepared by organizations like the NFPA to regulate the installation of individual building systems like automatic fire sprinkler systems (NFPA 13, *Standard for the Installation of Sprinkler Systems*) or standpipe systems (NFPA 14, *Standard for the Installation of Standpipes and Hose Systems*). See chapter 30, Fire Protection Systems, for a complete list of fire protection system standards.

Correct use of the building code ensures that the building will be built in accordance to the regulations that the jurisdiction uses for new buildings. Factors such as the construction of walls, allowable distance between exits, and flame spread ratings of interior finishes are all covered in building codes. A business that wishes to construct a building within a jurisdiction starts off by giving a copy of its proposed building to the city for a review, usually in blueprint form. The city building code officials ascertain whether the specified building meets the applicable codes and ordinances. This original blueprint will get sent back to the company with an approval or with notes that outline the changes necessary in the building to meet codes or ordinances that may have been overlooked.

Corrections are made, and any necessary clarifications are exchanged until a final plan is submitted that is agreed upon by the jurisdiction. A building permit is issued at this point, allowing construction to begin. As the building is in progress, the jurisdiction can send building inspectors out to make sure the building is being constructed as agreed upon. Once the building is completed, the jurisdiction conducts the final inspection to determine whether the building has been constructed and completed as submitted. Once the building meets inspection, it will be ready to open for business, and the jurisdiction will issue a certificate of occupancy stating such.

Once the building opens for business, the owner is then expected to maintain a level of fire safety for the employees and patrons. This is where the fire codes come in, to implement adequate maintenance of buildings. Some items covered in these codes are fire extinguishers in the building that have been inspected and are acceptable; illumination of exit signs in dark, well-traveled areas; and exit doors that are kept unobstructed. The **fire prevention inspection** is a legal inspection that should be completed annually or more frequently for high-risk hazardous occupancies.

In general, the building plan review and subsequent inspections are handled by the jurisdiction's building department, while the fire codes that cover the building's use and maintenance are part of the fire department's fire-prevention division's responsibility.

The fire inspectors' task is to make sure that the buildings within their jurisdiction are maintaining the level of fire safety outlined in the fire-prevention code. Some cities use fire-prevention division personnel to perform this function, while others train on-duty firefighters to conduct regular inspections.

Any building that is not in compliance with the jurisdiction's fire-prevention code will need to be corrected. It is for this reason that a building representative should accompany fire inspectors during the inspection. Although a receptionist may offer to accompany the inspectors, firefighters should suggest a manager or supervisor be summoned. Ideally, it should be someone who can authorize changes in the building that may be needed to bring the business up to code compliance. In most companies, the receptionist is in an entry-level position and does not have the authority to spend money to correct building issues.

We begin the building inspection by entering the main entrance door and asking to speak to a business representative. Once introductions are complete and the nature of the visit is outlined, the inspection can begin. *It is important to note that a fire inspection is an official government action; building owners can deny entry to fire inspectors under the "search and seizure" clause of the United States Constitution. In such cases, fire inspectors must obtain a warrant from an appropriate court to gain entry.*

The inspection actually begins on the outside of the building. A walk around the building will let the inspector understand the layout of the building, how accessible the building is from the four sides, and any additional concerns, like dumpsters too close to the building, overgrown brush growing up the side of the building, and the like. The inspector can also note from the outside the building the access to the closest fire hydrant and the utilities coming into the building.

The course of the investigation is determined by the inspector. If the inspector chooses to move from the front of the business to the rear, or a bottom to top

inspection on a multistory building, then stick to that plan. Doors that are not opened by the building representative must be noted at the time and inspected when the keys become available. Any confidential business that the inspector may see or hear is to be kept in confidence.

During the inspection process, inspectors should point out good points, where the business is exceeding fire code requirements, as well as the deficiencies. Formally, these deficiencies are documented, and a reinspection is needed to verify that the building is meeting the fire-prevention code. If a simple fix is undertaken by the building representative, that also should be noted. Some business owners may feel they want things done a certain way, and will make changes during the inspection, and then change back to their original way once the inspectors leave the premises. A well-documented fire inspection report is vital to enforce fire-prevention code compliance (fig. 33–4).

Fig. 33–4. Fire inspectors arrive at a business, ready to conduct a fire prevention inspection.

If the building has been in operation, the annual inspection starts off with reviewing past fire prevention inspections, to note the history of the building and business. If a business was found on each inspection to have continually violated fire codes, this matter should be discussed with the head of the fire-prevention division, usually called the fire marshal.

If any deficient items necessitate a reinspection, the inspector will need to visit the property again to ascertain fire code compliance. This inspection is usually brief and includes checking only the area or items that did not meet code during the inspection. If the inspector is satisfied that the business is now in compliance with the fire codes, the inspection is complete. Interestingly, businesses tend to fail their inspections in very similar areas that are common to almost all buildings. Burned-out exit lights, failure to maintain fire extinguishers and fire-suppression systems, improperly maintained emergency exits, and use of extension cords as permanent wiring are violations that are found quite frequently.

The subject of exits comes up so often in discussing large loss-of-life fires that it warrants further study here. Many patrons of businesses are familiar with the main entrance as their primarily intended exit. If an emergency arises, additional exits must be clearly identified and maintained to be used successfully. The **exit system** is made up of three components: the **exit access** (includes aisles within rooms or spaces as well as corridors), including how it can be seen and followed in an unobstructed manner; the **exit** itself (a stairwell in multistory buildings), consisting of the proper egress door mounted in the proper frame in the proper direction of swing; and the **exit discharge** (the door to the exterior of a building), which must also be kept clear to allow occupants to continue their travel to a safe area away from the structure.

If a complaint comes in to the fire-prevention division, the inspectors will determine if a visit is necessary. Complaints must be taken seriously and investigated, so the inspector must listen to the complaint and determine the course of action.

In addition to the duties just described, the fire-prevention division is often the fire department's investigative section. If fire company personnel are called to a fire that they would be of interest to the fire-prevention division, such as a large fire or one that seems to be intentionally set, they should call the division to investigate the fire to determine the fire's origin and cause.

FIRE SAFETY ORGANIZATIONS WITH AN ALLIED INTEREST IN SAFETY

FFII 6.5.1 The concept of fire safety is addressed by a number of organizations, and each will in some way affect firefighters and their lessons of fire safety for the public they serve.

After numerous fire disasters, fire insurance companies have become involved in fire safety efforts for their insured clients. **Factory Mutual (FM)**, an insurance company that insures industrial properties, maintains a laboratory for the testing of fire protection equipment, which may bear the FM seal of approval if so recognized.

Likewise, **Underwriters Laboratories (UL)** is an independent organization that does testing, listing, and examining items as they relate to fire protection and safety. The UL listing is another recognizable symbol that consumers look for when purchasing products.

The **Insurance Services Office (ISO)** is familiar to many fire departments, as they have developed and utilize the Fire Suppression Rating Schedule that determines a community's capabilities for firefighting, which is used to determine fire insurance rates for residents of the community. The Fire Suppression Rating Schedule does not incorporate an individual fire department's fire code enforcement or public education efforts into its rating. ISO does have another program called the **Building Code Effectiveness Grading Schedule**, however, which rates building code enforcement in individual communties.

The standards relating to fire safety are written by a number of agencies. The **American Society for Testing and Materials (ASTM)** writes standards that pertain to the flammability characteristics of wall finishes (ASTM Test Standard E84-08a *Standard Test Method for Surface Burning Characteristics of Building Materials*) and the hourly fire rating of wall, floor, and roof assemblies (ASTM E119-08a *Standard Test Methods for Fire Tests of Building Construction and Materials*). The **American Society of Mechanical Engineers (ASME)** writes codes that help maintain safety in elevators and escalators across the country. The NFPA, as described earlier, writes a variety of codes and standards that apply to many facets of fire prevention and suppression used throughout the world.

FIRE-SAFETY EDUCATION

FFII 6.5.1 It is the responsibility of the firefighters to educate residents in their district about fire safety at any opportunity that arises. This may be while visiting schools, at the fire station conducting a tour, or doing a **home fire-safety survey**.

A home fire-safety survey should not be confused with a fire prevention inspection. The fire prevention inspection is a legal inspection that demands compliance; whereas the home fire-safety survey is a voluntary inspection done by firefighters to help educate the occupants about the dangers of fire and how to be safer in their everyday lives.

Firefighters should not balk at conducting a home fire-safety survey. It is informational in nature; it does not imply that by following your suggestions, the occupants will never have a fire in their home. In any inspection or survey, we are looking to educate and make a safer environment. All buildings have heat sources, fuel, and plenty of oxygen, so thinking that fires can be eliminated in any structure is wrong.

The purpose of the home fire-safety survey is to educate. You only conduct this survey if the occupants have initiated contact with the fire department, or if your department does a door-to-door campaign and asks the owner for permission to conduct the survey beforehand. Let the occupants know that the survey is voluntary, and they can stop the survey if they wish. Inform them that there will be no follow-up inspections to make sure the suggestions you make are put into action, and the only paperwork the fire department will fill out is a simple form, a copy of which the occupants will receive at the completion of the inspection (fig. 33–5). The form should be in duplicate, so that one can stay on file with the fire department, for statistical purposes only. Firefighters assigned to home survey details should be able to articulate safety information clearly and concisely and be neat in appearance.

Once you have made contact with the occupants and received permission to conduct the survey, start from outside the house. Begin by looking at the property itself. If the home is located in a wildland–urban interface, it is suggested that the occupants keep a "green space" of living grass or vegetation at least 30 feet in all directions from their home. This allows firefighters an area to set up to try and save the home. If the home is nestled into the surrounding woods, it has little chance if a wildfire erupts nearby.

Next, look at the fixtures and storage items on the property. Outbuildings and sheds are often places where flammable liquids are stored. Explain the importance of keeping these areas secured, and that flammable liquids should be stored high and out of reach of children in approved containers. If vandals frequent the area, locks should be installed.

Storage of flammable and combustible materials should be considered, and the amount of flammable liquids (ignitable liquids with a flash point below 100°F [38° C]) should be kept to a minimum. In the arson field, it is interesting to note that majority of fires are set by juveniles. These misguided minors usually are looking for excitement rather than revenge or a statement of protest. By having plenty of combustible materials on the property, the missing ingredient is a simple match or lighter. Getting rid of accumulated flammable liquids, or locking them in a shed, barn, or a garage will deter juvenile fire setters. Since these children usually live in the area and do not want to be seen or recognized, installing motion-sensor lighting makes good sense, too.

The firefighters conducting the survey need to note the condition of the chimney, to see if it is in need of repair. Cracked or broken bricks are a sign that a chimney may need some repair. The condition of the roof should also be noted. Wooden shingles were once popular, but have fallen out of favor due to their vulnerability for fire spread. After years of use, they become thin pieces of wood that ignite easily, possibly from flying embers produced by an outdoor fire pit, if allowed.

Although some jurisdictions have a ban on any outdoor fires, others may not. Find out your local laws about outdoor fires and inform the residents in your area about them. If your area does allow outdoor cooking or pit fires, offer people information about how to do it safely. Proper use of camp fires, cooking fires, and the increased use of commercial fire pits are often the subject of questions that some residents may have. They are usually hesitant to bring this up, because they feel it may put them in a bad light.

You may be asked to look inside barns and garages. Inside these structures, you can address the same concerns of stored flammable liquids as you did with the sheds. You can also offer advice on accumulated storage items, if they are blocking access to and from the doors. If the garage is attached to the house, then the need for controlling storage and flammable liquids increases due to the close proximity to residents.

As you approach the entrance to the house, make sure that the address is clearly visible from the street. Night calls when people usually do not come outside to direct us can be difficult if the houses are not properly marked. The front porch light should be turned on if an emergency call has been made, and firefighters are expected to arrive. Aftermarket products are available that add an "emergency" function to the front porch light that turns it on and off, making it easy for firefighters to spot from a distance away.

The interior survey should include the main living areas of the home, as well as any additional areas the occupant may want inspected, such as a basement. If the survey does include the basement, housekeeping is a major issue. The basement should be clear of accumulated flammable combustible materials, and clear access should be maintained to the furnace, hot water heater and electrical panel, if located in the basement, as these are some of the main hazard areas common to basements.

If the basement is finished off into rooms, smoke alarms should be present throughout the basement to give early warning to occupants in case of fire (more on smoke alarms later in this chapter). If the basement is used for occupants to sleep within, certain safety considerations should be brought up to the occupants. First, if there are two clearly identified exits, they should be kept clear for easy access. This may include the basement door and stairs and large windows or a sliding door for backyard access. If the windows are smaller and high on the basement wall (unusable for egress), an appropriately sized escape window must also be installed near floor level as a required secondary means of egress (as required by the model building codes described earlier). Since you may not get homeowners to install this code-compliant secondary escape window (or stairwell to grade) in the near future, tell them of the dangers of using the basement as a sleeping area and how it is in violation of the building code.

If the basement is used often, such as a woodworking shop, laundry room, or a game room, installing a fire extinguisher is recommended. Regardless of whether the occupants choose an inexpensive model or a more expensive, rechargeable model, it should be an A-B-C rated fire extinguisher, and the adults should know how to use it if necessary. A short explanation on how fire extinguishers work may be necessary.

As you move through the home, find time to talk about safety related to some of the main causes of fire, such as arson (discussed earlier when outside), cooking-related, electrical and electrical distribution, heating equipment, and smoking materials.

Moving to the main level of the home, you can talk about kitchen fire safety. Safety topics in the kitchen are numerous, and many are common sense that need to be reinforced by a firefighter in uniform. Keep the cooking areas clean from grease and other combustibles that can easily ignite. Suggest that the occupants cook on back burners of the stove whenever possible, to prevent small children from reaching up and pulling hot items down onto themselves. Keep pot handles turned into the stove to avoid them being bumped and the pot contents being spilled. Children should not be allowed to play

in or around the cooking areas when cooking equipment is being used. Since the main cause of home fires is cooking-related incidents, having a fire extinguisher near the kitchen area also makes good sense. Besides the fire extinguisher, let the occupants know that keeping the lid to the pot or pan they are cooking with handy is also recommended. If a pan fire breaks out, the occupant can put a hand in a large oven mitt and grab the lid and place it over the flaming pot or pan. This takes away the oxygen, putting out the fire. Tell the occupant to keep the lid on and shut off the heat to the burner, then call the fire department to search for any fire spread that may have occurred. Another weapon that can be used against fire in the kitchen is baking soda. It can be kept nearby, or even left on the counter as a handy reminder. The family may choose to decorate a one-pound coffee can and put baking soda in it as their family kitchen fire extinguisher.

Also on the main level, you may find a room that is used by the family to spend quite a bit of time relaxing in. This may be called the living room, family room, or go by a different name. This may be a good time to discuss heating equipment, such as keeping furnaces and fireplaces clean and inspected annually. The screen of the fireplace should always be pulled into place when a fire is burning to keep any sparks contained. Portable space heaters have grown in popularity since the energy shortage of the 1980s, and they are still in use today (fig. 33–6). Although great for warming up a small area, like any open flame from cooking or a fireplace, they should never be left unattended, and there should be an adult supervising at all times. The safety of today's space heaters is a vast improvement over earlier models. Many of the newer models have a "tip over" switch that turns the unit off if it is tipped over. The safe distance that is recommended for combustibles to be kept away from any heating source (furnace, fireplace, space heater, etc.) is 3 ft (1 m).

HOME FIRE SAFETY SURVEY

This form is designed to help you check your home for fire hazards. All the questions are worded so a "YES" answer means the area is safe. A "NO" answer means a fire hazard exists and needs to be corrected. If you have any questions about how to correct a hazard, call your local fire and rescue station for assistance.

HEATING HAZARDS	**YES**	**NO**
1. Combustibles like clothes, curtains, and furniture are away from stoves and heaters.	_____	_____
2. Heating appliances are tested every year.	_____	_____
3. There is a screen in front of the fireplace.	_____	_____
4. Ashes are emptied into covered metal containers.	_____	_____
5. All alternative heating devices used are U.L. listed.	_____	_____

ELECTRICAL HAZARDS	**YES**	**NO**
1. Electric cords are checked to be sure they are not worn, frayed, or damaged.	_____	_____
2. Extension cords are not run under rugs, over nails, through water, or across passageways.	_____	_____
3. Proper size fuses are used in all sockets.	_____	_____
4. Each circuit is properly marked.	_____	_____
5. Electrical outlets are not overloaded by multiple plug devices.	_____	_____
6. Electric appliances are not used near water.	_____	_____

GENERAL HOUSEKEEPING HAZARDS	**YES**	**NO**
1. Closets, basements, attics, and garage areas are clean of old paper, boxes, paint cans, and other trash.	_____	_____
2. Rubbish is thrown away regularly.	_____	_____
3. Everyone in the family knows NOT to use a flammable liquid, like gasoline, for cleaning.	_____	_____
4. Flammable liquids and oily rags are disposed of after use or stored in a tightly closed metal container.	_____	_____
5. All combustibles are stored a safe distance away from any possible heat source.	_____	_____

SMOKING HAZARDS	**YES**	**NO**
1. Matches and lighters are kept out of the reach of children.	_____	_____
2. Smokers use ashtrays that are large, deep, and designed for use with smoking materials.	_____	_____

KITCHEN HAZARDS	YES	NO
1. The kitchen is kept clean all the time.	_____	_____
2. The stove and oven are in good working condition.	_____	_____
3. The stove area is kept clean and free of grease.	_____	_____
4. Combustible materials (like towels and pot holders) are kept away from open flames and heat sources.	_____	_____
5. Someone is always in the kitchen when food is cooking.	_____	_____

GENERAL FIRE SAFETY	YES	NO
1. The house address is clearly posted in large numbers that are easy to read from the street.	_____	_____
2. There is a working smoke alarm near the sleeping areas.	_____	_____
3. There is a working smoke alarm on every level.		
4. The smoke alarm is cleaned regularly and tested once a month.	_____	_____
5. You know the emergency telephone number for fire and rescue. (9-1-1)	_____	_____
6. This number is posted on all telephones for immediate reference.	_____	_____
7. You have portable fire extinguishers suitable for use in your home and family members know how to use them properly.	_____	_____
8. You have a home escape plan and practice it regularly.	_____	_____

If you have any "NO" answers, sit down with your family and discuss the problem and how it can be corrected. Take this opportunity to create fire safety awareness in ALL family members and, at the same time, make your home a safer place to live.

FIREFIGHTER II

Chapter 33

Fig. 33–5. Home fire safety survey form

Fig. 33–6. Homeowners need to be reminded of the rules of fire safety in their homes to build lasting changes in their behavior.

Electricity is a luxury that we have become accustomed to, and we enjoy its benefits every day. Whether it is listening to music, using our personal computers, or taking a cold drink out of the refrigerator, we all draw electricity into our homes. Although many safety measures are built into the electrical system in our homes and the products we purchase, we must be vigilant in our use of electricity at home. A good rule of thumb is one major appliance or power strip should be the maximum for any one outlet, and the power strips that are common today behind entertainment centers and computers should include a built-in circuit breaker that will shut off power to the appliances if a problem is encountered in the system. Most national codes today insist on outlets installed with ground fault circuit interrupters (GFCIs) when there is a chance of water being splashed with resultant electrocution, such as in kitchens and bathrooms.

If electrical extension cords are used in the house as part of a permanent wiring system designed by the homeowners, they should be informed about the danger of this practice. Extension cords are designed to bring electricity to a location where it is needed for a short time period, and then should be disconnected. An electrician may be needed to come out and install a few more electrical outlets in the home if they feel the need for more electrical outlets.

Ask the occupants if anyone smokes in the house. If so, some of the safety tips that we can tell them include having large, tip-proof ashtrays in the home that can hold the entire cigarette in case it is lit and forgotten, avoid emptying ashtrays with hot ashes into garbage containers, and never smoke in bed or when taking medicines that may cause drowsiness.

The items we use to light tobacco products, usually matches and lighters, are a problem themselves. Too often, children have easy access to these items. Children experimenting with matches and lighters account for far too many fires, some of which have injured or killed family members. Matches and lighters should be stored high up and out of the reach of children. Children should be taught that matches and lighters are tools used to start friendly fires, not toys for them to play with. Friendly fires can be enjoyed by all family members when properly supervised, such as fires in the fireplace, cooking on the stove, and candles.

Candles bring about a fire hazard that has been on the increase for several years. The development of gel candles and other decorative candles that provide aromatic pleasure has created additional risks in the home. Candles should be treated as the open flame they are, supervised by an adult, and with combustibles kept at least 1 foot away. Tell the occupants to make sure that no blowing curtains or other objects can come into contact with the open flame.

Bathrooms and bedrooms contain hazards that have been outlined, but if a special hazard is brought up by the occupants, listen and provide suggestions that address their worries. The main concern of parents is their children, so focus on this when discussing smoke alarms and fire-safety behaviors with the family.

Smoke alarm technology has come a long way since the 1970s, when a single unit cost over $50. Smoke alarms have been introduced to give occupants time to react and leave a building that has smoke (and probably fire) in it. *All* alarm activations should be taken as real, and family members should be encouraged to leave any building that has an alarm sounding. This may be going against the actions of the crowd, but it is always safest to leave first, then reenter if the "all clear" is given.

Smoke alarms should be installed throughout the homes in your area, with an absolute minimum of one smoke alarm per floor of the home (including the basement), and one outside of sleeping areas should be maintained in existing homes. The best level of fire protection, of course, includes installing alarms throughout the home. By doing this, wherever a fire may start, a smoke alarm (or heat detector in kitchens and bathrooms) is close by to alert the occupants of the smoke inside the home (fig. 33–7).

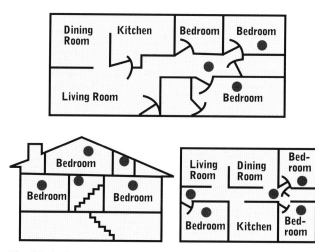

Fig. 33–7. Smoke detector placement

The most common type of smoke alarm is the battery-operated single-station unit that is a sensor and alarm all in one unit. Because they are operated by batteries, they can be easily installed almost anywhere in the home. Consult manufacturers' recommendations for suggested locations, but in general, smoke alarms should be mounted on the ceiling or high on a wall if a decorative ceiling is in the room. The corners of rooms have a "dead air" space where the walls meet the ceiling; air movement is restricted, so keep ceiling-mounted alarms at least 4 in. (10 cm) away from the wall, and wall-mounted alarms between 4 in. (10 cm) and 12 in. (30 cm) below the ceiling.

Many of the building codes that have been updated since the widespread use of smoke alarms have included the mandate of smoke alarms in the homes that are newly built or renovated. Current building codes call for hardwired (which uses a home's electrical supply instead of batteries), interconnected smoke alarms in the following locations: on all levels, outside all sleeping areas, and in all sleeping rooms. Wiring the smoke alarm to the home's electricity solves the problem of dead batteries rendering smoke alarm inoperable. The problem comes in during power outages, when many open flames from candles and fireplaces are in the home that is now without smoke alarm protection. For a slightly increased cost, most manufacturers offer a battery backup model of the hardwired smoke alarm to provide protection during these times.

Smoke alarms today come with many options, and different models should be considered carefully to see which ones are useful to the family. One option is a smoke alarm testing mechanism that allows a beam from a flashlight to test the alarm. This may be helpful to keep an elderly occupant from climbing on a chair to test the alarms. Others may have light beams that can be pointed at an exit, to help occupants find the way out of the house when smoke may obstruct their vision. Others have "silence switches" that will disarm the alarm mechanism for a short period, to allow time to investigate or clear out smoke that may have come from food cooking on the stove. Still other smoke alarms have 10-year batteries.

Another option should be considered by parents of children from the ages of about 5–12. This is a "vocal" smoke alarm that allows the parents to prerecord a message that will play after the alarm sounds. It has been found that children in this age group are so used to sleeping through unwanted sounds that they often sleep through smoke alarms going off. They are, however, more likely to awaken when they hear the familiar voice of a parent giving instructions. If this alarm makes sense for the family, it should be installed near the sleeping areas of the home where the children sleep.

Other smoke alarms are part of a home security package and are monitored by an outside alarm company. There should be a way to alert the alarm company or temporarily disconnect the alarm from the company during testing periods. The smoke alarms as part of a home security system should be individualized to meet the family's needs, and the system should be developed by both the occupants and the alarm company.

Regardless of type, smoke alarms cannot do their job if they are incapacitated. Each smoke alarm should be tested monthly by pressing and holding the test button until the alarm sounds. The whole family should take part in this activity to instill fire-safety behaviors in the next generation. Pick an easy day to remember and mark the calendars in the house. Maybe the first day of each month, the first Tuesday of the month, or some other system that works with the family should be selected.

The batteries in single-station units should be changed every 6 months to ensure that fresh batteries will enable the unit to respond to smoke. The International Association of Fire Chiefs and the Eveready Battery Company instituted the "Change Your Clock, Change Your Battery" campaign years ago, which tells consumers to change the batteries in their smoke alarms in the spring and fall when the time changes for daylight savings time. Although the daylight savings time may not be used by all areas, it is advertised widely enough for firefighters to remember to get their campaign underway to alert their citizens. A 2004 telephone survey found that 96% of the households surveyed had at least one smoke alarm. According to the NFPA, in one out of every five homes equipped with at least one smoke alarm installed, not a single one was working. The main reason for smoke alarms failing to work is missing, disconnected, or dead batteries. The statistics arm us with good information to tell residents about the importance of having working smoke alarms in the home (fig. 33–8).

Many fire departments make it a standard operating procedure to check the smoke detectors in a home after every call, regardless of the type of call. This is a public service to ensure the proper operation of a home's smoke alarms and to check for dead batteries. These same departments carry extra batteries and smoke detectors on the fire apparatus, ready to be installed. A notation is made in the incident report that the battery or detector was installed. This provides some legal protection, especially in the case of a call for a "smoke odor" that cannot be located by firefighters, followed hours later by a working fire in the same home. Although this may not provide immunity from lawsuits, it does show that firefighters took appropriate action for the residents' safety.

Fig. 33–8. Firefighters should test the smoke alarms in the homes. This shows residents how to test them and what the alarm sounds like if they haven't checked them recently. Show them how to replace the battery on battery-operated units.

Regardless of the options purchased on smoke alarms, today's smoke alarms operate on one of two principles. The sensing chamber is either an ionization type or photoelectric type. Much debate has taken place on which is better, but the research shows us that the ionization smoke alarm responds faster to flaming fires, while the photoelectric units respond faster to smoldering fires.

Ionization smoke alarm sensing technology consists of a small radioactive chip located between two electrically-charged panels, which ionize the air and move current between the panels. Smoke entering the sensing chamber disrupts the flow of ions, reducing the flow of the current, and sets the unit into the alarm mode.

Photoelectric sensing technology has a sensing chamber with a light-emitting source and a light-receiving source. As long as the two do not meet, there is no alarm. When smoke enters this sensing chamber, the light beam is refracted into the light-receiver, and the alarm is set into the alarm mode.

Carbon monoxide (CO) alarms are another important component is the overall safety picture of today's families (fig. 33–9). Many erroneously believe that smoke alarms and CO alarms are similar since all smoke contains carbon monoxide. They are also very similar in appearance. Carbon monoxide is the by-product of combustion of natural gas, which is present in most homes, as the use of natural gas is common for many stoves, furnaces, and water heaters.

Since carbon monoxide is similar in weight to air, some manufacturers suggest they be mounted on the ceiling or high on a wall, similar to smoke alarms. Others suggest a lower mounting, as evidenced by the plug-in type carbon monoxide alarms that are commonly available today.

Fig. 33–9. Carbon monoxide alarm

The CO alarm will sound when elevated levels of CO are attained within the home; families must be told to evacuate when the alarm sounds. Most fire departments respond first when a call for a CO alarm activation is received. Responding firefighters will use metering equipment to establish the levels of CO in the home.

JUVENILE FIRESETTER PROGRAMS

During the early phase of the home survey, arson was mentioned. Arson is a leading cause of dollar losses due to fire every year. While arson is the deliberate act of setting a fire, the majority of arson is juvenile arson. Do not assume a natural curiosity about fire is an unhealthy "arsonist" attitude. Almost all children are curious about fire. Hopefully they will have learned that using fire as a tool can be useful in the home and should not be used for other reasons.

FFII 6.5.1 It is important for today's fire departments to be ready for the call or visit from an adult or guardian who is concerned about catching a child playing with matches or lighters. The firefighter must know what action is appropriate to take when this occurs. Today, many parts of the country have **juvenile firesetter programs**, following the lead of organizations such as the Rochester, New York, Fire Department, which created one of the first such program in the 1980s. These programs bring together fire safety, law enforcement, mental health, and child safety advocates to provide community-based treatment to address this problem.

If your fire prevention division is not equipped with the appropriate training to handle this situation, arrangements must be made. This may include a neighboring department having a juvenile firesetter program, or an arrangement to visit a mental health professional.

TEACHING PROPER FIRE SAFETY BEHAVIOR

Fire-safety behaviors should also be reinforced in the families that you visit during your home surveys. While most of us have heard of **stop, drop, and roll**, many children may need some practice time to make sure the behavior can be duplicated when an emergency arises and they need to perform it. Having done it once or twice is not enough to make the behavior permanent.

If clothing catches fire, the person wearing the burning clothing should stop, drop, and roll to smother the flames out. Stopping keeps fresh oxygen from spreading the fire in the direction of travel, so that must be the first step. Explain and demonstrate to children how they should stop, drop, and roll: You should drop to the ground, where you can use the ground as a flat surface. You should then roll, to smother out the flames. If the sleeves are not involved in flame, use your hands to cover your face and protect it from heat. If your sleeves are involved in flame, keep them at your side as you roll. The rolling should be done until the flames are all extinguished, and all sides of your body must contact the ground as you roll. Once the flames have been extinguished, cool water should be applied to the burned area while an adult is summoned to inspect the burns.

Another fire-safety behavior that should be taught is the memorization of the emergency phone number for the jurisdiction they live in. Most of the country is covered by the 9-1-1 system, so this may be an easy number to memorize. In the few areas that are not covered, the 7-digit number should be taught to children and posted in the home and on telephones, so it can be called quickly during an emergency, without having to look up the number. This call should never be made from inside a house that is on fire or filling with smoke. The call should be made from outside the home, on a cell phone or from a neighbor's home.

Crawling low under smoke just makes good sense. When smoke is generated by a fire, it rises and spreads out. By standing and running through the smoke, you will probably breathe more smoke in, and possibly suffer adverse effects from it. It is important to have children practice these safety behaviors to help make them permanent. This can be done by having children crawl around the classroom toward the door, crawl under desks, or crawl under a blanket held by firefighters, simulating the smoke layer.

The home fire escape plan is a document that has a plan for escape in case of fire, and it must be discussed with all family members present. The escape plan should include a map of the home, including the outside and inside walls and doors to the rooms, and it should show two separate ways out of each room in the home. Usually, this includes a door and a window. If a room does not have two ways out, such as a bathroom, it should not be used for extended or overnight periods. The windows should be inspected by the family to confirm that they open properly and to see if children can open them if an emergency arises. Small children and others living in the home may need someone to look after them in case of fire, and this should be discussed during the home fire escape plan. Children unable to open windows, infants in cribs, and elderly in need of assistance should all be included in the plan.

Bedrooms that are up a flight of stairs can be handled in several ways. First, look out the window to see what is below the window. If a roof is there from a lower part of the home, such as a garage, it can be used as a secondary exit. If this is not the case, commercially made escape ladders can be kept under the bed in the bedroom. These take up very little room in their box, but deploy from the window down to the ground in case of a fire emergency. They are available in different lengths for use from second and third stories in the home.

The home escape plan should also include the locations of where the home's fire extinguishers, first aid kit, and family disaster kit are kept (fig. 33–10). This can help out during an emergency, or if a baby sitter is watching the children. The location of smoke alarms should also be marked on the plan, to make certain that all smoke alarms are tested at least once a month. The escape plan must also include a family meeting place, where all members of the family know exactly where to go during a fire emergency, regardless of which exit they used to get out of the house (fig. 33–11). This allows for an accurate head count to be given to first-arriving fire companies by the occupants.

Fig. 33–11. All family members should know where their family meeting place is, and it should be easily accessible.

The most important part of the home fire escape plan is to practice the plan at least twice a year. There is nothing like some actual practice to make behaviors permanent, and this is a plan that needs to be remembered in an emergency. To make sure the correct behaviors are likely to take place, practice the plan at night every once in a while. This may wake children up, but it's the best way to find out if they know what to do when confronted by a fire emergency.

The comprehensive home fire escape plan may also be called operation E.D.I.T.H., which stands for Exit Drills in the Home. Remember, once the plan is made, the most important part is practicing the plan twice a year.

Home fire sprinkler systems are getting more popular today. In some jurisdictions, building code requires that homes have residential sprinkler systems, and where they are not required, some homeowners may choose to have them installed. It is important that firefighters have information to give homeowners on what these systems are and how they would go about installing them in their homes. This can also educate the firefighters if they find homes that have fire sprinkler systems that they were unaware existed in their response district. This information should be documented and disseminated to the other firefighters in the area. Fire sprinklers can go a long way if we want to reduce the number of fire deaths in this country, and firefighters should be prepared to educate homeowners if approached (fig. 33–12).

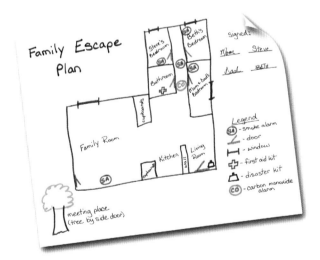

Fig. 33–10. The completed home fire escape plan should be prominently displayed in the home and practiced at least twice a year.

Fig. 33–12. Residential sprinklers are required in some communities, so be prepared to offer information about them if asked.

Although home fire escape plans have to do with the homes where people reside, make sure they can make them up when they go on vacation and stay at hotels and motels. Tell them to study the map of the building on the back of the hotel or motel room's door. A good meeting place can be the family car or under the hotel or motel sign, which is usually close to the main roadway.

Encourage families to discuss fire escape plans when they are planning a vacation or just going out for the evening, at popular places families frequent, such as restaurants and movie theatres. Although alarms may or may not be present, make sure everyone is encouraged to let one another know if unwanted smoke or flame is spotted. Many people are reluctant to alert others or take prompt action, often leading to devastating results.

FIRE STATION TOURS

FFII 6.5.1 Tours of the fire station should be a routine and expected part of any firefighter's daily activity. Preparation is the key to a successful program, and station tours are no exception. Knowing what time the tour is scheduled for, what group will be coming, the number of people in the group, and any specific information they

have requested should all be noted on the tour form that the fire company should have in their possession prior to the tour.

Make sure the fire station has been properly cleaned and the trucks and tools are clean as well. Special attention should be given to the path the tour is scheduled to take, removing any standing water and other hazards from the area. Greet the tour group promptly and start by discussing the rules for the tour, including where they can put coats during the tour and the procedures to follow on the tour. Start this off by telling them what their role will be when the fire station alarm sounds, so they know exactly where to go to be out of the way, and when it is okay to move from that spot, which is usually when the last bay door goes down fully. Make sure the group stays together for the tour, and that children are not allowed to wander off on their own.

Mix up some fun with the educational components of the tour. While it is always a good idea to discuss and practice fire-safety behaviors, show them the fire trucks and the tools on the trucks. Having a firefighter in full turnout gear at some point in the tour is a very personal way for children to recognize what firefighters look like when they go into a burning building. It is important not to scare children, but rather let them know that we are there to help them out of a building when it is on fire.

If your fire department provides emergency medical services (EMS), then show them the EMS vehicle and some of the supplies that are kept on that vehicle as well. Explain to the group how your fire department is staffed and describe the normal schedule you may have for station duties and vehicle maintenance. Remember to instill safety into your talk, by pointing out the fire station's working smoke alarms. This is a good time to discuss smoke alarms with the group, and all groups should hear our smoke alarm messages.

Handout materials for the group should be assembled prior to the beginning of the tour, and let the tour group representative know where they are in case you have to leave on an emergency call (fig. 33–13). When the tour is over, the main points can be summarized and handout materials passed out. If time allows, you can take several questions from the group and allow time during the tour for pictures to be taken by the parents, teachers, or caregivers in attendance. The fire station is a very interesting place for tour groups to visit. Be proud to show it off!

Fig. 33–13. Firefighters should have materials ready to hand out when conducting a residential survey.

FIRE SAFETY RESOURCES

FFII 6.5.1 Some very recognizable figures in the field of fire safety are **Smokey Bear** and **Sparky the Fire Dog**®. Smokey has been telling audiences his message of forest fire safety since 1944, while Sparky entered the fire-safety scene for residential homes in 1951. Children love both characters, and fire-safety material that features them can be purchased and given as tour handouts to the children. You can also suggest that children visit their Web sites, which are educational and very child friendly.

Some fire departments have educational and fun Web sites of their own. If that is the case, let your community know about it at every opportunity. Advertising your Web site address on fire department vehicles, on recorded phone messages, and in the media can help draw attention to your efforts. You can make bookmarks that have your Web address on them, and encourage a visit to your Web site to everyone who visits your fire station for tours.

The media can be very helpful for getting the message of fire and life safety out to your community. Television, local access cable television, newspapers, and community newsletters have all been used effectively for educating people about fires. For example, one topic could be recent fires in the news in your area, or some general fire-safety education tips. There are numerous resources for topics, including the USFA Web site. It has several topics to choose from, and you can add local flavor by including some local statistics, a background of a recognizable landmark, or your fire department uniform or patch prominently displayed. Some topics are general and can be used any time of the year, such as smoke

alarms and cooking safety, while others may be timely, such as Halloween safety tips in October.

Many fire departments take advantage of **Fire Prevention Week**, in recognition of the Great Chicago Fire on 1871. The NFPA is the official sponsor of Fire Prevention Week, and they have plenty of material for fire departments to use on their Web sites. During Fire Prevention Week, many fire departments hold a community open house event. This is a great way to showcase your fire department and firefighters, and teach fire safety in a fun way. Children love to put on a clean fire coat and squirt a fire hose, but you should also make it fun for them to practice the fire-safety behaviors discussed earlier in the chapter (fig. 33–14).

Fig. 33–14. The fire department open house should be entertaining *and* educational.

GIVING A FIRE SAFETY PRESENTATION

FFII 6.5.1 Many times, firefighters are called out to deliver a **fire safety presentation** to the public at a location other than the fire station. It may be at a school, mall, or business. Regardless, it is important to deliver appropriate safety information to the target group. Find out as much as possible about your audience prior to your presentation in order to customize the presentation to that specific group (age, particular fire safety issues, etc.). It would be good to know approximately how many people are expected to be in your audience (for handout material distribution), how long this talk is expected to last, any specific topics that should be covered, the availability of a room to present, and a system to meet any computer needs you may have. Topics can be recent newsworthy items such as fires in your area that have been covered in the news, or seasonal issues such as bicycle safety, swimming pool safety, or heating season safety.

The proper attire for this type of presentation is your fire department's approved uniform, so that you are easily recognized as the fire service professional to the group. While your firefighting gear is a must to show lower elementary school children, you may be able to skip the gear if you are addressing an adult audience.

Bring in a visual display or two to help you deliver your messages. A small display case containing a few objects destroyed in a house fire can create a visual message and be small enough to easily transport in a vehicle. When speaking to a group of adults that may have small children at home, such as a homeowners association meeting, a display of novelty lighters is usually a good attention-grabber (fig. 33–15). The novelty lighters bring about the subject of children playing with fire, keeping matches and lighters out of the reach of small children, and the dangerous novelty lighters that take the shape of ordinary childhood toys.

Fig. 33–15. Small displays, such as this novelty lighter awareness case, can provide a good visual message.

Remember to use simple descriptions here, and avoid our trade's jargon. Adult audiences can be quick to lose attention when they do not understand the message you are trying to get across.

Always schedule time to take questions. Questions make the person feel important enough that you take time to speak to their concerns directly. The best way to handle this for lower elementary school-aged children is by telling them that you will schedule a few minutes after your presentation for any questions. This will save time and effort during your presentation. Older audiences usually ask questions pertaining to your subject, so let them know at the outset to ask questions if and when they have them.

QUESTIONS

1. What is the name of the document that has helped pave the way for fire-safety education in the United States?

2. What is a fire inspection?

3. Does the fire company need to ask for the permission of the business to perform a fire inspection? Explain your answer.

4. Why it is important to sell the merits of the fire inspection to the business owner or manager?

5. What is the difference between home fire-safety and a fire-prevention inspection?

6. How can firefighters educate residents in their district about fire safety?

7. What items are important for firefighters to cover when conducting a fire station tour?

8. Name the main causes of home fires that firefighters can talk to families about when conducting home safety surveys.

9. How would you teach lower elementary school-aged children fire safety behaviors? How does that differ when you discuss the same behaviors with upper elementary school-aged children? Adults? Seniors?

Vehicle Extrication

by Dave Dalrymple

This chapter provides required knowledge items for the following NFPA Standard 1001 Job Performance Requirements:

FFII 6.4.1

This chapter contains Skill Drills. When you see this icon, refer to your Skill Drill book for step-by-step instructions.

OBJECTIVES

Upon completion of this chapter, you should be able to do the following:

- Describe the importance of the "Golden Hour"
- List modern vehicle technologies that have positive and negative impacts on vehicle extrication
- List common hand tools used by the fire service for vehicle rescue
- List the power tools used by the fire service for vehicle rescue
- List the equipment used by the fire service for stabilizing a vehicle in order to perform a rescue
- Describe the "operational cycle" used at vehicle rescue incidents by the fire service
- List the hazards that need to be identified during the initial size-up at a vehicle rescue incident
- Identify the proper protective clothing to be used by firefighters at a vehicle rescue incident
- Describe the importance of patient management and care at a vehicle rescue incident
- Identify the proper procedures to be used by firefighters for packaging and disentangling a victim at a vehicle rescue incident
- Describe the proper procedures to be used to safely remove a victim from a vehicle
- Identify the proper procedures to be used by firefighters for performing preventive maintenance on vehicle rescue tools

INTRODUCTION

After EMS calls, **motor vehicle crashes (MVCs)** are one of the most common types of incidents you will respond to. So it is a safe bet to call an MVC as a common, everyday emergency. However, is it a routine type of call? Every MVC is different, and yet the vehicle itself is the dynamic concern here. When vehicles crash, there are many systems in them to protect the occupants from harm, but these same systems can disrupt our efforts to disentangle the occupants and even injure us in the process.

FFII 6.3.4 Yet, we are tasked with rapidly managing the incident, mitigating the hazards, making patient contact, and managing that patient while displacing the vehicle components to create a proper pathway for the patient to be disentangled and transported to the appropriate medical facility. We clean up the scene, restock the vehicle, and return to service.

The golden hour

As with most operations fire departments perform, responding to an MVC is a time-sensitive task. We need to remember that while dealing with occupants who have been involved in an impact; there is great potential for trauma. There are procedures that can only be performed by doctors in a controlled facility. Therefore, it is imperative that occupants involved in an MVC get medical care from a trauma team as soon as possible. As rescuers, we pay a vital role in the outcome.

A term used in the emergency services for many years is the **Golden Hour**. This term describes the time that elapses between the moment of the patient's injury and the patient's arrival at the hospital and preparation for emergency surgery. The clock starts ticking once the injury occurs, not when the responders arrive on scene. It is a race against time, as notification of the incident is beyond our control, as well as the overall response time needed to get a crew on scene (fig. 34–1).

The only component of the Golden Hour within our control is the 15–30 minute window from the companies' first arrival on scene and through extrication operations. Keep in mind; this is a goal, not a definitive time frame. It may not always be possible to meet the components of the 60-minute window, as MVCs present many unpredictable challenges. The only way we can be most effective with extrication is through aggressive and consistent training.

In this chapter we present basic principles and methodology for vehicle rescue as a primer for the firefighter. First, let's look at some specific vehicle design issues and how they will impact our rescue efforts. We will cover tools and specific extrication techniques later in the chapter.

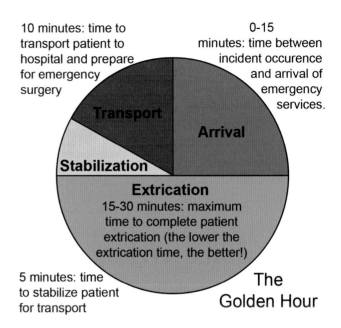

Fig. 34–1. The Golden Hour represents the 60-minute window of optimum response time for arrival, extrication, transport, and preparation of an injury victim for emergency surgery.

VEHICLE DESIGN AND TECHNOLOGIES

FFII 6.3.4 Today's motor vehicles challenge the emergency responder and pose many concerns (fig. 34–2). Each type of vehicle—car, pickup truck, sport-utility vehicle (SUV), or minivan—presents issues specific to the vehicle type, but they are also similar in some ways.

Fig. 34–2. New vehicle technology creates new challenges as well as tactics for extricating patients.

Although much of the focus on vehicles centers on safety systems such as air bags, we need to be aware of many other components, materials, and systems. And, we need to take into account not just motor vehicle crashes but also vehicle fires and even the simple medical response to an individual in a vehicle. To keep pace with the ever-changing components and features of these vehicles, we must keep updating our background knowledge.

Construction

Most vehicles are now built with a **unibody** configuration. This type of construction is strong and lightweight, and it is built around the concept of structural integrity: All its components must be intact.

So, when we remove or displace the vehicle's components (doors, side, roof, etc.) or if they are displaced by the crash, the vehicle's integrity is weakened. This can help or hinder us. The key here is to consider this in our on-scene action plan because it can assist our space-making. The two other construction types found today are **full-frame construction,** which was typical of older vehicles, and **space-frame construction,** which is much like a bird or roll cage in which the cage itself is the vehicle's structural integrity (fig. 34–3).

Fig. 34–3. This photo reveals the space-frame construction in a new vehicle.

Let's look at the **energy absorption areas (crumple zones)** in the vehicle. Throughout the vehicle are engineered areas designed to absorb energy (crush) during a crash; however, the largest area, and the one that has the greatest effect on us as responders, is the vehicle front. As the vehicle absorbs crash energy, the nose of the vehicle compresses, the engine/drivetrain drops downward, and often the front tires are forcibly

deflated. This basically places the nose of the vehicle on the ground.

Now, add into this mix the significant reinforcement built into the dash area. This reinforcement has gained significant strength (high-strength steels/alloys) over the recent past. The reinforcement is *tied* to the vehicle's sides, as well as to the floor and forward to the firewall.

So coupling the issue of crush zones with dash reinforcements, how does this construction affect moving a dash (fig. 34–4)?

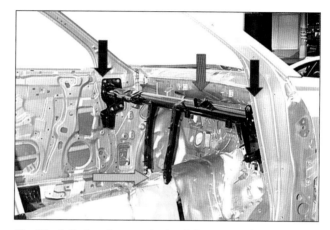

Fig. 34–4. Notice the new dash reinforcement in this vehicle.

Maybe we need to rethink how we perform **dash displacements**. Instead of performing a **dash roll-up**, perhaps a vertical lift of the dash would be more in order. Also, what if we place another relief cut to assist our dash displacement in a new location? We already make relief cuts into the lower dash—a post-area point for the dash—to move as well as pivot.

This **relief cut** might only look like a cut into the fender; the concept for the evolution is to *sever* the crush zone area behind the fender, thus allowing the dash area to move *independently* of the rest of the vehicle when displaced.

Therefore, even if the nose of the vehicle is on the ground, you can effectively displace the dash (fig. 34–5).

Fig. 34–5. Notice relief cut behind the fender on this 2007 Escape Hybrid.

Reinforcements

Because we've touched on reinforcements, let's delve into this area a little further. Although many vehicles are now made of lighter-weight materials than in the past, many more are reinforced with alternative materials and methodology. More points of reinforcement are found today, in addition to a greater percentage of **high-strength steels (HSS)**. Some vehicles have more than 63% of HSS and alloys. Many alloys, such as boron or microalloy steel, are difficult to cut, even with power hydraulic cutters. Even some of vehicle components and reinforcements are constructed of these materials. Imagine what might occur if a door side impact bar were displaced forward or rearward. Most components are made of either material (fig. 34–6).

Fig. 34–6. Notice the reinforcements revealed in the cutouts on a Mazda 6.

Another popular reinforcement in today's vehicles is **blown-in** polyester foam. Much akin to foam used to fill cracks and voids, this material adds to the structural integrity of the vehicle without adding significant weight.

However, think about how this material reacts when you are trying to sever it with a powered hydraulic cutter or a reciprocating saw! This material makes tool evolutions difficult because of the additional force needed to compress and then shear (with the powered hydraulic cutter), or the blade becomes dull and gummed up as the material adheres to it (with a reciprocating saw). Plastics are used significantly in vehicles today, even before you add in the large percentage of the vehicle's plastic-filled structural voids. Also, certain components, because of their location, have been given **extra duty** by changing their configuration and materials.

The seat belt attachment or bracket on the B-post is the best example of this type of reinforcement. Because most seat belt–attachment points on the B-post are adjustable, they are in the perfect location to reinforce the upper B-post area (fig. 34–7).

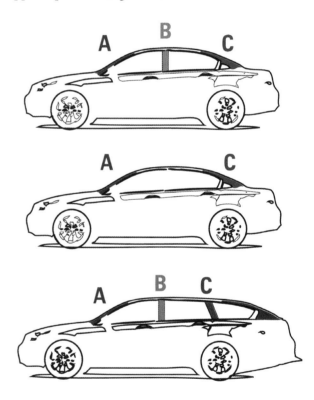

Fig. 34–7. The A, B, and C posts of a passenger vehicle

With all these construction concerns, what about our door displacement evolutions? Is just **popping** (or removing) the door enough? Is it any easier to pop the door these days? We used to accomplish the access we needed for patient care and removal with a door displacement. However, I would say it is now more difficult. Maybe we have to consider a side removal instead of a door pop. Using our knowledge of the vehicle's construction, we look for weaker areas and/or new pathways to displace, such as a B-post tear or rip evolution (fig. 34–8).

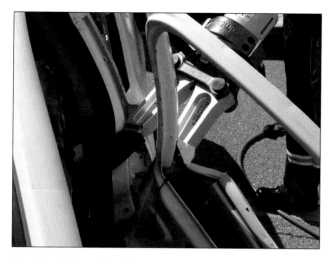

Fig. 34–8. Removing the door by tearing the door from the latch

Fig. 34–9. Notice how the laminated side glass (EPG) in this photo is shattered worse at the point of impact.

Windows

The two types of glass to which we have become accustomed, **laminated and tempered safety glass,** are still the most widely used. Laminated glass is a "sandwich", a series of layers of glass & plastic laminated together while tempered glass (safety glass) is a type of glass that breaks into small granular fragments when shattered. However, there are a few new curves out there. Enhanced protective glass (EPG) is basically a form of laminated glass placed in the side and rear windows. Dual-paned glass and polycarbonate glazing are also used. Some of these materials require a change in our methodology and tools for removing such windows (fig. 34–9).

Also, add dust masks to your personal protective equipment (PPE) for glass management (fig. 34–10). And factor in the issues of rear glass hatches in SUVs and minivans.

These glass hatches have a nasty habit of flying apart when broken because of the tension placed on them by the multiple hatch struts and the energy absorbed by the vehicle during the crash.

Fig. 34–10. Many departments now use reciprocating saws in their glass management.

Batteries

Although often helpful, by and large power in vehicles is a bane for rescuers. Today's vehicles have so much technology that the existing 12-volt systems cannot keep up with the demands. Experiments have been performed with different voltages (such as 24, 32, or 42) as well as multiple batteries. Remember, in approximately 42%

of vehicles the battery is located outside the engine compartment (fig. 34–11). However, voltage is not the greatest concern; it is the difficulty in finding the battery. Moreover, it is possible that there are alternative power sources in the vehicle. You must disconnect both battery cables at the MVC, and remove the key from the vehicle. Keep the key inside your apparatus.

Fig. 34–11. As previously mentioned, batteries may be located in many locations such as under the rear seat found in the 2007 Cadillac CTS .

Motive power

The buzzword here is **gasoline-electric hybrid vehicle.** Their high-voltage drive systems pose concerns, but there are other alternatively fueled vehicles out there. Compressed natural gas (CNG), E85, bio-diesel, and even hydrogen fuels are available today and on the street. Each vehicle is referenced in the *ERG (U.S. Department of Transportation Emergency Response Guidebook)*, which can be downloaded from the manufacturer's web site. The ERG reviews a wide variety of issues and concerns and contains background information for emergency responders.

Take note of the following *hybrid 101* points:

- All hybrids start on electric power alone

- Some travel up to certain speeds on electric power alone

- High-voltage (HV) power is direct current (DC)

- Some hybrids also generate 110 alternating current (AC)

- The HV circuit is self-contained (does not ground out to the vehicle chassis)

- Drivetrain power is computer-controlled and managed

- A crash and/or change in voltage results in a shutdown of the HV system

- All hybrids have a HV drivetrain circuit as well as a normal 12-volt automotive electric system

- The gas/diesel side of drivetrain is load dependent

- Even when the hybrid is shut down and secured, there is *always* power in the HV battery

- As emergency responders, there is *no need* to interact with the HV battery. Leave it alone!

- Colors to remember:

  - Bright orange = HV power (p-IR16)

  - Bright blue = *intermediate* HV power (GM)

Safety systems

Frontal supplemental restraint system (SRS). We have become accustomed to **frontal SRS**; however, we should look at them more closely (fig. 34–12). Generally, in the past if an air bag was deployed, it was considered spent. Many vehicles today are equipped with dual-stage frontal SRSs. Basically, this means the system has two inflation modules: a module designed to deploy at a lower speed or impact and a second for a higher rate of speed and crash severity. Also, a high-speed impact usually deploys both modules. Now the issue is how to know which modules have deployed. We can't tell by observation.

These systems can be found across the board in many vehicles of various types and brands. Disconnecting the battery drains the energy storage system in the air bag computer, but other energy (an alternate power source or static electricity, for example) might interact with the system.

Many large vehicles are equipped with frontal SRSs. In fact, one manufacturer has provided some of its models with inflatable tubular systems (a head protection air bag) and even seat belt pretensioners. Think about disarming the battery system in these vehicles!

Side safety systems. These systems are becoming more prevalent. They have expanded from the Volvo seat-mounted **side impact protection system (SIPS)** in 1995, to a door-mounted system, and then to a rear-seat and door-mounted system. Now, we have head-thorax side systems and **roof rail/side curtain head protection systems.** Unlike frontal SRS, these systems and side curtain systems work on the principal of stored energy caused by their reaction time (fig. 34–13). Many side systems are multi-chambered to give additional protection to the occupant's side and head. Side-curtain systems protect the head and give added protection during a rollover, keeping the occupants inside the vehicle. Disconnecting the battery to drain the energy storage system helps ensure a safe working environment.

Fig. 34–12. Has this air bag been inflated once or twice?

Fig. 34–13. Notice how both the Taurus side curtain and side impact bag were deployed.

However, we must keep in mind the following:

- Some side systems are mechanically activated; disarming the battery does not make these systems safe.

- Certain mechanical systems have emergency guides for disarming them.

- When operating power hydraulic tools in close proximity to these side systems, be extremely cautious, especially when the systems are not deployed. When you perform door and side tool evolutions, do not put yourself in the path of undeployed side systems. Be careful about where you place your tools during these evolutions.

Side curtain/head protection systems. A few years ago, only a handful of vehicles had side curtain/head protection systems (fig. 34–14). Now, they can be found in more than 65% of vehicle models, across all types of vehicles.

Fig. 34–14. With the trim of the 2007 Fusion removed, the undeployed side curtain is revealed.

The bag part of these systems is benign; the inflation system is of concern. The nature of the system is that it must react and deploy one-third of the time as frontal SRS; the inflation module is a pressure vessel topped with a small pyrotechnic charge. The gas stored in the module is an inert gas, but it is stored at approximately 3,000 to 10,000 psi (21,000 to 70,000 kPa). What could happen if you cut through one of these undeployed devices? At a minimum, there would be a release of high-pressure gas in close proximity to the tool operator and possibly the interior rescuer and even the patients. The worse-case scenario would be the pyrotechnic charge deploying, coupled with the release of high-pressure gas. There is also the potential for creating debris and even shrapnel. You must avoid cutting these devices. Even disconnecting the battery and electrically disarming the system does not help if you cut through the device (fig. 34–15).

Where are these inflation devices located? A few years ago, the inflation device was in the rear roof post. In 2002 all that changed. They now can be found in any of the roof posts, the roof structure itself, or even in the vehicle body.

Vehicle Extrication

FIREFIGHTER II

Chapter 34

Fig. 34–15. An accidental cut of live side curtain cylinder could be extremely dangerous for both the rescuer(s) and the patient(s).

How do we find them? How do we know in which vehicles to look for them? One clue is if one of the side curtains is deployed. Another clue is if the vehicle is a recent and high-end model. These facts should at least alert us to use more caution when dealing with roof posts. However, the best and surest approach is to strip interior trim before cutting the roof posts (fig. 34–16).

Fig. 34–16. Stripping the trim back shows side curtain cylinder.

You need not remove the trim completely, just move the trim enough so you can see the roof post structure and make sure a side curtain module is not mounted there.

Remember, this does not apply to models with these devices in the roof structure or the body.

What do you do if you find such a device? Ensure that you have disconnected the vehicle's battery to isolate the electrical power. Try to sever the roof post below the module if at all possible. If you cannot, cut the post well above the top of the module to be sure you do not cut through the pyrotechnic charge. The bottom line is that these systems are a very real concern for emergency responders and should be treated with caution (fig. 34–17).

Fig. 34–17. Once the trim is stripped back, locate and cut around side curtain cylinder.

Seat belt pretensioners. **Seat belt pretensioners** are powered devices that remove slack from the seat belt, ensuring that the occupant is seated properly when the air bag systems deploy. They are usually powered by a pyrotechnic charge; but some are powered by a gas cylinder and even high-torque electric motors. These devices are used in all front and rear seating positions in most vehicles. These devices are fairly benign to the rescuer, but it is a good idea to be sure that you cut the seat belts when working close to the belt. Even if you disarm the pretensioner by disconnecting the battery (just as with air bag systems), there is the potential for accidental deployment. Avoid cutting through these devices during tool evolutions, especially in the area of the B-post (figs. 34–18 and 34–19).

Fig. 34–18. The buckle side seat belt pretensioner is shown here.

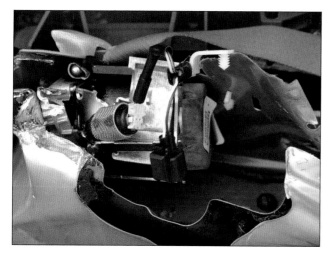

Fig. 34–19. The spool side seat belt pretensioner is shown in this photo.

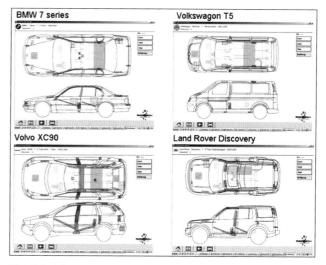

Fig. 34–20. It is important to review the crash recovery systems of as many vehicles as possible. These are a sampling of current crash recovery system information screens.

Other safety system locations. Last, let's take a look at the new locations we might find safety systems. We have had **knee air bag systems** since 1998 with Kia's Sportage, but we can now find such systems in a variety of vehicles.

These systems need careful attention when performing dash displacement evolutions. In the future look for new systems in the rear seat belts, head rests, and seat cushions, among other systems. Also, many convertibles have **pop-up rollover protective structures (ROPSs)** in conjunction with the other safety systems.

Construction, materials, and components affect our rescue efforts more and more as time progresses. We should review our methodology and tool evolutions more often and in conjunction with all vehicle concerns.

More background information is needed about vehicles and their components. Knowledge is power and key to our efforts when making changes and pushing the envelope is needed. Also remember that safety systems are becoming more widespread and comprehensive.

Safety systems already affect us and will continue to do so. Think about training issues and concerns. What do we get practice on today? Is it even fair to say the vehicles we encounter are much different from what we get to practice on? If we can't get the vehicles, can we simulate some of these hazards, issues, and concerns? The bottom line is this: Rescue teams must think and work smart when presented with issues and concerns of present and future vehicles (fig. 34–20).

TOOLS AND EQUIPMENT

FFII 6.3.4 We use tools for a wide range of tasks at an MVC, whether extrication, hazard control, patient management, or fire suppression (fig. 34–21). Time and space limit the depth to which we can hit on all these areas and tools, so the focus is on the common power tools used for extrication operations. But before we do that, think about what tools actually do for us as rescuers:

- *Sever*—dividing into two or more parts by cutting, piercing, penetrating, splitting, breaking, sawing, and so forth.

- *Distort*—changing the shape of an object in a plastic flow or other permanent manner without severing or parting.

- *Displace*—moving an object or portion of an object from its original position. The motion may be in any plane and the effect of the force applied is generally controllable. Minor distortion may occur during displacement.

- *Disassemble*—reducing objects to basic component parts in the reverse manner from which originally assembled.

Vehicle Extrication

FIREFIGHTER II

Chapter 34

Fig. 34–21. Pictured above is a typical tool staging as used on a MVC . This allows tools to be quickly and easily identified and retrieved when needed.

Extrication evolutions can require either or both hand tools and power tools. Power tools have become the accepted norm for vehicle extrication. It is easy to forget about hand tools as we carry hydraulic tools capable of cutting and crushing metals meant to withstand impacts of up to 70 MPH. But power tools can and will fail; therefore, it is important that the rescuer has a working knowledge of the basic hand tools that can be utilized as a backup plan when all else fails. The following are just a few of the various hand and power tools that can be used during extrication (fig. 34–22).

Hand tools

Hacksaw. A hacksaw is a fine-tooth saw blade held in a frame, designed to cut through various types of materials. A hacksaw can be a great primary tool for cutting through pillars or making a relief cut into the roof for a roof flap, especially while hydraulic tools are being set up. It is actually a good idea to have (4) hacksaws on scene. This can speed up the process while offering a backup saw.

Hand tool inventory. Here are a few of the hand tools that the rescue toolbox inventory should contain: tin snips, razor knives, hammers, chisels, crowbars, screwdrivers, and various types of wire cutters. It is also a good idea to carry a couple of rolls of duct tape to secure things such as tarps or cover sharp edges after components have been severed.

Center punch. This tool was used initially in the machine tool business. It has a pin that is operated by a spring. Once actuated the pin penetrates the material and leaves a dimple. The center punch is used in the rescue business to control glass of tempered windows. Once actuated, the glass will break into small pieces and access to the patient can be made.

Mechanic tools. Sometimes it is easier to "disassemble" the components of a vehicle than to cut or spread them. Socket sets, both metric and standard, ¼–½ in. (6–13 mm), as well as wrench sets are a great alternative for a door removal. As long as the hinges are exposed, you can remove the bolts that hold the hinges to the car. Once hinges are removed, you can roll the door off the "Nader Bolt."

Flathead axe & Halligan bar. As we know from our firefighting tools, these are two common tools carried on most apparatus today. The axe can be used as a striking tool in order to drive the Halligan into a tight crevice. The Halligan can be twisted or moved back and fourth to separate. These tools can be used to create **purchase points** or open a door completely by separating the door from the Nader Bolt.

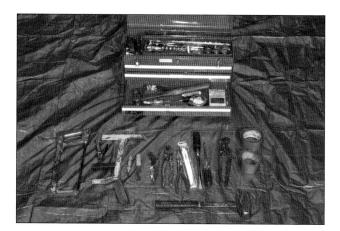

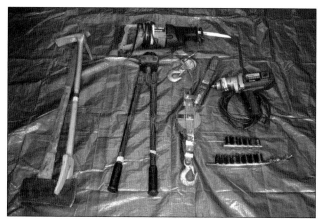

Fig. 34–22. Common hand tools used in extrication

Air impact wrench. This tool is also from the auto industry. It is operated by compressed air also and works great at disassembling vehicles bolt by bolt.

Bolt cutters. Bolt cutters are typically carried on most apparatus to cut locks. They can also be utilized to cut part of the steering wheel when the wheel is pining down the patient.

Come-along (hand winch). A come-along is designed to pull when it is used horizontally. It is designed to lift when used in a vertical situation. It may be used to displace a steering column when all other tools fail. It may also be used to hold tension on a vehicle on its side "pulling" the vehicle onto its crutches.

Power hydraulic tools

Power hydraulic tools are a system consisting of a power unit, hydraulic fluid and hoses, and one or more tools. The power unit can use gasoline, diesel, electric, or compressed gas power driving a hydraulic pump. The power unit has a reservoir of hydraulic fluid, which it supplies under force through connected hydraulic hoses to a tool, providing that tool with force to cut, spread, push, pull, and so forth. Most manufacturers use a mineral oil base fluid but not all. And the system operating pressure can vary from 3,000–10,500 psi (21,000–73,500 kPa).

Cutter. Power hydraulic cutters are used to sever components and materials. The blades can have a range of size openings as well as blade shapes.

Spreader. Power hydraulic spreaders are used to spread or push components and materials apart (fig. 34–23). They also can be used to pull components and materials together.

Fig. 34–23. The photo displays a spreading tool and power unit.

Combination tool. Power hydraulic combination tools are literally a cutter and spreader put together (fig. 34–24). The cutting surface is on the inside of the spreader arms. This tool is good in certain applications because of its size and storage space on an apparatus. However, it is a compromise of both tools as far as use.

Fig. 34–24. A combination tool

Ram. Power hydraulic rams are tools used to push components or materials over a greater distance than a spreader (fig. 34–25). They also can be used to pull over a greater distance.

Fig. 34–25. A ram

Air tools

Air Chisel. An air-powered impact tool using a variety of bits to cut vehicle materials. This tool, usually the version used in an auto body or vehicle mechanic shop uses compressed air to move a piston forwards and sometimes backwards to hammer a bit that is inserted in the end of the tool.

Today we can see purpose-made rescue air chisels that use high pressures, upwards of 300 psi to impact with greater force on vehicle materials (figs. 34–26 and 34–27).

Fig. 34–26. The air tool displayed is an Ajax tool.

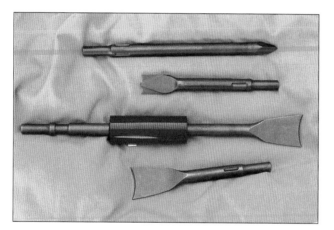

Fig. 34–27. A variety of Air chisel bits are good to have on hand to be used in many instances.

Impact wrench/gun. An air-powered wrench or gun that uses a socket to disassemble vehicle components (fig. 34–28).

Fig. 34–28. An impact wrench

Reciprocating saw. A reciprocating saw is a powered saw that uses a blade in a forwards/backwards motion to sever vehicle materials.

The saw's motive power usually comes from an electrical cord but can be battery powered or air powered today as well. The saw itself has a trigger to control the blade speed, speed setting for high or low or even orbital and an adjustable shoe to allow the operator to gain blade teeth access. While the motive power on saw is not usually a major issue blade choice can be. Purpose made extrication or demolition blades are the key factor in your choice for reciprocating saw use. The average bi-metal reciprocating saw blade is of little use for the extrication scene as it is not up to dealing with the kinds of vehicle materials we will encounter nor the environment it will be used in.

Key note of reciprocating saw use is "the saw stays at 0 MPH" basically meaning the saw stays stationary against the component you are severing and allowing the blade itself to do the work (figs. 34–29 and 34–30).

Fig. 34–29. Many rescuers have a reciprocating saw on their apparatus for a wide variety of rescue situations.

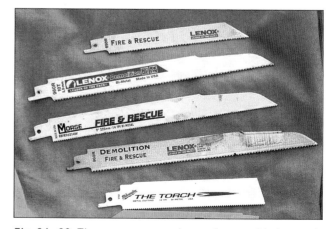

Fig. 34–30. There are many reciprocating saw blades used in today's fire/rescue service.

Stabilization equipment

Cribbing. This is the basis of ALL of stabilization tasks. Cribbing is usually cut into a certain length and dimensions such as 4 × 4 × 18 in. (10 × 10 × 46 cm), however, can come in many shapes and sizes (fig. 34–31). Cribbing can be made of wood or plastic and can be made into specialty devices such as step chocks or quick chocks to better facilitate our stabilization needs.

Cribbing will be our first tool for stabilization as it will fill the gaps between the vehicle and the ground, thus building the foundation for our tool evolutions to work from. Also, when we lift the vehicle, cribbing will secure and stabilize the vehicle by "following" that lifting device up (i.e., "lift an inch, crib an inch").

Fig. 34–31. Cribbing of various sizes

Tension buttress system. This stabilization adjunct greatly assists us when we are faced with a vehicle in a position other than on its wheels such being on its side, overturned or some sort of other precarious position. The concept of **tension buttress stabilization** is simple—we are going to build a right triangle against the vehicle and extending the vehicle's contact with the ground (fig. 34–32). We place a "strut" or brace at a 45-degree angle against the vehicle. Then we take ratchet strap from the base of the brace and extend it to the vehicle staying as low and straight as possible. We then tighten the strap thus putting tension into the brace.

There are many different devices on the market that employ this type of stabilization, such as ground pads and vehicle rescue struts by various manufacturers.

Fig. 34–32. Tension buttress systems

Ratchet strap. These nylon straps or belts that can be "ratcheted" or tightened can greatly assist our stabilization tasks (fig. 34–33). They come in a variety of sizes and strengths and relatively inexpensive. We can use these to tie vehicles together, used in tension buttress systems, hold back vehicle components such as a roof flap or a door, etc.

Fig. 34–33. Ratchet straps

Lifting bag. Lifting bags are an enclosed cell made of rubber or neoprene compounds reinforced with Kevlar that we will fill with compressed air to lift or spread objects (fig. 34–34). **Lifting bags** are made in a variety of sizes and shapes and utilize a variety of inflation pressures. These are usually grouped into either high

Vehicle Extrication

FIREFIGHTER II

Chapter 34

pressure lifting bags (100–124 psi [700–868 kPa]) or low pressure lifting bags (20–34 psi [140–238 kPa]). The lifting capability is directly related to contact area & inflation pressure. The lifting bag itself is just one part of the system, an air source, regulator, controller, and hoses complete the system.

Fig. 34–34. A lifting bag

Victim and rescuer protection equipment

Hard protection. **Hard protection** is a shatter-proof barrier empoyed when using tools in the occupant cell of the vehicle. These devices or cutting shields protect the patient and interior rescuer from flying debris and tool edges. In the past we used short boards and long spine boards for cutting shields but having a flexible shatter-proof barrier such as a Lexan™ or polycarbonate material shield is a better practice today. This is due to when severing high tensile strength reinforcements or even various vehicle components these can produce small fragments that have energy and can travel with force (fig. 34–35).

Fig. 34–35. There are various types of hard protection. This photo demonstrates how one type is used.

Soft protection. **Soft protection** is a barrier we will employ to protect the patient and interior rescuer when we remove glass or even as a barrier from the elements.

This device usually takes the form of a tarp, blanket, or specialty extrication blanket (fig. 34–36).

Fig. 34–36. It is important to place sharps cover between the glass to be broken and all persons in the vehicle.

Edge protection. A crashed vehicle can have quite a few sharp, jagged edges. Our tool evolutions will produce even more. Many of the vehicle materials can slice through our PPE readily so we will need to employ some sort of **edge protection** as we work.

Edge protection will cover those sharp edges and give us a safer and cleaner workspace. Edge protection can run from simple everyday items such are duct tape and spent firehose sections to purpose-made devices such as Kevlar blankets with sewn-in magnets (figs. 34–37 and 34–38).

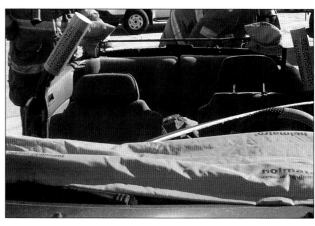

Fig. 34–37. It is very important to cover all sharp edges with some sharps covers.

Fig. 34–38. There are many ways to cover sharps from old hose sections to manufactured sharps covers.

MVC RESCUE OPERATIONAL CYCLE

Now let's take a look at our overall operational cycle at the MVC. Although many of the incidents to which we respond share many of the same components, MVCs have some unique issues all their own. The basic operational cycle includes the following steps:

- Size-up, initial actions, and scene management

- Hazard identification and control

- Vehicle stabilization and glass management

- Patient management

- Extrication evolutions

- Return to service

Now break down each part of the cycle. At every incident we provide for a continuous evaluation. Some steps may be necessary at a particular incident, and others may not. What we do or don't do—and what hazards are present—constantly change.

Our officers take charge, provide accountability, and develop sustained plans of action. Hazards are discovered and mitigated. Resources are requested to assist in mitigating the incident. We control the unwanted movement of the vehicles involved, create access to begin patient management, facilitate a path to remove our patient as we care for them, send the patient to the appropriate medical facility, and clear the highway before returning to service. The key here is to facilitate simultaneous operations on scene. That is what saves us precious time on scene.

Scene size-up, scene management, and initial actions

Arriving to an MVC can be overwhelming to even the most experienced incident commander. Motor vehicle crashes can be chaotic to say the least. People, multiple vehicles, and debris can make any country road or city street look like a combat zone. To properly size up one of these scenes there must be methodical approach in order to not miss any critical details; power lines, fuel leaks or multiple victims. This should all be part of the first arriving companies size up. In order to conduct a size up you must be able to look at the overall picture and not become too task oriented.

While not your responsibility as a Firefighter II, it is important to understand the responsibilities of the incident commander. These duties include the following:

1. Assume command and establish an Incident Management System

2. Conduct a size up identifying the number of victims, and their condition as well as their possibility of survival (manage the scene)

3. Recognize and manage common hazards: power lines, fuels, hazardous materials, etc.

4. Request additional resources as needed

5. Appoint a safety officer

Scene Size-up. The incident commander's size-up will establish the following:

- Number of vehicles

- Number of injuries

- Number of victims trapped

- Rapid patient assessment

- Condition and type of vehicle heavy damage to a SUV or compact sedan

- Hazards such as power lines, fuel leaks, or hazardous materials

Scene Management. As we do with hazmat incidents, we will create three zones in order to create a safe and organized scene. Once the incident has become organized and operations can begin, a circle should be established around the vehicle or vehicles involved. It is important to manage the scene by creating three "work zones": the hot, warm, and cold zones.

The extraction area ("hot zone"). The hot zone should extend out approximately 10–20 ft (3–6 m) in every direction or as large that is necessary. The only people allowed in the "hot zone" are the people directly involved in the extrication operation. Here again, our safety is key, we must ensure that the action circle is as free of tools and debris as possible. A tool staging area should be established in order to keep the action circle safe and keep personnel operating as efficiently as possible.

Tool staging area ("warm zone"). Establishing a staging area outside the "hot zone" will increase the overall effectiveness of the extrication. This is the place where only the rescuers supporting the extrication and patient removal will work. The tool staging area should be set up close to the vehicle involved with the extrication operation in order to ensure a place where tools can be found when needed, while ensuring a work zone with no trip hazards.

Setting up an organized work zone in the beginning of the incident can make or break the overall operation. Seconds count while trying to keep the extrication time to a minimum in order to work within the "golden hour."

Command post ("cold zone"). The "cold zone" is where the command post is established and where the PIO can work with the press. The "cold zone" is also the buffer between onlookers and the overall rescue operation.

Staging area. Having a staging area during the incident is the most effective way of managing resources. It keeps from having the incident commander bombarded with multiple units arriving simultaneously. Staging keeps any uncommitted apparatus and personnel available to assist in the extrication operation. Having a designated staging area can make the job of an IC much easier. It eliminates freelancing of incoming units as they are held back from the scene until requested. Staging also sets the tone for the incident by requiring members to stop and await instruction from the IC. This keeps the officer, from having to feel like they have to make up their own assignment in order to look busy. Just keep one thing in mind; it is easier to turn the companies back after the incident is over than it is to call for them when things start going bad.

Initial actions. Over time, think of how our response and the hazards we encounter have changed (figs. 34–39 and 34–40). The vehicle is still the dynamic hazard in the equation. However, think of what we need to look for: **supplemental restraint systems (SRSs)**, batteries and their subsequent locations, motive power, and vehicle glazing. Additionally, we must do this size-up

quickly and completely to ensure an effective and safe plan of action.

Fig 34–39. After securing the scene and hazards are mitigated, the victim is secured and a pathway is created to extricate the patient.

Fig. 34–40. Initial verbal patient contact must be made during the initial response size-up.

What initial actions will be taken? As we approach the vehicle, let's take in how the vehicle appears. What orientation is the vehicle: upright, on its side, or overturned? What kind of *stabilization* should we consider? How is the vehicle damaged? How much *crush* do you observe? This information should clue in potential *entrapment* and possible injuries. Do you see any deployed SRSs? Is there a fuel leak, presenting a fire hazard? We should make visual then verbal contact with the victims. Once we find the victims and establish contact, we should maintain it throughout the incident. We have assessed the scene and located and started to mitigate the hazards. When we are assured that the scene is safe, we must stabilize the vehicle to manage unwanted vehicle movement. This ensures a stable foundation for our space-making evolutions and minimizes movement to our patient.

Once we have the vehicle stabilized, we make access and begin hands-on victim management: airway, breathing, circulation (ABC); manual cervical spine (C-spine) management; cervical collar (C-collar); and oxygen (O$_2$) as indicated. Take a good look at the vehicle's interior. Where are any SRSs, deployed or undeployed? Is there damage to the interior? Is there any physical entrapment to our patient? Next we need to secure the vehicle's power.

Make sure that the vehicle is shut off, and remove the vehicle's keys. Remember, today's vehicles can have **proximity keys** that need to be more than 15 ft (4.5 m) from the vehicle, so it can't be accidentally started. Then disconnect the 12-volt battery. However, it may be hard to find the battery or even *batteries*, depending on the vehicle.

Remember, a substantial percentage of vehicles have the battery elsewhere than the engine compartment. But even there it can be hidden (fig. 34–41). Each vehicle has unique emergency procedures. However, if you do the following two actions they will disable the HV circuit and disarm or discharge the SRS system.

1. Turn the key to the OFF position, remove the key, and keep it AWAY from the vehicle.

2. Disconnect the 12V battery, both positive (+) and negative (–) cables.

Fig. 34–41. Batteries may be found in many locations such as under the rear seat, behind the front driver-side fender, under the floorboard, or, as in the BMW X3, in the trunk.

We need to make sure that the vehicle's power is secured for two important reasons. First, by shutting down the power, we start the process of draining the energy storage component of the SRS computer. This helps ensure our safety. Second, this also shuts down the high-voltage drive power in a **hybrid vehicle** (fig. 34–42). However, we also need to see what power accessories, such as windows and power seats, are in the vehicle before power is removed.

The officer in charge should document when power was shut down and document the items listed previously.

Fig. 34–42. This photo reveals the orange HV cable in the engine compartment of the 2007 Escape Hybrid.

How is our patient? Stable? What are the presented or potential injuries? And are they medically entrapped? Remember that we might need to make space to disentangle the patients, even if they are not physically pinned.

Do we need to extricate? Is the patient **physically entrapped** (encased in metal or pinned)? Consider the nature of the injuries and restricted space. Is the patient **medically entrapped**? Do we need to make space in order to prevent further injury by manipulating the patient during removal?

The officer in charge of the rescue effort must devise a tactical plan of action based on the information presented at the crash. The incident commander knows that the strategic goals at the MVC are life safety of our personnel and patient care of the injured. The tactical plan of action and various versions of it must account for many variables, much more than in the past, and must be performed much faster than ever before. We must protect ourselves and patients from traffic as well as evaluate scene hazards by following these steps:

- Scan the vehicle for damage, potential entrapment, and hazards.

- Find any patients and begin pre-hospital care for them.

- Stabilize the vehicle and then secure the vehicle's power.

- Evaluate the patient's injuries.

- Make space to disentangle the patient.

- Remove the patient to send to the appropriate medical facility.

Vehicle Extrication

FIREFIGHTER II

Chapter 34

- Check the equipment, service what is needed, and return to service.

So even if the MVC is a common emergency that we respond to regularly, how easy is it to manage today? Think about the present vehicle technology and various safety systems, as well as actual vehicle components, materials, and construction methodology. Let's take a close at these concerns first.

Hazard identification and control

We need to create a safe working environment, so we must identify hazards. Some hazards we might face are as follows:

- Fire hazard (every MVC has fire potential)
- Sharp objects
- SRSs (deployed/undeployed)
- Utilities
- Unstable objects
- Loads/cargo
- Fuel leakage
- Weather
- Crowds
- Hazardous materials
- Batteries (both *normal* automotive and HV drivetrain)
- Adequate lighting
- Debris
- Materials cut/displaced
- Rescuers themselves

Take a look at the list. There could very well be others. However, the thing to remember is that the vehicle itself is the most dynamic hazard we face. Scene hazards can and will be different each time, but they are pretty much consistent in how we mitigate them. The potential for fire exists at every MVC today because of fuels, electrical issues, and even the vehicle's materials. Vehicle power is our enemy. Although it can assist us with moving power seats, windows, doors, and the like, it can harbor issues that are not always visible or even considered, at times.

While protecting the occupants, safety systems such as air bags in various locations, ROPS, and even high-strength glass can hinder our operations. Even displaced vehicle components can be a hazard.

Now besides hazards, we must read the vehicle for potential injuries to our patients, such as possible physical or medical entrapment. Make and maintain contact with patients. Command needs to take our operational guidelines, develop a sustained plan of action, and put it into motion.

How do we do this rapidly? Start by taking a good windshield *snapshot* and then take a good 360-degree sweep around the incident. One sweep should be out far enough to capture all concerns of the incident and another should be in close to the vehicles. The officer then should also do a 360-degree sweep to prepare a plan accordingly. As we find hazards they should be relayed to the incident commander and all personnel on scene.

Our apparatus should be positioned effectively to work as well as protect the patients and personnel alike from traffic concerns.

PPE. We know you are first. Your crew or partner is second.

And the patient is third. MVC hazards are not what they used to be. We must use more caution than in the past; be more situationally aware than ever; and acquire more knowledge and, more importantly, up-to-date information on vehicles. Our tools generate hundreds of thousands of pounds of force and can injure us if we are not careful. Yet we need to work rapidly.

Many on-scene safety rules are common sense. Be aware of your surroundings. Do not get between tools and the vehicles. Always wear your PPE! (See fig. 34–43.) Use safety glasses or goggles for eye protection. Do not clear out windows with a gloved hand; use a tool. Verbalize your actions so the rest of your crew can hear what is going on.

Fig. 34–43. All rescuers must be wearing PPE to protect themselves from the many hazards associated with extrication incidents.

Always protect the patients with a barrier between them and whatever work is being done; the same goes for the interior rescuer. Cut wiring on a vehicle with a hand tool, not a power hydraulic cutter. Strip interior trim prior to cutting roof posts. Vehicle components we displace when removed are placed with the interior facing upwards because of possible undeployed safety systems.

Now what about fire protection? We must deploy a manned, charged hand line capable of at least 100 gpm (379 L/min) to provide adequate fire protection at an extrication scene.

Besides fuels, vehicle power and materials combined with vehicle fluids can make for a volatile mix. Thus, we must aggressively prepare for a potential fire at every MVC. Even with today's vehicles it is advantageous to have foam capability or a large quantity of water available because of these materials.

Vehicle Stabilization

Although neither glamorous nor high profile, vehicle stabilization is critical at an extrication scene and must be a consideration at all MVCs (fig. 34–44). Unwanted vehicle movement is a hazard at an MVC and needs to be addressed like any other scene hazard. Although most vehicles are upright and it is a very straightforward process to manage them, the vehicle in an unusual position is the situation that pushes the envelope and many times causes great stress. Additionally, as our tool evolutions remove and crash damage displaces vehicle components, the vehicle's structural integrity weakens.

Fig. 34–44. It is critical to stabilize any vehicle in which extrication is involved.

This weakening of the vehicle's structure can assist us, but it is vital to capture the vehicle and secure it on a foundation that is rock solid. Many tool evolutions require this foundation to work from. Think about it: How can you displace a dash if your vehicle is not sitting on a solid platform? So let's look at vehicle stabilization today in a variety of perspectives.

Vehicles. The vehicles of today and their construction affect every extrication effort, be it patient care, tool operations, or of course stabilization. The prevalent construction methodology of today is unibody construction. Basically the vehicle's framework is the occupant floor pan with subframes off the front and rear of the vehicle. The rest of the vehicle structure, including the glass, rounds out the structural integrity. In a crash, as vehicle components are damaged and displaced, the vehicle's strength weakens, as do the tool evolutions we perform to disentangle a patient. As we weaken the vehicle, the vehicle can twist, bend, and contort even if it is sitting on its wheels. This movement can trap doors that were previously open; add tension into glass, so when we break it, it *explodes* with magnified force; and even trap an occupants' feet and/or legs more by folding the footwell/firewall area. If we manage this movement by placing the vehicle on a *platform*, by securing it there we minimize the hazard, manage it better, and improve our tool evolutions.

OK, let's add another spin to the vehicles of today.

Consider ride height. Think about the ride height of today's vehicles or the distance between the underside of the vehicle and the ground. In the past most stabilization has been handled by step chocks (if the vehicle is upright). Step chocks are purpose-made cribbing blocks, built into a stair step fashion (fig. 34–45). But let's think about today's vehicle. Two of the most popular vehicle types today are SUVs and minivans. These vehicles tend to have a higher ground clearance (and higher center of gravity). Many times step chocks alone do not have enough height to properly capture and secure a vehicle alone; usually you must build a small box crib under the step chock for it to work well.

Fig. 34–45. A step chock

Conversely, many cars are much lower to the ground these days. In fact they are low enough that many times when we insert a step chock under the vehicle, we get only a few steps in and under the vehicle, leaving most of the step chock sticking outside the vehicle, becoming a trip hazard to us. Additionally, vehicles readily absorb energy when struck in a crash. This energy absorption principal can affect the vehicle by basically absorbing a certain amount of crash energy or **crush**, including the drivetrain and even tires; often the vehicle ends up sitting on the ground. How do we put a step chock under that? Well, you might ask why we bother, because it is sitting on the ground. However, we need to manage it and control ourselves to ensure it is mitigated properly. Last, add the addition of **run-flat tires** or tires with air monitoring/supplementation. How well can you deflate a run-flat tire today?

Tools and methodology. Cribbing, wedges, and step chocks make up our primary stabilization cache. We use cribbing of various sizes day in day out at a wide variety of incidents. Wedges fill up gaps and voids. Step chocks have been discussed a bit already. And all these are made of plastic as well as wood. However, I have mentioned the issue of both vehicle ride height and energy absorption principle, as well as the number of SUV and pickup trucks on the street as well. So I would like to take a look at some of the new and revisited concepts and tools for stabilization.

In the 1980s step chocks evolved from extrication challenges to assist with rapid stabilization of a vehicle on its wheels. Today's process has some additional options to help us. One of these is the rapid stair chock. This chock appears similar to a step chock but has a unique process to provide quick stabilization. It is a two-piece plastic device composed of a large chock but instead of stair steps it has an incline plane. The other part is a **traveling block** that has a mirrored incline plane to the large chock topped off with a large flat platform. Each incline plane has *teeth* that lock together when pressed. The rapid stair is placed much like a step chock, but the traveling block is placed near the base of the large stair. When the rapid stair is placed under the vehicle the traveling block is slid upward on the large stair, wedging the traveling block between the large stair and the underside of the vehicle.

This step maximizes contact between the vehicle underbody and the ground. This device makes for both rapid set up, stabilization, and securing of the vehicle.

Another type of chock is a **quick chock**. The quick chock is comprised of two pieces. The first piece is a platform of three or four 4 × 4–in. (10 × 10–cm) cribs, 18 in. (46 cm) long, screwed and glued together with a top plate of ½-in. (13-mm) plywood screwed on top of the platform. The second piece is a 6 × 6 or 4 × 6 in. (15 × 15 or 10 × 15 cm) wedge approximately 18 in. (46 cm) long. The quick chock is also placed under the vehicle like step chocks with the platform being the base and the wedge driven in between the platform and the vehicle underbody. This allows for rapid setup and a flexible approach. Depending on ride height and vehicle damage, you can add or subtract parts fill in space to stabilize.

Another idea that deserves a second visit is the lock blocks or Lego® block–type of cribbing. This crib made of plastic and manufactured by a variety of companies.

These cribs basically look like square or rectangular Lego-styled blocks of various heights that *nest* or lock together. These provide a large contact base, and because of various heights can be built and slid under the vehicle, placing a *column* of cribbing under the vehicle. Also, there are wedges that are also made to mesh with these blocks. All these adjuncts work well with the changes in vehicles; dynamics involved when these vehicles are crashed and interact with the tool operations as well as provide a more rapid and complete stabilization of vehicles upright on their wheels.

Also what about those vehicle tires? Think of the extremes we see out on the street today: from ultra-high performance tires that have almost no sidewall to the newest run-flat tires and the large sidewalls of SUV and pickup truck tires and then add aftermarket changes.

When we crib the vehicle, we capture the vehicle and its suspension, spreading that point of contact over a large area of the ground. However, depending on the vehicle's tires, we can still generate movement by *flexing* the tire sidewalls. Some sidewalls can be fairly large, so this movement can rock the vehicle off the platform we have created with our stabilization evolutions. This unwanted movement can be caused by accessing the vehicle or even tool evolutions. Remember, we need to minimize this unwanted movement in our patient care. So how do you deflate these tires? There are many options, but we want to strive for a controlled release of air from the tire. So stabbing the tire sidewall is not an advisable idea. Unscrewing the valve core from the stem, pulling or cutting valve stems, or using a purpose-made tire deflation tool are good choices.

Now let's look at stabilizing vehicles other than on their wheels. In the past, besides cribbing we relied on adjunct tools such as high-lift jacks, come-alongs, and even lifting bags to assist in our stabilization efforts. Although these items still give us options today, the trend today is the use of a technique called **tension buttress cribbing**, which resolves and mitigates stabilization of vehicles on their sides, overturned, or in an unusual situation. The concept is the placement of one or more right triangles against the vehicle. This shape ties a strut or brace with a ratchet strap to the vehicle, and then the strap is tensioned. This action basically extends the base of contact with the vehicle and the ground. There are many variations of this stabilization principal. From a simple homemade long crib with a ratchet strap, a section of cribbing with a manufactured base and strap combination, and crown or cap or a manufactured strut, base and strap combine all these to use the principal of tension buttress cribbing.

This principle allows us to *capture* a vehicle and hold it in place effectively and rapidly. This principal is also simple and straightforward to learn and apply in a variety of situations. The devices themselves also lend well to being stored on a variety of apparatus, and some have extensive accessories to enhance application options. Depending on vehicle orientation, this principal can be applied and vehicle stabilized in less than 2 minutes. Also depending on the device as the devices are adjusted they also can provide a source of controlled lift while stabilizing.

Some of the items mentioned chop away at that all-important scene time, making our extrications rapid and add in an enhanced margin of safety as well by making the vehicle we are working on rock solid.

We need to save time out there on the street so we can improve our patient's outcome. And this adds to our desire to always ensure a safe working environment. And remember, always recheck your cribbing and stabilization after every major action done on the vehicle (i.e., roof removal, side evolution, etc.).

Glass management. Primarily, we deal with two forms of glass or glazing in vehicles today. Laminated glass is found in windshields but is increasingly found in the side and rear windows as well. This type of glass is two layers of glass with a layer of plastic sandwiched in between the glass. This type of glass must be cut from the vehicle to be removed, which can be facilitated with an axe, a glass saw, or even a reciprocating saw by cutting the peripheral edge. This operation also produces glass dust, which is a respiratory hazard. Tempered glass usually found in side and rear windows when broken falls into small granular pieces. This breaking operation is facilitated by using an impact tool that imparts a large amount of force into a small concentrated area. We then clean out the window opening by pulling the glass onto the ground with a tool, not with our gloved hands.

Remember, today's vehicles can load the glass with energy from the crash, so when it's broken it can almost explode when that energy is released. We must protect our patient protective cover and even use hard protection to funnel glass pieces away from the patient. Make sure your own eye protection is in place, and you are wearing a dust mask to protect your airway from glass dust. Also, watch out for glass in hatches of vehicles. Not only might this glass become loaded with kinetic energy from the crash, but it might have up to four gas struts pushing on the glass and creating even more tension. When that glass is broken it might explode, and you might even have struts pushing out toward you.

Now let's think about managing all this broken and cut glass. Ideally, laminated glass we cut and remove should be folded slid in under the vehicle out of our way. If at all possible, tempered glass should be removed to the outside of the vehicle, away from our patient and the interior rescuer. However, in some vehicles, especially SUVs and minivans, we might encounter a lot of windows and/or a rather large window, which produce many glass particles.

A good practice is to sweep this under the vehicle, so we are not walking on it and our stabilization devices are on not on it either. Glass particles can be slippery, almost like marbles, when walked on.

Patient management

Vehicle rescue is a patient-care-driven skill. Although the focus of most education and training for mitigating issues at MVCs revolve around tool evolutions and vehicle concerns, let's consider patient care and considerations in the environment and our ability provide a better patient outcome. After all, the patient is the overall reason why rescue services are performed (fig. 34–46).

Fig. 34–46. Patient management begins as soon as the scene is safe enough to approach the vehicle and patient.

Good trauma care starts with good basic life support (BLS) care. Airway management, manual C-spine stabilization, application of C-collar, and oxygenation are basic BLS skills used in the initial care of a patient in a motor vehicle accident (MVA). Mass hemorrhage control comes next. It sounds simple and straightforward, but let's think about the many issues that affect our ability to provide the pre-hospital care necessary.

Think about how vehicles are configured today. Do you have enough room in the vehicle to perform basic patient care skills? Take a good look at how the dash and controls wrap around the driver and front passenger.

They form a cockpit-like configuration. How about seating? How many vehicles have bench seats, bucket seats, or racing styled seats? These make for tighter spaces, leaving less room and space for our equipment and ourselves (fig. 34–47).

Let's not forget about SRS items (fig. 34–48). We should observe space between those devices and ourselves, and our equipment as well. Visualize for a moment those spaces: frontal air bags, side impact air bags, and side curtain air bags. We even need to be aware of devices such as seat belt pretensioners and ROPS. Many times, the appropriate amount of space means displacing vehicle components. Consider packaging a patient in a **Kendrick extrication device (KED)** or similar device in today's cars, SUVs, and pickup trucks. Do you have the right amount of space to remove the patient with door access alone? Many mechanics of patient care and packaging taught today have been built around vehicles of the 1960s, 1970s, and even 1980s. Do they still apply in today's MVA environment? Recall that most education on access and patient removal revolves around either opening a door or displacing a roof. Although both are indeed viable, think of the additional variables that exist today. It is not as straightforward as it used to be.

Fig. 34–48. This photo shows typical SRS locations deployed and undeployed.

Take a good look at patient injuries and focus on where they occur. Do you see the same head and chest trauma that you used to see decades ago? How about injuries to the lower extremities and the pelvis? Why is that? There are a few paths here: frontal SRS, driver, and passenger side and front air bags and knee air bag systems, although sometimes causing injury, can and do protect occupants from injury sustained from the crash, even when seat belts are not used. When seat belts are not used, however, frontal air bags have a tendency to push the occupant down and under the dash. Now connect this with how vehicles are constructed and configured today. Vehicles are designed to absorb energy from the crash and crumple inward. If the vehicle structure is crushing in and the frontal air bags push the unrestrained occupants down, is there any wonder why we see such injuries? Even when the front occupants are restrained, the vehicle's structure can become crushed so badly in a high-energy crash that responders may see some of the same injury patterns (fig. 34–49).

Fig. 34–47. Smart cars, as shown here, are becoming more and more popular.

Fig. 34–49. The vehicle crumple zones are similar in most high-energy crashes.

Now how about side impact crashes? The same principle as with energy absorption still applies, but now the vehicle's structure is much stronger and more resistant to lateral forces than before; add to this side impact and side curtain air bags designed to protect vehicle occupants.

However, these days there is less space between the occupants and the impact. Although the various safety systems and the vehicle's construction and configuration do indeed effectively protect occupants from side impacts, think of how they hinder our work to provide care in the environment and package as well as extricate the patient from the wreck. We must strip interior trim prior to any sort of roof evolution today to avoiding cutting the gas generator for the side curtain air bags. We need to watch for side impact air bag systems when we force doors or perform side removal evolutions. Consider also vehicle construction material in these evolutions. We now end up pushing and prying against hardened materials for reinforcements and lightweight soft materials, such as enhanced and lightweight body skin alloys. Think of the necessary interactions to successfully mitigate the issues of both ends of the material spectrum.

To provide a better patient outcome, we must be aggressive when assessing MVCs and take a proactive approach in disentangling patient from the wreck and providing pre-hospital care. This requires us to perform simultaneous operations: patient care and space making, creating a pathway to remove that patient. EMS provides patient care in the same rescue real estate as the rescue team, which needs access to the exterior of the vehicle, especially the side between the wheels. EMS must be with the patient, comfortable working there, and keenly aware of the potential vehicle hazards as well. They must allow the rescue team to perform necessary tool evolutions to displace vehicle components to make appropriate space to remove the patient expediently.

The rescue team needs to be sharp. They must understand the issues and hazards involving the vehicle, their tools and evolutions, and how they will interact with the vehicle materials. Rescue personnel must also be aware of patient care considerations to make the best, safest, and most efficient pathway for that patient.

We need to provide prompt patient care simultaneously with our space-making efforts. Part of that requires us to get into the environment enhance patient care as well as create a rapid pathway for removal. A better patient outcome can be produced when these operations are fused together. Personnel operating tools and performing space-making evolutions must understand today's vehicle technology concerns, but so do EMS providers. As part of providing care, EMS providers operating in the environment interact with many vehicle hazards. They must have proper background knowledge of these concerns plus equip and use proper PPE for the environment in which they are working.

Patient care. We strive to perform proper pertinent patient care when we respond. We also focus on providing appropriate metal/material movement evolutions.

Yet how often do we combine these tasks, both in training and operationally? We need to practice these skills together, making the tempo of tasks at the MVC flow smoothly. The idea behind rescue real estate is that EMS must provide patient care in the environment (i.e., inside the vehicle) and the rescue team owns the vehicle's exterior, especially the vehicle's sides between the wheels. This concept allows both EMS and rescue team to operate together and enhance the speed of the rescue.

Next let's talk about patient care from our arrival on scene. Our visual survey approach should start our patient care process, even before we make contact. Reading the wreck, so to speak, gives us information about potential injuries, vehicle damage, and crush. Look at the windshield: Is it damaged or intact? Remember that frontal air bags cause damage to the windshield as part of their normal operating parameters. Check for interior damage: Are steering wheel and column intact? Are the air bags deployed? Don't forget side impact, side curtain, and knee bag systems. We should always try to approach our patients from the front of the vehicle. It is important to make visual contact first, keep their focus on us, and minimize movement prior to hands-on contact and C-spine management.

In addition to visual contact, we should attempt verbal contact. These contacts should be maintained throughout the rescue, ensuring communication to and from our patient as well as providing reassurance. This also provides a good presentation to our patient. Never leave the patient unless absolutely necessary. A good practice is having a rescuer maintain visual or verbal contact with our patient while another rescuer makes access to the vehicle to begin hands-on patient care.

After primary survey begins, ABCs are evaluated. Airway is a straightforward evaluation; with breathing remember to check quality as well as rate; for circulation, remember to look for and manage gross hemorrhage as needed.

C-spine management is next, both manual management and C-collar application. Oxygenation comes after that, managing proper fit and application of nonrebreather O_2 mask as warranted. Of note, the use of a nonrebreather O_2 mask on our patient also helps protect them from glass dust and other airborne particulates. As the rescue effort progresses, constantly reevaluate the patient for status changes, both good and bad. This information is communicated to the rescue team as well as the incident commander, facilitating appropriate decision making and operational planning. Communications are a key element no matter what part you play on scene, be it an EMS provider, tool operator, or incident commander.

This is just an overview of what basic care should be going on in the vehicle. However, depending on the skill level and ability of the caregivers on scene and what the patient needs, this care would be adjusted appropriately.

Space making/vehicle issues. Now let's take a look at the wreck so to speak. Even though we usually put tools to the vehicle to create a pathway for patient disentanglement, part of the concept of **space making** is to create space as required. That includes making space for us inside to work properly and safely. Re-proportion the inside of the vehicle as needed and performing strategic cutting operations. As vehicles become smaller, such operations are going to become the norm, not the exception.

There are many considerations. Displacing a roof off or away from a patient's head and/or face creates better airway control and C-spine management and has a positive psychological affect. How about cross-ramming the interior to make better access for us to work, to patients' lower extremities, or for that matter the patients themselves? The vehicles we have worked with in the past had plenty of space; with plenty of room for access, it was rarely necessary to consider such tool operations.

How about popping doors? Does such an operation have enough room in today's vehicles? Is a side removal more warranted these days? A side removal evolution is also many times easier than a door pop today as well. Why? With a door pop we are operating tools to force hardened components on both sides of the door. With a side removal we still need to force a latch. However, the balance we are working on usually has lesser strength materials. Remember that ultra-strength material reinforcements can now be found in the B-post areas as well (figs. 34–50 and 34–51).

Fig. 34–50. Rescuers are finding that the standard door pops are not enough space today.

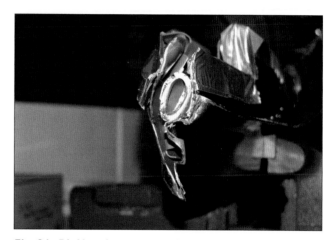

Fig. 34–51. Manufacturers are increasing the strength in vehicle supports such as B post with boron pipe reinforcement shown in this photo.

Also with this thread, let's add in strategic cutting. Many times today we are faced with dash areas that have dropped onto our patient's lower extremities as well as footwell areas that have folded up around these same extremities. Performing a fender evolution (strategically cutting the crumple or energy absorption zone) that severs the crumple or energy absorption area greatly helps the displacement of the dash and footwell. This same evolution also accesses the door hinges and the dash relief cut **cheat hole**. So by moving the fender as part of that evolution, we have helped with two other tool evolutions, thus saving time.

Remember, time saved helps produce better patient outcomes, especially if we can do these things on a consistent basis. If these operations must be provided often, we should go in with the notion to aggressively, proactively evaluate the wreck and set up for such evolutions, maybe even before we arrive on the scene or as part of our operational guidelines.

Note that you cannot forget that because we are cutting more often and materials are so much harder, it is increasingly important to provide a rigid barrier between our tool operation and the patient and interior rescuer. Also, the last roof post cut should be the one closest to the patient's head. Furthermore, don't forget to consider issues surrounding safety systems: air bags, seat belt pretensioner, or ROPSs. We should try to observe space between these systems and us and our patient. That also includes where we place our equipment.

Packaging/disentanglement.

Next let's talk about removing our patient. Once we have created our pathway, cover up any sharp edges (created with tool operations and by the crash) we must work around. If we can facilitate this, this should be done as tool work progresses.

Take a look at what the patient is sitting in. How much space is found in today's vehicle interiors? Then think about this: Many techniques to package patients evolved from vehicles of the 1960s, 1970s, and even 80s. Take a good hard look at how interiors of those vehicles are configured versus the interior of today's vehicles. Although bucket seats were available then, think of how those seats have evolved into the prevalent seat style today.

Also consider the equipment we use to package those patients. Many devices were also developed during the same time frame. Seats have become more like motorsport-styled racing seats. They are designed to hold the body firmly in the seat as the operator drives, regardless (relatively) of the situation at hand. However, how difficult is it to package a patient in a KED or similar device in these seats? Additionally, how much space is needed just to apply these devices, let alone disentangle the patient once it has been applied? Maybe we need to look long and hard at these devices. What else is out there in the market and how well would it work? These are more reasons to make space and proactively look at this concept. From casual observation it appears that many patients are removed directly from the vehicle onto a long spineboard (that is, a rapid takedown or extrication derived from **pre-hospital trauma life support [PHTLS]**). However, think about the criteria for such a maneuver. Rapid takedown or extrication focuses on an unstable trauma patient, a small percentage in the grand scheme of the MVC. Otherwise the KED-type device is warranted. So are these all unstable patients or are we cutting corners because of space issues? Maybe we need to revisit the concept of space making, incorporating the idea of being medically entrapped and planning in the appropriate amount of space to properly disentangle the patient.

Training/PPE. How are you preparing for an MVC today? Many of us are out in the salvage yards, training centers, and such practicing tool evolutions. We are reading trade publications; attending programs and presentations; and surfing the Internet to keep pace with current trends, issues, and concerns with vehicle technology. But how many of you are out setting up scenarios and solving the problem? Think about such training situations. Besides the obvious tool operations, think about what other situations to practice:

- Command and control issues and concerns

- Power management (finding batteries in alternate locations let alone multiple batteries)

- Finding potential SRS locations by using adhesive marking simulations (i.e., decals)

- Hazard control as well as looking for and managing possible scene and vehicle hazards

- Patient care and patient protection. Many times, we use training manikins to substitute for patients. Or we use our fellow rescuers as patients.

Are these substitutes suited for simulating patients? Sometimes the scenarios we set up are too hazardous for a live person, so a training manikin is warranted. And depending on where you are, regulatory constraints may not allow us to use a live person. But let's think about it for a moment. It is important to know and understand the various facets of interaction with that patient. And how else are you going to become comfortable and functional working in that vehicle unless it becomes a trained and practiced ability? One concept to help resolve the patient care skills is a medically trained and oriented *patient* or *casualty*. This concept is a crossover from the extrication challenges held in North America and around the world and from the International Centre for Emergency Techniques (ICET) in the Netherlands. These training events regularly use simulators to interact with the rescue team and EMS providers, which provides reality to the scenario in a controlled environment. One of the items of note that goes along with patient care is the EMS providers themselves. Although not operating tools, the EMS provider is a critical component at the MVC. Obviously, we are there to provide for a better patient outcome. However, often training, education, and personal protective equipment in relation to the MVC is a neglected area.

Although the facets and skills of patient management are practiced, how often is access in a wrecked vehicle practiced? How about vehicle technology concerns?

Because the EMS provider is in the vehicle working, aren't safety systems concerns just as important to them and the patient? Often, they are even closer to these systems than the tool operators. How many times do the EMS providers make access in the vehicle with minimal PPE? Will a helmet and maybe eye protection suffice today? Even if they have a bunker coat, does it fit or has it even been off the ambulance in weeks or months? Think of all the dynamic vehicle hazards of today and then add in working in an environment that doesn't always allow for quick exit. Shouldn't we be providing flash protection, proper head protection (helmet) that can stay on in the vehicle, proper gloves for the environment, and even respiratory protection from glass dust and other airborne particles? Take a good look at some the latest PPE that is on the market for EMS and technical rescue environments, and you will find some excellent solutions for these concerns.

Patient's rights. Patients have the right to a well-equipped, well-trained rescue effort. Think about that for a moment. It is not always about the best or newest tool out there. It is what you have and what you can and cannot do with it. Remember, vehicle rescue is a patient-care-driven skill. We are there to provide the best outcome we can in each and every response. This concept is carried through in all facets of our operations.

Plans are prepared with consideration for the vehicles we encounter today. We train as we operate: running rescue tools, providing patient care, operating a protective hoseline, or taking charge and mitigating the incident. Each part is important to providing a better patient outcome. Our equipment is always ready and prepared. We review our incidents to gain insight on the vehicles we work on, the hazards we face, and how we can enhance the patient's outcome.

Why do we extricate? Physical entrapment is what rescuers usually zero in on. The patient is physically trapped by a vehicle component, or we lack access to the patient (i.e., the doors are pinned). If our patients have relatively minor injuries and can move, they usually try and exit the vehicle prior to our arrival. In the past, most extrications revolved around such situations.

However, with the nature of vehicle construction and the vehicle's ability to absorb energy in a crash and crumple, think about another possibility that is actually more prevalent today: Vehicles are becoming smaller; add in the energy absorption principal; mix into this the way and position occupants actually sit today and the vehicle structure that surrounds them; finally, add into this

injuries themselves. We are faced with a smaller vehicle that is now crushed closer to the occupants, giving us less space to work on the patient, not to mention create a proper pathway to disentangle them. We call this situation medically entrapped. We might have access to the patient but not the space to properly care for them, let alone package and remove them. So how do we figure out who is medically entrapped whether we need to create space? Ask yourself these questions:

- Do we have adequate room to provide patient care?
- Do we have adequate room to work?
- Do we have adequate room to properly remove the patient?

If we cannot answer *yes* to those questions, we need to create space. Always try the simple things first: lift the tilt wheel, push the door farther back, and move the seat. In today's vehicles, even these simple things do not always give us the space we need.

Extrication evolutions

Roofs. Be they roof post cuts or relief cuts for a roof displacement, the big issue with all tool evolutions is the vehicle materials and construction. We have ultra-high strength reenforcements in the roof today. Some include boron steel, the same material as the door crash bar and beam.

We also can find side curtain air bag systems in the roof.

So before putting a cutting tool to the roof, displace the interior trim to look for side curtain air bag inflators and get a good look where the cut will be made (fig. 34–52).

Fig. 34–52. A reciprocating saw used to cut a C Post

The two primary tools we use for roof displacement is the power hydraulic cutter and the reciprocating saw or Sawzall®. These materials make the cutter twist and bend as it is weakened. Take a look at these cuts. The tool takes the path of least resistance, so anticipate where the cutter will go. Maybe even flip the tool over. Many times this methodology helps keep the cutter in line with the cut you wish to make, and it is even easier to cut. Make sure the blades go completely around the post and 90° to what is being cut. Don't forget to strip interior trim to locate the side curtain gas generators (this trim strip also allows us to look at the post and observe reinforcement locations and cut the post where it is weakest) (fig. 34–53).

Fig. 34–53. Always strip trim to find side curtain cylinder before cutting a roof or post.

Make sure there is a hard protection barrier between the tool and the patient and interior rescuer. This is even more important today; when hardened materials are cut, sometimes small hardened debris is created and sent flying about. When you make the cut, be sure the tool completely closes and makes the cut fully. Sometimes we have to wait for the second stage of the power unit to kick it to make the cut. Also, you must allow for foam reinforcement in the post to be compressed to make the cut. This means you need to visualize your cut, listen to the tool and its action as it cuts, and inspect the cut when the tool is removed to ensure it is complete. Always return the cutter blades to the tips touching position whenever a cut is complete for safety. With the reciprocating saw we must be sure the saw stays at 0 mph and the blade does the work. Don't try and saw with the saw itself. And like the cutter, make sure the blade is at a 90-degree angle to what's being cut. To minimize vibration make sure you are using a proper fire/rescue or demolition blade of 10 to 14 teeth per inch and that the shoe of the saw is tight against what is being cut. Remember to check the B-post for the adjustable seat

belt bracket; we don't want to cut through it because it is also made of hardened material. Also, remember the vehicle's structure has crash energy stored in it at times. When we sever roof posts, sometimes they snap or pop as this energy is released.

Besides a roof removal, you can also flap or section a roof depending on the size and damage as well as the patient location. Also, on certain vehicles such as SUVs and minivans, it might be a better option to flap or section the roof because of the size of roof structure in such vehicles. One tip to remember always: The last roof post cut is the one closest to the patient's head!

Doors. The basic tool evolution to gain access to a patient is usually a door displacement or pop. This evolution is the forcing of either the hinges or the latches of the door with a power hydraulic spreader. To begin this we must make a purchase point for our spreader tips to make better access and bite. We can use hand tools such as a Halligan tool, the spreader itself using the tips to grab and pinch the edge and pull it away. Or we can use the existing space made as a result of the crash itself.

When we pop doors today more times than not the door materials shred, tear, and rip apart, leaving us to try and spread another way or try and cut the door off. Why does this happen? Well, couple the light-weight door materials with high-strength latches and hinges and those *coupled* by the door crash beam and the whole tied together tighter than before because of vehicle construction and design and its inherent ability to move crash energy throughout the vehicle structure (figs. 34–54, 34–55, and 34–56).

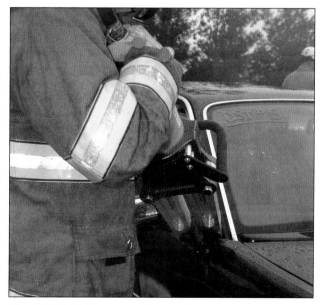

Fig. 34–54. Making a purchase point to remove the door at the hinge location

Fig. 34–55. Spreading the front of a door to remove the door by pulling the hinges off.

Fig. 34–56. Another angle of the purchase point.

Today's cutters make short work of cutting hinges and latches. Why not just cut them in the first place? Think about it. Cutting these items to remove the door creates much less stress and strain on the vehicle, which eases stress on the patient and the tool operator. The evolution actually goes faster and smoother, which also makes it safer for all as well. The key for this cutting is the ability to *visualize what you seek* (i.e., observe the hinge and or the latch) (figs. 34–57, 34–58, and 34–59). Ensure the cutter blades get completely around the hinge or latch. We don't want to place the tips of the cutter on the hinge, which causes the tool to be tip loaded and damages the blades.

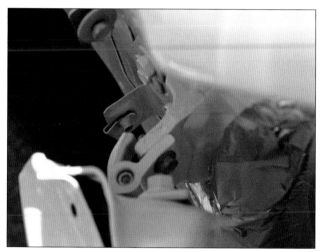

Fig. 34–57. Photo showing a top view of a door hinge

Fig. 34–58. Cutting the door hinge

Fig. 34–59. Cutting the door hinge—close-up

To do this, we need to make space between the door and vehicle body so we can get the blades in and around the objects to be cut. Watch tool reaction here as well, because often we are cutting square or rectangular material. This causes the cutter to swing or torque quickly, so we need to watch closely. Also, you ensure hard protection is in place between the tool work and the patient and interior rescuer. Now, like with roof post cuts, as we find wires in our path, remember to cut these with a hand cutter like medic shears or battery cable cutters. Why? Well, with more vehicles with side impact air bags in doors and side curtains in roof edges, these devices are affected by static electricity as well as pressure and shock (fig. 34–60).

Fig. 34–60. Debris with live SRS

Side evolutions. A thought to ponder: Do we make enough room when we perform a door pop? For patient access, yes. But what about patient removal? Not anymore. A side removal displacement works better and is usually easier than a door pop today. And because most vehicles have two real doors on each side, this configuration lends to a total side removal (figs. 34–61 and 34–62).

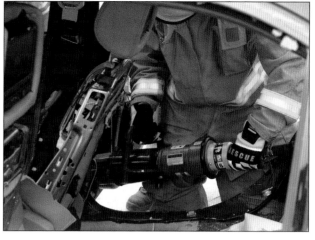

Fig. 34–61. After the trim is removed, begin creating a purchase point by tearing the B-post.

Fig. 34–62. With the purchase point made, use the spreaders to tear the B-post off.

As well as door pops, side removals call for power hydraulic cutters to use in relief cuts into the B-post. These areas are usually well reinforced, so cuts can be difficult. We need to displace trim at the base and top of the B-post to check for seat belt pretensioners as well as side curtain cylinders and the adjustable seat belt bracket. There are a variety of ways to facilitate a side removal, but one the most effective ways is to perform a **B-post tear**. We start off with forcing the latch on the back door. Open the door fully, in fact hyperextend the door forward a little.

Then taking the power hydraulic cutter make a relief cut into the base of the B-post, key point as deep and as straight as practical. Cut the top of the B-post as close to the roofline as possible. With the spreader place one tip or arm above the relief cut on the base of the B-post and the other tip or arm against where the floor rises vertically to meet the rear seat. Open the spreader. As the tool opens, the base of the B-post is pushed away from the vehicle's **rocker panel** and the relief cut tears forward.

As it does, the weakest points are the spot welds on the base of the B-post, they pop and the base of the roof post comes away. Sometimes the tear isn't straight and might have bits of metal still connected. Take the cutter and cut them away. Then the entire side swings out on the front door hinges.

Dash displacement. Now let's move onto dash displacement and strategic cutting (fig. 34–63). Here again we deal with newer, stronger alloys. Again we return to vehicle construction and its role in both energy absorption and those new hardened materials and dash reinforcement. We need to make appropriate relief cutting to raise the dash, but we also need to look deeper and strategically weaken the vehicle's structural integrity to displace the dash more effectively.

Fig. 34–63. After a relief cut is made, begin using a spreader to begin the end dash lift.

First, take a look at that strategic cutting (fig. 34–64). We want to make a vertical cut into the vehicle's **crumple** or **crush zone**. This isolates the dash area from the rest of the vehicle, especially when you make the relief cuts to actually displace the dash. We need to have a cutter that opens wide enough and has adequate power to make a deep cut into the crush zone and sever it completely. Many times we need to either cut and displace or spread and displace the fender to make that strategic cut.

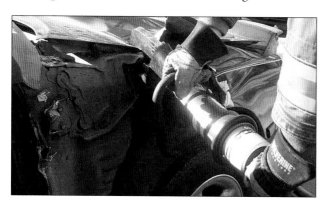

Fig. 34–64. Use the crumple zone cut to isolate the dash from the rest of the vehicle.

Next move onto the dash displacement. We need to make a relief cut to either roll or, preferably, lift the dash (figs. 34–65, 34–66, and 34–67). One of the areas to cheat for these cuts is the hole through which the wiring loom passes to the door.

Fig. 34–65. As relief cuts are made, pull the tab back.

Just pop that rubber boot out of the way and make a cut through both sides of the knockout hole area. To displace the dash either remove the roof or cut a 6-in. (150-mm) piece out of the A-post to allow dash travel as it is displaced. We then insert the tips of our power hydraulic spreader into our relief at a right angle to the side of the vehicle. We then open the spreader vertically. As the tool opens, the dash is lifted vertically and the footwell area is pushed down.

Fig. 34–66. Making a dash relief cut

Fig. 34–67. This photo displays dash lift relief cuts.

Fig. 34–69. A ram in place to perform a dash roll

Now as in the areas I have already discussed, ensure that cuts are complete by making sure the blades completely cross each other; and make sure you have that hard protection in place between the tool work and the patient and interior rescuer. The dash lift works so well because the dash reinforcement bar holds the dash and firewall integrity, and by applying force upward you can make that bar into a simple mechanical advantage (fig. 34–68).

Now let's take a look at the dash roll. For this evolution to work well, remove the roof first. Then make a relief cut at the base of the A-post under the bottom hinge of the front doors. Place a power hydraulic ram in the front door opening, from the base of the B-post to the A-post, roughly in the area of the top of the vehicle's dashboard. Make sure the base of the A-post is well cribbed, and have wedges ready to insert into the relief cuts as we operate the ram. As the ram is extended, the dash *rolls* upwards and forward. As it does, insert wedges into the relief cuts so if the ram slips the dash will not come back down (figs. 34–69 and 34–70).

Fig. 34–70. Notice how the dash rolls upward and forward.

Cutting first. Why thoughts on cutting? In the past rescuers didn't have a power hydraulic cutter capable of cutting hinges and latches, let alone hardened materials. We had enough power from our power hydraulic spreader to force apart these items, breaking them but the vehicle absorbed a large amount of kinetic energy in the process. Now we have a cutter that is capable and eager to do this job, but we have not always learned the proper technique to cut these items and materials well.

Take a look at the blades of the power hydraulic cutter. Straight blade cutters usually have two points of contact to grab the item to be cut. Curved blades usually have four points of contact for cutting. So think about that for a second. Curved blades usually pull the material they are cutting in toward the bottom of the blades where the highest amount of force is applied. Straight blade cutters cut like a pair of scissors; and with that sometimes the tool kicks back, and you need to reset the cutter back onto the area that was just gripped by the tool. Many times the straight blade produces more force and focused more at the base as well.

Fig. 34–68. This photo displays a side view of the dash lift end result.

Now look at some of the new cutters on the market. Some have a U-shaped blade design. This design also focuses whatever is in between the blades, pulling it into the base of the blades to maximize cutting force. However, the curved blade design allows the blade tips to grip whatever they cut. This helps hold the tool while it works. The straight blade works much the same way, but it is gripped by the inside of the blades as low as the cut will allow. The U shape does not, and you need to change your technique when cutting lighter weight materials. Hardened materials usually do not need this grip.

Return to service

Once the victims have been extricated and EMS personnel take them from the scene, it is important to maintain safety vigilance as the operation winds down. Ensure that proper safety precautions, such as handline protection, are maintained while the vehicles are removed from the scene. Maintain appropriate clearances from vehicles when they are being moved or uprighted; for example, tow truck cables have broken and injured responders during such activities.

Ensure that all equipment is retrieved on the scene, cleaned, and returned to its proper location on the apparatus (some equipment may need to be more thoroughly cleaned back at the firehouse). Take a thorough walk around the scene; do not leave anything behind. Take any damaged equipment out of service.

Remove damaged turnout gear from service. If it is contaminated with a victim's body fluids (blood, etc.) or motor vehicle fluids (gasoline, etc.), properly bag it and send it to an appropriate cleaning facility.

TOOL AND EQUIPMENT PREVENTATIVE MAINTENANCE

All of our equipment needs to be kept in a state of readiness. In order to do that, we must establish preventative maintenance (PM) procedures for our equipment.

This also helps with our training on equipment by familiarizing personnel on its operational needs and concerns. The equipment manufacturer many times has established the routine needs in the instruction manual or through

its dealer. However, the following are the key points in any PM program:

- After *every* use, inspect the tool for damage and service as needed (fuel, sharpen, etc)

- Routinely inspect all equipment, operate if needed, and document the inspection

- If a piece of equipment is damaged or inoperable, take it out of service and have it repaired by trained personnel, or if necessary, replaced it

- Keep required equipment fuels and fluids stocked and replenish as needed. Fuels should be stored with stabilizing solutions or kept fresh and not left in storage for extended periods of time

This routine inspection or tool checks can vary on recurrence, usually depending upon the equipment's usage, personnel shifts, etc. It is extremely important that *all* preventative maintenance and inspections are completely documented.

BEST PRACTICES FOR VEHICLE RESCUE

Command and control (C&C)

- Officer identifies any NVT (new vehicle technology) concerns/issues, communicates such information to the crew, and makes sure all personnel are aware of hazards.

- Officer documents NVT concerns.

Safety

- All personnel, especially those performing sizeup and evaluation, completely inspect vehicles for NVT concerns/hazards. When identified, such hazards are communicated to the rest of the crew.

- All personnel take appropriate caution and defensive measures when an NVT hazard is identified.

- Vehicle ignition is shut down and keys are removed from the vehicle.

- Battery and power is isolated and contained from the vehicle if possible and practical. Such power isolation is documented.

- Interior trims are displaced to evaluate if potential NVT hazards and concerns are present. If so, update the entire crew.

- Whenever using tools in the area of the passenger cell, place appropriate barriers between the patients and the crew members.

- When using cutting or spreading tools inside the occupant compartment, use of a good cutting shield (shatter proof barrier) is indicated.

- If part of departmental policy, use a postcrash AB protection device as indicated by hazard present.

- Debris with potential SRS devices are identified for wrecker and recovery personnel as well as all emergency personnel. Great care is taken with these objects.

Tool use and evolutions

- Observe a safe area in reference to observed NVT hazard or concerns.

- Use a high-quality proper cutting shield in conjunction with tool operations near a patient and/or crew personnel.

- Remove or displace interior trim prior to cutting roof posts or structure so there is no damage to any SRS inflation device.

- Pay attention to cutting material with possible NVT concerns with respective tools.

- Wear respiratory protection during glass management.

- Cut or sever wiring with a hand tool, not a power hydraulic cutter. Consider potential SRS reaction.

- Place debris from the vehicle into an identified debris pile, especially roof and doors. Be mindful of potential SRS reaction (i.e., doors placed with exterior panels faced down, interior facing upward).

QUESTIONS

1. What is the most dynamic hazard associated with responding to a motor vehicle crash? Why?

2. What is the purpose of positioning an apparatus in a "fend off" manner?

3. A vehicle's _____ can be found under the hood, in the trunk, or under the seat, depending on the manufacturer.

4. From the perspective of patient care, what does "reading the wreck" mean?

5. List two reasons for securing the vehicle's power.

6. Why might a traditional dash roll be less effective in today's vehicles as opposed to those of years past?

7. _____% of today's vehicles place the battery somewhere other than the engine compartment.

8. What are some of the hazards of cutting the inflation module for a side impact curtain?

9. What can rescuers do to determine presence and location of side impact curtains?

10. What kind of technique does this chapter offer in lieu of "popping a door"? Why?

11. In cutting roof posts, which post would you cut last?

Support of Technical Rescue Teams

by Larry Collins

This chapter provides required knowledge items for the following NFPA Standard 1001 Job Performance Requirements:

FFII 6.4.2

This chapter contains Skill Drills. When you see this icon, refer to your Skill Drill book for step-by-step instructions.

Fig. 35–1 Supporting technical rescue teams is an important responsibility for the Firefighter II.

OBJECTIVES

Upon completion of this chapter, you should be able to do the following:

- Describe the role of the Firefighter II in supporting technical rescue teams and the need to operate within the Firefighter II's level of training

- List and describe the proper procedures to be used during water rescue operations

- List and describe the proper procedures to be used during ice rescue operations

- List and describe the proper procedures to be used during mud and debris flow rescue operations

- List and describe the proper procedures to be used during structural collapse rescue operations

- Describe the placement considerations during structural collapse operations for fire service apparatus

- Describe the importance of proper staging of resources during technical rescue operations

- Identify the "victim search markings" approved by FEMA that are used during technical rescue operations

- List and describe the proper procedures to be used during void space rescue operations

- List and describe the proper procedures to be used during high-angle rescue operations

- List and describe the proper procedures to be used during trench and excavation collapse rescue operations

- Identify factors to consider for rescue operations during marine emergencies

- List and describe the proper procedures to be used during confined space rescue operations

- List and describe the proper procedures to be used during industrial machine operations

- List and describe the proper procedures to be used during elevator and escalator rescue operations

- Describe medical considerations that can impact rescue operations

- List and describe the proper procedures to be used during cave and tunnel rescue operations

- Describe what factors need to be considered during electrical emergencies

INTRODUCTION

According to National Fire Protection Association (NFPA) 1001, the Firefighter II should be prepared to help rescue companies and technical rescue teams safely manage water rescues, structural collapse rescue operations, trench and excavation collapse rescue, rescues in caves and tunnels, elevator and escalator emergencies, energized electrical line emergencies, high-angle rescues, motor vehicle entrapments, and industrial accidents.

In the sort of multitiered response system common in many progressive fire departments, the first-arriving engines, ladder/truck companies, and other first-responder units are tasked with sizing up the emergency and recognizing if it is a technical rescue. They then ascertain if there are immediate personnel safety hazards and react to them by establishing command; requesting additional resources as needed; stabilizing the scene (including isolating and denying entry to the public in the operational area); attempting immediate life-saving rescue within the limitations of their training and equip-

ment; and coordinating with the responding rescue company or technical rescue team to define, establish, and implement a definitive solution (rescue of the victim with safety measures for personnel). In this type of system, the first-due firefighters are responsible for supporting the rescue company or technical rescue team (see fig. 35–1).

FFII 6.4.2 Based on those goals, the Firefighter II should be capable of supporting rescue companies and technical rescue teams: establishing barriers, recognizing and retrieving rescue tools, understanding the hazards of rescue operations, and assisting as a member of the rescue team as needed and according to their SOPs.

Ropes and knots, vehicle extrication, and forcible entry are covered in other chapters this of textbook. This chapter concentrates on the remaining skills, knowledge, and abilities for the Firefighter II to support rescue companies and technical rescue teams. In all cases it's recommended that every Firefighter II supplement this information with formal didactic and manipulative training to develop and hone their skills and knowledge.

A final word about rescue: This chapter cannot describe every possible situation the Firefighter I and II may encounter. A sample of training requirements for some rescue companies is included in Appendix B to help illustrate the wide variety of rescue knowledge and skills that may be required for modern firefighters to get the job done. And even with this level of sophistication in the modern fire service, there are some situations for which a clear solution with designated protocols, procedures, and equipment may not be evident.

What would you do to resolve a similar rescue situation? Would you have the ability to adapt equipment, methods, and protocols from other disciplines into a seamless rescue operation? In addition to the basic skills covered in this chapter, it is the ability to innovate and take the best practices and use them to save lives in unusual emergencies that distinguishes top-grade firefighters and fire/rescue organizations. Starting with the skills and knowledge covered here, you will have an opportunity to take it to the next level of preparedness to manage the ever-expanding risks confronting modern firefighters.

LESSON FROM THE FIREGROUND

One example of this occurred as this chapter was written, when three men backed a truck up to the edge of a 70-ft-high (20-m) mountain of sand and began digging at the base to load their truck in a city next to this author's fire department jurisdiction. The men were buried when an entire slope of the mountain collapsed in an avalanche of sand.

The local fire department arrived to find one man buried to his chest, two others missing, and a 70-ft (20-m) high cornice of packed sand towering over their heads. They knew that the rest of the cliff could collapse at any moment, yet they also had a live victim trapped and talking to them in the collapse zone, with two other victims buried nearby.

Clearly, there was no way to erect protective shoring to stabilize the entire cliff in a timely manner, and entering the collapse zone would certainly place the lives of firefighters in jeopardy. It might be possible to bring in a trench box and employ an air knife and other trench/excavation rescue methods to this situation, and that's pretty much how the rescue was conducted, using lookouts, communication, escape routes, and safe zone (LCES) protocols adapted from wildland firefighting, using aerial ladders for lookouts and for moving equipment and personnel over the collapse zone (a method adapted from the New York City Fire Department [FDNY] structure collapse protocols), and other practices adapted from other rescue disciplines.

WATER RESCUE

Understanding conditions and hazards

A Firefighter II should have a clear understanding of the hazards of **moving water** and be able to recognize the conditions that occur during water rescue emergencies (fig. 35–2). When discussing directions with regard to rivers and other waterways, four basic terms are used:

1. **Upstream**

2. **Downstream**

3. **River right** (the right side of the river as one is looking downstream)

4. **River left** (the left side of the river as one is looking downstream)

Fig. 35–2. Water presents a wide array of hazards to firefighters and should be treated with great caution. (Win Henderson/FEMA)

Water rescue comes with one big advantage: The forces of moving water are governed by natural laws, which allows properly trained firefighters to predict what the water will do under specific conditions like gradients, obstacles, different water levels, and so forth. For example, water along the shore is slowed by friction with the sides, and water in the center typically moves faster. The deepest water is slowed by friction with the bottom, whereas the fastest water is often found near the surface, riding over the top of the slower current below. These are examples of **laminar flow** (fig. 35–3).

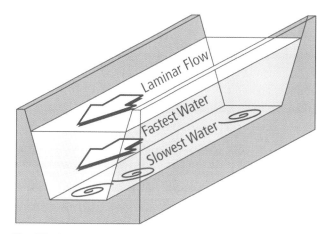

Fig. 35–3. The fastest water is usually found midstream just below the surface.

The slower moving water along the shore often circulates with water in the middle in a spiral motion, which we call a **helical flow**. The water along the shore is pulled to the middle and dives down, returning to shore along the bottom and then returning to the surface in a corkscrew motion.

When a river encounters a curve and strikes the shore at the outside of the curve, the water tends to carry away material and undermine the banks (unless they are lined with concrete or riprap). The water deflects off the outside bank and moves downhill once again in a straight line. Even if the current appears to make a graceful arcing change of direction, it's actually trying to move in a straight line until it's deflected by another curve or some sort of obstacle (fig. 35–4).

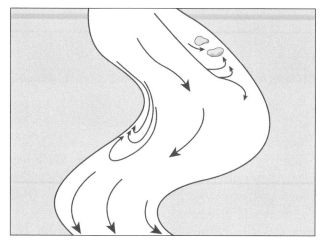

Fig. 35–4. Current flow and shore eddies on a curving stretch of waterway

The fastest moving water is found moving from the middle of the stream to the outside of the curve, then back to the middle (if the river straightens out). If there is a series of turns, the fastest water is found moving from the outside bank of the first turn to the outside bank of each subsequent turn. Conversely, the slowest water is found at the inside of the turn, just downstream of the bend. The difference between the fast and slow currents often creates an eddy effect in this area, known as a **shore eddy**. This can be used to escape the current, and it can also serve as a preplanned rescue point.

Eddies are calm areas separated from the main current flowing downstream. As the obstacle upstream of the eddy breaks the current, a gentle reversing current is often the result. This is an area where large amounts of floating debris (and victims) may be found and where tired rescuers may find a break from the main current.

The current water level has perhaps the greatest influence on the hydrology (and the look) of a waterway. Many small riffles indicate shallow water. This is particularly true where the current passes over gravel bars. As the water gets deeper, the surface tends to look smoother.

Submerged obstructions, such as rocks, cause a characteristic swelling on the surface just downstream of the obstacle. These bulges are an indication of objects below the surface (fig. 35–5).

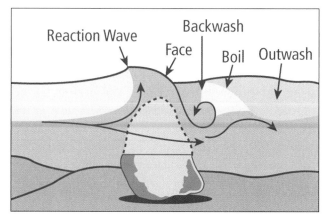

Fig. 35–5. How water level and its relationship to submerged objects affects the appearance of the surface of moving water.

The protruding object also causes the water to part into a V pointing upstream. We call this an **upstream V**. Swimmers approaching from upstream will see a V pointing upstream at them, indicating an obstruction to avoid. The downstream point of the eddy lines, where the main current resumes, is called the **eddy tail**. Where two eddy tails meet, or where the channel narrows and pushes the current together from both sides, a V pointing downstream forms. This is called a **downstream V**, and it's a good indicator of deeper, faster water with few obstacles (fig. 35–6).

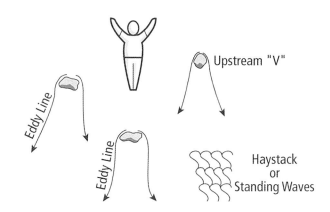

Fig. 35–6. Upstream Vs and downstream Vs

When water flows over a steep vertical drop, the force of the water creates a depression just downstream of the drop. The depression can get so deep that water normally flowing downstream is forced to move back upstream to fill the hole. Gravity has overcome the force of the current. This sets up a continuous recycling of the water we call a **hydraulic**, or **hole**.

The line where the recycling water is separated from the main downstream current is called the **boil line**, recognized for its constant white turbulent water that wells up from below and moves back upstream toward the drop. The turbulent white water found in a hydraulic is approximately 60% air. Even otherwise buoyant objects may not float well in white water. Hydraulics can be powerful enough to hold people and even boats for seconds, minutes, or hours. The configuration or shape of the drop has an effect on the holding power of a hole.

Low-head dams are artificial vertical or near-vertical drop structures that stretch across a waterway, resulting in a hydraulic from shore to shore with no downstream Vs, eddies, or other river features normally used to escape from fast moving water. People caught in the hydraulic of a low-head dam are forced down to the base of the dam, often through debris along the bottom, until they reach the boil line, where they may surface momentarily while being pulled back upstream to the face of the dam, where it happens all over again. Victims lucky enough to get to the side are often confronted with a high vertical sidewall. There is usually no escape unless rescue is available from shore (fig. 35–7).

The utmost caution is required any time firefighters are working near a low-head dam. Personnel should not enter the water upstream of low-head dams unless they are fully trained swiftwater rescue team members using precisely controlled means to prevent them from being swept over the falls (e.g., the use of helicopters, **inflatable rescue boats (IRB)** controlled by high-line systems, **live bait rescues**, or other positively controlled systems).

Fig. 35–7. Low-head dams should be treated with great caution as they can be potentially dangerous to responders.

A **strainer** is found where bridge abutments, trees, fencing, and other conditions that *strain out* floating objects (including people) from water moving past it. Naturally, strainers are dangerous because rescuers may become pinned against them in moving water.

Shallow, rocky areas are dangerous in fast-moving water, because rescuers trying to stand or walk across them may find an ankle wedged between submerged rocks (fig. 35–8). If the water is powerful enough, the victim may be forced under the water. The strength of the current and lack of adequate footing may prevent rescuers from reaching the victim in time. In these areas, it is best to crawl toward shore until the water is no longer deep enough to cause a problem, or unit an eddy is reached.

Mountainous areas, drainages, desert areas affected by intense monsoon storms, and regions affected by hurricanes are especially prone to flooding caused by heavy or excessive rainfall in a short period of time, or **flash flooding**.

Fig. 35–8. Water rescue responders must maintain a situational awareness to prevent being caught by debris or obstacles.

Support of Technical Rescue Teams

FIREFIGHTER II

Chapter 35

Water rescue equipment

Firefighters operating near moving water should use a minimum level of protection (fig. 35–9). **Personal flotation devices (PFDs)** used by fire departments typically are type III/V U.S. Coast Guard approved for use in rough water conditions. They are designed to keep an unconscious person upright and tilted slightly back in the water to maintain an open airway. A foam collar keeps the wearer's head out of the water. PFDs also provide limited torso protection. A whistle and rescue knife should be attached to a PFD. The whistle is for improved communication and warning. The knife is used if a victim or rescuer becomes tangled in rope or other debris and has a special blade for cutting rope safely and quickly.

Fig. 35–9. When working around moving water, responders must don appropriate personal protective equipment.

Structural firefighting helmets are generally not designed for use in water rescue situations. Although they provide excellent head protection from falling objects, they can cause more problems than they prevent when worn in moving water. The bill on the rear of structural firefighting helmets tends to catch water and create sufficient drag to rip the helmet off the wearer's head and tangle the chin strap around his neck. Rescue helmets provide full head protection and do not impair the wearer's head movement and vision. Rescue helmets differ from structure firefighting helmets in that they are lighter and do not have a rear bill.

Most fire department activities require safety shoes with steel toes. Water rescue incidents clearly have different footwear requirements. The use of heavy boots can be a hazard because they provide little traction on wet river banks. If firefighters fall into the water wearing boots, they are at a disadvantage from the start.

Firefighters typically have a pair of running shoes at their work site for participation in physical fitness programs. Running shoes are much more effective than work boots or turnout boots when working near moving water. They are the recommended footwear for many water rescue incidents if the alternative is turnout boots or work boots, which are slippery on wet shorelines and can impede the firefighter's ability to swim if water immersion occurs. There are also a wide variety of specialized rescue and outdoor recreation and water rescue footwear items available.

Fire and rescue agencies use a variety of devices as life floats. Some are commercially made, whereas others are as simple as inner tubes wrapped with **bungee cord** netting (fig. 35–10).

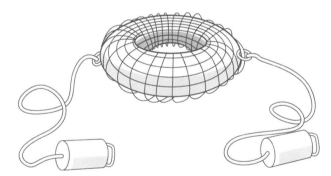

Fig. 35–10. Improvised flotation device with two throwbags for control

Hose inflators allow engine companies to inflate 2½-inch fire hose with air from SCBA bottles. The inflated hose is used in rescues from bridges, low-head dams, and other water rescue situations.

There is a great temptation for rescuers to tie themselves into rope systems when working in moving water. This may be inviting tragedy. If the line becomes tangled in debris, or if the rescuer is unable to get free of a static line, the rescuer can be forced to the bottom and drown. The effect is similar to a water skier who falls off his skis and attempts to hold onto the tow rope.

The Firefighter II should be prepared to support or conduct water rescues without actually entering the water. Throw bags are considered the single most versatile tool used for water rescue. They are similar in size and construction to the drop bags used for firefighting operations. One difference is the foam **flotation ring** sewn into the bottom of the bag (fig. 35–11). Rope stuffed into the float bags is a blend of nylon and polypropylene, which allows it to float on the surface.

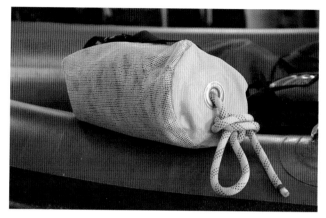

Fig. 35–11. Throw bags for water rescue include a foam flotation ring at the bottom of the bag (shown inside the metal grommet).

This rope is strong enough to haul victims to shore, but it is not generally rated as lifeline rope. When a victim is swept downstream, the quickest method of rescue is to toss the throwbag.

The average rescuer can normally toss the bag from 40 to 60 ft (12.2 to 18.3 m) using an underhand, overhand, or side arm throw. Once the victim grabs the floating drop bag, the rescuer begins to pull in the line. The victim moves toward shore in an arcing motion that resembles the swing of a pendulum. This is known as the **pendulum technique**, and it has a variety of other applications. Moving downstream as the rescuer pulls in the line helps keep the victim upstream of the rescuer, accentuating the pendulum effect.

Submerged victim rescues

When a victim is missing and presumed to be submerged in the ocean, lake, pond, or other body of water, the incident commander should immediately request a dive rescue team in addition to other units that may be responding. Helicopters are another good asset because helicopter crews viewing the scene from above can sometimes see submerged victims who are not visible to personnel working on the surface of the water. If conditions are reasonably safe, first responders may initiate a preliminary search. The following provides some guidelines to begin search operations until the arrival of a dive rescue team.

Search

Fire and rescue agencies are frequently called on to search for swimmers, boaters, fishermen, and others who have disappeared in lakes, ponds, the ocean, and other bodies of deep water. Searches under these conditions are usually hampered by lack of visibility caused by murky water or depth.

When a victim cannot be immediately spotted in deep water, the incident commander should ensure that the following objectives are met:

- Request one or more dive rescue teams and get their **estimated time of arrival (ETA)**
- Get a history of the victim's activities prior to disappearance
- Establish a **point last seen (PLS)**
- Request appropriate watercraft and helicopter resources for search

The PLS is commonly used as the basis for establishing a search perimeter. When responding to a search rescue in calm water, your only source of information about the victim's location may be witnesses on the shore. In some cases, firefighters or other rescuers approaching the victim may actually see the injured party go under water. In this event, your last visual contact with the victim is the PLS. When dive rescue teams arrive, give as much information as possible to assist them in locating the victim.

When you get to the PLS, begin a quick visual surface search to make sure you are in the proper location and the victim has not **popped up**. Attempt to get bearings from prominent geographical structures such as cliffs, points, mountains, or objects near the shore such as trees, buildings, and so on. Try to line up a couple of these points to *triangulate* the position.

Submerged vehicles

Firefighters responding to vehicles submerged in water are faced with several special problems ranging from the need for self-contained underwater breathing apparatus (SCUBA) or snorkeling gear, to powerful currents, to poor visibility in murky water. Add to that the inherent problems of vehicular damage resulting from collisions, the tendency of many automobiles to **turtle** (that is, turn upside down as they submerge and bury themselves in mud), air/water pressure differentials, failure of electrical systems, and other complications.

Fortunately, many passenger vehicles tend to float for several minutes (if there isn't severe damage) before submerging. Electrical windows and door unlocking systems tend to work long enough for conscious victims to make an escape before the auto goes below the surface. Many buses, however, tend to sink almost immediately.

One of the most important factors is the amount of impact a vehicle experienced before and after it entered the water. Regardless of the type and size of the vehicle, the amount of air trapped within is related to the amount of damage sustained as it hit the water (as well as whether or not the windows were down).

Low-speed crashes into water may present a greater chance for rescue than a high-speed crash off a bridge or cliff. It may be possible to make a surface before the vehicle sinks. The vehicle tends to tilt somewhat depending on where the center of gravity is. A front-engine car tends to tilt forward, exposing the rear window. This is ideal if the windows are rolled up because the tempered glass of the rear window shatters with a blow from a sharp object like an axe. A blow to one corner of the glass is most effective. Victims can then be pulled out through the rear window before the car goes down.

Rescue can be made from the side windows if the occupants are able to roll them down (or if they were down to begin with). Electric windows may still operate for a time even when a vehicle submerges. If the windows are inoperable or the victims are unconscious, the side windows (also tempered) can be shattered just like the rear window.

Windshields are notoriously difficult to break because of the lamination process that protects them from accidental breakage. Therefore, firefighters should avoid wasting valuable time trying to break a windshield unless there are no other options.

Note that the vehicle can suddenly tilt vertically and plunge to the bottom, and rescuers don't want to be climbing through a window (or in the car) when this happens. In fact, rescuers should move far away from the car if it appears to be ready to submerge. Rescuers do not want to be near such a large moving object in the water. Rescue efforts can continue once the vehicle has come to rest below the surface.

In deep or murky water, rescuers may have difficulty finding the vehicle. If it appears that the vehicle will submerge before victims can be removed, it may be possible to tie a rope to the bumper to guide rescuers to the vehicle after it goes to the bottom. A submerged vehicle leaves clues to its location. They may include a continuing trail of escaping air bubbles, an oil or gasoline slick, or articles floating to the surface. At night, headlights may be seen shining up from below.

In some cases it may be necessary to stabilize a submerged vehicle before rescue can proceed. The guide rope can be used for this purpose in calm water. Tying it to a bridge, tree, or other strong anchor at least lessens the chance of the vehicle moving and pinning a rescuer or victim. A winch, tow truck cable, or crane can follow the rope to provide additional stabilization. Other measures may be necessary under some conditions.

In some cases, the position of the vehicle can hinder rescue operations (i.e., a vehicle on its side with the exposed doors inoperable because of impact damage). Firefighters may need to move the vehicle to proceed with rescue operations. A tow truck, A-frame with a winch, or crane should be used when possible. If these devices are available, it may be possible to lift the vehicle to the surface. A heavy-duty crane may be able to pick the vehicle out of the water and set it on the shore. Obviously, this creates a much safer work environment for rescuers.

Under limited conditions, a rope hauling system could be used to move a vehicle in a life-and-death emergency. The human-powered pull raising system with a brake is one alternative. Mechanical advantage systems may also be used to move limited loads.

Doors may be difficult to open because of the pressure differential between the inside of the vehicle and the water. In some cases they may be opened when the vehicle fills with water, which equalizes the pressure. Doors may be difficult to open even when the vehicle is filled. Consider the possibility that the vehicle may have struck an object prior to going into the water. Previous impact, or even mud, may have jammed the doors.

ICE RESCUE

Ice rescues are complicated and dangerous because we have three main hazards to deal with:

1. Water is inherently dangerous to humans because it's a foreign environment in which we can't breath, and it robs the heat from our bodies.

2. Ice is a hard surface over the water that hides any danger below, and if broken through it may prevent us from getting back to the surface where the air is.

3. Cold is a rapid killer that gives victims just minutes and maybe only seconds to escape before their bodies fail and prevent them from climbing out.

The rules for ice rescue are much the same as for water rescue, emphasizing shore-based rescue first and contact rescue only if the shore-based rescue methods are not working (or not going to work because the victim is unconscious or out of reach). But they also take into account the other two main hazards: the hard ice over the water, which is subject to fracturing under the weight of rescuers, and the cold.

Firefighters responding to a potential ice rescue naturally want to be suiting up en route with appropriate gear to protect them from the cold. For many tailboard firefighters this still consists of bunker gear with an outer layer, such as a jacket, and should always include a PFD. Still, even with the cold, firefighters should try to avoid wearing turnouts near the water and when on the ice that might break under their weight. If you do fall in from the shoreline or go through the ice, you want to make a very quick escape, and bunker gear full of water only impedes that escape.

Ice rescue, dive, and some technical rescue teams responding to ice rescues typically wear thermal rescue suits built to maintain body temperature even during full immersion in ice water, and they train in that environment on a regular basis. Typically, other responding firefighters do not have that level of protection, so their tasks are limited to shore-based operations.

Thus, the order of the day for most firefighters includes tactics such as the following:

- Talking the victim through self-rescue

- Attempting to reach the victim with pike poles, rubbish hooks, or other reaching tools

- Tossing a rope or throw bag (or other tossing devices) to the victim in hopes of pulling the injured party out and over the ice

For specially trained firefighters with the proper equipment, the options expand further. The following are all tasks outside the realm of Firefighter II skills, so formal ice rescue training and the right equipment are required:

- Move across the ice using a commercial ice rescue platform and tools like ice picks (for traction) to

attempt a contact rescue, with ropes attached for retrieval by personnel on the shoreline

- Attempt the same type of maneuver using plywood to spread the weight, a ladder with fire hose weaved through the rungs and inflated with air, a large rescue board, or some other weight-spreading device, also with ropes for retrieval by shore-based personnel

- Attempt to plow and chop through the ice using an IRB with oars and/or with a motor, to reach the victim, also with retrieval lines attached for rapid return to shore

- Attempt a helicopter pick off with a firefighter lowered on a hoist cable or a short-haul system to capture and extract the victim

- For submerged victims, properly equipped dive rescue teams enter the icy water to search for and rescue the victim

- Other options that are beyond the Firefighter II level of skills, knowledge, and abilities

LESSON FROM THE FIREGROUND

We all know ice floats on water, and typically in the colder climates of North America it forms seasonally on lakes, ponds, and even some rivers. Ice rescues also happen in places you wouldn't normally expect. For example, during the writing of this chapter, a man died attempting to rescue children who broke through the ice in a lake in the 11,000-ft-high (3,352.8 m) San Gabriel Mountains right above Los Angeles (the lake is at approximately 6,500 ft [1981.2 m] elevation). According to witnesses, the children fell through the ice, and a desperate rescue effort was launched by citizens while the Los Angeles County Fire and Sheriff departments were called to respond. The would-be rescuer disappeared beneath the ice while helping the children, and he was never seen alive again. A specially equipped dive rescue team was required to locate and remove him.

MUD AND DEBRIS FLOW RESCUE OPERATIONS

Mud and debris flows are among the most hazardous emergencies because they combine some of the most dangerous characteristics of swiftwater, flash floods, and mud slides (fig. 35–12). They have been known to wipe out entire cities, kill thousands of people, and give little warning before leaving large areas buried under dozens of feet of mud and rocks. They are extremely dangerous because, unlike water, swimming in a mud and debris flow is generally not an option because of the load carried in the flow, which tends to batter victims and leave their bodies with severe physical trauma in addition to the drowning mechanism.

Fig. 35–12. Significant mud slides are rare events, but present a complex variety of hazards to emergency responders.

Mud and debris flows are common where steep mountains are affected by extreme erosion, earthquakes, volcanic action, fires, and other **debris flow producers**. Also, mud and debris flows and mud slides can sometimes create natural dams in canyons that are not visible (because of location, rain, darkness) to personnel working downstream. The only warning might be signs like water flow interruption. Failure of these natural dams can create a flash flood of mud, debris, trees, boulders, and vehicles with devastating consequences.

Wildfires are a particularly important trigger in some regions (especially the Western ranges), because after fire season come the winter rains (fig. 35–13). As the rain strikes, rocks and soil begin sliding off the mountain sides and falling into the canyon bottoms. Then, when intense downpours occur, tremendous amounts of debris can be quickly turned to a slurry and mobilized into a large flood of mud, rock, and water. The winters

following major wildfires require extra vigilance and planning to prepare for the possibility of damaging mud and debris flows.

Fig. 35–13. The winter season following a major wildfire is an opportune time for mud slides.

The Firefighter II should understand that mud and debris flows often arrive in multiple waves or surges. Firefighters attempting to rescue people from a mud and debris flow should assume they are in imminent danger of being affected by larger waves or surges of mud, water, and debris that can strike with little warning (fig. 35–14). Important considerations when arriving on the scene of a mud and debris flow include the following:

- Assess the condition of the incident site, including the stability of slopes, hazards like deep or moving mud and debris, shifting structures, and so forth. Is it a recently burned area? If so, an extra measure of precaution is required because the likelihood of multiple mud and debris flows is greatly increased.

- Establish upstream lookouts for *secondary* mud and debris flows or mud slides.

- Establish the following zones:

  - Exclusion zone: Within 100 ft (30.5 m) of the mud and debris flow and the debris field. Consider an exclusion zone of 500 to 1,000 ft (152.4 to 304.8 m) from debris flows on slopes 26° or greater.

  - Operational zone: To within 100 ft (30.5 m) from the edge of the flow

  - Support zone: At least 100 ft (30.5 m) from the outside edge of each side and the base of debris flow

- Strongly consider evacuation of all threatened areas to get people out of the potential path of secondary flows.

- Determine the potential number and location of victims (trapped and missing).

Fig. 35–14. Mud slides can occur in several "waves" and so emergency responders must be ever vigilant when operating in these conditions.

- Strategically stage resources in preparation for rescue operations in affected areas.

- Ensure all firefighters are wearing swiftwater personal protective equipment (PPE) or other gear appropriate for the conditions (personal flotation devices and other swiftwater gear is appropriate while active flows are occurring).

- Begin rescue operations (see the following text).

- Coordinate prehospital care and transportation.

Firefighters attempting rescue operations after a mud and debris flow should consider the following options to address common situations. Some tasks may exceed Firefighter I and II training. Others are in a gray area because they're nontraditional tasks, but they have been proven effective under mud and debris flow conditions, and they're mentioned here for context (fig. 35–15):

- Use front end loaders, bulldozers, helicopters, and other alternate-terrain units to transport personnel, equipment, and victims in and out of the incident site where fire apparatus generally cannot go.

- Breach the roofs and sides of buildings, and tunnel through debris to reach victims. Consider using trench shoring material and techniques to help secure areas around trapped/missing victims from further encroachment of mud and debris. It may be

necessary to use sandbags or other options to divert mud, debris, and water flow away from rescue sites.

- Create access over mud and quicksand-like conditions by placing plywood as ground pads or using air-inflated fire hose weaved through ladder rungs as a floating structure or inflatable rescue boats attached to rope systems to spread the weight of rescuers and equipment.

- Use helicopter hoist operations or heavy equipment to remove stranded victims.

- Lift and move heavy objects like trees or others pinning victims.

Fig. 35–15. Firefighters must be prepared to use conventional and unconventional methods to retrieve victims of mud slides.

- Pull victims out of mud by considering the following options:

  - Break the suction using reel lines blasting water into the mud (after harnessing the victim to gradually pull up the victim as suction is broken). Also use compressed air (air compressor lines from the **urban search and rescue [USAR]** apparatus, heavy lift rescue unit, or self-contained breathing apparatus [SCBA] bottles with lines) blasted into the mud with water.

  - Build an island of plywood around the victim on which an A-frame or tripod device can be established as a lifting system to slowly raise victim from the mud as suction is broken

STRUCTURE COLLAPSE OPERATIONS

Firefighters arriving at the scene of a structure collapse, regardless of the cause, typically need to complete the following tasks simultaneously: search for missing victims, prevent secondary collapse through shoring, rescue trapped victims, knock down fires from gas leaks and other causes, identify and react to possible hazardous material releases, and treat casualties (fig. 35–16). These are among the most challenging emergencies to which firefighters respond.

If the collapse is caused by a terrorist attack, **secondary devices** are a primary consideration. If it's a large earthquake, these simultaneous challenges may be multiplied many times over, across an entire city, county, or region. First-due firefighters may be on their own for an extended period of time before help arrives in the form of rescue companies, technical rescue teams, or regional/state/federal urban search and rescue task forces. So it's important to understand the basics of collapse emergencies and be prepared to take immediate action *and* assist rescue companies or technical rescue teams when they arrive.

Fig. 35–16. Managing structural collapse incidents involves a wide variety of tasks.

The modern fire and rescue service has developed a systematic approach to structure collapse emergencies. This approach is based on consensus of the most experienced fire departments and rescue organizations, and now it is recognized and used by international urban search and rescue teams in disasters around the world. The basis of this approach is the *five stages of collapse operations*. Regardless of the size or scope of a collapse

emergency or disaster, each particular collapse site can be effectively managed by conducting the five stages.

Stage 1: Response, size-up, and reconnaissance

When responding to a reported structure collapse, consider the possible causes and their associated hazards. Typical causes are fires, natural gas explosions, vehicles striking structures, construction accidents, mud slides, floods, avalanches, earthquakes, or bombs and other terrorist attacks. Each cause is often associated with particular hazards. Always consider the potential for explosion(s) caused by postcollapse gas leaks, secondary devices, and so on.

Size-up is critical on arrival (fig. 35–17). What is the extent of the affected area? Is it a single building or an entire neighborhood or city? Conduct an *eight-sided* size-up of the involved building(s) and the surrounding area. Check the top, bottom (basement), and four sides of the building; also check the air space around the building for falling hazards from adjacent structures and other aerial hazards. Finally, conduct a rotary sweep of the ground around the structure, looking for hazards like ruptured gas mains, broken water mains, railroad tracks, and other potential ground-level problems.

Fig. 35–17. When responding to structural collapse incidents, firefighters must consider how the collapse occurred and conduct a thorough size-up accordingly.

Consider factors that indicate how many victims might be trapped, and where they might be (fig. 35–18):

- What time of day was the collapse event?

- What day of the week?

- Is it a holiday?

- What is the building's occupancy type (e.g., offices and commercial versus residential or schools and hospitals)?

- What is the overall situation in the immediate area of the collapse?

- What is the condition of the area surrounding the actual collapse?

- What construction materials are involved?

- What is the pattern of collapse (pancake, lean-to floor collapse, lean-to cantilever, V-shape void, etc.) (fig. 35–19)?

- Are there basements or subterranean passageways?

- Are there heavy water tanks, air conditioning units, heating plants, communications, equipment, fuel tanks, or generators on the roof, upper levels, or in the basement?

- Is there heavy stock that can absorb water and cause secondary collapse after a fire?

- Are there vertical shafts for elevators and stairways?

- Is there a potential for secondary devices (possible terrorist attack)?

- Is there a hazardous materials (hazmat) problem?

- How many victims are missing or trapped?

- How many victims have been rescued and removed? From which locations?

- Is there an inventory of the occupants? Is there a seating chart for offices and schools?

- Is there an accounting of which occupants are missing, which ones have been accounted for, and which ones have left the area?

- Is there a need for additional resources?

- After finishing the size-up, the first-due unit typically names the incident, requests additional resources as needed, establishes command, and prepares to establish unified command when necessary.

Fig. 35–18. As always, life safety is the number one priority at structural collapse incidents.

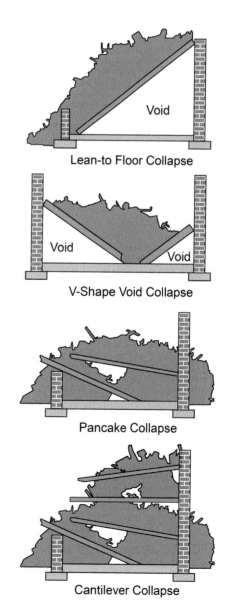

Fig. 35–19. Patterns of collapse

Apparatus placement. Just as in normal fireground operations, the placement of apparatus and vehicles is important for effectiveness of long-term operations. Parking heavy fire apparatus and bulky rescue vehicles in the wrong locations can complicate the situation by blocking access, placing personnel in the collapse zone, exposing units to the radiated heat of fires, preventing the deployment of supply hoselines and hand lines, preventing the proper placement of aerial ladders, and blocking egress and ingress for rescue companies, heavy equipment, and other critical resources. Some agencies have developed standard operating guidelines (SOGs) for collapse operations, including the placement of apparatus and personnel. The first-arriving officers must quickly develop a strategy for the incident, and the placement of apparatus should reflect and support those strategic decisions.

Aerial ladders/towers. Following the lead of FDNY, the SOGs for many progressive fire departments at structure collapse emergencies include the assignment of at least one tower ladder (aerial platform) at or near the front of the affected building(s). The ladder or platform is raised to an elevation from which a firefighter can observe the entire collapse zone and surrounding areas. This provides a constant lookout over the operational area, with particular emphasis on shifting walls, smoke or water appearing from cracks in walls, sagging roofs, and other signs of impending secondary collapse. The firefighter assigned as lookout should have the means to immediately notify everyone on the scene when signs of impending collapse or explosion are noted. This may include a handheld radio, an air horn, a whistle, or some other signaling device.

Firefighters should consider assigning tower ladders (aerial platforms) to different sides of the collapse zone to maximize the observation capabilities for lookouts (fig. 35–20).

Engine companies. To deal with the potential for fire and explosions occurring during collapse rescue operations, at least two sources of water should be secured for firefighting and protection of trapped victims and firefighters working to rescue them (fig. 35–21). Additional engines may be positioned to support effective water supply operations (relay pumping, shuttling water, etc.). Engine companies can also be used for personnel, cutting teams, medical teams, litter teams, and many other functions.

Fig. 35–20. Aerial ladders can be used at technical rescue incidents as observation towers.

Fig. 35–21. Engine companies will be responsible for fire suppression activities and supporting technical rescuers at structural collapse incidents.

Rescue companies and technical rescue teams. Rescue company and technical rescue team apparatus should be placed close to the collapse (but out of the collapse zone) where the heavy tools they carry can be put to the best use (fig. 35–22). Typically, this is directly in front of the collapse near an equipment pool.

Paramedic/advanced life support units and ambulances. Advanced life support and paramedic units and ambulances may be positioned in a **medical group** configuration, in a mass victim configuration, or somewhere else away from the collapse zone that allows victims to be triaged, treated, and transported in a timely manner.

Chief officers. If a chief officer vehicle is to be used as the command post, maintain a two-sided view of the incident, if possible, while remaining outside the collapse zone (fig. 35–23).

Fig. 35–22. Technical rescue apparatus should be placed as close to the collapsed structure as can safely be arranged to aid in tool accessibility.

Fig. 35–24. Numerous specialized apparatus are common at technical rescue incidents.

Fig. 35–23. Incident commanders should establish a command space in a conspicuous location where good visibility of the incident can be obtained.

Fig. 35–25. Although not normally considered emergency response equipment, heavy machinery is common at structural collapse and other technical rescue incidents.

Helicopters. Helicopters are useful for aerial assessments as well as transporting personnel, equipment, and victims in a collapse emergency. However, when personnel are working in an unstable collapse zone, helicopters should also be kept at a safe distance to reduce the noise at the scene, the chance of the rotor wash blowing loose material, blowing concrete dust and dirt, and other complications.

Specialized companies/units. The placement of lighting units, generator units, air compressor units, commercial vacuum trucks, and other specialized units is incident-specific (fig. 35–24).

Heavy equipment. Likewise, the placement of cranes, skip loaders, track hoes, bulldozers, dump trucks, and other heavy equipment is incident-specific (fig. 35–25). However, it's a good idea to leave room for these units to approach the collapse and potentially make direct access to the affected structure(s).

Staged resources. Staging areas should take into consideration such factors as ground vibration, debris-filled streets, the distance that equipment must be carried, and so forth.

Stage 2: Surface search and rescue

Stage 2 includes searching for victims while working from the exterior of the collapse, using whatever search means are available, and rescuing all victims trapped at or near the surface beneath *nonstructural* elements (desks, beds, bookcases, etc.). This includes firefighters pulling people from beneath bricks, walls, and roofing materials that are readily removable by hand, using hand tools, buckets, and other methods that don't require collapse rescue technical expertise and heavy equipment (fig. 35–26).

Victims found on top of the debris or lightly buried should be removed first. Initial rescue efforts should be directed at removing victims who can be seen or heard by firefighters combing the pile and calling out for victims (**hail searching**). The next efforts should be directed at reaching victims whose locations are known even if they cannot be *seen* or *heard*. It may be necessary for firefighters to use hand tools like saws, pike poles, pry bars, hammers, axes, and hydraulic jacks to lift or move debris off lightly trapped victims without cutting through or moving structural elements that might cause secondary collapse without proper shoring.

During stage 2 operations there is constant danger of causing secondary collapse or further crushing of trapped victims. Basic and advanced shoring systems may be necessary to prevent secondary collapse, and the Firefighter II may be requested to gather and assist with items such as hydraulic or pneumatic shoring; timbers and lumber for wood shoring; rescue air bags and jacks to lift, spread, and move items; and saws, coring tools, chain saws, and rescue saws with special blades to breach walls or cut through structural members and reinforced concrete slabs (fig. 35–27). The Firefighter II may be requested to help cut lumber for shoring, make wooden wedges, and associated tasks.

Fig. 35–26. Surface rescue is attempted on the outside of a structural collapse incident and involves rescue victims trapped beneath nonstructural elements.

Fig. 35–27. A chainsaw can assist rescuers in gaining access to victims trapped beneath collapse structures.

Firefighters should not allow passersby and relatives to scamper over the rubble pile (risking secondary collapse or the crushing of victims beneath), pick away indiscriminately at structural members (whose removal may precipitate secondary collapse), or use torches and other spark-generating tools without appropriate fire protection (because an out-of-control fire might render the victims **unsalvageable** and endanger the lives of firefighters and other rescuers).

Generally, during stage 1, 2, and 3 operations, firefighters should not allow heavy equipment to operate where surface rescue and void space search has yet to be conducted. Special caution and discipline are required whenever the use of heavy equipment is contemplated, especially when people may be trapped directly beneath the surface. Seek guidance from the rescue company or technical rescue team before putting heavy equipment to work in these areas.

Firefighters should avoid actions atop the collapse pile that could precipitate a secondary collapse event (fig. 35–28). Every move should be thought out by each person, because one wrong move could have devastating effects on people trapped beneath your feet, or adjacent to where you're standing and operating (including your coworkers).

Fig. 35–28. Firefighters operating on the surface of a structural collapse must be careful not to disturb the pile, as a secondary collapse can have deadly ramifications for victims.

Firefighters may be assigned to establish bucket brigades to remove debris from atop the collapse pile. If so, make use of designated open spaces to deposit debris where it is out of the way of emergency operations or where dump trucks, front-end loaders, and other equipment can later be used to move it to another site.

As the last readily accessible victims are removed, and as signs of additional victims trapped near the surface diminish, it's time to consider transitioning into stage 3 operations, or combining stage 2 and 3 operations. The incident commander typically makes this determination based on the conditions at hand, after considering reports from those doing the work and the recommendations of the most experienced rescuers.

Firefighters should use the nationally approved search marking system to identify buildings being searched as well as those where search has been completed (fig. 35–29). This helps prevent redundant searches by clearly identifying buildings and areas that have already been searched, and the results of those searches. It also includes a marking to indicate the stability of the structure itself and any special dangers, based on the assessment of the unit or team that searched it.

Fig. 35–29. Using a standardized marking system is important since it prevents duplication of effort and helps subsequent crews determine where further searching should continue.

This is critical information at a major collapse emergency, and even more important in a widespread collapse disaster where there may be many sites requiring search and rescue operations. These markings need to be readily identifiable from a distance, and typically they are made using fluorescent orange paint sprayed directly on the building, at the front or address side. Some newer systems use large stickers that can be applied to structure surfaces and marked appropriately.

The nationally approved search marking system is periodically updated by consensus by the major fire service and rescue agencies, including Federal Emergency Management Administration (FEMA) and state offices of emergency services, which have jurisdiction over disaster operations. It's recommended that firefighters consult their **field operations guides (FOG)** and updates from FEMA

and their state offices of emergency services for updates (fig. 35–30 to fig. 35–33).

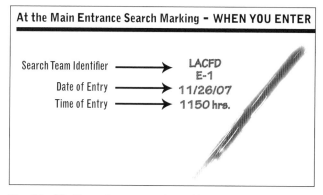

Fig. 35–30. Place these search markings at the main entrance when you enter.

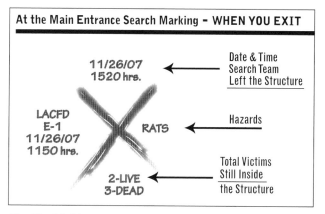

Fig. 35–31. Place these search markings at the main entrance when you exit.

Structure/Hazards Markings

Make a large (2' x 2') square box with orange spray paint on the outside of the main entrance to the structure. Put the date, time, hazardous material conditions and team or company identifier outside the box on the right hand side. This information can be made with a lumber marking device.

11/26/07
1310 hrs.
HM - nat. gas
LACFD-E-1

Structure is accessible and safe for search and rescue operations. Damage is minor with little danger of further collapse.

11/26/07
1310 hrs.
HM - none
LACFD-E-1

Structure is significantly damaged. Some areas are relatively safe, but other areas may need shoring, bracing, or removal of falling and collapse hazards.

11/26/07
1310 hrs.
HM - nat. gas
LACFD-E-1

Structure is not safe for search or rescue operations. May be subject to sudden additional collapse. Remote search ops may proceed at significant risk. If rescue ops are undertaken, safe haven areas and rapid evacuation routes should be created.

11/26/07
1310 hrs.
HM - nat. gas
LACFD-E-1

Arrow located next to a marking box indicates the direction to a safe entrance into the structure, should the marking box need to be made remote from the indicated entrance.

Fig. 35—32. Make these markings on the exterior of a structure so other firefighters will know the status of the building.

Interior Search Markings
– Each Room or Area

WHEN YOU ENTER   **WHEN YOU EXIT**

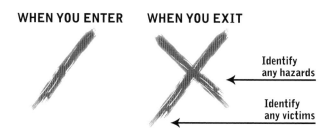

Identify any hazards

Identify any victims

Make a large (2' x 2') "V" with orange spray paint near the location of a potential victim. Mark the name of the search team or crew identifier in the top part of the "V" with paint or a lumber marker type device.

Paint a circle around the "V" when a potential victim is confirmed to be alive either visually, vocally, or hearing specific sounds that would indicate a high probability of a live victim. If more than one confirmed live victim, mark the total number of victims under the "V".

Paint a horizontal line through the middle of the "V" when a confirmed victim is determined to be deceased. If more than one confirmed deceased victim, mark the total number of victims under the "V". Use both the live and deceased victim marking symbols when a combination of live and deceased victims are determined to be in the same location.

Paint an "X" through the confirmed victim symbol after all the victim(s) have been removed from the specific location identified by the marking.

Arrow located next to a marking box indicates the direction to a safe entrance into the structure, should the marking box need to be made remote from the indicated entrance.

Fig. 35—33. Make these markings in each room or interior area as you search.

Stage 3: Void space search operations

After firefighters have removed all victims who are visible, lightly trapped, and readily reachable, the next step is to begin searching every potential **survivable void** space for victims, typically by breaching, shoring, creating, and crawling into void spaces, or using technical search devices or search dogs to check the voids (fig. 35–34).

Void space search is among the most dangerous tasks in collapse rescue operations and generally exceeds the Firefighter I and II skill level, because it requires physical entry into confined areas, establishing shoring, using search cameras and other technical search equipment, and other advanced skills. Firefighters voluntarily place themselves in harm's way to find victims. They break their way into, create, shore up, and crawl through confined areas that may be unstable. Typically, these tasks are conducted by firefighters and rescuers who have completed formal advanced rescue courses including confined-space rescue, shoring, rescue systems, and so forth. They are assigned to organize rescue companies or technical rescue teams. Nevertheless, first-due firefighters must be ready to assist rescue companies and technical rescue teams by providing shoring material, moving debris, providing lighting and other support, and so on (fig. 35–35).

In a large disaster, first-due firefighters may not have the luxury of rescue companies and technical rescue teams to assist them for many hours or even days. They may have to take extraordinary measures to attempt saving lives by performing tasks normally delegated to rescue specialists (fig. 35–36). So it's instructive to review these steps, with the caveat that they should be conducted with close supervision of experienced and properly trained officers, even in a disaster.

Under normal (nondisaster) conditions, the main role of the Firefighter II is to support these operations by gathering and delivering shoring materials and tools, cutting, breaching and lifting equipment, acting as litter teams and bucket brigades, and other associated tasks.

Fig. 35–35. Firefighters must be prepared to assist technical rescuers with gathering equipment and shoring materials for complex structural collapse incidents.

Fig. 35–36. Although it is preferred to have highly trained technical rescuers conduct structural collapse searches, under extraordinary circumstances firefighters may have to undertake these responsibilities.

Fig. 35–34. Searching for victims in void spaces occurs after all visible victims have been identified and removed.

In void space search we look for victims in void spaces and other places that could have afforded a reasonable chance of survival when the collapse occurred. The following places should be considered among the priorities for physical search:

- Between pancaked slabs

- In sheltered parts of structures with higher likelihood of surviving the collapse

- Beneath fallen walls

- In basements and other underground locations

- In voids beneath collapsed floors

- Beneath stairs and in stairwells

- Next to chimneys

- In spaces around sturdy furniture, safes, washing machines, desks, and so forth

- Rooms where access is difficult but where rooms have not yet collapsed

- Beneath other victims

It may be necessary for firefighters to assist rescue companies and technical rescue teams breaching walls, floors, roofs, and other structural elements, taking care not to further compromise the stability of the structure by cutting through **weight-bearing beams and columns**, and taking care to avoid cutting tensioned cables within concrete slabs (fig. 35–37).

Fig. 35–37. Assisting technical rescue teams by supporting breaching, breaking, and forcible entry operations is a common task for the firefighter.

Rescue companies and technical rescue teams often avoid breaching walls, as it may undermine the structural integrity of the building. They are trained to understand that it's generally safer to cut holes in floors and use the **vertical shaft** approach than to breach walls. If they must breach a wall or cut a floor, it's safer to cut a small hole first to ensure that they are not entering a hazardous area.

Rescue companies should understand that shoring should be used to support weakening walls or floors in the position they are found, *not* to restore structural elements to their original positions. Attempts to force beams or walls into place may cause secondary collapse. They should try to keep timber shoring as short as possible (the longer the timbers, the less weight they support and the more unstable the shoring system). Generally, any shoring that's been installed should *not* be removed once it is placed in an unstable building, because doing so may precipitate a secondary collapse from loss of support (fig. 35–38).

Fig. 35–38. Once supplemental shoring is placed in a building, it should not be removed, as it may cause secondary collapse.

In some situations, **engineered shoring**, designed and supervised by structural engineers (including FEMA USAR Task Force Structures Specialists), may be required. This was the case in the aftermath of the 1993 World Trade Center bombing, the Oklahoma City bombing, and the 9/11 attacks at the World Trade Center and the Pentagon.

Rescue company and technical rescue team (urban search and task forces, etc.) members probe all accessible void spaces and follow them when possible, looking for signs of trapped victims within the collapse zone. In some cases this is akin to following an earthquake fault or a narrow cave through the earth, exploiting existing weaknesses and openings in a journey that takes the searchers wherever the voids and cracks and faults lead.

As debris filling the cracks and voids is encountered, it is removed to allow forward movement, and shoring is placed where necessary to maintain stability for ingress and egress. Typically, the first-due firefighters in this system are positioned at the entrance to the opening to remove debris as it's passed out and hand requested materials to rescue companies or technical rescue team members working inside the voids.

Stage 4: Selected debris removal

After all known survivable void spaces are searched, **selective debris removal** begins. During this phase, rescue companies and technical rescue teams work with heavy equipment operators, structural engineers, construction and demolition contractors, and others to *delayer* the collapse zone (typically from top to bottom). As upper layers of the buildings are peeled away, additional void space search operations are generally conducted to check newly accessible parts of the building for potential survivors.

The role of first-due firefighters during stage 4 operations is similar to stage 3: Assist with moving equipment, debris, and victims as they are encountered, and providing support like hoselines for fire protection, cutting lumber for shoring, and so forth (fig. 35–39). It should be noted that sometimes the strategy of void space searches (stage 3) is alternated with selective debris removal (stage 4) until the entire collapse zone is dismantled and all victims are located and extracted (fig. 35–40).

Fig. 35–39. Removing debris from a collapsed structure to a safe area is a difficult task, but one common for the firefighter.

Fig. 35–40. Dismantling the collapse zone through selective debris removal is part of stage 4 operations.

Stage 5: General debris removal

Stage 5 generally signals the end of search and rescue operations and a transition to the **recovery phase**. These operations should be undertaken only after all other potential life-sustaining voids have been physically or technically explored for signs of victims, and after there is reasonable assurance that no survivors remain inside the collapse.

Even when stage 5 operations are proceeding, firefighters and other rescuers must remain alert to the possibility that some hidden parts of the collapse may reveal some sign of life (or life-sustaining conditions) that may require further exploration before the area is demolished and the rubble removed. They must also remain vigilant for human remains and potential evidence of the cause of the collapse, which helps identify and repatriate the deceased with their families and may assist in investigations into the factors that led to structural failure.

Stage 5 operations typically include the use of heavy equipment to bulldoze, demolish, and remove large sections of building as well as the debris piles left behind. This may involve hundreds of firefighters participating in the hand removal of tons of debris not accessible to heavy equipment. If victims are known or suspected to be missing, the search for deceased victims in the rubble continues through stage 5. It may be necessary to sift all the debris for evidence if the event is an act of terrorism, arson, or some other crime.

High-angle rescue operations

You've already learned about ropes and basic knots and how they're used in lowering and raising systems and for other purposes like maneuvering firefighting equipment (fig. 35–41). Now it's time to consider how you actually deal with **high-angle** rescues as a first-arriving firefighter, until the arrival of a rescue company or technical rescue team (at which point your responsibility is typically to assist these more highly trained rescuers).

Fig. 35—41. High-angle rescue operations can occur in a variety of locations including buildings, mountains and bridges.

Size-up. The following factors must be known about the incident, and this is information the first-arriving unit typically determines and communicates to the dispatch center and other incoming units:

- What is the exact location of the incident and the best access for ground units and helicopters?

- What is the victim's predicament (e.g., trapped or stranded on cliff, fallen to bottom, etc.)?

- Is victim able to assist in his or her rescue (e.g., injuries, age, frozen in place, etc.)?

- Is this a situation best handled by a helicopter hoist or short-haul operation, a high-angle rope rescue, or a combination of both?

- For vehicles over the side of a mountain road (possibly down a cliff or in a deep ravine), is there a vehicle extrication problem?

- What equipment is needed (battery-powered hydraulic rescue tools, battery-powered reciprocating saws, etc.)?

Rescue operations are as follows:

- Until the victim is rescued, rescue companies and technical rescue teams typically should not be canceled. Doing so may delay the rescue of the victim and may create unnecessary risks to firefighters.

- After ensuring firefighter safety, the next priority is to secure victims in danger of falling from their current position and securing vehicles in danger of rolling or falling. Typically, this is accomplished by having a first-responder firefighter rappel or be lowered over the side (by firefighters with appropriate training) to either place a harness and safety line on the victim, connect a rope or cable to the vehicle to prevent it from moving, or take some other stabilizing action that can quickly be accomplished. Sometimes this is done by specially trained firefighters lowered from a helicopter, with ground support by first-responder firefighters (fig. 35–42).

Fig. 35—42. An example of a situation where Firefighter IIs can assist rescue companies and teams

- The next priority is to treat the victim immediately for life-threatening conditions while waiting for the rescue company or technical rescue team to arrive, or for first-responding units to establish and insert a litter team and prepare to raise the victim and rescuers.

- If it has been determined that a rope system will be used, establish **bomb proof anchors** (fig. 35–43). If vehicles are used as an anchor, chalk the wheels and *remove the keys from the ignition.*

Fig. 35–43. Using vehicles as anchors for rope rescue systems is a common practice.

Fig. 35–44. For safety purposes, two ropes should be used when possible, especially when raising victims and/or rescuers.

- Any point where a rope passes, a stationary object must be padded with edge protection to prevent damage to the rope.

- Gloves, helmets, and other PPE should be worn by all firefighters engaged in the operation. At night, headlamps are recommended, and all members should carry at least one (preferably two) backup source of light. Goggles are mandatory around helicopters. Only NFPA-compliant harnesses or other approved rescue harnesses should be permitted for rescue operations.

- A helmet and goggles should also be provided for the victim and can be taken to the victim by the first rescuer or by the litter team.

- Whenever possible, two ropes should be used to lower the first rescuer over the side, and always when raising victims and rescuers (fig. 35–44). The second rope is the safety line. But single-line rappels are a common Firefighter II tactic, typically with some form of fall protection (prussic, bottom belay, etc.).

- In some cases (e.g., vertical cliffs where the rescuer is out of sight and requires split-second control to reach the victim), some fire departments allow the rescuer to **rappel** on the main line with a **safety line** attached to his sit harness and chest harness for fall protection.

- Non-rescue-rated cable winches are not recognized as appropriate raising systems.

- Even rescue-rated cable winches should be used judiciously. Caution is advised whenever the cable winch operator does not have *direct line-of-sight visual contact* with the rescuers (fig. 35–45). In the event of communication delay, it is possible for the powerful cable winch to pull rescuers through brush and rocks before the operator realizes it.

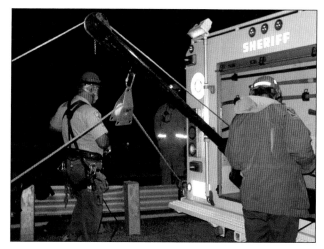

Fig. 35–45. Winch systems must be operated with care, especially when the operator does not have direct visual contact with the other rescuers.

- **Capstans**, machined that rotate to apply force to another used in conjunction with ropes or cabled winches, are often used in combination with winch systems to provide safety/belay capabilities for rescue loads, and so on (fig. 35–46).

Fig. 35–46. Capstans are used in combination with winch systems and offer additional rescue options.

- Injured victims should be securely packaged in a rescue litter bag before any raising or lowering operations.

- Solid rescue litters generally should be avoided for helicopter hoist or short haul operations because of their aerodynamic properties beneath Rotorwash®.

Potential jumper rescues. A twist on high-angle and rope rescues is in response to potential **jumpers** and hostage or crisis negotiation situations in high-risk environments like high rooftops, bridges, towers, and so forth. In many places, the primary responsibility of the fire department in these emergencies is to establish unified command with local law enforcement, provide safety support for the crisis negotiators, establish fall protection for the subject and potential rescuers, and be prepared to attempt a tactical rescue if conditions warrant.

Typically, law enforcement agencies are charged with primary responsibility for crisis negotiations and scene security. Fire department resources may be requested to be prepared to conduct or assist with tactical rescue operations of crisis negotiators, subjects, hostages, or even bystanders (fig. 35–47). Additionally, firefighters are frequently requested to stand by in case of injury to subjects, negotiators, law enforcement officers, or bystanders, or in case a fire erupts during the course of negotiations and/or tactical actions. Following are some considerations and actions that the Firefighter I and II should be aware of and capable of handling.

En route. Gather critical information from the dispatcher and mobile data terminal text descriptions that might indicate the nature of the incident (e.g., a possible jumper

perched on a tower, whether the subject appears to be armed, and so forth.)

Fig. 35–47. During jumper rescuers, the fire department should work with the police department under unified command to establish a common incident action plan.

- If available and appropriate for the situation, request a rescue fall cushion unit (e.g., stunt fall bags, carried by many U.S. fire department units) to respond to provide fall protection (fig. 35–48).

- Ensure law enforcement and crisis negotiators have been notified.

- Coordinate with the responding rescue company or technical rescue team via radio for any other needs.

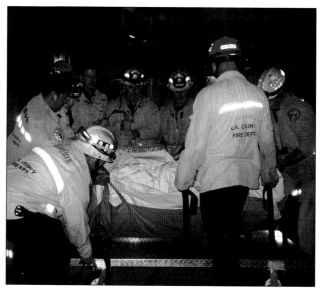

Fig. 35–48. If available, a fall rescue cushion can be a valuable resource at jumper incidents.

Fig. 35–49. A thorough size-up will determine the number of potential victims and other hazards that may exist to the victim or jumper.

Size-up. On arrival, firefighters should assess and report the following (fig. 35–49):

- The exact location of the incident and the best access and staging of fire department units and ambulances to maintain a secure perimeter around the operational area.

- The nature of the subject's predicament:
  - Is the subject injured?
  - If the subject falls or is dislodged from his present position, can the victim be injured?
  - Is the subject physically able to help exit to a safe location if compelled to do so?
  - Can the subject be convinced to move to a safer location/position until help arrives?
  - Are there hostages?
  - Are there obvious weapons?
  - Are there signs of explosive devices (including secondary devices), booby traps, or other unexpected factors that can cause injury or death to firefighters and negotiators?

  - What are the plans and needs of the crisis negotiators (fig. 35–50)?
  - Is there a need for fall bags or other special equipment like an aerial platform (fig. 35–51)?
  - Is there a need to provide physical protection (e.g., belay systems, harnesses, helmets) to crisis negotiators, the subject, and other involved parties?
  - Are negotiators in contact with the subject?

Fig. 35–50. Working with crisis negotiators is an essential requirement of firefighters operating at jumper incidents.

Fig. 35–51. Aerial platforms can be used to aid in gaining access to the jumper and providing for an added level of safety.

Operations.

- Until arrival of the rescue company or technical rescue team, firefighters can coordinate with law enforcement to develop the basic strategy (e.g., fall protection provided by the fire department, scene security provided by law enforcement, crisis negotiators make approach to the subject, fire department be prepared to attempt tactical rescue if necessary).

- It should be noted that some law enforcement crisis negotiations teams use a two-negotiator approach whereby one is the *talker* (to engage with the subject) and the other is the *shooter* in case the subject produces a weapon or takes action that threatens negotiators, firefighters, or the public. And other law enforcement officers on the scene may be compelled to take action if the subject becomes a threat. Firefighters should be aware of all these issues so they can stay out of the potential line of fire.

- If crisis negotiators aren't present when firefighters encounter a jumper, the incident commander should confer with law enforcement to determine how contact will be established, by whom, and under what parameters. Law enforcement typically has jurisdiction over crisis negotiations, although the fire department sometimes arrives first and must make a judgement about the situation (fig. 35–52). It's generally advisable to secure the scene, begin preparations for fall protection and tactical rescue, but wait for law enforcement to take the lead in negotiations. There are obviously exceptions, such as when it's obvious that the subject is serious about jumping, or if the subject is intent on doing harm to another person (such as holding a child). But before taking action, these questions must always be asked: If we take action, why are we doing it, and why now? What is the likely reaction of the subject if we take action? In most cases, the best solution is to wait, allow law enforcement to establish a presence, get crisis negotiators involved, and be prepared to provide fall protection and to conduct tactical rescue in a coordinated manner with law enforcement.

- Departments with rescue air cushion units can coordinate with law enforcement and crisis negotiators to establish fall protection.

Fig. 35–52. If crisis negotiators aren't present when firefighters contact a jumper, contact should still be established.

- Tactical rescue is generally assigned to the rescue company or technical rescue team, with support of the other firefighters (fig. 35–53). However, first-arriving firefighters should consider the potential need to initiate tactical rescue if conditions warrant.

Fig. 35–53. Tactical rescue is typically conducted by seasoned technical rescue personnel.

Marine emergencies. Marine emergencies refer to incidents in which victims are in need of rescue on the open sea, lakes, or wide rivers resulting from airplane crashes, capsized boats, boat collisions, boat fires, or other mishaps (fig. 35–54). In many areas where marine disasters are a hazard, progressive agencies have developed a coordinated response of all affected agencies (fire department, U.S. Coast Guard, law enforcement rescue, lifeguards, etc.) to get marine-based, air-based, and land-based fire/rescue/EMS units in place in a timely manner (fig. 35–55).

Fig. 35–54. Marine emergencies involve rescuing victims in the sea, lake, or other bodies of water.

Fig. 35–55. Using inflatable boats is a common practice for marine emergencies.

The goal of marine response is to deal with fires aboard ship or on the water, effect timely rescue and recovery, and provide rapid transportation to shore.

The role of firefighters may be to respond via fire boats, helicopters, engines, truck companies, paramedic squads, and other land-based units to provide medical care for injured victims transported to shore to assist in firefighting or hazmat operations or other tasks. Some tasks are outside the scope of Firefighter I and II, but it's worthy of consideration for firefighters who might respond to marine disasters to ensure they understand the plan, where they fit in, and what might be required of them.

Although the fire department often responds to off-shore search and rescue operations along the coast of the United States, ultimate responsibility is typically assigned to the local U.S. Coast Guard district as the Federal Search and Rescue Coordinator (SMC). However, the first on-scene agency (including fire departments) typically establishes incident command and then transfers command to the Coast Guard when they arrive. In some areas it has already been decided that unified command will be the order of the day for marine emergencies.

Trench and excavation collapse rescue. A common industrial accident resulting in fatalities is the collapse of trenches and excavations, generally at construction sites (fig. 35–56). These emergencies usually require rescue companies or technical rescue teams to provide specialized equipment, training, and rescuers to get the job done. However, first-arriving firefighters are a critical element; and they face dynamic and dangerous conditions requiring basic scene stabilization to prevent additional injuries or death as well as provide protection for trapped victims. Even as a tailboard firefighter without formal trench rescue training, it's important to understand the hazards of trench and excavation collapse and to perform basic scene stabilization. So let's review basic considerations for first-arriving firefighters.

Fig. 35–56. Trench and excavation emergencies involve rescuing victims from below grade earth cave-ins.

En route:

- Consider special information from the dispatchers (e.g., location is at a construction site, number of victims, special hazards) and potentially any preplanning that was done for the site in anticipation of potential collapse emergencies there.

- Consider the need for additional resources (shoring trailers, units equipped with **rescue vacuums**, hydrovac trucks, additional rescue companies, lighting, and utility companies are common requests for additional resources).

- Request law enforcement response to assist in traffic control and other vibration-elimination and crowd-control measures required for working trench collapse incidents.

On arrival:

- Park apparatus at a safe distance from the collapse to reduce potential of vibration causing secondary collapse. No vehicles should be within 50 ft (15 m) of the trench, except possibly the hydrovacs or aerial ladder if required for soil removal and as a high point for vertical extraction (fig. 35–57). Instruct other units to do the same.

Fig. 35–57. Emergency vehicles should be staged at least 50 ft away from trenches.

- Isolate and deny entry into unshored collapse areas and unshored trenches. Generally, rescuers should not enter unshored trenches and excavations more than 5 ft deep, even for rescue. Alternatives are to work from outside the collapse area: using reaching tools; lowering in breathing apparatus masks and other supplies to trapped victims; reaching in with shovels to remove soil; and using rescue vacuums, which have long handles designed to allow rescuers to work from outside the collapse. Once shoring is in place, rescuers can start working their way in.

- If construction workers, police, or others are digging in unshored areas to attempt rescue, they should be instructed to exit to a safe zone until adequate shoring can be placed. Failing to remove would-be rescuers from unshored areas risks additional victims if there is a secondary collapse, further complicating efforts. One alternative is to

convince them to help you begin the process of stabilizing the scene using plywood and/or timbers as edge protection around the trench or excavation, and moving **spoil piles** (excavated dirt) at least 2 ft (0.6 m) away from the edges.

- Remember that there is a greater than 50% chance of secondary trench excavation collapse following the original collapse. Isolating and denying entry until shoring is in place helps prevent additional victims if secondary collapse occurs.

- Eliminate vehicle traffic, heavy equipment, and other causes of vibrations. Shut them all down except critical items like hydrovac trucks. Don't forget to shut down nearby rail lines.

- Locate the site supervisor to determine potential number of victims, their last known locations, and site-specific hazards like utilities, pipelines, water mains, and so on. Keep the site supervisor with the incident commander; do not allow the site supervisor to venture off.

Rescue operations. Until the arrival of the rescue company or technical rescue team, first-arriving firefighters can begin performing the following tasks that keep them outside the unshored collapse zone.

- Place edge protection in the form of wooden planks, plywood sheeting, or even backboards around all edges of trench/excavation (figs. 35–58 and 35–59). This helps distribute weight of rescuers and eliminate secondary collapse.

- Consider options for helping to stabilize the area directly around the victim from secondary collapse. Examples can include the placement of ladders and plywood to prevent wall failure. Trench rescue operations eventually require the trench walls to be pressurized in the shoring process, and these skills and equipment are generally outside the realm of the Firefighter I and II.

- If the spoil pile is right on the edge of the trench, begin hand digging the pile back at least 2 ft (0.6 m) from the edge. Consider requesting an additional alarm for personnel for this labor-intensive work.

- If possible, lower a helmet and SCBA mask to the victim with instructions to don both to provide head and airway protection in the event of a secondary collapse.

Fig. 35–58. Edge protection along the sides of the trench can help distribute weight and prevent secondary collapse.

Fig. 35–59. Cutting and assembling lumber at a trench rescue incident will require several firefighters.

- If possible, lower a rope to the victim with instructions to tie it around the victim's body. This allows firefighters to trace the rope back to the victim in case of secondary collapse.

- *Do not* allow the use of backhoes or other heavy digging equipment to free victims.

- Ensure that water mains, electrical, and other utilities and pipelines are shut down in the collapse area.

- Develop an **equipment pool**, including buckets and rope, shovels, rope rescue equipment, and so forth.

- Assign companies to help the rescue company or technical rescue team unloading equipment on their arrival, and transport tools to the equipment pool.

- Develop a materials pool to store plywood, planks, and other shoring material.

- Consider potential high-angle rescue options in case rope systems are needed to *pick* the victim straight from the trench once the victim is freed (fig. 35–60).

Fig. 35–60. High-angle rescue techniques may have to be combined with the trench rescue operation in order to provide for safety and expedite victim removal.

- Approach trenches from the ends to avoid secondary collapse, and insert a ladder in each end. A ladder should be placed every 20 ft in the trench, for emergency escape by rescuers once they are working in the collapse zone with shoring in place.

- Be prepared for unanticipated release of water or other substances in the collapse zone, caused by rupturing pipes, ground movement, etc. (fig. 35–61). Have sump pumps and eductors positioned to insert at a moment's notice. A new device called the rescue vacuum (in combination with a Vactor or hydrovac truck) can rapidly remove water and mud flooding a collapsed trench. Also be prepared to quickly lower SCBA mask, dive mask, or some other source of emergency breathing air before the victim goes under water.

- When hazmat or rescue companies arrive, monitor the atmosphere in the collapse zone. Be mindful that apparatus still running may create carbon monoxide (CO) that could find its way into the trench or excavation.

Support of Technical Rescue Teams

FIREFIGHTER II

Chapter 35

Fig. 35–61. Controlling utilities, especially water service, is of extreme importance during trench operations.

- Precautionary ventilation into the trench and other collapse zones is advised under most circumstances to maintain a fresh atmosphere clear of contaminants. Consider the possible effects of dust from ventilation fans.

- Radio your findings to the incoming rescue company or technical rescue team.

- Identify the incident commander, operations section chief, rescue group supervisor, safety officer, shoring officer, cutting team, logistics, medical group, and other standard positions for these incidents based on your agency's standard protocols.

- For long-term entrapment with potential for crush syndrome, compartment syndrome, and trauma complications, consider requesting a medical director or physician to advise paramedics on treatment, and a helicopter to expedite patient transportation to trauma center after the victim is rescued.

Confined-space rescue. Confined-space rescue is one of the most difficult and dangerous duties, and most firefighters never encounter a true confined-space rescue in their careers. However, firefighters in some regions prone to confined-space conditions may respond to multiple rescues in this environment (fig. 35–62).

Firefighters assigned to active rescue companies and technical rescue teams may see multiple confined-space emergencies practically every year.

Fig. 35–62. Confined-space rescue can occur in industrial settings, transportation vessels, and a variety of other situations.

There is a relatively high incidence of mortality among would-be rescuers during confined-space emergencies. There are strict federal and state laws regulating who can attempt rescue in confined spaces, what equipment they require, and the level of rapid intervention that's necessary. Entry into confined spaces is typically beyond the scope of the Firefighter I and II, but it's important for all firefighters to understand the hazards and basic first-responder operations.

There are two major classifications of confined space: nonpermit spaces and permit spaces. A **nonpermit confined space** is any area that:

- Is large enough for an employee to bodily enter to perform work

- Has limited or restricted means of entry and egress, and

- Is not designed for continuous human occupancy

A **permit confined space** is any area meeting the aforementioned conditions, *and* the following additional hazards:

- Contains, or has a known potential to contain, a hazardous atmosphere

- Contains material with the potential for engulfment

- Has an internal configuration that may cause an occupant to become trapped or asphyxiated by inwardly converging walls, a floor that slopes and tapers to a smaller cross section, or other similar hazards

- Contains any other recognized serious safety or health hazard

Most firefighters recognize the following examples of confined spaces: storage tanks, pump wet wells, degreasers, sewers, manholes, tunnels, pits, tank trucks, underground vaults, boilers, silos, vessels, grain elevators, mixers, collapsed structures, storm drains, wastewater towers, railcar tanks, trenches, and excavations (fig. 35–63).

Fig. 35–64. Rescue company member making a confined space entry

Fig. 35–63. Underground vaults are merely one example of confined spaces.

A 1985 Occupational Safety and Health Administration (OSHA) study revealed that of 173 confined-space fatalities, 67 were in untested, oxygen-deficient atmospheres (fig. 35–64).[1] Even a small reduction of the oxygen percentage in a space indicates that some process is actively reducing it. It may be the result of consumption by fermentation, bacterial, or chemical reactions; absorption of hazardous substances into the lining of the shaft; displacement by other gases formed within the space or introduced from the outside; purging operations; oxidation from rusting steel casings or curing concrete shaft casings; or even as a result of respirations from a trapped victim, which can reduce the oxygen level to dangerous or lethal levels.

Combustible atmospheres may ignite or explode if a source of ignition is present or introduced. Combustible agents may include naturally occurring gases, vapors from liquids such as fuels or solvents, or dusts of combustible materials.

Combustibles are considered hazardous when they reach 10% of their lower explosive limits (LELs). Some flammable gases may flow into deep shafts naturally or be introduced by workers into the space accidentally. An oxygen-enriched atmosphere (23.5%+) increases the potential for ignition. Different gases, heavier or lighter than air, seek lower or higher levels (stratification) in a deep confined space such as a vertical shaft. **Desorption** of chemicals from the walls of the confined space may cause a combustible atmosphere. Dusts may become combustible in certain concentrations. Generally, dusts are considered possibly combustible when particulates reduce visibility to less than 5 ft, but some materials may reach dangerous concentrations long before that.

The atmosphere of a confined space might contain either immediate or delayed asphyxiates and irritants that can cause disease, illness, injury, or death. CO may be found where there has been incomplete combustion of fuels containing carbon and in decomposition of organic matter. CO is odorless, colorless, and may quickly reach lethal levels in a confined space and give little to no warning before a victim or rescuer is overcome. **Hydrogen sulfide** gas is produced from the natural decomposition of sulfur-bearing organic matter. Raw sewage can produce extremely high concentrations of hydrogen sulfide. Exposure to even very low concentrations may cause pulmonary complications, and exposure to higher concentrations rapidly cause unconsciousness and death. The rotten egg odor may not seem present at higher concentrations because it causes paralysis of the olfactory nerve, a double-whammy for rescuers and victims alike.

Mechanical hazards are another potential hazard, especially in industrial facilities. In these cases, power machines must be isolated and locked out/tagged out and a guard posted, if necessary, to prevent reactivation. Restrictive entry and egress openings often contribute to the dangers of confined space rescues (fig. 35–65).

Fig. 35–65. Restrictive ingress and egress openings in confined spaces present a large risk to rescuers.

Darkness is a key hazard in confined spaces. Getting lost in a shaft or tunnel without light is obviously something to be avoided. Consequently, three separate and intrinsically safe light sources are carried by each entry team member who enters a confined space. One option is for first-arriving firefighters to establish flood lighting and other high-intensity lighting outside a safe distance away to illuminate the confined space portal.

Engulfment and collapse is yet another potential hazard in confined spaces. Until proven otherwise, all confined space environments should be considered immediately dangerous to life and health (IDLH). As we have seen, the biggest danger is likely to be atmospheric. In every case it should be assumed that IDLH hazards exist throughout the duration of the entry.

In some cases, a dangerous situation might even be created by performing actual rescue work in a confined space. Certain cutting, shoring, and lifting operations carry a level of inherent danger in any environment. The danger is multiplied if these tasks must be performed in a confined space. For example, cutting metal with torches is accompanied by toxic by-product gases that might normally dissipate in open air. If this task is required to free a trapped worker in a confined space, it may lead to a concentration of gases which, combined with other atmospheric hazards, may quickly reach IDLH levels.

OSHA regulations require all employees (including fire and rescue personnel) who are expected to conduct or assist confined-space rescue to be protected from all existing and potential hazards through proper equip-ment, training, and procedures. Although only certified personnel typically enter confined spaces to attempt rescue, there are several actions that first-arriving firefighters can take before the rescue company or technical rescue team arrives to improve survivability for the victim(s) and rescuers.

En route. Consider special information from the dispatchers, as well as preplans for target hazards like refineries, industrial complexes, and other places prone to confined-space rescues.

The first-arriving firefighters set the stage for a successful operation if they can quickly determine what has happened, the potential number of victims, the probability of victim survival, and potential hazards to rescuers (fig. 35–66). Interview witnesses, the reporting party, and the site supervisor to obtain this information. If work was being conducted in the confined space, request the entry permit that contains information about the space, entrants, and potential hazards. Obtain material safety data sheets (MSDSs) if available. Victim information should include the number of entrants, their location, age, sex, general health, special health conditions, what they were doing in the space, and what protective clothing and equipment was being used.

Consider factors that indicate whether the situation is a potential rescue or a probable body recovery, based on the events that took place, the IDLH nature of the environment, the length of exposure, and other pertinent factors. The incident commanders and rescue company/ technical team officers must use a realistic risk-versus-benefit calculation when developing the incident action plan and rescue plan.

Fig. 35–66. First-arriving firefighters must gather as much information as possible from pre-incident surveys and on-site facility representatives.

Now first-responding firefighters can begin accomplishing the following goals that help the rescue company or technical rescue team when they arrive:

- Establish an **exclusion zone** (the danger zone into which no personnel should enter without suitable safety equipment). Typically, the exclusion zone is 50 ft (15 m) around the space opening at a minimum, but it is also based on the configuration of the incident site (fig 35–67).

- Establish an **operational zone** (a 100-ft [30.5-m] perimeter around the exclusion zone), in which primary and backup entry team operations and support operations are conducted (fig. 35–68). Outside the operational zone, establish an equipment pool, logistics, rehab, and entry control. Outside the perimeter of the incident, establish a zone for media, bystanders, and public officials who often gravitate toward extended deep shaft operations. Use fire line tape and other barriers. It may be necessary to request law enforcement to help secure the site and keep bystanders at a safe distance.

The initial efforts of first-arriving firefighters should generally be focused on preventing additional victims, establishing an effective incident command structure, and considering ways for rescuers to safely initiate *indirect* rescue operations without entering the confined space themselves, until arrival of the rescue company or technical rescue team.

Fig. 35–68. Equipment should be assembled and staged in the operational zone.

Indirect support for the victim may include tasks like lowering harnesses, wristlets, ropes, or even ladders to the victim for assisted self rescue, lowering SCBA to the victim to provide respiratory protection if he or she is conscious, lowering air hoses and fresh air blowers to ventilate the space and provide fresh air ventilation, and other tasks that assist the victim without placing rescuers inside the danger zone (figs. 35–69 and 35–70).

When a hazmat unit or other unit equipped with atmospheric monitoring equipment arrives, initial air sampling/monitoring can begin, conducted by personnel in the appropriate PPE (fig. 35–71).

Initial ventilation can also be conducted, which might make the atmosphere in the confined space more tenable for the victim until he can be rescued (fig. 35–72).

Fig. 35–67. An exclusion zone around the opening of a confined space is typically 50 ft (15.2 m), but may be modified based upon the specific situation.

Fig. 35–69. Firefighters may assist victims in self rescue by lowering ladders into a vertical confined space.

Support of Technical Rescue Teams

FIREFIGHTER II

Chapter 35

Fig. 35–70. Webbing can be lowered through a confined space opening, tied around the victim's hands and used to hoist them to safety.

Fig. 35–71. Monitoring of hazardous materials must occur in confined space rescue.

Fig. 35–72. Ventilation of the confined space can help alleviate a hazardous atmosphere and can make the space more tenable for the victim.

If there is machinery involved, or industrial processes that might introduce contaminants into the confined space, or electrical or other utility hazards, first responding firefighters can conduct **lockout/tagout** procedures as follows:

- All electrical, mechanical, or other forms of energy must be shut down and de-energized prior to entry. Post a firefighter to guard against someone turning the switches back on during the operation.

- All valves, switches, gates, or other control devices must be locked out with a keyed padlock and tag that reads, "DO NOT REMOVE. DO NOT TOUCH." Again, post a guard to make sure no one circumvents these safety measures.

- Hydraulic lines and pipelines must be blanked or blinded by disconnecting or using a provided steel plate blank out system. The system should then be bled to assure deactivation.

- The key should stay with the person who places the lock or be given to a responsible person, such as the safety officer, attendant, or incident commander.

- Locate a responsible party who is familiar with the systems to assist with this process and give any necessary technical advice about the facility and equipment.

As soon as a unit with atmospheric monitors arrives, at least a cursory assessment of the atmosphere around the opening can be attempted by personnel who are properly protected (SCBA, etc.) from potential hazardous atmosphere emanating from the confined space.

Entering a confined space with known or suspected IDLH hazards is generally not permissible unless personnel are trained in confined-space entry with appropriate recurrence. This is beyond the scope of the Firefighter I and II.

So, unless your department has a specific training program and policies that allow first-arriving firefighters to make limited confined-space entries, the next steps are to maintain a secure scene, continue ventilating and performing other tasks, maintain a medical group or team ready to treat victims (and any rescuers who get exposed by accident), and await the arrival of the rescue company or technical rescue team. Support them from that point forward.

All firefighters and rescuers operating near the opening to a vertical confined space (such as a shaft) should be properly harnessed and tied off (belayed) to prevent accidentally falling into the hole. Plywood or other decking material should be placed around dirt of soft edges to prevent collapse from point loading and to prevent objects and debris from being knocked into the space (fig. 35–73).

If it's technically a confined space that allows firefighters to operate safely from the outside to extract the victim (e.g., a person trapped in a chimney), firefighters can take actions within the scope of their training to safeguard and stabilize the victim and begin the process of extraction while operating from the outside (figs. 35–74 and

35–75). Even in some of the most basic of these rescues, however, specialized tools and training from the rescue company or technical rescue team may be required.

Fig. 35–73. Plywood or other decking material should be placed around the edges of the entrance.

Industrial and person-in-the-machine rescues.

Industrial rescue includes such a wide range of machinery, processes, and potential entrapment situations that they cannot all be covered here (fig. 35–76). For the purposes of this book we also include farming machines in this category, because the entrapment of people in machines has similarities regardless of whether it occurs in a factory or on a farm. There are some basic guiding principles that allow firefighters to effectively manage industrial entrapments of practically every shade.

Many progressive fire departments have developed **person-in-machine** tool kits on truck companies (and even some engine companies) that include items frequently used to extricate people from machines

Figs. 35–74 and 35–75. Even a person trapped inside a chimney constitutes a confined space rescue and may require specialized equipment.

(fig. 35–77). These kits may include cutting torches, whizzer saws, Dremel tools, small rescue air bags, fiber optic scopes, reciprocating saws, pneumatic rivet removers, assorted hand tools, and other items helpful in freeing people trapped in machinery.

Fig. 35–76. Industrial and machinery rescue involves extricating patients from heavy-duty machinery and processes.

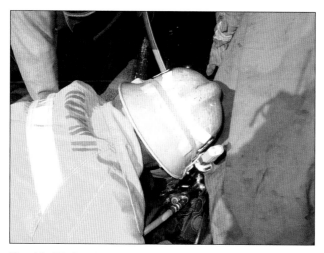

Fig. 35–77. Specialized tools kits may be assembled by departments to assist in extricating victims from known machinery hazards in their response area.

It should be reasonable to assume that your local rescue company or technical rescue team also has such a kit and/or an assortment of other tools that would be helpful in extricating victims from machinery (see Appendix A for a sample equipment inventory for rescue companies), but it's never a bad idea to make contact with them to familiarize yourself with their capabilities, limitations, operational guidelines, and expectations.

Let's consider actions that can be taken by first-arriving firefighters at the scene of industrial entrapment emergencies.

Conduct lockout/tagout procedures as follows:

- All electrical, mechanical, or other forms of energy must be shut down and de-energized prior to committing personnel to situations where machinery might suddenly move or become energized. Post a firefighter to guard against someone energizing machinery, switching the *on* button, or performing other acts that might endanger rescuers and the victim.

- All valves, switches, gates, or other control devices must be locked out with a keyed padlock and tag that indicates, "DO NOT REMOVE" or "DO NOT TOUCH." Again, post a guard to make sure no one circumvents these safety measures.

- Hydraulic lines and pipelines must be *blanked* or *blinded* by disconnecting piping or using a steel plate blank out system (usually provided). The system should then be bled to ensure deactivation.

- The key should stay with the person who places the lock or be given to a responsible person, such as the safety officer, attendant, or incident commander.

- Locate a responsible party familiar with the systems to assist with this process and to give any necessary technical advice about the facility and equipment.

First-arriving firefighters can also expedite the process of rescue by answering the following questions:

- What is the mechanism of entrapment? What was the person doing when trapped? What kind of machinery is it (what drives it, what does it do, how did it *grab* or trap the victim)?

- Has a similar mishap happened before, and how was it resolved?

- Can the mechanism be reversed safely in a way that will cause the least amount of pain, injury, and damage to the victim?

- Can the victim be freed by torching or cutting a chain, cutting a belt or band, disassembling a gear, and so forth (after securing the device from unwanted movement)?

- Can the machinery be carefully disassembled around the victim to free him?

- Can other elements of the machinery be torched, sliced, pried, peeled, moved, lifted, lowered, or otherwise manipulated to free the victim (fig. 35–78)?

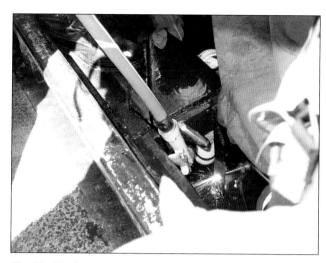

Fig. 35–78. A cutting torch can prove to be an effective way to extricate a victim trapped in heavy machinery.

- Is there someone at the site who knows how the machinery works, understands what happened, and might know what can be done to reverse it? If offsite, can this person be contacted and respond to the scene (with Code R escort by law enforcement if necessary)? As another alternative, is there some machinery or process expert available from another source (the manufacturer or another similar facility with the same machines), or even an instruction manual?

- Caution: Is there still **stored energy** in the mechanism (electrical, pneumatic, hydraulic, gravity, water, etc.) that could cause unwanted movement? If so, it's important to find a way to block or stop unwanted movement, such as chocking or wedging; or other alternatives such as securing with rope mechanical advantage systems, winch cables, chains, come-alongs, or heavily weighted devices or objects (fig. 35–79). For chocking and wedging, consider the possible need for materials heavier than normal wood cribbing and wedges, because some machines generate sufficient pressures to crush wood. If the mishap occurred in the middle of a machinery cycle, it may be necessary to prevent unwanted movement *in both directions*.

- What is the viability of the victim? Is the victim already pronounceable as dead on arrival (evisceration of the brain, lungs, or heart; incineration; decapitation; massive crushing; etc.)? Is the victim bleeding out quickly, being suffocated, in need of CPR but in a position that won't allow it, or in some other situation requiring

rapid and drastic action? Or is the victim trapped by one part of an appendage causing pain but not an immediately life-threatening situation as long as rescue is reasonably fast?

- Does the victim require immediate pain medication introduced by paramedics or a physician at the scene?

- Are advanced treatments such as surgery required for impending crush syndrome and other medical/trauma problems?

- Are other specialized tools and equipment required for extrication?

- Will vegetable oil, liquid soap, or some other nontoxic agent allow the victim's entrapped part to slip out of the machinery?

- Is field amputation possibly going to be required to free the victim? (If the answer is yes, immediately request the appropriate resources.)

- What are plans B and C if plan A doesn't work? (fig. 35–80).

Most questions can be answered by an experienced rescue firefighter in a matter of moments with the initial size-up, rapid patient assessment, and discussion with bystanders, the on-site supervisor, and of course the victim himself (fig. 35–81).

Fig. 35–79. Stabilizing and securing belts, pulleys, and other moving parts are essential since some machines may have trapped a victim during the middle of a cycle, thus presenting a further hazard as the person is freed.

Fig. 35–80. Firefighters must develop a back-up plan when dealing with complex machinery disentanglement situations.

Fig. 35–81. Conducting a proper scene size-up is always essential to a successful rescue incident.

First-arriving firefighters, however, do well to answer these questions while initiating basic stabilization operations (lockout/tagout, eliminating unwanted movement, dissipating stored energy, determining victim vitals and beginning appropriate medical treatment, requesting additional resources as needed, etc.).

It's also advisable to report conditions to dispatch and the other responding units to paint a picture of the victim's predicament and to dialogue with the on-scene expert and the responding rescue company or technical rescue team (via radio, cell phone, mobile data terminal [MDT], etc.) to determine the best course of action and consider other options.

Other initial efforts can include the following:

1. Establish an equipment pool close to the rescue site (with an equipment pool manager) to expedite the use of equipment and supplies likely to be needed off the responding apparatus.

2. Provide adequate lighting and ventilation.

3. Establish a medical group including immediate transportation to a trauma center or appropriate hospital once the victim is freed.

4. Begin basic efforts to free the person, constantly checking to see if the actions are improving the situation or making it worse and keeping alert for unexpected complications.

If the mechanism cannot be safely reversed without causing more damage or otherwise jeopardizing the victim and rescuers, it's typically necessary to begin disassembling the machinery in a strategic way or cutting it from around the victim. Be sure to employ basic precautions like fire extinguishers or protective hoselines for tactics like torching and cutting, providing spark and fire protection for the trapped victim (including, if necessary, a particulate mask, SCBA, or supplied air breathing apparatus), being careful of the use of oxygen in the presence of petroleum products and sparks.

Since firefighters respond to practically every rescue scenario imaginable, it's not unheard of for firefighters to be called on to enter hospital emergency rooms or surgery suites to attempt removal of items like stainless steel rings, case-hardened manacles, various types of rings, and practically anything else. This may require battery-powered tools or electric tools (instead of gas-powered tools that would obviously contaminate hospital atmospheres) and non-sparking tools that could be a hazard in close proximity to medical oxygen, and so on.

These cases may also require firefighters to scrub up and drape like doctors and nurses when conducting extrication operations in surgical suites, sometimes with victims under anesthesia. These are obviously unusual situations that typically require the rescue company or technical rescue team. But first-arriving firefighters may be the first to size up the situation and begin the process of setting up equipment pools, coordinating with hospital staff, communicating with the responding rescue company or technical rescue team, and so forth.

If the job is as simple as using a standard ring cutter to free a finger, typically the first-responding firefighters can complete that task. More complicated removal might require special tools or blades carried by truck companies, rescue companies, or technical rescue teams.

Elevator rescues. Many urban firefighters are accustomed to managing situations where victims are trapped in elevators, and increasing suburban and even rural areas are seeing multistory buildings outfitted with elevators, so it's no longer just an inner-city issue. The most common scenario is passengers in an elevator that stopped between floors caused by failure of power to the building or the elevator circuits or some sort of mechanical malfunction.

Other elevator emergencies involve repair technicians, building maintenance personnel, or kids engaged in the dangerous game known as **elevator hopping** who have become physically trapped and perhaps badly injured by an elevator.

Still other elevator rescues occur during the middle of larger incidents or disasters like high-rise fires, earthquakes, floods, hurricanes, or terrorist attacks, presenting firefighters with additional complications in already hectic situations. In the 1993 World Trade Center bombing, many elevator mechanics were required to help the FDNY locate and free people trapped in elevators at various elevations. Some mechanics were flown to the roof via helicopter and others were given SCBA that allowed them to operate in the smoky conditions within the building.

When terrorists attacked the World Trade Center on 9/11, dozens of people were trapped in elevators in the north tower (in some cases likely because of door restrictions—described below). In at least one case, firefighters reported they had to chop their way out of an elevator that became stuck between floors.

Even though elevator emergencies often end up being somewhat routine, they can be complicated and dangerous, and it's good for firefighters to be prepared to handle both.

When responding to a report of the most common type of elevator call (an occupied car stuck between floors), the first action is to ensure that dispatchers have requested the response of an elevator service mechanic (if it's known which company services that building). This information is ideally kept in fire department preattack plans for the building, and if that information is accessible to dispatchers, they can make that contact. If the information is unknown ahead of time, firefighters may have to arrive on scene and request the building manager or maintenance authorities to get the appropriate elevator repair company on the way. In any case, firefighters can never go wrong if they request and use the expertise of certified elevator mechanics.

On arrival, determine the general situation, the ETA of an elevator mechanic, and the type of elevator involved. Generally, there are two types of elevators: **traction elevators** (which use an electric motor and cable or "rope" to raise and lower the car) and **hydraulic elevators** (which use a piston under hydraulic pressure to raise and lower the car). Very tall buildings may have multiple sets of elevators staggered within. The control for traction elevators is found in the elevator **equipment room** at the top of the **hoistway** (fig. 35–82). Elevator cars travel within these hoistways (typically shafts), which contain hoistway doors at each floor level. The elevator cars themselves contain their own **car doors**.

Fig. 35–82. Motors for elevators are typically located in a designated elevator machinery room inside the building.

Buildings with up to five floors may have hydraulic elevator systems that rely on hydraulic pistons to lift and lower the cars, which are perched on the pistons. The power unit for hydraulic elevators is typically found at or near the lowest level.

Next, determine if there is any immediate life safety issue. For example, is there any sort of medical emergency among occupants of the elevator car? Is the lighting on with adequate ventilation, heating, or air conditioning? You can best determine that by making contact with the occupants using the elevator phone or intercom. To help determine the exact location of the car, this is a good time to ask what floor the indicator shows or what floor they recall the car passing (up or down) before it malfunctioned.

If there's no intercom or if it's out of service, firefighters can generally contact the occupants with direct voice contact talking through the elevator doors. Often, building maintenance or occupants have determined where the car is before firefighters arrive, having heard people calling for help within. Once contact is established, determine the condition of the occupants, reassure and calm them, and then act according to the urgency of the situation. You can also ask if occupants have cell phones that are getting service, and either call them directly with your cell phone, or have them call another specified phone that will allow you to talk with them.

If there is no contact, it is necessary to determine the car's location. Send firefighters to the **elevator pit** (to look up) or to the elevator equipment room (usually at roof level) to look down and determine the car's position (fig. 35–83). The location can then be confirmed by firefighters sent to the closest floor to visually check the car's position.

Fig. 35–83. Firefighters can determine the location of an elevator through the top or bottom of the elevator shaft.

This is also a good time to lockout/tagout the elevator system to prevent unwanted movement during the ensuing operations. A firefighter (preferably with a building maintenance person) can be assigned to go to the electrical panel (typically in the elevator equipment room) to de-energize the elevator. Just as in industrial rescues, post the lockout/tagout sign and use the kit's locks or assign the firefighter or a police officer, security guard, or a maintenance person to remain at the panel to ensure it's not energized until directed by the incident commander (fig. 35–84).

Fig. 35–84. Securing the electrical service to the elevator can be done by a trained firefighter or by a building maintenance person.

Some elevators can be freed (after ensuring the elevator banks were clear of personnel) by switching off and on the electrical switch to reset the system, allowing normal operation to proceed. Some elevators in certain buildings are known to have repeated problems with the electrical system that can be resolved in this way.

If your communication with the occupants indicates they are fine, the best action is often to await the arrival of the certified elevator repairman, who might be able to resolve the problem in minutes. Maintain contact with the occupants and continue to monitor their condition until the car can be moved to the appropriate landing for removal. You can reassure them by informing them that you can force doors and take other actions necessary to reach them if an emergency develops, but that under the current conditions the best strategy is to let the expert elevator mechanics free the car.

If information indicates there is some sort of medical or other emergency aboard the car that requires faster access, ascertain the ETA of an elevator mechanic, perform the lockout/tagout, and maintain communication with the occupants.

Work to open the hoistway door on the floor closest to the car. Firefighters can attempt opening these doors using hoistway door keys (sometimes stored in the equipment room, sometimes carried on engines, trucks, and rescue or other companies) (fig. 35–85). This takes some practice, and there are courses that firefighters can take to learn the best methods. Another option is to use a **Slim Jim** or another similar opening device to reach and manipulate the mechanism to open the door. If these options aren't available, yet another method is to force the hoistway door using wedges, irons, rabbit tools, hydraulic spreaders, or even small rescue air bags. Naturally, damage to the hoistway door system by forcing the doors should be weighed against the urgency of the situation in the car.

All firefighters operating in or near open elevator shafts must be secured with a rope and harness to protect against falls, including when removing occupants from a car.

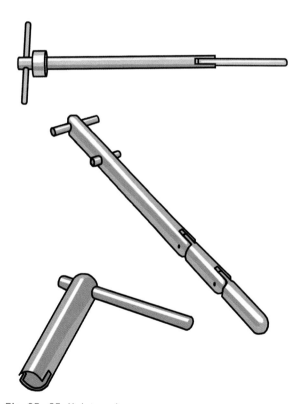

Fig. 35–85. Hoistway keys

Elevator systems are designed so that opening the hoistway doors automatically sets a safety interlock that prevents movement of the car. The switch is operated electrically and is naturally subject to damage or malfunction, and firefighters should not trust it absolutely to prevent movement of the car. Therefore, lockout/tagout is still necessary.

Some elevators use **door restrictors**. Typically these are metal bars that prevent the elevator hoistway door from opening when the car is outside the **landing zone**, 18 in. (45 cm) above or below the floor level of the lobby. Door restrictors are used to prevent people from opening the hoistway door from the inside and accidentally falling down the shaft when they try to exit the car. There are a variety of different types of door restrictors, depending upon the manufacturer of the elevator. Some can be bypassed with tools like a pike pole; others cannot. It is best to preplan the elevators in your response district to determine whether or not they have door restrictors and how you will be able to disable them during a rescue.

With the hoistway door open, block off any large openings (typically when the car is just above the landing, creating a large space near the floor level) by placing ladders or other obstacles across the opening to prevent accidental falls into the hoistway. Now, using appropriate caution to prevent personnel from becoming trapped *if* there is any unexpected movement of the car, and while communicating with the occupants ("stay back away from the doors, we're going to open them," etc.), push the elevator car doors, which should open freely (and also activate the safety interlock to prevent car movement even if the occupants themselves open the elevator car doors).

Alternate access into the elevator car doors can be made through emergency panels in the roof of all elevators, and the sidewalls of multi-elevator hoistways (to allow car-to-car emergency access).

Based on your access to the elevator car, its position in relation to the closest landings, and the condition of occupants, determine the best way to access and remove them. In some cases it might be as simple as a transfer from the car to the landing through the doors if the car is level with the landing. Consider placing a ladder or plank across the gap, and physically assist the occupants across.

If the elevator car is above the landing but reasonably accessible from that floor, block the gap in the hoistway as previously mentioned to prevent accidental falls, and place a ladder from the landing into the car (fig. 35–86). A firefighter can then climb in and determine the best way to move occupants out. Belaying harnessed occupants as they climb down on the ladder is a good method to prevent accidental falls. Occupants who are injured or medically impaired may need to be secured in a rescue litter and transferred down the ladder (using a ladder slide method with belay or another accepted method).

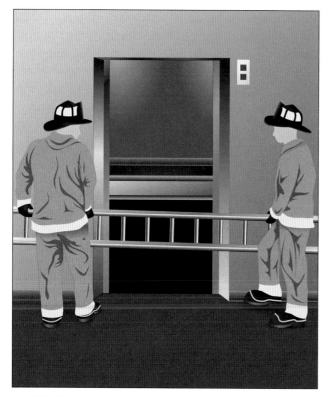

Fig. 35–86. A roof or attic ladder is held across the opening to prevent people from falling down the shaft as they are removed from the elevator car.

If the car is below the landing and enough of it is accessible to allow the movement of occupants, a ladder can be placed from the landing down into the car (fig. 35–87). Have a firefighter climb down into the car to assess the situation and assist occupants up the ladder.

If there is no access to the elevator car because of its position between floors, go to the floor above and open that hoistway door. Now the emergency roof panel should be accessible for a firefighter climbing down a ladder that's been placed from the landing onto the top of the car. The firefighter can lift the panel, assess the situation in the car, and go from there.

If the car is within reach, a ladder can be placed on the floor of the car and occupants can climb (with assistance) directly out to the landing (fig. 35–88). If not, consider using an attic ladder to allow occupants to climb out of the car, where firefighters assist them onto the other ladder to climb to the landing. Another option for multiple-elevator hoistways is to bring another elevator car to the appropriate level and transfer occupants across to that car. Use ladders or planks for a walkway, and consider belaying occupants as necessary.

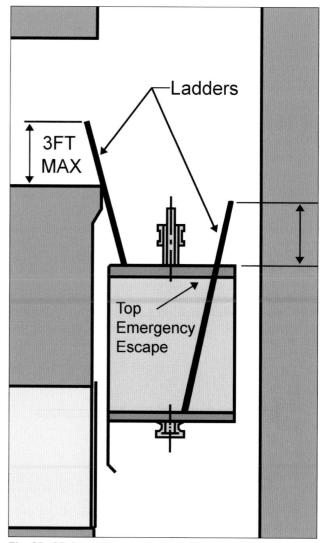

Fig. 35–87. A small ladder (attic ladder) can be placed into the elevator car, allowing victims to climb out to a floor above, if necessary.

Fig. 35–88. Victims using a ladder to evacuate an elevator car should be assisted by firefighters and given direction.

Some "express" elevators that access the upper reaches of a high-rise may travel through **blind shafts**—elevator shafts without hoistway doors since they don't stop on the lower floor. It may be necessary to breach the wall around such a stalled car; be careful when breaching walls as you may encounter electrical wiring and other utilities. Breaching a shaft wall in many cases will be a long, difficult, tedious task, especially in older buildings with a substantial concrete block or poured concrete shaft wall.

If the elevator system is hydraulic, lowering the elevator is a task that should be performed by a certified elevator technician. It is best to shut off the electrical power supply through lockout/tagout and to remove the passengers from the car using techniques described earlier for electric traction elevators (fig. 35–89).

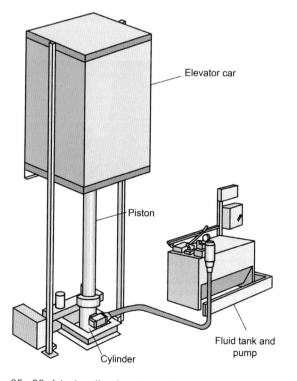

Fig. 35–89. A hydraulic elevator system

If a person is trapped between the car and a landing or bottom, or between cars in multi-elevator systems, lockout/tagout and other precautions must be taken. Then make a game plan for how best to support technical rescue companies/teams to extricate the person. Movement of the elevator is not always the best method of freeing people in these situations, but that also may be required. An elevator mechanic's advice and assistance is critical, and if necessary the mechanic's response can be expedited by a law enforcement escort or even by helicopter transport to the roof. Considerations similar to industrial entrapment are pertinent here, including the use of rescue air bags, cribbing, and possibly even field surgical intervention (amputation). First-arriving firefighters can assist the rescue company or technical rescue team by establishing an equipment pool and performing other stabilization and support tasks.

Escalator rescues. Although less common than elevator emergencies, escalator entrapment presents firefighters with serious hazards and potential complications. The first task is to ensure that the escalator is shut down (using the emergency shut down button or switch). Then ensure that an escalator mechanic has been requested, and provide a law enforcement escort if necessary to expedite his response (fig. 35–90).

Fig. 35–90. Escalator emergencies require the immediate response of a repair technician.

On arrival, assess the predicament and establish lockout/tagout. Typically, escalator electric power is provided through a motor located beneath the upper landing, inside a protective **landing plate**. There should also be an emergency stop switch at the top and bottom of the escalator, or on a nearby wall (which can also come in handy when firefighters must use escalators to access other floors with hoselines, etc.). Start by hitting the emergency stop button if it has not already been used by bystanders, and then disconnect power if feasible by lifting the landing plate (fig. 35–91).

Fig. 35–91. If not already done so by bystanders upon your arrival, the emergency stop switch should be activated.

If fingers are caught where the handrail glides into the underside, it may be possible to use a whizzer saw or reciprocating saw to cut the plate and expose the innards for further evaluation and action. Cutting through the handrail (a continuous belt) may allow you to manipulate it just enough to free the fingers. Reversing the escalator's direction of travel is usually not a good option because of multiple safeties that prevent backward movement in case of power loss. Fingers caught beneath the handrails can usually be freed by cutting the handrail belt or by using tools to access and free the fingers (fig. 35–92 a and b). Feet (or feet still in shoes) caught where the escalator stair dives beneath the landing plate, may be freed by lifting the plate to reveal the gears and motor for further evaluation and action.

As with any industrial entrapment, effective medical care including trauma, crush syndrome treatment, and pain management are critical. Equally critical are provisions for rapid transportation to the appropriate medical facility after the victim is freed.

Medical considerations during rescue operations.

Some major rescues take hours to complete, requiring a mix of ingenuity, good patient care, and patience. An informal rule of thumb when estimating the time it will take to extricate a victim is this: If you think it's going to take 1 hour, plan on it taking 2 hours. In other words, double the time you *think* it might take because often that's what actually happens during rescues, which are often slowed by a wide range of unexpected complications (fig. 35–93).

Figs. 35–92 a & b. Cutting through and manipulating belts, as well as moving stairs and other mechanisms can be done to free the victim.

Fig. 35–93. Rescuers should estimate the amount of time an incident should take by doubling what the time they think it will take.

Because of the potentially long time frames for extrication of trapped victims, firefighters must always keep in mind the potential for victims to suffer the effects of **crush syndrome**, **compartment syndrome**, and other maladies related to long-term crushing trauma (effects of which sometimes kill victims long after they are rescued). Another consideration is reducing pain of victims who are severely trapped, when medically feasible.

In addition to basic life support provided by first-arriving firefighters, it's important to allow paramedics to establish advanced life-support treatment when possible so that the victim does not suffer excessive pain or permanent (even deadly) complications that might otherwise be prevented (fig. 35–94). This requires good judgment and cooperation between the first-arriving firefighters, the incident commander, and EMS personnel.

Fig. 35–94. Although it may be difficult, firefighters and technical rescuers should allow advanced life support providers to have access to the patient when possible.

Rapid transportation to a trauma center should be strongly considered, including measures like having life-flight EMS helicopters dispatched to stand by for immediate transport once the victim is freed (fig. 35–95). This is especially true in remote areas like the mountains, where ground transportation is lengthy to begin with.

The time saved by aerial transportation to a trauma center sometimes literally means the difference between life and death for the victim. It certainly may have an effect on the victim's long-term recovery and whether or not the victim suffers permanent disability.

An uncomfortable but important consideration in industrial entrapment is the topic of **surgical field amputation**. Physical entrapment of one or more limbs sometimes compels firefighters to consider the possible need to request a physician and medical team to respond

to the scene to be ready to perform field amputation in the following cases:

- *If* the victim may not survive a long-term extrication because of uncontrollable internal or external bleeding, uncontrollable airway, or other uncontrollable medical issue

- *If* successful extrication may be impossible within the survivable limits of the victim's condition

Fig. 35–95. Utilizing helicopters for medical transportation is a good decision for long-duration rescue incidents.

In many regions there are preestablished protocols for requesting field surgical support when industrial entrapment or other difficult rescues present firefighters with conditions indicating a field amputation may be necessary. Protocols include potential helicopter transportation of the field surgical team and the victim to save time.

The key for first-arriving firefighters is to recognize situations that might require these extreme measures, and rapidly initiate the system that gets field surgical teams on the scene. In places without any sort of preestablished plan for this, it's even more important for the incident commander to get this ball rolling as soon as conditions indicate it may be needed.

Rescues in caves and tunnels. NFPA 1001 states that, in addition to other rescue situations, the Firefighter II should be prepared to help rescue companies and technical rescue teams safely manage rescues in caves and tunnels. When it happens, rescues in caves and tunnels are among the most hazardous situations that firefighters ever encounter (fig. 35–96).

Fig. 35–96. Cave and tunnel rescues are rare, but they present a serious risk to rescuers.

Many ingredients for disastrous situations can be found in mines, tunnels, caves, and other underground structures, including remote or restricted access to entrances and portals; tight spaces with minimal natural ventilation; potential for wall and ceiling collapse (possibly secondary collapse following a primary collapse that trapped victims); long horizontal or vertical travel distances to fresh air and the safety of the outdoors; the potential for sudden and massive flooding; the presence of atmospheric hazards like CO, hydrogen sulfide, methane, oxygen deficiency, and harmful dusts; potential for disease-causing organisms; complete darkness in the absence of artificial lighting; and the possibility of fires or explosions, which may create a fiery oven channeling heat and smoke, killing victims and rescuers where they stand.

In short, everything is more difficult underground: ventilation, lighting, communications, logistics, firefighting, physical disentanglement, movement of equipment and personnel, command and control, dewatering, atmospheric monitoring, and dive operations when necessary. Everything is made more complicated when it's happening in a hole in the earth (fig. 35–97).

The fire service has seen its share of underground rescues and disasters in recent times, including mining accidents that killed dozens of workers at a time (approximately 45 miners still die annually in the United States, and the toll is far higher in countries like China); automobile drivers roasted alive when fireballs erupted during collisions involving gasoline tankers in highway tunnels; the 1971 Sylmar (Los Angeles) tunnel explosion that killed 17 construction workers drilling through methane-laden soils and working with muck pocketed in the middle of a mountain near Los Angeles's San Gabriel Fault; a

number of subway crashes that required firefighters to spend many hours cutting apart subway cars to extricate trapped passengers; several cavers trapped below the earth; and many other examples.

Mine rescue teams, required for operations in commercial mining mishaps, are mandated to adhere to strict standards, including federal standards of Mine Safety and Health Administration (MSHA) for mine rescue teams (Code of Federal Regulations, title 30, part 49), and in some cases even stricter state standards.

There also are strict rules for workers and for rescue operations in tunneling operations for subways, rail tunnels, automobile tunnels, and water tunnels. The ironic thing about tunneling operations is that once the tunnel is completed and transitions from the *construction phase* to the *revenue phase*, the tunnel rescue rules change or don't seem to apply at all. A fire department or rescue agency responding to an emergency or disaster in an active tunneling operation during the construction phase must meet much stricter requirements than when responding to the very same tunnel after it's completed and is in the revenue phase.

Fig. 9–97. Cave rescues complicate ventilation, atmospheric monitoring, and logistics.

And in some cases there don't seem to be any rules at all. One example is abandoned mines and tunnels, which fall into a great big gray area with seemingly no formal regulation except common sense and adapting the rules of other disciplines like confined-space, high-angle, and tunnel rescue. Abandoned mines and tunnels are a particular problem because they are no longer maintained, they are often poorly marked (or not marked at all), and there is no reliable database that shows all their locations.

Thousands of abandoned mines can be found in the mountains and deserts across the United States (fig. 35–98). New Mexico alone has approximately 20,000 abandoned mines that the state has classified as dangerous because the openings present an attractive hazard to children and adults keen on exploring their depths. Utah also has approximately 20,000 mines, and it's common for snowmobile riders to plunge into the vertical shafts hidden by snow cover. California's inventory of abandoned and working mines easily exceeds 40,000. Every year about half a dozen explorers die in abandoned California mines. Dozens more are injured while climbing and crawling through them. And then there are the other mining states like Pennsylvania, West Virginia, and others.

Fig. 35–98. Abandoned and unmarked mines can attract children and adults, thus presenting a serious risk to responders.

Firefighters should understand that federal and state mine safety regulations were written for working commercial mining operations (fig. 35–99). Active mining, where there is ongoing penetration of the earth, has distinct inherent dangers that must constantly be monitored and dealt with. When disasters occur in working mines, there is the potential for large-scale life loss. Not surprisingly, regulations for mine rescue teams are basically intended to provide for rescue of miners lost or trapped in active commercial mines, including a requirement that team members have at least one year of working mine experience.

Fig. 35–99. Federal standards exist for commercial mine operations and their rescue teams.

So federally certified mine rescue teams are typically made up of miners employed in active commercial mining operations, who are required to have certain equipment, be trained in the use of certain equipment and techniques, and come together when a mining accident occurs to attempt the rescue of their own colleagues or miners who are lost or trapped in accidents in other commercial mining operations. They are required to be familiar with commercial mining equipment, methods, structures, and other information that would typically be known by people who work in the commercial mining environment every day.

This is important because active mines and tunneling operations have specific dangers such as deep vertical shafts, the use of heavy machinery, conveyer belts, explosives storage, the potential for collapse or sudden flooding, the potential for hitting methane pockets, and a long list of others potential hazards. Among other tools, mine rescue teams use devices (e.g., closed circuit SCBA for long-distance entry, long-term helmet lighting, etc.) and the so-called self rescuers (oxygen-generating device) that may be unfamiliar to the typical firefighter or rescuer.

As of this writing, MSHA is undertaking a review of existing policy, equipment, training, and capabilities for mine rescue as well as soliciting comments and recommendations. It is intended to improve the survivability of commercial miners when accidents happen in active commercial mines, as well as improving the speed, safety, and effectiveness of mine rescue operations.

Beyond working mines, what about underground situations is not covered specifically by federal and state mine safety regulations? Today, municipal fire and rescue departments across the United States are responsible for first-due (life-saving) response to fires, explosions, terrorist attacks, collapses, flooding, derailments, and other mishaps deep in the ground, sometimes hundreds of yards (or even several miles, in some cases) from portals (fig. 35–100). They can also be in subways, train tunnels, pedestrian tunnels, water tunnels, vehicular traffic tunnels, and other subsurface structures. This includes during the tunneling process, when an even wider range of mishaps can occur.

Fig. 35–100. Access and the construction of underground tunnels (including those under construction) should be inspected and surveyed by firefighters and rescue teams.

Municipal fire departments and other first responders are responsible for planning and executing life-saving operations in these below-grade structures using whatever equipment, training, and protocols are available, under conditions where far more lives may be at stake than in any commercial mining operation in the world. They are responsible for being prepared to assess conditions, establish incident command, make long-distance entry to fight fire, conduct searches, extract trapped victims, stabilize collapse zones, be aware of potential for secondary events (including, in the case of terrorist attacks, secondary explosive and delivery devices), mitigate hazmat releases, and remove victims to the safety of the surface.

But the existing rules for operations beneath the ground exist in a gray area. Firefighters and other first responders know that they will be the first response to trouble in these places, and they are usually the first and last line of defense for victims who might be trapped, lost, or in need of physical rescue from these places.

The potential for disastrous fires, collapses, explosions, flooding, derailments, and other mishaps has always been known by the first responders. And the potential is even more pronounced in the aftermath of the London subway terrorist bombings, the attacks on Spain's railway systems, the Tokyo subway sarin gas attacks, and the threat of future terrorist attacks on mass transit systems. First-arriving firefighters will be compelled to make risk-versus-gain decisions under life-and-death conditions that are not covered by the federal and state rules (fig. 35–101).

Fig. 35–101. Rescuers must make careful decisions when below-grade rescues are complicated with criminal intentions.

If there's any doubt about the special demands of these operations, try carrying a victim from a train wreck in a tunnel in zero-visibility conditions, with heat and smoke from uncontrolled fire, in a potentially explosive atmosphere, wearing full PPE and SCBA. How long do you think your 30-minute SCBA bottle will last? What about a 45- or 60-minute SCBA bottle? Which units in your area carry closed circuit SCBA, and how long will it take for them to arrive? Factor all this in, and it becomes evident that fire and rescue agencies with tunnels in their jurisdictions have special hazards that require special plans, training, and capabilities (fig. 35–102). Those issues exceed that scope of this text, but it's good food for thought for firefighters who may be called on to assist rescue companies and technical rescue teams when these emergencies occur.

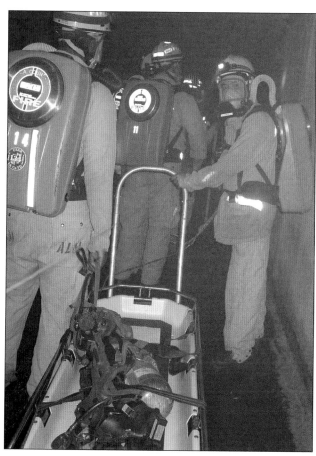

Fig. 35–102. Tunnel and cave rescue operations require significant planning and resources and should not be attempted without training and preparation.

ELECTRICAL EMERGENCIES

So, let's review some basic concepts that will allow firefighters to operate safely at the scene of emergencies where electrical hazards are likely to be present. The first priority is situational awareness: being heads-up about the potential dangers of any emergency scene. Everyone, from the tailboard firefighter to the incident commander (IC), should be scanning the area for possible hazards that can hurt responders and the public. Structure fires,

wildland fires, and automobile collisions are notorious for knocking down power lines or even the power poles themselves (fig. 35–103). All electrical lines and conductors should be considered energized until determined "cold." And even then, they should be avoided because power lines often become re-energized as the electrical grid often attempts (automatically) to reroute the power if there is a break in the system. Even guy-wires can become energized under some conditions (auto collisions that damage poles, expose energized wiring, and contact the guy-wires, etc).

Fig. 35–103. Downed power lines

When approaching the scene of a fire or possible electrical emergency, the engineer or driver must be "heads up" to potential electrical hazards. Responding units should not travel beneath or position apparatus below wires that are compromised and/or damaged or suspected to be. Consider positioning apparatus at least one span (the distance between two poles) from any damaged wire or pole, and think about the effects of a large fire on the wires and poles. If possible, avoid parking in or near puddles of water that may become energized if wires fall during the incident. All firefighters should carefully examine the immediate area before stepping off the rig to ensure it has not stopped atop a downed wire. Avoid stepping in puddles of water that may become energized.

Fire trucks and other apparatus provide protection from electrical currents, but they may become energized by live wires if they contact wires (or an object that is in contact with a live wire).

Remember, any metal part of an aerial ladder that touches high-voltage lines energizes the entire apparatus. Don't give the enemy easy access. Don't make your body the "ground" for an electrical contact. If it becomes evident that there is possible contact between the apparatus and an electrical source, stay on the rig (this is also the advice we give to the public in vehicles contacting wires and other electrical sources).

If it becomes necessary to get off the apparatus, do not step off. The way to exit is to carefully jump off as far away as possible, landing with both feet together and without losing your balance. Do not touch the ground with your hand, and don't fall backward or forward. Once on the ground, shuffle your feet as you walk away from the apparatus to maintain contact with the ground and prevent arcing.

Another way firefighters are sometimes injured or killed is when aerial ladders or baskets/snorkels touch or get too close to live wires. The operator should know his apparatus behavior intimately, and should allow for ladder swaying, rocking, and sagging when operating near power lines and cables, and should also take these factors into consideration when positioning apparatus and ladders. Operating, erecting, or handling of tools, machinery equipment, or apparatus over energized high voltage lines is generally prohibited. For wires and components of 600 volts or more, aerial ladders are required to maintain a minimum clearance of 10 ft (3 m).

Alternate methods than aerials for reaching upper stories and roofs must be considered rather than raising aerial ladders near high-voltage lines. Such methods, in addition to wooden ground ladders may call for using fire escapes, interior staircases, or adjacent roofs of buildings. In extreme cases, helicopters may be considered.

The use of ground ladders near electrical overhead wires must be done safely. Even if constructed of wood, ground ladders are still conductive due to metal parts and dirt and debris that may coat the ladder. Care must be taken when moving, raising, and lowering any ladders.

One of the first things your eyes should be drawn to as you approach these scenes is the telltale sign of power lines drooping over fences, dangling across streets and sidewalks, or the free ends of severed wires hanging around the scene. Right there you have a possible electrical emergency, and the IC should be made aware of the situation and should be requesting the jurisdictional power company to respond to the scene.

Windstorms, hurricanes, earthquakes, floods, landslides, and mudflows also cause power lines to go down, often over a large geographical area. Another colleague of the author was electrocuted after the 1987 Whittier earthquake when he stepped into the yard of a home near which a power line had fallen.

Whenever entering areas affected by these events, it should be assumed that power lines are down and other electrical hazards are present, often hidden from sight by debris. This is one reason that nighttime operations are considered high-risk during these types of emergencies or disasters. In some cases where most victims have been accounted for and the risk-versus-gain equation is such that the greatest life loss potential is to rescuers tromping around the scene at night and possibly encountering downed power lines, search operations may be suspended during hours of darkness.

Other electrical hazards are encountered at fires in homes, businesses, refineries, infrastructure, and other locations. They range from internal electrical hazards, such as wiring in walls to external hazards such as drip loops. In some cases, the likely electrical hazard locations are pretty clear (triplex drip loops between homes and power poles, underground electrical vaults, etc.). In other cases, they can be a surprise. How can you determine if electricity is present in any of these situations? In many cases, firefighters follow the practice of eliminating the source: they flip the switches at electrical panels, or carefully cut the drip loops (using proper PPE), or have the local utility company shut down power and confirm it.

Another option is to utilize "hot sticks" and voltage meters that detect the presence of electrical currents and signal you with an audible warning. They are carried on some rescue companies, truck companies, engines, and by some individual firefighters who find them useful. Not only can these devices detect electricity in bare wiring or being transmitted to objects like fences, they can also detect electricity being carried by wiring within walls (something to consider when breaching walls).

In life-threatening situations such as victims in contact with energized wires, victims trapped on high-voltage electrical towers, on billboards, in trees, in electrical vaults, and other places where victims might have been electrocuted and require physical extraction, or "jumpers" on or around electrical facilities, the IC should ensure the fastest response of a power company field team and a supervisor to assist and provide technical expertise. The request should be made for an "immediate/expedite" response, with a Code R (Code 3) escort by law enforcement as necessary to ensure timely response.

Part of the strategy should always include establishing a rapid intervention crew, and ensure that an ambulance and an advanced life support (ALS) unit are in place.

Firefighters attempting to control electrical hazards should wear full turnouts at minimum, to protect against the possibility of electrical arcing, flash fires, and explosions. This includes donning firefighting hood and gloves. Lineman's gloves (properly inspected and maintained) should be used where available (many departments now assign them to units that carry other electrical control tools). Full turnout clothing is not electrical protective clothing, and firefighters must be aware of the limitations. The composite material of SCBA bottles and the metal insoles of turnout boots can conduct electricity. Turnout coats and pants have metal clasps and buttons that are conductive.

One of the most common electricity-related situations you're likely to face is the task of de-energizing a building during an emergency. Consider the two most common methods. The first is to open the main switch or breaker switches at the electrical main panel. This is a practical method for de-energizing a building and reducing the hazard to the firefighter as well as the potential damage to the occupancy. However, responders should be aware of the inherent dangers of discontinuing the current in a high voltage application. Inspect the panel for signs of damage from fire or water. Avoid standing in water, and stand to the side of the electrical panel. Do not reach across your body to disconnect switches. Turn away from the panel when disconnecting switches to protect your upper extremities, and use your SCBA mask or shield to protect your face.

Never de-energize a building by pulling the electrical meter. This can cause arcing and possible explosion.

When turning off breakers, mark or remember any tripped breakers. Turn the main switch off first. If this does not turn the power off, shut off the individual breakers one at a time. If the panel cannot be accessed, contact the local power company.

The second common method is to cut drip loops using an approved mechanical axe and insulated electrical (lineman's) gloves. This method must be confined to low-voltage wires only. In an emergency when there is a need to de-energize a high-voltage line, the local electrical utility company should be requested to respond to the incident. Only qualified electrical workers should handle high-voltage lines. Firefighters should not for any reason attempt to cut high-voltage lines.

Many low-voltage service drops are found in the form of triplex cables. A triplex is three wires wound around each other. Triplexes should not be cut as a whole, because they will cause a short circuit that will damage or

destroy the blades of the mechanical axe and may injure the firefighter. They must be cut one at a time. Use the approved mechanical axe and insulated rubber gauntlet gloves. Stand on a dry object. Lock in when working on a ladder.

Do not reach over wires. Cut the closest conductor first. Do not touch another conductor or ground. After cutters are in place, turn your head to protect your eyes from flash and sparks, and make sure all insulated wires leading to service head are cut. When possible, the loops should be cut at the service head. If it's necessary to cut the loop at the pole, cut one wire at a time before it goes into the triplex.

If there are downed wires, visually inspect all other wires in the immediate area and adjacent to downed wires to determine the extent of involvement and possible flow of electricity to the ground. Identify all wires and their termination points. Visually follow all wires to determine if they are contacting fences, structures, trees, brush, etc., or if they are obscured from view. Remember, wires may be contacting metal fences or other conductors, causing them to become energized, creating a very hazardous condition for fire personnel and the public.

Establish a safety perimeter at least 30 ft (9 m) in all directions from the downed wires or objects in contact with them, and deny entry to the scene and control vehicle and pedestrian traffic. Use fireline tape or traffic barriers or assigned law enforcement to limit access, and request the local electrical utility company to respond. All power poles and towers and associated power lines, guy-wires, and/or communication wires should be considered energized until proven otherwise. Electrical utility employees determine whether electrical distribution lines and equipment are de-energized and the scene safe to operate.

Generally speaking, firefighters should avoid moving or cutting high-voltage lines that have not been de-energized. It's safer to allow the professional linemen to conduct these operations. Usually, communication wires located on the same pole as electrical distribution lines can be moved or cut by qualified firefighters with the proper PPE after a thorough inspection of all lines.

In electrical rescues or other circumstances where lives may be endangered but where initially is no other way to terminate power to low-voltage wires, the local electrical company should be requested and provided with a Code R escort by law enforcement as necessary to ensure timely response for life-threatening electrical emergencies. Here is where the risk-versus-gain decision will apply: to save a life, a qualified and properly equipped firefighter might be assigned to attempt separating the downed wire from the victim, with a rapid intervention crew with ambulance and ALS positioned.

One method is to move the wire away from the victim using a "hot stick" made for that purpose while wearing the proper gloves and other PPE.

If fire is at the base of an electrical pole and it's been determined that the fire was not caused by underground electrical sources or wires down, the pole fire may be considered a Class A and extinguished with water. If fire is near a pole top and/or involves electrical wires and/or equipment, fire should be considered Class C. Do not use water or foam to extinguish. Contact the local electrical utility company to advise them of the situation. Protect exposures, and establish a safety perimeter around poles and wires a distance of 1½ times the height of the pole.

If the situation is a vehicle that has crashed into an electrical pole, the IC should notify the local electrical utility company and law enforcement. If downed wires are contacting vehicle and victims are still inside, there is a decision point: if the person is conscious and no life hazard is present, instruct victim to stay inside vehicle. Provide instructions to the person from a safe distance away (30 ft) using a public address system. Direct your dispatch center to request an "immediate/expedite" response of the local electrical company, with a Code R (Code 3) escort by law enforcement as necessary to ensure timely response. Ensure a rapid intervention crew (with a squad and ambulance) is in place when conducting operations in any immediately dangerous to life and health (IDLH) conditions during electrical emergencies. Have hoselines in place in case a fire breaks out (in which case the priorities may change). Wait for the local power company representative to arrive to de-energize wires and other equipment before making victim contact.

If a fire breaks out and cannot be contained, or the area is flooding, or some other life safety hazard is present (for example, there is interior fire or other immediate life hazard), and the victim is conscious and ambulatory and able to follow your instructions, direct the victim to open the vehicle door, stand on the rocker panel (doorway) of the vehicle and jump to the ground with both feet together at once. Instruct the victim not to touch the ground with hands after jumping (they must remain balanced). Demonstrate the action to the person to make it absolutely clear before allowing them

to proceed. This is especially important with children. Once out of the vehicle, victim(s) should be instructed to shuffle (not walk or run) away from the hazard area to a safe zone at least 30 ft from the vehicle and/or downed wire.

If the victim is unconscious but no life hazard is present, wait for the local power company representative to arrive to de-energize wires and other equipment before making victim contact.

If a life safety hazard is present and the victim(s) appear unconscious, the IC must weigh the risk versus gain, considering all the hazards present to firefighters before ordering a rescue attempt. The IC should consider alternative means, such as a deck gun, to knock down fire using a deluge of water, or use another vehicle to push the involved vehicle to attempt to separate it from the power line, or other means.

Generally, one should not attempt to extinguish a vehicle fire with water or foam if wires are in contact or near the vehicle. Consider the fire Class C. Wait for the local power company to de-energize the wires before extinguishing the fire with water. Protect exposures and isolate and deny entry within 30 ft of the affected area.

If, after evaluating the risk-versus-gain equation, the IC determines that cutting the downed wires is prudent to save a life, only qualified personnel should attempt this procedure. Wear full PPEs, including protective goggles or SCBA facepiece. Use an approved mechanical axe and insulated rubber gauntlet gloves. Shuffle step (do not walk) to the best position to more closely assess the hazards and potential for successfully moving or cutting the downed wire. The qualified firefighter, after consulting with the IC and/or the on-scene safety officer, will determine if the best course of action will be to move or cut the downed wire. If the decision is made to cut the wire, stand on a dry object and follow the procedures outlined above.

Fires in electrical vaults, manholes, and pad-mounted equipment are an unusual but potent hazard. In 2008 a Los Angeles City firefighter was killed after several manhole explosions and fire caused the fire department to cut into a utility box. Unfortunately there apparently was an explosive atmosphere in the box, and it ignited/exploded when a circular saw was used to cut into it.

If the incident involves a potential rescue from a vault or manhole, ensure that a confined-space rescue response has been dispatched. Upon arrival, a priority is to determine whether there may have been personnel working in the space who are not yet accounted for.

LESSON FROM THE FIREGROUND

What is more dangerous than an enemy you can't see, can't hear, can't smell, can't taste, and can't feel until it's too late? What if that enemy can move at nearly the speed of light? What if that enemy had the ability to burn your insides, including your muscles, tendons, nerves, bones, brain, and all layers of your skin in an instant? What if that enemy had the ability to blow off the ends of your limbs and kill anyone who touched you while trying to rescue you? How would you protect yourself against such an enemy?

In the past two decades, more than 25 American firefighters have been killed in the line of duty from electrocution. Hundreds of firefighters have suffered electrical injury, and many of those have been career-ending events. When I came on the job in 1980, one of the best mentors was a training captain who had for many years been assigned full-time to light duty. He was a wealth of knowledge, a true firefighter's firefighter.

Wondering why the captain spent all his time in training, this author remembers being stunned to find out that he had barely survived an electrocution that killed another firefighter. They had arrived on the scene of what appeared to be a "typical" traffic collision, with one car having plowed into a fence. Unknown to the firefighters, a power line had been knocked loose and was draped over the chain-link fence beyond their initial vantage point.

When the captain went to help a victim still trapped in the car, he in essence became "the ground" between the now-electrified fence and the earth. Not only did he suffer severe electrical burns to his internal organs and extremities, but he was made nearly deaf and would forevermore rely on a hearing aid to communicate normally.

The enemy was unseen, unheard, and unfelt until it was too late. That's how it goes with electrical mishaps. Another colleague firefighter was once killed by contact with piping that became electrified at a construction site. The list of firefighters killed or injured by electricity is far too long.

Make no attempt to extinguish fires involving underground or pad-mounted electrical equipment. This equipment should be considered Class C until de-energized by the local power company. Never put water or foam into a vault until it is de-energized. Use only nonconducting extinguishers (CO_2, BC, or ABC-type) and only when requested to do so by the local power company representative.

Upon arrival at a manhole fire, care must be taken on apparatus placement. No emergency vehicle should stop over or within close proximity to manholes because they may fill the holes with carbon monoxide. Control traffic, set up a safety perimeter, and keep vehicles and pedestrians away from the area. Manhole covers often weigh 300 lb and have been blown 75 ft vertically into the air and a lateral distance of 125 ft.

If smoke or flames are showing from a manhole cover, do not attempt to remove the cover. A flammable atmosphere may be present which may be toxic or explosive.

Do not enter a vault or manhole until a power company representative confirms that it is safe to enter. Any entry made to rescue a downed worker or victim should be considered a confined-space rescue emergency, and a confined-space rescue response should be requested with confined-space rescue protocols and a rapid intervention crew (with an ambulance and ALS unit) in place.

Fires in electrical substations are high-risk operations, and unless there is an immediate threat to life, it's best to hold back, go slow and deliberately, and don't get tunnel vision on the fire and smoke. Your enemy here is the unseen electrical forces that are present all around. Generally speaking, it's best not to enter electrical substations without approval from the local power utility company, which should be able to guide you about next actions.

Do not fight electrical substation fires from outside the gates.

Protect exposures and isolate and deny entry until a local power company representative arrives. Follow the power company representative's instructions when entering and driving inside a substation. If victims are injured, missing, or trapped within the facility, the IC should determine whether personnel with full PPE including SCBA have a reasonable chance of completing a rescue. The risk-versus-gain decision must also take into account the potential for a successful rapid intervention operation if a mishap occurs. Ensure that a rapid intervention crew (with ambulance and ALS unit) is being assigned if a rescue is attempted.

Fires in electrical substations should be considered Class C until de-energized. Do not attempt to extinguish with water or foam. If fire involves transformers, fire shall be considered Class B once the equipment is de-energized.

Transformers and capacitors contain oil coolants that have a tendency to explode when subjected to intense fire. Older capacitors may contain a liquid substance called polychlorinated biphenyls (PCBs), which is toxic, non-biodegradable, and environmentally hazardous. All capacitors owned by SCE have been converted to mineral oil; however, this assurance cannot be made for those owned by other power companies. If a capacitor has ruptured for any reason, the liquid should be considered a hazardous material until determined otherwise by the local power company representative or a health hazmat officer.

Many wildfires affect electrical power poles and towers, and they can present a significant hazard to firefighters. Maintain a safe distance from electrical power lines, poles, and towers equal to 1½ times their height when involved in wildland firefighting activities. If fire has ignited the base(s) of electrical power pole(s), fire may be considered Class A and should be extinguished with water to prevent the pole from collapsing and causing wires to drop. Extinguish smoldering pole fires (below electrical wires only) to prevent power line failure or dropped lines. Consider all downed or compromised wires and associated poles, towers, and other equipment to be energized.

Fires on electrical poles at or near the level of electrical wires shall be considered Class C. Do not attempt to extinguish using water or foam. Isolate and deny entry until a local power company representative arrives to de-energize lines. Do not use areas below wires as safe zones, escape routes, ICP locations, or for any other use. Avoid ordering aerial water or retardant drops directly over electrical power lines, which can cause arcing, shorting, down-strikes, and explosions. Wires create a hazard for aircraft because they are hard to spot in even normal conditions. Be aware that heavy smoke conditions can cause electrical down-strikes below transmission and distribution power lines.

Another electrical hazard is found where potential jumpers or victims of industrial mishaps are found trapped or stranded on high-voltage towers. This can also include victims trapped in trees with electrical lines, and other high-angle electrical emergencies. The IC should ensure the most appropriate response is dispatched, and then double check that the correct units are coming. Furthermore, he should ensure that the local electrical company has been requested on an expedite/immediate response, with a Code R escort from law enforcement.

If the situation is a jumper with electrical hazards, ensure that a rescue fall bag and a crisis negotiation team are also dispatched. The responding rescuers can work with these units to coordinate high-angle and negotiation operations.

If the emergency is some sort of entrapment on a power tower, billboard, or other above-ground electrical hazard, consider rescue fall bags and coordinate with the rescue company and other units to establish a rescue plan once the electrical lines have been de-energized, or until it's determined that a rescue can proceed before all the electrical lines are de-energized. Ensure a rapid intervention crew (with ambulance and ALS) is being/has been assigned if a rescue is attempted.

NOTES

1. Atwood, Rich, Tod Mitcham, Wayne Ibers. *County of Los Angeles Fire Department Confined Space Rescue Technician Training Manual*, 1996.

QUESTIONS

1. Water rescuers benefit from understanding laminar flow and helical flow. Explain both terms.

2. Name five water hazards.

3. Name five good devices for water rescue equipment.

4. A submerged vehicle leaves clues to its location. Name at least three.

5. _____ are a particularly important trigger for mud and debris slides in some regions.

6. Name the five stages of collapse operations.

7. There is a _____% chance of secondary trench excavation collapse following the original collapse.

8. You've arrived at a trench collapse before the rescue crew. List five tasks you and your crew could perform outside the unshored collapse zone while waiting for the rescue crew to arrive.

9. List three forms of indirect support for a victim that the first-arriving firefighter can provide while waiting for a rescue company to arrive.

10. At an escalator rescue, what should be the first task?

APPENDIX A

Sample Inventory of Equipment and Tools Carried on Rescue Companies

Equipment Names

Camera, thermal imaging system

Rotary hammer bit kit

Radio, handheld, intrinsically safe, command frequency

Wrench, torque

Technical search camera, snake-eye

Radio, handheld, intrinsically safe, tactical frequencies

Axe

Tote set, 2 pieces

Air bag, rescue, 21.8 ton, 11.1-in. lift

Air bag, rescue, 17 ton, 9.2-in. lift

Air bag, rescue, 12 ton, 8-in. lift

Chains, tire

Drill, wood ½ in. × 18 in.

Wrench, impact ¾-in. drive

Reducer, 2½ in. to ⅝ in.

Chain, cutting, Diamond

Drill, wood, ¾ in. × 18 in.

Air bag, rescue, 43.8 ton, 15.5-in. lift

Driver, screw, flat 10 in.

Wrench, spark plug

Chisel, pneumatic

Air bag, rescue, 1.5 ton, 3-in. lift

Air bag, rescue, 73.4 ton, 20-in. lift

Air bag, rescue, 35 ton, 10-in. lift, (rectangle)

Air bag, rescue, 3.2 ton, 3.5-in. lift, (rectangle)

Air bag, rescue, 4.8 ton, 5-in. lift

Drill, pneumatic ⅜ in.

Rotary hammer & charger

Chains, tire, snow

Chain, tensioner

Arcair rods, box, ⅜ in.

Chairs, folding, for confined-space rescue equipment donning and standby team readiness, and for personnel rehab

Coupling, set

Saw, rotary, blade, 16, in., concrete, dry

Ram set bolts, 7 in. × ½ in.

Ram set nails, 3.5 in.

Saw, rotary, blade, 14 in., concrete, wet

Ram set bolts, 9 in. × 1 in.

Ram set bolts, 7 in. × ¾ in.

Ram set bolts, 5.5 in. × ½ in.

Saw, rotary, blade, 16 in., diamond

Saw, rotary, blade, 14 in., concrete, dry

Saw, rotary, blade, 16 in., concrete, wet

Saw, rotary, blade, 16 in., carbide tip (wood)

Saw, rotary, blade, 16 in., metal cutting

Blade, wood cutting, 16 in.

Boat motor, 25 horsepower outboard with fuel tank

Supplied air breathing apparatus (SABA) air hose, 100 ft/sec

Saw, rotary, 14 in., K-700

Fiberoptic technical search system

Boat, rescue, inflatable

Drill/hammer drill-24V

Pneumatic rescue system (airgun 40)

Bit, pilot point set, 19 piece

EMS backpack for mountain rescue, collapse, confined space, and other limited-access patient treatment

Chuck, ½ in. with key for DW5351

Map books and maps for Los Angeles County, Orange County, Ventura County, Santa Barbara County, Riverside County, San Bernardino County, San Diego County, San Luis Obispo County, Kern County, State of California, State of Arizona, State of Nevada, and State of Oregon (e.g., jurisdictional and regional counties, jurisdictional state, and adjacent states)

Adaptor, chuck Bosch SDS-Max®

Building triage/marking kit

Rotary hammer, 1½-in., kit, electric

Stanley® rescue system parts kit

Bolt cutter, 36 in.

Pump, hand-fuel

Bolt cutter, 12 in.

Life Detector Technical Search System & Accessories

Hose, garden

Power unit, hydraulic, Stanley-HP1 Rescue system

Chain saw, Diamond-Stanley rescue system, hydraulic, DS11

Saw, skill, worm drive 7¼ in.

Cutoff saw, Stanley rescue system, 14 in., hydraulic, CO23

Technical search device, Olympus fiber-optic

SABA air cart air supply system

Breaker, 90 lb, Stanley rescue system, BR89

Bit, moil point, Stanley rescue system breaker

Pump, trench shore

Ducting, ventilation, accordion,15 ft

Chain saw, gas

Half-backboard; laser safety personnel (LSP), Miller Half Back; for confined-space vertical extraction and other limited access vertical rescues

Saw, reciprocating, 18 V rechargeable

Adaptor, rotary hammer, spline to a taper shank

Saw, rotary, 16 in., Partner K-1200

Kit, pneumatic shoring feet, in hardened carrying case

Chain kit, for combo hydraulic spreader

Heavy duty lockout tags, package

Air horns, handheld

Cutting torch, oxyacetylene

Tool, release, trench shore

4:1 mechanical advantage rope system, prerigged; in high-angle rescue packs

Fluid, hydraulic, trench shore

Rotary hammer bit, core bit adapter

Hydraulic rescue tool system power unit

Ice chest for Bio-Pak® SCBA canisters & rehab

Kit, air bag, rescue, low pressure

Ram, hydraulic rescue system, 20 in.

Hose, airbag, rescue, 16 ft, black

Ram, hydraulic rescue system, 30 in.

Wrench, pipe, 14 in.

Ram, hydraulic rescue system, 60 in.

Air bag, rescue, master control package

Breaker, hammer, 60 lb

Resuscitator with airways, bag valve mask, etc.; in backpack for mountain rescue, vehicles over the side, confined-space rescue, and other limited access patient treatment

Saw parts & repair kit, in ammunition box

Atmospheric monitor kit, hardened case, with organizer

Confined-space communications kit, in hardened case

Saw reciprocating-24V

Lockout/tagout kit, in hardened case

Drill, hammer rotary

Extinguisher, dry chemical

Bit, wood eater set, 5 piece

Ear plugs, package

Chain saw, electric, 16 in.

Spinner, rivet

Rescue frame

Burn sheet-set

Kit, trailer hitch for towing personal watercraft (PWC) trailer

Dirt vacuum system

Air knife system

Clipboard, technical rescue, with technical rescue Incident Command System (ICS) worksheets and other incident documentation items

Swiftwater rescue hose inflator system

Swiftwater rescue line thrower system

Chain saw bar, 20 in.

Chain saw chain blade, 16 in., carbide tip

Swiftwater rescue board

MRE (meals ready to eat), case, for disaster operations and overnight hike in rescues in the mountains

Confined-space scene management kit, case

SCBAs, with masks: one per post position

Night vision goggle systems

Hammer, sledge 16 lb

Radio, handheld, mountain rescue frequencies

Confined-space communications talk box

Rope, rescue, 7/16 in., 200 ft

Rope, rescue, 1/2 in., 250 ft

Water, bottled, case, for disaster operations, long-term rescues, and rehab

Kit, IRB (inflatable rescue boat)

Confined-space communications: operator external mic/ mute switch,1 ft

RIC (rapid intervention crew) pack, air with bottle, to supply emergency air to trapped firefighters (with or without their SCBAs on) and to trapped citizens during fireground or rescue scene extraction

Hook, grappling

RIC straps, CMC, one per post position Tripod rescue system: for cliff rescues, deep shaft rescue, confined-space vertical entry, rooftop operations on high-rise rescues, etc.

Alarms, personal safety system (1 per post position)

Rescue straps (Cearley straps), for helicopter/swiftwater, marine rescue, and cliff rescue operations

Helicopter-high-rise rescue pack

High-rise officer's hose pack

Litter, rescue, junkin

Litter, rescue, Ferno (for PWC rescues)

Breaker, Bosch, handheld

Confined-space communications command module

Atmospheric monitor calibration kit

Bolt cutter, 42 in.

Dikes, crosscut

Pliers, needle-nose

Pliers, lineman

Liter with prerig

Chain, 20 ft

Ram bar, sliding

Technical rescue system-search camera

Shovel, round point, 3 ft

Shovel, long handle, square point

Night vision monocle system

Atmospheric monitor, sampling pump

Ram set, powder-actuated nail gun

Kit, tripod, pneumatic

Wrench, crescent, 8 in.

Pneumatic shoring system

Lifeguard rescue can for surf rescue, marine rescue, lake rescues, swiftwater rescue

Wrench, crescent, 12 in.

Blanket, rescue, reflective

Confined-space communications: operator external mic/ mute switch and cord, 20 ft

Set, index, drill

Litter, confined-space rescue (Sked® sled)

Victim rescue harnesses, 4

Probe, rescue, telescoping, 6 ft, stainless steel

Spray paint, fluorescent orange, case (for structural and victim-marking systems)

Combination tool, hydraulic spreader/cutter

Anchor bolt box, ½ in. × 7 in.

Ram, rescue, 40 in.

Anchor bolt box, ¾ in. × 7 in.

Anchor bolt box, 1 in. × 9 in.

Rebar cutter, hand pump

Rope, rescue, 600 ft (2 sets)

Saw, beam, 16¼ in.

Bit, concrete ⅜-in. L-10 depth 10

Bit, concrete ½-in. L-10 depth 10

Clipboard, medical (for EMS documentation)

Bolt cutter,14 in.

Pneumatic shore regulator

Electrical adaptors, various, in kit

Set, wrench, ignition

Electrical adaptors

Bit, concrete 1 in. L-10 depth 10

Rope bags, for all ropes carried on USAR company

Sprocket, drive, chain saw, Stanley rescue system

Bio-Pak closed-circuit SCBAs: one per post position (for mine/tunnel rescue, high-rise fires, helicopter/ high-rise operations, long-distance confined-space operations, etc.)

Dive rescue kit: one per post position

Ice and snow rescue kit: one per post position

Avalanche poles, kit

Pump, water, Stanley rescue system chain saw

Wrench, crescent, 10 in.

Wrench, combination 1¼ in., Stanley tool

Wrench, combination 1¹⁄₁₆ in., Stanley tool

Plug, spark, Stanley rescue system power unit

Prerig rings, steel, O

Saw, concrete, circular, Stanley rescue system

Electrical adaptor

Filter, air, power unit, Stanley rescue system

Rope, utility, ½ in. 200 ft in bag

Filter, oil, Stanley rescue system

Pulleys, knot pass 2 in., in high-angle rescue packs

Bar, chain saw, Stanley rescue system

Ducting, ventilation, accordion, 25 ft, 2 sets, for confined-space and mine/tunnel rescue

Rebar cutter, electric, 1-in. capacity

Perrigo systems for litters

Rotary hammer, battery power

Oil, hydraulic 5 gal, Stanley rescue system

Blade, rotary, metal, 16 in.

Respirator, dust and mist

Prussicks, long, in high-angle rescue packs

Edge pad, canvas, in high-angle rescue packs

Rope, anchor, 25 ft, in high-angle rescue packs

High-angle rescue pack, industrial (steel hardware)

Edge rollers, in high-angle rescue packs

High-angle rescue pack, Ponypack, mountain (aluminum hardware)

Rescue platforms, 10-person marine rescue platforms, for helicopter deployment into ocean during marine disaster operations

Sawzalls, with hardened cases & blades, electric

Search and recon kit, in backpacks

Plumb bob

Rods, cutting, 50/box × 4 boxes, for arc-air rescue metal cutting system

Brooms, corn

Pressurized water spray can, Hudson type

Anchor bolt box, ½ in. × 5½ in.

Air bag, rescue, hose, 16 ft, yellow

Air bag, rescue, dual controller

Chain saw chain, 20 in. carbide tip, spare

Funnel, 7½ in. diameter

Chain saw chain, 16 in., standard, spare

Cutting torch cylinder, oxygen

Axes, flathead

Cutting torch cylinder, acetylene

Kit, chain breaker, Stanley

Axes, pick-head, with belt: one per post position

Helmet, victim, rescue

Wrecking bar, 3 ft

Filter, hydraulic, Stanley rescue system

Air bag, rescue, hose, 16 ft, black

Bit, chisel point, Stanley rescue system breaker

Pliers, vice grips

Digital camera, still

Wrench, Allen 15-piece set

Come-alongs, 2–4 ton

Kootenay carriages, in high-angle rescue packs

Straps, 2 in. × 20 ft, tie down

Hoses, hydraulic, Stanley rescue system, twin, 50 ft

Air horn canister, spare

Bars, digging, 16 lb, 72 in.

Hydraulic jacks, 12 ton, bottle

Devices, friction, 8 plate, aluminium, in high-angle rescue
packs

Air bag, rescue, hose, 16 ft, red

Pneumatic adaptors, kit

Pneumatic shore, 36.3 in. to 58.0 in.

Hydraulic adaptors, kit

Rope, rescue, 200 ft

Rope, rescue, 300 ft

Shovel, long handle, round point

Electrical adaptor kit

Prussics, short, in high-angle rescue packs

Chisel, cold ⅞ in. × 11 in., SDS Max tool

Collection plate, aluminium, in high-angle rescue packs

Bank chargers, battery, various

Radio, handheld, USAR talk around entry frequency

Tygon tubing, (1 each 25 ft, 50 ft)

Point, bull 12-in. Bosch SDS-Max® tool

Cribbing, 4 × 4 × 24, kits

Salvage covers

Oil, engine, 2 cycle, 8 oz.

Radio, handheld, aviation

Pick-off straps, in high-angle rescue packs

Sigg bottle, 1 qt.

Swiftwater rescue equipment packs

Sprocket, nose, bar, Stanley rescue system

Bags, drop: one per post position

Brady single-pole circuit breaker lockout, package

Brady multipole lockout

Shores, speed, trench shores

Arcair® rods, box, ¼ in.

Lights, portable, ground, 500 wt

Charger, 1 hr with 3-stage charging f/24 V
DEWALT cordless

Atmospheric monitors: one per post position

Sawzall® blades, package, metal

Sawzall blade, package, wood

Pneumatic shore, 18.8 in. to 24.5 in.

Screwdriver, common

Radio Batteries, VHF and UHF, Charged

Radiation monitoring kit, civil defense

Vests, orange, position assignment, kit

Pneumatic shore, 55.5 in. to 87.3 in.

Underwater radio kit

Swiftwater strobe lights, on each PFD

Hydraulic rescue system hose, 20 ft sec.

Pneumatic shore, extension 36 in.

Tape, duct, box

Device, friction, 8 plate, steel, in high-angle rescue packs

Carabiner, extra large, steel, in high-angle rescue packs

Confined-space communications cable, 200 ft
with connectors

Helmets, helicopter operations: one per post position

Headlamps, Pelican VersaBright II:
one per post position

Confined-space rescue communications cable, 50 ft, with
connector

Edge protection, Ultra-Pro, in high-angle rescue packs

Confined-space rescue communications, face mask rescue
set, with speaker

Bit, ½-in. wood eater

Confined-space rescue communication cable, 100 ft, with
connector

Personal Watercraft, for River and Flood Rescue
Operations as well as Submerged Victim
Search Operations

Bit, ½-in. straight shank

Trailer, personal watercraft, rescue

Bit, ⅜-in. straight shank

SABA escape bottles, spare, 10 min:
one per post position

Swiftwater personal flotation device (PFD):
one per post position, one for victim

Light, hand, King Pelican

Rotary hammer, Hilti®, battery, 36 V

Fuel can, 1 gal, safety

Swiftwater knives: one per PFD

Horse rescue harness, large

SABA mask kit, case

Mask, swim: one per post position

Harness, full-body, class 3: one per post position

Pulleys, 4 in., in high-angle rescue packs

Blade, rotary, concrete, 16 in.

Pneumatic shore, extension 12 in.

Pneumatic shore, 24.8 in. to 35.4 in.

Swiftwater throw bags, with 70 ft-rope

Radiation pager: one per post position

Cordage, utility 10 M, in high-angle rescue packs

Blade, Diamond continuous rim, 16 in.

Horse rescue harness, medium

Dog rescue harness

Fins, swim, pair: one per post position

Whistles, on each PFD

Cyalume light sticks, boxes with different colors

GPS (global positioning system), handheld

Saw, electric, 16 in. (beam)

Saw, circular, electric, 10¼ in.

Saw, rotary, blade, 14, in. Diamond

Air chisel/impact wrench, pneumatic, kit

Air bag hose, green, 32 ft

Distance measuring device

Griphoist, TU28, with 50-ft cable

Hand truck

Air bag hose, blue, 32 ft

Mechanical grabber (electrical line)

SABA air hose reel, with 250-ft air line, victim

Lumber crayon, red, box

Shovel, scoop, D handle

Parts cleaning station

Parts cleaning station flow-through brush

Air bag hose, 32 ft, red

Confined-space rescue communications boom mic wind
   screen

Lumber crayon, yellow, box

Nut driver set, standard

Search camera reel system, 300 ft with standard camera/
   two-way communication head: for observation and
   communication in deep shaft rescues, mine & tunnel
   rescue, confined-space rescue, structural collapse
   rescue, etc.

Screw driver bit set, 60 piece

Ratchet, standard tooth flec head, $\frac{3}{8}$ in.

Ratchet, 5½ in. stubby flex head, $\frac{3}{8}$ in.

Punch & chisel set, 24 piece

Pliers, lineman ft

Pliers, arc joint

Pliers set, reach needle nose

Short arm hex set, metric, 11 piece

Pliers set, locking

Short arm hex set, standard, 11 piece

Nut driver set, metric

Multimeter, digital liquid crystal display (LCD)

Handle, spinner, ¼ in.

Handle, flex T, ½ in.

Wrench set, adjustable, 5 piece

Respirator canister, replacement, case

Chain saw bar, 16 in.

Electric detection device, hot stick

Respirators, air purifying respirator (APR):
   one per post position

Pliers set, pro

Wrench, combo, metric, 23 mm

Anchor plate, hanger, stainless steel, box

Binoculars, 10 × 25

Ram, hydraulic rescue, accessory kit

Slings, 2 in. × 20 ft, in high-angle rescue packs

Label machine

Brady plug lockout

Wrench, combo, standard, $1\frac{5}{16}$ in.

Wrench, combo, metric, 6 mm

Screw driver set

Wrench, combo, metric, 25 mm

Backboard, with straps (Miller board)

Wrench, combo, metric, 20 mm

Wrench set, combo, metric, 12 pt.,17 piece

Wrench set, combo, 12 pt., 17 piece

Socket wrench set, 235 piece

Socket tray set, 3 piece

Socket tray set, 3 piece

Socket tray set, 3 piece

Socket tray set, 3 piece

Socket Set, Bit, 19 piece

Wrench, combo, metric, 26 mm

Anchor eye nut, ¼ in.

Saw, rotary, kit

Level, 4 ft

Drill, variable speed, ½ in. DEWALT

Drill bit set, steel, ⅛ in. to ⅝ in.

Drill bit set, carbide, ¼ in. to ⅝ in.

Die grinder, pneumatic, kit

Water, drinking, case

Laser pointer

Dosimeters: one per post position

Anchor eye nut, ⅜ in.

Nail kit

Anchor eye nut, ½ in.

Awning anchor kit, heavy duty

Video camera, with light, spare battery, in case

Awning heavy duty leg set, EZ-UP, for rehab and
   equipment pool

Awning, EZ-UP, for rehab and equipment pool

Level A entry suits: one per post position
   (for weapon of mass destruction [WMD] terrorist
   attacks, potentially contaminated structural collapse
   sites, etc.)

Metal detector

Stanley breaker, 45 lb, hydraulics, BR45

Ladder, Little Giant®

Anchor eye nut, ⅝ in.

Search camera video transmitter and connector

Firefighters United for Safety, Ethics, and Ecology
   (FUSEE), highway, box

Hall runners

WMD Terrorism Antidote Kit

Nail gun nails, case, 8 piece

Nail gun, pneumatic, kit

Tow straps, nylon

Tool chest

Hose, 1¾-in. 50 ft/sec.

Mechanical axe, (electrical line cutter)

Ducting, lay-flat L

Respirator parts kit

Swiftwater rescue briefcase with log book, waterway rescue preplans, inundation maps (for dam failure, fast-rise flooding), and tsunami inundation maps (for coastal zones vulnerable to tsunamis)

Picket anchor set: in backpack for mountain rescues, mine/tunnel rescues, swiftwater rescues, etc.

Nail gun nails, case, 16 piece

Breaker bit, bull point, 1⅛ in., hex

Breaker bit, chisel, 1 in. 1⅛ in., hex

Chain saw kit,

Air bag, rescue, hose, black 32 ft

Air bag, rescue, hose, 32 ft, yellow

Rope, tagline 300 in., 8 mm in bag

Screwdriver, straight

Exothermic cutting torch

Pliers, pair, slip joint, 10 in.

Target hazard fire attack preplans

SABA air hose kit, case

Funnel, 3½-in. diameter

Hydraulic rescue tool pump, manual, with foot pedal

Ground-penetrating radar, technical search, field ready system

Rotary hammer bit, 1 in.

Ventilation blower, electric, intrinsically safe

Ventilation blower conductive duct, 8 in. × 4 ft

Tape, electrical, black, roll

Breaker, chain

Ventilation duct coupler

Rotary hammer bit, coring

Rotary hammer bit, ⅜ in.

Pipe cutter, multiwheel

Hacksaw, (heavy duty), with 10 blades

Crosscut hand saw

Camera, digital

Ventilation blower 12 in. duct adaptor

Electrical junction box, 4 outlet, with ground fault interrupter (GFI)

Level, line

Electrical adaptor, wye

Thermal imaging system, handheld, with video transmitter link

Saw, skill, blade, 7¼-in. carbide tip

PS wave detectors, for early warning of incoming earthquakes and aftershocks during collapse rescue operations

Halligan

Smart levels

Ventilation duct storage bag

Sledgehammer, 10 lbs.

Bauman bag vertical extrication C-spine immobilizer

Oxygen bottle, 55 cu ft

Ram set studs, box, ⅜ in.

Tape measure, 25 ft

Nail puller (cat's paw)

Brake bars, in high-angle rescue packs

Hammer, framing, 24-oz. straight claw

Sledgehammer, 3 lb

Ram set booster, red, Hilti

Dewatering pumps

Ram set booster, yellow, Hilti

Cutting torch cutting tip #2

Camera, digital, motion picture

Carpenters pencil, box

Cutting torch cutting tip #000

Exothermic torch, ⅜ in., conversion kit

Compasses, type 3: one per post position

Cutting torch, cutting tip #1

Cutting torch, Welding tip #00

Cutting torch tip, multiflame #8

Cutting torch tip, multiflame #6

Cutting torch cutting tip #00

Saw, rotary, blade, 14 in. carbide tip (wood)

Exothermic torch washers

Carabiners, large, locking, aluminum, in high-angle rescue packs

Electrical cords, 50 ft, 12/3

Carabiners, lg., locking, steel, in high-angle rescue packs

Ram set fasteners, 2.25 in. × ⅜ in.

Ram set fasteners, 1.75 in. × ⁷⁄₁₆ in.

Wedges, pair, 6 × 6 × 30, Case

Wedges, pair, 6 × 2 × 18, Case

Lumber, plywood, 1 in. and 2 in.

Carabiner, standard, locking, aluminum

Wedges, pair 2 × 4 × 18

PalmPilot® for information technology (IT) applications

Picket anchors, 1 in. × 4 ft, cold rolled steel

Webbing, green, 5 ft, in high-angle rescue packs

Screw jacks 1½ in. × 18 in., with foot

Cribbing, 6 × 6 × 30, cases

Stick, light, 12 hr

Air bag, rescue, pneumatic components kit

Air bag, rescue, 31.8 ton, 13.1-in. lift

Auxiliary electrical adaptors, kit, assorted

Electrical adaptor, wye

Chain saw air filter

Saw, rotary, air filter

Cutting torch wrench, 8 MC

Label machine tape, 4 in.

Saw, rotary, drive belt, spare

Rotary hammer bit, 1¼, in.

Rotary hammer bit, ⅞, in. spline shank

Awning sidewall, EZ-UP, for rehab and equipment pool

Level, 6 in.

Rebar cutter blades

Engraver, electric

Lineman gloves, pair

Pliers, tongue & groove, 14 in.

Cell phones: one per post position, for emergency communications

Screw driver, Phillips

Nails, box, 25 lb, 8 piece

Nails, box, 25 lb, 16 piece

Adapter kit, air knife and air vacuum, to use SCBA bottles to provide compressed air to victims trapped in quicksand, mud flats, and trench/ excavation collapse remote from USAR apparatus

Screwdriver, Phillips, stubby

Chalk line, chalk, 8 oz.

Rebar cutter, battery

Rebar cutter, battery, spare blades

Screwdriver, slotted, stubby

Horse rescue harness, small

Animal rescue snare

Rotary hammer bit, ¹¹/₁₆ in. spline shank

Electrical cord reel, 10/3

Nails, box, 25 lb, 16-piece duplex

Etriers, in high-angle rescue packs

Crane operators manual

Ram set boosters, purple, Hilti

ICS field operations guide (FOG)

Battery, 12-volt lead acid, spare for exothermic cutting torch and other similar-powered tools

Ventilation blower ducts, 8 in., 1 ea., 25 ft, 15 ft

Bars, pry and pinch-point, 60 in., 18 lb.

FEMA USAR national response system FOG

Rescue resource list: with contact numbers for local/ state/ federal response agencies, OSHA, public works, crane operators, structural engineers, demolition contractors, etc.

Cribbing, 2 × 4 × 24 cases

Wedges, pair, 4 × 4 × 24 cases

Generator, 5 kw, portable, gas

Swiftwater helmets

Fireground search rope pack

Blade, carbide tip, 14-in. fire rescue

Ellis jacks

Lumber, 6 × 6 × 20 ft

Lumber, 2 × 12 × 12 ft

Petrogen metal burning systems

Cans, gasoline, 1 gal, for Petrogen metal burning systems

Cribbing, 2 × 6 × 30

Ram set pins, box, steel, ⅞ in.

Osborn aluminum lockouts, 1 in. hasp

Osborn aluminum lockouts 1½ in. hasp

Ram set pins, box, 1⅞ in.

Ram set pins, box, 2⅞ in.

Anchor kit, in ammo boxes, 1/size

Communicable disease kits: one per post position

Chock block, metal

Line, chalk

Eight plate, rescue, aluminum, in high-angle rescue packs

Eight plate, rescue, steel, in high-angle rescue packs

Carpenter belts: one per post position

Hydraulic tool, fluid, 3 gal

Square, trispeed

Shovels, folding

Rope, rescue, 100 ft

Chalk line

Lumber, 2 × 4 × 20 ft

Lumber, 4 × 4 × 16 ft

Respirator dust prefilter

Haul buckets, metal, 5 gallons

Light saddle, pelican

Electrical adaptor

Diagonal cutters,

Swiftwater dry suit: one per post position

Electrical plug, L14P, male plug

Swiftwater goggles: one per post position

Swiftwater gloves, pair: one per post position

Spark plug, for rotary saw

Swiftwater fins, pair: one per post position

Kneepads, pair, CORDURA®, with plastic cover: one per post position

Elbow pads, pair, CORDURA with plastic cover: one per post position

Swiftwater booties, wet suit, pair: one per post position

Atmospheric monitor, battery shell pack

SABA air hose reel, with 250 ft of air line & comm

Electrical plug, L14R, female receptacle

Spark plug, for Stihl 044 chain saw

Economy lockout padlock with 2½ in. shackle

Electrical adaptor

Webbing, blue, 12 ft

Floodlight, 500 wt, portable

Atmospheric monitor, spare batteries, lithium

Canvas bag, tool, carpenters, extra-strength: one per post position

Saw, rotary, blade, 14 in. metal cutting

Ellis clamps

Filter, water/dust stop

Paddles, Carlson, for inflatable rescue boat operations

Radio harness, chest: one per post position

Exothermic cutting torch collet nuts, ¼ in.

Exothermic torch flash arrestor

Zip ties, medium duty, 10 in.

Radio bone microphones, for Motorola® Saba radio: one per post position

Topographical maps for mountainous areas in jurisdictional and surrounding regions

Pipe, schedule 40, 1½ in. × 20 ft

Webbing, red, 22 ft, in high-angle rescue packs

SCBA bottles, 60 minute: one primary and one spare per post position, with 5 extra for equipment operations

Pulleys, Prussik minding, in high-angle rescue packs

Electrical plug, L5P, male plug

Post screw jacks

Electrical plug, L5R, female receptacle

Pipe, steel schedule 40, 1½ in. × 4 ft

Air bag, rescue, regulators, in hardened case for industrial and street operations

Pulleys, 2 in., in high-angle rescue packs

Air bag, rescue, regulators: in back pack for rapid intervention operations and collapse rescue operations

---

Source: L.A. County Fire Department Urban Search and Rescue Task Force 103 and 130 (Rescue Company) Inventory

APPENDIX B

Sample of Training Required for Some Rescue Companies

Primary Training Courses

Rescue Systems 1	40 hours
Rescue Systems 2	40 hours
Emergency Trench Rescue	24 hours
Swiftwater 1/River, Flood 1	24 hours
Confined-Space Operational	40 hours
Collapse Structure Technician	16 hours
Swiftwater 2/River, Flood 2	24 hours
Closed-Circuit SCBA	24 hours
Marine Disaster Rescue	24 hours
Tunnel Awareness	8 hours
Weapon of Mass Destruction (WMD) Training	30 hours
Large Animal Rescue	24 hours
Helicopter/High-Rise	16 hours
Inflatable Rescue Boat (IRB)/Personal Watercraft (PWC)	24 hours
Mine Rescue	24 hours

Annual Continuing Education

Confined Space	16 hours
Swiftwater 2	8 hours
Swiftwater Ground	8 hours
Closed-Circuit SCBA	32 hours
Swiftwater Helicopter	8 hours
Marine Disaster	16 hours
Building Shoring	16 hours
WMD Training	16 hours
Emergency Trench Rescue	8 hours
Large Animal	24 hours
Cutting and Breaching	8 hours
Helicopter High-Rise	16 hours
Heavy Lifting	8 hours
IRB/PWC	8 hours
Rope Rescue	16 hours
Auto Extrication	8 hours
Dive Rescue	48 hours
Total:	**272 hours**

Source: Los Angeles County Fire Department, Training Requirements for Urban Search and Rescue Task Forces 103 and 130 (Rescue Companies)

Support of Technical Rescue Teams

FIREFIGHTER II

Chapter 35

KEY TERMS

1 New York Plaza. The site of a major blaze in 1970.

¾ rubber boots. Boots that do not meet the NFPA 1971 standard. Hip boots (also known as ¾ rubber boots) can serve an important role in the event of water emergencies, from a flooded basement to minor street flooding, to keep you dry and protected.

4-Gas Meter. An atmospheric monitoring instrument used to monitor oxygen levels, flammability, carbon monoxide, and hydrogen sulfide.

A

ABC. Monoammonium phosphate, "ABC," or "multi-purpose" dry chemical. It differs from potassium bicarbonate or sodium bicarbonate in that it is acidic in nature. When it contacts the burning surface of an ordinary combustible, a molten residue (metaphosphoric acid) is formed. This residue coats the burning ember and excludes oxygen.

abrasion. The friction damage caused by two objects coming in contact, as in a rope being pulled over an unprotected edge.

absorbent booms. A barrier made from various materials that can collect compatible materials that have been released during a spill.

absorption. The physical process of picking up a liquid with a solid sorbent material.

acetylene. A gas that, when combined with oxygen at the right mixture and ignited, burns at a very high temperature. Acetylene is commonly used in cutting torches and welding, but when an acetylene tank is exposed to fire, it can overpressurize and potentially BLEVE.

acid. A chemical compound containing one or more hydrogen ions that will liberate hydrogen gas on contact with certain metals, has a pH of less than 7.0, and may be very chemically active.

ACP. Area contingency plan.

actinide series. One of two series of metals at the bottom of the periodic table, the other being the lanthanide series. Collectively, they are the rare earth metals.

acute exposure. A single exposure to a toxic substance.

addressable device. A fire alarm system component with discrete identification that can have its status individually identified or that is used to individually control other functions.

adjustable gallonage fog nozzle. A nozzle that allows a nozzle operator to choose a desired flow using a flow-selection ring.

admin. The tracking of costs and requirements of the resource required to mitigate an event.

adsorption. The chemical process by which the spilled product adheres to the surface of the sorbent.

ADULTS. Mnemonic used for identifying conditions where a high-flow handline (usually a 2½ in. [65 mm]]) should be used instead of the standard low- or medium-flow handline (1½ or 1¾ in. [38 or 45 mm]).

advanced life support system (ALS). A system in which the paramedic provider level is a component.

aerial ladder. A firefighting apparatus that has a permanent, mounted, telescoping ladder usually constructed of steel, aluminum, or a combination of metal alloys and that is operated via a hydraulic fluid and lift system in conjunction with steel cables and pulleys. These ladders vary in size and reach heights of 100 feet (30 m) or more.

air consumption rate (ACR). The rate at which a wearer will use up the capacity of air carried in an SCBA cylinder.

A-frame ladder. A ladder that when closed resembles a small extension ladder without any halyard or pulleys. It has two pins and two receiver brackets mounted at the ladder's tip. Most of these ladders have two stationary ladder locks that hook onto a rung to keep them closed or locked together when extended manually. This ladder can be used in the A-frame position or as a small extension ladder. Because of its size, it can be transported conveniently throughout a structure. Also called a combination ladder.

after action review (AAR). An informal discussion conducted after and incident is completed to review the strategy and tactics employed at the incident to determine if the incident was handled correctly, safely, and to offer suggestions on future similar incidents. AARs are also referred to as critiques or post-mortems.

air and light shafts. Vertical spaces in some multistory row houses, intended to bring sunlight and air into rooms of the apartments. These shafts have windows built into the walls, allowing rapid vertical fire spread from floor to floor.

air bills. A set of hazardous material shipping papers containing the name and address of the shipper and receiver, identification of the material being shipped, and the quantity and weight of the shipment. Air bills are kept in the cockpit of aircraft, under the supervision of the pilot.

air management program (AMP). A system that recognizes the factors related to air consumption rates (ACR) and develops guidelines allowing firefighters to exit hazardous environments prior to using their reserve supply of air.

air purifying respirator (APR). Respiratory protection through a partial or full face piece which uses removable cartridges to filter certain types of particulates and contaminants from the air.

air-reactive material. A substance that will self-react and/or ignite when exposed to air.

air-sampling detector. An air sampling device that uses suction tubes to draw air from the environment.

AKA/vanity name. A designation used when the name of the building may be more distinctive to the fire department than its post office address, e.g., the Empire State Building, the Pentagon, etc.

alarm signal. Indicates that an emergency condition exists and that some type of response is required.

alarm time. The time between feeling a painful heat stimulus and being able to remove oneself from the environment or take action to improve the environment.

alarm-initiating devices. Automatic or manual mechanisms that cause a system to indicate an alarm condition.

alarm-notification appliances. A device that notifies the occupants of a dangerous condition, by means of audible appliances, visible appliances, or a combination of both.

alcohol. Hydrocarbon derivatives having a hydrocarbon backbone and a hydroxyl radical.

alcohol-resistant foam. A synthetic or protein based foam resistant to the actions of alcohols.

aldehydes. Hydrocarbon derivatives having a hydrocarbon backbone and an aldehyde radical.

Alfred P. Murrah Building. A federal building in Oklahoma City bombed by anti-government, right-wing radicals in 1995.

algorithms. A specific set of instructions for carrying out a procedure or solving a problem.

alkali metals. The Group IA elements on the periodic table, headed by lithium (even though hydrogen sits above lithium.)

alkaline earth metals. The Group IIA elements on the periodic table, headed by beryllium.

alkanes. The analogous series of saturated hydrocarbons that has the general formula C_nH_{2n+2}.

alkenes. The analogous series of unsaturated hydrocarbons that has the general formula C_nH_{2n}.

alkynes. The analogous family of unsaturated hydrocarbons that has the general formula C_nH_{2n-2}.

allergies. A condition in which a person has been sensitized to a substance, subsequently reacting adversely to further exposure.

alpha particle. A specific particle ejected from a radioactive atom, having low penetrating power and short range.

aluminum oxide abrasive blade. A non-toothed circular abrasive disc made up of composite and metallic materials held together by an organic bonding agent and used with rotary power saws to cut metal.

aluminum stile door. An outward-opening and heat treated tempered glass door in an aluminum frame commonly found in storefronts.

America Burning. A 1973 report from the National Advisory Commission on Fire Prevention and Control that noted that the mission of the American fire service has expanded rapidly beyond fire prevention, suppression, and investigation. Recognizing that firefighters are the first line of defense for citizens facing any type of disaster or emergency, the report presented an agenda for improving firefighters' ability to deal with such situations in the future. It lead to the development of the United States Fire Administration and the National Fire Academy.

American Society for Testing and Materials International (ASTM). A voluntary standards development organization that develops technical standards for materials, products, systems, and services. Examples are ASTM Test Standard E84-08a Standard Test Method for Surface Burning Characteristics of Building Materials, and ASTM E119-08a Standard Test Methods for Fire Tests of Building Construction and Materials.

American Society of Mechanical Engineers (ASME). An organization that develops voluntary standards and promotes the art, science, and practice of mechanical and multidisciplinary engineering and allied sciences around the globe. Examples are standards that maintain safety in elevators and escalators.

amines. Hydrocarbon or ammonia derivatives having a hydrocarbon backbone and an amine radical.

analog. An older type of radio signal that relies on measurable quantities of voltage, resistances, or rotations.

analogous series. A series of compounds in which each successive compound differs from the previous one by the same variation.

ANFO. A blasting agent composed of ammonium nitrate and fuel oil.

angle stickers. Stickers affixed to each side of the base section of a portable ladder between the fourth and fifth rungs that warn of electrical hazards overhead, question whether a ladder is in a correct angle, and remind of the proper direction the fly section should face. Also called danger or electrical stickers.

angry smoke. A heavy volume of thick, black, pressurized smoke that can be disgorged from a fire compartment.

anhydrous. Chemical term meaning "no water present."

appliance. A piece of portable equipment through which water flows.

approved. Having met the requirements of the authority having jurisdiction.

aqueous film-forming foam (AFFF). A water-based Class B firefighting foam that controls Class B spills/fires by forming a blanket on the surface of the fuel, creating a barrier between the fuel vapors and the air. AFFF is a low-expansion foam.

arbor. The shaft on which the saw blade mounts on a saw and is held in place with a nut.

arch. A basic construction component that is constructed in two basic shapes: round or curved arch, and flat arch.

area of refuge. The designated area within a building where occupants with limited mobility or extended exit paths can remain without exiting until the fire is under control. The area can typically be isolated from smoke.

area of rescue assistance. An area where persons unable to use stairways can remain temporarily to await instructions or assistance during emergency evacuation.

arm-lock maneuver. A position that secures a firefighter to a portable ladder during window venting that is accomplished by the positioning of the firefighter's arms.

aromatic hydrocarbon. A type of hydrocarbon with a specific type of ring structure.

arson. The intentional setting of fire to a building or object for the purpose of destroying it.

arsonist. A person who intentionally starts fires.

articulating ladder. A ladder that may incorporate the use of boom, tube, or ladder construction with an articulating joint that allows one section to be placed above, behind, or over an object. At the end of the boom, a bucket is attached with a pre-piped monitor.

asbestos. A naturally occurring mineral fiber that can pollute air or water and cause cancer or asbestosis when inhaled.

asphalt siding. Thin asphalt shingles that often look like bricks.

asphyxiants. A substance, either a gas or a vapor, that interferes with the respiratory process.

atmospheric pressure. A constant force of pressure (14.7 psi [100 kPa]) caused by the atmosphere of the planet.

atom. The smallest particle of an element that can still be identified as that element and that is electrically neutral.

atomic mass unit (AMU). The unit of weight used to state atomic or molecular weights of atoms or molecules.

atomic number. The whole number found above the symbol of an element in its box on the periodic table and by which the elements are arranged. The atomic number is equal to the number of protons in each atom of an element.

atomic weight. The weight of the nuclear parts of an atom, the proton and neutron, measured in atomic mass units, or AMUs.

atomization. A process that breaks a liquid into a mist, creating maximum surface area of the liquid.

attack hose. A hose designed to be small and lightweight enough to be easily moved around, which ranges from 1½ to 2½ in. (38 to 56 mm) in diameter, and flowing up to 325 gpm (1,230 L/min). It is considered an attack/handline hose.

attack stair. The stairwell (usually the one closest to the seat of the fire) in a multi-story building with more than one stairwell designated as the one from which an interior fire attack will be initiated.

attic ladder. A narrow, collapsible ladder that folds into itself for transportation through small, narrow spaces. Also called a folding, scissor, suitcase, or closet ladder.

authority having jurisdiction. A person or entity enforcing local codes, standards, or laws concerning the construction of and the life-safety issues of a particular building or structure, including adopted building codes and standards.

autoignition temperature. The minimum temperature to which a material must be raised before combustion will occur. Also called ignition temperature.

automatic aid. A plan developed by two or more fire departments for the immediate, joint response to incidents.

automatic dry-deluge sprinklers. A system containing all open sprinkler heads that can be triggered by an air pilot line, heat detectors, or a remote pull station, which results in water flowing to all heads, which are open all the time.

automatic dry-pipe sprinklers. A sprinkler system where compressed air holds back the dry-pipe valve until sprinkler heads start to open from the heat of the fire. Air will then rush out of the heads, dropping the pressure, which allows the dry valve to open and fill the system with water.

automatic foam spray sprinklers. A system that is similar to all other sprinkler systems, except with a tank of firefighting foam connected to it that delivers finished foam to the sprinkler head.

automatic preaction sprinklers. A dry sprinkler system used indoors and in water sensitive areas. Heat or smoke detectors actuate a valve in the room, causing water to flow.

automatic sprinkler heads. A component of an automatic sprinkler system that contains either frangible bulbs or fusible links that open an orifice when heated to a certain temperature, allowing water to be discharged.

automatic sprinkler system. A system of pipes and sprinkler heads, designed under fire protection principles, that is thermally activated and, when activated, discharges water onto a fire without requiring manual activation.

automatic vehicle location (AVL). Using satellite or wireless phone signals to produce an approximate location of a vehicle or person.

automatic wet sprinklers. A sprinkler system in which water is at the head at all times. They are most commonly found in heated places and are the quickest and most efficient type of sprinkler system.

auxiliary boxes. A type of municipal fire alarm system that is tied directly to a specific building. If the fire alarm in the building is tripped, the auxiliary box will notify the fire department.

average molecular weight. An approximation of the molecular weight of a substance, such as air, calculated with the atomic weight of its component elements.

awning windows. Similar to casement windows, these open upward instead of sideways, and are often found in basements.

azides. Explosive compounds containing the azide ion.

B

backdraft. The term given to a type of explosion in a confined space caused by the sudden influx of air into a mixture of gases that has been heated to above the ignition temperature of at least one of its components.

backup position. The firefighter who aids in providing momentum to the nozzle operator.

balance point. The spot on a ladder where it balances evenly when lifted. It may not be the true center of the ladder's length because other mechanisms attached to the ladder may render the balance point more toward one end.

bale. The handle on a nozzle used to open and close the valve controlling the flow of water from the nozzle.

balloon frame. A building with studs running two or more stories without fire stops.

balloon frame construction. A structure with studs running two or more stories without fire stops. Open spaces between studs extending from foundation to the attic allows for quick and easy fire travel.

Baltimore fire of 1904. A fire that raged for more than two days with mutual aid companies responding from as far away as Philadelphia,

Washington, New York City, Wilmington, and Atlantic City. Tragically, most mutual aid companies found that the lack of standard fire hose couplings and threads and the absence of adaptors limited their usefulness.

Bangor ladder. A larger extension ladder with tormentor poles to maximize stability during raising and lowering. Also called a pole ladder.

bank down. A term referring to a situation in which smoke rises and ultimately fills a room with smoke to the floor.

barn roof. Another name for a gambrel roof.

barrier booms. Barriers constructed of nonporous materials that float on the water to contain spills, such as oil.

base. The end of a ladder that contacts the ground when positioned against a structure. In a truss-construction ladder, spurs or spikes are usually mounted onto the base. In other types of ladders, a permanently mounted precast aluminum foot, butt, or shoe attaches to the base. Also called the heel or butt.

base. 1. That location at which the primary logistics functions are coordinated and administered.
2. A chemical compound that contains the hydroxide ion, is active chemically and has a pH greater than 7.0.

basic emergency medical technician (EMT-B). The minimum level of certification required to function on an ambulance.

basic life support system (BLS). A system in which the first responder, EMT-B, and EMT-I provider levels are usually components.

BC. Sodium Bicarbonate or "BC" is also known as "regular dry chemical." In addition to its effectiveness on Class B and C fires, it does have some effect on the flaming stages of a Class A fire but no effect on the embers or deep seated Class A fire.

beam. 1. A horizontal supporting member that transfers weight from one location to another and from one structural component to another. 2. The main structural component of a ladder that supports a firefighter's weight and transfers it from the rungs to the ground. The beams run the long sides of the ladder and support the rungs at 14-inch intervals.

bed section. The bottom section of a ladder that remains in touch with the ground or apparatus. Usually this is the widest section because upper or fly sections retract into it. The bed section is normally the only section with a designed foot or butt attached to it.

belay. A rope that secures a climber to an anchor point as a safety; also, the act of securing a climber in this way.

bench calibration. The ability to provide accurate readings on detection equipment by exposing meters to a predetermined concentration of gases.

benchmarks. Measurable outcomes used by personnel operating at an incident scene to confirm and communicate the completion of strategic goals or tactical objectives.

benzene ring. The six-sided, closed molecular structure with a carbon atom at each apex and alternating double bonds.

benzene. The first in the series of six-carbon cyclical hydrocarbons called the aromatic hydrocarbons.

beta particle. A charged particle emitted from the nucleus of some atoms as part of those atoms' radioactive decay, with moderate penetrating power and a range of up to a few meters.

Beverly Hills Supper Club fire. A May 28, 1977, fire that broke out in the Zebra Room in Southgate, Kentucky, in which 165 people were killed, many of the victims caught in a crowd crush (jam of people) at exits while fire and smoke moved in.

big box retail. A large (greater than 50,000 sq ft) undivided single-story commercial building (usually of non-combustible construction) with a single retail tenant and few or no interior divisions.

bight. A rope that is bent back on itself and parallel.

Bilco type fold-up doors. A metal enclosure found on the outside of buildings and homes with hinged doors leading to a basement or cellar.

bills of lading. A set of hazardous material shipping papers containing the name and address of the shipper and receiver, identification of the material being shipped and the quantity and weight of the shipment. Bills of lading are for over-the-road shipments and are also called freight bills.

bi-metal. A reciprocating saw blade used to cut both wood and metal.

black fire. Thick, black superheated smoke that will ignite explosively when conditions are perfect, such as with the introduction of oxygen.

Black Tom Island. A major munitions depot situated in the Hudson River near Jersey City, N.J., where, in July 1916, two million pounds of explosives were detonated with such force that it could be felt 90 miles (145 km) away.

blasting agent. A substance made up of a mixture of materials, none of which is classified as explosive, but operates by exploding.

bleeding the line. The process of releasing entrapped air from a charged line by opening the nozzle fully to ensure the attack line is supplied with sufficient water flow and pressure.

blind shaft. An elevator shaft that has passenger openings only at the top and bottom of the shaft, and does not stop at any floors between. Blind shaft elevators are frequently used in high-rise buildings where individual elevators serve different sets of floors (zones) within the building.

blitz attack. A structural fire attack tactic in which high-flow exterior fire streams are initially used to reduce/contain visible fire in the hope of allowing a follow-up interior fire attack for final extinguishment. A blitz attack is often used with visible fire in several rooms or when an initial company is awaiting the arrival of additional companies prior to entry.

blood asphyxiant. A substance that will attach itself to red blood cells and render them incapable of carrying oxygen.

blow-up. A sustained rapid increase in the size and speed of a wildland fire, which often places fire crews at great risk.

bobtails. Small, local delivery tanker trucks that carry between 2,000 and 3,000 gallons of liquefied petroleum gas.

body chemistry. The various features of a victim that determine how that victim will react to an exposure.

body to the building. A term that describes a firefighter's positioning his or her body on the side of the ladder that provides a constant view of the fire building.

boiling liquid expanding vapor explosion (BLEVE). An event in which a container of liquefied flammable gas fails and the resulting release allows the contents to expand to hundreds of times their liquefied volume. When ignited, the rapidly expanding vapor violently explodes.

boil line. The line where the recycling water is separated from the main downstream current.

boiling point. The minimum temperature at which the vapor pressure of a liquid equals atmospheric pressure.

bomb proof anchor. An anchor able to hold the intended load and then some.

booster or reel line. A rubber hose with either a ¾- or 1-in. (20- or 25-mm) diameter used for nuisance fires and small vegetation fires, with less than 60 gpm (227 L/min) flow.

bottom chord. the lower supporting member of a truss.

bowstring. A structural truss consisting of a hump-like curved top chord meeting bottom chords at each end and used on large structures where a wide open floor space is required.

box keep. A component of mortise locks that lines the hole in the frame into which the bolt fits.

boxer's stance. Standing with one leg forward and the other back.

Braidwood, James. Superintendent of the London Fire Brigade, appointed in 1833 and credited with organizing the first effective paid fire department, offering a model for an effective urban fire department.

branched-chain hydrocarbon. A configuration in which a carbon atom is attached to more than two other carbon atoms, forming a side or "branch" chain.

branches. That organizational level that can be functional or geographic and have responsibility for major segments of incident operations.

breaching. Breaking through or make an opening, hole, or gap in a wall or floor.

bread and butter. Single- and two-family homes.

brick ordinance. Enacted on April 20, 1863, this rule required all new buildings to be constructed of brick or stone.

brisance. The explosive power of an explosive or a material that explodes.

British thermal unit (BTU). The amount of heat energy required to raise 1 gram of material 1 degree Celsius or 1 pound of material 1 degree Fahrenheit.

Brooklyn Theater fire. An 1876 incident that led to improved laws for high-occupancy structures.

bucket brigade. A line of people formed for the purpose of passing buckets filled with items. This can be debris removal technique used when life is still suspected in a collapse.

buddy breathing. A previously taught practice of two firefighters or a firefighter and civilian sharing a single facepiece in an emergency situation. Buddy breathing is no longer a recommended practice.

buddy system. A safety practice used to pair first responders together when encountering a potentially hazardous or risky environment.

Building Code Effectiveness Grading Schedule. Developed by ISO, this rates building code enforcement in individual communities.

building intelligence. Critical building data that is available to the fire department during an emergency response.

building reconnaissance. The gathering of critical building data during a pre-incident planning site visit.

built-up roof. A type of roof covering with a layer of fiberboard insulation panels, then a base sheet of roofing material and several layers or roofing felt (paper).

bulk terminal. A facility where flammable/combustible liquids or gases are transported, then either held in large capacity storage tanks or transferred into smaller vehicles or cylinders for customer use.

bulkhead. An enclosure at the roof level accessed by a wood or metal door from the interior stairs below and used when occupants are trapped by fire below to gain access to the roof for safety.

bumper spikes. Metal spikes on a chainsaw's body found below the guide bar.

bungee cord. Elasticized rope.

bunker boots. The boot typically used today, they can be pull-on leather or rubber boots, which are typically 14 to 16 in. (36 to 40 cm) high; or they may be laced/speed laced boots, which are typically 10 in. high. For efficient donning, bunker boots are typically placed within the pants.

bunker gear. Protective clothing that includes the helmet, coat, pants, boots, and gloves normally worn by firefighters during structural firefighting operations. See also structural PPE and turnout gear.

burglar bars. Commonly known as "window bars," these bars are attached or set into the wall.

burst pressure. A test done by the manufacturer when the hose is new that tests the hose at at least three times the specified service test pressure.

butt. The end of a ladder that contacts the ground when positioned against a structure. In a truss-construction ladder, spurs or spikes are usually mounted onto the butt. In other types of ladders, a permanently mounted pre-cast aluminum foot, butt, or shoe attaches to the butt. Also called the heel or base.

bypass. Emergency Bypass. Part of the SCBA system, a valve that, when activated, will deliver air directly from the cylinder to the facepiece, bypassing the regulator. The bypass is activated to deliver short bursts of high-pressure air (often to clear a fogged mask) or in emergency situations when the regulator has failed.

C

CAA. Clear Air Act.

CAD. Computer-aided dispatch system.

call box. A direct communication device that puts the caller and the telecommunicator in direct voice contact. This allows the caller to request a specific type of assistance and the telecommunicator to gain valuable information about what type of incident is occurring. They are often found along roadways, highways, and footpaths.

call taker. The first person to receive the information in a communications center and who then passes it on to the telecommunicator. The call taker may be a state highway patrol dispatcher at a public safety answering point (PSAP) in a remote area far from the caller, or it could be a local agency, depending on how the wireless call is routed.

camps. A geographical site, within a general incident area, separate from the base, equipped and staffed to provide food, water, and sanitary services to incident personnel.

capstan. A machine that rotates to apply force to another used in conjunction with ropes or cabled winches.

carabiner. Metal connecting links used extensively in rope systems.

carbides. Binary compounds of carbon and another element, usually metals.

carbide-tipped blade. A 12- or 24-toothed steel tipped circular blade used with rotary power saws to cut wood, Lexan, acrylic glass panels, and light-gauge metal.

carbon dioxide suppression system. A non-water based suppression system that inhibits combustion by displacing oxygen to smother a fire. This is a colorless, odorless gas.

carbon dioxide. Also known as CO_2, it is an odorless and colorless gas that does not conduct electricity. It is stored in extinguishers as a liquid under pressure and when expelled turns into a "snow" (dry ice) on contact with the moisture in the atmosphere.

carbon-based compounds. Hydrophobic and nonpolar, including materials such as activated carbon and graphite.

carboys. Small, round, or square containers kept inside of another box and used for storage of acids and other corrosive materials. The outer box can be made of wood, polystyrene, or other materials to protect the container during transport, use, or storage.

carburetor. A pressure differential device on an engine that mixes air and fuel in the correct proportions to allow even combustion.

carcinogen. Any substance that has been identified as possibly leading to the development or aggravation of cancer.

card systems. A system that still exists in smaller agencies used to determine a pre-designated response to an emergency. Radio and computer equipment provide quicker responses in higher-volume agencies.

carriage bolt. A round-headed bolt used mostly for fastening pieces of timber together and inserted into pre-drilled holes.

CAS. Chemical Abstract Service.

cascade system. A series of larger compressed air bottles, often connected to an air compressor and an air refill station, used to refill SCBA cylinders.

case-hardened steel. The result of a process in which the steel is heated to give it more strength. For theft prevention, lock shackles are often case-hardened to resist cutting while remaining less brittle inside to resist impacts.

casement windows. A sideways-opening window operated by cranking a handle.

cell phone sites. Cell-phone-service-provider-installed structures found on parapet walls and roofs that can restrict the area available for cutting the roof for vertical ventilation and pose an electrical, gas, and tripping hazard.

cellar pipe. A nozzle with a directed stream that can be pointed in any direction through the use of a lever at floor level.

cellulosic materials. Ordinary combustibles, such as wood, paper, and cloth.

Celsius. A temperature scale denoted by °C, where the normal freezing point of water is 0°C and the normal boiling point of water is 100°C.

cementitious. Densely packed and non-fibrous, friable material.

center core floor plan. A type of building construction typically used in modern high-rise buildings where utilities, elevators, bathrooms, and exit stairways are built near the center of the building and are typical on every floor.

center hall layout. A building layout in which each floor has a main central hallway running the long axis of the building and individual occupancies are accessed from that hall. The building's central functions are often located at either end of this hallway, as well as the axis mid-point.

central core layout. A building layout common in high-rise construction where a building's central functions (HVAC, electrical, plumbing, elevators, etc.) are contained within a vertical central core, with open floor space surrounding the core on each floor.

central-station alarm system. A system in which the operations of circuits and devices are transmitted automatically to a central station, where they are recorded, maintained, and supervised. This station is constantly staffed with trained operators.

CERCLA. Comprehensive Environmental Response Compensation and Liability Act.

cervical collar. A device used by first responders to immobilize a victim's neck and head in cases where they have undergone trauma.

CFC. Chlorofluorocarbon.

CFR. Code of Federal Regulations.

chafing block. A block of material with a channel designed for the hose to rest on, which prevents damage to the hose from rubbing on the ground due to vibrations or hose reactions.

chain brake. A safety feature used to lock the chain from spinning when transporting chain saws.

chain guards. The safety guard that houses the chainsaw guide bar to prevent accidents and to allow cutting at the tip of the chainsaw only.

chain of custody. The method of preserving the integrity of an item of evidence. A form stays with the item and documents the security of the evidence.

chain saws. A portable wood or concrete cutting power tool with an endless chain made up of sharp teeth.

chain. A molecule of bonded carbon atoms, resembling a chain with carbon atoms existing as links.

channel guide. A section, channel, or slot in a ladder that supports and interlocks with a corresponding section of a ladder as it is raised.

Channing, William F. Inventor of the street box fire-alarm telegraph system.

chase kinks. The process of following the hoseline and removing any kinks to allow the water to flow unrestricted.

cheater. A short section of air tube attached to the inhalation valve on the facepiece as a way of reducing SCBA-supplied air use. Cheaters are not approved for use.

check valve. A valve assembly consisting of a body and a clapper, which restricts flow to only one direction.

chemical biological radiological nuclear (CBRN). Agents that pose a general health threat, especially if released as part of a terrorist attack. CBRN-rated protective equipment will provide protection against all four types of threats.

chemical reaction. A chemical change that occurs when two or more substances are brought together and energy is either absorbed or liberated. Examples include oxidation, condensation, hydrolysis, ionization, photosynthesis, polymerization, pyrolysis, and reduction.

chemistry. The science of matter, energy, and reactions.

Chicago Fire. The most serious late 19th-century fire, lasting for four days in early October 1871. The fire destroyed almost 20,000 buildings in a four-square-mile area in the city center, and left 100,000 people homeless.

choke lever. The device on small engines that regulates the amount of air allowed to enter the carburetor. When closed, it enriches the fuel/air mixture and enables the power tool to start and run more easily when cold.

choker hitch. A rigging technique used when rope, sling, or webbing is looped and girthed on itself to wrap around something.

chronic exposure. Multiple exposures over an extended period of time.

cinch. A tool used as part of speed laces to quickly secure or tie boots.

circle dike. Used as a secondary containment to capture a released material that escapes or overflows the V-dike. It is a beam that is placed 360° around a leaking container. It does not form a perfect circle but rather an enclosure for the product.

circle of danger. The term used when firefighters are operating dangerous power tools and the need for a 10-foot safe working radius is needed to prevent injury to other firefighters.

cistern. A watertight underground tank used for storing liquids, especially water.

Class A foam. Firefighting foam intended for used on Class A fires. Foam concentrate is mixed with water and, when applied to burning Class A materials, breaks down the surface tension of the water, allowing it to remain on the surface of the material, providing a longer cooling period, preventing regrowth of the fire.

Class A uniform. A full dress uniform used for special, official occasions.

Class A. Ordinary combustibles—wood, paper, rubber, fabrics, and many plastics.

Class B foam. Class of firefighting foams intended for use on Class B (flammable/combustible liquids) spills or fires. Class B foams suppress the vapors given off by spills or fires, eliminating the oxygen and cooling the fuel, helping to prevent reflash.

Class B. Flammable liquids and gases—gasoline, oils, paint, lacquer and tar.

Class C. Fires involving live electrical equipment.

Class D. Combustible metals or combustible metal alloys.

Class I standpipe system. A system of pipes and hose outlet valves designed exclusively for fire department use.

Class II standpipe system. A system of pipes and hose outlet valves designed for occupant use.

Class III standpipe system. A system of pipes and hose outlet valves designed for both fire department and occupant use.

Class K. Fires in cooking appliances that involve combustible cooking media—vegetable or animal oils and fats.

clean-agent gases. Gasses designed to replace Halon as a suppression agent without harming the ozone layer.

closed-circuit SCBA. A self-contained breathing apparatus (SCBA) that uses compressed oxygen and a filter system in which exhaled air from the user is filtered and re-oxygenated then delivered to the wearer. The advantage is a longer use cycle for the wearer.

closed shaft. A light and air shaft that is enclosed on all sides and cannot be identified from street level.

closet ladder. A narrow, collapsible ladder that folds into itself for transportation through small, narrow spaces. Also called a folding, attic, scissor, or suitcase ladder.

cloud-to-cloud lightning. The visible flow of electron discharge between clouds when they have different levels of electron charges.

CO. Carbon monoxide. A colorless, odorless gas released as a by-product of incomplete combustion. CO molecules replace oxygen molecules in the bloodstream, depriving body tissues of needed oxygen.

CO_2. Carbon dioxide.

cockloft. The common roof space. The cockloft is defined as the large concealed space between the top-floor ceiling and the underside of the roof deck. Fire may spread with explosive speed inside the cockloft.

Coconut Grove Night Club. Location of a November 1942 fire in Boston, Mass., that resulted in 492 deaths and hundreds of injuries.

code. A document with mandatory wording suitable for adoption into law. It must be legally adopted by a jurisdiction to be enforceable.

coffin cut. A 3 × 6 ft or 4 × 8 ft rectangular roof ventilation hole.

cold zone. The clearly marked and controlled area where the command post and support functions that are necessary to control an incident.

cold-formed steel stud. A steel stud formed from a steel rod without using heat.

collapse zone. The area on the ground that includes the height and width of a building or part of a building that may collapse, plus additional space for safety.

collapse zone. The distance from the unstable wall equal to the height of the wall.

column. A vertical structural element that transmits a load imposed at its top or side to another structural element at its base.

combination attack. An attack method used in structure fire situations where the room or space has flashed over or is well-involved. Water is first applied into the room from the doorway using a wide fog to absorb the greatest amount of heat, allowing fire crews to enter the room and make a direct attack on the base (seat) of the fire.

combination ladder. A ladder that when closed resembles a small extension ladder without any halyard or pulleys. It has two pins and two receiver brackets mounted at the ladder's tip. Most of these ladders have two stationary ladder locks that hook onto a rung to keep them closed or locked together when extended manually. This ladder can be used in the A-frame position or as a small extension ladder. Because of its size, it can be transported conveniently throughout a structure. Also called an A-frame ladder.

combination method of fire attack. A method of fire extinguishment where a fog stream is rotated in a clockwise direction hitting the ceiling, walls, and floor. It is preferred to inject the fog stream through either a window or a doorway.

combustible liquid. An ignitable liquis with a flash point above 100°F according to the NFPA.

combustible gas meter. A handheld meter that fire personnel can use to detect the presence of combustible gases in an enclosed structure. This meter reports the presence of a combustible gas as a percentage of product in an air sample.

combustible liquid. A liquid with a flash point of 100° F (37.8°C) or higher.

common cockloft. A cockloft in a building that is divided into single commercial or residential occupancies and spans from end to end with no fire stopping or firewall.

common names. The name originally given to a chemical compound upon its discovery prior to the adoption of an organized system of assigning proper names.

communications unit. The unit that provides on-site communications at large incidents.

community risk reduction. Programs that address the contemporary educational, regulatory, and enforcement requirements of a modern fire department involved in such activities as life- and fire-safety education, hazardous materials, EMS, technical rescue, homeland security, code application and enforcement, fire investigation, and special operations.

compartment syndrome. Increased pressure within a confined space that leads to micro-vascular compromise and ultimately to cell death as a result of oxygen starvation.

compartmentation. The division of a large area into smaller areas.

compensation/claims unit. The unit responsible for all workers' compensation claims reported at an incident. The unit also files all injury and illness reports associated with the incident.

compressed air foam system (CAFS). A foam delivery system that delivers low concentrations of Class A foam mixed with water and compressed air to create a finished product that is projected onto burning materials (or fire exposures) and the then held on the surface, limiting or extinguishing the burning or heating process of the fuel and preventing ignition or re-ignition.

compressed gas cylinders. Cylinders that can hold flammable gases, toxic materials, poisons, corrosives, or mixtures of these.

compressed gas tube trailers. Trailers that run with pressures between 3,000 and 5,000 psi and are a series of steel tubes or cylinders banded together. These often carry helium, hydrogen, and other gases under pressure.

compressed natural gas (CNG). One of the cleanest motor vehicle fuels because of low hydrocarbon emissions. As a fuel, it produces very little ozone. However, vehicles fueled with CNG do emit a significant quantity of nitrogen oxides.

compression. The action of squeezing or pushing a component; a load or weight imposed on a structural column that result in a compressive force.

Computer-Aided Management of Emergency Operations (CAMEO). A database used to identify hazardous materials and determine what, if any, precautions should be taken in their handling.

concentrated load. A load applied to a relatively small area, such as a steel column bearing on the buildings footing.

conduction. Heat transfer by direct contact.

conductor. A medium that allows the flow of electrical current or power in the form of electrons. This is usually a metal wire but can be any material that will allow the flow of electrons.

cone roof. A roof on a bulk storage tank that is shaped like an inverted cone. The roof is welded to the tank side with "weak seams" so that the roof could easily blow off if the tank explodes or over pressurizes.

consist. A list of each car in a train and what they are carrying during railway shipments.

constant gallonage fog nozzle. A nozzle designed to flow a specific gallonage when operated at a specific pressure.

control line. Used to contain wildland fire, control lines are created ahead of a spreading wildland fire by removing or treating fuel in the fire's path to create a gap that the fire cannot burn across and then can be controlled by firefighters.

control the door. A technique that confines fire spread and protects firefighters and civilians on or around the fire floor by keeping a door with fire behind it closed but not locked.

controlled breathing. A method an SCBA wearer can use to reduce the rate at which their air supply is consumed, extending the amount of time they can continue to work while operating in a hazardous environment.

convection. Heat transfer via a fluid medium.

copolymer. A rubber or plastic material made by the copolymerization of two monomers, such as styrene and butadiene to make styrene-butadiene rubber.

corrosive. A chemical agent that reacts with the surface of a material, causing it to deteriorate or wear away.

corrosiveness. The susceptibility of a material to attack, damage, or destruction by chemical reaction.

cost unit. The unit responsible for collecting all information relating to the cost of the incident and providing cost-saving recommendations.

coupling. The component, made of brass or aluminum, that makes the joining of lengths of fire hose possible.

covalent bond. A bond between atoms, formed by the sharing of electrons.

covered top floating roof tanks. A bulk storage tank where there are eye vents around the top rim of the tanks. Like a floating roof tank there is an internal floating pan that floats on the surface of the product. This tank looks similar to the cone roof tank.

crazed. A pattern of small cracks in glass left by fire.

Creed method. A single-firefighter ladder drag developed by Creed McClelland of the Orlando Fire Department in which a firefighter slides an extension ladder bed section down on a roof ladder and drags it by the first rung of the foot section.

critical application rate. The minimum rate at which an extinguishing agent must be applied to the fire.

critical-incident factors. A list of different aspects of the incident, along with the incident hazard, that have a major effect on completing tactical priorities and have a major impact of firefighter safety. They vary from incident to incident, and include size, age, and condition of a building; occupancy type; and fire size, intensity, extent, and location.

cross-zoned alarm system. A fire alarm system in which two detection devices must activate before initiating a fire alarm condition.

crown fire. Large wildland fire that spreads through the tops of the trees, often moving rapidly, out of reach of fire crews on the ground.

crowning. During childbirth, this is when the baby's head begins to emerge from the vaginal opening.

crush syndrome. Caused by a prolonged and continuous pressure on muscle tissue found in victims of building and trench collapse, as well as auto extrication.

cryogenic liquid tanks. An insulated and vacuum jacketed pressure tank commonly used for carbon dioxide, liquid oxygen, liquid nitrogen, and similar materials.

cryogenic tank cars. A railcar that carries liquids such as oxygen, nitrogen, carbon dioxide, and other gases that have been converted to a liquid by refrigeration.

cryogenic. Pertaining to the behavior of matter at temperatures of –150°F (–101°C) and below.

CSB. Chemical Safety Board.

curb valve. Secondary natural gas valve branching from a distribution line to an individual occupancy or building. This valve is usually located below-ground at the street.

curie. A unit used to define the rate of decay of a radioactive material.

curtain wall. Lightweight exterior wall system used in high-rise construction where thin panels of aluminum or glass are hung from supports joining the building's steel skeleton to form the exterior wall. This system leaves gaps between the floor decking and exterior wall.

cyclical hydrocarbon. A hydrocarbon with a molecular structure that forms a closed ring instead of being open-ended.

cylinder. The part of a fire extinguisher containing the extinguishing agent. Stored-pressure extinguishers store their extinguishing agent in a cylinder with a gas that provides the pressure to operate the unit.

D

dado. A groove cut into wood.

danger stickers. Stickers affixed to each side of the base section of a portable ladder between the fourth and fifth rungs that warn of electrical hazards overhead, question whether a ladder is in a correct angle, and remind of the proper direction the fly section should face. Also called electrical or angle stickers.

dangers cargo manifest. Set of hazardous material shipping papers containing the name and address of the shipper and receiver, identification of the material being shipped and the quantity and weight of the shipment. This manifest is found on marine vessels normally found in the wheelhouse with the captain of the vessel.

day boots. Boots meeting the standards for slip-resistant, hardened toes and shank, and body fluid-borne pathogen resistance.

dead bolt. A lock bolt, usually rectangular, that has no spring action, and that becomes locked against end pressure when fully projected.

dead load. The weight of materials of construction incorporated into the building, including but not limited to walls, floors, roofs, ceilings, stairways, built-in partitions, finishes, cladding, and other similarly incorporated architectural and structural features.

deck gun. A device mounted on the top of an engine company used to apply water from the ground onto burning piles of debris, over walls, and sometimes into unoccupied buildings to get a quick knockdown.

decompression button. A button found on gas-powered saws and used to reduce the pressure in the cylinder so the saw is easier to start.

decontamination. Removal of harmful substances such as noxious chemicals, harmful bacteria or other organisms, or radioactive material from exposed individuals, rooms, and furnishings in buildings, or the exterior environment.

dedicated channel. A specific radio bandwidth that is only able to be used by a certain entities like public safety radio systems.

deductive reasoning. The use of logic to test the validity of a hypothesis.

defensive strategy. Employed when the fire or incident hazard exceeds the capabilities and firefighter safety systems of an offensive attack. The primary focus of defensive fires is cutting off the main body of the fire and protecting exposures by using larger master streams.

deflagration. An explosion moving at subsonic speed (slower than the speed of sound).

deluge guns. Portable monitors that are similar to detachable deck guns except that they are always used on the ground.

deluge sprinkler head. A component of a deluge sprinkler system that is in capped, and open by design to facilitate the flow of water in high hazard installations.

deluge system. A system of pipes with open sprinkler heads that are open to ambient atmosphere, with water flow being controlled at the deluge valve. Once the deluge valve releases the clapper, all heads flow water simultaneously. Such systems are used in high-hazard areas where much water is necessary to extinguish a fire.

demobilization unit. On large or complex incidents, the unit works with the IC and operations section to develop a plan to release personnel and apparatus no longer needed at an incident and ensures the incident is adequately staffed to meet the IC's objectives and strategies.

demonstrative evidence. Any physical evidence after a fire that can demonstrate the origin or cause, such as a defective appliance or a fire pattern.

density. The ratio of mass to volume of an object or substance.

Department of Transportation (DOT). An agency, either federal or state, that regulates shipments and transfer of hazardous materials.

deployment procedure. The cycle companies follow in 1) responding to the scene of an incident, 2) how they are assigned to positions around the scene, 3) how long they can safely operate in the hazard zone, and 4) methods to cycle companies in and out of the hazard zone (work-rest cycles, on deck, etc.).

depth gauge. A gauge found at the tip of chainsaw chain guards to adjust the depth of cutting roofs.

derivative. A compound made from a hydrocarbon that substitutes another atom or group of atoms for one of the hydrogen atoms in the compound.

designed loads. A load that the building designer or structural engineer has calculated into the building based on sound engineering principles.

desorption. The process of removing a material from the surface of another material on which it is adsorbed.

detonate. To explode.

detonation. An explosion moving at supersonic speed (faster than the speed of sound).

Dewar's flask. Small, round, or square containers kept inside of another box and used for storage of acids and other corrosive materials. The outer box can be made of wood, polystyrene, or other materials to protect the container during transport, use, or storage.

diamond-cut grit blade. An expensive circular steel blade with industrial diamond tips used with rotary power saws to cut metal, concrete, and wood without the aid of lubricating fluids or water.

diatomic molecule. A molecule made up of two atoms bonded covalently.

dicing. A method of roof ventilation consisting of making multiple downward cuts.

digital. A more modern type of radio signal that relies on digitally encrypted data.

digital technology. Communications technology in which the user's voice is converted to digital data, then converted back to voice when received.

diking. The process of constructing a land-based barrier using dirt, sand, clay and other materials found on scene to control the movement of liquid hazardous material.

dilution. The act of adding water (or other material) to a water soluble material, thereby lowering its concentration.

dimension lumber. A size classification of lumber that is from 2 in. (52 mm) up to, but not including, 5 in. (125 mm) thick, and that is 2 in. (52 mm) or more in width.

direct fire attack. A method of fire attack in which a solid or straight fire stream is applied directly to the base (seat) of the fire. Direct fire attack disrupts the burning process and quickly contains the fire.

direct fire damage. That which is caused by the actual combustion process, where there is physical destruction from flame, heat, or smoke. Also known as primary fire damage.

disinfection. A chemical or physical process that kills pathogenic organisms in water, air, or other surfaces.

distributed load. A load distributed over a large area of the supporting surface, supporting a uniform load over the area (e.g., a ballast stone applied on a rubber membrane roof).

distribution system. The system of treated water storage reservoirs, tanks, pumps, and water mains or pipes that ultimately supply the fire hydrants with water.

distributor. A spinning 1½- or 2½-in. (38- or 65-mm) nozzle with multiple orifices pointed in different directions, spraying water in all directions.

distributors. Small diameter lines (from the outdated 4-in. [100-mm] main to 12-in. [305-mm] mains) that make up the bulk of most water main systems and are the primary supplier for hydrants.

diversion. The process of changing the direction of a liquid material by using constructed barriers such as sandbags to direct the material to an area were it poses less harm.

divided highway. An area of highway where traffic is separated by a median, concrete embankment, guardrail, or combination thereof.

divisions. The organizational level having responsibility for operations within a defined geographic area or with functional responsibility. The division level is organizationally between the strike team and the branch.

documentary evidence. Evidence after a fire in written format such as an inventory list or insurance policy.

documentation unit. Responsible for all documentation related to an incident, including distributing copies of the IAP, objectives, and strategies to all supervisory personnel involved in the incident.

doffing. The act of taking off or removing chemical protective clothing or other protective gear.

dogs. The parts of an extension ladder that travel over each rung and make clicking noises as the fly section rises. When the ladder locks into a rung just after the click of the dogs, the fly and bed section rungs align. Also called ladder locks, pawls, and rung locks.

dome top/dome roof. Low-pressure tanks for flammable and combustible liquids stored up to 15 psi (105 kPa).

door position. The position that ensures the smooth and sustained movement of hose to the seat of the fire and eliminates any kinks in the hoseline.

dormer. A small structure that rises up out of the roof to provide light, ventilation, and increased usable floor space on the story directly below the roof.

dosage. The actual quantity of a chemical administered to an organism or to which the organism is exposed.

DOT406. A nonpressurized (less than 3 psi [21 kPa]) tank, commonly used to transport gasoline, fuel oil, kerosene, and other flammable and combustible liquids. This tank is also known as a MC306.

DOT407. A low pressure (less than 40-psi [280 kPa]) tank with a normal maximum capacity of 7,000 gallons (26,500 L). This tank is double shelled for leak protection and has recessed manheads for rollover protection. This tank typically transports flammable liquids, caustics, or acids.

double bond. Two covalent bonds between two atoms.

double-hung windows. A window both of whose sashes move up and down vertically.

double-sheave pulley. A device that allows for two ropes to pass to help create a mechanical advantage for raising or lowering a load.

double-action pull station. A manual fire alarm box that requires two steps to activate, such as breaking a glass window or lifting a hinged cover to access the handle.

double-jacketed hose. Hose utilizing two layers of protective and reinforcing materials around the inner core.

downgraded rope. Utility rope not used for search and rescue or life safety.

downstream V. Indicating deeper and faster water with few obstacles, a V forms downstream when two eddy tails meet.

downstream. With the direction of natural movement or flow of a stream or river.

draft riots. When heavy losses forced the Union to draft young men for the army, opposition to the draft was expressed, and riots broke out. The most serious occurred in July 1863 in New York City, where pre-existing tensions between the Irish and black workers over jobs and housing had precipitated conflict long before the war.

drafting hydrant. A specialty hydrant built to access a static or moving water source. It consists of a strainer basket submerged at least 2 ft (0.6 m) below the surface, 6-in. (150 mm) diameter piping, and an accessible pumper connection.

drafting or hard suction hose. A rigid hose that is used by a pump to acquire water from static water sources.

draft-stop. A piece of glass, Lexan®, plastic, or drywall.

drag rescue device (DRD). A webbing loop that wraps around the back and shoulders when deployed and is used to drag a downed firefighter.

drifting into failure. Failures at a fire that happen incrementally until the sum is greater than the parts, resulting in injury or death.

drop ladder. A small vertical ladder that connects the first-floor landing of an exterior fire escape to the ground when released.

drop point. When completing the hose stretch, the point at which the crew prepares to enter the hazardous environment. Additional hose is flaked at this point to allow for improved mobility.

drop tank. An easily deployable, folding, portable water tank, placed at a dumpsite that has a slightly larger capacity than a water tender tank.

dry barrel hydrant. A hydrant that incorporates a draining mechanism to remove water from the portions above to prevent freezing.

dry bulk cargo tank. A tank used for transporting goods such as cement, bakery flour, plastic pellets, and fertilizers. When viewed from the side, these tanks can form a series of connected cones.

dry chemical suppression system. A non-water based suppression system commonly found under self-serve gas station canopies, commercial cooking hoods, and many other places. ABC dry chemical can be used for wood (ordinary combustibles), petroleum, and electrical fires.

dry hopper cars. Railcars configured in three different models: pneumatically unloaded, covered hopper car, and open top hopper car. Each car carries different types of dry products from grains and fertilizers to plastic pellets and coal.

dry pendant sprinkler. A section of pipe, known as a drop nipple, which consists of a standard pendant sprinkler head, and a shaft inside the top of the drop nipple holds a cap to prevent water.

dry sprinkler heads. Heads that are designed for installation in areas subject to freezing. They are installed in the upright position.

dry-chemical extinguishing systems. A system that uses dry chemicals powdered agents for extinguishment of fires by coating the fuel. The powder is kept in pressurized tanks or separate in adjoining tanks, which hold the expelling agent (pressurized air or nitrogen) and the extinguishing agent separate.

dry-pipe system. A sprinkler system whose piping system is filled with pressurized air or nitrogen instead of water, which holds the clapper shut, controlling water flow. In order for water to flow, a head must open, releasing the air or nitrogen pressure and allowing the clapper to open. This in turn allows water to enter the pipes and discharge through open sprinkler heads.

dry-pipe valves. The alarm valve on a dry-pipe sprinkler system in which the pipes are normally filled with air to avoid freezing.

drywall. A building material that is composed of a layer of gypsum sandwiched between layers of a paper material.

due process. A course of formal proceedings carried out regularly and in accordance with established rules and principles.

dumbwaiter bulkhead. An enclosure at the roof level accessed by a small door located over the shaft of where dumbwaiters were once used in multiple dwellings.

dumbwaiter shaft. A shaft that contains either a mechanical or a manual lift intended to move material from one floor to another floor so the occupants need not carry materials up and down the stairs.

dump site. An easily accessible location on a fire scene where a dump tank can be accessed by water tenders.

duplex. A term referring to radio operations in which one frequency is used for transmitting while a second frequency is used for receiving.

duplex system. A radio system using two frequencies that can be active at all times. This allows all users to transmit and receive simultaneously.

dynamic load. A load with dynamic effects or that is in motion when applied to a building such as strong earthquakes, gusting winds, etc.

dynamic rope. A very flexible rope with high stretch. Used in rock climbing to absorb falls and put less stress on the anchoring system.

E

early-suppression, fast-response (ESFR) sprinkler heads. Heads designed to quickly discharge a density of water droplet sizes that provide fast suppression, which are usually used in warehouse rack storage and other high challenge areas.

eave. The area of a roof that extends beyond the edge of the exterior wall.

eccentric load. A load imposed on a structural member at some point other than the center section of the supporting member.

eddies. Calm areas separated from the main current flowing downstream.

eddy tail. The downstream point of the eddy lines, where the main current resumes.

edge roller. A device used to protect moving ropes from abrasive surfaces.

eductor. An appliance used to draw raw foam from its storage container (usually a five-gallon bucket) and feed it into a flowing hoseline.

egress. A place or means of exiting.

electric strike. A door entry system, often the "buzz-in" type.

electrical distribution panel. Commonly known as the "fuse box" or "breaker box," this is the area where electrical power enters a structure and then branches off into specific areas.

electrical stickers. Stickers affixed to each side of the base section of a portable ladder between the fourth and fifth rungs that warn of electrical hazards overhead, question whether a ladder is in a correct angle, and remind of the proper direction the fly section should face. Also called danger or angle stickers.

electrically neutral. Having no electrical charge, as in an atom.

electron cloud. The theory that electrons in a benzene ring are shared by all six carbon atoms. Represented by a circle drawn inside a hexagon.

electron configuration. The number and position of the electrons(s) orbiting the nucleus of each atom.

electron. A subatomic particle with an electrical charge of –1 and essentially no weight.

element. A pure substance that cannot be broken down by chemical means.

elevation head pressure. The pressure created by gravity on a column of water, and also the amount of resistance exerted when raising a water column. For every foot of elevation, 0 .434 pounds of pressure are in resistance (when raising a water column) or exerted at the base of a tower.

elevator bulkhead. An enclosure at the roof level accessed by a door and located over an elevator shaft where the elevator's mechanical equipment is housed.

elevator door restrictor. A collapsible, electromechanical, or mechanical device installed on an elevator to prevent opening of a car door when the elevator is outside the landing zone.

elevator equipment room. Usually at roof level, the room that houses the power machinery for operation of the elevator.

elevator hopping. A dangerous game played in the shaft atop moving elevator cars.

elevator landing zone. A zone extending from a point 18 in. (45 cm) below a landing to a point 18 in. (45 cm) above the landing.

elevator mechanical room (EMR). An area enclosed with fire barriers with a fire-resistance rating not less than the required rating of the hoistway enclosure served by the machinery.

elevator pit. The portion of the hoistway extending from the lowest landing sill to the bottom of the hoistway.

emergency escape slide. A life saving rope rescue evolution where harness-equipped firefighters on a roof tie off a rope to a substantial object and rappel down to safety.

emergency medical services (EMS). An existing central dispatch resource, strategically place stations, a centralized training resource, and a 24-hour career and/or volunteer staff. A fire-department-based EMS generally depends on the department having the required infrastructure to provide this service.

emergency medical system. The system staffed by paramedics and emergency medical technicians.

Emergency Response Guidebook (ERG). A book published by the Department of Transportation (DOT) that assists responders in making initial decisions upon arriving at the scene of a hazardous materials incident.

emergency voice alarm. Used when verbal instructions can be helpful to speed up evacuation and provide direction to building occupants, and may be live broadcasted or prerecorded.

Empire State Building. The site of an incident, just before V-J Day in 1945, when FDNY responded when a B-25 bomber lost in fog crashed into the 79th floor. The crew and at least 11 office workers died.

empirical data. Information that is obtained through observations, experiments, or other direct data-gathering means.

employee assistance program. A benefit provided to firefighters to assist them and their families with coping with the stresses commonly found in the fire service.

encoder. A device at the dispatch center that transmits a coded tone that activates a radio pager and allows the pager to then receive a voice message from a dispatch center and to call back career firefighters for major incidents.

endothermic reactions. A reaction between combustibles that absorbs heat.

endothermic. Characterized by the absorption of heat, as in a chemical reaction.

engine company. The unit composed of apparatus, usually a pumper or engine, staffed with firefighters and a company officer, and primarily assigned to deliver water to a fire and other duties as designated by the department.

engine compartment. The area underneath the hood containing the engine components, the radiator, battery, hood struts, and other potentially dangerous flammable/combustible liquids.

engineered shoring. Shoring systems pre-built without the use of wood. Examples are plastic cribbing and aluminum screw jack struts.

entrainment. A process whereby air is drawn into a fire.

entry route. The path by which a toxic substance enters the body.

environmental load. Factors that include snow, rain, wind, and earthquakes.

EPA. Environmental Protection Agency.

equilibrium. The state at which the vapor pressure is no longer rising or falling.

equipment pool. A staging area to organize tools and supplies to assist with tasks.

escalator landing plate. A protective metal plate located at the upper landing and, when uncovered, houses the motor that provides electric power.

esters. Hydrocarbon derivatives having two hydrocarbon backbones or radicals, joined by a radical of oxygen and carbon.

ETA. Estimated time of arrival.

ethers. Hydrocarbon derivatives having two hydrocarbon backbones or radicals, joined by an oxygen molecule.

ethyl mercaptan. A pungent additive that can alert responders to a liquefied petroleum gas leak.

evacuation signal. An audible signal that indicates that the decision has been made to evacuate firefighting or rescue operations inside a building because of excessive danger to firefighters or because the scene has become too dangerous to continue tactical operations.

evacuation stair. A designated stairwell (usually the one farthest from the seat of the fire) in a multi-story building with more than one stairwell from which building occupants are directed to use to evacuate the building.

evaporation. The process by which a liquid changes into a vapor.

exclusion zone. Danger zone into which no personnel should enter without suitable safety equipment. These are typically 50 feet around the space opening at minimum, depending upon the configuration of the incident site.

exempt firefighter. Volunteer firefighter who served a set number of years and were rewarded by being excused from jury and militia duty forever.

exit access. Routes including aisles within rooms or spaces as well as corridors that lead from inside a building up to a doorway (the exit) that must remain unobstructed and free of hazards at all times.

exit discharge. The pathway leading through and away from a door, which must also be kept clear to allow occupants to continue their travel to a safe area away from the structure, which is usually a public area.

exit system or egress. An unobstructed pathway from the inside of a building to a public area of safety. It consist of a the exit access, the exit way itself, and the discharge area.

exit. The doorway or stairwell in a multistory building leading to a doorway consisting of a properly marked egress door, which is mounted in the proper frame, and which will swing out in the direction of travel to the discharge. The exit must not be locked (except in limited circumstances), must use panic bars or other easily operated opening hard ware, and must be kept free of obstructions, debris, and combustibles.

exothermic. A reaction between combustibles that creates and releases heat.

exothermic. Characterized by the liberation of heat, as in a chemical reaction.

explosion. The phenomenon characterized by the instantaneous release of heat and pressure caused by the oxidation of fuels or the decomposition of molecules.

explosive limit. The amount of vapor in the air that form explosive mixtures.

explosive train. A sequence of events in which a primary explosive detonates a secondary explosive, which in turn detonates a main charge.

explosive. Any pure substance or mixture whose principal purpose is to explode.

exposure. A building (exterior) or adjoining space (interior) threatened by the heat being generated by a fire.

extension ladder. An adjustable ladder with a bed section and one or two fly sections that rise as a firefighter operates the halyard. In an extension ladder with one fly, the ladder rises in 14-in. (36-cm) increments. With a two-section fly, the ladder rises in 28-in. (71-cm) increments.

exterior fire attack. The method of fire attack in which fire streams (usually high flow) are applied to the fire from outside the fire building in an attempt to contain the fire. Exterior fire attack is used when there is a high risk to firefighters entering the building with no chance of saving a life or the structure.

external force. A force applied to a building on the exterior, such as environmental effects (weather, earthquakes, etc.).

extremely hazardous substances. Substances defined by the EPA as chemicals that must be reported to the appropriate authorities if released above the threshold reporting quantity. Each substance has a threshold reporting quantity. The list of extremely hazardous substances is identified in title III of Superfund Amendments and Reauthorization Act (SARA) of 1986 (40 CFR Part 355).

exterior insulation and finish system (EIFS). A lightweight synthetic wall cladding that includes foam plastic insulation and thin synthetic coatings that produce a finish that resembles stucco.

F

facilities unit. The unit that sets up any fixed facilities (for eating and sleeping, for example) that may be required for an incident. Typically, this unit is not established except for very large incidents.

facilities. All buildings, equipment, structures, and other stationary items located on a single site, or on contiguous or adjacent sites. The size and scope of an incident determines if and what incident facilities are needed.

Factory Mutual. An insurance company that insures industrial properties, and maintains a laboratory for the testing of fire protection equipment, which may bear the FM seal of approval if so recognized.

Fahrenheit. The temperature scale devised in 1717 by D.G. Fahrenheit and denoted by °F. The normal freezing point of water is 32°F and the normal boiling point of water is 212°F.

false alarm. The activation of fire alarm systems in the absence of an emergency or fire condition, due to malfunction, good intent, or malicious intent.

family effect. The phenomenon in which all the elements in the group or family have similar chemical properties. The family effect is strongest on the edges of the periodic table, and it weakens toward the middle of the table.

fascia. A vertical surface that spans across the top of columns or across the top of a wall.

FCC. Federal Communications Commission.

FEMA. Federal Emergencies Management Agency. Designed to coordinate emergency services during major disasters.

female coupling. The receiving coupling that has the swivel end, with threads inside of the rotating portion.

field operations guide (FOG). A document usually carried by USAR teams and filled with information such as shoring diagrams and the proper use of search markings.

figure eight plate. A common descending device shaped like an eight.

filament. One strand in a nylon rope.

fill site. An easily accessible location close to the fire scene that can provide a minimum capacity of 1,000 gpm for the filling of apparatus.

film-forming fluoroprotein foam (FFFP). Foam that will form a film over a flammable liquid surface, much like AFFFs.

finance/administration section. The section responsible for monitoring incident-related costs and administering any necessary procurement contracts.

fingerprints. Fire patterns.

fingers. Smaller, more narrow areas of a wildland fire, extending out from the head or main body of the fire.

fire alarm control panel (FACP). Also known as a fire alarm control unit (FACU), this is the central system that connects and supervises all of the components, including initiating, notification, detection, and suppression.

fire and building codes. Regulations enacted by the authority having jurisdiction regarding the necessities of fire protection and building construction to ensure public safety.

fire blanket. A fire-resistive cloth blanket made up of Kevlar and Nomex and deployed above the fire and lowered down to cover windows affected by high winds when battling fires in high-rise buildings.

fireboat. A marine apparatus used to access waterfront property for suppression and to supply water for suppression activities on land.

fire control. Also referred to as incident stabilization, the second of the three strategic priorities, which identifies the fire as no longer extending from its current state and able to be extinguished with current resources. The benchmark for meeting this priority is "fire stopped," or "fire under control."

fire department communication systems. This usually takes the form of a fixed, dedicated "firefighter's telephone system" that permits two-way communications between firefighters in different locations, including stairwells, elevator cabs, and elevator lobbies in high-rise buildings by use of fixed jack locations with portable phone units, or permanently mounted phones.

fire department connection. A Siamese connection used by apparatus to connect to a standpipe and to support the sprinkler system during operations.

Fire Department of the City of New York (FDNY). Department established under the terms of the Tweed Charter (1870), thus restoring home rule to the City of New York.

fire load. The total amount of combustible (or flammable) material present in a precisely defined area where a fire might occur.

fire marks. A distinctive metal marker once produced by insurance companies to identify their policyholders' buildings.

fire patrol. Personnel or units, paid by insurance companies, whose only job was salvage on the fireground. The equipment carried on their apparatus was strictly for that purpose. These units no longer exist today.

fire point. The lowest temperature at which a liquid produces sufficient vapor to flash near its surface and then continue to burn.

fire prevention inspection. A legal inspection that demands compliance under the authority having jurisdiction, performed to determine the adherence to fire and life safety codes adopted in the jurisdiction.

Fire Prevention Week. Established in recognition of the Great Chicago Fire in 1871, it is sponsored by the NFPA, who develop material, based along a yearly theme, for fire departments to distribute.

fire problem. Any condition(s) present in a community that causes an increase in the number of fires in a particular area or for a specific reason.

fire safety presentation. A demonstration on safety made to the public at a location other than a fire station.

fire stop. A construction consisting of the materials that fill the openings around penetrating items such as cables, cable trays, conduits, ducts, pipes, and their means of support through the wall or floor opening to prevent the spread of fire.

fire stream. The shape of the water as it leaves the nozzle on a fire attack hoseline.

fire tetrahedron. A three dimensional fire triangle illustrating the interrelationship of the chemical chain reaction in the combustion process.

fire triangle. A graphic representation to illustrate that fuel, oxygen, and heat of ignition are needed for a fire to start and continue burning.

fire watch. The person(s) chosen to stay at a structure to watch for fire after a sprinkler system is deemed out of service after a fire until the system has been restored. Often the fire prevention bureau performs this task.

Fire Zouave. Firefighters who enlisted in the Union and Confederate Armies during the Civil War.

fire-extinguishing agents. The liquid, solid, or gaseous materials applied to extinguish or control fires.

Firefighter I. The first level of firefighter based on knowledge, skills, and abilities in basic areas of firefighting.

Firefighter II. The second level of firefighter based on knowledge, skills, and abilities in basic areas of firefighting including all those from Firefighter I and based on the level of supervision required.

Firefighter phase II elevator key. Elevators shall be provided with Phase I emergency recall operation and Phase II emergency-in-car operation in accordance with ASME A17.1.

firefighter soup. The condition that exists when the destruction of thermal balance, excessive steam generation and accumulation, and loss of tenability occurs during the application of a fog stream.

Firefighting Resources of Southern California Organized for Potential Emergencies (FIRESCOPE). The organization that initiated a version of the incident command system (ICS) for wildfire operations.

fire-resistive construction. Type I construction; the structural members including columns, beams, and sometimes floor slabs are protected from the fire's heat to prevent the loss of the structural element's integrity.

first responder. The team that provides first aid and cardiopulmonary resuscitation.

fission. The splitting of an atomic nucleus by bombardment with neutrons.

fixed facilities. Permanent structures or installations as opposed to mobile operations. Common fixed facilities that contain hazardous materials are bulk oil storage terminals, refineries, and other major industrial sites.

fixed-temperature detector. A device that activates when a predetermined surrounding temperature is reached.

flake. The process of laying a hoseline in an accordion style to facilitate the deployment of the hose to the seat of a fire.

flame detector. A device that monitors for the ultraviolet or infrared light spectrum, which is released by the combustion process but invisible to the naked eye.

flammable. Easily ignitable and rapidly burning.

flammable liquid. A liquid with a flash point below 100° F (37.8°C).

flammable or explosive limits. The concentration of gas or vapor in air between a lower point of concentration or limit and an upper point of concentration or limit that forms a flammable or explosive mixture.

flammable range. The concentration of a flammable gas vapor (between an upper and lower limit) between which the mixture of the gas vapor in air is capable of igniting.

Flanders, William, F. The first American steam-powered fireboat, commissioned by the Boston Fire Department in 1873.

flanks. Sides of a wildland fire that allow the fire to extend laterally, but usually at a slower rate than the head of the fire.

flare-up. A sudden increase in the speed of a wildland fire for a short period of time.

flash flood. A flood caused by heavy or excessive rainfall in a short period of time.

flash point. The minimum temperature of a material at which it produces vapors sufficient to form an ignitable mixture with the air at the surface of the liquid or near the container.

flashover. The phenomenon that may occur during a fire when the surface of everything in a compartment appears to break into flame at the same time because all combustibles are giving off ignitable vapors.

flat roof. A type of roof where the members supporting the roof decking are horizontal or have a slight pitch.

flatbed cars. Railcars that may be used to transport one-ton bulk intermodal containers, which could contain hazardous materials. Other items may be hauled on flatbed cars such as lumber, steel, or heavy machinery.

floating roof tank. A bulk storage tank in which the roof is set on floating pontoons that float up and down on the surface of the product contained therein.

floor open. Denoted in the building marking system by an "FO," it means that there are holes in the floor and firefighters should be aware of the possible hazard.

floor slab. A concrete floor either cast in place or pre-cast and erected.

floor truss. A lightweight wood parallel chord truss used in wood frame construction.

flotation ring. A piece of foam sewn into the bottom of a water throw rope bag to prevent it from sinking.

flow switch. A device that utilizes a paddle or vane, inserted into the rises above the clapper, to detect water flow in sprinkler pipes.

flow test. A test to determine the available water supply from a given hydrant for fire suppression purposes.

fluoroprotein foam. A biodegradable type of firefighting foam consisting of products made from a protein hydrolysate to produce thick foam blankets for use on Class B. flammable liquid fires.

flush feature. A device that allows small pieces of debris to be discharged.

flush fitting. A surface exactly even with an adjoining one, forming the same plane.

flushstrip-flush. The process of flushing large amounts of water, stripping contaminated clothing, and repeating flushing of water to hazardous materials contaminated victims in the warm zone.

fly section. A section of a ladder that fits inside a channel of the bed section and extends to gain height and distance.

foam. Firefighting foam consists of small bubbles that are produced by the mixing of air, water, and a foaming agent concentrate (often a surfactant or detergent-like material), which acts as a blanket, excluding air and blocking the escape of volatile vapor. Foam may be protein, synthetic, aqueous-film forming, high expansion, or alcohol type.

foam blanket. The result of a slow and dispersed foam application to reflect radiant heat away from the fuel source, insulates fuel by dispersing the heat away, and assists in smothering the fuel to create a fuel vapor barrier between the fuel and the fire.

foam concentrate. The pre-mixed ingredients of fire extinguishing foam. It is mixed with water before application.

foam eductor. A device for mixing foam concentrate in proper proportions with a stream of water to produce a foam solution.

foam solution. A foam concentrate diluted with water in varying proportions depending on the type of foam used.

fog nozzle ricochet. A phenomenon that occurs during the application of a fog stream when a significant portion of the products that cannot be vented when forcefully pushed forward by the fog stream then impact the wall surface and roll back over and around the nozzle team.

fog nozzle. A nozzle that discharges water that is characterized by small droplets of water in a dispersed pattern; the distinct droplets of water produced from a fog nozzle evaporate more readily, generating steam.

folding ladder. A narrow, collapsible ladder that folds into itself for transportation through small, narrow spaces. Also called an attic, scissor, suitcase, or closet ladder.

food unit. The unit responsible for ensuring that incident responders have food and drinking water for a long-term incident.

foot bracket. The bottom part of a gas-powered saw.

force. Any action that maintains or alters the position of a structure or a part of a structure.

forcible entry. A technique used by fire personnel to gain access to building structures, motor vehicles, or any other obstruction preventing us to perform our firefighting duties. Locked doors, roll down security gates, barred windows, vehicle doors; trunks; or hoods, are a few examples of obstructions which may require this technique.

forcible entry team. Firefighters assigned to gain entry into secured structures and areas of fire to allow search and rescue and assist hoseline access to fire.

forward lay. Hoselay designed to be laid from the hydrant to the fire.

fox lock. Commonly found in the rear of commercial buildings or occupancies where high security is a concern, the lock mounted on the outside of a steel door, which is made up of two crossbars installed into the metal door jamb adding extra security.

frangible disc. On a container, a safety relief device that bursts when the pressure in the container reaches a predetermined level.

frangible. Capable of bursting.

frangible bulb sprinkler head. A sprinkler head with a glass bulb that holds an orifice cap in place and prevents water from flowing until it reaches its designed activation temperature and breaks, allowing water to flow.

freeboard. 1. The vertical distance from the normal water surface to the top of a confining wall.
2. The vertical distance from the sand surface to the underside of a trough in a sand filter.

freelancing. Operating outside of the established fire attack plan, operational guidelines, or operating protocols.

freezing point. The temperature at which a liquid changes to a solid.

freight bills. A set of hazardous material shipping papers containing the name and address of the shipper and receiver, identification of the material being shipped, and the quantity and weight of the shipment.

Freight bills are for over-the-road shipments and are also called bills of lading.

Fresno ladder. A narrow extension ladder with no halyard or pulleys that provides access in narrow areas. It rises manually when the fly section is pushed up and locks in position as spring-loaded dogs pass over the rungs. Also called a two-section attic ladder.

friction loss. A loss of energy, measured in PSI, due to friction between a fluid in motion and the walls of the hose or other device.

frontpieces. Also known simply as fronts or shields, these display fire company identification and rank information on the front of a firefighter's helmet.

frostbite. Injury caused to skin or other tissue by very low temperatures and/or cold materials.

fuel controlled. This describes a fire in which oxygen is in abundant supply but the growth and development is controlled by the amount of fuel available to burn.

fuel. Anything that will burn.

fusible link sprinkler head. A sprinkler head that opens when the solder holding two pieces of metal together fuses or melts, releasing the orifice cap and allowing water to flow.

fusible plug. On a container, a safety relief device which melts when the temperature of the container reaches a predetermined level.

fusion. The act of melting.

G

gable end venting. A metal or plastic vent placed on the exterior near the top peak of the side of the home that can be removed to assist in ventilation.

gallons per minute (gpm). Measure of the amount of water flowing through a hoseline.

gambrel roof. A roof made up of two sides that slope away from the ridgepole; a gambrel roof begins at the ridgepole with a slight pitch and changes to a steeper pitch. Similar to a gabled roof.

gamma radiation. Extremely short wavelength and intensely high energy electromagnetic radiation.

garden apartment. A multi-family apartment building where individual units are on a single floor and each unit is accessed from a common interior hallway or stairway with limited exterior access.

garden hose adapters. Plumbing fittings used to adapt to fire department fittings so that a garden hose can be supplied from a hydrant or fire engine to assist in low-water pressure decontamination at hazardous materials incidents.

gas detectors. Devices that detect dangerous chemical components produced during combustion.

gases. Fluids with vapor pressures of 40 psia (280 kPa) or more at 100°F (48°C).

gasoline siding. Another name for asphalt shingle siding due to the rapid combustibility of the material.

gasoline. A highly flammable liquid made up of pentane, hexane, heptane, octane, nonane, and addititves.

gateways. Mobile devices used to link different frequencies together at a specific location.

gauntlet glove. An interface component that extends from the end of a glove and provides limited protection to the area where the coat and glove meet.

girder. A structural support member usually found in the horizontal position.

gooseneck ladder. The top vertical ladder that connects the top-floor landing of an exterior fire escape to the roof.

gooseneck-style, hand-pumped fire engines. American designed fire engines with solid metal play pipes much like modern-day deck guns.

gooseneck ladder. A metal ladder that leads to a roof, attached to a fire escape on the outside of a building.

Grandcamp. A French Liberty ship, loaded with ammonium nitrate fertilizer, caught fire and blew up in April 1947, killing 26 Texas City volunteer firefighters.

gray water. Water that is not safe for consumption but is safe for use during firefighting activities.

grease trap. In a commercial cooking system, part of the overhead duct system intended to catch and hold airborne cooking grease in a series of filters, reducing potentially combustible grease build-up in remote duct-work.

Great Fire of London. A fire that destroyed almost 80% of the city in 1666.

ground support unit. The unit that maintains and refuels any vehicles assigned to the incident and provides transportation of personnel to and from the incident.

groundwater. Water that exists beneath the ground in naturally occurring aquifers and is accessed by wells.

Ground Zero. The site of the aftermath of the collapse of the World Trade Center Twin Towers.

group. Within the operations section, a method of dividing an incident scene into functional areas of operation for the purpose of maintaining effective command and control.

guide bar. The long bar on a chainsaw where the chain rides and lubrication occurs.

gunning a saw. Squeezing the throttle handle trigger on a gas-powered saw repeatedly.

gypsum board. See drywall.

gypsum roof. Sheetrock with a waterproof coating. It has little to no load bearing strength and a firefighter cutting will notice a white or gray powder-like residue.

H

hail search. A visual and verbal evaluation of whether victims may be trapped at or near the surface of a collapse or in a deeper space where victims' voices may carry to the outside.

halocarbons. Gaseous agents that work by cooling the fire and chemical reaction with the fire. Halocarbon gases have a NOAEL concentration meaning they have "no observed adverse effect level." This is the concentration below which testing authorities consider safe.

halogenated agents. Halogenated agents have been used for firefighting since the early 1900s. Of the ten halogenated that have been used, two have been the most common since the early 1970s: Halon 1211 and Halon 1301. Halogenated agents suppress fire by interrupting the chemical chain reaction in the combustion process, working in the fire chemically instead of physically. Exactly how this "chain breaking" process works is not completely understood. It is generally agreed that bromine is released from the agent as it decomposes in the fire carrying away the "free radicals" that cause the combustion and releasing more bromine to continue the "chain breaking" process.

halogenated hydrocarbons. Hydrocarbon compounds that have had one or more hydrogen atoms replaced by a halogen.

halogens. Group VIIA elements on the periodic table, headed by fluorine.

halon. A fire-extinguishing gas that chemically interrupts the combustion reaction. Usually used in total-flooding systems, some local-application systems, and fire extinguishers, it is banned in most countries because of its effect on the environment.

halyard. A manila or nylon rope that makes use of a pulley or pulleys to extend and retract a ladder's fly section or sections from the bed section.

handheld portable radio. A small personal communication device that is usually powered by disposable or rechargeable batteries. They usually have a limited range.

handle. The means by which an extinguisher is carried. The actual design of the handle varies from model to model. In most cases, the handle is located just below the lever that you squeeze for discharge.

Happyland Social Club. The location of an arson fire on March 25, 1990, in Bronx, New York, which killed 87 people.

hasp. A hinged metal strap designed to be passed over a staple and secured in place.

hasp and staple. A fastening in two pieces for a door or box to be secured by a padlock. The hinged part is called the hasp and shuts over the staple.

Havemeyer, William F. The first American steam-powered fireboat, commissioned by the FDNY in 1875.

Hayes, Daniel. Of the San Francisco Fire Department, the developer of the first successful aerial extension ladder truck that allowed firefighters to reach the upper portions of many of the newest, tallest buildings (1868).

hazardous material. 1. A substance or material that has been determined by the secretary of the Department of Transportation (DOT) to be capable of posing an unreasonable risk to health, safety, and property when transported in commerce, and which has so been designated. 2. Any material that when it escapes from its container, can cause damage to life, health, the environment, or property. 3. Any material that can cause damage to life, health, the environment, or property.

hazardous material PPE. Specialized personal protective equipment used when there is a danger of hazardous materials being present. Hazardous material PPE is classified into four levels. Level A provides the highest level of skin and respiratory protection with integrated gloves and boots. A self contained breathing apparatus (SCBA) is donned under the suit to provide respiratory protection. Level B has a lower level of skin protection because the gloves and boots are not integrated with the suit. SCBA is donned under the suit for respiratory protection. Level C provides the same level of skin protection as Level-B but a lower level of respiratory protection because an SCBA is not required. Level D is a normal work uniform and in many cases is structural PPE or a "jump-suit."

hazardous substance. 1. Any material that poses a threat to human health and/or the environment and is toxic, corrosive, ignitable, explosive, or chemically reactive. 2. Any substance designated by EPA to be reported if a designated quantity of the substance is spilled in the waters of the United States or is otherwise released into the environment.

hazardous waste. A material that can no longer be used for its original intended purpose, and that possesses at least one of four characteristics (ignitability, corrosivity, reactivity, or toxicity).

hazmat. Shortened form of "hazardous materials." Inspired by Capt. Ron Gore, the first hazmat team formally went online in Jacksonville in January 1977, inspiring the introduction of such units all over the nation.

HAZWOPER. Hazardous Waste Operation and Emergency Response.

HCS. Hazard Communication Standard.

head. Leading edge of a wildland fire, moving in the direction of the wind, is usually the hottest and most rapidly advancing part of a wildland fire.

Health Insurance Portability and Privacy Act (HIPPA). Law that defines and limits the circumstances under which a person's health information may be released.

heat detector. A device that warns of a fire condition by sensing a specific high temperature, high rate of rise in temperature, or both. Heat detectors are alarm initiating devices.

heat exhaustion. The condition that results from the body's compromise of the ability to cool down properly from prolonged exposure to intense heat. It causes excessive sweating and sodium deficiency.

heating, ventilation, air conditioning (HVAC). A system of air handlers and connecting ductwork which delivers heated or chilled air throughout a building. Air handling units are usually located out of sight on the ground level or on the rooftop.

heat release rate. A value of the heat energy generated when a material is burned.

heat stroke. A life-threatening condition that can occur during prolonged exposure to intense heat. The body is unable to sweat, resulting in extremely high body temperature and collapse.

heat-sensor labels. Stickers that are usually small, round, and orange that turn black when a ladder has been subjected to more than 300°Ft. They are affixed below the second rung from the top of each section of a ladder and on each side of the beams. They also have expiration dates.

heavy gauge steel stud. A skeletal building component of lightweight curtain walls made from a heavy gauge steel.

heavy timber or mill buildings. Type IV construction; The buildings were constructed of exterior brick walls, wood joisted floors, and massive interior wood columns and beams (more than 5 in. in any dimension).

heel. The end of a ladder that contacts the ground when positioned against a structure. In a truss-construction ladder, spurs or spikes are usually mounted onto the heel. In other types of ladders, a permanently mounted precast aluminum foot, butt, or shoe attaches to the heel. Also called the base or butt.

helical flow. Slower moving water along the shoreline circulates in a spiral motion with water in the middle.

helispots. Temporary locations where helicopters can safely land and take off. This term is used by the NIMS/ICS.

higbee indicator. A visible notch denoting the start of the threading inside a female coupling.

high angle. Denotes operations in which members are dependent on life safety rope and not a fixed surface for support.

high density polyethylene (HDPE). A polymer commonly used in the fuel tanks of newer cars. It can fail under direct fire conditions.

high explosive. An explosive that may or may not be combustible.

high point. A system of anchors and mechanical advantage hardware used to gain maximum clearance when raising victims out of below grade confined space or trench rescue situations.

high-pressure water systems. Water supply systems capable of providing high pressures to support fire attack apparatus on a fire scene.

high-expansion foam. A low-water content Class B foam which uses a foam generator and aerator which when activated cause the foam to expand to nearly 1,000 times its original volume. High-expansion foam works in enclosed spaces by excluding the oxygen from the fuel, extinguishing the fire.

hip boots. Flexible three-fourths rubber boots firefighters wore in the past.

hip roof. A type of roof that has three or more sides that slope to the exterior walls of the building.

HMIS. Hazardous Materials Inventory Statement.

HMMP. Hazardous Materials Management Plan.

hockey puck lock. A case-hardened steel hockey-puck-shaped lock where the locking pin is located inside.

hoistway. The opening through which an elevator travels. It is also referred to as the shaft.

home fire-safety survey. A voluntary inspection done by firefighters to help educate the occupants about the dangers of fire and how to be safer in their everyday lives.

Homeland Security Presidential Directive 5 (HSPD-5). This directed the federal government and state and local agencies to work under a newer version of ICS (Incident Command System) called the National Incident Management System (NIMS).

hook ladder. A form of a straight ladder with curved metal hooks permanently attached to its tip. When these spring-loaded hooks deploy, they allow the ladder to bite into the ridge of a roof, which provides a stable platform for a firefighter working on a steep.

hook-in leg-lock (Hill) maneuver. A way of securing oneself to a ladder by placing a boot in the center of a rung with the heel slid into the rung.

horizontal load test. A test that places weight on a horizontally supported ladder to determine its serviceability by measuring the amount of deflection or bending.

horizontal pressure tanks. High-pressure storage with capacities from 500 to 40,000 gallons of product. They are not normally insulated and so are usually painted white to reflect light and heat.

horizontal tanks. A horizontal bulk storage tank. These tanks sit on legs, usually a steel frame on a cement pad. Horizontal tanks can contain any combination of flammable or combustible liquids and may have some form of fixed protection.

horizontal ventilation. Removing heat, smoke, and fire gases by opening doors and windows.

hose bridge. A device placed around a section of hose to prevent it being driven over by vehicles.

hose clamp. A clamp that can be screwed down, use lever action, or is even hydraulic, which clamps shut a section of hose at a given point.

hose fittings. A manufactured fitting, not permanently attached to the hose or device, which adapts the coupling size, type, or thread style between different hoses or devices to allow them to be connected.

hose gasket. A rubber ring that helps to create a watertight seal between hose couplings and devices.

hose jacket. A hose tool that is put around a portion of hose that is leaking.

hose load. The tactical manner in which hose is stored and is intended to be deployed on an apparatus.

hose reel. A cylindrical piece of equipment used to store fire hose and allows the hose to be rapidly deployed.

hose rope tool. A section of rope or webbing, which may incorporate a cast hook, which is used to control, move, and secure hose.

hose tools. Tools that aid firefighters in the use and handling of fire hose.

hoselines. Hoses used for firefighting operations, normally ranging from 1 ½ in. to 2 ½ in. in diameter.

hot zone. The clearly marked and controlled area immediately surrounding a dangerous goods or hazardous materials incident that extends far enough to prevent adverse effects from released hazardous materials to personnel outside the zone.

hourly fire rating. The level of fire resistance of a building.

H-type apartment. A multi-story apartment building (usually of ordinary construction) laid out in an "H" with long center-hallway and wings on either end. Access to the wings may be via an offset or separate stairwell.

HUD window. A means of sealing up vacant buildings accepted and approved by the US Department of Housing and Urban Development

that uses plywood and dimensional lumber secured in place with bolts and nuts.

Heads-Up Display (HUD). A display found in the facepiece of the wearer's SCBA, a series of LED lights gives the wearer visual clues regarding air consumption and environmental temperatures.

hurricane-resistant window. Three-paned windows resistant to hurricane-force winds and theft from break-ins.

hydrant appliance. An appliance that is attached to a hydrant to alter its characteristics, such as the number of outlets, output pressure, or to begin or cutoff water flow.

hydrant gate valve. A slow turning valve that operates a sliding gate which occludes the water way.

hydrant inspection program. An annual program of systematic inspection to insure the operational capabilities of a hydrant.

hydrant key or tee wrench. A specially designed, long handled wrench used to shut of the gate valve of a hydrant.

hydrant. A device placed in water supply systems that incorporates discharge orifices, usually two 2½ in.- (65-mm) and one 4-, 4½-, or 5-in. (100, 115, or 125 mm) connection called a "steamer." These connections are designed to supply water for firefighting and maintenance purposes.

hydraulic or hole. Water formation following a sudden drop in the riverbed or over an obstruction that creates a powerful circulating force at the base of the drop. A powerful hydraulic can hold boats and people for an extended time.

hydraulic ventilation. The use of fog nozzles for ventilation.

hydrides. Compounds containing hydrogen and another element. The inorganic hydrides are flammable, water-reactive and very dangerous fire risks.

hydrocarbon fuels. A term given to any of the flammable or combustible liquids with a molecular make-up of hydrogen and carbon, created when crude oil is refined. Hydrocarbon fuels will not mix with water and either float on top (specific gravity < 1.0) or sink to the bottom (Specific Gravity > 1.0).

hydrocarbon. A chemical compound made up of carbon and hydrogen.

hydrogen cyanide (HCN). A colorless, odorless gas often released as products found in structural fires are exposed to heat and break down. The gas is highly toxic and causes severe respiratory distress.

hydrogen sulfide (H₂S). Gas emitted during organic decomposition. Also a by-product of oil refining and burning. Smells like rotten eggs and, in heavy concentration, can kill or cause illness. A chemical blood agent.

hydrogen sulfide. Gas emitted during organic decomposition. Also a by-product of oil refining and burning. Smells like rotten eggs and, in heavy concentration, can kill or cause illness; H₂S. A chemical blood agent.

hydrostatic hose testing machine. A machine designed to generate the high pressures required for modern fire hose.

hydrostatic test. Hydrostatic testing involves subjecting the cylinder (known as the pressure vessel) to water pressure or pressure applied by some other noncompressible fluid, usually through the cylinder's valve opening, using a specially designed test coupling.

hydroxyl radical. A radical (-OH) that, when combined with a hydrocarbon backbone, produces a class of chemicals called alcohols.

hyper extended leg-lock (Hell) maneuver. A leg-lock developed by Michael Ciampo of the FDNY to assist firefighters who momentarily lose their grip on a ladder, slip, or who perform rescues. At the proper working height on the ladder, a firefighter positions both feet on the same rung. Then, he or she raises one leg, similar to standing on the tip of the toe or flexing a calf muscle. The firefighter may use either leg to perform this tactic and should be well-balanced, not attempting to balance on the toe itself. As the leg extends upward, the firefighter wedges the lower thigh or knee under the ladder's rung. Also called the Hell maneuver.

hypothesis. An idea or assumption made based on the analysis of evidence and data and the experience of the investigator.

I

I-beam. A type of ladder construction in which the beams are shaped in an "I"-like configuration, with the rungs attached to the beams. Fiberglass and common homeowner ladders often carry this design.

IC command mode. This mode places the IC in a strategic command position. The best strategic position is inside a vehicle designed to serve as a command post.

IC fast-attack mode. This mode allows the IC to put a quick hit on the incident problem while managing the incident using a portable radio.

IC investigative mode. This mode allows for the IC to conduct an investigation for "nothing-showing" situations.

ice rescue PPE. The ice rescue ensemble consists of the suit, helmet, and harness (typically integrated with the suit itself), and will seal your body from the water leaving only the face exposed. The suit is in one piece, much like coveralls with attached boots, gloves, and hood. The integrated gloves and boots are formfitting and do not require additional internal apparel for use. Once donned and closed, the hood creates a tight seal around the face to keep water from entering the suit. Additionally, ice shoes, which are like sandals with spikes, make maneuvering on ice quicker and safer. A helmet much like the technical rescue helmet is required for protection in case of a fall.

IDLH. Immediately dangerous to life and health. 1. The maximum level to which an individual can be exposed to a chemical for 30 minutes and escape without suffering irreversible health effects or impairing symptoms. 2. The amount of material, usually expressed as parts per million (ppm) of air or other material, or milligrams per cubic meter (mg/m^3) of air that will pose an immediate life-or health-threatening situation to the exposed person.

IFC. International Fire Code.

ignitable liquid. Any liquid that is capable of being ignited including both combustible and flammable liquids.

ignitable mixture. A mixture of fuel and air within a flammable range.

ignition temperature. The minimum temperature to which a material must be raised before combustion will occur. At this temperature, no ignition source is required to be present.

impact load. A force delivered in motion such as a blow, or a force delivered by an object in motion striking a fixed object (e.g., an axe striking a roof).

impact resistant drywall. Drywall manufactured with fiberglass and other materials that make the finish of the drywall harder and therefore more difficult to open or breach.

incendiary fire. A fire that is intentionally started.

incentive program. When smoke, heat, and fire conditions compel a firefighter to abandon a search and quickly escape the structure.

incident action plan (IAP). An oral or written plan containing general objectives reflecting the overall strategy for managing an incident. It may include the identification of operational resources and assignments. It may also include attachments that provide direction and important information for management of the incident during one or more operational periods.

incident commander (IC). 1. The person responsible for the management and coordination of all incident operations. 2. The person in charge at the scene of an incident, who uses an ICS to manage operational personnel.

incident command post (ICP). A facility located at a safe distance from an emergency site, where the incident commander, key staff, and technical representatives can make decisions and deploy emergency manpower and equipment.

incident command system (ICS). 1. The organizational arrangement in which one person, normally the fire chief of the impacted district, or in some cases, the first responding chief officer, is in charge of an integrated, comprehensive emergency response organization and the emergency incident site. 2. A management system of specific procedures for controlling personnel, facilities, equipment, and communications from different agencies to coordinate effectively. 3. The chain of command and leadership at the scene of an emergency.

incident management system (IMS). A flexible on-scene system that identifies key roles and tasks that must be fulfilled to safely manage an emergency incident. It stipulates that one person (the incident commander) is responsible for overall operations during the incident.

incipient fire. A fire that is in the early stages of growth and has not developed past a point where a portable fire extinguisher or a small hand held hoseline flowing up to 125 gpm (473 L/min) can control the fire.

indicating valve. A valve that visually indicates either an open or closed condition.

indirect fire attack. Method of fire attack in which a solid or straight fire stream is applied against a ceiling or wall in an attempt to break the stream into smaller water droplets for increased heat absorption. Indirect fire attack is used when fire crews cannot directly access the base (seat) of the fire.

indirect fire damage. All other damage caused by fire suppression efforts and other activities on the fireground. Also known as secondary fire damage.

inductive reasoning. A method of analyzing all of the data collected and observed to reach a hypothesis.

inert gas. A gaseous agent that doesn't react with most chemicals, such as helium, neon, argon, nitrogen, and carbon dioxide. They extinguish fires by lowering a room's oxygen concentration from the normal level of 21 percent to below 15 percent, which is a safety hazard to humans.

infection. The growth of a parasitic organism inside the body. A person with an infection has an organism, such as a pathogenic virus, parasite, or bacterium, that is capable of invading body tissues, multiplying, and causing disease.

infectious disease. An illness or disease resulting from the invasion of a person's body by disease-causing organisms including bacteria, viruses, fungi, or parasites.

information officer. The officer responsible for dealing with the news media and general public. The information officer provides accurate, complete information about an incident's cause, size, and current situation; resources committed; and other matters of general interest. Also called the public information officer (PIO).

inherent fire stopping. Fire stopping accomplished by the characteristics (composition and size) of the materials used or the construction type used.

inhibitor. Any substance used to slow down or prevent a chemical reaction.

initiator. A chemical added to a monomer that will overcome the stabilization action of the inhibitor to allow a polymerization reaction to begin.

inline pumper. The apparatus that receives water from a source pumper and relays it to the attack pumper or apparatus.

inorganic acid. An ionic compound containing the hydrogen ion. Sometimes called mineral acids.

inorganic chlorides. A classification that includes some materials that are stable in water and others that are very water-reactive.

inorganic peroxides. Inorganic compounds containing the peroxy anion O_2^{-2}.

inspection holes. Small holes cut in floors or roofs to gain more information about the fire before cutting a larger hole, or to determine fire spread after a trench cut.

Insurance Services Office (ISO). This office develops and utilizes a prescriptive fire suppression rating schedule that determines a community's capabilities for firefighting, which is used to determine fire insurance rates for residents of the community.

interface component. A material used to construct or is a part of the protective equipment that provides limited protection where each portion of a protective material meets another, such as the area where a glove and coat sleeve meet.

interior finish. Any material(s) found on the floors, walls, or ceilings of a structure. Examples include carpet, paint, wood flooring, wallpaper, etc.

interior fire attack. A tactic used as part of an offensive strategy in which fire crews advance handlines into a fire building to attack and contain the fire.

intermediate emergency medical technician (EMT-I). This provider level serves to bridge the practical skills and capabilities of EMT-Bs and paramedics. EMT-I's are frequently found where the paramedic provider level is not provided.

intermediate web members. The supporting members of a truss that connect the top chord and the bottom chord.

intermodal tank. A tank often found in fixed facilities normally identified by a surrounding steel frame. There are two models of non-pressurized intermodal tanks and one model for pressurized materials. These tanks carry materials such as flammable and combustible liquids, toxic materials, or corrosives.

International Association of Firefighters (IAFF). A national union established in 1918 to support the professional interests of firefighters.

International Building Code. A consensus standard written by the International Code Council to ensure safe building construction; may be adopted by local and state governments.

International Code Council (ICC). A membership association dedicated to promoting safety and fire prevention and which develops the codes used to construct residential and commercial buildings, including homes and schools.

International Fire Code. An ICC code providing regulations governing the safeguarding of life and property from all types of fire and explosions hazards.

inverted roofs. Spongy roofs tapered to permit water runoff.

inward collapse. A type of collapse usually associated with post and beam construction in which the walls fall into the structure.

ionization smoke detector. A device that uses a small amount of radioactive material, usually Americium, to charge the air passing through two oppositely charged electrodes. When smoke enters the chamber, it lowers the conductance, initiating the alarm or initiating a signal to a fire alarm system.

ionize. To produce charged particles (ions) in a medium.

ionizing radiation. Radiation that can strip electrons from atoms.

ions. Electrically charged atoms or groups of atoms.

IRB. Inflatable rescue boat.

Iroquois Theater fire. A 1903 fire in a Chicago theater during the performance of *Mr. Bluebeard* in which 602 people died. The theater was claimed to be fireproof. It remains the worst theater disaster in U.S. history and led to improved laws for high-occupancy structures.

irritant. A corrosive material that may cause injury by irritation of the eyes, skin, or mucous membranes.

irritating material. A liquid or solid substances that, upon contact with fire or when exposed to air, emit dangerous or intensely irritating fumes.

isomer. One of two or more chemical compounds with the same molecular formula but different molecular structures.

isotopes. Different types of atoms of the same element with identical chemical properties but which differ in the number of neutrons.

J

jalousie window. A window constructed of glass louvers that overlap one another. A hand crank handle operate the louvers to tilt for opening.

James Gordon Bennett Medal. One of the first medals for bravery that was introduced in New York in 1869.

jet siphon. A device incorporating the venturi effect used to move water from one portable tank to another in water shuttle operations.

JLSC/DM. Joint Logistics Systems Center Depot Maintenance Directorate.

joint powers agreement (JPA). A contract between a city, county, and/ or special district in which the city or county agrees to perform services, cooperate with, or lend its powers to an operation.

joist. A supporting member used in building construction to support a floor, roof, or ceiling.

jumper. A suicidal person jumping from a height.

juvenile firesetter programs. Programs that bring together fire safety, law enforcement, mental health, and child safety advocates to provide community-based treatment to address and intervene upon fire setting by juveniles.

K

Kalamein doors. Doors set in metal frames that are pliable and made up of a composite construction with a wooden core.

Kelvin. An absolute temperature scale in which absolute zero is assigned the value zero. One Kelvin (K) is the same size as a Celsius degree. The normal freezing point of water is 273.15 K, and the normal boiling point of water is 373.15 K.

kerf. A notch, channel, or slit made in any material by cutting with a gas powered saw.

kerf cut. A quick and easy plunge cut made with a chain or rotary saw creating an opening the width of a single blade used to determine the location or existence of fire.

Kernmantle rope. A rope design featuring an inner, stronger core covered by an outer sheath.

ketone. A hydrocarbon derivative having two hydrocarbon backbones, or radicals, joined by a carbonyl radical.

key box. A locked container often used to store building entry keys, plans, and related emergency data.

keyed mortise cylinder. A device that operates the locking and unlocking function of a lock body.

key-in-the-knob-lock. A lock or latch that fits around bored openings in the face and edge of a door. If they are key operated, the cylinder is contained in the knob.

kinetic energy. The energy of motion.

kink. A sharp bend in a hoseline that reduces the flow of water.

knockdown. The ability of a finished foam product (raw foam, water, air) to be successfully applied to a burning product and contain the fire.

Knockdown is also a term used to indicate that a fire inside a building has been contained at the point of origin.

knockout cut. An additional relief cut made in a large ventilation hole used to assist roof firefighters to open up the roof and inspect the location of the hole.

L

ladder locks. The parts of an extension ladder that travel over each rung and make clicking noises as the fly section rises. When the ladder locks into a rung just after the click of the lock, the fly and bed section rungs align. Also called dogs, pawls, and rung locks.

ladder company. The company composed of apparatus, usually an aerial apparatus, staffed with firefighters and a company officer, and primarily assigned to place ladders, search and rescue, and other duties as designated by the department. Also called the truck company.

ladder pipe. A nozzle attached to the rungs of an aerial ladder. Ladder pipes can flow in excess of 500 gpm (1,893 L/min).

ladder tower. A heavier-duty aerial ladder with a bucket and pre-piped waterway attached to it.

laid rope. Rope constructed by three large strands twisted together.

laminar flow. Water flowing in layers of varying speed that do not interact because of friction.

laminated drywall. Drywall panels that have multiple layers laminated (glued) together to increase strength; often used in high security areas.

landing zone (LZ). An area where it is safe to land a helicopter for medical evacuation.

LAN. Local Area Network.

lanthanide series. One of two series of metals at the bottom of the periodic table, the other being the actinide series. Collectively, they are the rare earth metals.

large diameter hose. Supply line made of extruded or traditional means with a diameter of between four and five in.

last meal. What a patient last ate, a vital piece of information because of possible food allergies.

latent heat. The thermal energy that is absorbed when a substance is converted from a solid to a liquid or from a liquid to a gas.

latent heat of vaporization. The amount of heat a substance must absorb when it changes from a liquid to a vapor or gas.

LC$_{50}$. The concentration of gas or smoke required to produce lethality in 50% of exposed organisms.

LD$_{50}$. The dose of substance that will produce lethality in 50% of exposed organisms.

lean-to type collapse. A type of collapse where a floor falls down but one side stays attached.

length of services awards programs. Any program where an employee is recognized for service time with an organization.

LEPC. Local Emergency Planning Committee.

lever. The device squeezed or depressed to discharge a fire extinguisher's agent. In cartridge operated extinguishers, the discharge is accomplished by releasing the pressurizing gas into the cylinder. On most extinguishers the lever is located above the handle.

Lexan®. A polycarbonate resin thermoplastic glazing that has an impact resistance.

liaison officer. The officer responsible for coordinating with any outside agencies that respond to an incident.

life hazard. The first of the three strategic priorities, identifies the presence of potentially trapped incident victims. The benchmark for meeting this priority is "all clear."

lifeline. A rope used in searching larger areas such as stores, warehouses, or theaters. It is tied to a large, immovable object outside the fire building, then carried by the as he searches. The rope then can be used for egress if a firefighter becomes disoriented.

lifter roof tank. A bulk storage tank whose roof slides up and down on tracks, and when the contents pressurize, the roof lifts slightly to relieve the pressure.

light scattering. Projecting a beam of light from a smoke detector across a sensing chamber. When smoke is present, the particles reflect the light onto a sensor, which initiates the device.

light search. A quick search technique that can be performed when smoke conditions are several feet off the floor. The searching firefighter either crouches below the smoke layer or lies down on the ground and uses a powerful flashlight to completely scan the floor area and any furniture for victims.

lighting up. Fire re-igniting when more air is introduced into an area.

lightweight construction. System of construction in which structural support components are pre-engineered using a method to minimize weight/mass. These systems, which are more cost-effective than traditional construction methods, are prone to early failure when exposed to fire.

lightweight wood frame. Any wood frame construction using any lightweight engineered structural components, including lightweight parallel floor trusses, lightweight peaked roof trusses, and engineered wood I-beams.

lightweight wood truss roof. A roof whose wood truss components are connected by thin galvanized metal gusset plates that penetrate into the wood about ¼ to ⅜ in. (6 to 10 mm).

limited area sprinkler system. Fewer than 20 sprinkler heads on any single connection.

limited combustible construction. Another name for noncombustible construction.

line dam. A barrier, constructed of any suitable material available, intended to stop or slow the flow of liquid on an incline into the environment.

linear detector. A device in which detection is continuous along a path, essentially a cable that may run through a large portion of a building or loop around the ceiling of a room.

lined hose. A hose with an inner core of rubber compounds, thermoplastics, or blends of both, as well as polyurethane or natural rubber latex, and an outer layer for protection and reinforcement.

line-of-duty deaths (LODD). Fatalities to fire service and other emergency service personnel that occur as the result of injuries sustained during the performance of duty. There are approximately 105 deaths in the line of duty each year in the United States. Even one preventable death is unacceptable.

lintel or header. A horizontal beam that usually supports the wall above an opening such as a window or door.

liquefied gases. Gases that have been converted to a liquid by pressure and/or cooling.

liquefied petroleum gas (LPG). A category of easily liquefied , petroleum-based hydrocarbon fuels that include propane, butane, isobutane, methane, and propylene.

liquid natural gas (LNG). A colorless, odorless, tasteless, non-toxic, flammable liquid that has an odorant added to it to make it detectable by smell well below its lower flammable limits. It is mostly methane (depending on its source, it may be as high as 90% methane), with ethane making up the vast majority of the balance of the mixture.

listed. Items or components of a detection or suppression system that haves been listed by an approved testing laboratory, such as Underwriters Laboratory or Factory Mutual.

live bait rescue. Method of rescue in which a tethered rescuer wearing a PFD swims out to a victim.

live load. A non-fixed (sometimes moving) variable load that is added to the structure, including people, materials, and other transportable items.

load. The common term for the total weight of personnel and equipment being supported by a rope system.

local fire alarm system. A system that only warns occupants of a building that there is a fire, and sends no signal, other than audible, off site.

local-application system. A suppression system designed to protect only the area directly around a hazard.

lock body. The part installed inside the mortise cut-out in the door.

lockout/tagout. A procedure to prevent use of any equipment that should not be used, generally tagged and locked closed or off.

lock trim. The trim surrounding a lock based on style, look, and design.

locking mechanism. A simple and quick release device that secures an extinguisher's lever to prevent accidental discharge.

locomobile. The first gasoline-driven fire apparatus, assigned to the chief of New York City's fire department in 1901.

logistics section. The section that manages all resources required for the incident that are not assigned to the hazard zone. This includes staging and rehab.

loop. Made by placing a twist in a rope and having the standing part of the rope continue in the same direction.

low explosives. Explosives that usually deflagrate and do not detonate unless confined.

low-air alarm. Part of the SCBA system, an audible (and sometime sensory) warning to the wearer that their air supply cylinder is now at the level considered to be their air reserve, usually less than 25% of the cylinder's rated capacity.

lower explosive limit (LEL). The concentration of a compound in air below which the mixture will not ignite.

low-head dams. Artificial vertical or near vertical drop structures that stretch across a waterway, resulting in hydraulics from shore to shore with no downstream Vs, eddies, or other river features normally used to escape from fast moving water.

low-rise. A multi-story office building (up to seven floors) utilizing elements of modern high-rise construction techniques, such as a steel skeleton with metal-decking floors and curtain-wall exterior walls.

M

magnetic lock. A fail-safe lock that operates on DC electrical current.

main charge. A high-explosive.

main group elements. The tall, vertical columns on the periodic table marked IA through VIIIA that are also called representative elements and are made up of both metals and nonmetals. They are the alkali metals, alkaline earth metals, halogens, and noble or inert gases.

mainline valve. Part of the SCBA system, the valve that controls the flow of air from the cylinder though the regulator to the facepiece. The mainline valve must be activated to begin the flow air to the wearer.

make a door. The term used for completely clearing all glass, molding, and sashes from a window.

male coupling. The coupling end which has the visible threads extending from the hose.

mandatory mask rule. A rule that requires firefighters to wear SCBA in any IDLH environments.

manifold system. A special connection to water main system, wet or dry, utilizing non-potable or raw water for fire suppression activities, which are supplied by fire boats.

Mann Gulch fire. A fire in Helena Forest in Montana in 1949 that killed 16 smoke jumpers.

manual fire alarm boxes. Equipment that activates a fire alarm when manual action is applied by operating a lever that opens or closes a circuit.

mask-mounted regulator (MMR). A style of SCBA in which the regulator mounts directly to an opening in the front of the facepiece.

mass decontamination. Emergency decontamination on a large scale, involving the reduction or elimination of contamination through expeditious procedures on a large number of victims.

master stream. A water stream with a flow in excess of 300 gpm (1,136 L/min).

matter. Anything that occupies space and has mass. Matter is made up of atoms and may be solid, liquid, or gas.

Mayday message. A radio callout intended to clear the channel of traffic in order to transmit critical information. This callout is only used when there is an immediate threat to the lives of firefighters.

MC306. A nonpressurized (less than 3 psi [21 kPa]) tank, commonly used to transport gasoline, fuel oil, kerosene, and other flammable and combustible liquids. This tank is also known as a DOT406.

MC307. A low pressure (less than 40 psi [280 kPa]) tank with a normal maximum capacity of 7,000 gallons (26, 500 L). This tank is double shelled for leak protection and has recessed manheads for rollover protection. This tank typically transports flammable liquids, caustics, or acids. This tank is also known as a DOT407.

MC312. This tank is a similar to a MC307 except that it is designed to carry corrosive liquids and run with pressure less than 75 psi (525 kPa) with a normal capacity of 7,000 gallons (26,500 L). These tanks have numerous rings around the tank shell for strength and stiffening purposes and have built-in rollover protection.

MC331. A high-pressure tank containing gases or liquids under pressure starting at 100 psi (700 kPa). They typically have capacities at 11,000 gallons (41,640 L) and have a bolted manway at the front or rear. They will be painted white or some other heat reflective color. These tanks carry LPG, anhydrous ammonia, and other gases that have been liquefied.

MC338. A heavily insulated steel tank with a round endhead at the front and a squared off cabinet or compartment at the rear that contains the valves. This tank is for cryogenic liquids and may be marked with a "refrigerated liquid" label.

McCormick Place Exhibition Hall. Site of a major blaze in Chicago in 1967.

mechanical advantage. The advantage created by a rope system that enables people to do work while using less force.

mechanical equipment room (MER). A room that houses building services, such as heating, electrical, water, air-conditioning and ventilating systems, refrigeration, etc.

mechanical fastening. The use of bolts, screws, etc. to secure a building material.

mechanical ventilation. Ventilation consisting of machines and building systems to force smoke and hot gases by means of electrical, gas, or hydraulic powered exhaust fans or blowers; a hoseline to provide hydraulic ventilation; and a building's heating, ventilation, and air-conditioning (HVAC) system.

mechanical ventilation. See hydraulic ventilation.

med-evac. Medical evacuation by helicopter.

medical group. The team accountable for tasks such as victim decontamination and victim care.

medical PPE. Personal protective equipment used to provide body substance isolation to greatly reduce the possibility of cross contamination. It has a moisture barrier, which will prevent any liquids such as blood and vomit from penetrating the PPE and reaching the skin of the responder.

medical unit. The unit whose functions include providing medical treatment for incident responders and developing an incident medical plan that includes transportation route, available hospitals, and emergency medical services (EMS) organizations. The unit is also responsible for implementing and maintaining the rehabilitation area at an incident.

melting point. The temperature at which a solid changes to a liquid.

membrane roof. A rubber, waterproof, and flammable roof covering.

Meridian Plaza blaze. An incident in Philadelphia in 1991 described by officials as the "most significant fire of the twentieth century."

metals. Elements to the left and below the dividing line on the periodic chart. Metallic elements lose electrons easily.

metering valve. A device on foam eductors to regulate the percentage of foam to concentrate with a stream of water.

Metropolitan Fire Department. The paid New York fire department that replaced the volunteer fire service disbanded in 1865. The paid department was placed under the direction of commissioners appointed by the insurance-influenced, rural-based state legislature.

Michigan v. Tyler (436 U.S. 499). A case heard by the U.S. Supreme Court in 1978 that upheld that an investigator has the right to delay entry into a fire scene for origin and cause investigation until the scene becomes safe for them to do so.

minerals. Inorganic compounds found in nature formed by natural processes.

miscellaneous ladders. Portable ladders such as the collapsible, combination, and various sizes of the common stepladder that many fire departments carry on their apparatus. It is common to find many types of collapsible and telescoping portable ladders.

mobile computer terminal (MCT). A computer terminal that enables increased data collection and information retrieval. They are usually found in fire department vehicles and provide speed and storage capabilities similar to stationary office computers.

mobile data terminal (MDT). A terminal that allowed greater communication and information transmission than simple radio devices. They were developed in the 1980s and have more recently been phased out in favor of mobile computer terminals.

mobile radio. Radio units that are mounted on fire department apparatus. They are more powerful than handheld portable radios.

mobile water supply apparatus. A vehicle (tanker or water tender) designed primarily for transporting (pickup, transporting, and delivering) water to fire emergency scenes to be applied by other vehicles or pumping equipment.

Model Building Code. A generically written code created after the Baltimore fire of 1904 that could be adopted by any city in the United States, known as the National Building Code (NBC).

model fire and building codes. Codes that are designed to ensure the safety of buildings.

moderately soluble irritants. Irritants that dissolve in the moisture of the upper respiratory tract and lungs.

molecular decomposition explosion. A reaction in which materials do not burn, but instead undergo an instantaneous decomposition of their molecules, releasing enormous amounts of energy in a fraction of a second.

monomer. A small molecule that possesses the unusual chemical property of being able to react with itself to form a polymer.

mop-up line. A hoseline used for overhaul operations.

mortise and tenon connections. A connection consisting of a tenon (tongue) cut onto the end of the beam that is inserted into the mortise (hole) cut into the post.

mortise locks. A lock or latch that is mortised to let into the thickness of the door from the meeting edge and held in position by screws through the far end.

Mose the Fireman. A somewhat crude but big-hearted and brave fireman, who became a standard feature of the American theater.

mounded above-ground tanks. Tanks found in older terminals, usually fuel oil depots, that are half in-ground and half above-ground, mounded over with dirt and grass or gravel. These tanks are connected to a fuel oil truck loading rack and are protected with a bulk foam system.

moving water. A body of water that does not stand still. Examples of moving water are rivers and streams.

MSDS. Material Safety Data Sheet.

multicasting. Uses different frequencies on adjacent towers to increase range without.

multiple bond. A double or triple covalent bond.

multiple commands. More than one person assuming command or giving orders on an incident scene.

multiple roofs. Roofs built on top of existing roofs post-renovation.

municipal fire alarm system. Boxes around a community that can be used to notify the fire department in an emergency. They transmit a coded signal to the communications center, but they can also transmit directly to fire stations or other monitoring buildings. Also knows as street boxes.

municipal water system. A public water system that provides sufficient clean water for consumption while providing adequate residual capacity of that same water for fire suppression, which is maintained by a public or private water department.

mushrooming. The horizontal flow at ceiling level and subsequent banking down to floor level of smoke and heat generated by a fire in a confined space. The rapid mushrooming of smoke and heat can trap and disorient firefighters during search and rescue operations. It occurs more rapidly in small rooms. Venting roof skylights, stairways, and windows can delay or eliminate mushrooming of smoke and heat in confined spaces during a fire.

muster. A gathering of fire apparatus (usually antique pieces) for purposes of display and competition.

mutal aid. Agreements between fire departments that involve reciprocal assistance under a prearranged plan. This type of agreement is also used in the event the closest fire department to a particular incident is committed to another response.

N

NAERG. North American Emergency Response Guide.

National Association of Fire Engineers. Association formed in 1873 and later known as the International Association of Fire Chiefs (IAFC).

National Board of Fire Underwriters. Group established by a consortium of insurance companies in 1866 with the purpose of urging communities to upgrade their firefighting forces and building regulations.

National Fire Academy (NFA). A branch of the Federal Emergency Management Agency, under the Department of Homeland Security, whose mission is to educate America's firefighters to prevent, prepare, and respond to emergencies.

National Fire Protection Association (NFPA). A voluntary membership organization whose aims are to promote and improve fire protection and prevention. NFPA has published several volumes of codes known as the National Fire Codes. It was established in 1896 with the original intention of standardizing codes for sprinkler and electrical systems. An organization dedicated to fire safety that produces many standards, including the four-color diamond (NFPA 704) used on labels to indicate hazard.

National Incident Management System (NIMS). A systematic, proactive approach to guide departments and agencies at all levels of government, nongovernmental organizations, and the private sector to work seamlessly to prevent, protect against, respond to, recover from, and mitigate the effects of incidents, regardless of cause, size, location, or complexity, in order to reduce the loss of life and property and harm to the environment.

National Interagency Incident Management System (NIIMS). A command system developed in the early 1970s by FIRESCOPE, a California-based command consortium, to manage large-scale wildfires, later used to manage other large-scale disasters, including forest fires, earthquakes, civil unrest, etc. This system is used to manage massive amounts of necessary resources during incidents that can last from weeks to months, require thousands of incident responders, and generally include federal and state resources.

National Institute for Occupational Safety and Health (NIOSH). A division of the U.S. government's Centers for Disease Control (CDC). The purpose of NIOSH is to gather data documenting incidences of occupational exposure, injury, illness and death in the United States.

national standard hose thread. A national standard thread size that standardizes the connections on fire hydrants, fire hoses, and hose devices.

National Urban Search and Rescue System. Regional task forces established in 1989 under the jurisdiction of Federal Emergency Management Agency (FEMA).

natural ventilation. Ventilation consisting of cutting holes in roofs, opening up doors, windows, and any other possible source of wind that would allow the products of combustion to naturally and escape to the outside atmosphere.

negative pressure ventilation. Using blowers in windows or doorways to force smoke out of a structure.

nerve agents. Substances that interfere with the central nervous system.

neutralization. Decreasing the alkalinity or acidity of substance by adding alkaline or acidic materials, respectively. The result is a breakdown of the material.

neutron radiation. A deeply penetrating and highly dangerous form of radiation, being larger than the beta particle and lighter than the alpha particle.

neutron. The nuclear particle with an atomic weight of 1 atomic mass unit and no electrical charge.

New London, Texas, Junior-Senior High School. Site of a natural gas explosion in March 1937 killing 298 student and teachers. Because natural gas is odorless, this explosion led to the requirement of using mercaptan as an odorant so leaks can be detected quickly.

New York City's Great Fire of December 1835. A fire that consumed more than 650 buildings, including most of the Wall Street financial area and the lower east side wharf and dock district.

Newsham hand pumper. A 100 gpm (379 L/min) manual pump operated by two people lifting and lowering wooden handles called "brakes." The pumper can hold about 170 gallons (644 L) of water.

NFIRS. The National Fire Incident Reporting System.

NFPA 1. Uniform Fire Prevention Code dealing with fire prevention in the built environment.

NFPA 1962. Standard for the inspection, care, and use of fire hose, couplings, and nozzles and the service testing of fire hose.

NFPA 25. Standard for the inspection, testing, and maintenance of water-based fire protection systems.

NFPA 5000. The building construction and safety code developed by NFPA.

NFPA 921. The National Fire Protection Association publication titled A Guide for Fire and Explosion Investigations.

NFPA Fire Officer I. A level of fire officer designation based on training and education for the company officer. Generally holds the rank of sergeant, lieutenant, or captain and is responsible for the supervision of the personnel and resources assigned to a single or multiunit engine, ladder, or other company.

NFPA Fire Officer II. A level of fire officer designation based on training and education for the chief officer. Generally holds the rank of battalion chief or district chief and is responsible for the supervision of the personnel and resources associated with multiple units/stations or organizational disciplines within a fire department.

NFPA Fire Officer III. A level of fire officer designation based on training and education for the chief officer. Generally holds the rank of deputy chief or assistant chief and is responsible for the supervision of the personnel and resources associated with a major functional discipline (training, EMS, etc.) within a fire department.

NFPA Fire Officer IV. A level of fire officer designation based on training and education for the chief officer. Generally holds the rank of fire chief or fire commissioner and serves as department head and must possess advanced administrative, financial, communications, political, legal, managerial, analytical, and information management skills and abilities.

NFPA Hydrant Color Codes. A visual system used in indicating the hydrant's available flow at 20 PSI residual pressure.

night latch. A rim or mortise latch with a beveled spring bolt or roller bolt that shoots when the door is closed, but can be withdrawn by key from outside and by a knob or lever handle from inside.

NiMH. Nickel metal hydride. A common component of hybrid vehicle batteries.

nitrides. Water-reactive compounds made up of a metal and nitrogen.

no command. When no one on an incident scene assumes command of the incident, resulting in freelancing.

noble gases. Group IIIA elements on the periodic table, headed by helium. Also called inert gases.

nonpermit confined space. A space large enough a person can enter and perform work, but has limited or restricted means for entry or exit, and may not be designed for continuous human occupancy.

non-polar. Chemical species not having positive and negative ends.

non-coded alarm. An alarm condition that does not give any information as to the location, type, or reason for initiating devices activation.

noncombustible construction. Type II construction; the structural members are of noncombustible materials and have little or no fire resistance.

noncombustible materials. Any building materials that are not capable of combustion under specified test conditions.

noncompressible. Describes fluids with a given volume that will retain that volume regardless of pressures being applied. This makes it capable of being pumped.

nonconductive. Does not conduct electricity when dry.

nonionizing radiation. Radiation that does not change the structure of atoms but does heat tissue and may cause harmful biological effects.

nonmetals. Elements to the right and above the dividing line on the periodic table. Non-metallic elements will accept electrons.

nonpressure tank car. A rail car that may or may not be seen with expansion domes. These carry a wide variety of materials including, flammables, combustibles, oxidizers, organic peroxides, poisons, irritants, reactive liquids, and other similar materials.

nozzle. The device through which an agent is expelled and that gives the shape of the fire stream and the direction it will travel. Also known as the horn.

nozzle operator. The person in control of the operation of the nozzle on a fire attack hoseline.

nozzle pressure (NP). Pressure of water as it is discharged from the nozzle orifice.

NTSB. National Transportation Safety Board.

nucleus. The center of an atom that contains all its positive charge and essentially all the weight of the atom. It contains protons and neutrons.

O

Occupational Safety and Health Administration (OSHA). A federal agency charged with creating and enforcing laws regarding occupational safety and health.

octet rule. In chemistry, the rule that states that an element becomes stable or satisfied when its outer ring has eight electrons in it, with the exception of helium, which can only have two electrons (known as the duet rule.)

offensive strategy. Structure fire situation in which the incident commander determines that the best course of action to contain the fire is to commit crews into the building. An offensive strategy is usually employed when civilian lives are at risk or the fire has not yet consumed a large portion of the building.

off-gassing. A signal that your gear is superheated. The gear is literally smoking when you leave a building. This process is your gear releasing heat absorbed from the fire.

ohm. A measure of electrical resistance.

old-style sprinkler heads. A type of head that directs about half the water to the ceiling and half on the fire. These are considered obsolete.

OPA. Oil Pollution Act.

open fracture. A fracture in a bone where the bone pierces the skin creating a wound.

open shaft. Light and air shaft that opens to one side of the building and easily identifiable from that side of the building.

open-circuit SCBA. A self-contained breathing apparatus (SCBA) that uses compressed air only. Pressurized air is delivered to the wearer, and exhaled air is expelled from the facepiece through a one-way valve.

opened up. An overhaul term used when all the building material affected by fire is removed to inspect for extension.

open-web steel bar joist roof. A light weight steel truss system covered with multiple layers of insulation material, tar, and composition and engineered to span between load bearing points.

operating/working pressure. The maximum pressure a hose should be exposed to under field conditions, which is 10% of the service/test pressure.

operational zone. Area where primary and backup entry team operations and support operations are conducted. Typically a 100-ft (30 m) perimeter around the exclusion zone.

operations group. Responsible for tasks such as fire control and direct fire fighting evolutions including ventilation, forcible entry, search, rescue, salvage and overhaul.

operations section. The section in the incident command system responsible for all tactical operations related to an incident.

ordinary construction. Type III construction; the building consists of exterior masonry load-bearing walls and wood joist floors and roof. The interior bearing walls may be of wood frame or, when required, an interior bearing wall that is a firewall is constructed of masonry.

organic (natural). 1. Referring to or derived from living organisms. 2. In chemistry, any compound containing carbon, with certain exceptions. 3. Pertaining to organic chemistry, which is the chemistry of compounds that were part of living things. Generally recognized as the chemistry of carbon compounds, hydrocarbon compounds, and their derivatives.

organic acid. A covalent hydrocarbon derivative that contains a carboxyl group. Weaker than inorganic acids of the same concentration.

organic chemistry. The study of compounds that are or once were part of living things.

organic peroxides. A group of highly dangerous materials used as initiators for thermoplastics and curing agents for thermosetting plastics.

oriented strand board (OSB). An engineered wood product formed by layering strands (flakes) of wood in specific orientations. In appearance it may have a rough and variegated surface with the individual strips lying unevenly across each other.

origin and cause investigation. The procedure of finding where (origin) and how (cause) a fire started.

outside stem and yoke (OS&Y). A valve that can be shut off to stop water flow at a sprinkler riser in the event of sprinkler system activation with water flow.

outward collapse. A type of collapse usually associated with post and beam construction in which the walls fall outward.

overfill protection device (OPD). A device built into fill valves on compressed flammable gas cylinders that prevents overfilling by using an interior float switch to close off the valve when the cylinder is full.

overflow dam. The products at the base of the dam while the moving water flows over the top; used for products with a specific gravity of greater than 1.

overhaul. The process that takes place after the main body of fire has been controlled or extinguished. In this process firefighters use tools to open walls, ceilings, and floors and to examine furniture and anything that looks like it may contain any hidden fire.

overpressurization. Occurs during interior fire attack when a fog fire stream is applied to a fire in a room or space that is not well-ventilated, resulting in a disruption of the thermal layering which makes conditions throughout the room untenable for fire personnel. Also referred to as thermal inversion.

oxidizer. A substance that either is oxygen, a substance that contains oxygen and gives it up readily, or another substance that will support combustion. Also known as an oxidizing agent.

oxanions. Complex, negatively charged ions that contain oxygen and at least one other element.

oxygen-containing compounds. Hydrophilic and polar compounds, including materials such as silica gel and zeolite.

P

PASS. Pull, aim, squeeze, sweep. The acronym that describes the operation of a fire extinguisher.

padlock. A portable detachable metal hinged shackle lock often found on roll down security metal gates. Normally unlocked using a key or a dialed or numerical combination.

painting the box. A way of marking a solid-beam ladder's balance point when it falls directly between a set of rungs by painting the inside and outside of both beams.

pancake-type collapse. A type of collapse where one floor falls totally on another.

paraffin series. An older name given to the alkanes.

paramedic. This certification level provides for the administration of various medications and invasive EMS procedures under medical direction.

parapet. The front section of a building's wall that extends above the roofline.

parts per million (PPM). Units commonly used to express contamination ratios, as in establishing the maximum permissible amount of a contaminant in water, land, or air.

passenger compartment. The area of the car where passengers ride. It can burn vigorously when vented and contains many potential fuel loads including foam seats, a padded dash, and vinyl trim components. A firefighter should also be wary of air bag deployment and the possible explosion of pressurized air bag inflator tanks.

penciling. The use limited amounts of water for short durations to delay flashover.

pendant sprinkler head. A sprinkler head that is mounted on the underside of sprinkler piping and incorporates a deflector designed to direct the water stream down.

Performance Based Fire Prevention Code. A code that uses engineering principles and mathematical models to meet an acceptable level of fire and life safety.

periodicity. The regular repeating of chemical properties of the elements.

permit-confined space. A space large enough for a person to enter and perform work, but with limited or restricted means for entry or exit, and may not be designed for continuous human occupancy due to poor or restricted air quality and other life-threatening hazards, such as flammable atmospheres and awkward interior layouts which may cause a worker to be injured or trapped.

peroxides. Hydrocarbon derivatives having two hydrocarbon backbones or radicals, joined by a peroxide radical.

personal alert safety system (PASS). A device that can be either removable (clipped on a strap) or integrated as a component of an SCBA. When in alarm the PASS will notify firefighters working in and around the scene that a firefighter is down, trapped, or in some life-or-death emergency. A PASS device can be activated manually or when the wearer is motionless for a period of time.

personal fire shelter. A self-deployable shelter constructed of an aluminized material used as a last resort to reflect the extreme heat during a fire roll over.

personal protective equipment (PPE). The system of protective garments and respirator protection designed to encapsulate a firefighter and offer protection from a variety of hazards, including heat, toxic gases/smoke, and puncture injuries.

personnel accountability report (PAR). A roll call from the IC, to ensure all troops are out of harm.

personnel accountability system (PAS). A system that provides for the tracking and inventory of all members operating at an emergency incident using passports consisting of Velcro and plastic cards attached to various apparatus and status boards to track assignments of divisions, groups, companies, teams, and individuals at emergency incidents.

person-in-machine. When a person's body part, such as a limb, is trapped or pinned in a device requiring removal.

PFDs. Personal flotation devices.

Philadelphia Gazette. Benjamin Franklin's newspaper, which led to the forming of America's first volunteer fire brigade, the Union Fire Company (1736).

phosphide. A compound made up of a metal and phosphorus.

photoelectric light-obscuration smoke detector. A device that measures how much of a light beam is blocked by smoke. The detector uses a projected beam, which is projected from a sending unit to a receiving unit. When smoke enters the sensing chamber, the beam is blocked, initiating the device.

piercing nozzle. A tapered nozzle with a pointed end that can be driven through a wall or floor surface to penetrate the void space. The nozzle is charged and discharges a fog spray into the burning void space, such as attics, walls, and floors.

planning section. The section responsible for collecting and evaluating incident situation information, preparing situation status reports, displaying situation information, maintaining status of resources, developing an IAP, and preparing required incident-related documentation.

plastics. Materials that contain as an essential ingredient one or more organic polymeric substances of large molecular weight, is solid in its finished state, and at some stage in its manufacture or processing into finished articles can be shaped by flow.

plate glass. Glass produced in thin sheets, used for windows and mirrors.

platform frame. A type of wood frame construction that generally uses dimensional lumber with each story built one at a time, which provides inherent fire stopping.

point last scene (PLS). A primary search area established by interviewing witnesses to determine where the victim was last seen

poison. Any substance that causes injury, illness, or death to living tissue, usually in small doses.

polar. In chemistry, having positive and negative ends.

polar solvent. A term given to any solvent made from polar molecules (opposing electrical charges). Polar solvents will mix with water and when ignited burn at a higher temperature than hydrocarbon fuels.

polymer. A large molecule made up of up to thousands of monomer molecules that have reacted with themselves in a special type of chemical reaction called polymerization.

polymer-based compounds. Polar or nonpolar functional groups in a porous polymer.

polymerization. A chemical reaction in which a monomer reacts with itself to form a larger molecule called a polymer.

polypropylene rope. A type of rope that floats, resists rot and mildew, and has a strong tolerance to chemicals and acids. Used primarily for water applications and rescue.

polyvinyl chloride (PVC). A form of plastic commonly used in building construction and contents within a structure. When exposed to heat, PVC products break down easily and produces toxic, carcinogenic gases.

Pompier ladder. A historic fire service ladder that is no longer recognized by the National Fire Protection Association, but is still used by some fire departments and training facilities to increase a firefighter's trust in tools and equipment. Its construction includes one center beam with rungs attached to each side. A large, solid, forged hook at the top of the beam was used for breaking windows and then could be hooked onto a window's ledge. Then, a firefighter could climb the ladder and proceed up the side of a building floor.

pony length. A short section of hose used to fill short runs of hose or to hook to a hydrant for filling.

positive pressure ventilation (PPV). Using blowers in windows or doorways to force clean outside air into a structure.

post and beam or braced frame. Wood frame construction in which the frame of the structure is formed by vertical wood posts (located at each corner of the building) connected to horizontal beams (located at each floor level) that support the floors.

post control window ventilation. A public-friendly technique used when the fire is extinguished and care is given in carefully removing windows to ventilate without doing any damage.

post-indicator valve. A water control valve with a window that reads either open or shut depending on its position.

potable water. Treated water that is safe for consumption.

potential energy. Energy stored within a physical system.

pounds per square inch gauge (psig). This gauge has been corrected to zero, with the reading already wakening into account the atmospheric pressure which is constantly being exerted.

preaction system. A system of pipes with closed sprinkler heads where water flow is controlled by to actions. The first is the release of a locked clapper, which prevents water from entering the piping, and the fusing of a closed sprinkler head, to allow water to discharge from that sprinkler head. In order for water to flow, both actions must occur.

precast panels. Any of a variety of panels such as windows that are made off-site and delivered to the building site.

preconnect. Hose that is attached to a discharge or suction during loading.

prefire plan. A plan for firefighters that details all hazards, ingress and egress points, alarms, sprinkler systems, water supplies, and any information that will prepare the fire department to handle a fire or other emergency at the occupancy.

pre-incident plan. A document developed to gather building intelligence data used by the fire department to determine resources and decision-based actions necessary to mitigate anticipated emergencies at a specific facility.

Prescriptive Based Fire Prevention Code. A code that outlines exact methods for compliance.

pressure indicator/gauge. A device that lets you know whether an extinguisher has adequate pressure to operate properly.

pressure tank car. A railcar with valves that are protected by a dome with a hatch. Flammable liquids and toxic gases are usually found in these types of cars.

pressure. Force applied over a given area, commonly expressed as pounds of force per square inch (psi).

pressure-regulating valve. A device that controls pressure at the outlet of a standpipe to prevent excessive nozzle pressure in hoselines.

pressure-relief explosion. The release of material after the failure of a container due to the rise of pressure above the container's design strength.

pressurized gases. Gases that are still in a gaseous state, but under pressure higher than 14.7 psia (100 kPa).

pressurized ventilation. Ventilation technique consisting of machines and building systems that force smoke and hot gases by means of electrical, gas, or hydraulically powered exhaust fans or blowers; a hoseline to provide hydraulic ventilation; and a building's heating, ventilation, and air-conditioning (HVAC) system.

primary explosives. High explosives that explode or detonate by heat or shock with enough brisance to initiate the detonation of the main charge.

primary feeders. Large diameter (between 30 in. and 48 in. in diameter) water mains found in areas of high demand that act as the primary connections to secondary feeder lines.

primary search. A rapid check of a fire building, focused on areas that are normally used by occupants for egress.

principal hazard. The most dangerous property or reactive tendency of a substance.

procurement unit. The unit responsible for processing rental and purchase paperwork for specialized equipment to be used at an incident.

The unit is also responsible for reporting when the equipment arrives, is used, and leaves.

products of combustion. In the case of hydrocarbons, for example, carbon, carbon monoxide, carbon dioxide, water, and several intermediate products that are all matter.

proof/acceptance test pressure. The pressure the hose is subjected to by the manufacturer at the factory prior to shipment.

propellants. An alternate name for certain low explosives.

proper name. The agreed-upon system of naming organic compounds according to the longest carbon chain in the compound.

property. A structure, mobile or permanent, and all possible contents in or around it. Contents usually have value, and are worth trying to saving during suppression efforts.

property conservation. The third of the three strategic priorities, which identifies when the incident has reached a point where no further damage is likely to occur and units will begin de-committing from the incident. The benchmark for meeting this priority is "loss stopped."

proportioner. Connected to the eductor, the proportioner allows the pump operator to select the ratio of raw foam to water that will be discharged as finished foam. The ratio (or proportion) depends on the type of raw foam being used and the type of incident (spill or fire).

proprietary system. A system, common on college and office campuses, where the same group manages and is responsible for protecting many buildings. It contains a monitoring station, staffed by trained operator, who work directly for the managers of the property.

protected. A fire pattern created by an item "protecting" the area from the effects of fire, smoke, heat, soot, etc.

protected premises. A building protected by fire alarm systems.

proton. The nuclear particle that has an atomic weight of 1 atomic mass unit and an electrical charge of positive 1.

proximity PPE. Personal protective equipment with an outer shell comprised of an aluminized surface to reflect rather than adsorbs the vast radiant heat created from aircraft and petroleum based fires. Proximity PPE provides close proximity protection for short periods of time at radiant heat temperatures as high as 2,000°F (1,093°C).

psi. Pounds of force being applied per square inch of surface area.

public safety answering points (PSAP). Facilities operated by local law enforcement where calls for assistance are initially received and then transferred to the fire department for dispatch. A PSAP may be staffed with civilian and law enforcement personnel, uniformed firefighters, or an appropriate combination as determined by the local community or jurisdiction.

pull loops. Loops extending from a preconnected line to assist with deployment.

punched hole. An examination cut made with a sharp point of a hand tool to determine the location or existence of fire.

Purple K. Potassium bicarbonate, a dry chemical developed by the U.S. Naval Research Lab, precluding the use of the term "Purple K" as a trade name. It was discovered that the salts of potassium were far more effective on flammable liquid fires compared to the salts of sodium.

push. Term used to describe the process of feeding hoseline into a structure to ease the burden on the nozzle team pulling the hoseline.

pyrolysis. The chemical decomposition of matter by heat.

pyrophoric. The property of a material that ignites spontaneously upon exposure to air.

Q

QAP. Quick Action Plan.

Q-decking. A light-weight flooring system used in high-rise construction with a corrugated metal deck resting on a steel truss support system and covered in a thin layer of poured concrete. A Q-decking flooring system has less weight and is easier to construct at elevation than traditional flooring systems.

queue. A backed up line of vehicles.

quick release maneuver. A technique that allows a firefighter to remove their SCBA if they have become entangled.

quint. A fire department vehicle equipped with a permanently mounted fire pump, water tank, hose storage area, and aerial device with a permanently mounted waterway and complement of portable ladders.

R

rad. The unit of radiation in an absorbed dose.

radiation. Heat transfer through space by light waves.

radical. A highly reactive molecular fragment that, when attached to another molecular fragment or hydrocarbon backbone, will impart specific properties to the new compound.

radio frequency. A specific oscillation between 3Hz and 300GHz. These are used by first responders for communication purposes.

radio headset. A combination headphone and microphone that allows hands-free communication between a captain and his crew.

radioactivity. The property of some substances to emit invisible and potentially harmful radiation.

rafters. A series of sloping roof framing members that support the roof sheathing and roof covering.

Rankine. An absolute temperature scale named after 19th century Scottish engineer William Rankine, and denoted by °R. One Rankine degree is the same size as a Fahrenheit degree, so absolute zero (-460°F) is 0°R. The normal freezing point of water is 492°R and the normal boiling point of water is 672°R.

rapid intervention crew (RIC). A team of equipped and trained firefighters standing by while other firefighters operate in hazardous fire conditions. The RIC is ready to be deployed should any of the operating firefighters become unable to exit the building.

rapid oxidation explosion. A very fast combustion reaction. A deflagration.

rappelling. The common term for personal descending techniques.

rare earth metals. The lanthanide and actinide series of metals at the bottom of the periodic table.

ratchet adjustment. A changeable headband inside a helmet that will allow its wearer to adjust the fit. Enables the helmet to fit when donned with or without the SCBA facepiece and hood.

rate compensation detector. A heat detector that accurately senses surrounding air temperatures regardless of temperature changes in the air around it. These are particularly useful in spaces where large temperature changes or cooling air movement occurs.

rate-of-rise detector. A device that activates when the temperature surrounding it rises.

Rattle Watch. Created in 1648, these night patrols and fire wardens inspected chimneys, thatched roofs, and household cooking fires in New Amsterdam. Also known as "the prowlers."

Rattlesnake Fire. Incident in the Mendocino Forest in 1953 that took 15 firefighters' lives.

RCRA. Resource Conservation and Recovery Act.

reaction force (RF). The force applied to a nozzle operator when the nozzle is in operation.

rear-mount apparatus. Turntable devices mounted at the rear of an apparatus with the ladder's tip/bucket mounted over the cab of the apparatus.

recessed. A mounting method requiring a cutout to be made into a finished wall or other type of surface.

recharge. To refill an extinguisher. Recharge shall be done by trained and certified personnel immediately after use. The extinguisher must be recharged with the extinguishing agent listed on the nameplate. Substitutions could cause damage or injury.

reciprocating saw. An air, electric, or battery powered saw with a blade that moves back and forth. Various blades can be used to cut wood, metal, plastic, or automobile components.

recoil spring. The gasoline powered engine's rope starter assembly used to wind up the starter cord and prevent the cord from pulling out.

recovery phase. When search and rescue for life operations have ceased and life is no longer suspected with the preservation of evidence.

reduced-profile maneuver. A technique that allows a firefighter to move through small areas that would normally be too small to fit through.

regimen. A plan of exercise and proper diet designed to keep a firefighter in good health and always prepared for the job.

regulator assembly. Part of the SCBA system that reduces the cylinder-supplied air from its compressed pressure (up to 4,500 psi [31.500 kPa]) to a level just above normal atmospheric pressure.

reinforced concrete. Concrete with imbedded rebar or other types of metal, mesh, or tensioned cables to increase the overall strength and support.

rekindle. The reignition of a fire because of latent heat, sparks, or smoldering embers.

relative response factor. The inaccurate readings obtained when attempting to detect the concentration of other types of flammable gases not calibrated to the meter.

relay pumping. The use of one or more apparatus to supply water to additional apparatus for fire suppression operations.

rem. A measure of radiation dose related to biological effect.

remote annunciation panel. A small alarm panel located at the entrances of a building that help to notify the fire department and others concerned of the alarm system status and the location of the initiating device that has activated.

representative elements. The tall, vertical columns on the periodic table marked IA through VIIIA that are also called "main group elements" and that are made up of both metals and nonmetals. They are the alkali metals, alkaline earth metals, halogens, and noble or inert gases.

rescue air kit (RAK). An air supply kit carried by rapid intervention crews that includes an air supply cylinder, a quick-fill hose, and an extra facepiece. A RAK is intended to deliver an emergency air supply to a trapped firefighter.

rescue company. A fire company that is tasked with the rescue of victims from fires, confined spaces, trenches, and high-angle situations.

rescue pickup evolution. A lifesaving rope rescue performed when one firefighter is lowered by another firefighter on rope and picks up a civilian or firefighter in danger at a window below and lowered down to the street or a lower window.

rescue vacuums. Large diameter vacuums used to aid in the removal of debris, water, mud, dirt, or sand, trapping victims in trench rescue or building collapse. These vacuums are commonly mounted on Hydrovac or Vac Trucks owned by utility and construction companies.

residential sprinkler. A sprinkler designed for use in residential settings. These sprinkler heads activate quickly to enhance occupant survivability in the room of origin.

residential system. A system used in residential settings that is designed to prevent flashover in rooms of origin, improves chances for occupant escape, and prevents fire spread to adjacent rooms.

residual pressure. The pressure remaining in a hose or water main while water is flowing.

Resigned Firemen's Association. An association formed in 1848 when a significant number of volunteer firefighters walked off the job.

resistance. The potential for molecular collisions that occur as electrons move along a conductor making the flow of the electrons more or less difficult. The lower the resistance, the easier it is for the electrons to flow. The higher the resistance, the more difficult it is for the electrons to flow.

resources unit. The unit responsible for checking in and maintaining status on all personnel, apparatus, and equipment assigned to the incident.

respiratory paralyzers. Materials that will, upon entering the body, short-circuit the respiratory nervous system.

retard chamber. A chamber located between a sprinkler valve and water-flow alarm that prevents false alarms by allowing pressure surges to dissipate before setting off the water-flow alarm.

retroreflective. The reflection of light in which the reflected rays are preferentially returned in the direction close to the opposite of the direction of the incident rays, with the property being maintained over wide variations of the direction of the incident rays.

returns. The small walls that extend down from the inside of a skylight or scuttle.

reverse lay. Hose lay designed to be laid from the hydrant to the fire.

Rex tool. A beefier version of the A-tool. It is a U-shaped, lock-pulling tool, with sharp, tapered blades that bite into lock cylinders of all shapes and sizes. The opposite chisel end is used to drive rim locks after cylinders are removed.

ridge beam or ridgepole. The uppermost horizontal framing member of a roof system located at the peak or uppermost point of the roof.

ridge vent. An area at the peak of a roof where a space is made between the sheathing and covered with a decorative aluminum vent or roofing material that allows the roof to vent the hot air from the attic space.

ridging the roof. A technique used to ventilate a peaked roof by removing or cutting downward on both sides of the ridge vent.

rim lock. A lock or latch typically mounted on the surface of a door or drawer.

Ringling Brothers and Barnum & Bailey Circus tent fire. An incident in Hartford, Conn., killing 167 and injuring nearly 500 in early summer 1944.

risk management. The process of planning, organizing, leading, and controlling resources and activities of an organization in order to minimize the adverse impact of accidental losses on that organization at a reasonable cost.

risk management plan. A major tool the IC uses to determine the level of risk to be taken, to determine the incident strategy based on the risk versus the gain.

risk versus gain. A comparison of the risk of loss against the potential for gain in an operation deemed unsafe.

river left. The left side of the river as one is looking downstream.

river right. The right side of the river as one is looking downstream.

road flares. Flares used at night to alert motorists. They should be used judiciously because they present an ignition source that might not be desirable at some incidents.

rock lath. A gypsum board material in 16 in.- to 2 ft-wide boards with holes every couple of inches.

rocker lugs. Tabs that extend from the body of a coupling that allow the connection of a spanner wrench for tightening of the connection.

roentgen. The unit of exposure from x-rays or gamma rays.

roll-down gate. A gate that is operated manually, mechanically, and/or electrically, made of metal and that opens and closes vertically. Often found in shopping malls, storefronts, schools, food concessions, loading docks, supermarkets, and pharmacies to provide security.

rollover. When heated gases in a compartment, such as a room, rise to the ceiling and become ignited, traveling over the heads of occupants in the compartment or space. Also called flameover.

roof hooks. Permanent curved, spring-loaded, metal hooks that secure the tip of a roof ladder to a pitched roof.

roof is open. A radio transmission given by a firefighter on the roof to communicate that initial vertical ventilation over the stairwell is complete.

roof joist. A term used for rafters in buildings constructed with a flat roofs.

roof ladder. A form of a straight ladder also commonly called a hook ladder because of curved metal hooks permanently attached to its tip. When these springloaded hooks deploy, they allow the ladder to bite into the ridge of a roof to provide stability.

roof open. Denoted in the building marking system by an "RO," a term that means that there are holes in the roof and firefighters should be aware of the possible hazard.

roof ventilators. Ventilators that differ in type, size, and shape and may be found on roofs for venting a particular area within a building or providing some type of ventilation for a device or appliance such as kitchen appliances.

rope rescue. Any operation where a life-dependent rope evolution is required.

rotary power saw. A gasoline fueled two-cycle engine power tool that can be equipped with multiple types of blades used to cut through materials such as wood, metal and concrete.

round turn. A loop made with rope in which the standing part goes back in the direction from which it came.

RPM. Revolutions per minute.

rule of air management (ROAM). A method used to remind personnel about an increased awareness in their air capacity and the need to exit hazardous environments prior to using reserve air.

runaway polymerization explosion. An instantaneous release of energy from an uncontrolled polymerization reaction.

runaway polymerization. The almost instantaneous, uncontrolled conversion of monomers to polymers, with a great release of heat energy.

rungs. Circular, horizontal cross members of a ladder spaced 14 in. apart that tie two beams together, serve as footrests for climbers, and transfer weight into the beams and then the ground. Some aluminum ladder rungs have raised extrusions or flat tops.

running end. The end of a rope that is to be used for work such as pulling or hoisting.

runoff. Excess water produced during firefighting efforts, rain, or from contaminated liquids produced as a result of decontamination.

S

safety brake handle. The part of a saw that prevents the blade from rotating across the bar as the throttle lever is engaged and allows the operator to apply the brake, which immediately stops the blade.

safety briefing. A briefing conducted to inform responders at a long-term hazardous materials incident about safely operating.

safety factor. An additional distance added to a collapse zone to account for misjudging the height or width and any bouncing of materials when they fall.

safety line. A secondary rope line used as a backup in case of primary or main line failure.

safety officer. The officer responsible for keeping the IC advised on all operational safety matters relating to an incident.

safety. This includes the concept of "embedding" safety elements and the communications flow plan the command team uses to connect all organizational elements to ensure worker safety in the hazard zone.

salt. An ionic compound formed by a metal and a nonmetal.

saltbox roof. A form of a gabled roof where the sloping sides of the roof are asymmetrical and each side ends at a different story.

salvage. In firefighting, the process of protecting the contents of a building from fire, smoke, and water damage. Also known as loss control.

San Francisco's Great Earthquake and Fire of 1906. A fire that destroyed more than 28,000 buildings. Originally reported to have cost fewer than 400 lives, researchers revealed a cover-up by the city after the event and now suspect the loss of life to be in excess of 3,000. This was the largest fire in American history.

saponification. The process by which an alkaline solution reacts with fatty acids in a cooking medium to form a soapy foam on top of burning material. This secures the vapors and cools the cooking medium as the foam drains out and converts to steam.

SARA. (1986) Superfund Amendments and Reauthorization Act.

saturated hydrocarbon. A hydrocarbon compound that contains only single covalent bonds between each carbon atom.

saw sling. A removable carrying strap attached to a power saw for a safe hands-free operation.

scaling ladder. A historic fire service ladder that is no longer recognized by the National Fire Protection Association, but some fire departments and training facilities still use it to increase a firefighter's trust in tools and equipment. Its construction includes one center beam with rungs attached to each side. A large, solid, forged hook at the top of the beam.

scene control group. The group responsible for establishing and enforcing perimeters used to isolate affected areas.

scientific method. A systematic approach to conduct the origin and cause investigation using proved scientific procedures. NFPA 921 identifies seven steps for this process.

scissor ladder. A narrow, collapsible ladder that folds into itself for transportation through small, narrow spaces. Also called a folding, attic, suitcase, or closet ladder.

scrubbed out. When a natural gas leak occurs underground, a term indicating the odorant added to natural gas giving it a distinctive smell has been trapped below-ground and stripped off the natural gas molecules, rendering the gas odorless.

scuttle. A small hinged square hatch at the roof level accessed by a wood or metal ladder at the top floor of a structure and used when occupants are trapped by fire below to gain access to the roof for safety.

secondary collapse. Any additional collapse event after the original collapse incident caused by falling debris, vibrations, unstable structures, explosions, and/or earthquake aftershocks.

secondary contamination. Contamination by emergency response personnel of medical or related personnel outside of the hot zone.

secondary devices. Intentionally placed devices intended to detonate and/or cause further destruction or injuries after the initial event has occurred.

secondary explosives. High explosive used to build up the relatively weak shock of the primary explosive.

secondary feeder. A medium diameter (from 12 to 24 in.) hose that branches off of primary feeders to supply distributor lines. Many fire hydrants are connected to these secondary feeders.

secondary search. A slower, more methodical, and more thorough search than a primary search that requires that firefighters search for victims in every possible spot both inside and outside the fire structure.

sector officer. The officer in charge of a rapid intervention team.

sector. A division or part of an incident scene (geographic or functional) used to maintain span of control and provide adequate incident control.

security roof fence. A chain link, steel bar, or ornamental aluminum fence with or without barbed wire to prevent traversing from roof to roof on adjoining buildings.

selective debris removal. The process of taking a building apart piece by piece, usually from top to bottom, conducted by heavy equipment operators, structural engineers, construction, and demolition contractors.

self-accelerating decomposition temperature (SADT). The temperature at which a molecule begins to decompose, liberating enough energy to increase the speed of decomposition until it becomes self-feeding and irreversible.

self-contained breathing apparatus (SCBA). Respiratory protection through a full face piece with supplied air from a cylinder carried by the user. SCBAs are designed to protect against heat, smoke, poisonous gases, and low-oxygen levels.

semiconscious removal. The act of removing a disoriented, dazed, confused, or semiconscious victim from a fire building. The firefighter may place a knee into the victim's buttocks as they descend the ladder. As the firefighter goes from rung to rung, he or she may transfer the victim's weight from knee to knee or use just one knee.

semiduplex system. A radio system that allows multiple users to communicate, but not all users can simultaneously transmit and receive. It is equivalent to a two-frequency simplex system.

senior advisor. The person responsible for confirming that enough resources are assigned to the incident, verifies that the strategy and IAP match current and forecasted incident conditions, confirms that the incident organizations matches the size and complexity of the incident, and manages the command post.

SERC. State Emergency Response Commission.

service test pressure. The pressure used during annual field service testing to determine if fire hose is still suitable for use.

shackle. A U-shaped piece of metal. In a padlock the shackle is the part which passes through an opening in an object or fits around an object and is ultimately locked into the case.

Shaler, Alexander T. Appointed as New York's fire commissioner in 1866, he is credited with creating New York's paid department.

shear. A condition or force causing two structural members to slide past each other in opposite directions (away from or toward each other).

shed or single pitched roof. A type of roof built on a single sloped plane that slopes from between parallel walls of different heights.

shell. The outer layer of the PPE.

shore eddy. An area of water created by the difference between fast and slow currents.

shoring. Temporary bracing used to support a structure or trench in order to prevent collapse so that search and rescue can proceed.

short circuit. A situation in which the insulation around two electrical conductors in a wire are broken and they make contact with each other creating sparks and heat.

Siamese. A device that takes two female inlets and turns them into one male outlet, and can be straight or incorporate a spring operated clapper that occludes the water way.

sidewall sprinklers. Sprinkler heads designed for installation on one wall of a rectangular room, incorporating a distinct deflector that distributes water sideways along the length of a room.

silicon carbide blade. A non-toothed circular abrasive disc made up of composite and metallic materials held together by an organic bonding agent and used with rotary power saws to cut concrete.

simple asphyxiant. A substance that will replace the oxygen in the air to a level below that required to sustain life.

simplex system. A radio system that uses one channel for both initiating and receiving traffic. This system allows only one person to speak at a time.

simulcasting. A type of communication that relies on a common frequency on multiple transmit sites under computer control to ensure that their transmissions are synchronized in order to avoid conflicting with each other.

single bond. The presence of one covalent bond between two atoms.

single command. Situation in which one person handles the command.

single jacketed hose. Hose having a single outer protective and reinforcing layer around an inner core.

single resources. Individual apparatus or a crew of firefighters with an identified supervisor that can be used in a tactical application on an incident.

single-sheave pulley. A device through which a single rope passes and is used to change the direction of pull on a rope.

single-action pull station. A manually operated fire alarm box that requires only one step to activate, usually pulling down a switch or handle.

single-station carbon monoxide (CO) detectors. A device that incorporates detection and notification systems in one device. This device is used to detect the presence of carbon monoxide, a common and deadly by-product of the combustion process.

single-station smoke alarm device. A combination smoke detector and notification device used typically in existing private homes without detection-system code requirements.

situation unit. The unit responsible for collecting all current incident information and, based on this, prepares maps, displays, and projections.

situational awareness. Knowledge of all aspect of an incident.

size-up. A systematic process of gathering pre-incident information and current incident conditions including factors that impact the development of strategy and tactics, including factors which may impact firefighter safety.

SK. A teletype code at the end of a sentence that means "stop talking" and cues the other party that it is time to respond.

skip breathing. Method the SCBA wearer can use in an emergency setting to greatly reduce the rate at which their air supply is consumed. Method requires the wearer to focus solely on controlling their breathing.

SKSK. A teletype code at the end of a conversation that means the party will be hanging up.

skylight. A glass or plastic window or dome set into a ceiling or roof to provide natural light and/or ventilation.

slag. 1. Small stones used for roofing that are usually mixed with hot tar. 2. Hot molten metals from a welding or cutting operation.

slash cut. A roll-down-gate cut using a forcible entry saw by making two parallel cuts from top to bottom.

sliding windows. Windows that operate like, but are smaller than sliding patio doors.

slightly soluble irritants. Irritants that dissolve in the lungs, destroying alveoli by chemical action.

smoke cessation program. A program designed to assist firefighters who wish to quit smoking.

smoke control system. A system of HVAC components that uses air pressure differences to keep smoke away from building occupants so they can be evacuated safely.

smoke detector. A device that activates when it detects products of combustion, commonly called smoke, and is wired to and initiates a separate fire alarm system.

smoke ejector. A mechanical fan or blower that rapidly forces the by-products of combustion out of a contaminated area.

Smokey Bear. Character originating from the U.S. forest service that has represented forest fire safety since 1944.

smooth bore nozzle (tip). A nozzle that produces a tight, compact, unbroken pattern upon discharge.

solid beam. A type of ladder construction that makes use of solid-core side components as in wood ladders or a rectangular tube design as in aluminum ladders.

solid frame window. A non-opening window.

solid gasoline. A term used to describe the behavior of hydrocarbon-based materials. When under fire conditions, these solid materials behave in the same manner as gasoline.

solidification. The process of adding a product that causes a chemical to turn into a solid so that it can be easily captured and removed.

soluble in water. Able to dissolve and disperse in water.

sounding the roof. The act of banging a boot or tool onto a pitched or flat roof to test for structural soundness. In many instances, this tactic informs firefighters that a roof's underside is weak or burned away.

source pumper. In relay operations, the apparatus located at the water source which supplies water to an inline or attack apparatus.

source of ignition. The type of heat energy that initiates a fire by causing a fuel to ignite.

South Canyon Glenwood Spring, Colorado. Site where, in the summer of 1994, 14 wildland firefighters died when shifting 70-mile-per-hour winds trapped them and fire swept over their position.

span of control. The number of personnel one supervisor can effectively manage. The range is two to seven, with five being the optimal number.

spanner wrench. A tool designed to tighten the connections between two sections of hose.

spark plug. A device screwed into the combustion chamber of a gas powered tool that supplies the spark that ignites the air/fuel mixture so that combustion can occur.

Sparky the Fire Dog®. Fire safety character whose accompanying fire-safety material can be purchased and given as tour handouts to children.

speaking trumpet. A funnel-shaped device used by early fire officers to enhance their voices when giving orders on the fireground.

special operations. Any of several specialized operational units that a fire department may choose to deliver in their jurisdiction. These include hazardous materials, swift water rescue, ice rescue, confined space rescue, technical rescue, etc.

specific gravity. The ratio of weight density of substance to the weight density of another substance that is a standard measure, usually water but sometime air.

specific heat. 1. The ratio between the amount of heat necessary to raise the temperature of a substance and the amount of heat necessary to raise the same weight of water the same number of degrees. 2. The ratio of the heat capacity of a substance to that of water.

speed laces. Laces located in the surfaces of the boot and tightened/secured by a cinch system rather than a knot.

spherical pressure vessels. High-pressure storage for up to 600,000 gallons. These vessels are used mostly for LPG and vinyl chloride.

splint. A device that is used for the immobilization of a victim's limbs or spine.

split lay. Hose lay where two engines are used to complete one water supply evolution from the fire to the hydrant.

spoil piles. Excavated materials consisting of topsoil or subsoils that have been removed and temporarily stored during construction and trenching.

spontaneous ignition. A process by which oxygen combines slowly with a fuel, usually on its surface, with the slow evolution of heat energy. The heat energy is absorbed by the fuel, raising its temperature slowly, until the fuel's ignition temperature is reached, and the fuel breaks out into flaming combustion.

spot fire. Smaller, isolated fire off of the main wildland fire, often started by wind-blown embers. Spot fires are often the reason a wldland fire is able to cross fire control lines or fire breaks.

spray nozzle. See fog nozzle.

sprinkler alarm valve. A valve designed to indicate water flow. This is essentially a check valve that permits flow in only one direction. An alarm valve redirects a portion of that flow to a notification or imitating device, such as a water motor gong or a pressure switch.

sprinkler deflector. A device attached to the end of a sprinkler head and serves to break the water stream into droplets and push them to cover an area larger than a straight stream of water would.

sprinkler wedge. A tool used to stop the flow of water in a sprinkler head to prevent further property damage and that could possibly allow the sprinkler system to remain in service.

squad or rescue company. A company composed of a vehicle carrying specialized rescue equipment, staffed with firefighters and a company officer, and primarily assigned to perform forcible entry, search and rescue, and other duties as designated by the department.

stacked tips. A set of decreasing nozzle tips threaded into each other.

staging area. A locations set up at an incident where resources can be placed while awaiting tactical assignment.

standard. A document referenced by a code that includes suggestive wording and or guidance on how to perform a specific action.

standard of cover. The number of fire stations required to meet a community's response time.

standard operating procedure (SOP). Within an organization, a written plan outlining specific tactics or tasks and how they are to be completed.

standing part. The section of the rope between the working and running end.

standpipe systems. A series of pipes, valves, and hose connections installed in buildings and used by firefighters to supply water to fire hoses in different building locations and on different floors.

staphylococcus aureus. A staph infection, also known as MRSA.

starter cord. A strong braided cord with a plastic handle used for non-electrical start gasoline engines.

static load. A relatively unchanging load, which may be delivered over an extended period.

static pressure. The amount of pressure in a hoseline or water main in a street while no water is flowing.

static rope. Rope with very low stretch. Used in most fire department rescue applications.

The Station Nightclub. A West Warwick, RI, nightclub where, on February 20, 2003, polyurethane foam lining the walls was ignited by indoor pyrotechnics used during a performance of the band, Great White. One hundred people eventually died as a result of the fire; lethal conditions in the nightclub developed in about 90 seconds.

steam burn. A burn injury that can occur when large volumes of steam are produced during fire attack.

steel bar joist truss. A lightweight truss using steel bars; usually replaces steel I-beams for roof systems.

steel skeleton frame. The supporting members of a building, constructed of steel.

STEL. Short-term exposure limit.

sterilization. The removal or destruction of all microorganisms, including pathogens and other bacteria, vegetative forms, and spores.

still alarms. Nonemergency calls that require a less urgent response and are usually handled by one company, such as assisting people with animal rescues, helping individuals off a floor, or stringing a halyard on a school flag pole. These types of responses are common and help continue the good name of the fire department organization and their role in the community they serve.

stop, drop, and roll program. A fire prevention program aimed at children to teach them the basics of fire safety, including dialing 911, crawling low in smoke, exit drills in their home (EDITH), two ways out of each room, and the value of smoke detectors.

Stortz coupling. A unisex coupling style utilizing a slot and tab connection, and may incorporate a locking mechanism.

straight ladder. A lightweight, single-section ladder with a fixed length, usually 12 to 20 feet. Also called a wall ladder.

straight-chain hydrocarbon. A molecular configuration in which each carbon atom is attached to only one or two other carbon atoms.

strainers. Dangerous obstructions in moving water causing someone to be pinned and ultimately drown.

strategic level. The incident commander is responsible for managing the strategic level of the incident organization. The IC sets the overall incident strategy, develops and manages the incident action plan (IAP), and assigns and controls the position and function of all incident resources.

strategy. The overall plan developed to control an incident, which factors in information gathered during pre-incident planning, size-up, and includes specific goals that will mark the successful control of the incident. This strategy is often written down into an incident action plan.

street boxes. See municipal fire alarm system.

stretching. The process of determining the distance from the apparatus to the fire, then deploying an adequate length handline to the drop point where the line is to be charged and entry into the fire area will be made.

strike plate. A shaped flat metal plate fixed to a door frame or jamb with one or more bolt holes into which the bait or bolts shoot.

strike teams. Specified combinations of the same kind and type of resources, with common communications and a leader.

strip mall. A commercial building of one or two floors with a series of adjoining, unconnected occupancies (usually divided by some type of fire separation), each with their own front and rear egress.

stripflush-cover protocol. A decontamination procedure in which the victim's clothing is removed, body is flushed with a large amount of water, and then covered with a non-contaminated garment for warmth and privacy.

structural hierarchy. The determination of which structural components are most important, factored with locations of the structural members within the building.

structural PPE. Protective clothing that includes helmet, coat, pants, boots, and gloves normally worn by firefighters during structural firefighting operations. Also known as turnout or bunker gear.

subatomic particles. The nucleus and electrons that make up an atom.

sublimation. When matter changes phases directly from a solid to a gas.

suitcase ladder. A narrow, collapsible ladder that folds into itself for transportation through small, narrow spaces. Also called a folding, attic, scissor, or closet ladder.

supervisory signal. A signal that provides a way of monitoring an alarm system.

supplied air respirator (SAR). Respiratory protection through a full face piece with supplied air from a remote source delivered by means of an air supply line. SARs require an emergency air supply carried by the user.

supply hose. Hose designed to move large volumes of water with a larger diameter than attack hoses, ranging from 3 in. to 3 ½ in., considered a medium diameter hose.

supply unit. At large incidents, the unit responsible for ordering personnel, equipment, and supplies. It also stores and maintains supplies, services, and nonexpendable equipment.

support officer. The officer responsible for managing the tactical worksheet, recording the position and function of all assigned resources, and verifying that correct strategy and IAPs are used based on the critical incident factors.

surface water. Above-ground water. Salt water and freshwater sources are lakes, creeks, rivers, deltas, as well as engineered freshwater storage such as large reservoirs.

surface-area-to-mass ratio. A ratio of the surface area of a material in relation to the total mass of the material. The greater the surface area to mass ratio, the easier it is for the material to absorb heat, reach the material's ignition temperature faster and burn.

surface-to-mass ratio. The amount of surface area compared to the actual mass (weight) of an item such as a truss; the greater the surface area and the less mass, the more likely the object will start on fire and burn.

surfactant. Any substance that changes the properties of the surface of another material.

sweep-and-sound maneuver. The technique in which a firefighter's head is kept outside a fire building toward the window's side while using the structure's wall for protection. Next, the firefighter sweeps the floor with a hand tool to look for a victim. If the tool meets no resistance, the firefighter sounds the floor with a tool to ensure there is a stable floor in the immediate area and moment. Then the firefighter may drop the tool forward and listen for the distinct sound, reinforcing that the floor exists.

Swick method. A single-firefighter ladder drag created by Robert Swick of the Fairborn Fire Department in Ohio in which a firefighter connects an extension ladder to a roof ladder and drags them by the extension ladder's bottom rung.

swim method. A technique used by firefighters to avoid entanglement.

switch-controlled. A term that describes an electrical circuit that is controlled by a switch that opens and closes the conductor.

synthetic. Made by humans as opposed to being made in nature.

systematic approach. The way an investigator takes photographs of the fire scene. This approach is done the same way at every scene.

systemic poison. Any poison that interferes with any vital bodily process.

T

tactical level. The coordinated tasks of multiple companies at an incident scene each performing task-level work.

tactics. The specific methods or objectives to be used to complete the goals established in an incident strategy.

tag line. An additional rope tied to the objects being lowered and used to keep tools and equipment from being caught up when being lowered or raised.

talk groups. The assigned groups on a trunked radio system.

tamper switch. A device that monitors the position of a valve and initiates a supervisory signal when a valve is moved from its normal condition, either normally open, or normally closed.

target hazard. Unique characteristic(s) within a building that are ranked according to their potential threat(s) to firefighters and/or occupants.

task. A specific skill completed by an individual firefighter or fire crew as part of an assigned tactical objective.

task force. Any combination and number of single resources (with span of control limits) assembled for a particular tactical need. May be a mix of different kinds of resources, be of the same kind but different types, or be several resources of one kind mixed with other resources.

task level. The level performed by firefighters where actual work is done. These combined efforts complete the tactical priorities of rescue, fire control, and property conservation for the incident (for structure firefighting).

taxpayer. 1. A single or multi-family building, usually two or three floors, with some type of commercial occupancy on the ground floor and living units on the upper floors. Units may or may not have direct access to the commercial occupancies below.
2. One- and two-story buildings that line the streets of some older commercial districts; these taxpayers are cheaply constructed ordinary buildings. 3. Longer, single story, commercial stores with flat roofs. These structures are also referred to as strip malls.

technical rescue PPE. Lightweight flexible PPE used to offer protection during special rescue operations. Technical rescue PPE comes in the form of a coat and pant or jumpsuits and must offer abrasion, liquid, and flame resistance. Boots are similar to medical boots with toe, foot, and general penetration protection. For head protection, special technical rescue helmets are employed. A rescue harness, rope, and rope accessories can be included as part of technical rescue PPE.

telecommunicator. A person trained and responsible for receiving all nonemergency and emergency calls for service and dispatching the appropriate equipment.

telematics. The blending of computers and wireless telecommunications technologies, with the goal of efficiently conveying information over satellites.

temperature. The measure of how fast a group of molecules are moving.

tempered glass. A strong, safe, and high heat resistive glass that shatters into small and rounded edge fragments when broken.

temporal 3 pattern. A standard audible alarm signal to alert a building's occupants to evacuate.

tenement. A multi-story (usually 3–5), ordinary construction apartment building with a center-hallway layout. Tenements are normally found in urban settings, often grouped in developments.

tension. the action of stretching or pulling of a component.

tent-type collapse. A type of collapse where the middle section of floor stays attached but the sides fall downward.

testimonial evidence. Evidence after a fire that is provided by people such as witnesses or experts.

tether line. Attached to the main search line by a carabineer, this extension of the search line allows firefighters to search off of the main line in smaller areas such as cubicles.

thermal balance. What some firefighters refer to when discussing thermal layering.

thermal imaging camera (TIC). A device that sees through smoke by reading heat signatures, using very slight variations in temperature that exist between different objects to create an image on the camera's screen.

thermal layering. The layering of heat and smoke when fire occurs in a room or enclosed space, with the highest temperatures and more dense smoke at the ceiling and lower temperatures and less dense smoke near the floor.

thermal pane windows. Double- or triple-glazed window that improve energy efficiency and eliminate drafts.

thermal protective performance (TPP). A test to measure the time it takes for convective and radiant heat to penetrate through the three layers of a complete PPE system: the outer shell, moisture barrier, and thermal liner-and injure the wearer.

thermally thick. When a material exposed to a heat flux on its front face has not had an appreciable temperature rise on the material's back face.

thermally thin. When at a given instant a material's back face is at a temperature close to that of the front face.

thermoplastic. A class of plastics that can be subjected to heat and pressure more than once without degradation.

thermoset. A class of plastics that can be subjected to heat and pressure only once. Any further exposure will cause the material to degrade and/or decompose.

thief line. A stretch of 2½-in. (65-mm) hose with an attached gated wye which, when connected to a hi-rise pack, gives the fire crew the additional length necessary to fight fires a further distance from the truck without pumping at an excessively high pressure. Also referred to as a fire line.

three-dimensional fire. A term referring to flammable liquids that are being pumped or sprayed as they burn (under normal conditions, flammable liquids fires are two-dimensional, forming pools).

three-firefighter perimeter search. A search plan in which three firefighters enter a room. The first two proceed around opposite sides of the perimeter and the third remains in the doorway with a light. When the two searching firefighters meet, they return to the third.

throttle handle trigger. A part found on the handle of gas-powered tools that, when squeezed, increases the speed of the engine for the tool to operate.

throttle lock. A button located near the throttle handle trigger on a gas-powered tool to lock the trigger in an open position, but not used as a safety.

through-the-lock. An entry technique involving the removal of part of a lock, then using a "key" tool to duplicate the action of the key in non-emergency situations to reduce property damage.

tie-rods. Metal rods usually only on wooden ladders that run under the rungs and through both beams. They help secure both beams together with the rungs.

tilt-slab. A method of non-combustible construction in which walls are large pre-fabricated concrete panels that are raised into place and then tied together and held in place by the roof system.

time unit. The unit responsible for keeping track of personnel arrival and departure times at the incident to help with accountability and aid the resource unit in tracking personnel and apparatus.

tip. The top one to few rungs of a ladder when it is propped over the roofline of a structure.

tissue asphyxiant. A substance that replaces oxygen in the red blood cell and poisons the cell body to which it is transferred.

TLV-TWA. Threshold limit value-time weighted average.

tone encoding. A function on some radios allowing the user to transmit an audible or subaudible tone in emergency situations.

top chord. The uppermost supporting member of a truss.

tormentor poles. Metal poles attached with a swivel connection to the bed section of a ladder that help stabilize the ladder as it is raised and lowered. They also have a single spur at their bottoms to assist in footing the ladder.

torsion. The action of twisting a building component such as a nut on a bolt.

torsional loads. Loads applied parallel to the cross section of the supporting member,

total heat loss (THL). A test that measures the ability of the PPE to allow heat to pass away from the body through the three layers that make up the garment.

total working length of a ladder. The distance from a ladder's base to the spot of its upper support.

total-flooding system. A system that completely fills a room or compartment with suppression agent.

tower ladder. 1. A ladder whose original design came from the telescoping sections of a crane and is still used today. Engineers adapted this to include a bucket or basket attached to the end of the boom with a pre-piped waterway and monitor nozzle.
2. Fire vehicles that have permanently mounted ladders that can be elevated to an area for rescue or access.

townhouse apartments. Multi-family apartment building where individual units share common walls sitting side-by-side, have two or three floors, and are accessed from individual ground-level entryways.

toxic. Harmful, destructive, poisonous, or deadly to the body.

toxicity. The ability of a chemical substance to produce injury once it reaches a susceptible site in or near the body.

tractor drawn tiller aerial trucks. They are recognizable with a tiller operator driving the rear of the apparatus and pivot on a fifth wheel. These apparatus are commonly used in areas with narrow roadways and alleys.

traffic cones. Items carried on all apparatus to identify safe perimeters.

traffic control. Awareness and direction of traffic in the vicinity of an incident.

trailers. Anything used by an arsonist to help spread the fire to as many locations as possible. May also be used to keep the arsonist farther away from the actual fire.

transceivers. Radios with the ability to receive and transmit.

transfill. Using an SCBA bottle to provide air to a downed firefighter by filling his SCBA bottle.

transition elements. The short columns on the periodic table marked I through VIIB and VIII that are all metals.

transmutation. The changing of one element into another.

treated water aqueducts. Waterways up to 20 ft (6 m) in diameter in cities with heavy water demand like New York or Los Angeles.

trench cut. A defensive roof operation cut for cockloft fires to prevent further extension into different building wings or adjoining stores or homes.

Triangle Shirtwaist factory fire. A fire in New York City in 1911 in which 146 women died. As a result of the fire, the state of New York enacted a labor law requiring fire drills in heavy timber factory buildings in New York City. The law is now the legal basis for requirement that fire safety organizations be established in high-rise office buildings.

triangular inspection hole. A three-legged cut shaped like a triangle to determine the location or existence of fire as well as inspection of roof construction. Also known as an "A" or "Teepee."

trimming a window. Clearing a window of remaining broken glass using a hand tool.

triple bond. The presence of three covalent bonds between two atoms.

triple-combination pumper. A piece of fire equipment that consists of three key critical items: a pump, fire hose, and a water tank.

trouble signal. A signal that identifies system problems that can influence the system's reliability.

trunk. The car storage area usually found behind the passenger compartment. Many dangerous articles can be transported in a trunk and special care should be taken when approaching. Gas tanks and fuel lines are usually located near the trunk, so it should not be approached or opened until the fire has been knocked down.

trunked radio systems. An efficient use of available radio frequencies and channels. These constantly readjust the frequencies used for conversations, allowing for a more efficient use of the limited frequencies because each conversation does not require a dedicated channel. However, it also makes it very difficult to scan trunked conversations because it is usually unknown on which frequency the next portion of the conversation will appear. Trunked radio systems use a data or control channel system.

truss. A structural component using one or more triangular units to attain stability.

trussed beam. A type of ladder construction that makes use of a top and bottom rail joined together with gusset plates, usually at the rung position. It is of open construction and usually made of wood or aluminum. Most have spikes or permanent cleats mounted at the base.

try before you pry. Turning a door knob or opening a window before doing any damage.

TTY. A device that assists people with hearing or speech impairment in using a telephone. It is also called a text telephone or teletype.

tubular pin tumbler lock. A lock in which six to eight pins are arranged in a circular pattern, and the key for unlocking is similar in tubular or cylindrical shape. Examples are found on bicycle locks and vending machines.

turnout gear. Protective clothing that includes helmet, coat, pants, boots, and gloves normally worn by firefighters during structural firefighting operations. See also structural PPE and bunker gear.

turtle. When automobiles in water turn upside down as they submerge and bury themselves in mud.

Tweed, William M. "Boss." Controversial Tammany leader, who began his rise to political power as foreman of Americus Engine 6 on Henry Street in lower Manhattan.

Twin Towers. World Trade Center towers in New York City attacked by terrorists using airliners on September 11, 2001.

two cycle-engine. An engine found on power tools that uses a fuel mixture of both gasoline and oil.

two-firefighter perimeter search. A search plan in which two firefighters place a flashlight at the room's entrance, then proceed around the perimeter, meeting on the opposite side and returning to the light source through the middle of the room.

two-in, two-out standard. During interior structural firefighting, the standard that states that a fire department shall ensure that at least two employees who enter the immediately dangerous to life and health atmosphere (IDLH) shall remain in visual or voice contact with one another at all times; at least two employees are located outside the IDLH atmosphere; and that all employees engaged in interior structural firefighting will use SCBA.

two-section attic ladder. A narrow extension ladder with no halyard or pulleys that provides access in narrow areas. It rises manually when the fly section is pushed.

Type 1. Very large operations that are led by a specific federally-trained Type 1 overhead teams. This level of incident command is typically conducted over long operational periods, usually lasting weeks or months.

Type 2. Incidents that are also federal large-scale events, but require a smaller management team, fewer resources, and less time to bring under control.

Type 3. Incident operations that are managed by resources on a statewide level.

Type 4. Operations organized for local incidents. Type 4 and Type 5 responses represent more than 99 percent of all fire department incident activity.

Type 5. Operations organized for local incidents. Type 4 and Type 5 responses represent more than 99 percent of all fire department incident activity.

type. A resource designation based on its size, capability, staffing, qualifications, and ability to accomplish a task or function.

U

ultra-large diameter hose (ULDH). Supply lines of extruded hose in diameters of 6, 8, 10, and 12 in.

UN. United Nations.

Uncle Joe Ross. The Latta brothers' horse-drawn steam fire engine introduced in 1853 in Cincinnati.

unconscious removal. The act of removing an unconscious victim from a fire building. A firefighter may place both arms out and onto the beams of the ladder, accepting a victim across both arms.

underflow dam. A barrier used to contain products that are lighter than water and other products which have a specific gravity less than 1.

underground storage tank. A non-pressure bulk storage tank that is found mostly in gas stations where the tanks are buried below grade and the materials are pumped to the surface for dispensing.

undesigned loads. Loads that a designer or structural engineer did not anticipate or calculate.

Underwriters' Laboratories (UL). Formally known as the Underwriters' Electrical Bureau, this was founded by William H. Merrill in the spring of 1894 and began laboratory testing of materials for combustibility in the upper floors of a Chicago Fire Patrol house. Today it serves as an independent organization that does testing, listing, and examining of items as they relate to fire protection and safety. UL listing is another recognizable symbol of safety.

undetermined. A classification of the cause of a fire when there is insufficient evidence to prove a particular cause.

unified command. An element of NIMS/ICS that allows agencies to work together to develop common objectives and strategies to handle a more difficult incident.

unit identifiers. The field unit's ID number that appears on the dispatchers monitor when they transmit.

unit status. The availability of a field unit: in service, out of service, responding, or at scene.

universal rescue connection (URC). A male air inlet found on SCBAs intended for emergency use that allows the SCBA cylinder to be transfilled from another air source, possible a rescue air kit (RAK).

unsalvageable. Not capable of being repaired or saved.

unsaturated hydrocarbon. A hydrocarbon compound that contains at least one multiple covalent bond between two carbon atoms.

unstable. Having the qualities of spontaneous decomposition, polymerization, or self-reaction.

unstable materials. Any substance that will decompose spontaneously, polymerize, or otherwise self-react.

upper explosive limit. The maximum percentage of gas or vapor in air above which ignition will not occur.

upright sprinkler head. A sprinkler head that is mounted above sprinkler piping, and incorporates a deflector to divert the upward-flowing water stream down to the floor.

upstream. In the direction against the natural movement or flow of a stream or river.

upstream V. When an object protrudes in moving water, this creates the water to part into a V pointing upstream.

urban-wildland interface. Boundary areas where urban development (usually residential) is encroaching into wildland areas. Structures are exposed to significant fire risks associated with wildland fires.

urgent message. A radio callout intended to clear the channel of traffic in order to transmit critical information.

USAR. Urban Search And Rescue.

V

V-pattern. A common char pattern often found after a fire; the pattern is in the shape of a "V" and will point toward a source of fire.

valley. The intersection where the sides of a sloping roof meet at an inside corner.

vanity. A motive for arson that involves the fire setter seeking praise for "heroic" actions or a monetary gain such as a raise for saving an employer money.

vapor density. The relative density of a vapor or gas (with no air present) as compared to clean, dry air, which has a vapor density of 1.0.

vapor dispersion. The movement of vapor clouds in air due to wind, thermal action, gravity spreading, and mixing.

vapor pressure. The pressure exerted by a gas or vapor on the sides of its container at equilibrium.

V-dike. A barrier that captures released material by using the small end of the V as the collection point.

vehicle fire. Any fire that occurs in an automobile, truck, bus, train, plane, or boat.

vent and soil pipes. Pipes that extend through a given roof at various locations and provide exhaust ventilation for plumbing fixtures on the waste side on the plumbing system.

vent/enter/search (VES). A structural search tactic in which a crew must ventilate fire products from a room prior to conducting a search. VES is often completed above a fire where a victim is likely to be found and search crews cannot gain access to the interior stairs due to high heat or fire conditions.

ventilation controlled fire. A fire in which the growth and development is controlled by the amount of air that is supplied to the fire.

venting for life. A method that assists a firefighter's movement into an area where there is a known or suspected life in danger. Also assists the engine company's advance and is coordinated to aid in the extinguishment of fire.

venturi effect. The principle that holds that a moving column of water or air will have a lower internal pressure than the surrounding environment. As a result, a partial vacuum is created in the area adjoining the column and any surrounding liquid or solid will be drawn into the moving column. Venturi is the operating principle behind foam eductors and positive pressure fans.

vertical ventilation. Removing heat, smoke, and fire gases by means of openings at the roof of a structure.

Victaulic coupling. A mechanical coupling designed to be field repairable, which is used on very large hose (up to 18 in. [460 mm] in diameter).

Vigiles. The watchmen of Rome and the first public force of firefighters. Emperor Augustus was credited with creating the force.

VIN. Vehicle identification number.

Voice over Internet Protocol (VoIP). Phone systems using the internet to make phone calls. The caller's origin is unknown to emergency call takers.

void space. Any space within a building not normally accessible where fire/products of combustion can spread without being easily detected.

volatility. The tendency of a liquid to evaporate at a given temperature.

W–Y

walk-in alarm. A verbal face-to-face notification of an actual emergency or non-emergency reported directly to a fire station and not a dispatch center.

walkthrough bulkhead. A barrier that cuts the roof section of a building into two sections and has doors at both ends.

wall ladder. A lightweight, single-section ladder with a fixed length, usually 12 to 20 feet (4 to 6 m). Also called a straight ladder.

warm zone. The clearly marked and controlled area between hot and cold zones where personnel and equipment decontamination and hot zone support take place. It includes control points for the access corridor and thus assists in reducing the spread of contamination.

warrant. A legal document issued by a court to allow an investigator to search for evidence.

The War Years. The early 1960s, during which the fire service entered into an era of confusing and often violent social, racial, and economic confrontation.

water cannon. See water monitor.

water chute. A trough made using salvage covers or tarps, pike poles, and ladders to catch dripping water and divert it to a specified location.

water hammer. Violent dissipation of kinetic energy that occurs when flowing water is stopped rapidly in a closed system.

water knot. A knot used to tie two pieces of webbing together.

water main valves. Any valves used by the water district to shut down certain areas of the system or grid for issues like repair and maintenance.

water miscible. Any substance that can be mixed with water and will remain mixed under normal conditions.

water mist. A type of extinguisher that uses de-ionized water that is discharged as a fine spray onto the burning material. It is designed as an alternative to halon in areas where contamination must be kept to a minimum without the expense of halon substitutes. Using de-ionized water causes little damage to most electronic circuits and it is the safest agent available for use on humans (such as in operating rooms).

water mist system. The use of low quantities of water at very high pressure, creating a fine spray of water to suppress fires. Generally they are installed in total-flooding systems similar to deluge sprinkler systems, but the quantity of water applied is much lower.

water monitors. Nozzles mounted to tower ladders that can flow 1,000 gpm (3,785 L/min).

water motor gong. A type of local alarm notification device that is powered by water moving through an alarm check valve. When water flow unseats the clapper, water is redirected through a retard chamber and into the water motor gong, which causes an arm to spin and strike the body of the gong, making a bell-like noise.

water shuttle operations. The use of water tenders and other apparatus to move water from a fill site to a dumpsite to supply fire suppression with necessary water.

water tender. An apparatus that holds up to 3,500 gallons (13,250 L) of water, or more, and is used as a water source during fire suppression or during water shuttle operations.

water turret. See water monitors.

water-reactive materials. Any material that enters into a chemical or physical reaction in the presence of water.

water-soluble irritants. Irritants that dissolve in the first moisture they encounter, usually the eyes, mouth, nose, and upper respiratory tract.

waybills. A set of hazardous material shipping papers containing the name and address of the shipper and receiver, identification of the material being shipped, and the quantity and weight of the shipment. Waybills are for shipments by rail.

webbing. A flat or tubular woven fabric often used for anchoring, slings, and patient packaging.

weight bearing beams and columns. Structural beams carrying or supporting an active load.

weight effect. The change produced in certain properties as the molecular weight of compounds in an analogous series is increased or decreased.

wellness program. A department program designed to keep all firefighters in good health.

wet barrel hydrant. A hydrant that constantly has water in its above-ground portion. These are used in climates with no or little risk of freezing temperatures.

wet chemical. Solutions of water mixed with potassium acetate, potassium carbonate, potassium citrate, or combinations thereof. They are specifically designed for Class K fires but they have demonstrated superior effectiveness on Class A fires when compared with plain water. They have limited capabilities on Class B fires and can be used in extinguishers with special wand applicators that achieve a Class C listing, verifying that electricity cannot be conducted back to the operator.

wet-chemical extinguishing systems. A system using a proprietary liquid agent, often a potassium solution, as an extinguishing agent, which suppresses fire by a process of saphonification, or the formation of a soap-like barrier that disrupts the fire tetrahedron.

wet-pipe system. A system of pipes that contains water up to a thermally activated, automatic sprinkler head.

wide fog. Rotational control to adjust the pattern from straight stream to the wide-angle spray (characteristically, a 100-degree angle).

wide-flange beam. The modern name for the I-beam, so named for the increase in the horizontal dimensions of the bottom and top flanges.

wildland firefighting. A professional specialty, prevalent in the western states. Wildland fires are large, unfriendly fires in which the natural cover of the fire area constitutes the primary fuel supply.

wildland hose. A type of single jacketed specialty attack hose designed to work well for combating vegetation fires. It is less than 1½ in. (38 mm) in diameter, flowing between 30 to 70 gpm (114 to 265 L/min).

wildland or brush PPE. PPE designed to protect firefighters from flash fire and abrasion during wildland fires while allowing the greatest amount of mobility and heat recovery possible.

window guards. Made of metal, this folding, stationary, or swinging gate is installed to prevent theft or to prevent small children from fall accidents. Sometimes they are secured with a padlock.

wired glass. Glass that is reinforced with a wire mesh to prevent security break-ins and fire spread.

wood frame construction. Type-V construction; the supporting structural members are wood but are not of large dimension.

wooden I-beam. An engineered floor joist manufactured with a top and bottom chord and a web in the middle of the joist.

working end. The part of the rope that forms the knot.

working length. One folded length (50-ft [15-m]) of hose.

wristlet style cuff. Typically, a specially designed piece of fabric that extends from the end of a coat sleeve that provides limited protection to the area where the glove and coat meet.

wye. A device in which water enters through a single female inlet and then exits.

wythe. A single vertical stack of brick.

Z

zero impact factor. The amount of time it will take for a company to make an impact on a Mayday situation.

zone non-code alarm. The geographic area within a protected facility from which a signal has been received, and may indicate the specific device that has activated.

zone coded alarm. Per NFPA 72, this is an audible or visible signal that conveys several discrete bits or units of information.

INDEX

C

E

INDEX H

I

M

N

O

S

INDEX S

INDEX S—T

INDEX T

U

V

Y

Z